ENCYCLOPEDIA OF PHYSICAL SCIENCE AND TECHNOLOGY

SECOND EDITION

VOLUME 8 Imp - Lip

EXECUTIVE ADVISORY BOARD

ENCYCLOPEDIA OF PHYSICAL SCIENCE AND TECHNOLOGY

SECOND EDITION

VOLUME 8 Imp - Lip

An Encyclopedic Reference Complete in Eighteen Volumes, with Volume 18 the Index Volume

ROBERT A. MEYERS, EDITOR
TRW, INC.

ACADEMIC PRESS, INC.
Harcourt Brace Jovanovich, Publishers
San Diego New York Boston London Sydney Tokyo Toronto

This book is printed on acid-free paper. ♾

Academic Press, Inc.
1250 Sixth Avenue, San Diego, California 92101-4311

United Kingdom Edition published by
Academic Press Limited
24–28 Oval Road, London NW1 7DX

Library of Congress Cataloging-in-Publication Data

Encyclopedia of physical science and technology / Robert A. Meyers
[editor]. – 2nd ed.
p. cm.
Includes index.
ISBN 0-12-226930-6
1. Physical sciences–Dictionaries. 2. Technology–Dictionaries.
I. Meyers, Robert A. (Robert Allen), date
Q123.E4974 1992
503–dc20 92-6959
CIP

PRINTED IN THE UNITED STATES OF AMERICA
92 93 94 95 96 97 MA 9 8 7 6 5 4 3 2 1

EDITORIAL ADVISORY BOARD

CONTENTS

GUIDE TO USING THE ENCYCLOPEDIA

Articles in the *Encyclopedia of Physical Science and Technology* are arranged alphabetically by subject. A table of contents appears in each volume. The volumes may be consulted directly by checking the contents of the appropriate volume. Thus, a reader who needs information on Air Pollution Control will find an entire article on that subject in Volume 1 (A–An). An article on X-Ray Analysis appears in Volume 17. The final volume in the set, Volume 18, contains a combined subject index for all 17 text volumes.

The reader may check the subject index in Volume 18 to find the volume (in boldface) and page numbers (lightface) for the information sought. The reader may also refer to the relational index found in Volume 18 for groupings of related articles. For example, under the heading Earthquake Prediction, the following articles are listed:

Plate Tectonics
Seismology, Observational
Seismology, Theoretical

Alphabetization of articles within the Encyclopedia follows the letter-by-letter method based on the main subject of the title (i.e., modifying words or phrases enclosed in parentheses or set off with a comma are not considered). For example, Volume 1 contains articles in the following order:

Airplanes, Light
Air Pollution (Meteorology)
Air Pollution Control

Volume 4 contains articles in the following order:

Electronic Displays
Electrons in Solids
Electron Spin Resonance
Electron Transfer, Transition Metal Complexes
Electron Transfer Reactions, General

Each article is designed to present the subject in a standard format. An outline and a glossary of key terms precede each article. A defining paragraph appears as the opening text of each article. Following the main text of each article is a list of bibliographic references.

Cross-references within articles lead the reader to related articles for background information.

A complete list of the contributing authors, their affiliations, and the titles of their articles is given in Volume 18.

IMPACT CRATERING

William B. McKinnon *Washington University*

GLOSSARY

Catastrophic disruption: Impact so energetic that it breaks the target body apart instead of forming a crater.

Complex crater: Impact crater of relatively large dimension and shallow depth, characterized by a central uplift and peripheral slumping or terracing that develops during the modification stage as a result of yielding of the underlying rocks (or ice).

Coupling parameter: Single scalar measure of the impactor that determines the characteristics of the cratering flow field during excavation.

Ejecta: Material ejected from a crater during its formation.

Excavation stage: Stage in the cratering process, following initial shock compression of the impactor and target, in which the crater bowl forms.

Hugoniot: Locus of points describing the pressure–volume–energy relations or states that may be achieved within a material by shocking it from a given initial state.

Impactor: Cosmic object that strikes a planetary or satellite surface.

Late heavy bombardment: Early period of heavy cratering expressed on the most ancient (3.8–4.5 Gyr-old) surfaces of the Moon, Mercury, and Mars.

Modification stage: Stage in the cratering process for large craters that promptly follows the excavation stage and results in such morphologies as flat floors, slump terraces, central peaks, peak rings, or multiple rings.

Multiringed basin: Large circular depression, hundreds of kilometers in diameter, with one or more zones of concentrically arranged mountains caused by large-body impact.

Regolith: Layer of fragmentary debris produced by meteoritic impact on the surface of any celestial body.

Secondary crater: Impact crater produced by a fragment or fragments ejected from a larger primary crater.

Simple crater: Impact crater of relatively small diameter characterized by a uniformly concave-upward shape and maximum depth in the center and lacking a central uplift or marginal slumping.

Transient crater: Crater formed at the end of the excavation stage, which, if the crater is large enough, promptly collapses to a complex form.

Impact craters form when a smaller object strikes a larger one at hypervelocity. The resulting crater has a simple bowl shape at small physical scales, but several more complex morphologies can arise at larger physical scales. Impact craters are a dominant landform of the Solar System, identified on nearly every solid body studied to date. The effects of cratering have been profound, if only because all solid planets and satellites formed by the collision and accretion of numerous smaller bodies. Space exploration during the last 25 yr has documented the fundamental role of impact cratering in the geological and atmospheric evolution of Earth and the other planets, and especially in the biological evolution of Earth. The level of activity in the field of impact studies has never been higher. The recognition of impact cratering as a fundamental geologic process, particularly when contrasted with the vigorous impact-versus-volcanic origin debates 30 yr ago, represents a revolution in geologic thought.

I. Introduction

Impact craters are relatively rare on Earth, so debate originally centered on the origin of lunar craters observed through the telescope. The lack of *in-situ* examination, coupled with a dim understanding of planetary surface and evolutionary processes, allowed many dubious scenarios to be entertained. The few, relatively well-preserved impact structures on Earth were considered to be volcanic, but because there was no evidence for lava or other volcanic materials, they were termed cryptovolcanic. Even G. K. Gilbert, a famous geologist who advocated an impact origin for lunar craters and found abundant meteoritic iron at meteor Crater, Arizona (both in 1891), concluded that Meteor Crater was volcanic in origin.

Gilbert was led astray by an incomplete understanding of cratering mechanics. This situation began to change after World War II, when analogies to large explosion craters were developed, notably by R. B. Baldwin and E. M. Shoemaker. Their arguments helped convince H. C. Urey and G. P. Kuiper (the chemist and astronomer, respectively, who founded modern planetary science), and thus other scientists, that lunar craters were created by impact. Geologic evidence accumulated supporting the impact hypothesis, such as the discovery of shocked polymorphs of quartz and other minerals at crater sites, but it was not until the early 1960s, with the return of spacecraft images of the Moon showing an abundance of craters at every scale, that the volcanic hypothesis was laid to rest. Even at this time, the appreciation of impact cratering as a general phenomenon was incomplete. When *Mariner 4* returned images of the cratered highlands of Mars in 1965, researchers were surprised. In contrast, cratered terrains were expected in images of the satellites of the outer planets returned by *Voyagers 1* and *2* during the last 10 yr. Analysis of crater morphologies, spatial distributions, and size-frequency distributions is now a major tool for understanding the geologic histories of planetary bodies, including Earth. [*See* MOON (ASTRONOMY); PLANETARY SATELLITES, NATURAL.]

II. Mechanics

Excavation of an impact crater form begins when a smaller object, the impactor, strikes a larger target, initiating a rapid (but orderly) series of events. Momentum and energy are transferred to the target, and a shock wave is set up that propagates through the target. This shock wave deposits internal and kinetic energy, which results in the melting and vaporization of the impactor as well as target material near the impact point and the creation of a flow field in ruptured target material. Expansion of the flow field creates the crater.

The pressure P, density ρ, shock velocity U, particle velocity u, and internal energy E (per unit mass) of the shock-compressed material are determined by the Rankine–Hugoniot equations, which express the conservation of mass, momentum, and energy, respectively, across the shock front:

$$\rho_0 U = \rho(U - u) \tag{1a}$$

$$P - P_0 = \rho_0 U u \tag{1b}$$

$$E - E_0 = \frac{P + P_0}{2}\left(\frac{1}{\rho_0} - \frac{1}{\rho}\right) = \frac{1}{2}u^2 \tag{1c}$$

Here, P_0, ρ_0, and E_0 are the unshocked values, and these equations apply in the frame of reference where unshocked material is at rest. Shock and particle velocities are empirically related for a given material and must be measured. Such a U–u curve is one example of a shock Hugoniot. Typical impact velocities in the Solar System are on the order of 10 km sec^{-1}, which lead to initial shock pressures in the range of 10^{2-3} GPa (1–10 Mbar). Equations (1) plus Hugoniot data, when coupled to the hydrodynamic equations of motion and appropriate boundary conditions (at the impactor–target interface and the impactor and target free surface), allow a complete description of the initial stages of the cratering process. While computationally intensive, such calculations can now be carried out at reasonable cost.

Impact crater formation is conventionally divided into stages. The first, compression, begins with the initial contact and ends when the resulting shock wave reaches the back of the impactor (see Fig. 1). Unloading also begins immediately, at the free surface near the impactor–target interface. An unloading or rarefaction wave propagates inward, and the material undergoing rarefaction is subjected to a steep high-pressure

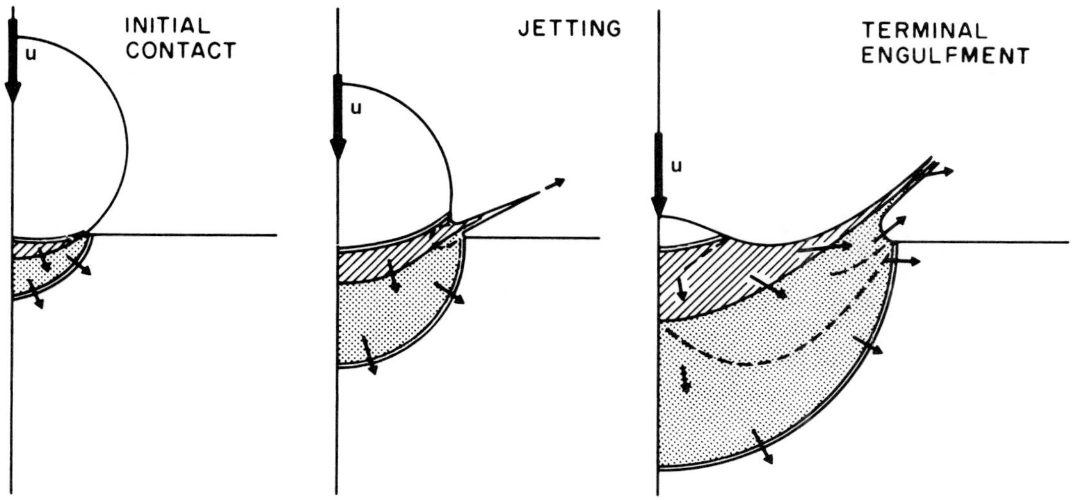

FIG. 1. The compression stage of impact mechanics. The left panel shows the shock wave geometry just after initial contact with a spherical impactor moving at velocity *u*. Shocked impactor and surface (target) material is lined and stippled, respectively. Arrows indicate particle velocities. Rarefaction waves (dashed lines) unload the shocked zone, causing jetting. Jetting segues into the beginning of formation of the ejecta curtain. [From Chapman, C. R., and McKinnon, W. B. (1986). Cratering of planetary satellites. *In* "Satellites" (J. A. Burns and M. S. Matthews, eds.), pp. 492–580. Univ. of Arizona Press, Tucson, Arizona.]

gradient and accelerated upward and outward in a jet of what is usually melt or vapor.

Momentum and energy transfer are completed during the first part of the excavation stage. Here, the shock wave continues to propagate into the target, but the rarefaction front from the free surface of the target (and impactor) eventually catches up and combines with the original hemispherical shock in the target. The resulting geometry resembles a detached shock. The overall effect is to rotate the velocity vectors of the flow field, from basically radially outward from the point of initial contact, toward the original target surface (Fig. 2). The pressures behind the detached shock are relatively high, and the original mechanical integrity of the target material is destroyed. Material close to the impact point may be vaporized or melted, but most target material is thoroughly fractured and comminuted. The flow field created is approximately steady-state and incompressible, and the crater bowl, or transient cavity, opens up as the flow field expands. Expansion of crater dimensions is a power-law function of time and is accomplished by both ballistic ejection and displacement (Fig. 2).

The detached shock expands and dissipates. The flow field expands hydrodynamically until arrested by some combination of gravity, strength, or viscosity. Except for small craters in competent materials, the ultimate limitation on crater size and shape is the dissipation of flow field kinetic energy, either frictionally or viscously, or its conversion to gravitational potential energy.

Crater dimensions at the end of the excavation stage are typically one to two orders of magnitude greater than that of the original impactor. Excavation lasts orders of magnitude longer than compression and scales as the square root of the diameter. Thus, on Earth a 1-km-diameter crater may form in ~10 sec and a 100-km-diameter crater in ~100 sec.

The crater at the end of the excavation stage is termed the *transient crater*. It may also be the final one, but for craters larger than a threshold diameter (which varies from planet to planet) and for all craters in liquids, the transient crater is not in mechanical equilibrium and promptly collapses under the influence of gravity. This modification stage results in the creation of many different morphological features, discussed later. For larger craters, the end of the excavation stage and the modification stage are one continuous process, because both phases are gravity dominated.

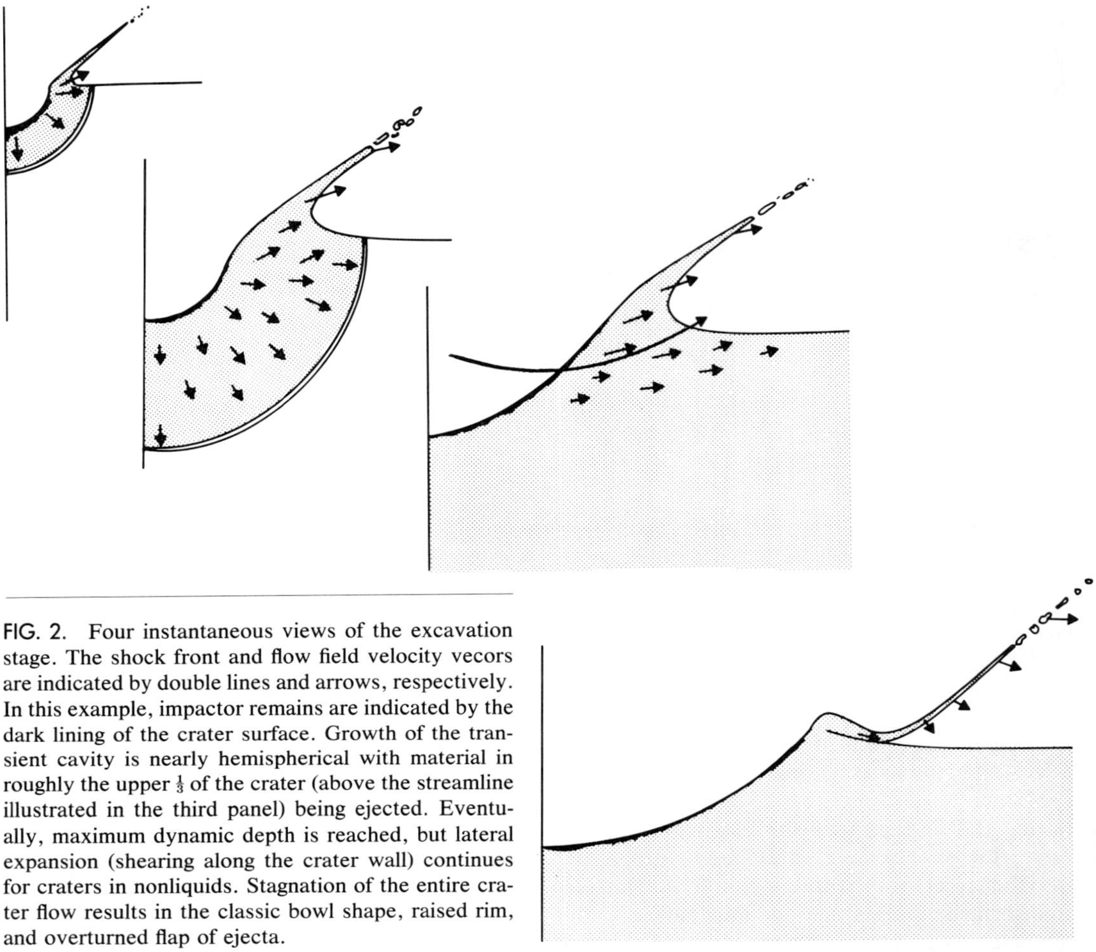

FIG. 2. Four instantaneous views of the excavation stage. The shock front and flow field velocity vecors are indicated by double lines and arrows, respectively. In this example, impactor remains are indicated by the dark lining of the crater surface. Growth of the transient cavity is nearly hemispherical with material in roughly the upper $\frac{1}{3}$ of the crater (above the streamline illustrated in the third panel) being ejected. Eventually, maximum dynamic depth is reached, but lateral expansion (shearing along the crater wall) continues for craters in nonliquids. Stagnation of the entire crater flow results in the classic bowl shape, raised rim, and overturned flap of ejecta.

III. Scaling

Early scaling relationships derived from explosion crater studies assumed that the final diameter depends solely on impactor energy. Energy and momentum are both important in impact cratering, however, as might seem obvious. The coupling of kinetic energy and momentum into a restricted region near the impactor nevertheless allows the impactor to be characterized by a single measure or variable, the point-source coupling parameter. The coupling parameter is intermediate in dimensionality between energy and momentum. Its form must be determined experimentally for each material of interest. For nonporous materials, which are appropriate in most planetary situations, the coupling parameter has dimensions closer to energy.

A convenient way to express crater scaling is through dimensionless variables, in particular, the gravity-scaled size

$$\pi_2 = 3.22ga/u^2 \qquad (2)$$

where a is the spherical equivalent radius of the impactor, u is its velocity, and g is the gravitational acceleration. The best estimate for the scaling of a large crater forming in solid rock (or ice) is

$$V\rho/m = 0.2\pi_2^{-0.65} \qquad (3)$$

where vertical incidence is assumed, V is the excavated volume below the original ground plane, ρ is the target density, and m is the impactor mass. In terms of the transient crater radius R,

$$R\,(\rho/m)^{1/3} = 0.8\pi_2^{-0.22} \qquad (4)$$

As an example, a 1-km-diameter impactor striking Earth at 25 km sec^{-1} (a typical collision velocity for an asteroid) creates a 34-km-diameter crater. Finally, formation time is close to $0.8V^{1/6}g^{-1/2}$. Smaller craters can be affected by the strength, or cohesion, of the target, but craters on the terrestrial planets and icy satellites greater than ~1 km in diameter should be mainly affected by gravity.

IV. Observations

Craters, whether in rock or ice, or on planets and satellites of greatly varying gravity, form similar size-dependent morphological sequences. The smallest craters are called simple craters because they have simple bowl shapes. The depth to diameter ratio for such craters, when freshly formed in rock, is always close to 0.2. Those formed in ice (as on the satellites of the giant planets) are somewhat shallower. They all exhibit raised rims built of plastically deformed rock (or ice) units overlain with ejecta. The trajectories of the ejecta cause the stratigraphy of the target to be emplaced in an inverted sequence at the rim, an occurrence sometimes called an overturned flap. Away from the rim crest, ejecta is laid down more violently and is more thoroughly mixed. The ejecta forms a blanket that thins away from the crater, becoming discontinuous at a distance of about one crater radius. Along with discontinuous ejecta, individual and groups of secondary craters are distributed even further out. Secondary craters form from more coherent individual blocks and fragments that are ejected from the growing crater (probably from the near-surface region). The distance they travel depends on the target body's surface gravity, and although secondary craters are seen on the larger icy satellites, they are generally absent from small satellites. The most distant ejecta is distributed as bright (or sometimes dark, depending on the composition of the terrain) albedo streaks or rays.

The floors of simple craters are covered with a breccia or rubble lens that is the accumulation of material unable to escape from the crater during the final stages of lateral expansion (Fig. 2). It overlies a thinner more heavily shocked unit that lines the crater floor. Terrestrial studies show that this unit includes crystallized shock-melted rock (and similar units can be imagined for craters formed on the icy satellites). The presence of impact-melted rock becomes more pronounced for the larger complex craters. These craters have undergone modification in response to gravity, have lower depth to diameter ratios than simple craters, and generally have

FIG. 3. Mosaic of *Apollo 15* metric camera frames of the lunar farside crater Tsiolkovsky (~180 km in diameter and several kilometers deep). Slump terraces can be seen, as well as ponds of impact melt on and beyond the rim to the east (right) and a lineated ejecta blanket to the northwest (upper left) that indicates ground flow. The floor is covered with impact melt and breccia (rock rubble), which is in turn overlain with dark mare basalt.

more complex morphologies (see Fig. 3, for example).

For each planet and satellite, there is a distinct size above which craters are complex and below which they are simple. This transition size is inversely correlated with surface gravity and is also generally lower for icy bodies than for rocky bodies. The smallest complex craters have flat floors. Somewhat larger complex craters show slump blocks along their rims, sometimes organized into wall terraces. An uplift in the central region of the crater, corresponding to the downward and inward slumping movement, produces central peaks. At still larger scales, the central peaks are apparently not stable and collapse into a mountain ring form (peak rings), or on the larger icy satellites, into what are termed central pits.

For the very largest impacts, the response of a planet (or satellite) during the modification stage is widespread. The rigid outer shell of the planet is fractured by a coherent system of faults that encircle the collapsing crater but at large distances beyond the rim. Displacements on these faults give rise to great circumferential mountain ranges and valleys. These impact structures are the multiringed basins, the most magnificent crater forms of all. They occur on only the largest bodies: the Moon, Mercury, Mars, and the icy satellites Ganymede and Callisto. They are created by collision of the largest asteroids or comets (on the order of 100 km in diameter) and are generally over 1000 km in extent. The largest involve entire hemispheres of their respective worlds.

Impact craters, once formed, are subject to further modification. On airless worlds, they can be eroded by further bombardment; indeed, a perpetual rain of small impactors churns up such surfaces, creating a fragmental soil layer or regolith. Impact craters can also be eroded by the action of wind and water, as on Earth and Mars, or buried by volcanic units. On large, icy satellites, their topography may be reduced by slow viscous creep of the surface. It is characteristic of the larger craters on the Moon, Mars, and Mercury to act as preferential sites for the later eruption of basaltic lavas. On the Moon, these form the well-known maria, or seas.

V. The Solar System Cratering Record

Understanding the distribution of impact craters in space and time remains one of the most challenging tasks of cratering science. The distribution of craters on Earth (Fig. 4) is very nonuniform. This is partly a reflection of more detailed exploration in the Northern Hemisphere, but it also reflects a concentration of impact cra-

FIG. 4. Areal distribution of known impact structures on Earth. Open symbols are those craters with associated meteorite fragments. [From Grieve, R.A.F. (1982). *Geol. Soc. Am. Spec. Pap.* **190,** 25.]

ters on the oldest and most geologically stable regions of North America and Europe. There are always many more small impact craters than large ones, so only a few, deeply eroded, large structures survive on Earth.

The level of geological activity on the Moon, compared to Earth, is very low, and an enormous number of impacts survive. When the number of craters per square kilometer, or crater density, is plotted against surface age as dated by traditional radioactive isotope methods, an astonishing fact emerges (Fig. 5). Most of the Moon's craters formed a long time ago, and nearly all formed in the first 700 Myr or so of Solar System history. This torrential rain of debris is called the late heavy bombardment, and can be thought of as the final sweep-up of the material that originally built the planets. Curiously enough, no rock units from this time period survive on Earth.

Only a few places on the Moon have been visited and sampled, so the information in Fig. 5 can be turned around and used to date other portions of the lunar surface through their impact crater densities. The probability of having a crater form anywhere on the Moon is uniform, so terrains of equal age should have equal crater densities. Using impact craters as a chronometer, the stratigraphic column of the Moon has been worked out.

It would be marvelous to be able to extend the Moon's impact timetable to other Solar System

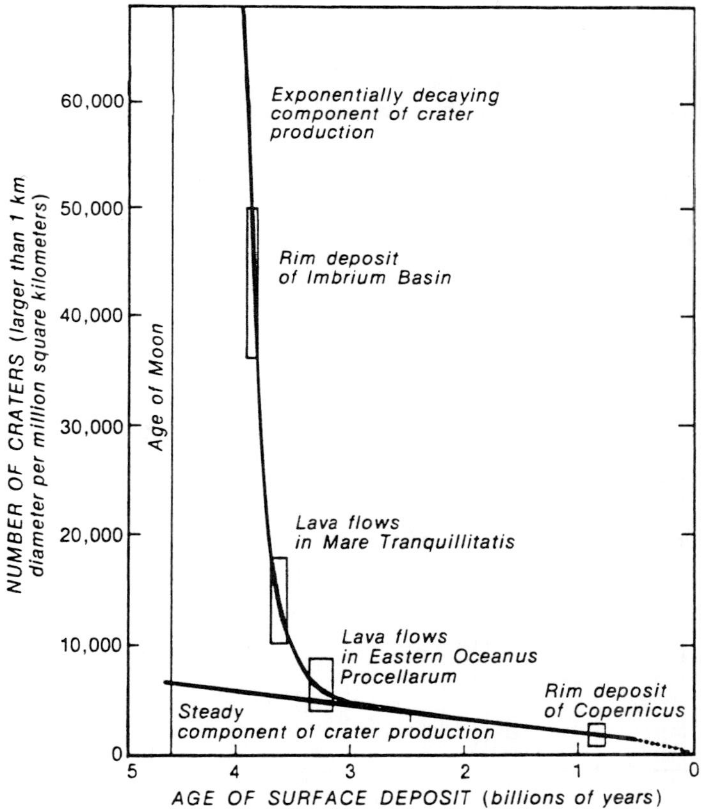

FIG. 5. The variation of crater density on lunar surfaces of different ages. Widths of the small rectangles, which correspond to Apollo landing sites, indicate the uncertainty in age of each radiometrically dated surface. The heights indicate the statistical uncertainty in crater density. The high cratering rate of the late heavy bombardment dropped rapidly between 3.9 and 3.3 Gyr ago, giving way to a lower, more steady rate of crater production. [From Shoemaker, E. M. (1982). *In* "The New Solar System" (J. K. Beatty, B. O'Leary, and A. Chaikin, eds.), p. 33. Sky Publishing Corporation, Cambridge, Massachusetts.]

bodies, that is, to establish an interplanetary correlation of geologic time. To do this means that it must be shown that the same population of impacting objects has struck each body. It is thus necessary to look at the detailed characteristics of the impact flux. The distribution of crater sizes is strongly weighted toward small craters, as mentioned previously. The cumulative number of craters N greater than diameter D, per unit area, generally follows a steep power-law function close to

$$N(>D) \propto D^{-2} \tag{5}$$

The number of craters in each logarithmic size bin, or the crater frequency, goes as D^{-3}.

Figure 6 shows the crater population frequencies for various Solar System bodies divided by a D^{-3} power law. This has the effect of flattening all the curves (removing their steep slopes) and emphasizing their differences. The well-determined curves for the heavily cratered terrains on the Moon, Mars, and Mercury all resemble each other. Hence, the late heavy bombardment occurred on all the planets of the inner Solar System. The case for the outer Solar System is more controversial. The largest icy satellites, Ganymede and Callisto, are missing large craters (>100 km in diameter) compared to the Moon. This may mean either that large craters are preferentially erased on these satellites (perhaps by viscous relaxation) or that a different population of impactors was dominant in the Jupiter region and beyond. This different population could be comets, in contrast with asteroids in the inner Solar System. Some of Saturn's small satellites show crater populations that are strongly peaked in the 10-km-diameter range. These may indicate a population of secondary debris generated within the Saturn system, perhaps by the catastrophic disruption of a small satellite.

VI. The Impact Crater Revolution

Impacts are now felt to play a major role in nearly every aspect of Solar System evolution. The following is an incomplete list of recent discoveries or active research areas.

1. Collisional accretion is thought to be the mechanism of formation for solid planets and

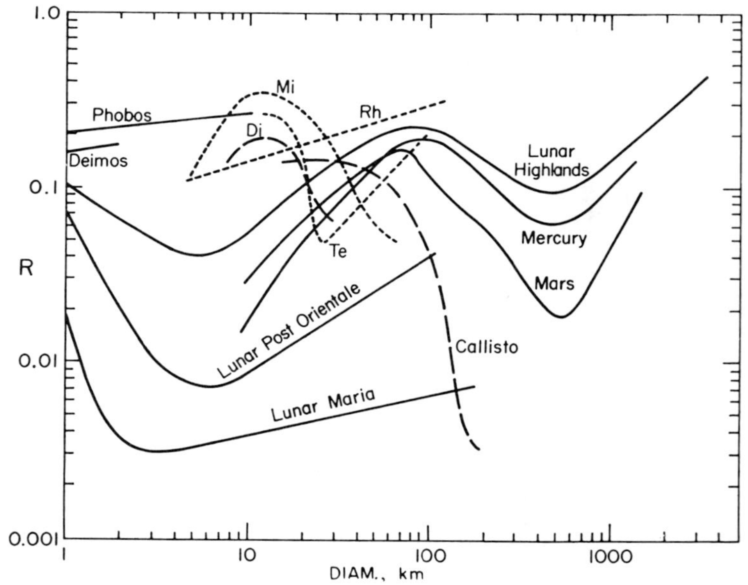

FIG. 6. Characteristic relative-plot diameter-frequency relations for various satellites and terrestrial planets. These are approximate average relations, generally for heavily cratered terrains. Phobos and Deimos are the moons of Mars; Callisto orbits Jupiter; and Mi, Rh, Di, and Te identify Mimas, Rhea, Dione, and Tethys, respectively (all satellites of Saturn). The curves for the older terrains on the Uranian satellites resemble that of Rhea. [From Chapman, C. R., and McKinnon, W. B. (1986). Cratering of planetary satellites. *In* "Satellites" (J. A. Burns and M. S. Matthews, eds.). Univ. of Arizona Press, Tucson, Arizona.]

satellites and for the cores of the giant planets (the latter are thought necessary for giant planet formation).

2. The impact of a Mars-sized object early in the Earth's history may have driven enough material of the right composition into permanent orbit to form the Moon.

3. The impact of a very large asteroid with the northern hemisphere of Mars may ultimately be responsible for the hemispheric dichotomy of that planet, whereby the north is plains and the south is cratered highlands.

4. The impact of a very large object with a differentiated proto-Mercury may have stripped it of its silicate mantle, leaving it with an anomalously large iron core.

5. Collision of an Earth-sized object with Uranus may have tipped its rotation axis substantially and blown or spun out a disk of material from which its satellites formed.

6. Triton may have been captured from solar orbit by Neptune because it collided with an original Neptune satellite.

7. A proto-Pluto could have been collisionally disrupted by collision with a similar object, leading to the formation of the Pluto–Charon planet–satellite pair.

8. Small satellites whose orbits have evolved inside the Roche limit of a giant planet may have been catastrophically disrupted by cometary impact, creating spectacular ring systems such as we see today around Saturn and Uranus.

9. Impacts with planetary and asteroid surfaces have launched meteorites and lunar samples to Earth. Certain young meteorites have been deduced to come from Mars.

10. Early cometary bombardment may have supplied Earth with its inventory of water.

11. Asteroid and comet impact may have stripped away the early atmospheres of the terrestrial planets; in particular, Mars's atmosphere may have been much more massive and allowed liquid water on its surface.

12. Early cometary bombardment may have supplied Earth with its initial inventory of organic molecules, thereby setting the stage for the origin of life.

13. Early giant impacts on Earth may have frustrated the origin of life.

14. Microbes may be launched in ejecta from Earth, potentially seeding other worlds of the Solar System.

15. A large comet or asteroid strike at the end of the Cretaceous, for which there is abundant physical and chemical evidence, may have initiated a sequence of events that led to the extinction of 90% of all the species on Earth at the time, including the dinosaurs. The evolution of *Homo sapiens* ultimately depended on the mammalian radiation that followed.

16. The course of evolution on global and regional scales has probably been profoundly affected in a stochastic way by impacts. According to Steven Jay Gould, evolution, as Darwin saw it, may need major revision.

Just as the paradigm of plate tectonics unified the geological sciences in the 1960s by giving an accurate picture of how Earth behaves as a system, so is impact cratering, or more generally, the collision of Solar System bodies, giving a unified picture of terrestrial and planetary evolution in the 1980s and 1990s. It is no longer valid to speak of earth science and planetary science as distinct entities. Earth and the other planets are part of one system, a system that interacts and evolves via impact.

Bibliography

Anderson, C. E., ed. (1987). Hypervelocity impact: Proceedings of the 1986 Symposium. *Int. J. Impact Eng.* **5,** 1–759.

Chapman, C. R., and McKinnon, W. B. (1986). Cratering of planetary satellites. *In* "Satellites" (J. A. Burns and M. S. Matthews, eds.), p. 492. Univ. of Arizona Press, Tucson, Arizona.

Holsapple, K. A., and Schmidt, R. M. (1987). Point source solutions and coupling parameters in cratering mechanics. *J. Geophys. Res.* **97,** 6350–6376.

Hoyt, W. G. (1987). "Coon Mountain Controversies." Univ. of Arizona Press, Tucson, Arizona.

Mark, K. (1987). "Meteorite Craters." Univ. of Arizona Press, Tucson, Arizona.

Melosh, H. J. (1989). "Impact Cratering: A Geologic Process." Oxford Univ. Press, New York.

IMPEDANCE SPECTROSCOPY

J. Ross Macdonald *University of North Carolina*

GLOSSARY

Admittance: A complex quantity usually symbolized by $Y = Y' + iY''$. It is the inverse of impedance and is sometimes called complex conductance. Here $i = +(-1)^{0.5}$, and the single and double primes denote in-phase and quadrature components, respectively.

Complex dielectric constant: The ratio of the (complex) dielectric displacement to the small-signal AC electric field that induces the displacement. Conventionally written as $\varepsilon = \varepsilon' - i\varepsilon''$. It is given by $Y/(i\omega C_C)$, where C_C is the capacitance of the empty measuring cell.

Complex forms: Impedance spectroscopy data may be expressed in two different forms. Rectangular: $I = I' + iI''$, where I' and I'' are the real and imaginary parts of I, respectively; or Modulus: $I = |I|e^{i\phi}$, where $|I|$ is the modulus, or absolute value, of I and ϕ is its phase angle, or argument. Note that the complex conjugate of I is $I^* = I' - iI'' = |I|e^{-i\phi}$.

Complex modulus: $M = M' + iM''$. It is the inverse of the complex dielectric constant and is also equal to $i\omega C_C Z$.

Debye length: A characteristic length that determines the extent of a space charge region near a discontinuity. It depends on temperature, dielectric constant, and the valence numbers and bulk concentrations of the mobile charges present. The diffuse double-layer capacitance present near a non-ohmic electrode is inversely proportional to the Debye length.

Immittance: A general term denoting any of the four basic impedance spectroscopy response quantities: Y, Z, ε, or M. $I = I' + iI''$.

Impedance: The ratio of a sinusoidal voltage, applied across two terminals of a measurement cell, to the sinusoidal component of the current flowing between the terminals that results from the applied potential difference. Unless the system is purely resistive, impedance is a complex quantity because the current will have a different phase from the applied voltage: $Z = Z' + iZ''$.

Impedance spectroscopy (IS) is a general term that subsumes the small-signal measurement of the linear electrical response of a material of interest (including electrode effects) and the subsequent analysis of the response to yield useful information about the physicochemical properties of the system. Analysis is generally carried out in the frequency domain, although measurements are sometimes made in the time domain and then Fourier transformed to the frequency domain. IS is by no means limited to the measurement and analysis of data at the impedance level (e.g., impedance vs. frequency) but may involve any of the four basic immittance levels; thus, most generally, IS stands for immittance spectroscopy.

I. Short History of Impedance Spectroscopy

Since impedance spectroscopy (IS) deals directly with complex quantities, its history really begins with the introduction of impedance into electrical engineering by Oliver Heaviside in the 1880s. His work was soon extended by A. E. Kennelly and C. P. Steinmetz to include vector diagrams and complex representation. It was not long before workers in the field began to make use of the Argand diagram of mathematics by plotting immittance response in the complex plane, with frequency an implicit variable. Electrical engineering examples were the circle diagram introduced by C. W. Carter (1925) and the Smith-Chart impedance diagram of P. H. Smith (1939). These approaches were soon followed in the dielectric response field by the introduction in 1941 of the Cole–Cole plot: a plot of ε'' on the y (or imaginary) axis vs. ε' on the x (or real) axis. Such complex plane plots are now widely used for two-dimensional representation of the response of all four immittance types. Finally, three-dimensional perspective plots that involve a log-frequency axis were introduced to the IS area by the author and his colleagues in 1981; these plots allow complete response at a given immittance level to be shown in a single diagram.

Because IS analysis generally makes considerable use of equivalent circuits to represent experimental frequency response, the whole history of lumped-constant circuit analysis, which particularly flowered in the first third of the century, is immediately relevant to IS. Since then, much work has been devoted to the development of theoretical physicochemical response models and to the definition and analysis of various distributed circuit elements for use in IS-equivalent circuits along with ideal, lumped elements like resistance and capacitance. The preferred analysis method for fitting of IS data to either equivalent circuits or to a mathematical model is complex nonlinear least squares fitting (CNLS), introduced to the field in 1977 by Macdonald and Garber. In this procedure, all the parameters of a fitting model are simultaneously adjusted to yield an optimum fit to the data.

Early experimental work in the IS field is discussed in the book on IS listed in the bibliography. Here it will suffice to mention the work of Grahame on electrolyte double-layer response, the technique of AC polarography pioneered by D. E. Smith, and the electrolyte studies of Randles and Somerton, Sluyters and Oomen, R. P. Buck, and J. E. Bauerle. Since the late 1960s, IS has developed rapidly, in large part because of the availability of new, accurate, and rapid measuring equipment.

II. Categories of Impedance Spectroscopy: Definitions and Distinctions

There are two main categories of IS: electrochemical IS (EIS) and everything else. EIS involves measurements and analysis of materials in which ionic conduction strongly predominates. Examples of such materials are solid and liquid electrolytes, fused salts, ionically conducting glasses and polymers, and nonstoichiometric ionically bonded single crystals, where conduction can involve motion of ion vacancies and interstitials. EIS is also valuable in the study of fuel cells, rechargeable batteries, and corrosion.

The remaining category of IS applies to dielectric materials: solid or liquid nonconductors whose electrical characteristics involve dipolar rotation, and to materials with predominantly electronic conduction. Examples are single-crystal or amorphous semiconductors, glasses, and polymers. Of course, IS applies to more complicated situations as well, for example to partly conducting dielectric materials with some simultaneous ionic and electronic conductivity. It is worth noting that although EIS is the most rapidly growing branch of IS, nonelectrochemical IS measurements came first and are still of great value and importance in both basic and applied areas.

In the EIS area in particular, an important distinction is made between supported and unsupported electrolytes. Supported electrolytes are ones containing a high concentration of indifferent electrolyte, one whose ions generally neither adsorb nor react at the electrodes of the measuring cell. Such an added salt can ensure that the material is very nearly electroneutral everywhere, thus allowing diffusion and reaction effects for a low-concentration ion of interest to dominate the AC response of the system. Support is generally only possible for liquid electrochemical materials; it is often, but not always, used in aqueous electrochemistry. Solid electrolytes are unsupported in most cases of interest, electroneutrality is not present, and Poisson's equation strongly couples charged species. Because of this difference, the formulas or models used to analyze supported and unsupported situations may be somewhat or completely different.

Another important distinction is concerned with static potentials and fields. In a material-electrode system without an applied static external potential difference (p.d.), internal p.d.s and fields are, nevertheless, generally present, producing space-charge layers at interfaces. For solids such regions are known as Frenkel layers and arise from the difference in work function between the electrode and the material. Because the static fields and charge concentrations in the material are inhomogeneous, exact small-signal solutions for the impedance of the system are impossible and numerical methods must be used.

In an electrolytic cell such static space-charge regions are only absent when the external static p.d. is adjusted so that the charge on the working electrode is zero—the point of zero charge (PZC)—a flat-band condition. Such adjustment is impossible for systems with two symmetrical electrodes because an applied static p.d. increases the space-charge region at one electrode while reducing it at the other. But the use of a working electrode of small area and a large-area counter electrode ensures that the overall impedance of the system is little influenced by what happens at the counter electrode; in this situation the PZC can be achieved for the working electrode. In general, the current distribution near this electrode is frequency dependent and thus makes a frequency-dependent contribution to the overall impedance of the system, which is dependent on electrode geometry and character.

Figure 1 shows a flow diagram for a complete IS study whose goal is characterization of important properties of the material-electrode system from its electrical response, one of the major applications of IS. The experimental data is denoted by $Z_e(\omega)$, the impedance predicted by a theoretical fitting model by $Z_t(\omega)$, and that of a possible electrical equivalent circuit by $Z_{ec}(\omega)$, where $\omega = 2\pi f$ and f is frequency. When an appropriate detailed model for the physicochemical processes present is available, it should certainly be used for fitting. Otherwise, one would employ an equivalent electrical circuit whose elements and connectivity were selected, as far as possible, to represent the various mass and charge transport physical processes thought to be of importance for the particular system.

Note that a complete IS analysis often involves more than a single set of measurements of immittance vs. frequency. Frequently, full characterization requires that such sets of measurements be carried out over a range of temperatures and/or other externally controlled experimental variables. IS characterization may be used to yield basic scientific and/or engineering information on a wide variety of materials and devices, ranging from solid and liquid electrolytes to dielectrics and semiconductors, to electrical and structural ceramics, to magnetic ferrites, to polymers and protective paint films, and to secondary batteries and fuel cells. Other important applications of IS, not further discussed herein, have been made in the biological area, such as studies of polarization across cell membranes and of animal and plant tissues. Finally, the analysis techniques of IS are not limited to electrical immittance but apply as well to measurements of mechanical and acoustic immittance.

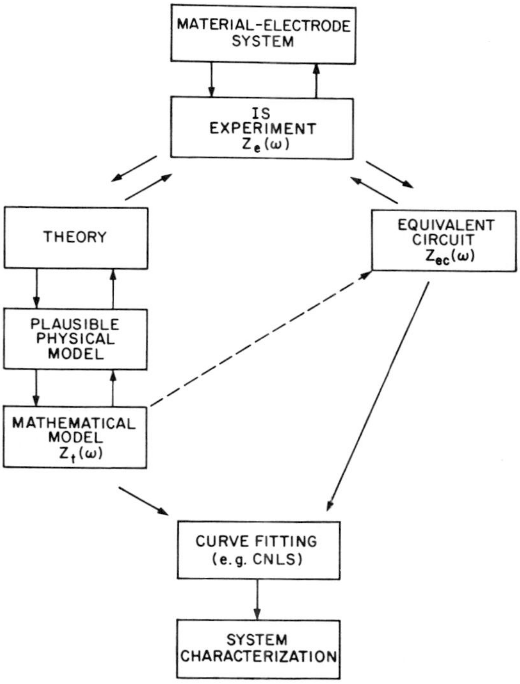

FIG. 1. Flow diagram for the measurement and characterization of a material-electrode system. (Reprinted by permission of John Wiley & Sons, Inc., from "Impedance Spectroscopy—Emphasizing Solid Materials and Systems." J. R. Macdonald, ed. Copyright © 1987, John Wiley & Sons, Inc.)

III. Elements of Impedance Spectroscopy

A. Measurement Methods

Although IS measurements are simple in principle, they are often complicated in practice. Part of the difficulty arises because the resistive and capacitive components of IS response have ranges, when one considers different materials, electrodes, and temperatures, that span 10 or more orders of magnitude. Measurements require comparison with standard values of these components and are thus only as accurate as the standards. Second, the IS frequency range may extend over 12 orders of magnitude or more: from as low as 10 μHz for adequate resolution of interfacial processes, up to 10 MHz or higher, sometimes needed to characterize bulk response of the material of interest.

Although IS measurements on solids or dielectric liquids usually involve cells with two identical plane, parallel electrodes, the situation is often much more complicated for measurements on liquid electrolytes. There, one usually employs one or more small working electrodes, a very small reference electrode, and a large counter electrode. Such an arrangement ensures that everything of interest (related to immittance) happens at or near the working electrode(s). Further, a rotating-disk working electrode is frequently used to control hydrodynamic conditions near the electrode.

Because the kinetics of electrode reactions often depend strongly on the static (dc) potential difference between the working electrode and the bulk, or, equivalently, the working electrode and the reference electrode, a potentiostat is needed to fix this p.d. to a known and controllable value. The simultaneous application of both ac and dc signals to a three- or four-electrode cell makes it particularly difficult to obtain accurate frequency-response results above 50 kHz or so.

Although a calibrated double-beam oscilloscope, or the use of Lissajous figures with a single-beam instrument, can be used to determine immittance magnitude and phase, such measurements are generally insufficiently accurate, are time consuming, and apply only over a limited frequency range. A superior alternative is the use of audio-frequency or high-frequency bridges. Several such bridges are discussed in the IS book. Of particular interest is the Berberian–Cole bridge, which can cover a wide frequency range and can allow potentiostatic dc bias control. Another important technique using a bridge and special error reduction procedures has recently been developed by Schöne and coworkers that allows potentiostatic control and yields very accurate impedance results up to 3 MHz. But manual balancing of a bridge is often disadvantageous because of its slowness, especially for corrosion studies where the properties of the system itself may be slowly changing.

Manual balancing is avoided in various automated network analyzers and impedance analyzers now commercially available. But the measuring instrument that has virtually revolutionized IS measurements and principally led to the burgeoning growth of the field in the past 20 years is the frequency-response analyzer (FRA). Typical examples are FRAs produced by Solartron and by Zahner. Although space does not allow a full description of their many features, such instruments allow potentiostatic control for three- or four-terminal measurements, they are highly digitized, they incorporate automatic frequency sweeps and automatic control of the magnitude of the applied ac signal, they can yield 0.1% accuracy, and they carry out measurements automatically.

Although FRAs such as the Solartron 1260 cover a frequency range from 10 μHz to 32 MHz, impedance results using them are not sufficiently accurate above about 50 kHz when potentiostatic control is used. A typical FRA determines impedance by correlating, at each frequency, the cell response with two synchronous signals, one in phase with the applied signal and the other phase-shifted by 90°. This process yields the in-phase and out-of-phase components of the response and leads to the various immittance components. A useful feature is autointegration, a procedure that averages results over an exact number of cycles, with the amount of such averaging automatically selected to yield statistically consistent results.

B. Analysis and Interpretation of Data

1. Graphics

Before carrying out a detailed analysis of IS immittance data, it is a good idea to examine the data graphically, both to search for any outliers and to examine the structure of the data, structure that will usually reflect, at least in part, the physical processes present that led to the data. From the experimental situation one will generally know whether one is dealing with an intrinsically insulating material, such as a nonconducting or a leaky dielectric, or whether the situation is of intrinsically conducting character: mobile charges dominate the response but may be completely or only partially blocked at the electrodes. For complete blocking, no DC can pass, a case that could be confused with dielectric response. In the intrinsically conducting situation, dielectric effects are generally minimal, and Z and M representations of the data are often most useful. In the nonconducting case, Y and ε are frequently most appropriate, but it is nevertheless a good idea initially to examine plots of the data for all four immittance levels, whatever the conducting/nonconducting situation.

When mobile charges are present, five principal physical processes may influence the data; these are bulk resistive-capacitive effects, electrode reactions, adsorption at the electrodes, bulk generation-recombination effects (e.g., ion-pairing), and diffusion. The double-layer capacitance is the reaction capacitance C_R, and the reaction resistance R_R is inversely proportional to the reaction rate constant. It is important to distinguish C_R from the usually much larger low-frequency pseudocapacitance associated with the diffusion of mobile charge or with adsorption at an electrode. Note that in general a process that dissipates energy is represented in an IS equivalent circuit by a resistance, and energy storage is usually modeled by a capacitance. Detailed CNLS analysis of IS data can lead in favorable cases to estimates of such basic material-electrode quantities as electrode reaction and adsorption rates, bulk generation-recombination rates, charge valence numbers and mobilities, diffusion coefficients, and the (real) dielectric constant of the material.

There are many ways IS data may be plotted. In the IS field, where capacitive rather than inductive effects dominate, conventionally one plots $-\mathrm{Im}(Z) \equiv -Z''$ on the y-axis vs. $\mathrm{Re}(Z) \equiv Z'$ on the x-axis to give a complex plane impedance plot. Such graphs have (erroneously) been termed Nyquist plots. They have the disadvantage of not indicating frequency response directly, but may, nevertheless, be very helpful in identifying conduction processes present. Another approach, the Bode diagram, is to plot $\log[|Z|]$ and ϕ vs. $\log[f]$. Alternatively, one can plot Z' (or any I') or $-Z''$ (or $-I''$), or the logs of these quantities vs. $\log[f]$.

An important IS building block is Debye response, response that involves a single time constant, τ. A Cole–Cole plot of such response is shown in Fig. 2. The arrow shows the direction of increasing frequency. Debye response can be represented in complex form as $\varepsilon = \varepsilon_\infty + [\varepsilon_0 - \varepsilon_\infty]/[1 + (i\omega\tau)]$ and, in circuit form, involves a capacitance $\varepsilon_\infty C_C$ in parallel with the series combination of a resistor R, modeling dissipative effects, and a capacitor $C \equiv (\varepsilon_0 - \varepsilon_\infty)C_C$, representing stored charge. Finally, the time constant or relaxation time is given by $\tau \equiv RC$.

Three-dimensional perspective plots are particularly useful because they allow complete response to appear on a single graph. Figure 3

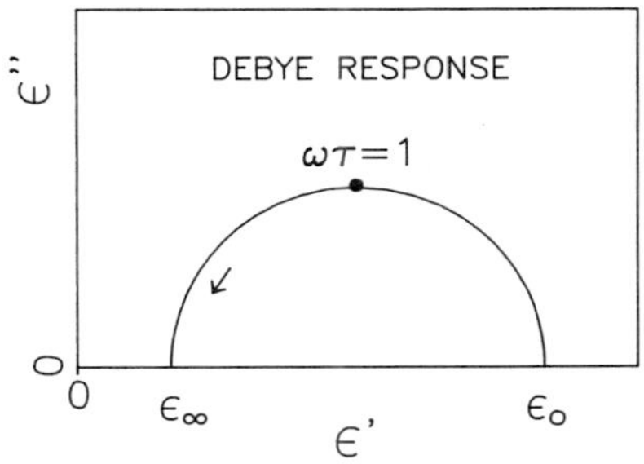

FIG. 2. Complex-plane plot of the complex dielectric constant for Debye frequency response.

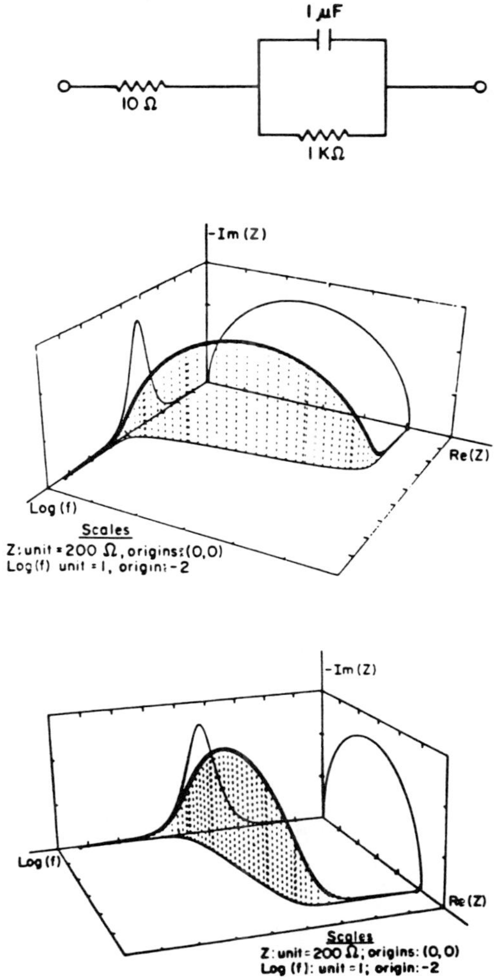

FIG. 3. A simple circuit and 3-D perspective plots of its impedance response. (Reprinted by permission of John Wiley & Sons, Inc., from "Impedance Spectroscopy—Emphasizing Solid Materials and Systems." J. R. Macdonald, ed. Copyright © 1987, John Wiley & Sons, Inc.)

shows such plots at the impedance level for the analog of Debye response for a conducting system. By including projections of the 3-D curve of the response in all three perpendicular planes of the plot, one incorporates all relevant 2-D plots in the same diagram. Note that the curve in the back plane, the complex-plane impedance plot, is just the usual Debye semicircle, one with its center on the real axis.

To demonstrate some of the power and weaknesses of 3-D plots, Fig. 4 includes three types of such plots, all for the same EIS data taken on single-crystal Na β-alumina. Graph A is an impedance plot and shows that only two out of the four curves indicate that the lowest frequency point is in error. In this plot, ν denotes frequency f. Clearly, one should not rely on the conventional log[f] curves alone. Since the diagram shows that much high-frequency data are not resolved by this kind of plot, graph B involves the logarithms of the data. Although high-frequency response now appears, the error in the low-frequency point is nearly obscured by the reduced resolution inherent in a log plot.

Much improved results appear in graph C, a 3-D M plot. Resolution over the full frequency range is greatly increased; the error in the lowest frequency point is clearly shown; a mid-frequency glitch now appears that is not evident in the other plots and arises from a switch of measuring devices without adequate cross-calibration; and nonphysical behavior is now apparent

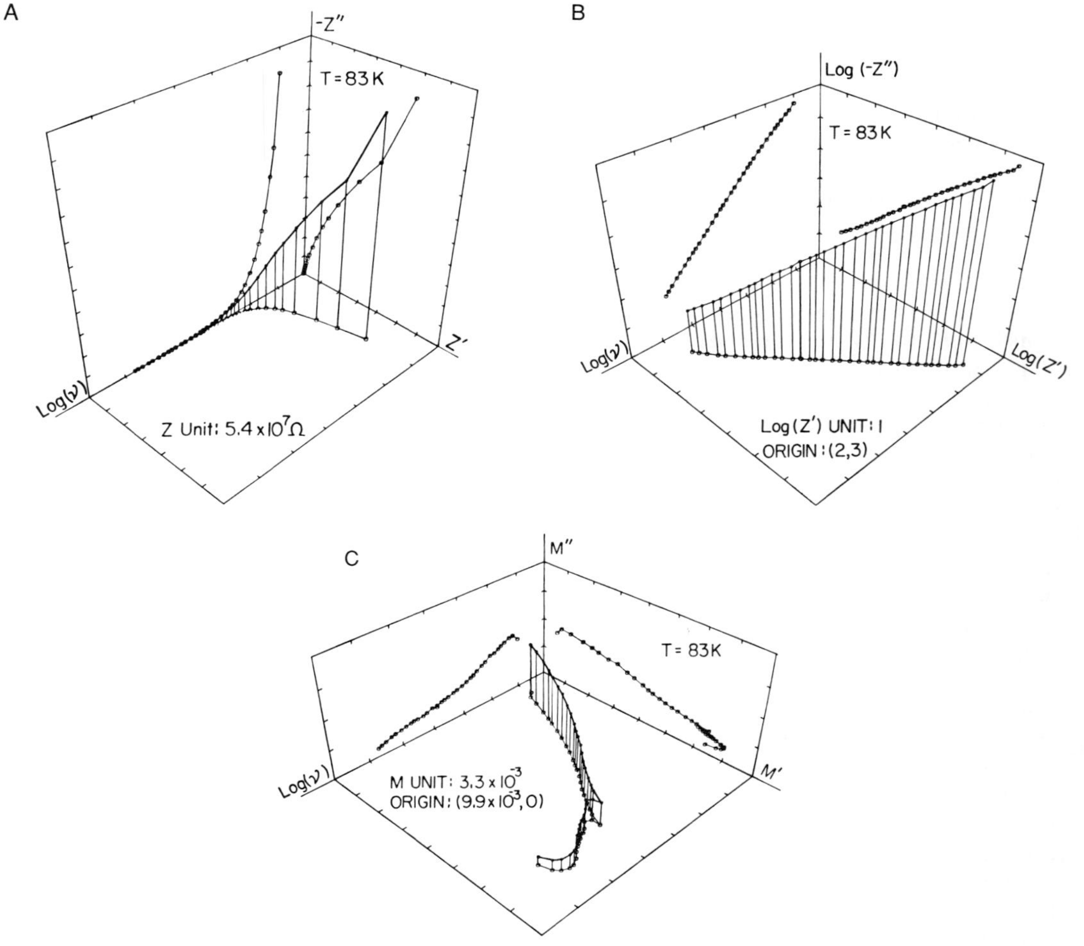

FIG. 4. Three-dimensional perspective plots of Na β-alumina data at (A) the impedance level, (B) log impedance level, and (C) complex modulus level. (Reprinted by permission of John Wiley & Sons, Inc., from "Impedance Spectroscopy—Emphasizing Solid Materials and Systems," J. R. Macdonald, ed. Copyright © 1987, John Wiley & Sons, Inc.)

at the highest frequencies. These results make it clear that even when 3-D plots are used, it is always desirable to explore the results of different transformations of the data and to pick the one with the best resolution.

2. Complex Nonlinear Least Squares Data-Fitting

a. Strengths and Weaknesses. Although graphic examination of IS data is an important analysis step, only in the simplest cases can it be used to obtain even rough estimates of some system parameters. Since good parameter estimates are needed for adequate characterization of the material-electrode system, a fitting technique such as CNLS must be applied to obtain them. In doing so, the data, at any I level, are fitted to a mathematical model involving the parameters or to the response of an equivalent circuit. Such fitting models are discussed in Section IV, A. Not only does CNLS fitting yield estimates of the parameters of the model, but it also provides estimates of their standard deviations, measures of how well they have been determined by the data fit. These standard deviation values are valuable in deciding which parameters are crucial to the model and which are useless, or at least not well determinable from the data.

CNLS fits are produced by a program that minimizes the weighted sum of squares of the real and imaginary residuals. A residual is the difference between a data value at a given frequency and the corresponding value calculated from the model. The weights used are the inverses of the estimated error variance for a given real data value and that for the corresponding imaginary value. Weighting is the most subjective part of least squares fitting, yet it can often have crucial effects on the results of such fitting and is thus of prime importance.

Since individual error-variance estimates are usually unavailable, it has been customary to use simplified variance models to obtain values to use in the fitting. The simplest such model is to take all weights equal to one: unity weighting (UWT). Another popular and important choice is to set the error variance of each data value equal to the square of that value. Since the uncertainty of the value is then proportional to the value itself, this defines proportional weighting (PWT). It has recently been shown, however, that such weighting leads to biased parameter estimates; it should be replaced, when the fitting model is well matched to the data, by function-proportional weighting (FPWT), where the calculated rather than the direct data value is employed in the weighting.

PWT or FPWT is particularly important because the range of typical IS data can be as large as 10^3 or even 10^6. When UWT is used in fitting such data, only the largest parts of the data determine the parameter estimates, and the smaller values have little or no effect. Alternatively, with PWT or FPWT, which is equivalent to assuming a constant percentage error, small and large data values contribute equally to the final parameter estimates.

Figure 5 presents the results of PWT CNLS fitting of β-PbF_2 data using an equivalent circuit with a distributed element, the constant phase element (CPE). Both the original data and the fit results are shown in the 3-D plot. The figure

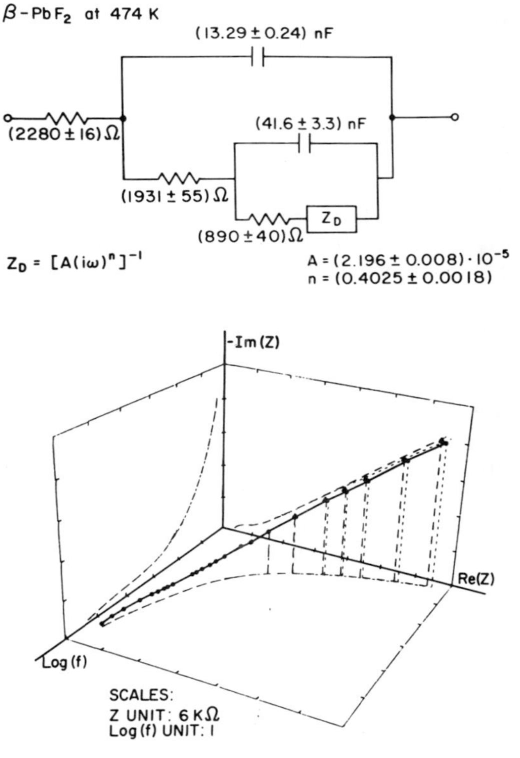

FIG. 5. Three-dimensional perspective impedance plot of β-PbF_2 data (——, ---) and fitted values and curves (— — —); the fitting circuit used and parameter estimates and estimates of their standard deviations. (Reprinted by permission of John Wiley & Sons, Inc., from "Impedance Spectroscopy—Emphasizing Solid Materials and Systems," J. R. Macdonald, ed. Copyright © 1987, John Wiley & Sons, Inc.)

indicates that seven free parameters have been quite well determined by the data, a remarkable result when one considers the apparent lack of much structure in the data themselves.

A detailed physico-chemical model is always preferable to an equivalent circuit for fitting, especially since such models often cannot be expressed in terms of an equivalent circuit involving standard elements. But most IS situations involve many-body problems currently insolvable at the microscopic level. Thus one must usually be satisfied with simpler continuum models, often expressed as equivalent circuits. One weakness of equivalent circuits involving only ideal elements is their ambiguity. The same elements may be interconnected in different ways and yet, with appropriate values, yield exactly the same frequency response at all frequencies. Thus, IS fitting cannot distinguish between the different possible structures, and only other measurements, such as IS fitting of data over a range of temperatures and/or potentials, can help one establish which of the possible circuits is most physically reasonable.

Figure 6 shows all possible potentially equivalent conducting circuits involving two resistances and two capacitances. Specific parameter value choices that make them all have exactly the same response are also indicated. Here the values for circuit D were taken exact, and approximate values for the other elements are denoted with a ~ sign. Let the units of these elements be MΩ for resistances and μF for capacitances. Note that the two RC time constants of circuit A, a series connection, differ by less than 17% and are thus very close together. Can IS procedures resolve such a situation? Figure 7 shows the exact complex-plane response of these circuits at both the *Z* and the *M* levels, compared to single time-constant Debye response. The *M* curve shows much better separa-

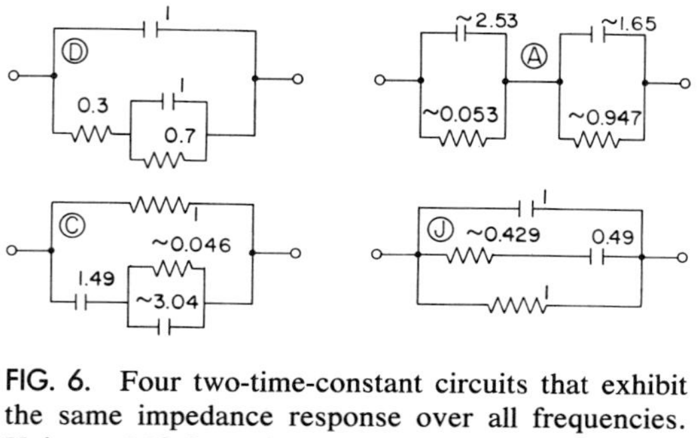

FIG. 6. Four two-time-constant circuits that exhibit the same impedance response over all frequencies. Units are MΩ for resistances and μF for capacitances.

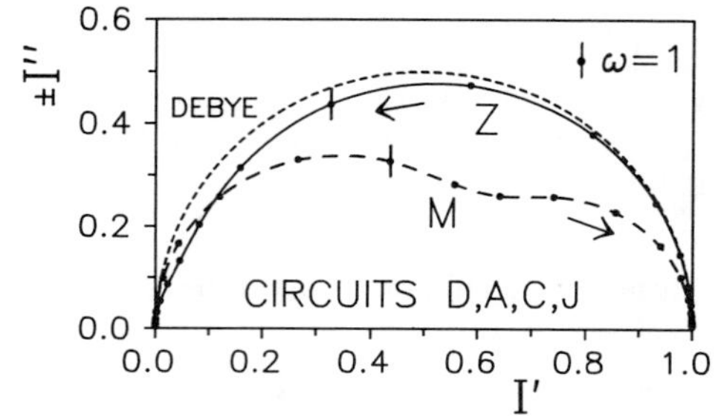

FIG. 7. Complex-plane immittance responses, at the *Z* and *M* levels, of the circuits of Fig. 6.

tion of the two response regions than does the *Z* curve. Thus, adequate graphical resolution is indeed possible. Further, it turns out that CNLS fitting of synthetic data calculated from any of these circuits with appreciable proportional random errors added still yields excellent parameter estimates. In fact, with reasonably good data, CNLS can resolve response involving considerably closer time constants than those involved here.

Although several CNLS fitting programs now exist for use on personal computers, two commercially available ones have ben especially tailored for the IS field. The first, EQUIVCRT, can be obtained from Dr. B. A. Boukamp, Twente University, P.O. Box 217, 7500 AE Enschede, The Netherlands: the second, LEVM, can be obtained from the Department of Physics and Astronomy, University of North Carolina, Chapel Hill at nominal cost. The programs to some degree complement each other, but LEVM is more general and flexible in many ways and incorporates much more sophisticated weighting possibilities.

b. Recent Developments. Currently, the capability of using various types of weighting involving model predictions instead of data values exists only in LEVM, first released in the summer of 1989. Although weighting such as FPWT is somewhat more complicated than PWT because it varies with each nonlinear least squares iteration as the parameter estimates change during the fitting procedure, its bias reduction potential makes such complexity worthwhile. Although LEVM allows the fitting of real or imaginary parts of the data separately, fitting both together, as in CNLS, ensures that the best use is made of all the data in determining the parameter estimates and is thus preferred when both parts are available.

Real IS data often has independent random errors that have both an additive term and one that depends on the true model predictions. A rather general error-variance model incorporating these possibilities is included in LEVM. For a specific angular frequency ω_j, the real and imaginary parts of ν_j, the error variance used in determining the weighting, may be written as

$$\nu_j' = U^2 + |F'(\omega_j)|^{2\xi}$$

and

$$\nu_j'' = U^2 + |F''(t_j)|^{2\xi}$$

where U is associated with the additive random errors and ξ is an arbitrary positive fractional exponent.

When $U = 0$, $\xi = 1$, and F is a data value, one has PWT; whereas when F is a model prediction the result is FPWT. Another widely used weighting, modulus weighting, follows when the same values of U and ξ are used but both F' and F'' in the above equations are replaced by $|F|$. It is usually inconsistent, however, with the types of errors likely to be present and generally leads to appreciably more bias in parameter estimates even than PWT. CNLS fitting yields a standard deviation S_f of residuals, which is a measure of the overall goodness of fit. For proportional random errors having a proportionality constant of σ_r, S_f is an unbiased estimate of σ_r for FPWT, is nearly so for PWT, and is appreciably biased on the low side for FMWT and MWT, types of modulus weighting.

When the data involve one or more inductive-type loops, such as arise from adsorption of a mobile charge at an electrode, it is desirable to use a nonzero U along with PWT or FPWT or to use modulus weighting. Otherwise, because values of the imaginary part of the data may become very small and even pass through zero in the loop region, PWT or FPWT alone can strongly overemphasize the effect of these values near zero and thus lead to poor fitting.

Although U and ξ may be given fixed values during CNLS fitting, a way has been found to incorporate them as free parameters in LEVM least squares fitting. When this is done, the data themselves determine the most appropriate weighting for their fit, thus removing an appreciable part of the subjective element present in prior weighting approaches. Further, Monte Carlo fitting studies have shown that the statistical uncertainties of U and ξ in CNLS fits with them both taken free, or with only ξ free, are usually quite small compared to their estimates, and their biases are even smaller. Thus, their fit estimates may be used with confidence.

Although for much IS data one would expect that ξ would be close to unity, this need not always be the case. Consider, for example, a set of real data arising from the sum of the radioactive decay of two different species. Now the statistics of such decay follows a Poisson process, one for which $\xi = 0.5$. The radioactive background count will also involve such a process. Thus the appropriate variance model would involve $U = 0$ and three terms, each with $2\xi = 1$. The first two would be the two exponential decays and the last, the background. In such a fitting situation, where ξ is known absolutely it should be held fixed at its proper value.

IV. Applications

A. Basic Analysis of Material Properties and Electrode Effects

1. Bulk and Reaction Response

Although IS is of great value for the characterization of the electrical properties of material-electrode systems, its use for this purpose requires that connections be known between model and/or equivalent circuit parameters and the basic characterization parameters. One must be able to pass from estimates of macroscopic quantities, such as resistances and capacitances, to estimates of average microscopic quantities. Here only a brief overview will be given of some of the large amount of theoretical IS-related work of the past 40 years. More details appear in the IS book.

Because of the charge decoupling present in a supported situation, it is often an excellent approximation to treat the effects of the various physical processes present independently. On the other hand, for unsupported conditions where strong coupling is present, a unified treatment of all the processes together is necessary. The most complete such theory, which incorporates all five of the processes mentioned in Section III,B,1, was published by Franceschetti and Macdonald in 1978. It is a continuum (i.e., averaged, not microscopic) theory, includes intrinsic and extrinsic charge effects, and applies to either ionic or electronic conduction conditions. Even though it strictly applies only to flat-band conditions, its results are still sufficiently complicated that only in simplified cases does it lead to response that may be modeled by an equivalent circuit.

It is useful, particularly in the EIS area, to separate the electric processes present into bulk- and electrode-related groups whenever possible. The first group includes bulk resistance and dielectric effects and the homogeneous reactions associated with dissociation and recombination of the charges present. It is generally associated with response effects at the high end of the frequency range, while electrode effects usually occur near the low end, possibly at very low frequencies. Bulk resistance and capacitance are extensive quantities, dependent on the effective separation between electrodes.

The second group involves what happens in the neighborhood of the electrodes (within a few Debye lengths of them) and is thus intensive. No charge is transferred to an electrode if it is completely blocking for all mobile charges. The next simplest EIS situation is that where a mobile metallic ion is of the same species as the atoms of a metallic electrode: a parent-ion electrode. Then, in a symmetrical-electrode situation there is a sink/source of ions at each electrode, since electron transfer at an electrode can transform ions into atoms and vice versa, depending on the polarity of the electric field at the electrode. Such a reaction can be written

$$\mathrm{Me} \leftrightharpoons \mathrm{Me}_{z+} + ze^-$$

where Me denotes a metal atom and z the number of electrons transferred. An example of a symmetrical cell of this type is Ag|AgCl|Ag.

Particularly important for the aqueous electrolyte area is the redox electrode, where charge crosses the interface at the electrode only in the form of electrons. The species Red and Ox are usually soluble in the electrolyte, satisfy

$$\mathrm{Red}^{(z-n)+} \leftrightharpoons Ox^{z+} + ne^-$$

and involve the forward and reverse reaction rate constants k_f and k_r, respectively. If $z = n$, the Red species is uncharged and may diffuse in the electrode, or may evolve if it is a gas.

2. Distributed Circuit Element Response

a. Diffusion. Since diffusion is not localized at a point in space but is distributed over a finite region, it leads to electrical response characteristic of a distributed circuit element (DCE). Such elements cannot be described by means of a finite number of ideal elements such as resistances and capacitances. Here, the response of several DCEs important to IS will be discussed.

In addition to possible diffusion of uncharged species within an electrode, diffusion of mobile species in the electrolyte may contribute significantly to the impedance of a IS system. Generally, diffusion response is neither intensive nor extensive. At sufficiently high frequencies, diffusion effects are confined to the immediate neighborhood of the electrode (or within a hydrodynamic boundary layer at a rotating electrode) and so are intensive; whereas at low enough frequencies, diffusion occurs throughout the material between electrodes, and the response becomes extensive as the frequency decreases and the effective diffusion length l_d, proportional to $(\omega)^{-0.5}$, becomes comparable to the size of the cell.

The diffusion impedance, appropriate when there is a fast electrode reaction, is of the form

$$Z_W(\omega) = Z_W(0)[\tanh\{i(l/l_d)^2\}^{0.5}]/\{i(l/l_d)^2\}^{0.5}$$

where l is the separation between symmetrical electrodes and $Z_W(0)$ is a resistance proportional to l and thus is extensive. Such response is known as finite-length Warburg behavior. At high enough frequencies that the tanh term goes to unity. $Z_W(\omega)$ becomes proportional to the intensive quantity l_d and is termed (ordinary) Warburg response.

As the electrode reaction rate decreases toward zero, a more complicated expression for $Z_W(\omega)$ must be used, but it reduces to the form

$$Z_W(\omega) = Z_C[\mathrm{ctnh}\{i(l/l_d)^2\}^{0.5}]/\{i(l/l_d)^2\}^{0.5}$$

when the electrode is completely blocking (open circuit diffusion). Here Z_C is given by $(l/l_d)^2/\omega C_{DOC}$ and C_{DOC}/C_C is the effective low-frequency limiting dielectric constant associated with the process.

For general unsupported situations, those with positive and negative charged species mobile and having diffusion coefficients of D_n and D_p and valence numbers of z_n and z_p,

$$(l_d)^2 = (4D_nD_p/\omega)[(z_n + z_p)/(z_nD_n + z_pD_p)]$$

No diffusion effects appear when only charge of a single sign is mobile; this often is an excellent approximation for solid electrolytes.

For supported conditions, matters are different. Consider a single species with diffusion coefficient D and valence number z (possibly zero). Then $(l_d)^2 = 4D/\omega$, a result that follows from the above expression when one sets $D_n = D_p = D$ and $z_n = z_p = z$. Further, when both positive and negative charges are mobile, diffusion under unsupported conditions leads to a single expression involving tanh, as above, but for supported conditions, as in the redox case, two such terms appear, one for each species—in keeping with the lack of coupling between the species.

b. Other DCEs. A characteristic signature of diffusion is $(i\omega)^{\pm 0.5}$ response, but IS data more often exhibits CPE response $(i\omega\tau)^{\pm\psi}$, where $0 \leq \omega \leq 1$. But such response is not physically realizable over all frequencies, and so other DCEs have been introduced that approximate such behavior over a limited frequency range. They may be written as impedances or complex dielectric constants, depending upon which I level is appropriate. Here they will be given at the Z level.

An empirical DCE of the above type is Havriliak–Negami (HN) response, written as

$$Z_{HN}(\omega) = R_{HN}/[1 + (i\omega\tau)^{\alpha}]^{\beta}$$

where $0 \leq \alpha \leq 1$ and $0 \leq \beta \leq 1$. It reduces to Cole–Davidson response when $\alpha = 1$ and to Cole–Cole response (termed *ZC* response at the Z level) when $\beta = 1$. The first of these yields an asymmetric arc in a complex-plane plot and the second one a symmetric arc. Both shapes appear often in practice, and *ZC* fitting is frequently used to represent data that yield an arc of a semicircle with its center below the real axis. Such behavior is usually ascribed to the presence of a distribution of some physical quantity in space, time, or energy. Rough electrodes are one example. Although fitted values of α and/or β often show appreciable temperature dependence, there exists no theory yielding such dependence for HN response.

Another important DCE is that of Kohlrausch–Williams–Watts (KWW) response. It yields a stretched exponential in the time domain, response proportional to $\exp[-t/\tau]^{\psi}$, with $0 \leq \omega \leq 1$. Here there are, if anything, too many different theories yielding such response, but again they do not predict the temperature dependence of ψ. The corresponding frequency response is very difficult to calculate accurately, but an excellent approximation for it is available in LEVM. Complex plane plots of KWW response yield an asymmetric arc for any $\psi < 1$ until $\psi = 1$, when a Debye semicircle appears.

Another DCE category is associated with the presence in a material of a distribution of activation energies (DAE). Such distributions are likely in IS materials and may be expected even in single crystals when there are many competing possibilities for the individual motion of mobile charges. Both Gaussian and exponential distributions have been considered in detail and can lead to either symmetric or asymmetric complex-plane arcs. But only an exponential DAE yields CPE-like fractional-exponent frequency response over a finite frequency region. This exponent, ϕ, is not limited to the range from 0 to 1 but satisfies $-\infty < \phi < \infty$. Further, unlike the other DCEs considered, an exponential DAE predicts temperature dependence of ϕ in good agreement with many experimental results.

3. Equivalent Circuits

Many different equivalent circuits have been proposed over the years for IS fitting, and no one circuit structure is appropriate for all situations. Figure 8 shows a circuit, however, that has been found useful for a variety of materials and experimental conditions. Bulk properties are represented by C_g, the geometrical compacitance, and R_∞, the high-frequency limiting resistance. C_R, associated with an electrode reaction, is the double-layer capacitance (possibly including both a compact inner-layer capacitance and a diffuse double-layer capacitance), and R_R is the reaction resistance. Finally, C_A and R_A are associated with adsorption at an electrode. The Z_D elements, when present, are DCEs. Also, not all the other elements need be present; for example, in the absence of adsorption C_A and R_A would not appear.

For an unsupported, fully dissociated material with charges of only a single sign mobile, the Fig. 8 circuit with all Z_Ds absent has been found to yield an accurate representation of the impedance resulting from a flat-band theoretical anal-

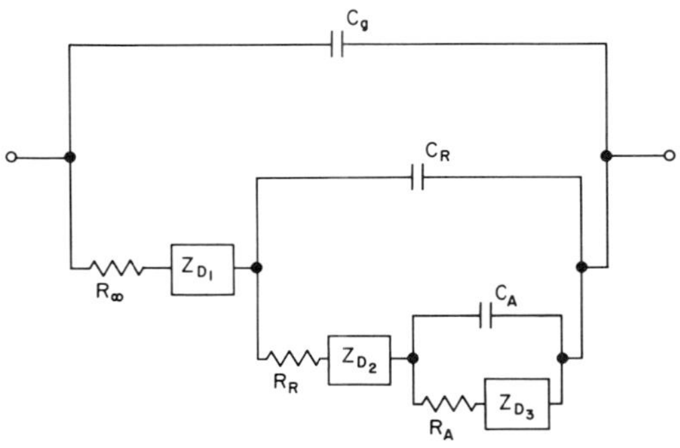

FIG. 8. An equivalent circuit of hierarchical structure useful in fitting much IS data. (Reprinted from "Interface Effects in the Electrical Response of Non-Metallic Conducting Solids and Liquids," J. R. Macdonald, *IEEE Trans. on Electrical Insulation*, Vol. EI-15, pp. 65–82, Fig. 3. Copyright © IEEE 1981.)

ysis of the situation. Since only *R*s and *C*s are involved, ambiguity is present, and many other circuit structures with the same elements and the same frequency response are possible. Nevertheless, the present hierarchical ladder-network connection is more physically reasonable than the others for homogeneous material. It ensures that bulk charging and conduction effects take place before reaction/adsorption ones. For polycrystalline materials, however, circuits involving series rather than hierarchical connection of parallel *RC* subcircuits are often found appropriate.

For the conditions above, no diffusion DCE element is present. The $Z_W(\omega)$ one discussed earlier appears, however, in the Z_{D3} position when charges of both signs are mobile and at least one of them reacts at an electrode. When static fields are present in the material, either intrinsic and/or externally produced, numerical analysis of the nonlinear transport equations governing the IS response shows that the Fig. 8 circuit still applies to good approximation but elements such as C_R and R_R then depend appreciably on the static p.d. present. Finally, the circuit of Fig. 8 has often been found appropriate for the fitting of data for supported conditions as well as unsupported ones.

B. Uses of IS for Evaluation and Control of Electrochemical Processes of Industrial Interest and Importance

1. Corrosion and Surface Protection

Corrosion of metallic structural materials leads to immense damage each year (an estimate for the United States for 1988 is 200 billion dollars); thus its control and amelioration are of tremendous economic importance. EIS has played and is playing a valuable role in quantifying and mitigating corrosion effects. For example, it has been successfully applied to complicated corrosion systems to determine corrosion rates as well as the mechanisms and efficiency of corrosion inhibitors. The use of EIS has broadened the range of corrosion phenomena that can be studied using electrochemical techniques and has been particularly valuable in evaluating the corrosion behaviors of polymer-coated metals and anodized aluminum alloys. In addition, it has been incorporated into a quality control test for anodized aluminum surfaces and for chromate-conversion-coated aluminum alloys.

The application of EIS techniques has resulted in a great deal of information on methods of corrosion protection that are difficult or impossible to study with traditional dc techniques, such as conversion and polymer coatings, anodic films, and inhibitors. Not only can EIS measurements provide greater sensitivity and more information about the processes investigated than can conventional dc methods, they are particularly appropriate when impedances are high and/or when low-conductivity media are used.

EIS measurement and analysis has been used to provide fast and sensitive information on the protection properties of chromated galvanized steel. Such measurements may be used as a quality control procedure, since the charge transfer resistance has been found to be well related to the corrosion rate. EIS has been used to detect corroding areas of large structures accurately and has been applied for corrosion monitoring of steel reinforcing bars in concrete to yield a nondestructive estimate of the amount of corrosion damage.

Since the roughness of an electrode surface is reflected in the results of EIS measurements involving the electrode, EIS may be used to identify surface inhomogeneities produced by corrosion. It provides (averaged) information on surface morphology on a much smaller scale than does even electron micrography. EIS has been employed as a means of nearly continuous evaluation of localized corrosion processes such as pitting, crevice corrosion, stress corrosion, cracking and fatigue corrosion, abrasion, and corrosion under a porous surface layer.

EIS measurements over a relatively wide frequency range have been found to yield valuable detailed information about the properties of aluminum oxide layers formed under different anodizing and sealing conditions. Discrimination was possible between properties of the dense barrier layer and the porous outer layer, and changes arising from aging and from the effects of natural environmental conditions were reflected in the results.

An EIS monitor has been used for the detection of paint degradation under atmospheric exposure. A model is being developed to help predict the lifetime of protective organic coatings on steel based on short laboratory tests. The model includes the steps of defect formation, transport of corrodents, loss of adhesion, and corrosion. EIS helps elucidate how these four processes interact and depend on coating processes and environmental effects.

Although IS analysis should properly be carried out only on time-invariant data—data obtained from a system whose properties are independent of time—some of these properties are often not time-invariant during measurement of a corroding system. If the change is slow compared to the required measurement time and/or if it is approximately linear in time, improved results may be obtained by making a set of measurements from low to high frequencies immediately followed by one from high to low frequencies. Averaging of the results will then eliminate much of the variation with time.

A test of time invariance can be made by analyzing the data with the Kramers–Kronig (K–K) relations, integral transforms connecting real to imaginary parts of the data and vice versa. They are only applicable for time-invariant systems. All useful fitting models and equivalent circuits are minimum phase and so automatically satisfy the K–K relations. Thus, a good fit is evidence of time invariance. Strong failure of the K–K relations for a given set of data is immediate evidence of unwanted time variation, and, unlike CNLS fitting, no model or circuit is required to carry out such a test. But be warned that K–K analysis requires a lot of computation and can be difficult to apply accurately.

2. Batteries and Fuel Cells

EIS studies have been made of the kinetics of the insertion reaction in solid-state batteries based on such reactions. A single EIS experiment allows information to be obtained about the electrode-interface reaction and diffusion in the electrolyte or electrode. Measurements at different battery voltages to determine the dependence of the results on the charge of the battery have led to increased understanding of the discharge process and thence to improved battery design.

An interesting EIS study has been carried out on electrochemically impregnated Ni electrodes from four different manufacturers of Ni/H cells. The EIS measurements were made in KOH electrolyte, and large differences were found in the impedance behavior of the electrodes from the different manufacturers. The results indicated a probable correlation between impedance parameters and cell life and performance.

EIS studies of molten carbonate fuel cells have increased the understanding of processes going on under operating conditions of the cell. In particular, they have helped identify and elucidate the reactions that occur both at the anode and at the cathode.

3. Other Devices and Techniques

Electrolyte-insulator-semiconductor sensors meld integrated circuit technology with traditional chemical technology. They can be used to monitor pH changes, for example, and can be constructed with ion-selective membranes to make them sensitive to a specific ion. IS measurements and analysis can yield, in favorable cases, information on the electrical characteristics of the electrolyte, the insulator, the semiconductor, and the various interfaces and on interface states. The IS approach allows very low surface-state densities at the insulator-semiconductor interface to be determined. Measurements have shown, however, that it is the electrolyte–insulator interface that responds to pH changes.

Solid-electrolyte chemical sensors are electrochemical cells designed to measure the concentration or pressure of chemical species in gases or fluids; for example, zirconia-based solid electrolytes have been used to measure oxygen concentration. Such sensors are employed to measure the oxygen concentration in steel melts and the air–fuel ratio in automobile engines. EIS has been found very useful to study (and to help optimize) electrode materials and appropriate pretreatment preparation for such sensors.

Photoelectrochemical solar cells involve a semiconductor electrode, an electrolyte interface, and a redox reaction in solution. EIS can yield information on surface states and other electrode properties of such devices. It is an important tool for probing the processes occurring at the interface and for finding ways to increase cell conversion efficiency.

In recent years a number of variants on and extensions of IS have been developed. An important one is electrohydrodynamic impedance. Here the speed of a rotating-disk electrode is modulated sinusoidally, resulting in modulation of the mass transport in a liquid electrolyte. Such modulation allows the minimization of the coupling with interfacial kinetics. Modulation of numerous other quantities in an IS experiment is also possible, such as light, temperature, or magnetic field. Thus analysis of other transfer functions, cause and effect relations that go beyond potential and current, can add valuable additional information to IS studies. It is likely that much future development will be concerned with such possibilities.

Bibliography

Archer, W. I., and Armstrong, R. D. (1980). The application of A. C. impedance methods in solid electrolytes. *Electrochemistry* **7,** 157–202.

Armstrong, R. D., Bell, M. F., and Metcalfe, A. A. (1978). The AC impedance of complex electrochemical reactions. *Electrochemistry* **6,** 98–127.

Franceschetti, D. R., and Macdonald, J. R. (1978). Theory of small-signal AC response of solids and liquids with recombining mobile charge. *J. Chem. Phys.* **68,** 1614–1637.

Gabrielli, C., ed. (1990). Proceedings of the First International Symposium on Electrochemical Impedance Spectroscopy. *Electrochim. Acta* **35,** 1483–1670.

Macdonald, J. R., ed. (1987). "Impedance Spectroscopy—Emphasizing Solid Materials and Systems." Wiley–Interscience, New York.

Macdonald, J. R. (1987). Impedance spectroscopy and its use in analyzing the steady-state AC response of solid and liquid electrolytes. *J. Electroanal. Chem.* **223,** 25–50.

Macdonald, J. R., and Potter, L. D., Jr. (1987). A flexible procedure for analyzing impedance spectroscopy results: Description and illustrations. *Solid State Ionics* **23,** 61–79.

Mansfeld, F. (1988). Don't be afraid of electrochemical techniques—but use them with care. *Corrosion* **44,** 856–868.

Schöne, G., Wiesbeck, W., and Lorenz, W. J. (1987). High-frequency impedance spectroscopy of fast electrode reactions. *J. Electroanal. Chem.* **229,** 407–421.

Sluyters-Rehbach, M., and Sluyters, J. H. (1984). AC Techniques. *In* "Comprehensive Treatise of Electrochemistry." (E. Yeager, J. O'M. Bockris, B. E. Conway, and S. Sarangapani, eds.), Vol. 9, pp. 177–292. Plenum Press, New York.

INCLUSION (CLATHRATE) COMPOUNDS

Jerry L. Atwood *University of Alabama*

GLOSSARY

Calixarene: Cyclic oligomer made by the base catalyzed condensation of a phenol and formaldehyde.

Clathrate: Inclusion compound in which the guest is completely surrounded by the host.

Crown ether: Macrocyclic polyether, so called because of its appearance in molecular models.

Cyclodextrin: One of a family of cyclic oligosaccharides produced by the enzymatic degradation of starch.

Guest: Molecule or ion that is held within a molecule (or ion) or within a host lattice without the formation of a covalent bond.

Host: Molecule, ion, or lattice capable of entrapping other molecules or ions (guests).

Inclusion compound: Arrangement of two substances that are intimately linked, but not with covalent bonds.

Intercalation: Reaction of a guest molecule (or ion) with a layered host lattice.

Zeolites: Extensive group of porous tectosilicates.

Inclusion compounds are those formed between two substances that are intimately linked, but not with covalent bonds. One substance is designated as the host and the other as the guest. The original designation, clathrates, was used to describe the situation in which the guest was completely encapsulated by the host. The field has expanded vastly since the initial elucidation of the clathrate structures in the late 1940s.

I. Historical Perspectives

The concept of inclusion is as old as humankind. The hand is capable of a variable assortment of inclusions, and many analogies are appropriate. The first verified examples of inclusion compounds date from the early 1800s. It is instructive to list the dates of record for the preparation of inclusion compounds of various types: the chlorine clathrate hydrate by Faraday in 1823, graphite intercalates in 1841, the β-quinol H_2S clathrate in 1849, cyclodextrin inclusion compounds in 1891, Hofmann's clathrate in 1897, tri-o-thymotide aromatic inclusion compounds in 1909, Dianin's compound in 1914, choleic acid inclusion compounds in 1916, phenol clathrates in 1935, urea inclusion compounds in 1940, and amylose inclusion compounds in 1946. These early studies were hard to understand since the compounds were often nonstoichiometric. A firm knowledge of any of the systems had to await developments in X-ray structure determination. All events came to a junction when H. M. Powell carried out his pioneering studies of β-quinol clathrates in 1947. We also owe to Powell the designation of the term clathrate.

Not all of the host–guest systems listed above fit under the meaning of the term clathrate, and we now use the designation inclusion compound to encompass solution behavior as well as many different types of solid state phenomena. The area has grown rapidly since 1970 and is now recognized as an important interdisciplinary subject. In 1983, a periodical, the *Journal of Inclusion Phenomena*, was launched to collect work in the inclusion area. The maturity of this field is measured in part by the award of the Nobel Prize for Chemistry in 1987 to D. J. Cram, J.-M. Lehn, and C. J. Pedersen.

II. Inorganic Hosts

A. Werner Compounds

Werner compounds are named after the coordination chemist who made important contributions to inorganic chemistry at the turn of the century. Specifically, these hosts have the formula MX_2A_4, where M stands for practically any divalent transition metal cation, X represents an anionic ligand, and A is a neutral ligand, most commonly a substituted pyridine. The structure of one of the most studied, $Ni(NCS)_2$(4-methylpyridine)$_4$, is shown in Fig. 1. The molecular conformation is a propeller, in which the pyridine rings are twisted by about 50° from a coplanar arrangement. In the solid state the molecules pack in layers. Guest molecules may pack between the layers in a space bounded by the NCS^- ligands. This is seen most clearly with reference to Fig. 2, which shows the naphthalene inclusion compound. There are rather large openings between the cavities occupied by the guests, and these are connected by two-dimensional windows. This is similar to the situation in zeolites discussed below.

Werner compounds have been used to effect separations between closely related molecules: for example, the xylene isomers. In these situations it is important to consider both the shape of the cavities and the kinetics of the absorption and desorption processes.

B. Hofmann-Type Compounds

The compound as initially formulated by Hofmann was $Ni(CN)_2 \cdot NH_3 \cdot C_6H_6$. However, it is now recognized that the actual formulation is $Ni(NH_3)_2 \cdot Ni(CN)_4 \cdot 2C_6H_6$. There are two kinds of nickel atoms, one that exhibits square planar four-coordination [tetracyanonickelate(II)] and one that exhibits an octahedral array of nitrogen atoms around the nickel. The host has a layered structure, with the NH_3 units protruding into the layers. The cavities thus formed are illustrated in Fig. 3. The benzene is completely enclosed, and the compound is a true clathrate. Because of the limitation in space, only molecules smaller than substituted benzenes can be entrapped.

The original Hofmann clathrate may be modified in several ways to produce new inclusion compounds. First, the ammonia molecule may be changed for another amine, even a bi- or tridentate one. Second, the square planar nickel may be replaced by another square planar metal or by a tetrahedral one (for example, cadmium

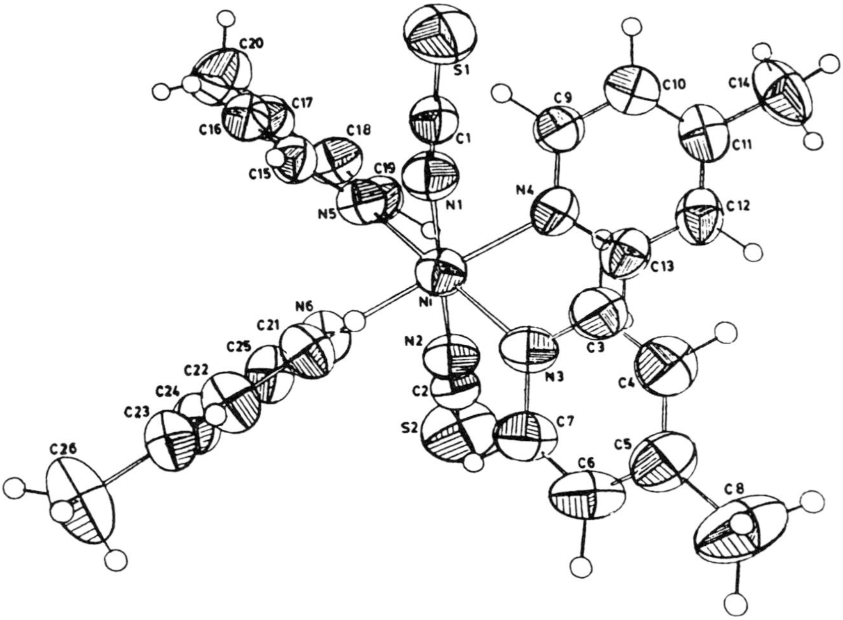

FIG. 1. Structure of $Ni(NCS)_2(4\text{-}MePy)_4$. [From Atwood, J. L., Davies, J. E. D., and MacNicol, D. D. (Eds.) (1984, 1985) "Inclusion Compounds," Vols. 1–3. Academic Press, Orlando.]

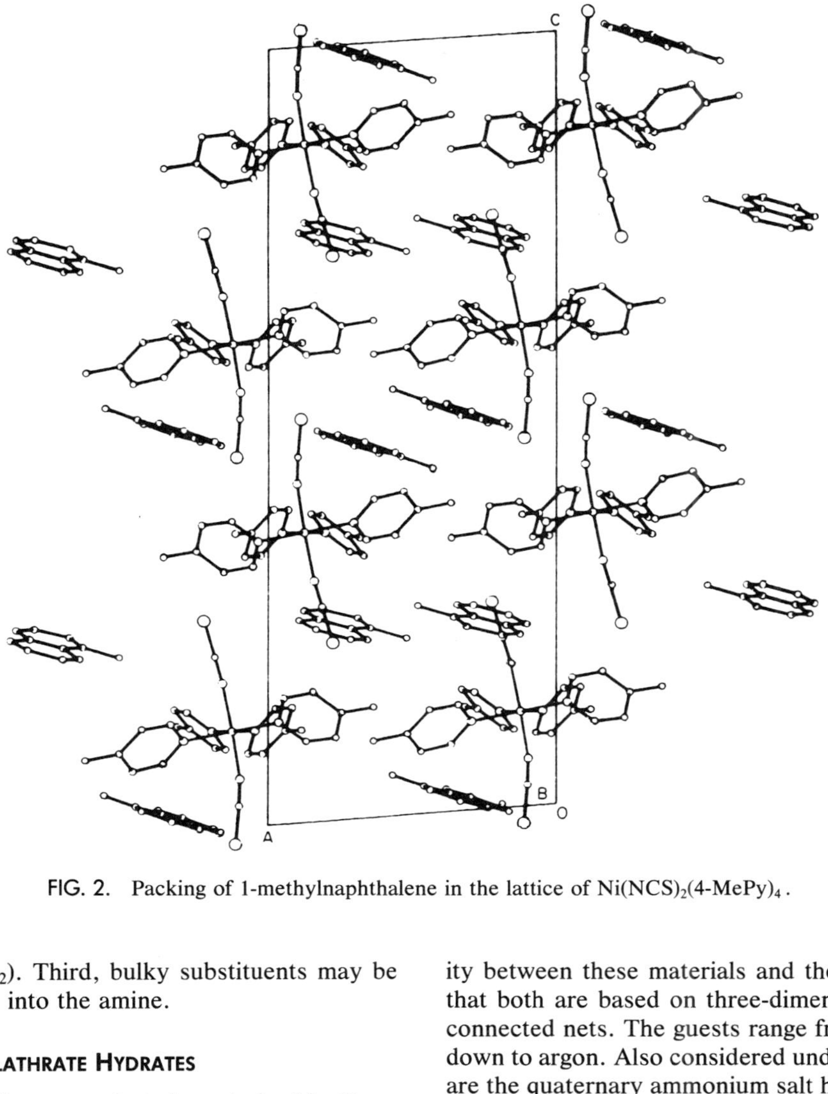

FIG. 2. Packing of 1-methylnaphthalene in the lattice of $Ni(NCS)_2(4\text{-}MePy)_4$.

in $Cd(CN)_2$). Third, bulky substituents may be introduced into the amine.

C. Gas Clathrate Hydrates

These substances, first characterized by Faraday in 1823, are based on the ice structure. The gases are included in voids in the hydrogen-bonded network. There is a geometrical similarity between these materials and the zeolites in that both are based on three-dimensional four-connected nets. The guests range from dioxane down to argon. Also considered under this topic are the quaternary ammonium salt hydrates and the alkylamine hydrates. With a number of guests the gas clathrate hydrate structure is thermodynamically more stable than that of ice. Indeed, several have melting points in the 0–15°C range and one is reported to melt at 31.5°C.

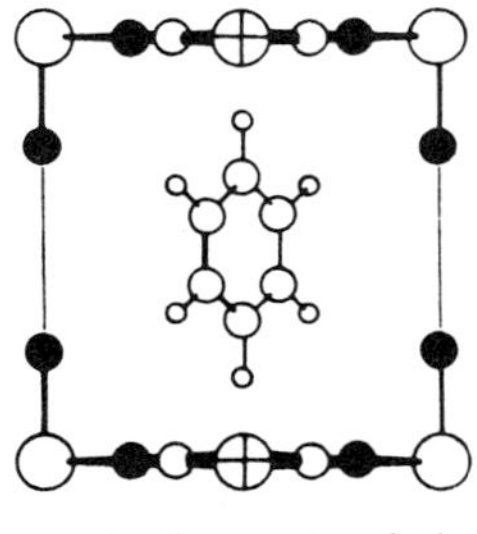

FIG. 3. Hofmann's benzene clathrate, $Ni(NH_3)_2$ $Ni(CN)_4 \cdot 2C_6H_6$.

The true gas clathrate hydrates, with few exceptions, crystallize in one of two structures, I and II. In general, the smaller guests belong to structure I and the larger ones to structure II, while those of intermediate size may belong to either under slightly different conditions. The ideal unit cell contents for a type I is $6X \cdot 2Y \cdot 46H_2O$ and for a type II, $8X \cdot 16Y \cdot 136H_2O$, where Y refers to the guests in a 12-hedra and X to those in 14-hedra or higher. The polyhedra can be understood with reference

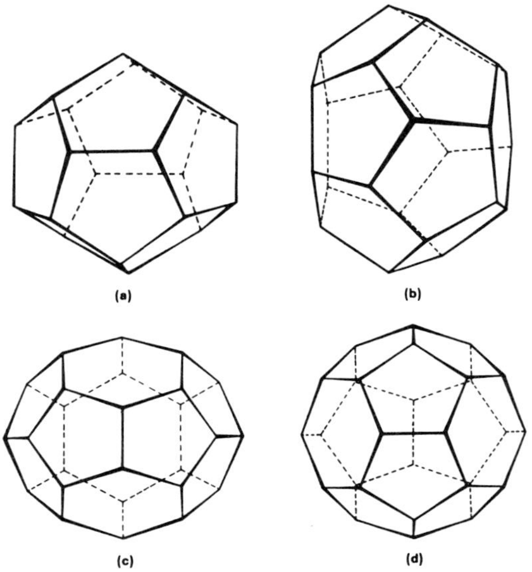

FIG. 4. Clathrate hydrate voids: (a) 12-hedra, (b) 14-hedra, (c) 15-hedra, and (d) 16-hedra.

to Fig. 4. X and Y type spaces may both be filled by a small molecule. For example, the ideal stoichiometry is $8CH_4 \cdot 46H_2O$ for the gas clathrate hydrate of methane. It is also possible to form mixed hydrates in which a smaller guest is trapped in the smaller cavity and the larger in the more spacious void.

Structure I belongs to the cubic space group Pm3n, and can be viewed as a close packing of 12- and 14-hedra sharing faces in the ratio 1 to 3. Structure II falls in the cubic Fd3m group and is viewed as 12- and 16-hedra sharing faces in the ratio 2 to 1. A hexagonal hydrate structure (type H) requiring both large and small guests to stabilize the lattice has been found to be isostructural with dodecasil-1H. Lower symmetry structure types III–VII have been observed for the ammonium salt hydrates and alkylamine hydrates. Description of these structures is beyond our scope, but it is instructive to note the differences between the ammonium or amine structures and those of the gases. In the case of simple salts that contain anions such as F^-, the latter is not surprisingly found involved with the hydrogen-bond framework. For anions such as benzoate, the oxygen atoms are a part of the framework, while the phenyl group is located in a void. The cations are entrapped, but much larger voids are required when an ion as large as $[N(i\text{-}C_5H_{11})_4]^+$ is utilized. Alkylamine hydrates are hydrogen bonded to the framework and penetrate the cavities as well. Figure 5 illustrates this situation. [*See* HYDROGEN BONDS.]

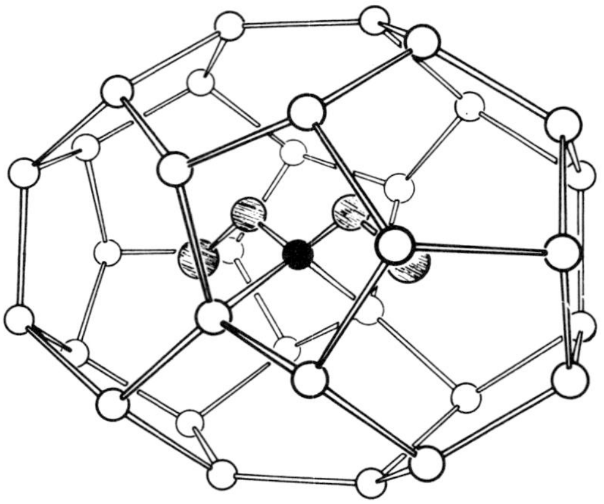

FIG. 5. Structure of the diethylamine hydrate, $12(CH_3CH_2)_2NH \cdot 104H_2O$. The nitrogen atom is the dark sphere; the carbon atoms of the ethyl groups are shaded spheres.

Gas clathrates are of considerable importance industrially, even though they have gained some infamy by being held responsible for plugging the Alaska natural gas pipeline. The methane clathrate has a melting point well above that of ice itself, so the substance can crystallize at temperatures above the freezing point of ice. This very property has also caused speculation about the use of the substances as heat storage media. It is possible to allow an underground reservoir to freeze in Minnesota and then use the ice as a source of air conditioning during the summer. The gas clathrates have nearly the same heat of fusion as ice, and a reservoir of a high melting one could conceivably be used in a like manner in Georgia.

D. Zeolites

Zeolites are porous tectosilicates of typical formulas such as $Li_2[Al_2Si_4O_{12}] \cdot 2H_2O$ (bikitaite), $Ca_4[Al_8Si_{28}O_{72}] \cdot 24H_2O$ (heulandite), or $(Na_2,Ca,Mg)_{29}[Al_{58}Si_{134}O_{384}] \cdot 240H_2O$. About sixty naturally occurring framework topologies exist, and many new ones have been synthesized. Each of the topologies gives rise to a unique system of cavities and channels that characterize its structure. The exchangeable cations (Li in bikitaite) may share cavities or channels along with guest molecules or ions. However, there are many more positions for guests than the exchangeable ions can inhabit.

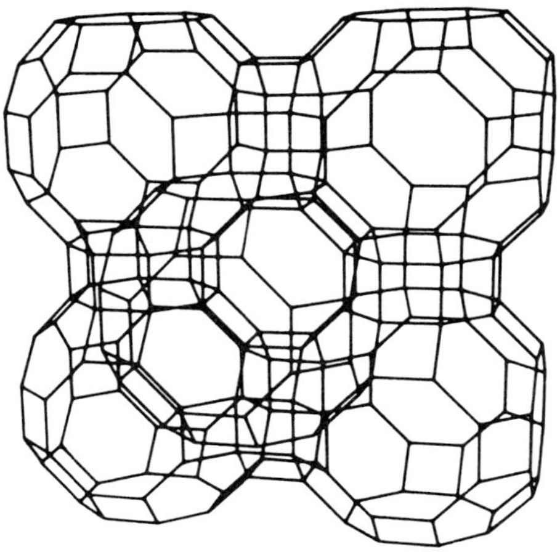

FIG. 6. Framework structure of zeolite RHO.

Framework structures are shown in Figs. 6 and 7. The networks are rigid, but access to cavities may be controlled by the type of guests present. For example, a zeolite with rather vast cavities may be rendered useless for adsorption purposes by the presence of smaller ions that specifically block channels giving access to the large cavities.

The internal channel systems may be classified as one-, two-, or three-dimensional. When the channels are too small to permit diffusion of the guest between them, then only one-dimensional diffusion is possible. An example of channel patterns is given in Fig. 8. The window concept is of importance in understanding molecular diffusion. The most important windows are 8-rings, 10-rings, and 12-rings. The openings are themselves constrained by the supporting framework. The 8-rings may be nearly

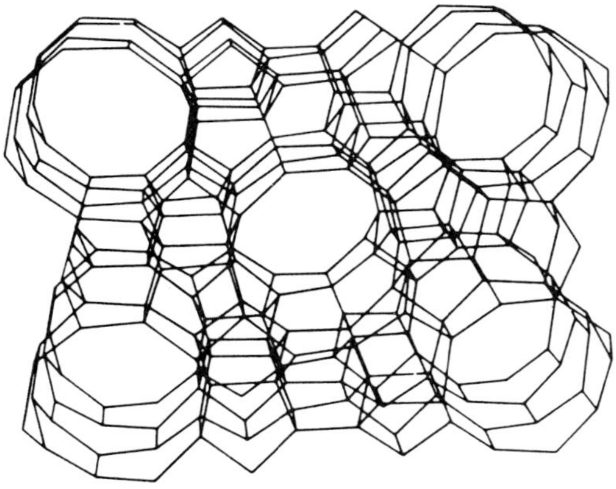

FIG. 7. Structure of zeolite ZSM-5.

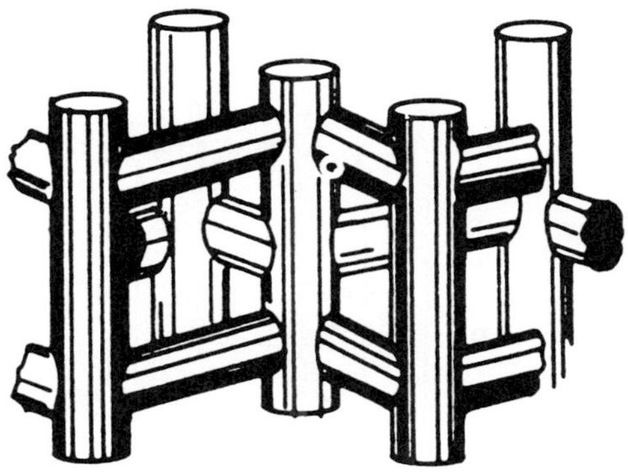

FIG. 8. Channel structure of ZSM-5.

planar (in which case the opening is about 4.2 Å) or substantially elongated. A schematic representation is shown in Fig. 9. As an example of practical importance, consider the sorption of organic molecules by ZSM-5. The 10-ring openings, as shown in Fig. 9, allow entrance to *n*-parafins and simple aromatics. However, the opening is so narrow that benzene or *p*-xylene (critical dimension ~6.3 Å) may be differentiated by the rate of sorption from o-xylene, 1,2,4-trimethylbenzene, or naphthalene (~6.9 Å) and will exclude pentamethylbenzene or 1,3,5-trimethylbenzene (~7.8 Å).

Zeolites have found uses in many areas: adsorptive separation of hydrocarbons, purification of gases and liquids, catalytic cracking of hydrocarbons, and ion exchange, to name the largest applications. Further developments in shape selective catalysis, molecular electronic devices, and sensors are anticipated. [*See* CATALYSIS, INDUSTRIAL.]

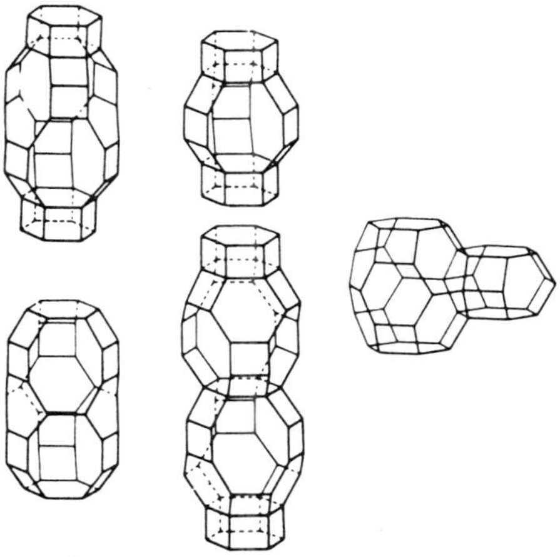

FIG. 9. Openings between cavities in zeolites.

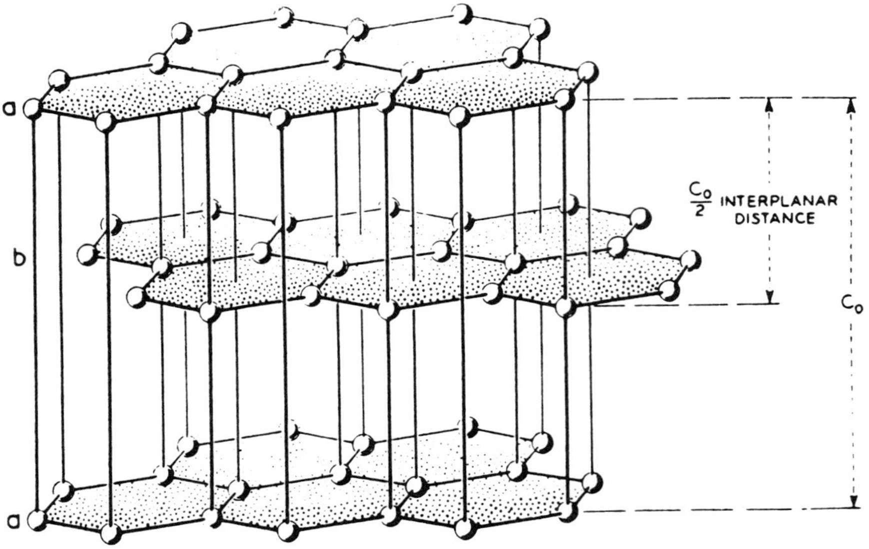

FIG. 10. Layered structure of hexagonal graphite.

E. Intercalates

Intercalation compounds are produced by the insertion of an atomic or molecular species into a host lattice. Many common solid materials possess this property: graphite (structure shown in Fig. 10), MoO_3, H_xMoO_3 (a hydrogen bronze), V_2O_5, $Zr(HPO_4)_2$, FeOCl, and many clays to mention but a few. The reactions that lead to the intercalated substances are classified as reversible, topotactic solid state reactions. These are therefore processes in which the solid matrix is essentially unchanged with regard to structure and composition. The reaction may conveniently be divided into two types: (1) intercalation of mobile guest species into an empty host lattice that provides adequate free volume and appropriate geometry, and (2) intercalation by exchange reactions with a host that already contains a guest. In these reactions temperature is a very important factor. If the temperature is too low, the solid lattice is too rigid, but if the temperature is too high, the lattice may disintegrate. [*See* SOLID-STATE CHEMISTRY.]

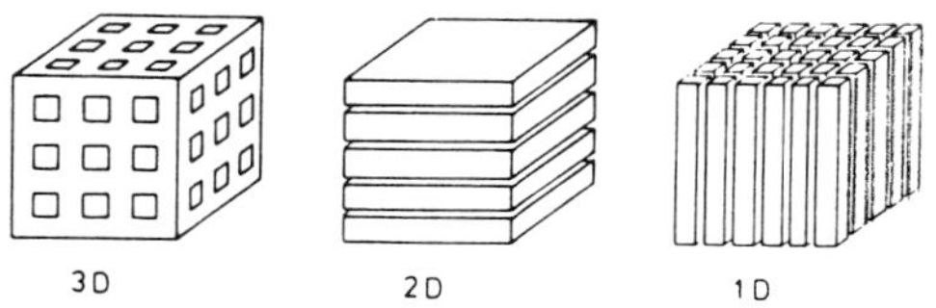

FIG. 11. Host dimensionality.

Structurally, there are three types of hosts, as shown in Fig. 11: three-dimensional, layered, and chain structures. The concept of staging is important, and it may be visualized with reference to Fig. 12.

Applications of intercalates have been numerous. Sorption and ion exchange properties of zeolites and related substances are regarded under this heading. Catalysis of the heterogeneous type is emerging on the industrial level. Hosts with conductivity properties are seeing activity in energy storage. On the laboratory scale, new analytical techniques are being based on this type of phenomenon.

F. Cyclophosphazenes

This class of materials is composed of paddle-wheel-shaped molecules, and the way in which the molecules pack in the solid state is illustrated in Fig. 13. The combination of layer types 1 and 2 gives the tunnel as depicted in Fig. 14.

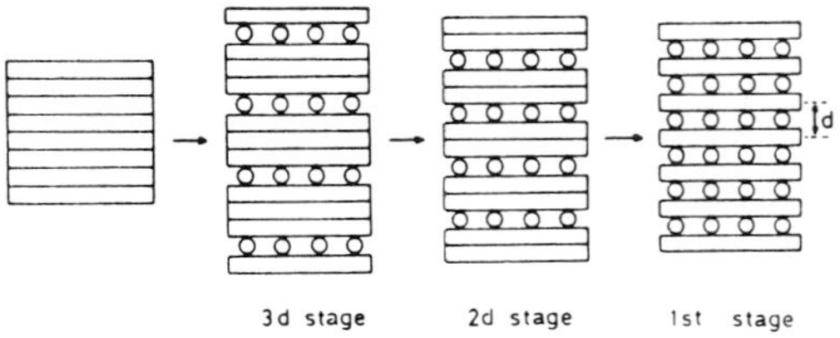

FIG. 12. Staging in intercalation reactions of layered host lattices.

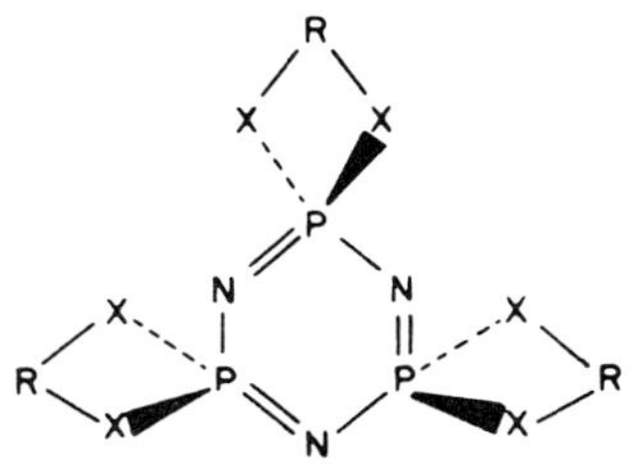

FIG. 13. Paddle-wheel-shaped molecule of the host cyclophosphazene.

The view leads one to expect that long-chain aliphatics should be preferentially entrapped. This is most dramatically realized by exposing crystals to a mixture of *n*-heptane and cyclohexane. The long-chain aliphatic is adsorbed to the total exclusion of the cyclic one. It is also worthwhile to note that the adsorption process is quite rapid, even though large crystals are used.

Molecular motion in the channels has been studied in detail and has been related to solid state polymerization results (inclusion polymerization). It was found that *p*-bromostyrene can be polymerized, but styrene cannot be. The explanation was found in the orientation of the molecules in the tunnels.

G. Liquid Clathrates

The term *liquid clathrate* presents a paradox. Clathrates are by definition solid substances, but it is possible to apply the same basic concepts to liquids as well. A liquid clathrate is a member of a group of liquid inclusion compounds that form upon the interaction of aromatic molecules (guests) with certain species related geometrically to salts such as $[NMe_4][Al_2(CH_3)_6I]$. The substance thus formed contains a certain maximum number of guest molecules and is immiscible with excess aromatic. The hydrocarbon molecules in the liquid clathrate are trapped as they would be in a solid clathrate and can be freed by a change in temperature and reclaimed unaltered.

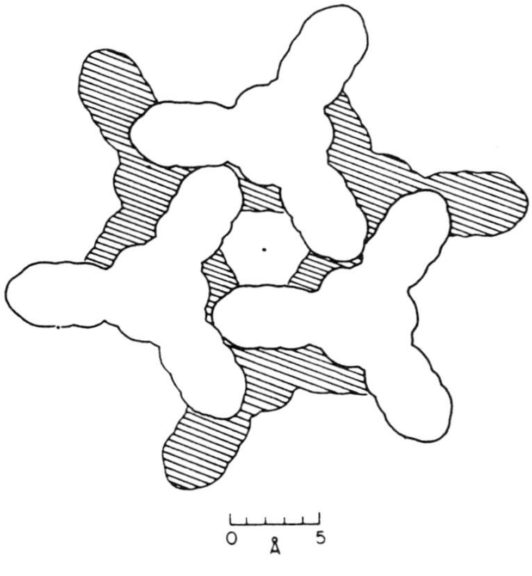

FIG. 14. View of the tunnel that results from the packing of layer type 1 and layer type 2 upon each other.

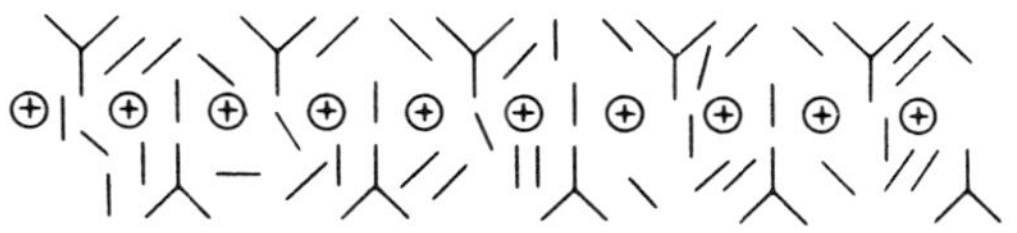

FIG. 15. Two-dimensional model of liquid clathrate behavior.

A model for liquid clathrate behavior is presented in Fig. 15. It is believed that the ions interact in a cooperative manner. One cation may be associated with two or more anions and vice versa. The cation–anion interaction must be strong, or the ions will separate and a normal solution will result. The aromatic molecules are necessary constituents of the layerlike structure. They are guests, but they are also in effect components of the host. The analogy to certain solid state inclusion compounds of the Werner type is to be noted.

Of the several interesting applications of liquid clathrates the most promising is in the area of separations. Since the behavior is found for aromatic molecules but not for aliphatic ones, a separation is possible. It is possible to envision even difficult problems such as the separation of the xylene isomers being attacked by liquid clathrates. Liquid clathrates have also been reported to be useful as solvents for the liquefaction of coal.

III. Organic Hosts

A. Crown Ethers and Cryptates

Crown ethers are cyclic polyethers, and typical examples are shown in Fig. 16. They were first recognized as a new class of macrocyclic compounds in 1967, but thousands of articles on aspects of the subject have been published since then. Crown ethers form the simplest models for the structured complexation that is central to the function of enzymes. They are also useful as

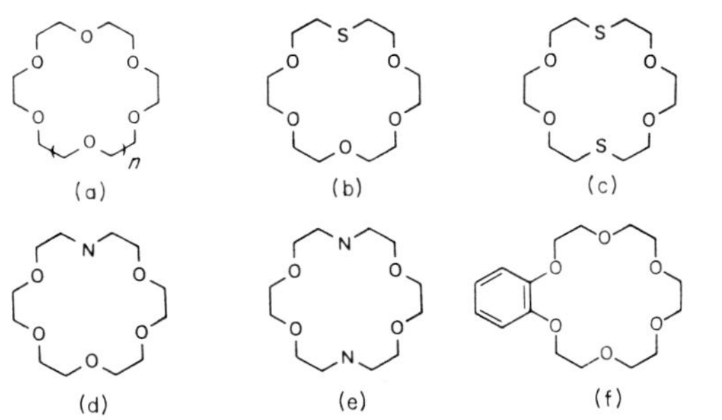

FIG. 16. Crown ethers. (a) $n = 0$, 15-Crown-5; $n = 1$, 18-Crown-6; $n = 2$, 21-Crown-7. (b) Thia-18-Crown-6. (c) 1,10-Dithia-18-Crown-6. (d) Aza-18-Crown-6. (e) 1,10-Diaza-18-Crown-6. (f) Benzo-18-Crown-6.

models for ion transport. Indeed, the hole in the crown ether can be tailored so as to fit any simple cation: K^+ is best accommodated by 18-crown-6, while Na^+ fits into 15-crown-5. Recently, substantial effort has been expended in the study of the complexation of neutral molecules and anions by crown ethers.

Crown ethers are essentially two-dimensional complexing agents. Macrobicycles, first reported by Lehn in 1968, represent an important move to three-dimensionality. Simple examples of these so-called cryptates are shown in Fig. 17. Three-dimensionality has also been imparted to crown ethers by the addition of one or more side-chains onto the crown (lariat ethers). The construction of hosts with specific complexing ability has proved to be an interesting area of synthetic organic chemistry. Since the number of naturally occurring organic hosts is limited, important advances in medicinal chemistry can be expected in this area. [*See* ORGANIC MACROCYCLES.]

B. CYCLODEXTRINS

Cyclodextrins are cyclic oligosaccharides formed by the enzymatic degradation of starch. In the process, one portion of the starch helix is hydrolyzed off, and the ends are joined together. The most common results are molecules made up of 6, 7, or 8 glucose units, α-, β-, or γ-cyclodextrins, respectively. A schematic view of these structures is shown in Fig. 18.

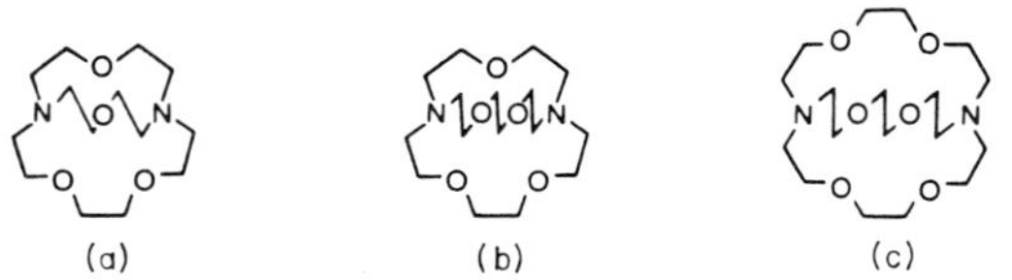

FIG. 17. Cryptates. (a) Cryptand [2.1.1], (b) cryptand [2.2.1], and (c) cryptand [2.2.2].

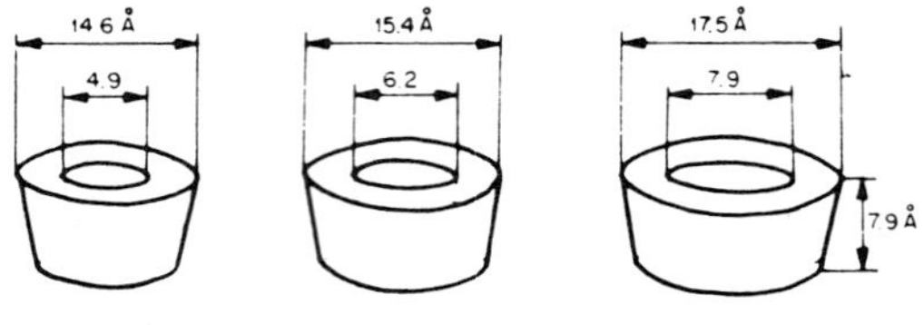

FIG. 18. Representations of the structures of α-, β-, and γ-cyclodextrins. (The α-cyclodextrin is the smallest.)

Since the glucose unit is a rigid one, the cyclodextrins possess cavities even as isolated molecules in the absence of guests. All cyclodextrins have a height of about 8.0 Å and an outer diameter of 15–18 Å. The diameter of the cavity is 4.7–5.2 Å for α-, 6.0–6.4 Å for β-, and 7.5–8.3 Å for γ-cyclodextrin. These values are comparable to molecular dimensions for many simple organic molecules. Figure 19 shows a model view of the complex of *p*-iodoaniline with α-cyclodextrin.

It is significant to note that the cyclodextrins have good water solubilities. They are finding extensive use in the pharmaceutical industries of some countries as vehicles either to solubilize drugs or to protect them as they pass through the digestive system. Other applications in such diverse areas as that of food additives and in pesticide formulations have been realized.

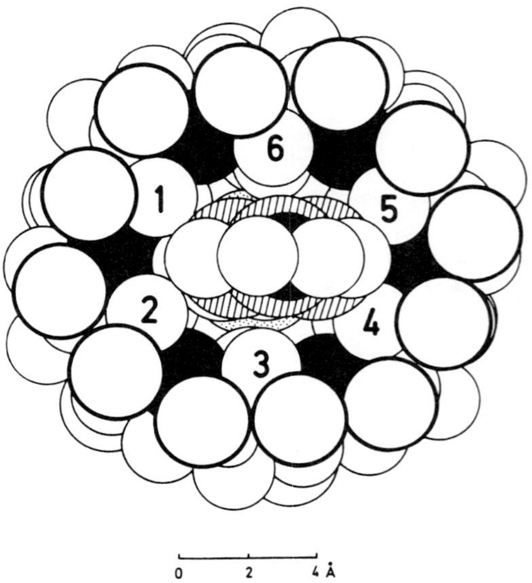

FIG. 19. Structure of the complex of α-cyclodextrin and *p*-iodoaniline. Space-filling models have been used.

FIG. 20. The inclusion compound formed by urea (the host) and a normal hydrocarbon (the guest).

C. Urea and Thiourea

The simple organic molecule urea, $(NH_2)_2C{=}O$, was discovered in 1940 to form adducts. These differ from the previous two examples in this section in that the host–guest interaction occurs only in the solid state. Urea crystallizes in the presence of long-chain hydrocarbons, as illustrated in Fig. 20. Thiourea behaves in the same fashion with only minor modifications.

Since urea is a common, abundant substance, it is of interest to exploit its inherent selectivity toward hydrocarbons. Attempts have been made to use it to separate benzene and cyclohexane from *n*-heptane, but commercial reality has not been achieved.

D. Hydroquinone, Phenol, and Dianin's Compound

These molecules, represented schematically in Fig. 21, exhibit host lattices based on the use of hydrogen bonding to build a hexameric unit.

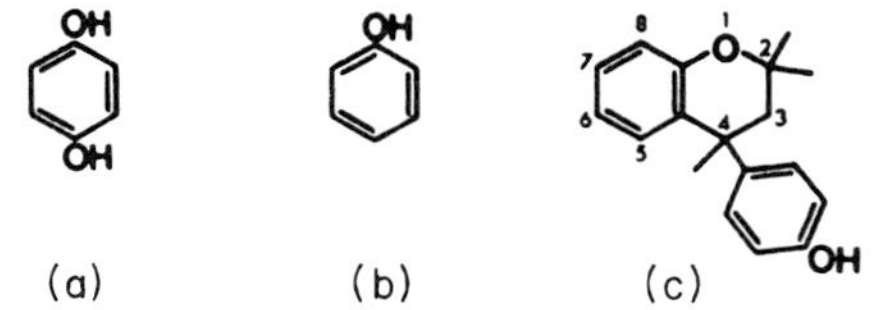

FIG. 21. Formula representations of (a) hydroquinone, (b) phenol, and (c) Dianin's compound.

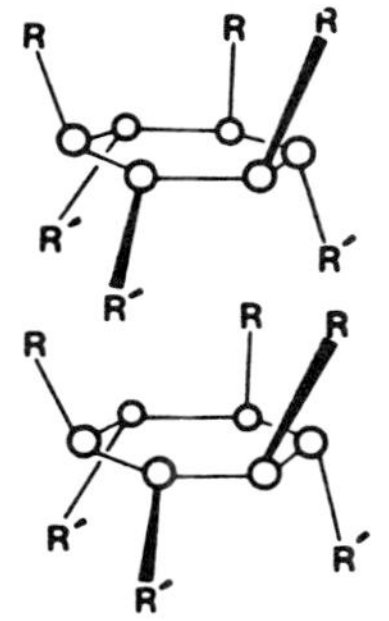

FIG. 22. Schematic view of the packing of two hexameric units to form a cavity. The O—O represents a hydrogen bond.

In the case of Dianin's compound, the hexamer consists of three molecules of one configuration R, pointing upwards, and three of the other configuration R′, pointing downwards. When these units pack in the solid state, the result is the formation of a cavity, as shown in Fig. 22.

The extension of the naturally occurring hexameric units to synthetic analogues is significant. The hexa-hosts, shown in Fig. 23, have the same overall geometry as the phenolic hosts, but the hydrogen bonding in the latter has been replaced with full covalent bonds in the former. The result is particularly important since it shows that molecules can be constructed or engineered to have a specific shape.

There are several uses for these hosts in the area of separations, but none are industrially important as yet. It is instructive to note that the inclusion compound of SF_6 and Dianin's compound has been used as a method of storage of SF_6. This aspect of inclusion may prove to be important for a wide variety of reactive or unstable molecules.

E. Calixarenes

Calixarenes, shown schematically in Fig. 24, are prepared by the condensation of *p*-tert-bu-

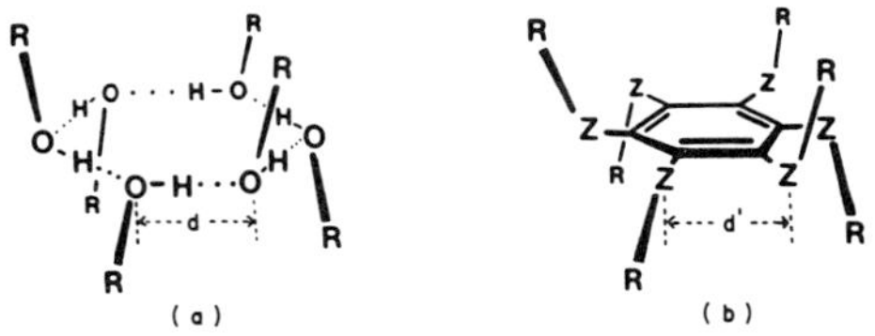

FIG. 23. Analogy of the hydrogen-bonded hexameric unit (a) to the hexahost (b). Z denotes a general atom: S, for example.

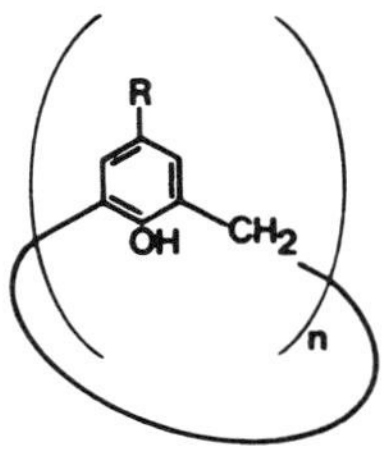

FIG. 24. Schematic view of the structure of a calix-[*n*]arene. The most common values of *n* are 4, 6, and 8.

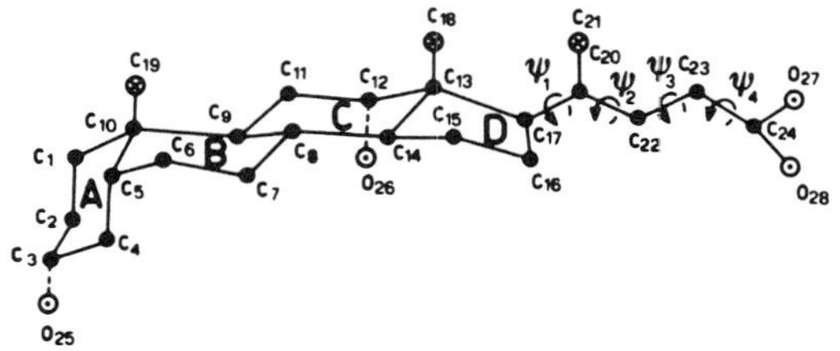

FIG. 26. Structure of deoxycholic acid: ● represents C; ⊙, O; and ⊗, CH_3.

tylphenol with paraformaldehyde. In the cone conformation, calix[4]arene has the shape of a chalice or vase. Figure 25 exhibits this geometry, and the inclusion of a toluene molecule is apparent. Closer observation of Fig. 25 shows that an Na^+ ion is also held in the base of the chalice. Thus, this calixarene can include both neutral molecules and ions at the same time. The similarity to the cyclodextrins is clear, but the calixarenes are not as rigid.

F. Other Organic Hosts

The synthesis of new types of inclusion hosts is an active area of organic research. The number and diversity of such materials makes even a summary treatment beyond the scope of this presentation. This section contains representative examples only.

Deoxycholic acid, $C_{24}H_{40}O_4$, has an arched shape (Fig. 26) and forms inclusion compounds of the channel type with a wide variety of organic molecules.

FIG. 27. Two representations of the structure of perhydrotriphenylene.

Perhydrotriphenylene, $C_{18}H_{30}$, has the schematic structure shown in Fig. 27 and forms inclusion compounds with linear and branched chain hydrocarbons and with macromolecular compounds such as polyethylene.

Cyclotriveratrylene, $(C_9H_{10}O_2)_3$, has the shape of a saucer (Fig. 28a). The molecule can be used as a base upon which to chemically construct the so-called octopus molecules (Fig. 28b). These molecules can be used to include molecules in solution as well as in the solid state.

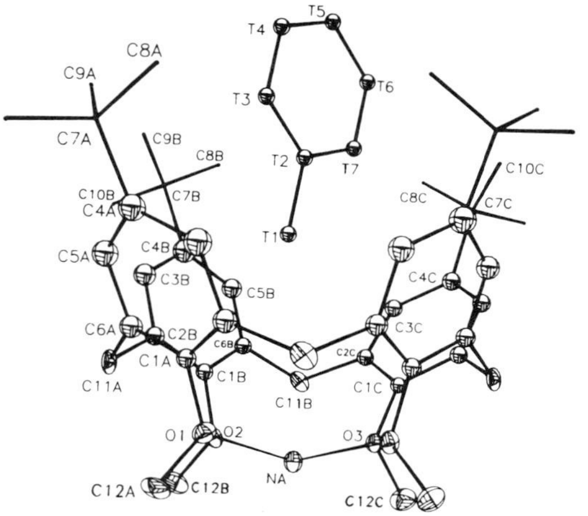

FIG. 25. The methyl ether of calix[4]arene with included toluene (T) and sodium ion.

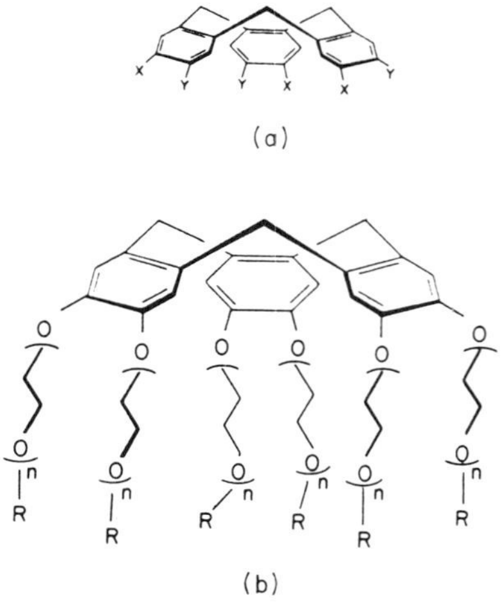

FIG. 28. (a) Saucer-like structure of cyclotriveratrylene and (b) related octopus molecule.

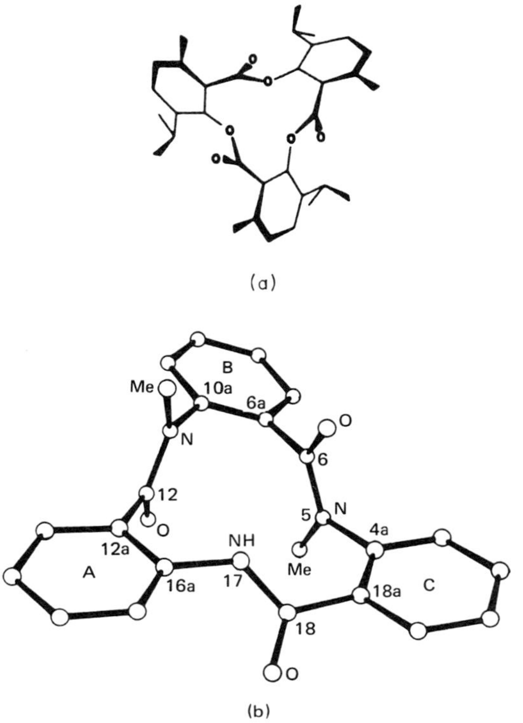

FIG. 29. (a) Propellerlike structure of tri-o-thymotide, TOT, and (b) related structure of *N,N'*-dimethyltrianthranilide.

Tri-o-thymotide (TOT), Fig. 29a, exists in a propellerlike configuration and has features in common with the trianthranilides, Fig. 29b.

IV. Biochemical Relationships

A. Enzyme Models

The chemist seeks enzyme mimics or models so as to bridge the gap between chemical reactions in the laboratory and those of the life processes. Since the way in which most biological transformations occur is obscure, model reactions can provide insight. Reactions out of the realm of true biochemistry have two features in common: They are catalyzed very effectively, so that they occur rapidly even under mild conditions, and they are very selective. A true enzyme mimic must exhibit both of these features.

The most studied class of enzyme mimics is the cyclodextrins. The rigid hydrophobic cavity is rimmed with hydroxyl groups that may be further functionalized.

As an example of a well-studied biomimetic process, consider the chlorination of anisole,

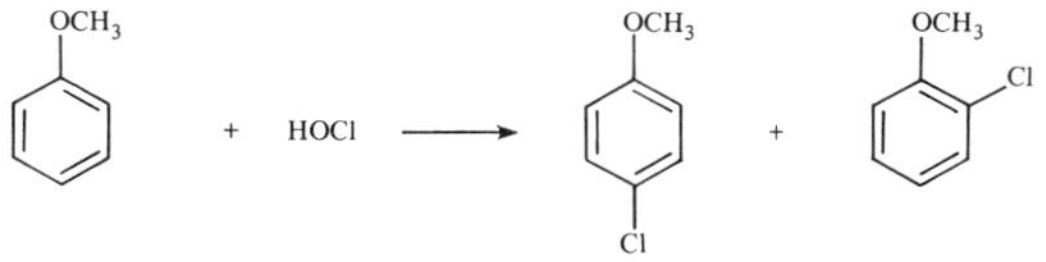

In aqueous solution both the ortho- and the para-isomers are produced (in about 40 : 60 ratio, respectively). Addition of α-cyclodextrin changes the ratio to 4 : 96. The ortho-position is clearly shielded from attack, as is shown in Fig. 30. The cyclodextrin also has the effect of substantially speeding up the chlorination of anisole. This catalysis is due to the existence of a new pathway for the reaction, which is also shown in Fig. 30.

The construction of synthetic iron(II) dioxygen carriers as a model for myoglobin has long been sought. Advances based on transition metal complexes of cyclidenes have now provided the result. Cyclidenes, given in Fig. 31, are composed of two fused rings, one which is useful for metal coordination and the other for molecular design purposes. A model which serves to illustrate the biological discrimination of O_2 over CO is displayed in Fig. 32.

The synthesis of molecules with shapes and functional group orientation (Fig. 33) appropriate for catalytic functions has been achieved by the use of the Kemp triacid as a structural unit to effect U-turns. This strategy has led to hosts capable of the recognition of numerous substrates such as is shown for chiral alcohols in Fig. 34.

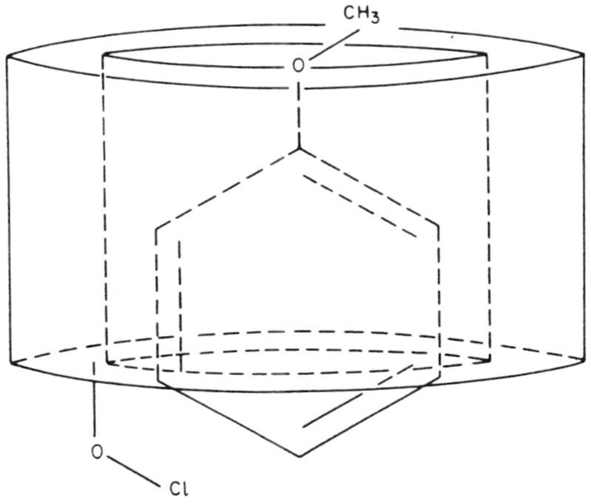

FIG. 30. Schematic view of the structure of the complex of anisole with cyclodextrin.

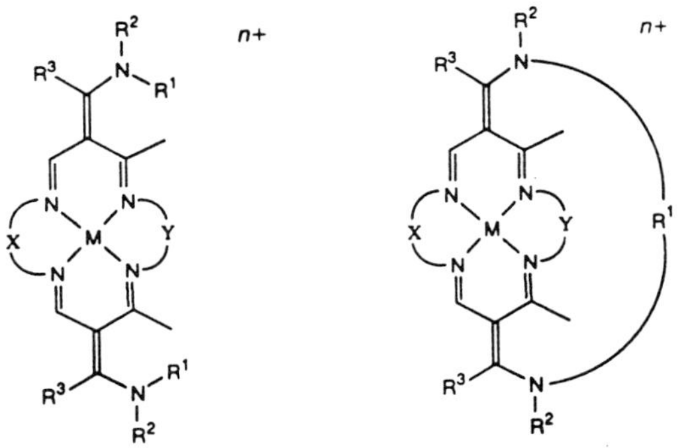

FIG. 31. General cyclidene structure. [From Atwood, J. L., Davies, J. E. D., and MacNicol, D. D. (Eds.) (1991), "Inclusion Compounds," Vol. 5, Oxford University Press, Oxford.]

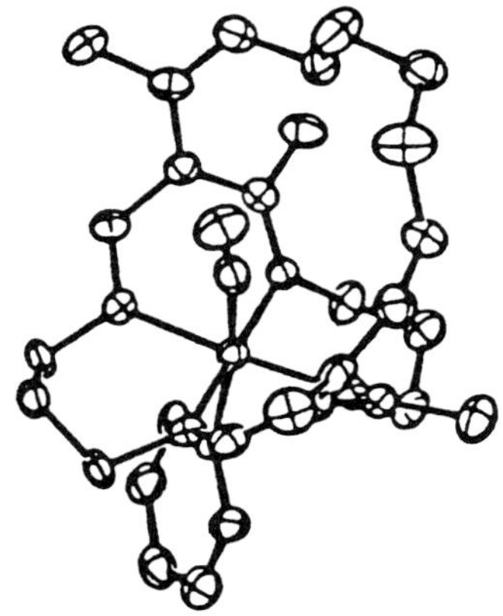

FIG. 32. Cyclidene complex of iron(II) with bonded carbon monoxide.

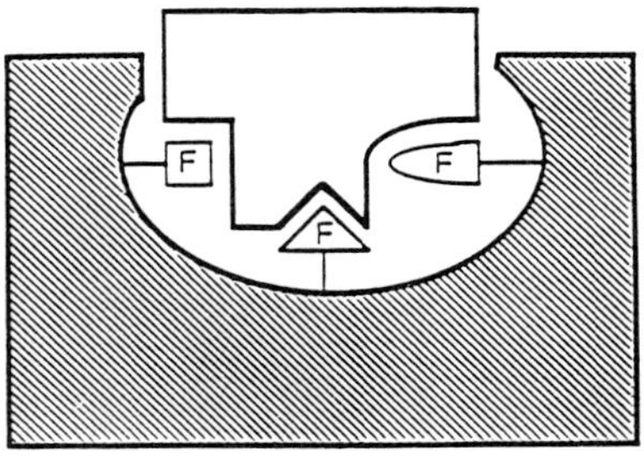

FIG. 33. Schematic view of U-shaped host. [From Atwood, J. L. (Ed.) (1990), "Inclusion and Molecular Recognition," Plenum Press, New York.]

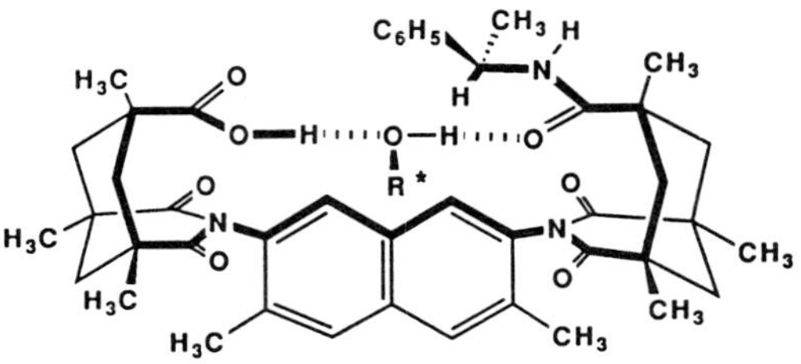

FIG. 34. Rigid, U-shaped molecule capable of binding chiral alcohols.

Many other classes of enzyme mimics are under investigation, but the general principles are covered in the examples above. One of the first benefits expected from studies of this type is a new way to catalyze known chemical reactions.

B. Cation Transport

A necessary feature of the life process is the solubilization of cations in low dielectric constant media. The way in which both electrolytes and nonelectrolytes cross membranes has received much study. A useful model of cation transport is the motion of ions affixed to macrocycles. Crown ethers and cryptates have been studied the most. One of the features of biological transport is selectivity. The simple crown ethers are particularly suited for experiments on selectivity, since the hole or cavity is of rather specific size. Thus, 15-crown-5 is better matched to Na^+ than to K^+, while the reverse is true for 18-crown-6.

Bibliography

Atwood, J. L. (Ed.) (1990). "Inclusion Phenomena and Molecular Recognition." Plenum Press, New York.

Atwood, J. L., Davies, J. E. D., and MacNicol, D. D. (Eds.) (1984, 1985). "Inclusion Compounds," Vols. 1–3. Academic, New York.

Atwood, J. L., Davies, J. E. D., and MacNicol, D. D. (Eds.) (1991). "Inclusion Compounds," Vols. 4–5. Oxford University Press, Oxford.

INCOMMENSURATE CRYSTALS AND QUASICRYSTALS

J. D. Axe *Brookhaven National Laboratory*

GLOSSARY

Antiphase domains: Spatial regions of an ordered structure in which some aspect of the order reverses. For example, in a binary AB alloy, an A lattice site in one domain becomes a B lattice site in the other, and vice versa. The average spacing of these antiphase regions may or may not be a rational multiple of the underlying structure.

Lock-in transformation: Abrupt thermodynamic phase transition that converts an incommensurate structure into a commensurate one.

Modulated structure: Atomic arrangement in which a simple periodic pattern is broken only by (in some sense) small distortions (the modulation) with another period. This new period may or may not be a rational multiple of the simpler pattern (that is, the modulated structure may be commensurate or incommensurate).

Traditionally, solids are classified as either crystalline or amorphous (glassy), depending upon whether or not their macroscopic structure can be described by a space-filling repetition of a much smaller microscopic subunit, a so-called unit cell. Although this classification scheme retains its usefulness, over the past decade there has developed a realization that other modes of large-scale organization of atoms are not only possible, but do in fact exist rather commonly in nature. These newly recognized forms of matter are almost crystalline in a precise sense, to be discussed later, and have come to be termed incommensurate crystals. Recently (1984), a new and in some sense more radical manifestation of this same quasi-periodic organizing principle has come to light. These materials are called quasicrystals, and the considerable interest that they have generated has resulted in a deeper understanding and appreciation among physicists and crystallographers of the nature and subtlety of quasi-periodic order.

I. Periodic versus Quasi-Periodic Order

The lattice-forming property (translational long-range order), which defines conventional crystalline arrays and is the simplifying concept upon which much of modern solid-state physics rests, reveals itself in many of the mechanical, optical, and electrical properties of these materials, but nowhere more directly than in electron, X-ray, and neutron scattering, in which the spatially periodic array of atoms acts as a grating and gives rise to a diffraction pattern consisting of sharp spots (Bragg peaks) that define a lattice in a dual three-dimensional momentum (or Fourier transform) space.

$$\mathbf{Q} = \sum_{i=1}^{3} h_i \mathbf{a}_i \qquad h_i = \text{integer} \tag{1}$$

The diffraction patterns of amorphous materials do not contain these sharp Bragg peaks, which are a unique signature of the translational long-range order of the atomic arrangements that produce them. From the lattice symmetry of the diffraction spots in this dual space, it is possible to deduce the lattice symmetry of the atoms in real space, which must be 1 of 14 allowed space-filling Bravais lattices. [*See* CRYSTALLOGRAPHY.]

Incommensurate crystals and quasicrystals, unlike amorphous materials, have sharp diffraction patterns, but are also unlike crytalline solids in that these peaks do not form a three-dimensional dual-space lattice, and irrational (that is, incommensurate) numbers rather than integers, h_i, must be used to index the Bragg peaks when described in terms of Eq. (1). Only by postulating one or more additional basis vectors, $\mathbf{a}_i$ ($i = 4, 5, \ldots$) does one recover a rational indexing scheme:

$$\mathbf{Q} = \sum_{i=1}^{n} h_i \mathbf{a}_i \qquad h_i = \text{integer} \tag{2}$$

If there exist no integral linear relations among the n basis vectors, Eq. (2) defines a quasilattice of rank n. Such a set of discrete momenta or Fourier components represent what is known mathematically as a quasi-periodic function as long as n is greater than the spatial dimension, ($n > d = 3$). Moreover, and this is an important insight, a quasilattice of rank n can be viewed as the projection onto the three dimensional space of a completely periodic n-dimensional lattice. (Fig. 1 shows an example of a one-dimensional lattice of rank two formed in this way.) Incommensurate crystals and quasicrystals cannot, of course, be classified into any of the known 230 crystallographic space groups. However, analogous and equally powerful symmetry analyses of quasi-periodic structures are possible, making use of the higher n-dimensional imbedding spaces. [*See* QUASICRYSTALS.]

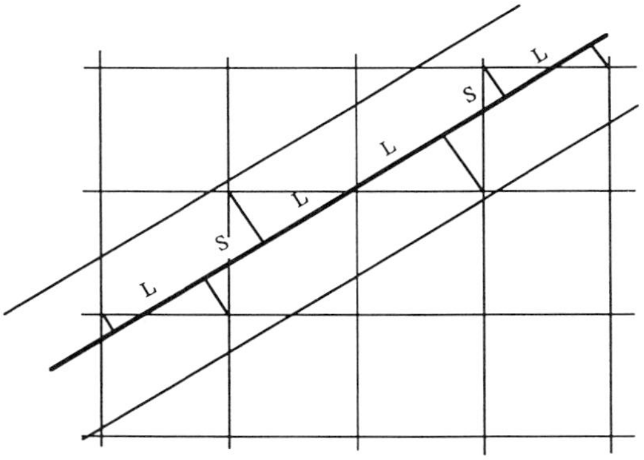

FIG. 1. Construction of a one-dimensional quasicrystal. The vertices of a two dimensional square lattice are projected onto a line with a slope given by the golden ratio $\tau = (\sqrt{5} - 1)/2$. When the projections are restricted to lie within the indicated strip, the line is cut into a sequence based upon two intervals, one long (L) and one short (S). The resulting sequence, . . . LSLLSL . . . , is known as a Fibonacci chain.

(It seems most sensible to continue to define crystals as periodic structures, in which case the term incommensurate crystal is an oxymoron, but one which may perhaps be justified by their generally crystalline properties and the by now firmly fixed common usage. As a generic term, quasicrystal is more logical and arguably more insightful nomenclature. Unfortunately, the term has been equally firmly appropriated to denote a specific subclass of quasi-periodic structures.)

From a geometrical point of view, quasi-periodic pattern formation in two dimensions is the problem of covering an area with tiles in a nonperiodic way, which can be accomplished with a minimum of two sets of tiles of different shapes, known as Penrose tiles. The resulting global patterns (more than one is possible) have interesting self-similarity properties. (For example, any given fragmentary local pattern, of whatever size, can be shown to recur within a distance of the order of the diameter of the local size. It is this property that gives rise to the sharp diffraction patterns that these Penrose tilings generate in spite of their lack of translational long-range order.) Penrose tilings can be generalized to higher dimensions. One way of accomplishing this, the cut-and-project method, is demonstrated for a one-dimensional example in Fig. 1. The resulting construction, known as a Fibonacci chain, has among other interesting properties those of local self-similarity, as discussed previously.

Incommensurate structures, although now known to be rather common in nature, are at best marginally stable with respect to fully ordered structures. Often, such phases are stable only over relatively small ranges of temperature and pressure. There are forces present that act to drive the modulation period from an incommensurate to a commensurate value, giving rise to lock-in transformations in which the structure reverts to a commensurate one, albeit often with a very greatly enlarged unit cell.

II. Examples of Incommensurate and Quasi-Crystalline Structures

Although there are many examples of quasiperiodic structures, there are a relatively smaller number of basic phenomena that produce them. Briefly, they are explained in the following subsections.

A. Modulated Structures

In this important class, there is an underlying three-dimensional periodic structure and a superimposed deviation with a different incommensurate period. For example, in a rank four modulated structure ($\mathbf{a}_1$, $\mathbf{a}_2$, $\mathbf{a}_3$) might define the dual of a conventional three-dimensional periodic structure, and $\mathbf{a}_4$ the period of the modulation. The modulation wave might represent static fluctuations in composition (for example, antiphase domain boundaries in metal alloy systems such as CuAu) or small-amplitude displacement of atoms from regular lattice sites (for example, charge density wave systems such as TaS_2). Because the modulation is often small in amplitude, the Bragg reflections are readily classified into strong parent reflections and weaker satellites (with nonzero $\mathbf{a}_4$ components). Often, the incommensurate length scale, $\mathbf{a}_4$, can be traced (for example, a Fermi surface dimension in metals) and used to identify a specific physical mechanism responsible for stabilizing the incommensurate structure. Novel low-energy excitations associated with dynamical fluctuations in the phase of the modulations with respect to the underlying periodic structure are also of some importance in the understanding of this class of materials.

B. Intergrowth Structures

Three-dimensional examples of this type occur when a sublattice A, of a regular periodic structure, is open enough to accept an interpenetrating or intercalated sublattice B, of a different substance. In general, the two sublattice spacings can be incommensurate. Often, but not always, additional constraints, such as charge neutrality, enforce commensurability of A and B. When this is not the case, the resulting quasiperiodic diffraction pattern cannot be readily classified into intense peaks and weaker satellites. Two-dimensional manifestations of this type are even more common, as when substance B forms a monolayer on the surface of a crystal of substance A.

C. Incommensurate Magnetic Structures

In most magnetic materials, the long-range magnetic order is of a simple commensurate ferromagnetic and antiferromagnetic type. However, in some materials, the competition between magnetic exchange forces of different ranges gives rise to spiral or antiphase magnetic structures with periods incommensurate with the chemical structures. Such magnetic arrangements, which occur commonly but not exclusively among rare earth metals, were the first known examples of incommensurate systems, having been studied extensively by neutron diffraction since the early 1960s. The full significance of the concept and its generalization to the chemical-structural context were slow to develop.

D. Quasicrystals

In 1984, it was discovered that certain very rapidly cooled Al–Mn alloys produced diffraction patterns with crystallographically unallowable fivefold rotational symmetry and, it was subsequently discovered, could be accurately indexed in terms of integral linear combinations of 12 basis vectors pointing to the faces of a regular dodecahedron. It was this discovery that provoked the present and ongoing examination of quasi-period structures at a greater depth than had hitherto been attempted. It is now widely believed that these materials do indeed represent new examples of quasi-periodic structures of rank six (only half of the 12 basis vectors are independent) and are thus unlike other known apparent examples of fivefold symmetric structures that are created by macroscopic twinning. Identical and related phases have also been reported in other rapidly cooled binary and ternary alloys, as have single quasicrystalline samples of AlCuLi of millimeter size and faceted growth habits. These later were grown under conditions much more favorable for thermodynamic equilibrium.

Bibliography

Blinc, R., and Levanyuk, A. P., eds. (1986). "Incommensurate Phases in Dielectrics," 2 Vols. North-Holland Publ., Amsterdam.

Currat, R., and Janssen, T. (1988). Excitations in incommensurate crystal phases. "Solid State Physics," Vol. 41, pp. 201–302. Academic Press, San Diego, California.

Janssen, T., and Janner, A. (1987). Incommensurability in crystals. *Adv. Phys.* **36,** 519–624.

INFORMATION DISPLAY SYSTEMS

George M. Krembs *IBM*

Glossary

ANSI: American National Standards Institute.

Bridge: Used between different kinds of media, such as coax to fiber-optics, to connect subnetworks of identical protocol. Bridges look at each packet address, keep their own local traffic, and send on packets intended for other stations across the bridge. If one local network is overburdened, a simple bridge is often used to try to subdivide the load.

CASE: Computer Assisted Software Engineering.

CCITT: Consultative Committee on International Telegraph and Telephone.

Client-server: Defines the relationships involved among interconnected computers. For end users with desktop machines, the remote capabilities provide service on request, so that the remote machine is a server to the desktop client. With the proper application software, one computer may assume both roles, being a server to some and a client to others on the network.

Gateway: A node that takes packets from one type of network, disassembles them, and reassembles them into new packets compatible with the destination. Because this processing usually involves all layers of the architecture, gateways process fewer packets per second than bridges or routers, depending on how many levels of dissimilarity exist between the networks.

ISO: International Organization for Standardization.

Multitasking/multithreading: Multitasking allows a system to have multiple applications running at once, whereas multithreading lets multiple processes exist within a single application; in other words, if the user pulls down a print menu while a spreadsheet application program is doing a recalculation, or if the CAD program will accept a user interrupt of a time-consuming redraw of the screen without waiting for it to finish, the system is performing multithreading.

NTSC: National Television Standards Committee; the group that defined the method for encoding and transmission of color television broadcasting in the United States.

POSIX (Portable Operating System Interface): Document created by several different committees of the IEEE. The Federal Information Processing Standard (FIPS) uses POSIX as its base. While it was originally derived from UNIX, non-UNIX-based operating systems can be compliant with POSIX. Intended for varied and divergent platforms, so that the operating system is independent of the particular run platform, POSIX defines common OS calls, command languages interpreter programs, and a verification suite of programs to test POSIX compliance and conformance.

Repeater: Electronic box that regenerates electrical or optical signals; it has no capability to detect addresses, so it cannot interrupt or analyze data. The repeater can support different types of media and does not care what kind of software protocols or address data exist on the media.

RISC (reduced-instruction set computer): Computer that avoids use of complex instructions that may take several clock cycles to execute. Some designers believe that

ENCYCLOPEDIA OF PHYSICAL SCIENCE AND TECHNOLOGY, VOL. 8

such a simplification not only increases the rating of the processor in MIPS (millions of instructions per second) but also the speed at which the computer can execute the application by keeping the pipeline flowing smoothly. RISC-like processors strive for one or more instructions executed per clock cycle. An architecture that executes one instruction per clock cycle on average has a quoted performance of 33 MIPS at 33 MHz; if it could sustain three instructions per cycle, with a 50 MHz clock, you might be able to get 150 MIPS.

Router: When many subnets need to be interconnected and more bridging does not seem beneficial, then a router is needed. More than a bridge, routers possess a plan to determine the best way to move the packet from source to destination among many alternative paths; they may also be capable of responding to changes in traffic loading by revising the plan and thus achieving a better balance among interconnecting networks. They can react to network errors or any failures by rerouting around problems. The most sophisticated routers do a least-cost analysis for bulk files.

SCSI (Small Computer System Interface): Technology that defines a design for attaching devices together across multiple vendors of products. Similar but different designs are called high performance parallel interface (HIPPI) and intelligent peripheral interface-3 (IPI-3).

SPEC (Systems Performance Evaluation Cooperative) performance benchmark: The Systems Performance Evaluation Cooperative (SPEC) was established by a number of computer system vendors to develop a set of mutually acceptable programs to measure primarily the CPU's integer and floating-point run time in engineering and scientific applications; the first suite released had 10 benchmarks in the set, and the geometric mean for all 10 is the published SPEC performance result.

TCP/IP: Internet Protocol (IP) for ISO Level 3 datagrams, Transmission Control Protocol (TCP) for ISO Level 4 data streams; it is an open system protocol that is media independent (ISO Levels 1 and 2).

Window manager: Software program that controls the presentation of several different applications at the user interface and has a viewing screen as a composite of overlays that appear to be in three-dimensional space. The 3D effect can be achieved by shading the pictured icons.

Workstation: Broadly used term connoting direct attachment to a local-area network, with more function at a higher price than a personal computer. Originally, workstations were used for engineering CAD/CAM applications, but now they are finding cost-effective usage in the financial and securities industry and have good potential for use on the manufacturing factory and shop floor. The distinction between the personal computer and the workstation will lessen as the power of microprocessors increases and the price differential decreases between workstations and personal computers.

X windows and terminals: Standard developed by Massachusetts Institute of Technology for distributed computing, where the device controlling the end-user interface is called the server, and the host system executing the application is called the client. Thus, a DOS machine can be an X server, as well as a special-purpose display called an X terminal. If the X server is implemented on the host, the overhead of X and TCP/IP protocols is eliminated over the serial link. The purpose of the X terminal is to achieve a workstation-type interface for close to the price of a dumb terminal.

An information display system typically consists of a cathode-ray tube monitor for displaying output, a keyboard and associated hand-movable mouse to position the screen cursor, a printer for generating text-oriented documents, a plotter for graphic hard copy, and store-and-forward units for storing/retrieving records and for sending/receiving communications. Continued advances in the technology of display devices and electronic components have resulted in industrial products that progress to twice the computational performance and capacity every 2 years. In 1990, the semiconductor industry was in early production of 4-Mbit dynamic random access memories (DRAMs), was exchanging published technical papers on its 16- and 64-Mbit prototypes, and had begun manufacturing the optical step-and-scan lithography systems to be installed at its ultra large scale integration (ULSI) research centers for investigation of 256-Mbit DRAM devices. (These ULSI optical systems can print 0.35, maybe 0.25, micrometer line-widths on chips.) To make the more aggressive 512 Mbit density, semiconductor technologists have experimented with excimer laser lithographic systems. By the end of the century, it is anticipated that an X-ray energy source, synchrotron or stand-alone, will be used to expose X-ray sensitive photoresist in a helium-atmosphere camera and produce 1 Gbit dynamic RAMs.

This relatively fast rate of technical progress indicates that aggressive pricing and functional improvements are to be the norm for information display systems in the 1990s. Whereas home computers in the early 1980s had 64 Kbytes of RAM and an 8-bit microprocessor unit (MPU), in 1990 the minimum configuration of the IBM PS/1 home computer contained 512 Kbytes of RAM and a 16-bit Intel 80286 microprocessor. Listed prices for the PS/1 ranged from $999 to $1,999, and the base model included a monochrome monitor, one 3-1/2 in. floppy drive, an internal 2400-baud modem, and PC-DOS software to drive a VGA graphics display generator.

For the high-performance users of desktop workstations, the microprocessors available in 1990 contained more than one million transistors on a single chip; for example, the Intel 80486 MPU has 1.2 million transistors. Very large scale integration (VLSI) chips processed with complementary metal oxide semiconductor (CMOS) technology were practical at 1.27 × 1.27 cm; for example, IBM's chip used in its RISC workstations resulted in enough space for up to 256 Mbytes of real memory. Figure 1 gives a picture of these large silicon VLSI CMOS chips used in the IBM RISC workstation. The expectation for the end of the 1990s is to achieve 100 million transistors per chip, 250-MHz clock rates, 2 billion instructions per second, ... and be architected for parallel throughput using four CPUs on a single chip.

FIG. 1. IBM's new RISC desktop workstations feature 1.27 × 1.27-cm chips. (Photo courtesy of International Business Machines Corporation.)

The continued impact on information display systems caused by the decline in prices and the rise in speed and capabilities of integrated circuits is described in this article.

I. Organization of an Information Display System

A. Physical Hardware Elements

Most modern desktop units contain a 16-bit or 32-bit microprocessor. Motorola has announced a RISC microprocessor for speeds over 60 MIPS. The clock speed of most microprocessors is usually between 12 and 65 MHz. Beyond 60 MHz, the motherboard or backplane electronics become expensive for a workstation environment, and the challenge is to control the critical tolerances necessary to avoid out-of-spec distributed capacitance delays in the packaging. More predictable is the cost savings that can be realized by combining several earlier chips on one denser silicon substrate; not only is the total cost lower, but also less strip-line delay exists across the several pinouts connecting the individual chips on the board.

Figure 2 shows the IBM POWERstation 320 desktop workstation, which offers a very high price/performance, namely 20 MHz clock speed, 27.5 MIPS, 48 K Dhrystones, and 7.4 Mflops at a price starting at $12,995. (For comparison, an IBM 3090 E-class mainframe sold during the mid-1980s has a system performance for a uniprocessor of about 15 Mflops when doing double precision arithmetic on a matrix of linear equations on the order of one hundred; the IBM 3090 600E was rated by the Gartner Group at 77 MIPS.) The IBM RISC System/6000 Mod 320 supports thick/thin Ethernet, IEEE 802.5 standard 4/16-bit Token Ring, Micro Channel, OSF/MOTIF, POSIX, OSI, X

FIG. 2. IBM's RISC System/6000 desktop workstation. (Photo courtesy of International Business Machines Corporation.)

Window System, and Display PostScript. Housed in a floor-standing tower, a fast member of the IBM RISC System/6000 is POWERserver 540, using a 30 MHz microprocessor to achieve 41.1 MIPS, 13 Mflops, and a SPEC performance benchmark rating of 34.7 units. The 540 has 4-Mbit DRAM chips for its standard 64 Mbyte memory, and the tower can accommodate a maximum 256 Mbytes of real memory, which was the maximum central storage on many mainframe designs in the mid-80s. To provide the file storage, magnetic or optical diskette and hard-disk devices are added. Small magnetic and optical hard disks have a capacity of hundreds of megabytes or gigabytes of personal storage. Sun Microsystems, Inc. offers an entry-level, diskless RISC-based workstation that runs at 12.5 MIPS, is priced just under $5,000, and can be used as a network node. This Sun desktop unit comes with a 20 MHz MPU, 8 to 16 Mbytes of memory, 64 Kbytes of cache, two serial ports, a 17-in. monochrome monitor, keyboard and mouse; bundled in all Sun's Sparc-based machines is the SunOS operating system, the Open Look graphical user interface, and its Open Network Computing/Network File System (ONC/NFS) software.

Because of these low-cost hardware elements provided by VLSI, function that once was performed on the central system has moved into the workstation. Consequently, local-area networks are assembled for purposes other than time-sharing a central processor to create the display screen. Instead, distributed file servers and network routers were invented. Mainframe applications are becoming more oriented to managing large-transaction corporate files, doing long computer server simulations, and managing the networks. Central services are also still needed to procure the expensive I/O and the high-speed wide-area networks at the site. The impact of the physical hardware is so pervasive that multiple microprocessors are now being designed into workstations, to perform floating-point and Fourier transform algorithms, generate the screen, be protocol engines, and do database searching. Consequently, the end user can personalize the desktop workstation by plug-in cards controlled by the bus master. Card options define the memory size, special processing, the printer interface, the communications protocol, the input device options, and indicate whether there is a tape-backup unit or other special equipment within the workstation's control. For example, the Sun entry workstation has options to add 104 Mbytes to 2.7 Gbytes of external disk storage, CD-ROMs, and a 150 Mbyte 1/4-in. or 2.3 Gbytes 8-mm tape drive.

The $3\frac{1}{2}$ in. disk drive is the most prevalent size sold in contemporary desktop workstations. The technology has attained an amazing level of performance and reliability, packing 300 to 425 Mbytes, with average seek time of 12 msec for read commands, less than 14 msec for write commands, and data transfer rates to 5 Mbytes per sec. The drives contain embedded SCSI IC controllers for robust test capability. IC options are various caching schemes and command queuing. Examples of this drive IC function are: (1) unit self-testing, including proper servo operation and read/write (R/W) electronics across the 1600 tracks per platter inch default mode without dependency on the host bus accept for the power; (2) a write cache that will get off the bus immediately after receipt of the data and writes onto disk later when it is free; (3) an adaptive prefetch algorithm that enables the drive to tailor the access pattern of the operating system. These disk IC drive features do not necessitate that system manufacturers include such features in the disk drivers of their operating systems, since the algorithms are automatically executed. Error monitoring and reporting provide details on error patterns should a drive fail and can be used to predict potential catastrophic failure. Vendors claim an impressive 75,000 hr mean time between failures (MTBF). Without this concurrent improvement in the permanent storage hardware elements such as the small-form-factor disk drive I/O, the benefits of faster MPUs in terms of system performance could not have been accomplished.

SCSI drives require a device driver to interface between the operating system and the host bus adapters. To find an official standard so that systems integrators can just "plug-in and play," be it DOS, OS/2, or UNIX, the ANSI X3T9.2 standards committee has written a specification, called the Common Access Method (CAM), with hopes that eventually the SCSI CAM devices become compatible with a variety of operating systems.

B. Programmable Software Elements

Giving end users at their desktop the equivalent capability of what was a central mainframe just a decade ago has moved the application and presentation manager control programs into these end-user workstations. End users become the clients who request some kind of service from the central servers. In the early days of window management by the central server, the mainframe needed to know the parameters of the workstation software system if it was to be responsible for the screen format displayed in the window. For more advanced window management, the workstation control program may choose to keep the overlay appearance and style to itself and let the central server application program write to a full-screen or full-window buffer, even though only a portion is shown to the end user on the composite screen. As the instruction processing speed of these distributed systems increases, this potential is being utilized to write more sophisticated software with longer path lengths. Thus, the end user still experiences a subsecond response time to most keystrokes that are controlling the function within the workstation. RISC processors have been built to optimize the system response of the most frequently executed instructions, and the workstation performance is critically dependent on the ability of the compiler to make use of the multiple execution modes of superscaler architectures. That is why the MIPS rating of a microprocessor is not as informative as a comparative benchmark performance study using an agreed-to suite of application programs.

It is the essence of the information display system to provide the end user with a cost-effective, helpful application. As the hardware and software elements increase in complexity, the rate of progress is paced by the ability of the total software industry to create timely products that can be developed before the next generation of hardware makes them obsolete. For personal computers, the most frequent applications used on personal computers are

- Word processors
- Spreadsheets
- Database managers
- Desktop publishing
- Graphics for desktop publishing
- CAD/CAM/CAE
- Mainframe access
- Accounting and tax preparation
- Recreation
- Languages and tools
- Electronic mail
- Education

Figure 3 shows a graphical screen with a windowing application. The graphical screen has icons representing the many office tasks performed in a typical business day, and the format conforms with the OSF/Motif interface objectives.

In distributed environments, the listed applications share resources stated in the application program, such that the client can call for data stored on a network server and receive it back in some cases with no knowledge of how the network server actually found and moved it, that is, through transparent computing network facilities.

With such a diversity of detailed designs, the software industry has had to seek CASE toolkits

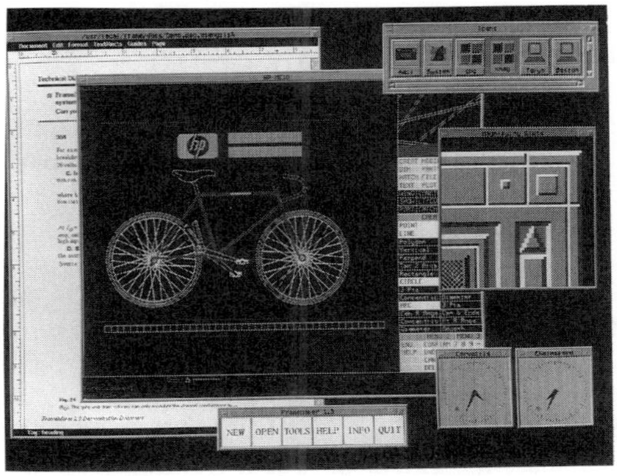

FIG. 3. "Bike" windowing display based on OSF's MOTIF graphic user interface. (Photo courtesy of Hewlett-Packard Company.)

to accelerate productivity, just as the hardware design engineers made major investments in computer-aided design tools. Semiconductor technology allows VLSI chips to control multitasking within the operating system, but realization of that potential has been slow, and more attention is being drawn to standardization of architectures that are open to all participants. Consortiums and open foundations are now organized to meet the challenge of distributed processing, both for suppliers and for the customers involved in this fast-moving technology. Upward compatibility and portability across several different types of operating systems have forced together industry representatives who were once strong rivals. Such alliances will continue to appear on a worldwide basis, as the price/performance of solid-state devices is projected to continue to improve for the next decade.

Thousands of applications exist for each major computing system, and therein lies the potential problem of inertia. Some technologists believe that programs must be composed of "objects," just as building contractors construct various architectural edifices out of some standardized hardware that conforms to local building and zoning codes. CASE tools are being designed to generate a windowing management program by manipulating icons on a screen to build a program. A software developer connects these icons on a display screen with arrows in a logical flowchart representation of the program. The CASE software will generate the specific code when you compile the object code of each invoked icon. The libraries in such a CASE windowing program are reusable graphical-code modules that are object-oriented and modifiable.

II. Progress in Related Physical Science and Technology

A. Display Devices: CRTs and Flat Screen

Despite impressive recent technological progress in flat panels, the cathode-ray tube still dominates. CRT designers continue to push out the limits, selling 38-cm diagonal monochrome monitors with 3300-by-2560 pixel capacity for a few thousand dollars; 48-cm diagonal models are also appearing more frequently for demanding applications. The display quality currently available for color graphic workstations now consists of 1600-by-1200 pixels on a 19-in. or 27-in. diagonal screen; Fig. 4 is photograph of a high-resolution 27-in. color monitor with a video bandwidth of 175 MHz, 74 KHz horizontal line rate, 60 Hz vertical frame rate; the dot trio pitch is 0.37 mm, and power consumption is 300 W. On a 19-in. CRT, these 1.9 million viewable pixels have been accomplished with a 0.25-mm pitch shadow-mask, a 75-KHz horizontal scan frequency, and a vertical frequency of 60 Hz noninterlaced. The 1.92 million pixels on this 19 in. color monitor were generated by a 32-bit, 6 MIPS graphics processor executing from up to 4 Mbytes of display list memory. From such a list, the Texas Instruments 34010 graphics processor can fill in areas at 48 million bits per second, draw lines at 1.2 million pixels per second, or create text characters at 25,000 per second. In the 1990s, the functional specifications of a graphic processor to drive CRTs for commercial professional workstations would be required to generate 10 K quadrilateral polygons per second, with Z-axis smoothing in its display buffer.

FIG. 4. 1600-by-1200 pixel high resolution color display system. (Photo courtesy of Lundy Computer Graphics—A Division of TransTechnology Corporation.)

The color-monitor revenue has now surpassed monochrome sales, with color growing at an annual rate of more than 10% overall, and even faster in high-resolution segments for CAD/CAM/CAE and imaging. For such complex screens based on windows, highlighting data via intensity is not adequate ease of use. Thus, the ever-increasing demand for color highlighting and identification will affect the design of information display systems for years to come.

The push into high-definition television (HDTV) will simply continue to fund advances in CRT technology and cause the data processing industry to introduce new multimedia applications. HDTV shows its best potential on large display screens, which is why the CRT is also dominant in HDTV displays. All proposed HDTV standards accommodate any window with the TV image having a smaller raster scan. Figure 5 illustrates such a composite; the information shown in the video windows comes from the NTSC (or PAL) color TV standard signal. The entire screen is managed by Microsoft Windows. The available real estate on the HDTV screen will appear to be about five times larger in size. Symbolics, Inc. has applied HDTV technology to the production of entertainment motion pictures. With its software for computer-animated rendering, the company generated a humanlike character to talk to the real human being in the inserted NTSC window. To create the animation film, Symbolics film producers first made on HDTV digital tape recording at the data rate of 1.188 Gbytes per sec, consisting of a single 30 MHz bandwidth of luminance, plus two color difference signals at 15 MHz each. Thereafter, they created a sequence of frames, 1970 pixels by 1035 scan lines. To generate the final composite shown in the figure, an electron-beam recorder was used to combine both HDTV and NTSC images together onto a 35 mm film that could be shown in movie theaters.

CRTs exist from 0.5-in. diameter for helmet-mounted displays to 45 in. for entertainment applications. (Such a CRT weighs 250 lb and is 28 in. in depth, just under the 30 in. limit to move the TV set through doors.) Paper-white phosphors have been developed especially for the information display system, now that the need for long-persistence phosphors and multibeam CRTs has almost disappeared due to the increase in electronic circuit speed and density (plus improvements in yokes and amplifiers for conventional single-beam raster scan monitors).

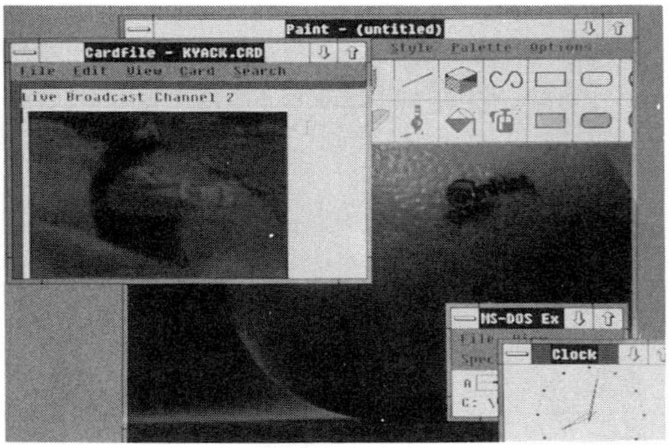

FIG. 5. Multimedia display demonstrating full-motion and still video overlays. (Photo courtesy of New Media Graphics, Billerica, Mass.)

Projection CRTs are predominant in the TV industry and thus enjoy a production cost advantage over light valves for general-purpose data displays. Resolution of 640-by-400 is typical, with adequate lumens for board, class, or conference rooms. However, the military and special-purpose information centers create a market for the oil-film CRT, the light-emitting diode array, solid-state light modulators, cathodochromic CRTs, direct-view projection lasers, and so on.

Flat-panel devices, with their lower weight, size, and power needs, are prevalent in portable displays. The flat-bulb CRT has diminished in prominence, and three physical sciences are in competition: electroluminescence, gas plasma, and liquid crystals.

1. Electroluminescence

The thin-film electroluminscent (TFEL) panel is growing in popularity because it is rugged and fast-writing. Ranging in size from 2-by-3 to 12-by-14 in. at 1024-by-800 pixels, the technology gives high brightness (up to 100 foot-Lamberts) by increasing the refresh rate with a power consumption between that of the liquid crystal display (LCD) and the ac/dc plasma panel. Full-color TFEL displays are contingent on an efficient blue phosphor, which is still a laboratory science project.

2. Gas Plasma

The ac plasma offers a good contrast ratio and viewing angle, so that laptop computer buyers often purchase this high-priced display device instead of the passive liquid crystal display. The dc plasma panel provides 16 or 256 levels of gray scale, although the poorer contrast ratio detracts from the low price of the current dc panel. As for size, a 150-cm diagonal screen with 2048-by-2048 pixels has been fabricated. Compared to CRTs, the monochrome plasma panels have lower resolution, around 0.4 mm (62.5 lines/in.).

Full-color plasma panels exist in the laboratory; photoluminescence is being tried to achieve greater white luminance efficiency. A 640-by-448 pixel dc display for the cell array of each of the three colors can be made. With 256 gray levels, the dc plasma panel displays a full-color television picture with a quality nearly comparable to a CRT. Thomson Tubes Electroniques demonstrated a 17.4-in. multicolor ac plasma screen, with the hope that full-volume production could begin in 1991. To achieve this demonstration, the standard structure was modified with a coplanar sandwich, so that the gas discharge emits UV to activate the individual red, green, and blue phosphor dots. However, the unit has a low resolution of 384 by 384, no true gray scale, and the single-unit price is a hefty $10,000. (A 24-in., 512 by 512 display is the next objective for that experimental group.)

3. Liquid Crystals

Liquid crystal displays have become the most popular flat panel display. The LCD display does not emit light but does polarize it during reflection and refraction. Nowadays flat panels are manufactured with all the necessary drive electronics to control the polarizing direction of each pixel in the array, from the simple on/off state to a frame modulation scheme that causes the visual effect of 4- or 16-level gray-scale images.

The passive-matrix LCD stands alone in long-battery-life applications. With ASICs chips as the enabling technology, a portable computer is commercially available for Poqet with an 80-character by 25 line display and a 77-key typewriter style keyboard designed to be a fully MS-DOS IBM-compatible PC, yet it measures only 8.75 × 4.3 × 0.9 in., and weighs just under 1 lb; this palmtop portable computer operates up to 100 hr on 2 AA alkaline batteries, contains 512 Kbytes of memory, and has a 7-in. LCD display. The Poqet palmtop is shown in Fig. 6.

With built-in backlighting from an electroluminescence foil or fluorescent tubes, LCDs can be read under any ambient light conditions. The Airis VH-286 has an 11-in. SuperTwist LCD VGA screen with EL back light, a 20-Mbyte 2.5-in. hard disk, and 12.5 MHz 80C286 processor in a package a little bit bigger than a loose-leaf notebook; this $1,899 system weighs 6.5 lb, measures 10.25 × 11.9 × 1.8 in., and has 2 Mbytes of RAM that's user-expandable to 4 Mbytes. The average access time for the hard disk drive is 23 msec, and this notebook computer also features a built-in 256 Kbyte disk cache to speed software execution and limit disk access frequency to save power. (The 2.5-in. drive is 40% smaller than 3.5-in. units seen in desktops and stores in the range of 20 to 40 Mbytes per single platter.) MS-DOS and Traveling Software's LapLink are loaded on the standard hard disk (LapLink does lap-to-desktop file transfer), and the VH-286 notebook computer has the ability to download (via modem) new system BIOS software for updating its flash electrically programmable read only memories (EPROMs). Flash EPROMs, up to 2-Mbits per IC, come in a thin, small-outline package, which is 20 × 8 × 1.2 mm called TSOP. That package permits 16 ICs on a dense "PC card" measuring 2 × 3 in., which means about 4 Mbytes of rewritable, nonvolatile, low cost storage is available for the downloading software. The DOS operating system is capable of enabling programs for direct execution from ROM; additional DRAMs are needed to provide the memory space for the data manipulation.

The Airis VH-286 is supplied by either a rechargeable nickel-cadmium battery pack or 10 C alkaline cell batteries. The 6.5 lb includes all 10 batteries loaded from the front drawer as shown in Fig. 7. The unit also comes with an external 120 V ac power adapter and voltage converter. NiCad batteries are the more commonly used

FIG. 6. MS-DOS compatible palmtop computer. (Photo courtesy of Poqet Computer Company.)

FIG. 7. MS-DOS compatible notebook computer. (Photo courtesy of Airis Computer Corporation.)

laptop power source. With a 4 A/hr energy reserve, the VH-286 notebook computer can achieve 6 hr of normal activity; the 2.5-in. hard drive is designed for low-power surges and has limited mechanical mass. Airis claims that 12 hr of operation can be squeezed from its alkaline battery operation due to extraordinary battery-saving features. For example, power is maintained to the system RAM when shut off, and will remember where it was (auto-resumes) on reactivation by the end user.

Texas Instruments, Inc. (TI), together with Sharp Corporation, makes a TravelMate 2000 laptop computer with a 640-by-480 VGA LCD display, using cold-cathode fluorescent side-lighting and triple SuperTwist technology, allowing 16-gray-scale imagery; the MS-DOS and LapLink are in ROM to conserve weight at 4.4 lb. The 80287 coprocessor socket and both Centronics and serial ports are standard; the microfloppy system is external, as well as an expansion chassis with $1\frac{1}{2}$ PC slots. It is interesting that TI extended the power of Traveling Software's Battery Watch power manager to include real-time control of the system; the operator can assess the laptop's "time to empty" at any time and allow the user to demand more power or throttle back the power consumption.

Another innovative LCD product is a computer-driven overlay plate to be placed on an overhead transparency projector that functions in the manner of a light valve or shutter; these units are PC-compatible and have a typical resolution of 640-by-400. In considering future LCD enhancements, laboratory prototypes of full-color LCDs have exhibited impressive image quality and size (14 in.) for information display systems. Contrast ratios up to 100 : 1 are claimed, with 60-degree viewing angle and 17.5-msec response.

B. Other Input and Output Devices

The television camera has become a practical scanning device to capture an image in gray tones and manipulate it within the workstation. The composite screen is then sent on the local-area network to the print server, which is probably a laser electrophotographic printer. PC/fax boards convert computer-generated documents into the standard code understood by fax machines, and this direct conversion and transmission of stored text and images will preserve the graphics quality at the receiving fax. (Some manufactures of PC/fax boards include an optical scanner interface.) For the desktop printer/hardcopy device, ink-jet printing technology is still the most cost-effective for an acceptable image, although it is not laser quality, nor equal to a plain-paper electrographic copier.

In terms of future hardcopy technology, the LCD shutter may compete with laser light sources, or the LED printer could become the high-speed bulk printer; yet the ubiquitous dot-matrix impact low-price printer head now comes in 9, 18, 24, and 48 pins to move ink from the everlasting cloth ribbon spindle.

C. Electronic Control Circuits and Components

To accommodate the various product raster formats, the CRT monitor frequency comes equipped with a multiple-scan feature. Commercial application software packages are written to support specific graphic adapters. Therefore, when a new version gains popular appeal, it takes time for new display-driver software to be developed and released for that version. The earlier color graphic standard was 320-by-200, later enhanced to 640-by-350 with 16 colors. Eventually, video quality arrived in a price range for the desktop models with 640-by-480 pixels, each capable of 256 possible colors. For the novice, it can be perplexing to find a monitor, a graphics card, and a shrink-wrapped software package that will match up and work together. And there is more to consider, such as whether the expansion slot for the plug-in card has 8-bit, 16-bit, or 32-bit capacity. Moreover, some slots will run at only half the CPU speed or are found to be not bus-compatible with the boards in the older machines when it comes time to move up to the next purchase. Multiscan monitors contain auto-synchronous circuits to overcome some of these problems of forward and backward compatibility across the graphic standards. Some advanced monitors will provide a switching function to convert a color monitor into the appearance of a higher-resolution monochrome quality image.

In 1990, the stage was set for putting 1024-by-768 pixel resolution into the lower-priced systems as part of the ongoing merger of the personal computer and workstation capabilities. (There are noninterlaced versions as well as interlaced rasters, similar to the TV frame, to reduce cost.) Such adapters require display buffer memory from 512 Kbytes to 1 Mbyte from which the system graphic coprocessor generates and stores the image. The medium 512 K board list price in 1990 was $580, and such generators will continue advancing with the DRAM IC growth in density during the 1990s. Since the main processor within the workstation simply sends graphics instructions to these adapter cards, the main control program has instruction cycles available to do other tasks, such as managing the overlay windows of the multitasking environment and policing the traffic between coprocessors that share the bus on the backplane or motherboard.

Performance measurements on the total system can determine which element shows down the end user throughput. While the microprocessor may operate at 25 or 33 MHz, the performance edge may go to the system with the fastest hard disk, or disk-caching software, or static-RAM cache, or the speed of the network, or the bit size of the motherboard slot to be used for memory expansion, depending on the overall design. The horsepower of a fast MPU can be wasted waiting for another element to respond. To overcome bottlenecks, gallium arsenide chips have been used for design of static RAM cache memories to cut delay time in half over current silicon parts and improve the workstation throughput. Another approach involves putting on chip an 8-Kbyte cache that handles both data and instructions. On the system bus connecting these VLSI chips together, transfer can occur at several hundred megabytes per second. Some chips have been designed to have a physical address range of 4 Gbytes (4×10^9 bytes) and a virtual address range of 64 Tbytes (64×10^{12} bytes).

Performance is not the only customer concern. Too many microprocessor engine options can splinter the software development industry, already struggling with incompatible graphic adapters and network protocols. The serious purchasers of information display systems invest more in their applications and database than in outlay of money during the original purchase, so upward compatibility is usually a key concern. Because RISC CPUs strive for a performance advantage over the more complex instruction CPUs, there is more risk that a family of RISC CPUs will be neither backward nor forward compatible. At the present pace of technology, the speed advantage of the RISC architecture can last for about 2 years before the next generation is needed to keep the lead in stated performance within a predetermined price range. As chip density increases, more pipelining is added to avoid pushing the RISC system designer into the off-chip stray capacitance problems associated with higher clock speeds. Thus, RISC machines are adopting more of a parallel-processing architecture, as well as putting more functional parts onto the chip. The IBM RISC System/6000 achieved its breakthrough performance with a superscalar design technique based on logic that executes more than one instruction in parallel.

D. Transmission Lines, Modems, and Switching Nodes

In less than a decade, many applications have been written and installed at the desktop. Network systems architectures have had to accommodate the intelligent desktop equipment, because the central mainframe becomes a peer of the end user's personal system. Having become the functional appearance to the end user of the mainframes built back in the 1970s in terms of horse-power, memory, and storage, these workstations are programmed to process the application and to communicate with other peers via messages and files. To keep a balanced system, all subnets must move ahead orders of magnitude in transmission speed. During the 1970s, mainframes in the information center communicated with each other in the range of 1–4 Mbytes/sec. In the late 1980s, workstations needed to talk to each other and to any central servers at that rate, while the central mainframes needed to progress toward gigabyte-per-second linkages. Fortunately, the physical science and technology of fiber-optical transmission has become available to solve this quest for higher speed.

1. Local Area Networks (LANs)

In the early 1980s, the workstation would often emulate the older terminals and then switch to stand-alone PC mode, coming back into the emulator when there was a need to transmit or receive mainframe messages. While many terminals were connected directly to central mainframes, the advent of the personal computer/workstation created the need for the local area network, or LAN.

A LAN can address more than 256 workstations. All LANs are based on time-sharing; a workstation may grab the token to begin transmission, or just start transmitting in a contentious way, as long as no other peer workstation tries to communicate; if another does, then the collisions are detected and the workstation continues trying to transmit until the LAN is free.

Transmission line losses per meter have improved in the fiber cable so that one transceiver pair can extend the linkage about 2 km for bit rates that would travel 25 m on a copper coaxial cable with one repeater. LANs with coaxial or shielded twisted-pair copper wire usually operate with a digital bit rate between 4 and 16 Mbit per second. A fiber-optic LAN will need to run at one order of magnitude better (that is 100+ Mbit per second) to be acceptable in the LAN speed spectrum. A proposed standard, called Fiber Data Distributed Interface (FDDI), has been defined by ANSI committees as a new ring technology to achieve this order of magnitude at reasonable cost per attached node. Figure 8 is a diagram of a possible FDDI local area network that will be utilized as backbone and eventually could become the wall outlet for the desktop workstation.

Some very high-powered workstations are built with dual frame buffers. While the graphics adapter is generating the visualized image from one buffer, the computer server can be loading the next frame into its twin. Some supercomputer centers have demonstrated synthetic real-time video by this method, although the supercomputer is usually dedicated to serving a few high-powered workstations, since the LAN speed must be in the range of gigabits per second. If the workstation frame buffer is fast and large enough, these few workstations can share the supercomputer high-speed channel via a cross-point switch. Information is sent in bursts across that star topology, which is similar to the switching hub of a major railroad yard or train depot. An early prototype of this network switch architecture allows concurrent transmission by each workstation at about 1-Gbit/sec rate for 30 workstations; eventually, the goal is to link 1700 workstations and handle an aggregate capacity of 850 Gbit per second. A VLSI device has been fabricated in a standard 2-μm CMOS process to function as a 16-by-16 cross-point switch; it transfers data at 70 Mbit per second, indicating that the speed of networks will increase rapidly in the 1990s.

Why a star and not the shared ring for gigabit rates? Laser devices exist to build such very high-speed LANs, but the difficulty with a shared ring comes during the protocol analysis which the star topology avoids. CPU with 50-MHz instructions per second are too slow for protocol interpretation at gigabits per second. VLSI research projects are underway to build the protocol analysis into dedicated processors and to convert a gigabit-per-second serial stream back to a parallel CPU stream to slow down the arrival rate of each transmitted packet per CPU.

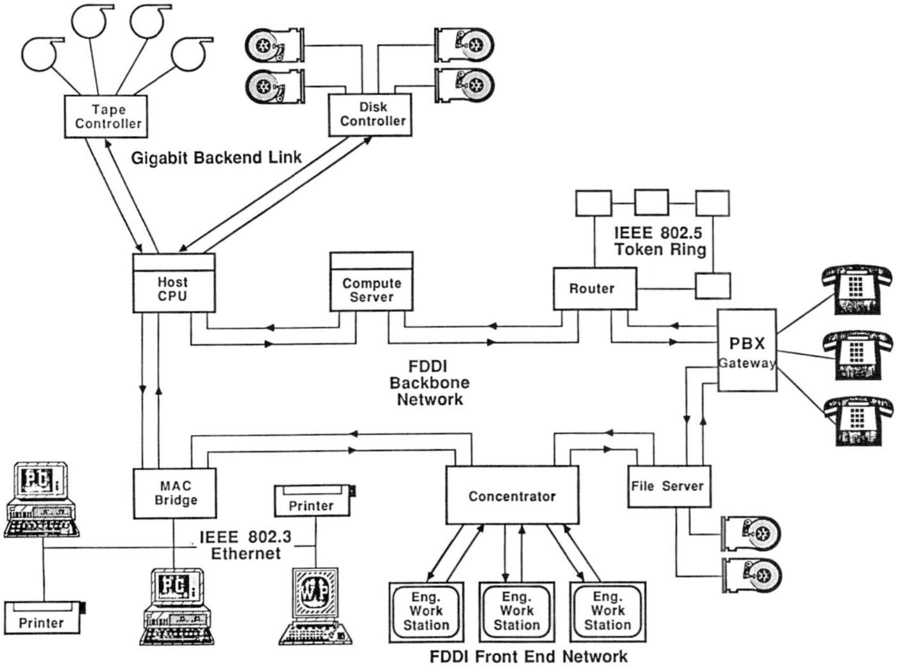

FIG. 8. Fiber Data Distributed Interface (FDDI) network. (Drawing courtesy of Advanced Micro Devices.)

Possibly a string of CPUs, architected like the INMOS "Transputer" could be linked together to examine the data in a pipelined flow, each doing one task like the coordination on a high-speed assembly line.

A bridge is more intelligent than a repeater because it looks at the data-link sublayer of the OSI reference model to decide whether to pass on the frame, hence a media access control level or "MAC-level" bridge. Slower than repeaters, bridges nevertheless may connect Ethernets to token rings that use the same protocols, for example. (Ethernet is a bus broadcasting technology without central authority needed to attempt to transmit; access is granted by avoiding collisions.) Lower-speed networks can be built with MAC-level bridges, but three or more bridges subnets can cause out-of-order packets, because unintentional delays create confusion when the packets are collected at the destination. (In some instances, packets are filtered out continuously and looped around the bridged networks on the chance that some subnet would claim them.) Routers link LANs to OSI Level 3, the network layer, and are usually protocol specific. The term "brouter" just means the unit is programmed to act as a bridge for one protocol and as a router for another one. To get from TCP/IP to the X.25 protocol requires a translator that probably operates at the OSI model's Level 7, or the application layer. Via that translator, users on either type of network can make virtual terminal-connecting sessions to the other type of network. Figure 9 shows these network node differences among bridges, routers, and gateways on the seven-layer OSI reference model.

2. Wide Area Networks (WANs)

A LAN covers a distance of about 2.5 km, although optical technology such as the FDDI media can be linked together over 60 km. WANs cover the world and are often networks of networks, called internets; metropolitan-area networks (MANs) are simple two-way shared medium to a community of users within a 50-km diameter. Unlike the internal corporate building or the campus setting, much more heterogeneity is involved in WANs. The more physical elements involved, the more the solution introduces new subnet architectures. National supercomputer networks interconnecting the centers funded by the U.S. government at major universities have built backbones based on the public tariff T1 (1.54 Mbit/sec), and can be expected to grow into T3 (44.5 Mbit/sec). The T1 circuit bundles the equivalent of 24 64 Kbit-per-second circuits, and one T3 line can contain up to 28 T1 channels. In 1986 most of the installed T1 lines were applied to voice-only usage, but data applications existed on over half of the T1 lines in 1990. (Fractional T1 fast-packet switches can be installed to provide incremental data rates between 64 Kbit per second and 1.544 Mbit per second, using portions of an entire T1 line, in order to add more bandwidth later.)

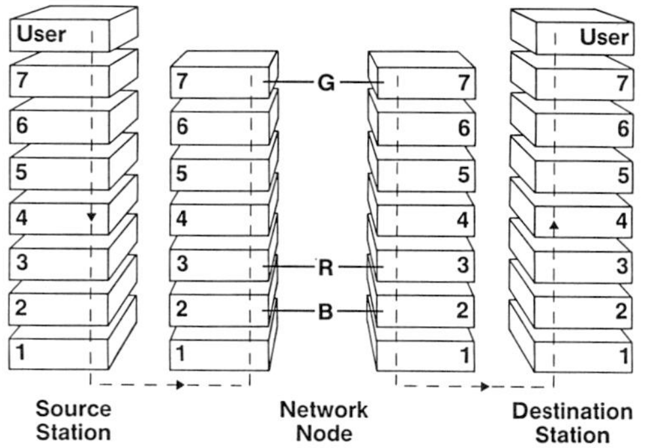

FIG. 9. Network node differences. Key: G, gateway; R, route; B, bridge. (Drawing courtesy of International Business Machines Corporation.)

At still higher data rates, data/voice products named the synchronous optical networks (SONET) strive for hundreds of megabits per second; furthermore, the 1990 U.S. Congress has funded research to build a 3 Gbit-per-second fiber-optic network to link universities, industry, and government databases into a "National Research and Education Network." With coherent light, the distance can be greater, but today's expense of lasers puts coherent light beyond that appropriate for a workstation attachment. A promising advance has occurred at British Telecom Research Laboratories in England, which demonstrated the feasibility of noncoherent transmission using a direct detection method (no heterodyne) to run a fiber-optic link at several tens of gigabits per second over a distance of 100 km. The design uses erbium-doped active fiber that amplifies the light in-line (the Kerr nonlinearity effect) and prevents linear dispersion of the transmitted pulses in the optical fiber. Solitons are pulses of light that travel along optical fibers with no dispersion. Field trials for future transoceanic communications have begun.

The first popular WAN protocol developed for the internet routing function was the Department of Defense's TCP/IP. The IEEE's 802.6 Working Group on MANs has developed a distributed-queue dual-bus (DQDB) protocol. To provide even more flexibility and standardization, the ISO has published Open Systems Interconnection, or OSI, based on a reference model first proposed in 1977. Because of the much larger investment involved in WANs, there will be a longer gestation period to build high-speed WANs around the world. Electronic mail between desktops could be as useful as the telephone, but the design approach involves many business and regulator issues, as well as the physical sciences and technology. Beginning in 1989 the major E-mail providers announced interconnection between disparate services and across national boundaries. To accomplish that goal, CCITT endorsed the X.400 standard for data communications that described seamless interconnections. Now even the more open Soviet Union is looking to build a fiber-optical cable across the USSR linking Europe and the Far East.

How is the progress in semiconductor devices being applied to overcome E-mail barriers? Multiprotocol routers are being designed to handle two or more protocols at once, such as TCP/IP and the ISO TP-4 that closely resembles TCP/IP (because both use basically the same techniques of positive acknowledgment and retransmission). But, for most business and education budgets, the T1 and T3 private links are too expensive to justify, so such users purchase the CCITT's X.25 packet-switched links or bridges that run up to 64 Kbit per second. A dial-up public network can operate to about 19.2 Kbit per second with the right type of phone line and modem, but the dial-up 2400 and 9600 Kbit/sec modems are still dominant in the number of modems sold within the United States. It is hoped that someday these modems can be replaced by local-loop digital networks, called the Integrated Services Digital Network (ISDN); CCITT controls the ISDN technical and protocol standards. Another fast-moving WAN facility is the cellular phone system; it won't be long before a global network of low-orbit satellites will handle voice and data over land, sea, or air by means of digital switching and transmission among the cells.

E. Software Control Programs and Components

Choosing an operating system requires merging the hardware to the desired application tasks sought by the end user. Operating systems have many different parameters that need to be carefully considered, especially if one intends to write one's own application programs:

1. Memory addressibility, matching with 8, 16, 32, or 64-bit CPUs
2. CPU type, since newer versions obtain additional instructions
3. Associated coprocessor, and whether it is on or off the CPU chip
4. Binary instruction compatibility
5. Compiler design and efficiency, especially if recompiling upward
6. Code compatibility at both the source and object levels
7. Bidirectional code compatibility, including downward
8. Pipelining and other optimizing instruction flow architectures

Traditionally, a new version is released when the performance for standard benchmarks can increase two to four times the earlier product. Unless stated clearly, it is not necessarily true that applications written and tested on an earlier model in the same CPU family will run on the newer family member without modification. The need for upward compatibility and migration of existing applications and databases is a strong customer requirement in the data processing industry.

What does all this increased system capability accomplish for the end user? Some people can be totally satisfied with an 8-bit system for word processing. Usually, these systems are character-oriented screens of data. The need to operate with displayed italics, super- and subscripts, symbols, and graphics with acceptable performance caused the growth of 16-bit systems; graphics run with even more responsiveness at 32 bits. The 32-bit systems are now beginning to do page-layout and multitasking in the windowing overlays. The more powerful systems also can serve their lower power clients, handling file transfer, backup and recovery, or archival data and network routing as well as perform network-error statistical analysis. Operating systems take about one microprocessor generation to develop, so the industry expects the majority of operating systems to be 16-bit when 32-bit MPUs attain full production. Similarly for the 1990s, 32-bit operating systems will be the software growth area when 64-bit MPUs come into full production.

While the performance increases, the price and size of existing products decrease. Present logical functions become the standardized building blocks for next-generation, more highly integrated silicon products. Often the microcode control programs are converted into ASIC random logic chips to gain more speed. To illustrate this historical trend, in 1984 the PC/AT comprised about 180 chips without memory, including the disk controller cards, the I/O ports, and the EGA graphics adapter card. By 1987 when the PS/2 was introduced, all the aforementioned functions were consolidated onto the motherboard within about 70 chips; and during 1990 only 10 chips plus memory constitute the full 32-bit 386-class personal computer with VGA graphics. By 1993 it will be possible to integrate all those core functions (sans memory) onto a single chip! Soon modems and LAN controllers will also become standardized and suitable for integration. Later in this decade, functions such as real-time video and speech recognition will move onto the motherboard.

III. Applications in High Performance Computing

A. Database Management

Many people want to do more than send E-mail, share printers, and exchange files. The mother lode of the data processing industry is the multiuser application that consolidates and modifies a database. In computational fluid dynamics (CFD), a single solution may produce 40 Mbytes of output, require 100 concatenated time-steps, and necessitate several computations per week; over the duration of a year, this individual user might want to store 500 Gbytes of newly created data. If a CFD research lab had 600 professional employees and only 10% were that prolific, nevertheless, the additional storage capacity per year would amount to a significant 30 Tbytes! Yet that requirement seems small in comparison to the estimated 1 Tbyte per hour collected by the Earth Orbiting Satellite (EOS) or the 4 Tbytes per hour of raw data to be produced by the future Superconducting SuperCollider, which planners think will spawn in a 3000 Tbyte archival storage facility.

A typical national supercomputing center has mass-storage system hardware that supports 100 Gbytes of disk space and cartridge tape capacity for 3 processor channels and 12 transports. (Probably the uniprocessor has 64 Mbytes of memory and 32 channels divided into 24 at 3.0 Mbytes per second and 8 at 4.5 Mbytes per second.) The peak data transmission rate would be about 1.2 Mbytes per second on such a system, which is capable of running up to four operating systems simultaneously, each independent, so that more than one file server and one mass storage system can be resident. If the center houses 45,000 cartridges, the tape library has more than 7 Tbytes, given a tape capacity of 200 Mbytes per square cartridge. That represents around 400,000 files that on a daily basis create 3000 requests. Each high-speed disk drive in the "farm" transfers at nearly 24 Mbit per second. Each center establishes a time period before the seldom-used disk data is moved to the tape cartridge (e.g., 5 days). A read request will find data on the disk farm 67% of the time. In 1989, it would be likely that 10,500 more cartridges would be added to this kind of a data center, or 2.1 more Tbytes per year. To manage that physical inventory, robotic pickers retrieve and replace the cartridges, and the mean time to load can be tens of seconds, followed by additional read/write-access and transmission times on the LAN/WAN network. Even if the transmission rate were 100 Mbytes per second, the storage transfer rate per head is usually limited to less than 10 Mbytes per second due to unstable "flutter and wow" and mechanical inertia, once the disk track containing the wanted data has been located. To establish and maintain a totally balanced system is indeed a challenge for the database administrator of a hierarchical storage management system in a high performance computing center.

Seeking to increase the read/write access rates, product developers are trying to read multiple disks in parallel, called "data striping" to transfer data one order of magnitude faster. Striped disks allow a single logical file to be spread across multiple physical devices. Called a redundant array of inexpensive disks (RAID), a possible design could house 80 Gbytes of data on sixty-four $5\frac{1}{4}$-in. disks. Given enough financial resources, arrays of arrays can be assembled into on-line storage with terabyte capacity. Because there are fewer data stored under each head, and the head doesn't travel as far across the surface, overall access time is less. (The reliability can be increased by mirroring the data on the multiple platters.) The space taken up by such an 80-Gbyte design would be similar to the IBM 3390.

To interconnect higher speed storage subsystems, channel striping has been used to speed up the I/O transfer rate. If each channel has a raw data speed of 3 to 5 Mbytes per second, an eight-channel striping attachment could provide 20 to

30 Mbytes per second of data transfer. If the central data server and the disk array controller supported the approved ANSI X3T9.3 High Performance Parallel Interface (HIPPI), the system throughput goal could approach 60 Mbytes per second. (The HIPPI standard supports either two independent 800 Mbit per second operations or a single higher performing 1600 Mbit per second connection, opening further growth to 120 Mbytes per second of data transfer.)

Furthermore, with data compression ICs built into future drives, the same space could contain 450 Gbytes or more, but unlike tape drives, the file structures formatted on a disk are tightly defined sectors that don't change size. Disk data compression can be difficult to implement reliably, but new Reed-Solomon ICs hold promise. Unlike the initial attempts with randomly generated codes of fixed length, the Reed-Solomon code appends a redundant check code, typically adding an additional 4 to 8 bytes per 512-byte sector message block. With high error recovery rates accomplished by these ICs, designers estimate that the improvement will fall somewhere between 20% and double the capacity of existing $5\frac{1}{4}$ in. form factors.

When storage space is a premium in either the office or the computer center, and the read/write media must be low in price per volume, many end users have selected 8-mm helical-scan video tape cassettes for their digital computer tape storage solution. With tape lengths to 112 m, the data capacity per 8-mm cartridge is 5.5 Gbytes at a transfer rate of 500 Kbytes per second and a search speed of 37.5 Mbytes per second. Packaged in the standard $5\frac{1}{4}$ in. form factor, these tape units exist at the desktop as well as mounted on standard 19-in. NEMA racks in many institutional data centers. Manufacturers of 8-mm tape drives claim that the nonrecoverable error rate is less than one in 10^{13} bit reads during the data interchange mode, because within the drive's ICs, they have included error correction and recovery while the head-to-tape speed is effectively 150 in. per second. EXABYTE Corporation sells an 8-mm $\frac{1}{2}$-Tbyte capacity handled via a robotically driven mechanism that needs only 4 square feet of floor space.

If that capacity is still insufficient, the 4-mm digital audio tape (DAT) cassette with 1.3 Gbytes per drive and higher areal density may be a future step toward greater economics, given the cost benefits of the consumer audio tape decks.

So what is the role of optical storage? In 1990, the half-height optical $5\frac{1}{4}$ in. disk drive has a formatted cartridge capacity of 650 Mbytes (less than either the 8-mm or 4-mm physical units). Projected to have a 15 to 20 year life (longer than microfilm), the write-once read-many optical disk (WORM) seems best suited for long-term data archival applications.

B. Numerically Intensive Computing

The constantly increasing requirements for compute power are largely driven by engineers and scientists who need to make more complex simulation models of the real and imaginary world. What is labeled a supercomputer by these high-performance computing end users is a constantly moving target. Historically, the Cray 1S, introduced in the late 1970s, demonstrated 12 Mflops on a Linpack performance benchmark. That Linpack performance was accomplished by a single chip in 1989. For a listed price of $7000 in 1989, an IBM i860 add-on board to the PS/2 provides 10 Mflops for numerically intensive computing at the desktop in the DOS/OS environment. The 1979 CRAY 1S power has become a plug-in card in the course of one decade of real time.

To meet the price/performance (dollars/MIP) of modern workstation competition for numerically intensive computing (NIC) applications, the central supercomputers in the 1990s must be capable of gigaflop performance and form clusters to reach 10 to 1000 Gflops; in such an environment, the multiprocessors share a main memory approaching 1 Gbyte, and the system manager will need to plan for 10 to 100 Gbytes of extended store. The I/O channel data speed should be above 20 Mbytes per second to the hard disk arrays.

Meteorology is the science of weather forecasting. The National Center for Atmospheric Research in Boulder, Colorado, has a community climate model for three-dimensional space simulation having nearly 100,000 mesh points, with 25 variables at each point; that amounts to 2.5 million words (one word = 64 bits) to contain the data. Simulating 1 year of weather would require 30 hr to run on a supercomputer capable of calculating 80 Mflops per second. In the late 1980s, supercomputers had eight processors; by 1995, they are expected to have sixty-four, and provided that the problem can be broken down into parallel processing, a massively parallel system with 1 Tflop is forthcoming. (To accomplish 1 Tflop in the 1980s would take something equivalent to 2566 NEC Technologies, Inc. SX/

2 processors, or 7,376 Cray Y-MPs, or more than 24,000 IBM 3090 S-class machines.)

But what about the parallel or clustered FORTRAN application software needed to operate these processor arrays? In this field of research, creation of new software to take advantage of the speed of parallelism determines its degree of acceptance more than the hardware advances. One research team with 1024 processors has claimed to achieve 500 Mflops, and future versions may surpass 25 Gflops on real problems. Not just for scientific exploration in the international research labs, parallel-processing computers have also become the target for major business and commercial NIC applications as well, including macro/micro economic models.

In leading laboratories, research teams are building parallel-processing arrays interconnecting 2000 chips with 1 million transistors per chip. It would take only 20 such chips to wire up the equivalent at 100 million transistors per chip. A "superchip" with a 64-bit floating-point unit, a memory management unit, message routing hardware, and input-output processor is said to deliver 27 billion scalar flops; up to 8192 such processors can be connected in parallel, or the potential of more than 100 Gflops.

Embedded in research on parallelism lies the answers to the question in vogue: What will be the uses for 100 million transistors per chip?

C. Image and Multimedia Processing

Consider an international financial operation in credit-card transaction services as an illustration of practical image processing in high-performance computing (HPC) solutions. For its card holders, American Express Travel Related Services Co., Inc. receives charge receipts that total 3 million pieces of paper each day from its 30 million members. This company's policy is to mail a monthly statement with each original receipt printed at two-thirds size, so the required HPC image processing system must scan, compress, store, retrieve, and print electronic images of these receipts.

After arrival at the service center, the paper is fed at 28 receipts per second under a charge-coupled video camera, so the mechanical transport is moving the paper at 240 in. per second. An OCR scanner also reads the paper to generate the image ID consisting of both the account and invoice numbers. Then the image is enhanced to sharpen the foreground information for readability on the displays, is rotated for alignment during later printout, compressed electronically to the 15 Kbyte range, and stored on 12-in. WORM disks at 100,000 images per platter. (Since one disk has 2 Gbytes capacity, it holds the equivalent of six filing cabinets of paper; 1 year's repository of card receipts is 5,000 WORM disks.) The WORM disks are mounted in on-line jukeboxes at 64 platters per box, meaning that 11 jukeboxes would contain about 1 month's worth of arriving paper. Using the OCR tags, these images are sorted by zip code to gain postal mailing discounts, and then the images are decompressed and routed electronically to sixteen laser printers where the hardcopy output (to be mailed to customers) is generated at the rate of 6500 billing-statement pages per hour. Until the credit card information can be verified at the source electronically, this service center is a huge paper-in/paper-out image processing application.

For multimedia processing, let's consider the challenge of generating synthetic real-time television by means of a high-performance supercomputer. The NTSC flicker-free frame rate is 30 per second. If we assume each of the 1024-by-1024 pixels has 24 color bits per pixel, uncompressed visualization requires 90 Mbytes per second. So another developing high-performance computing application for the 1990s is visualization via image and video processing and related database growth, just as color graphics dominated the innovations of the 1980s. (Already synthetic audio/video cards can be purchased for workstations, and corresponding DSP chips are being mounted directly on the motherboard to process video, image, audio, sound, music, and voice data.) Normally, a compact disk will store only 30 sec of video, but compression algorithms are being designed into integrated circuits that achieve 1 hr of video storage per CD. Read-only videodisks that can store entire movies are generated by laser-machining of minute holes that are burnt into a thin layer of reflective metallic material on a substrate of glass or plastic. The recording code is a combination of the video and sound signals based on pulse-code modulation (PCM), which does not promote easy content recognition electronically. To permit search for an image on videodisks, each frame must have a digital number recorded on its header. (It is conceivable to invent database-search algorithms that find icon features within the image store; one example is the ability to identify iconic patterns from a TV camera recording or to use digital video to assist in locating prerecorded patterns in microscopy.) The resultant digital video could appear in a display screen window, just as conventional graphics and text have developed into everyday acceptance, but in the early 1990s one supercomputer is just about consumed generating one synthetic real-time HDTV sequence of frames.

Multimedia technology will be an opportunity for creativity and another way to take advantage of progress in semiconductor technology during the 1990s.

Bibliography

1988 Technology Roundup (1988). *Information Displays*. Vol. 4, No. 12.

Computer Technology Review (1990). Special Spring Issue, Vol. X. No. 5.

Comer, D. E. (1988). "Internetworking with TCP/IP." Prentice-Hall, Englewood Cliffs, New Jersey.

Rose, M. T. (1990). "The Open Book: A Practical Perspective on OSI." Prentice-Hall Englewood Cliffs, New Jersey.

INFORMATION RETRIEVAL

Brian Vickery *University College London*

GLOSSARY

Boolean operators: Operators AND, OR, and NOT used in query formulation.

Data: Content of information messages or sometimes the numeric values they contain.

Database: Collection of records containing data with associated indexes.

Data bank: Database containing numeric or factual data.

Field: Demarcated section of a record.

Format: Sequence and arrangement of fields in a record.

Host: Computer system, comprising databases and a retrieval program, accessible for search via telecommunications networks.

Index: Ordered set of terms that may be used to access the records in a database.

Indexing: Process of selecting and assigning terms describing the information content of an information message.

Inverted index: Index of terms extracted from records and arranged sequentially with pointers to the corresponding records.

Key: Term in an information record by which it may be accessed.

Message: Sequence of symbols (numbers, text, drawings, etc.) that carry information.

Posting: Pointer, in an index, to a specified record to which the index term refers.

Precision: Proportion of items in an information output that are judged relevant to the initial information need.

Primary information: Messages (texts, documents, etc.) collected by a system that carry the full information.

Query: Expression of an information need in the form that can be searched by a retrieval system.

Recall: Proportion of relevant items in the system that are retrieved in a search.

Record: Information message as stored in a retrieval system.

Relevance feedback: Process of modifying a query on the basis of a relevance assessment of the output of the initial search.

Stop list: List of common terms (and, of, by, etc.) that are excluded from use as index terms.

Thesaurus: List of words and phrases allowed as index terms in a particular database, with semantic relations among terms shown

Truncation: Suppression of right-hand or left-hand letters in a term used for search, so that all occurrences of a root stem are located.

Weight, weighting: Assignation of a numerical weight to an index term to indicate its relative importance to the information content of a record.

Information retrieval is the process of selecting information from a store in response to a query. The topic has two aspects of interest to physical scientists and technologists. First, in their studies and professional work, all scientists and engineers need a regular supply of information and should be aware of the modern sources and mechanisms of supply and of the problems they may encounter as users of those sources and mechanisms. Second, information retrieval processes are becoming increasingly dependent on physical mechanisms, in particular, on computers and telecommunications; and the design of information retrieval systems based on these physical devices has become an important area of applied information technology. The purpose of this article is to summarize the present state of practice and research on information retrieval in science and technology.

I. Entities to Be Stored and Retrieved

The information required by a scientist or engineer is factual and conceptual: the value of a physical property, the details of a technical method, the description of a device, an equation for a relation between variables, the ideas behind a physical theory, and so on. As these facts and ideas are mentally absorbed, they become "information" for the recipient.

In contrast to this, the information stored in a retrieval system is in the form of messages: physical records bearing graphic markings (numbers, text, drawings, etc.) that carry meaningful content that the recipient can interpret. The records in retrieval systems can be of several kinds, for example:

1. Quantitative and qualitative data about variables of interest to science and engineering
2. Texts (including illustrations) on physical and technological subjects
3. Drawings, graphs, charts, maps, and other graphics material
4. Computer programs
5. Descriptions of objects (e.g., minerals, laboratory apparatus, and industrial equipment)
6. Names and locations of people, institutions, and manufacturers
7. Bibliographic references (i.e., indicators of the identity and location of texts where any of the above types of information may be found)

The total process of information retrieval is often multistage. To give a complex example, a search for some quantitative data on the properties of a manufactured material might require a series of steps:

1. Search bibliography for references to texts about the material.
2. Locate the texts and find one that mentions the name of a manufacturer and another that mentions a computer data bank that could include data on the material.

TABLE III. World Acetylene Usage[a]

Location	Chemical	Industrial	Total
United States	282	114	396
Western Europe	814	200[b]	1014[b]
Japan	106[b]	100[b]	206
Others	200[b]	150[b]	350[b]
Total	1402[b]	564[b]	1966[b]

[a] In millions of pounds.
[b] Estimated value.

FIG. 1. Information message: table with headings.

3. Search directories to locate the manufacturer and the databank.
4. Contact manufacturer and receive a brochure containing relevant data.
5. Access data bank and retrieve further data.

The entities stored and retrieved are therefore messages of the kinds indicated above. Incorporated in each message are one or more keys or index terms by which the content of the message is designated and through which it may be retrieved. Figures 1–6 illustrate some messages and their keys. In Fig. 1 the table heading and its column and row headings can form the retrieval keys; in Fig. 2, the title and abstract of the text may furnish index terms, and this holds also for the caption in Fig. 3; words in the text of a description (Fig. 4) provide index terms; the names in a directory (Fig. 5) are the search access points; and keyword terms for a bibliography (Fig. 6) may be assigned by an indexer.

The technical problems of information retrieval are concerned with the efficient organization of stores of messages and the choice and manipulation of search keys. The variety and

ANTENNAS

Ronold W. P. King *Harvard University*

I.	The Dipole Antenna in Air	595
II.	Antennas Used in and near Material Media	601
III.	The Loop Antenna	606
IV.	The Slot Antenna	608
V.	Horn Antennas	609
VI.	The Dielectric-Rod Antenna	610
VII.	Pulses and Nonsinusoidal Waves	610
VIII.	Conclusion	611

FIG. 2. Information message: text with title and contents.

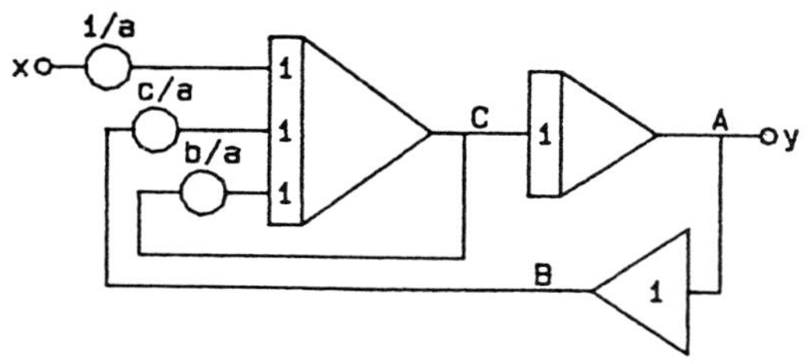

FIG. 94. Configuration for the solution of the differential equation $a(d^2y/dt^2) + b(dy/dt) + cy = x$.

FIG. 3. Information message: drawing with caption.

S. Chandrasekhar
The University of Chicago
Linus Pauling
Linus Pauling Institute of Science and Medicine
Vladimir Prelog
Swiss Federal Institute of Technology
Abdus Salam
International Center for Theoretical Physics
Glenn T. Seaborg
University of California, Berkeley
Kai Siegbahn
Uppsala University
Edward Teller
University of California

FIG. 5. Information message: directory entry.

complexity of these problems have increased with the development of retrieval systems based on computers.

As well as systems specifically concerned with retrieval, other computer systems incorporate retrieval processes. For example, database management systems search files to locate data before manipulating it; and computer-aided design systems retrieve wanted design data from store to feed it into design programs. Indeed, the kind of retrieval system described above is regarded by some as only one of the possible varieties of information retrieval, one that does not involve the processing of data subsequent to retrieval but simply reports on the messages found in response to a query. Other varieties of systems involving retrieval are those that use statistical processing to reduce the response to a manageable size or use deductive inference to draw conclusions from the data retrieved.

II. Tools, Techniques, and Agencies

The conventional tools of information retrieval have been and still are printed materials of various kinds:

1. Books with chapter headings and indexes
2. Handbooks and manuals with section headings and indexes
3. Catalogs and bibliographies of books and other printed materials
4. Abstracting and indexing publications, arranged by topic and with indexes, that give references to journal articles, technical reports, patents, and so on
5. Printed directories to people, institutions, manufacturers, and so on

Increasingly in science and technology, the various kinds of message stores are becoming available in machine-readable form. In a Delphi forecasting study, it has been predicted that (a) by the year 2000, 50% of existing indexing/abstracting services will be available only in machine-readable form; (b) up to 25% of science/technology periodicals will be available in that form; and (c) by 1995, 50% of newly issued technical reports will be in a similar situation.

Readers of this article will be broadly familiar with conventional retrieval tools; for those who wish to widen their knowledge, some references to guides to the literature of physics and engineering are given in the bibliography. Here we shall concentrate on electronic tools and techniques, based on machine-readable stores.

The essence of electronic retrieval is that a collection of messages is stored on some computer-readable medium (currently the preferred medium is magnetic disk) and is accessed by software run on a computer to which the store is linked. A system may be personal (using a mi-

C. Hydraulic Design

This design phase determines the types, dimensions, location, and orientation of the multitude of internals used in absorption columns. It usually leads to refinements to the column design and sizing and, most important, is critical for ensuring trouble-free operation.

FIG. 4. Information message: narrative text.

Encyclopedia of physical science and technology.

Includes index.
1. Science—Dictionaries. 2. Engineering—Dictionaries. 3. Technology—Dictionaries. I. Meyers, Robert A. (Robert Allen), Date
Q123.E497 1987 503'.21 86-1118
ISBN 0-12-226901-2 (alk. paper)

FIG. 6. Information message: bibliographic reference.

crocomputer and small-scale disk storage), institutional (using a mini or mainframe computer to which a number of users have wired access from terminals), or public (with the store and software housed in a mainframe with many ports to telecommunication networks to which any telephone has access). Computer hardware and telecommunications are dealt with in other articles in this Encyclopedia. It is the use of these technologies for retrieval purposes that is of concern here. [*See* ON-LINE INFORMATION SYSTEMS; TELECOMMUNICATIONS.]

There are now many publicly available systems, such as the DIALOG Information Service in Palo Alto, California; Pergamon Infoline in London; or Datastar in Zürich. Each of these data processors or hosts has powerful computing facilities and stores a considerable number of databases. Each database is produced by a publisher and leased to processors. The machine-readable database is often linked to, and may be the source of, a printed version of the messages in it. For example, the Institution of Electrical Engineers in London owns the database publisher INSPEC, which is responsible for producing databases in physics, electrical engineering, computers, and control and for publishing printed abstracts and current titles of periodicals. Each database may be leased to more than one processor; for example, the INSPEC databases are available not only from DIALOG and Pergamon Infoline but also from other hosts.

There are now many hundreds of science–technology databases mounted on publicly available processors. Some indication of the range of content is given by the following examples:

CA SEARCH (chemistry and chemical technology references)
Compendex (engineering references)
Computer Database (references)
Encyclopedia of Associations (directory)
Energyline (references)
INSPEC (physics, electrical technology and computer references)
Kirk–Othmer Encyclopedia of Chemical Technology
Mathematical Reviews Online (references)
Metals Abstracts (references)
Microcomputer Index (references)
National Aeronautics and Space Agency (references)
National Technical Information Service (references)
Robotics Information
Smithsonian Science Information Exchange (directory)

These databases are accessible through terminals linked by modem to the national and international public telecommunications systems. In recent years, material from many databases has become available on CD-ROM disks, searchable via retrieval software mounted on microcomputers. Readers wishing to widen their knowledge of the facilities available are directed to items in the bibliography. [*See* SCIENTIFIC INFORMATION SERVICE; VIDEOTEX AND TELETEXT.]

III. Design Problems in Information Retrieval

The central problems of information retrieval arise from the nature of the messages stored as records in the system and the relation of these messages to the queries likely to be put to the system.

The messages are not generally of uniform structure, in contrast to the situation in, for example, database management systems, which normally process files of data described by a small set of prespecified attributes: their record structure is uniform and restricted, each attribute may be expected to carry only one of a small number of specific values, and the search keys required are largely specified in advance. In information retrieval systems, the values (for example, the texts) stored are of unlimited variety, the search terms presented in queries are unpredictable, and the relationships between messages stored and queries processed are often ambiguous.

The overall structure of the storage and retrieval process can be represented as in Fig. 7 (INFO stands for INFORMATION):

Information is input to the system in any of the forms previously noted. The information is placed in a primary information store, which may be a collection of documents (library, filing cabinet, microform collection, etc.) or a machine-readable store. It is indexed (process 1), that is, its content is analyzed to determine possible search keys. This process can take one of three forms: (a) the information can be humanly inspected to decide on index keys, (b) the information can be put into machine-readable form and keys extracted by computer program, or (c) the machine-readable information can be itself used as a message for storage in the retrieval

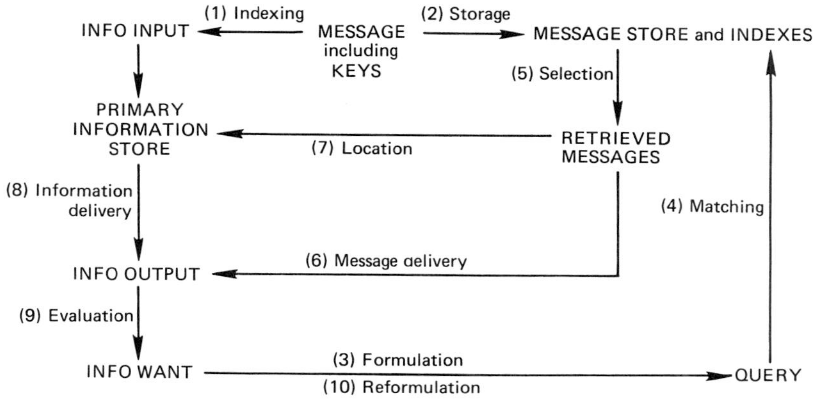

FIG. 7. The storage and retrieval process.

system. The storage of messages and indexes (process 2) completes the input phase.

Output begins when an enquirer approaches the system with an information need, a desire to fill some gap in his or her knowledge. A query expressing this need is formulated (process 3). This formulation process may be assisted by a human intermediary or by a computer interface. The query is matched against index keys (process 4), resulting in the selection of certain messages from store (process 5). In modern retrieval systems these processes are carried out by computer program. This immediate output may be delivered to the enquirer (process 6) for evaluation of the information carried by the messages retrieved. Alternatively, if the retrieved messages do not themselves include the primary information, they may be used to locate the primary information (process 7) for delivery (process 8) and evaluation (process 9). If the information need appears to be satisfied by the information delivered, the output process ends. Otherwise, there may be a reformulation of the query (process 10) and an iteration of the search.

IV. Information Analysis

Human analysis of a primary information message consists of a scan to select from it terms, phrases, and other expressions that are believed best to express its information content. The structure of the primary message itself often guides the human indexer (e.g., the title of a paper, a summary provided by the author, or his conclusions). There is considerable evidence of inconsistency in analysis, both between two indexers of the same input and by one indexer over time.

To achieve at least some terminological consistency (although this does not prevent the selection of different concepts), many retrieval systems use a standard terminology, a list of indexing terms known as a thesaurus. A typical example is shown in Fig. 8. The terms acceptable for indexing are listed alphabetically. Terms not used in indexing are included with a direction to "use" another term (see, for example, the term "Plumbicons"). Under each accepted term are listed terms that are related in meaning and use. Three kinds of relationship are indicated: (1) "Color television camera tubes, BT color television" indicates that Color TV is regarded as a wider term that may be used if the initially chosen term is too specific; (2) the narrower term (NT) "Thermionic tube" is a specific kind of electron tube, and (3) RT indicates a term that is related in some less definite way to the thesaurus term. The UF links (as in "Electron tubes") point to unacceptable terms at which "use" directions exist. These thesaurus relations can be used to aid the indexer in allocating terms or to aid the searcher in choosing terms.

Indexers are required to translate the concepts selected from the information input into terms chosen from the thesaurus where possible, otherwise tagging them as additional indexing terms. The very act of selecting concepts and terms assigns to them a greater importance than those not selected. In addition, the indexer may give a greater weight to some terms than to others. In some retrieval systems, selected terms are tagged as more or as less important; in a few systems, weights from 10 to 1 have been used.

Computer-based indexing systems have, in

b: TEST model

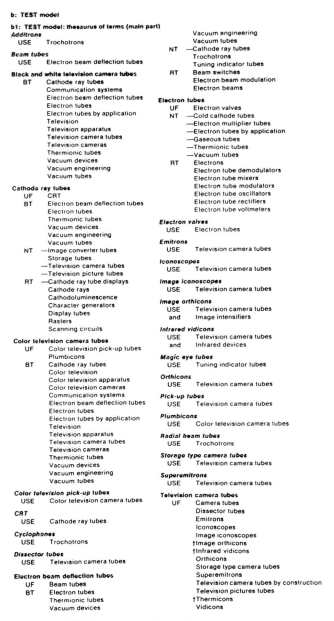

b1: TEST model: thesaurus of terms (main part)

Additrons
USE Trochotrons

Beam tubes
USE Electron beam deflection tubes

Black and white television camera tubes
BT Cathode ray tubes
Communication systems
Electron beam deflection tubes
Electron tubes
Electron tubes by application
Television
Television apparatus
Television camera tubes
Television cameras
Thermionic tubes
Vacuum devices
Vacuum engineering
Vacuum tubes

Cathode ray tubes
UF CRT
BT Electron beam deflection tubes
Electron tubes
Thermionic tubes
Vacuum devices
Vacuum engineering
Vacuum tubes
NT —Image converter tubes
Storage tubes
—Television camera tubes
—Television picture tubes
RT —Cathode ray tube displays
Cathode rays
Cathodoluminescence
Character generators
Display tubes
Rasters
Scanning circuits

Color television camera tubes
UF Color television pick-up tubes
Plumbicons
BT Cathode ray tubes
Color television
Color television apparatus
Color television cameras
Communication systems
Electron beam deflection tubes
Electron tubes
Electron tubes by application
Television
Television apparatus
Television camera tubes
Television cameras
Thermionic tubes
Vacuum devices
Vacuum engineering
Vacuum tubes

Color television pick-up tubes
USE Color television camera tubes

CRT
USE Cathode ray tubes

Cyclophones
USE Trochotrons

Dissector tubes
USE Television camera tubes

Electron beam deflection tubes
UF Beam tubes
BT Electron tubes
Thermionic tubes
Vacuum devices
Vacuum engineering
Vacuum tubes
NT —Cathode ray tubes
Trochotrons
Tuning indicator tubes
RT Beam switches
Electron beam modulation
Electron beams

Electron tubes
UF Electron valves
NT —Cold cathode tubes
—Electron multiplier tubes
—Electron tubes by application
—Gaseous tubes
—Thermionic tubes
—Vacuum tubes
RT Electrons
Electron tube demodulators
Electron tube mixers
Electron tube modulators
Electron tube oscillators
Electron tube rectifiers
Electron tube voltmeters

Electron valves
USE Electron tubes

Emitrons
USE Television camera tubes

Iconoscopes
USE Television camera tubes

Image iconoscopes
USE Television camera tubes

Image orthicons
USE Television camera tubes
and Image intensifiers

Infrared vidicons
USE Television camera tubes
and Infrared devices

Magic eye tubes
USE Tuning indicator tubes

Orthicons
USE Television camera tubes

Pick-up tubes
USE Television camera tubes

Plumbicons
USE Color television camera tubes

Radial beam tubes
USE Trochotrons

Storage type camera tubes
USE Television camera tubes

Superemitrons
USE Television camera tubes

Television camera tubes
UF Camera tubes
Dissector tubes
Emitrons
Iconoscopes
Image iconoscopes
†Image orthicons
†Infrared vidicons
Orthicons
Storage type camera tubes
Superemitrons
Television camera tubes by construction
Television pictures tubes
†Thermicons
Vidicons

FIG. 8. Extracts from thesaurus.

general, not tried to emulate the mental functions of a human indexer. To program a computer to select significant terms from natural language text requires that the program incorporate much linguistic understanding and a knowledge of the subject being analyzed, which is too great a task at present for any but the most specialized of retrieval systems. Instead, automatic indexing has relied on methods based on the relative frequencies of the words in the text. Word analysis of information text displays the distribution shown in Fig. 9. There is a group of very frequently occurring nonsignificant words (e.g., a, the, to, for, not, from, by, who, when, is, it), and there is a group of very infrequently occurring words that may be regarded as not significantly representative of the information content of the text. There also is an intervening group of words

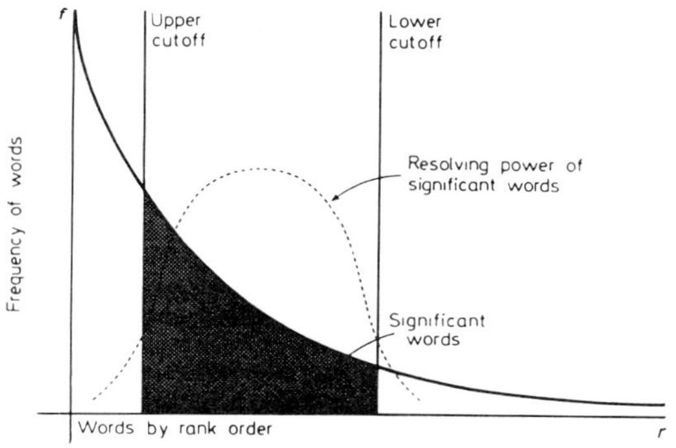

FIG. 9. Word frequency distribution.

A	AMONGST	BECOMES
ABOUT	AN	BECOMING
ACROSS	AND	BEEN
AFTER	ANOTHER	BEFORE
AFTERWARDS	ANY	BEFOREHAND
AGAIN	ANYHOW	BEHIND
AGAINST	ANYONE	BEING
ALL	ANYTHING	BELOW
ALMOST	ANYWHERE	BESIDE
ALONE	ARE	BESIDES
ALONG	AROUND	BETWEEN
ALREADY	AS	BEYOND
ALSO	AT	BOTH
ALTHOUGH	BE	BUT
ALWAYS	BECAME	BY
AMONG	BECAUSE	CAN
	BECOME	

FIG. 10. Extract from stop list.

of appreciable frequency of occurrence that are regarded as having high resolving power (are best able to represent the information and discriminate between information texts); it is from this central group that automatic analysis seeks to select.

Several term-weighting functions have been derived from these basic considerations. The simplest is the inverse document frequency weight. This assumes that the importance of a term in a particular text is proportional to its frequency of occurrence F in that text and inversely proportional to the total number T of texts in which it occurs (a term that occurs widely has little resolving power). A derived term-weighting function is $W = F[\log N - \log(T + 1)]$, where N is the number of texts analyzed, and logarithms are to the base 2.

In practice, automatic indexing usually operates as follows:

1. The texts analyzed are often not the full primary information. An abstract, précis, or summary of the primary text is humanly produced, and a machine-readable version of this is analyzed by computer.
2. The very frequent nonsignificant words are removed from this summary text by matching against a stop list, an example of which is given in Fig. 10.
3. The remaining words are then passed through a stemming process to remove suffixes (and perhaps some prefixes) and reduce each word to its root stem. An example of the suffixes removed is given in Fig. 11. It has been found that such stemming results in improved retrieval performance.
4. The occurrence frequencies of the stems in the text collection analyzed are then computed to derive weighting functions for each stem.
5. Each stem with a weighting function greater than some arbitrary threshold value is assigned as an index key to the text in which it occurs. In some systems, the key may be assigned a weight proportional to its weighting function value.

If the threshold value is put too high, infrequently occurring terms are not selected as keys, yet these may on occasion have significant resolving power, although normally they are too specific to be useful in retrieval. One compromise is to select them, using a low threshold value, but to associate them with other terms in "term clusters," similar to the grouping of narrower terms in a thesaurus. If the term "Gaseous tubes" in Fig. 8 were such a low-frequency term, it could then be searched either as itself or as a member of the broader group "Electron tubes." Such term clusters can be contructed humanly, as a thesaurus, or automatically.

ABILITIES	ACIDOUS	AIC
ABILITY	ACIDOUSLY	AICAL
ABLE	ACIES	AICALLY
ABLED	ACIOUSNESS	AICALS
ABLEDLY	ACIOUSNESSES	AICISM
ABLENESS	ACITIES	AICISMS
ABLER	ACITY	AICS
ABLES	ACY	AL
ABLING	AE	ALISATION
ABLINGFUL	AGE	ALISATIONAL
ABLINGLY	AGED	ALISATIONALLY
ABLY	AGER	ALISE
ACEOUS	AGES	ALISED
ACEOUSLY	AGING	ALISEDLY
ACEOUSNESS	AGINGFUL	ALISER
ACEOUSNESSES	AGINGLY	

FIG. 11. Some suffixes removed in stemming.

	T_1	T_2	$\cdots$	T_t
D_1	d_{11}	d_{12}	$\cdots$	d_{1t}
D_2	d_{21}	d_{22}	$\cdots$	d_{2t}
$\vdots$	$\vdots$			$\vdots$
D_n	d_{n1}	d_{n2}	$\cdots$	d_{nt}

FIG. 12. Text/term matrix: texts D are linked to terms T. A value such as $d_n t$ represents the weight of term t in text n.

The automatic method is to follow step 5 above by the construction of a text/term association matrix, as shown in Fig. 12. A similarity measure is then computed between each pair of terms. For example, if t_{ik} indicates the weight of term k in text i, then a measure of the similarity of terms k and h is $S = \sum t_{ik} t_{ih}$ (summed for $i = 1$ to n). When all pairs of terms have been thus compared, a term/term association matrix may be constructed (Fig. 13). A variety of automatic classification or clustering methods can now be used to construct clusters of terms (equivalent to thesaurus groups) by collecting into a common cluster all terms whose similarity values exceed an arbitrary value.

The stop list removes high-frequency nonsignificant words from the text, but there remain other high-frequency words that are characteristic of the text (not occurring too much in other texts) and so become keys for retrieval: For example, in the present article, the terms "information" and "retrieval" are of this type. As single words (or rather, stems), they may have insufficient resolving power but could be a useful retrieval key if compounded into the phrase "information retrieval." As can be seen in Fig. 8, such phrases are common in humanly constructed thesauri.

There are automatic phrase-generation methods. For example, from the term/term matrix can be derived values of the pair frequency P_{kh}, the number of texts in which two terms k and h jointly occur. If C_k and C_h represent the collection frequencies of the two terms, then the cohesion of the term pair is proportional to $P_{kh}/C_k \cdot C_h$. Word-pair phrases may then be chosen that have a sufficiently high cohesion. Refinements of this approach are possible in which simple co-occurrence of terms in text is replaced by criteria such as the adjacency of the terms, but this of course requires that information about word positions in the text be recorded during the prior analysis. As will be seen, this kind of information is indeed often included in the messages stored in retrieval systems.

	T_1	T_2	$\cdots$	T_t
T_1	$s(T_1,T_1)$	$s(T_1,T_2)$	$\cdots$	$s(T_1,T_t)$
T_2	$s(T_2,T_1)$	$s(T_2,T_2)$	$\cdots$	$s(T_2,T_t)$
$\vdots$	$\vdots$			$\vdots$
T_t	$s(T_t,T_1)$	$s(T_t,T_2)$	$\cdots$	$s(T_t,T_t)$

FIG. 13. Term/term matrix: similarity values are shown for each pair of terms.

It is to be noted that only the simpler processes of automatic indexing (word extraction, the use of a stop list, and stemming) have so far been generally implemented in operational retrieval systems. The use of term/term association matrices is rare outside experimental studies.

V. Record Structure

In information retrieval systems, there is usually only one set of records carrying messages, each record having the same basic structure: a set of fields. The elements to be included as fields are of the following kinds:

1. Generally, a unique record identification number
2. A set of fields that together carry the information content of the message
3. Fields carrying specifically assigned search keys, whether humanly or automatically derived

The content and format of the record naturally vary according to the type of message in the system. Unlike the situation in database management systems, many of the fields are likely to be of variable length to cope with the variations in length of the values of some data elements (e.g., book titles). In the record, the fields follow each other sequentially. The boundaries between fields may be indicated

(a) by placing markers or field separators,
(b) by recording the length of each field and/or the starting position of each field in the record, and
(c) by starting each field with a tag that is a coded indication of its name.

For bibliographic files, the International Standards Organization has developed a standard communication format upon which record formats in large bibliographic retrieval systems are often based. It is illustrated in Fig. 14. There is a

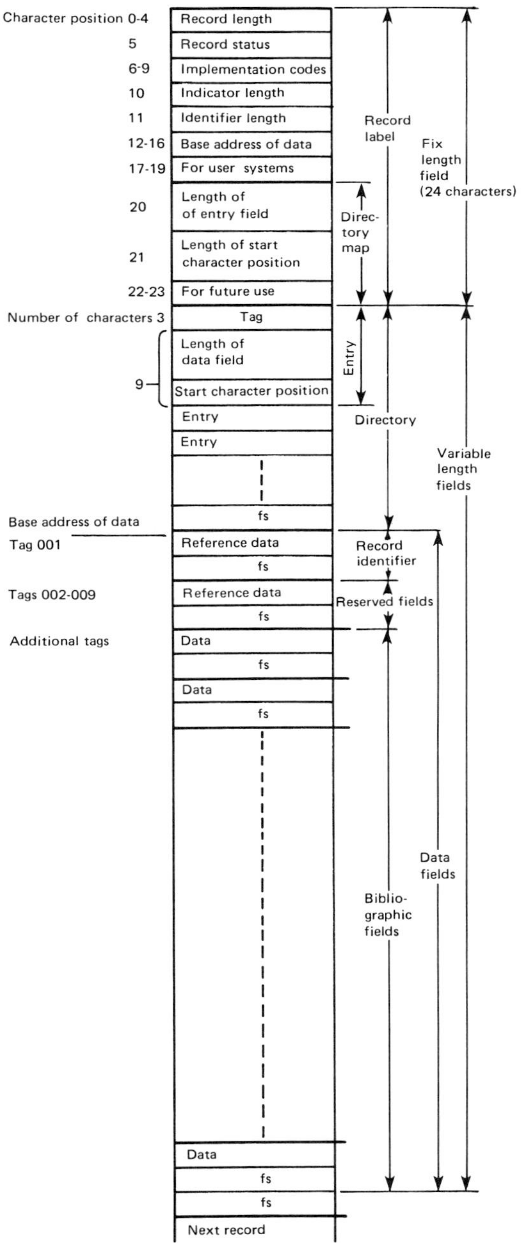

FIG. 14. Bibliographic information interchange format.

fixed-length leader (label) at the beginning of each record, indicating the total record length, its status (e.g., new or amended), space for fixed-length codes to be implemented by the individual system, lengths of tags (indicators or identifier), the starting position of the data (base address), more fixed-length space for individual use, and details of the directory map. There is then a variable-length directory to the data in the record: Noted for each field (entry) are its tag, the length of the field, and its starting position; the directory is concluded by a field separator (fs). A series of data fields then follows in sequence, the first few of which may be of fixed length and the remainder of variable length; each is concluded by a field separator. The first fixed-data field carries the unique record identification number. At the end is a record separator (rs).

VI. File Structures

Records of the kind just discussed are normally stored in direct access files on disk. The sequence of records may be mapped into the store using the record identification number, which is translated into a store address by a hashing algorithm. If the size of the system is relatively small, a direct address method can be used in which a supplementary file is created linking the record identification number to a store address. To access the main file it is then necessary to create an index of search keys, each of which can be linked to the record numbers to which it relates. Most operational retrieval systems use the so-called inverted index. All the keys are ordered sequentially (typically, in alphanumeric order). The record for each key generally includes a note of the number of data records to which it applies (the number of postings) and the actual data record numbers concerned.

The keys for inclusion in the inverted index may be drawn from search key fields in the data records. However, index creation may be carried out at this later stage and not during the earlier information analysis that created the record. In many systems, as each data record is input, it is subjected to an automatic indexing process: Words are extracted from all or from designated fields in the record, screened through a stop list, perhaps stemmed, and merged into an inverted index. There may even be at this stage a screening of the extracted words or stems against a thesaurus: Thesaurus words are admitted into the index, and others are reported to the system operator as candidates for approval or rejection. Further elements may then be included in the record for each search key. First, for each occurrence of a key, there may be not only the record number but also the name of the field in which it occurs. If the data fields being indexed consist of text, the relative positions of words in the text may be important for retrieval, as will be seen later. So, for each occurrence of each indexed word, there may be included in its record a note on the paragraph number in the text, the sentence number, and the word number within the sentence.

At this stage, the file organization is as follows:

1. Inverted index with data record number pointing to ...
2. Direct access data file, either through hashing or via a supplementary file linking record number and storage address

The inverted index may be held as a linear list, and during the retrieval process it may be searched sequentially or by a binary method. If the index is large, there is usually a hierarchical approach to it through further supplementary files, for example, a dictionary file pointing to letter pairs and a word file pointing to the inverted index, as shown below.

Dictionary file:
header—pointer to letter pair 1—pointer to letter pair 2—pointer to letter pair 3—...

Word File:
letter pair 1
word 1—pointer to inverted file
word 2—pointer to inverted file
letter pair 1
word 1—pointer to inverted file
⋮
⋮

VII. Query Formulation

An information need initially arises in the mind of an enquirer who expresses it in natural language, either to himself or to a system operator (so-called intermediary). To carry out a matching process against index keys, the natural language expression must be transformed into an appropriately structured query. Such a query can differ from the natural language statement in several ways:

1. A query almost always uses a type of syntax different from the natural language.
2. The query often substitutes for the significant words of the need statement standardized terminology from a thesaurus.
3. The query as initially stated may be an inadequate formulation of the need and may have to be expanded or amended.

The syntax of queries will be discussed in the next section in relation to the file searching process. A thesaurus is used in the ways already noted in Section IV.

The formulation of a query so that it is an adequate expression of information need requires more than an understanding of its syntax and standard terminology. Also required are knowledge of the subject area of the retrieval system, so that the query topic can be accurately located in the subject structure, and knowledge of the ways in which the subject is organized in the database. To the casual user of a retrieval system, query formulation may be a difficult and time-consuming process. Much current searching of large systems is carried out with the aid of an intermediary, an operator with a background knowledge of its subject area and good familiarity with the database structure.

After matching a query with the indexes of a system, some sample output may be evaluated (as described later), and if it is not fully relevant to the need, then the query may be reformulated in ways suggested by the nature of the output. This relevance feedback may be carried out humanly by the enquirer and/or intermediary or automatically by computer program. It will be considered further in Section XI.

VIII. Matching Queries and Indexes

In most retrieval systems, the query syntax makes use of the Boolean operators AND, OR, and NOT. To identify all records indexed by the terms "information" and "retrieval," the query INFORMATION AND RETRIEVAL is input to the system. Each term is individually searched in the inverted index, and a report is made on the number of postings for each:

SET 1	INFORMATION	*m* POSTINGS
SET 2	RETRIEVAL	*n* POSTINGS

The intersection of sets 1 and 2 (i.e., the number of items that have been indexed by both terms) is then reported:

SET 3 1 AND 2 *p* POSTINGS

The record numbers in set 3 are then sought in the main file, and the records are appropriately displayed.

To identify all records concerned either with information retrieval or with document retrieval, the following Boolean query could be input:

RETRIEVAL AND (INFORMATION OR DOCUMENT)

This would result in the display

SET 4	INFORMATION	m POSTINGS
SET 5	DOCUMENT	q POSTINGS
SET 6	4 OR 5	r POSTINGS
SET 7	RETRIEVAL	n POSTINGS
SET 8	6 AND 7	s POSTINGS

Set 6 is the union of sets 4 and 5 (i.e., the number of items indexed either by "information" or by "document" or by both). A search for RETRIEVAL NOT COMPUTER might be expected to identify a set of records indexed by "retrieval" but not by "computer" (set difference).

Most systems permit the use of right-hand truncation. A search for INFORM: might produce a report such as

SET 9	INFORMATICS	t POSTINGS
SET 10	INFORMATION	m POSTINGS
SET 11	INFORMATIVE	u POSTINGS
SET 12	INFORMED	v POSTINGS

Such truncation is of course less needed if word-stemming has already been carried out at the indexing stage. Left-hand truncation (e.g., :COMPUTER to retrieve not only COMPUTER but also MICROCOMPUTER and MINICOMPUTER) is less often available, being less sure in its operation and more costly to implement.

If the inverted index contains information as to the field in which a key occurs in each record, it is possible to restrict search to particular named fields. For example, a search for WATER: (AU) might identify only authors whose names start with WATER and avoid other keys concerned with water that occur in other fields.

Where the data searched are numerical, systems may offer the possibility of range search, such as >97 AND <103.

If the inverted index contains information about the relative positions of words in the records, as described in Section VI, then it is possible to carry out "adjacency" searches. For example, the query INFORMATION (1W) RETRIEVAL (TI) might identify records that in their title fields had the words "information" and "retrieval" next to each other and in that sequence. The query RETRIEVAL (3W) INFORMATION (TI) might identify titles containing strings such as "retrieval of information," "retrieval of physics information," and "retrieval of current information." A query such as INFORMATION (S) RETRIEVAL might restrict reports to records containing the two words in the same sentence, and INFORMATION (P) RETRIEVAL to those with the words in the same paragraph.

Many systems also offer the possibility of string search: the scanning of text fields for named strings of characters, even if these have not been specifically indexed. Since this is very costly in processing time, it is usually restricted to small sets of records that have previously been identified by Boolean search.

IX. Selection and Display of Records

It is often possible in retrieval systems to vary the display of retrieved records on terminal and/or printer. The fields and the sequence of items to be displayed may be varied. Some systems offer wide or even complete flexibility as to which of the many fields in the record are to be displayed. The default sequence of display may be the order in which the records were input to the system or the reverse of this (in which case the most recent addition comes first). Other sequences may be achieved by sorting on named fields.

In Section IV it was noted that automatic indexing may result in keys being assigned weights corresponding to the weighting functions that have been used in selecting them for indexing. These weights may be used to rank retrieved records according to the weights of the search terms related to them. In principle, this can mean that records more likely to be relevant to the search query appear earlier in the display.

X. Evaluation of Information Output

The immediate output of a retrieval system is a set of messages that have been input to the system. As explained in Section III, these messages may sometimes include the actual primary information (e.g., in full text systems or in databanks of numerical information). It is then immediately possible for the enquirer to judge whether the output satisfies the information need. In other cases, the output messages simply serve to identify the primary input, which is held in another store. If this store is not readily accessible, the enquirer must make an evaluation of the output from the retrieved messages alone. If the number of records in the retrieved set is large, it may be necessary to make the evaluation on the basis of a sample of these.

The procedure in an operational system is to examine each member of the set (or the sample) and to decide whether it is relevant to the information need; if a sufficiently high proportion of the set examined is judged to be relevant, the whole retrieved set is accepted, and the enquirer may then proceed to locate the primary information that it identifies.

Ideally, an enquirer would like to ensure two things: that a high proportion of the retrieved set is relevant (the search achieved high precision) and that the search had retrieved a high proportion of the potentially relevant items in the database (high recall). Unfortunately, in an operational situation there is no simple way of determining whether the second criterion has been met. (One way of exploring the unretrieved bulk of the database is to formulate a query designed to retrieve a wider set than that already selected and see whether many more relevant records appear. But this increases the time and cost of the retrieval process.)

A great deal of research effort has been expended on developing the theoretical basis of retrieval evaluation and on the testing of experimental systems, to assess the relative performance of various indexing techniques and search strategies. Results are fully reported in books listed in the bibliography. One well-attested generalization that has emerged from this work is that precision and recall tend to vary inversely: A change in a query that results in improved precision (a higher proportion of the output is relevant) is likely to result in a loss in recall (fewer of the potentially relevant records in the database are retrieved), and vice versa. It is the constant aim of system design to achieve improved performance on both criteria.

XI. Query Modification

If a sufficiently high proportion of the sampled output is judged not to be relevant to the information need, then there may be a reformulation of the query. For this purpose, various aids can be used. The thesaurus for the database being searched may be examined to pick out broader, narrower, or otherwise related terms that may be substituted for the terms originally chosen. The initial search output may be examined: Terms occurring in it (other than those used in the original query) may suggest an alternative search formulation. Finally, reference texts in the subject field of the query (dictionaries, encyclopedias, manuals, etc.) may suggest new search terms.

In a number of experimental retrieval systems, various automatic methods of query modification have been tried. The simplest method is to widen the search by an automatic procedure. For example, if the original query is a Boolean intersection of terms A, B, and C, a term may be dropped from the query to give an expression A AND B. Rules may be developed to determine which category of term should be dropped first. Again, in a Boolean search A AND B, a thesaurus may be used to replace first A by its broader (BT) term, then B by its BT term, and finally both terms may be replaced. More sophisticated forms of query modification are based on relevance feedback. A sample of the initial output is evaluated as to relevance to the information need, and a subset D_R of the sample is identified as relevant and a subset D_N as nonrelevant. The text/term matrix for these two sets is examined by program. According to specified rules, terms with high weights in the relevant set are added to the query formulation, and terms with high weights in the nonrelevant set are removed; thus a modified query is constructed. This is then searched as before. Several such iterations may take place, until a satisfactory output is achieved.

XII. Intelligent User Aids

Most operational retrieval systems offer the user the following aids:

1. A user manual that contains a description of the databases accessible and an explanation of the command language in which searches are formulated, with examples
2. Help messages that can be called by program during the search, usually explanations of the command language
3. An interactive display of a chosen section of the index
4. A printed thesaurus or an interactive display of a chosen section of the thesaurus or both

Experimental systems, as already described, may also offer automatic query reformulation. Further intelligent aids that are being developed include the following:

1. User interfaces that can accept natural language input of search questions and transform this input into an appropriate Boolean or other search query.

2. Interfaces that can further analyze the input search statement and evaluate its suitability as a query for the system; it may be outside the subject scope of the system, contain words not present in the database index, or give insufficient information for formulation of a satisfactory query, in which cases the interface may proceed to hold an interactive dialogue with the user in an attempt to achieve a more usable query.

3. In systems comprising a set of databases, an interface that can make a subject analysis of the query and on this basis select the most appropriate database for search.

Such intelligent aids are being constructed using techniques derived from artificial intelligence programming.

XIII. Primary Information Store

If the information stored is brief, as in the case of numerical data or directory names and addresses, it may be included in the recorded messages in the retrieval system and so be immediately accessible to search. If the primary information comprises longer texts or includes graphic material not readily stored in digital form, then the primary information store may consist of printed materials or microform reproductions of these. Many mainframe retrieval systems now include full texts in their records; this has been particularly developed for news databases and legal texts, so that access to any string of characters in the text is possible. [*See* INFORMATION DISPLAY SYSTEMS.]

Automated access to primary information stores is taking a number of forms. The simplest is to provide the retrieval system with an electronic mail facility, so that after identification of records that relate to needed information, a message can be sent to a primary store (e.g., a library) requesting provision of the primary texts. A method that has been used with microcomputer retrieval systems is to link the microcomputer with a videodisk player, so that the retrieval program can call up required images from the videodisk.

The development known as electronic document delivery consists of the storage in digital form of extended primary information, including both text and graphics. The text is converted to digital form by the usual methods of input (keyboarding, optical character recognition, etc.); the graphic material is scanned by facsimile camera, which transforms images into digital form. The store can be accessed by electronic mail in just the same way as a library, and requested documents can then be transmitted electronically and converted to legible form by a digital facsimile display. [*See* SIGNAL PROCESSING, GENERAL.]

Bibliography

Ashford, J. A., and Willett, P. (1989). "Text Retrieval and Document Databases." Chartwell Bratt, Bromley, England.

Coblans, H. (Ed.) (1975). "Use of Physics Literature." Butterworth, London.

Hartley, R. J., et al. (1990). "Online Searching." Bowker-Saur, London and New York.

Heaps, H. S. (1978). "Information Retrieval: Computational and Theoretical Aspects." Academic, New York.

Mildren, K. W. (Ed.) (1976). "Use of Engineering Literature." Butterworth, London.

Salton, G., and McGill, M. J. (1983). "Introduction to Modern Information Retrieval." McGraw-Hill, London.

Sparck-Jones, K. (Ed.) (1981). "Information Retrieval Experiment." Butterworth, London.

van Rijsbergen, C. J. (1979). "Information Retrieval," 2nd ed. Butterworth, London.

Vickery, B. C. (1987). "Information Science." Butterworth, London.

Wiederhold, G. (1983). "Database Design," 2nd ed. McGraw-Hill, London.

INFORMATION THEORY

Richard E. Blahut *IBM*

Glossary

Codeword: A string of symbols from a finite alphabet that satisfies a given need.

Channel capacity: The maximum rate, in bits per symbol or bits per second, that information can be transmitted reliably through a channel.

Communication system: A system for the transmission of information between two points.

Discrimination: A measure of information describing the average information within a measurement for separating two hypotheses.

Entropy: A measure of information describing the average uncertainty in a random measurement.

Mutual information: A measure of information describing he information that one random variable gives about another.

Reed–Solomon code: A byte-organized code for the correction of errors in a digital message.

Surveillance system: A system for the extraction of information from the environment.

Transcription system: A system for presenting information in convenient notation.

Trellis diagram: A graph useful for the description of dependent sequences of symbols.

Waveform: A continuous real-valued or complex-valued function of time.

Information theory is the formal subject that deals with precise definitions of the term "information," with ways to measure it quantitatively, and with limitations on the extraction of information from the environment and on the transmission of information between two points. Information theory has close connections to the fields of statistics, of communications, and of signal processing, and partially overlaps these subjects. The distinction is that information theory approaches its problems with the primary goal of learning what is possible in principle, and only secondarily with practical methods that approach the optimum.

Information systems may be subdivided into systems for the transmission of information between two points, systems for the extraction of information from the environment, and systems for the transcription of information into a convenient system of notation. We shall refer to these as *communication systems, surveillance systems,* and *transcription systems,* respectively. Systems of each kind have a long history of engineering development, and many kinds of such systems are in existence. Information theory attempts to provide a unified and formal mathematical development of these topics from first principles so that areas of potential improvements may be found.

All communication systems and surveillance systems involve the estimation of unknown data based on noisy measurements. If the data were known beforehand, there would be no need for communication or surveillance. Moreover, if all measurements were perfect, uncontaminated by measurement noise, and all communication channels were perfect, uncontaminated by channel noise, then the tasks of surveillance and communication would be trivial. It is the noise that limits performance and makes these interesting problems. Consequently, information theory is inevitably built on the theory of probability and of random processes.

The simplest form of the information transmission problem is shown in Fig. 1. A message is to be transmitted from a source to a user

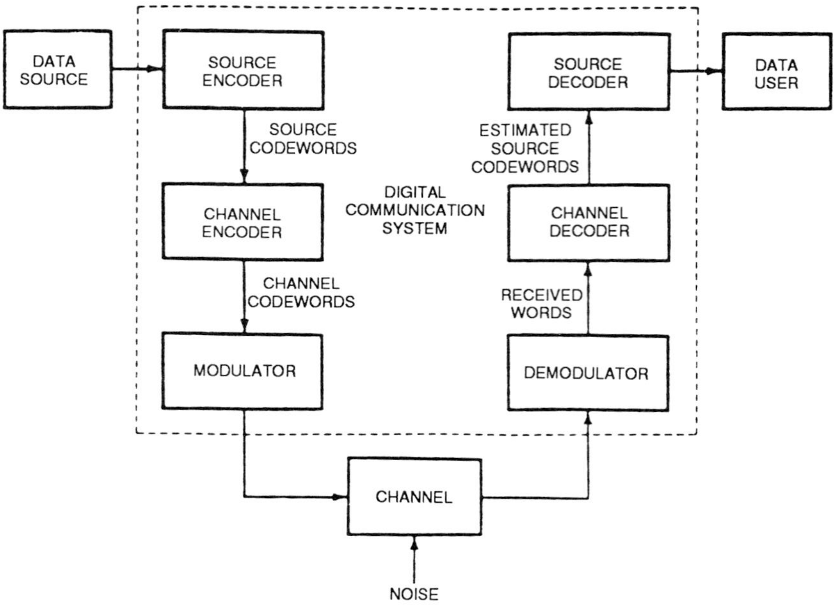

FIG. 1. Structure of a Digital Communication System.

through a communication channel. The important *separation principle* of information theory says that every data transmission problem is equivalent to the communication of a serial binary bit stream through the channel because every kind of source output can be represented as accurately as desired by a binary bit stream and every channel can be used to convey a binary bit stream. This means that the data transmission problem can be divided into the task of transcription of the data into a binary bit stream and the task of the communication of a binary bit stream.

I. Measures of Information

Three basic mathematical functions are used to quantify average information in various situations. These measures are the entropy, the discrimination, and the mutual information. Each of these is a function of the probability distributions describing that situation.

Entropy is the first measure of average information. If an event a_j occurs with probability $p(a_j)$, abbreviated p_j, then the amount of information associated with the occurrence of the event is defined to be

$$I(a_j) = -\log p_j$$

When logarithms are to the base 2, information is measured in units of *bits*. When logarithms are to the base e, information is measured in units of *nats*. The nat is usually more convenient for theoretical developments. The conversion factor is: one nat equals 1.443 bits.

The symbol a_j will, on average, occur $np(a_j)$ times in a total of n outputs of a source with independent outputs, so the expected amount of information obtained from n source outputs is

$$\begin{aligned} np_0 I(a_0) + \cdots + np_{J-1} I(a_{J-1}) \\ = np_0(-\log_2 p_0) \\ + \cdots + np_{J-1}(-\log_2 p_{J-1}) \text{ bits} \end{aligned}$$

Divide by n to obtain the expected amount of information per symbol.

$$H(\mathbf{p}) = -\sum_{j=0}^{J-1} p_j \log_2 p_j \qquad \text{bits/symbol}$$

This is known as the average information, the uncertainty, or the *entropy*, $H(\mathbf{p})$. The term entropy is used because the function is the same as that derived in statistical mechanics for the thermodynamic quantity entropy. The source output may also be described as the random variable X; then $H(\mathbf{p})$ is also denoted, imprecisely, as $H(X)$.

For example, a single gambler's die has six possible outcomes, each of which occurs with probability one-sixth, so the entropy in one role of the die is

$$H(\mathbf{p}) = -\sum_{j=0}^{5} \tfrac{1}{6} \log \tfrac{1}{6} = 2.58 \text{ bits}$$

and the entropy in two rolls is twice this. If a pair of dice are rolled and only the sum is recorded then there are eleven possible sums, from 2 to 12, that occur with a nonuniform probability distribution; the probabilities range from $\frac{1}{36}$ to $\frac{1}{6}$. The entropy is

$$H(\mathbf{p}) = \tfrac{1}{36} \log \tfrac{1}{36} - \tfrac{1}{18} \log \tfrac{1}{18} - \tfrac{1}{12} \log \tfrac{1}{12} - \cdots - \tfrac{1}{36} \log \tfrac{1}{36} = 2.95 \text{ bits}$$

This entropy is less than the entropy of the two rolls; there is less average uncertainty in the sum of the outcomes than in the outcomes themselves.

The entropy function can be formally motivated in several quite different ways, such as its role in source compaction coding theorems for the transcription of data and its role in combinatorics. Another satisfying approach is to formulate several natural and intuitive properties to be required of any measure of average uncertainty in an experiment (for example, that the uncertainty in a pair of independent experiments is the sum of their individual uncertainties) and then to show that entropy is the only function that satisfies these properties.

A *binary source* is one that can emit only two source symbols, a_0 and a_1; their probabilities are given by p and $1 - p$, respectively. The *binary entropy function* is

$$H_b(\mathbf{p}) = -p \log_2 p - (1 - p) \log_2(1 - p)$$

The output of a binary source is a binary digit. The distinction between the bit used as a measure of information and the bit used as a binary output symbol should be carefully noted. On average, the amount of information provided by a binary source is always equal to or less than one bit of information per data bit. The binary source provides one bit of information for each selected symbol only when the two symbols are equiprobable.

For a continuous random variable X, with probability density function $p(x)$, the entropy is replaced by the *differential entropy*, which is defined as

$$H(X) = -\int_{-\infty}^{\infty} p(x) \log_2 p(x)\, dx$$

The differential entropy is not the limiting case of the entropy; the entropy of a continuous distribution is infinite. The differential entropy is not invariant under coordinate transformations. By itself, it has no fundamental physical meaning.

Of all probability distributions with variance σ^2, the Gaussian distribution

$$p(x) = \frac{1}{\sqrt{2\pi}\sigma} e^{-x^2/2\sigma^2}$$

has the largest differential entropy, given by

$$H(X) = \tfrac{1}{2} \log_2(2\pi e \sigma^2)$$

The differential entropy of a vector X^n of length n whose components are independent, identically distributed, Gaussian random variables is $H(X^n) = nH(X)$. Consequently, if a Gaussian noise process of ideal rectangular spectrum is sampled at the Nyquist rate of $2W$ samples per second, the differential entropy rate of the resulting source is $W \log_2(2\pi e \sigma^2)$ bits/second. A Gaussian noise process whose spectrum is constant for frequencies below W hertz and is zero for larger frequencies is called *bandlimited* white noise.

Discrimination is the second measure of average information. Given two probability distributions on the same alphabet, $\mathbf{p} = \{p_0, \ldots, p_{J-1}\}$ and $\mathbf{p}' = \{p'_0, \ldots, p'_{J-1}\}$, the *log-likelihood ratio* is a function of j defined as

$$\ell(j) = \log \frac{p_j}{p'_j}$$

The expected value of the log-likelihood ratio with respect to $\mathbf{p}$ is the function known as the *discrimination*.

$$L(\mathbf{p}; \mathbf{p}') = \sum_{j=0}^{J-1} p_j \log \frac{p_j}{p'_j}$$

The discrimination describes the average amount of information that a measurement gives about the truth of a given hypothesis as compared with an alternative hypothesis. Although the log-likelihood function may be positive or negative, the discrimination is always nonnegative and equal to zero if and only if $\mathbf{p}$ and $\mathbf{p}'$ are equal. On average, every measurement contains some information unless the probability distribution on the outcome is independent of which measurement is true.

Mutual information is the third measure of average information. It measures the amount of information that one random variable X gives about a second random variable Y. Let X take values in the set $\{a_0, \ldots, a_{J-1}\}$ and let Y take values in the set $\{b_0, \ldots, b_{K-1}\}$, possibly $J \neq K$. The joint probability distribution $P(a_j, b_k)$, abbreviated P_{jk}, is the probability that X takes value a_j while Y takes value b_k. The marginal probability distributions are $p_j = \Sigma_k P_{jk}$ and $q_k =$

$\Sigma_j P_{jk}$. The entropy of the pair of random variables X, Y is

$$H(X, Y) = -\sum_j \sum_k P_{jk} \log P_{jk}$$

The individual entropy terms are given by $H(X) = -\Sigma_j p_j \log p_j$ and $H(Y) = -\Sigma_k q_k \log q_k$. The *mutual information* is defined as the difference

$$I(X; Y) = H(X) + H(Y) - H(X, Y)$$

which can be written as

$$I(X; Y) = \sum_{jk} P_{jk} \log \frac{P_{jk}}{p_j q_k}$$

The mutual information describes the amount of information that one random variable Y gives about a second random variable X. It is always nonnegative, and $I(X; Y) = I(Y; X)$.

The mutual information can also be stated in the context of a discrete communication channel with input X and output Y. Let $Q(b_k \mid a_j)$, abbreviated $Q_{k|j}$, be the probability that the received symbol Y takes value b_k given that the transmitted symbol X takes value a_j. The matrix $(Q_{k|j})$, called the transition matrix of the channel, satisfies the Bayes formula $P_{jk} = p_j Q_{k|j}$.

The mutual information can now be viewed as a function of the probability distribution $\mathbf{p}$ and the transition matrix $\mathbf{Q}$. It is denoted by $I(\mathbf{p}; \mathbf{Q})$ rather than $I(X; Y)$ and is given by

$$I(\mathbf{p}; \mathbf{Q}) = \sum_{j=0}^{J-1} \sum_{k=0}^{K-1} p_j Q_{k|j} \log \frac{Q_{k|j}}{\Sigma_i p_i Q_{k|i}}$$

This form of the mutual information disguises the fact that it is symmetric in X and Y but is convenient for problems stated in terms of the conditional probability $Q_{k|j}$.

The *conditional entropy* $H(Y \mid X)$ is defined as

$$H(Y \mid X) = \sum_j p_j \left[-\sum_k Q_{k|j} \log Q_{k|j} \right]$$

Then

$$\begin{aligned} I(X; Y) &= H(Y) - H(Y \mid X) \\ &= H(X) - H(X \mid Y) \end{aligned}$$

where the second line follows by symmetry.

II. Communication Systems

A communication channel is a medium through which data can be sent from a source to a user. Usually we think of the channel as the fixed part of the system not under the designer's control. We may regard channel time to progress discretely or continuously, and we may regard the input amplitude to be discrete or continuous. A *waveform channel* allows arbitrary functions of time called *channel waveforms* to be transmitted from one point to another. A *discrete channel* is a system by means of which an arbitrarily long sequence of symbols, called the *channel code stream,* each symbol chosen from a finite alphabet of J symbols $\{a_0, \ldots, a_{J-1}\}$, can be transmitted from one point to another. Teletype, telegraphy, and the compact disc are three simple examples of discrete channels. A *noiseless* channel is one in which the output is completely determined by the input (and the input by the output); errors do not occur. A *constrained* channel is one that forbids certain subsequences of symbols from being transmitted. A discrete *noisy* channel is one for which the output symbol is not completely determined by the input symbol; only some probability distribution on the set of output symbols is determined by the input symbol. A *memoryless* channel is a channel for which the response to each input does not depend on previous inputs or outputs of the channel. The deep-space Gaussian noise channel and the noisy binary magnetic storage channel are two important examples of noisy channels.

Between the source and the channel is a device for preparing the source data for the channel, called a *transmitter* or an *encoder*. The former name is usually considered appropriate for waveform channels and the latter for discrete channels. Between the channel and the user is a device called the *receiver* or the *decoder*.

The function of the communication system may be broken into three subfunctions for convenience of discussion. These are data translation, data transmission, and modulation. The purpose of data translation is to translate the data stream into a code stream that satisfies sequence constraints peculiar to the channel. The purpose of data transmission is to encode the data stream into a code stream that can combat errors that would be made by a noisy channel. Common practice is to treat the translation code that satisfies sequence constraints separately from the error control, cascading the two codes. An inner encoder/decoder matches its input symbols to the channel. When the channel makes an error, the inner decoder makes an error. An outer encoder/decoder corrects errors and has no constraints on its input sequence or output sequence.

Error control codes are one form of data transmission code and are routinely used for many purposes: to protect against various forms of noise and other interference; to protect against hostile interference in military systems; to protect against noise and media defects in magnetic recording systems; and so forth. Error-control codes can be used for error detection or error correction. When they are used for error detection, a request for retransmission (called automatic repeat request) is fed back to the transmitter. When they are used for error correction (called forward error correction), the link operates without interruption, and the error control is transparent to other levels of the system. Forward error correction can operate with very noisy links and low transmitted power, whereas automatic repeat request cannot.

The performance of a modulation system is measured by the probability of bit error p_e, also called the *bit error rate*. The bit error rate can usually be reduced by increasing transmitted energy per bit, but it is by the performance at low transmitted power that one judges the quality of a digital communication system. The better of two systems, otherwise the same, is the one that can achieve a desired bit error rate with the lower transmitted power.

A. Structure of Codes and Waveforms

Information theory is concerned with the structure of waveforms and with the structure of codes. A code is a string of symbols from a finite alphabet that satisfies a given need. The operation of the encoders and decoders is to map sequences of symbols from one alphabet into sequences of symbols from a second, possibly the same, alphabet.

For any code, a stream of data symbols is entered into the encoder and a stream of codeword symbols comes out of the encoder. Usually the data stream is so long as to appear infinite to the encoder and the decoder. In a practical system, the input data stream must be broken into pieces that are small enough for the encoder to work on. Long codes must be constructed from small pieces according to some plan. A *block code* breaks the data stream into blocks of fixed length k and encodes each block into a codeword of fixed length n. The blocks are concatenated to form the code stream. The *code rate* R of a block code is equal to the ratio k/n. One can also use block codes of variable blocklength. If the ratio of the input blocklength to the codeword blocklength is a constant independent of codeword, then the code is called a *fixed-rate* code.

A *variable-to-fixed-length block code* breaks the data stream into blocks of variable length and encodes each block into a codeword of fixed length n; the codewords are concatenated to form the code stream. A *fixed-to-variable-length block code* breaks the input data stream into blocks to fixed length k and encodes each block into a codeword of variable length; the codewords are concatenated to form the code stream. It must be possible for the decoder to break the code stream back into the individual codewords that were concatenated in the encoder. Therefore most fixed-to-variable-length block codes satisfy a condition known as the *prefix condition*, which allows self-punctuation of the code. This kind of code is called a *prefix code*.

There are also codes that cannot be broken into noninteracting segments. The encoding operation has a structure whereby as a few data symbols enter the encoder, a few codeword symbols leave the encoder. A *tree code* breaks the input data stream into frames of length k that are encoded into codeword frames of length n with the encoding map depending on the previous m input data frames. The codeword frames are concatenated to form the code stream.

When time is continuous, we speak of waveforms rather than of codes. A waveform may be real-valued or complex-valued. A real-valued waveform is a real-valued, usually continuous, function of time. Most transmitters construct a waveform from a discrete sequence, as may be generated by a code, using a rule such as

$$d(t) = \sum_{\ell=-\infty}^{\infty} c_\ell s(t - \ell T)$$

where $s(t)$ is a fixed, finite-energy pulse used to fill in the time axis.

B. Coding for Discrete Noiseless Channels

The capacity C (in units of bits/second) of a discrete noiseless channel is defined by

$$C = \lim_{T\to\infty} \frac{1}{T} \log_2 N(T)$$

where $N(T)$ is the number of sequences of duration T that can be accepted by the channel. The limit in the definition will exist and be nonzero in most cases of interest. It is clear from the definition that about 2^{CT} different messages can be transmitted through the channel in T seconds for large enough T. We say that the channel can carry C bits per second. In the teletype channel, there are 32 symbols of the same duration, and any sequence of symbols is allowed. Each symbol can be used to represent five bits of information. It is easy to see that, if it can carry r symbols per second, the teletype channel has a capacity of $5r$ bits per second. The teletype channel need not always be transmitting information at this maximum rate. The actual rate depends on how the source of information is connected to the channel.

The telegraphy channel has four symbols which we formalize as follows: (1) a dot, consisting of line closed for one time unit and then line open for one time unit; (2) a dash, consisting of three time units closed and one unit open; (3) a letter space, consisting of three time units of line open; (4) a word space, consisting of six time units of line open. Allowable sequences must satisfy the constraint that no space may directly follow another space.

The number of sequences of duration T, $N(T)$ must satisfy the difference equation

$$N(T) = N(T - 2) + N(T - 4) + N(T - 5) + N(T - 7) + N(T - 8) + N(T - 10)$$

as is seen by counting sequences of symbols according to the last or next-to-last symbol occurring. Standard methods for the solution of difference equations can be used to show that $N(T)$ will be dominated by the term λ^T where λ is the largest real zero of the characteristic polynomial $x^{-10} + x^{-8} + x^{-7} + x^{-5} + x^{-4} + x^{-2} - 1$. Hence, C equals $\log_2 \lambda = 0.539$ bit per unit of time. This is the maximum rate at which information can be conveyed by the telegraphy channel. One may devise many codes whose rates are close to the capacity, but never greater.

The well-known Morse code is a widely used code for transmitting text over the telegraphy channel. However, one may properly question the efficiency of the Morse code. Does the Morse code perform near the limit that information can be conveyed through the telegraphy channel? These questions are answered by information theory.

The Morse code combines both source encoding, described in a later section in terms of the entropy of the source, and channel encoding, described above. The Morse code does not exploit the memory in the structure of natural language. Therefore, we will evaluate the code for use with a memoryless model of English whose 27 output letters (including the space) occur with the same probabilities as in English text. The entropy of this model is 4.03 bits per letter, and the capacity of the telegraphy channel is 0.539 bits per unit time. Hence, an optimum code uses an average of 7.48 units of signaling time per source letter. The Morse code uses an average of 9.296 units of signaling time per source letter, which is 124% of the time needed by the otimum code for use with the memoryless model of English text. The Morse code is an excellent compromise between performance and simplicity.

C. Coding for Discrete Noisy Channels

Information can be sent reliably through a discrete noisy channel by the use of an elaborate cross-checking technique that is known as a data transmission code or as an error control code. The *channel capacity* C of a noisy channel is defined to be the maximum rate at which information can be transmitted through a channel. At any rate below channel capacity, an error control code can be designed so that the probability of decoded error is arbitrarily small. Specifically,

$$C = \lim_{p_e \to 0} \lim_{T \to \infty} \frac{1}{T} \log_2 N(T, p_e)$$

where $N(T, p_e)$ is the number of messages in the largest set of messages that can be distinguished with probability of error p_e. This definition of capacity is unsatisfactory for computations because we have no hope of ever knowing the function $N(T, p_e)$. A major accomplishment of information theory is that the limit can be evaluated in a way that completely sidesteps the enormously difficult task of optimum waveform design.

A noisy memoryless channel is described by a transition matrix $\mathbf{Q}$. Intuitively, in a well-designed message an isolated channel input symbol a_j should occur with a probability $p(a_j)$ such that the average mutual information $I(\mathbf{p}; \mathbf{Q})$ between input and output is maximized. This is indeed the case, and the channel capacity of a memoryless channel can be expressed mathematically by the formula

$$C = \max_{\mathbf{p}} I(\mathbf{p}, \mathbf{Q})$$

where the maximum is over all probability distributions on the input alphabet. This formula is quite different from the definition of capacity, and the equivalence is far from trivial to prove. The curious feature is that this formula for capacity is a so-called *single-letter formula* for capacity. Even though good messages require complex dependencies between successive transmitted symbols, nevertheless if only a single input symbol is observed, it is random and the probability $p(a_j)$ of taking value a_j is the $p(a_j)$ that maximizes $I(\mathbf{p}, \mathbf{Q})$.

The single-letter formula for capacity can be evaluated for many examples. The *binary symmetric channel* has a symmetric translation matrix $\mathbf{Q}$ with diagonal elements $1 - p_e$, and its capacity is achieved when the two inputs are equiprobable. Then

$$\begin{aligned} C &= 1 + p_e \log_2 p_e + (1 - p_e) \log_2(1 - p_e) \\ &= 1 - H_b(p_e) \end{aligned}$$

bits per input symbol. When $p_e = 0.11$, $C = 0.5$.

The *binary erasure channel* has input alphabet $\{0, 1\}$, output alphabet $\{0, 1, e\}$, and transition matrix

$$\mathbf{Q} = \begin{bmatrix} 1 - \rho & 0 \\ 0 & 1 - \rho \\ \rho & \rho \end{bmatrix}$$

The capacity of the binary erasure channel is $C = 1 - \rho$ bits per input symbol. This says that the erasures cause a loss in capacity exactly equal to the average fraction of symbols erased despite the fact that the encoder does not know which symbols will be erased.

The *M-ary symmetric channel* has M input symbols and M output symbols. Each transmitted symbol is in error with probability p_e and each of the M-1 incorrect symbols occurs with equal probability $p_e/(M - 1)$. The capacity, in bits per channel symbol, of the M-ary symmetric channel is

$$C = \log_2 M - H_b(p_e) - p_e \log_2(M - 1)$$

Data transmission codes are used to obtain channel rates approaching channel capacity. Codes in use can achieve extremely small probability of symbol error, but the known codes are not good enough to achieve code rate near the channel capacity. Powerful data transmission codes are available for use with M-ary symmetric channels whenever M is a prime or a prime power. Error-control codes in common use work with a code alphabet of size 2^m where m is a positive integer. It is common to use byte-organized codes whenever the channel has memory because errors in such systems tend to occur in bursts and because the hardware is simpler. The most important block codes in use are those known as the (binary) *Hamming codes,* the (binary) *BCH codes,* and the (byte-organized) *Reed–Solomon codes.*

Table I shows the set of 16 codewords for the (7,4) Hamming code, a binary code, that can

TABLE I. Examples of Block Codes

Hamming (7,4) Code							Reed–Solomon (7,5) Code						
Information				Parity			Information					Parity	
0	0	0	0	0	0	0	0	0	0	0	0	0	0
0	0	0	1	0	1	1	0	0	0	0	1	6	3
0	0	1	0	1	1	0	0	0	0	0	2	7	6
0	0	1	1	1	0	1	0	0	0	0	3	1	5
0	1	0	0	1	1	1				⋮			
0	1	0	1	1	0	0	0	0	0	1	0	1	1
0	1	1	0	0	0	1	0	0	0	1	1	7	2
0	1	1	1	0	1	0	0	0	0	1	2	6	7
1	0	0	0	1	0	1	0	0	0	1	3	0	4
1	0	0	1	1	1	0				⋮			
1	0	1	0	0	1	1	0	0	0	7	0	7	7
1	0	1	1	0	0	0	0	0	0	7	1	1	4
1	1	0	0	0	1	0	0	0	0	7	2	0	1
1	1	0	1	0	0	1	0	0	0	7	3	6	2
1	1	1	0	1	0	0				⋮			
1	1	1	1	1	1	1	0	0	1	0	0	7	3
							0	0	1	0	1	1	0
							0	0	1	0	2	0	5
							0	0	1	0	3	6	6
										⋮			

correct a single bit error. Table I also shows some of the codewords of the (7,5) Reed–Solomon code, an octal code, that can correct a single octal symbol in error. This code has 8^5 (or 32,768) codewords. The (7,5) Reed–Solomon code is actually a very small code compared to some in use, although the number of codewords is already too great to enumerate. Codes as large as the (256,224) Reed–Solomon code are now quite practical. This code consists of 224 (eight-bit) bytes of information followed by 32 bytes of parity and can correct 16 symbol errors; an error is an eight-bit byte that is wrong in any possible way.

The rules for constructing good block codes for error control make use of an arithmetic system known as a *Galois field*. A Galois field with 2^m elements, denoted GF(2^m), is an arithmetic system containing the operations of addition, subtraction, multiplication, and division defined in such a way that most arithmetic and algebraic procedures are valid. The arithmetic operations themselves are unconventional but have the enormous advantage that there is no overflow or round-off error. The error-control code is used to process bit packages but not to do real computations, so it does not matter that the arithmetic rules are unconventional. Table II shows addition and multiplication tables for several simple Galois fields. Notice that GF(2) and GF(2) are modulo 2 and modulo 3 arithmetic, respectively, but GF(4) is not modulo 4 arithmetic. Large fields such as GF(256) are very important in practice, but the multiplication tables are too large to show here.

Efficient decoders exist for BCH codes and Reed–Solomon codes, based either on the *Berlekamp-Massey algorithm* or on the *Sugiyama algorithm*. To correct t errors, the hardware or software complexity is proportional to t^2.

A *convolutional code* for data transmission encodes a stream of data symbols into a stream of code-word symbols. However, the duration of each stream is so long that it is effectively infinite and does not enter into the design of the encoder and decoder. The stream of incoming data symbols is broken into segments of k symbols called data frames, which may be as short as one symbol. The encoder stores the most recent m frames, a total of mk data symbols. During each frame time, a new data frame is shifted into the encoder, and the oldest data frame is shifted out and discarded. At the beginning of a frame, from the new incoming data frame and the m stored data frames, the encoder computes a single code frame of length n symbols. This code frame is shifted out of the encoder as the next data frame is shifted in. Hence, the channel must transmit n code symbols for each k data symbols. The rate R of the code is defined as $R = k/n$. The *constraint length* v of a convolutional code is defined as the number of memory stages in a minimum encoder.

Figure 2 shows an encoder for a simple convolutional code, one with $k = 1$, $n = 2$, and $v = 2$. A *trellis description* of the code is shown in Fig. 3. The convolutional code is the set of all semi-infinite binary words that may be read off any path through the trellis. A 0 data bit entering the encoder at any node is encoded into the upward path out of that node, and a 1 data bit is encoded into the lower path. This convolutional code is

TABLE II. Examples of Finite Fields

Galois Field	Addition Table					Multiplication Table				
GF(2)	+	0	1			·	0	1		
	0	0	1			0	0	0		
	1	1	0			1	0	1		
GD(3)	+	0	1	2		·	0	1	2	
	0	0	1	2		0	0	0	0	
	1	1	2	0		1	0	1	2	
	2	2	0	1		2	0	2	1	
GF(4)	+	0	1	2	3	·	0	1	2	3
	0	0	1	2	3	0	0	0	0	0
	1	1	0	3	2	1	0	1	2	3
	2	2	3	0	1	2	0	2	3	1
	3	3	2	1	0	3	0	3	1	2

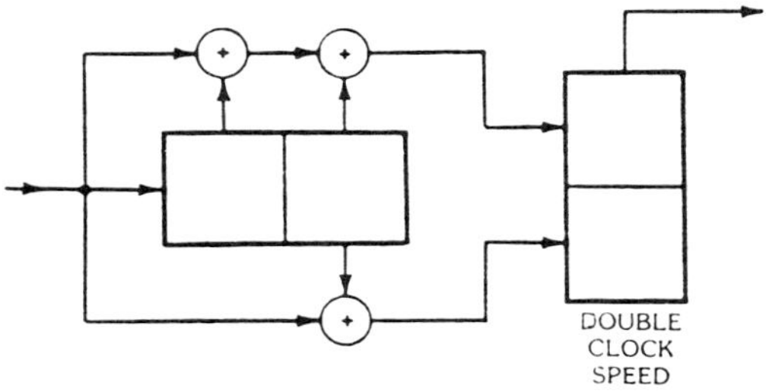

FIG. 2. Encoded for a simple convolutional code.

able to correct any number of error events each containing one or two bit errors provided the error events are spaced far enough apart for the decoder to clear one error event before it sees the next.

Most decoders for convolutional codes either use the *Viterbi algorithm* or use *sequential decoding*. The Viterbi algorithm has a complexity proportional to 2^v and so is practical only for small v. Sequential decoding, using either the *Fano algorithm* or the *stack algorithm,* has a complexity that grows only slowly with v, but has a random decoding delay and will occasionally overflow any finite-sized decoding buffer. Binary convolutional codes used in practice may have a constraint length in the range of about seven to forty.

D. MODULATION

The average mutual information between two continuous random variables X and Y with joint probability density function $p(x, y)$ is

$$I(X; Y) = H(X) + H(Y) - H(X, Y)$$

Each term on the right is a differential entropy and is not invariant under a coordinate transformation. However, because it is defined as a difference, the mutual information does not suffer this limitation.

A continuous channel usually has some constraint on the input probability distribution. The

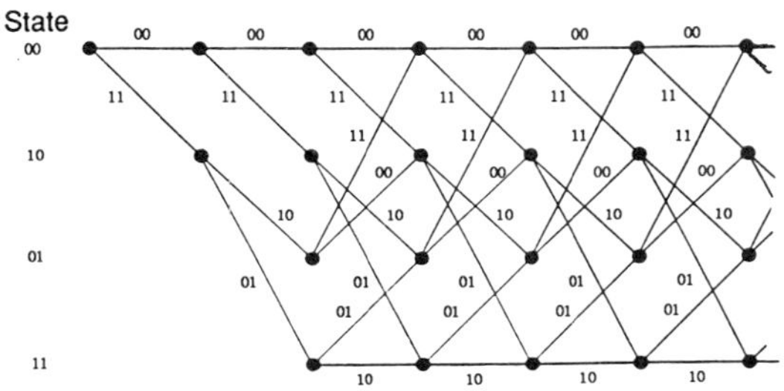

FIG. 3. A trellis for a simple convolutional code.

average power constraint

$$\int_{-\infty}^{\infty} x^2 p(x)\, dx \le S$$

is, by far, the most important constraint.

The capacity of the continuous channel is the maximum value of the average mutual information

$$C = \max_{p(x)} I(X; Y)$$

where the maximum is taken over the set of probability distributions on the channel input that satisfy the constraints.

Calculation of the capacity can be a difficult task requiring a computer, but the important case of an additive discrete-time Gaussian-noise channel subject to an average power constraint can be solved analytically. The channel output Y is given by $Y = X + Z$ where X is the channel input and Z is additive Gaussian noise of variance N. Because X and Z are independent, $H(Y \mid X) = H(Z)$, and $I(X; Y) = H(Y) - H(Z)$. For Gaussian noise, $H(Z) = \frac{1}{2} \log_2 2\pi eN$. Then

$$C = \max_{p(x)} [H(Y) - \tfrac{1}{2} \log_2 2\pi eN]$$

The output Y has variance $S + N$ and the entropy $H(Y)$ is largest if Y is Gaussian, which will be true if X is Gaussian of variance S. Then

$$C = \tfrac{1}{2} \log_2 2\pi e(S + N) - \tfrac{1}{2} \log^2 2\pi eN$$
$$= \tfrac{1}{2} \log_2 (1 + S/N)$$

This is Shannon's formula for the capacity of the additive discrete-time Gaussian noise channel with an average power constraint.

A continuous-time channel with an ideal rectangular transfer function of bandwidth W hertz and additive bandlimited white noise has capacity $C = W \log (1 + S/N)$ because it can be sampled at the Nyquist rate of $2W$ samples per second to form an equivalent discrete-time channel.

An additive Gaussian noise waveform channel, modeled as a linear filter with a general transfer function $H(f)$ followed by additive Gaussian noise with power spectral density $N(f)$, has the same capacity one would obtain if the transfer function $H(f)$ were approximated by many thin ideal rectangular transfer functions of different amplitudes. The capacity is given parametrically in terms of the parameter θ.

$$C(S, \theta) = \tfrac{1}{2} \int_{-\infty}^{\infty} \max\left[0, \log \frac{\theta}{N(f)/|H(f)|^2}\right] df$$

$$S(\theta) = \int_{-\infty}^{\infty} \max[0, \theta - N(f)/|H(f)|^2]\, df$$

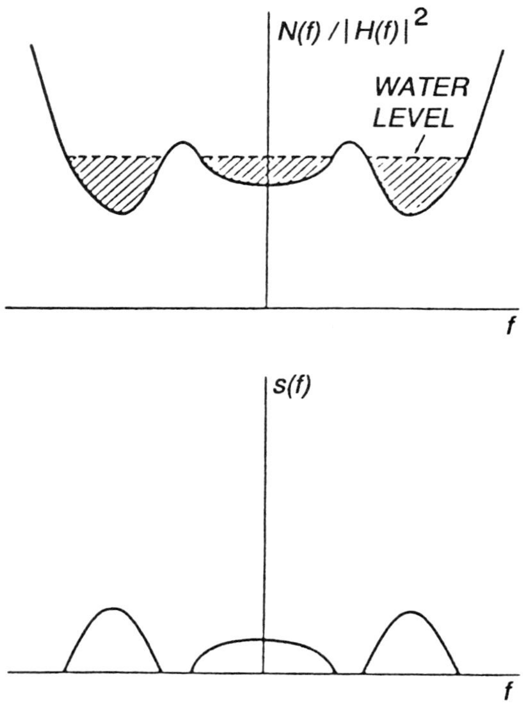

FIG. 4. The analogy of water pouring.

These so-called water-pouring formulas can be understood from Fig. 4. The input informations is imagined as "poured" into a vessel whose shape is defined by $N(f)/|H(f)|^2$. This produces the optimum spectral shape of input waveform $S(f) = \max[0, \theta - N(f)/|H(f)|^2]$ that achieves the channel capacity. The important lesson given by the water-pouring principle is that optimum waveforms put most of their energy in the spectral region where the channel is good. The optimum strategy is exactly the opposite of an often-used equalization strategy that puts extra power in the spectral region where the channel is poor.

Given a message $s(t)$ of duration T containing K information bits, the *bit energy* E_b is given by $E_b = E_m/K$ where E_m is the message energy. For an infinite-length message of rate R information bits/second, E_b is defined by $E_b = S/R$, where S is the message average power.

The bit energy E_b is calculated from the message energy and the number of information bits at the input to the encoder/modulator. The channel message may appear to contain a larger number of bits because of parity symbols for error control, or symbols for frame synchronization or for channel protocol. These symbols do not represent transmitted information, and their energy increases E_b.

In addition to the signal, the receiver also sees white noise of one-sided spectral density N_0 watts/hertz. A linear demodulator's performance cannot be affected if both the signal and the noise are doubled. Only the ratio E_b/N_0 affects the bit error rate. Signaling schemes are compared by comparing their respective graphs of bit error rate versus required E_b/N_0.

It is possible to make precise statements about values of E_b/N_0 for which good waveforms exist; these are a consequence of the channel capacity formula for the ideal rectangular channel in additive Gaussian noise. Define the *spectral bit rate* r (measured in bits per second per hertz) by $r = R/W$. Besides the bit error rate p_e, the spectral bit rate and E_b/N_0 are the two most important figures of merit of a digital communication system. The signal power can be written $S = E_bR = E_brW$ and the noise power can be written $N = N_0W$.

The rate R is less than the capacity, so $r < C/W$. From this, the capacity formula can be rewritten as

$$\frac{E_b}{N_0} > \frac{(2^r - 1)}{r}$$

This inequality, shown in Fig. 5, tells us that increasing the information bit rate per unit bandwidth increases the required energy per bit. This is the basis of the energy/bandwidth trade of digital communication theory where increasing bandwidth at a fixed information rate can reduce power requirements.

Every communication system can be described by a point lying below the curve of Fig.

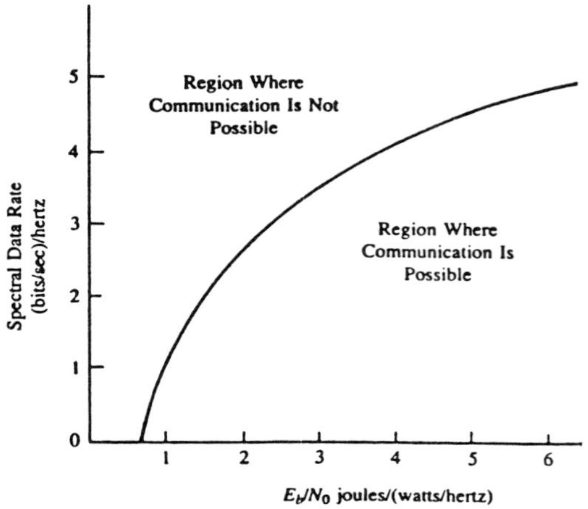

FIG. 5. Capacity of the Additive Gaussian-Noise channel.

5. Any communication system that attempts to operate above the curve will lose enough data through errors so that its actual data rate will lie below the curve. For any point below the curve one can design a communication system that has as small a bit error rate as one desires. The history of digital communications can be described in part as a series of attempts to move ever closer to this limiting curve with systems that have very low bit error rate.

If bandwidth W is a plentiful resource but energy is scarce, then one should let W go to infinity and r to zero. Then we have

$$E_b/N_0 > \log_e 2 = 0.69$$

This is a fundamental limit. The ratio E_b/N_0 is never less than -1.6 dB, and by a sufficiently expensive system and enough excess bandwidth one can communicate with any E_b/N_0 larger than -1.6 dB.

If the bandwidth is much larger than the data rate, then one can signal by using an M-ary signaling alphabet. An M-ary signaling alphabet is a collection of M sufficiently distinct waveforms; usually $M = 2^k$ for some k. The modulator maps each k-bit code symbol from the channel encoder into one of the 2^k waveforms in the signal alphabet. The demodulator compares the received signal in each signaling time interval to each of the 2^k possible transmitted waveforms and chooses the most likely as its estimate of the code symbol.

The M-ary signal alphabets with the best performance known are those known as *simplex* waveforms, but *orthogonal* waveforms are almost as good and are usually used in practice. M-ary signaling is more energy efficient than binary signaling because the modulator puts k bits into one waveform, so it has k times as much energy as it would for a binary waveform. Part of this energy advantage is offset by the fact that the demodulator must make a 2^k-way decision rather than a binary decision. The net effect, is a system that can operate at a very low E_b/N_0 and arbitrarily close to the limit of 0.69 dB. However, the waveforms occupy a bandwidth much greater than the bit rate.

When bandwidth is expensive, one no longer attempts to transmit with very small E_b/N_0. Now it becomes important to transmit with large values of the spectral bit rate r. Good performance can be achieved by careful combination of modulation and error control. The *Ungerboeck trellis codes* are a class of modulation codes that provide good combinations of spectral bit rate and E_b/N_0. The rate $k/(k + 1)$ codes are designed to work with code symbols in a set of 2^{k+1} fixed complex numbers, called a *signal constellation,* which represent phase/amplitude modulation patterns of a carrier sinusoid. An encoder for an Ungerboeck code with $v = 4$ for the 8-point PSK signal constellation is shown in Fig. 6.

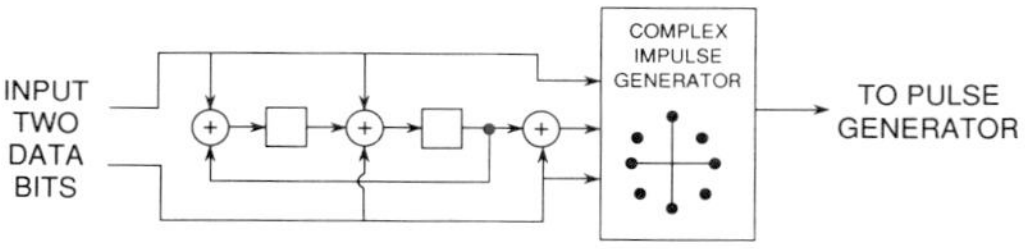

FIG. 6. Encoder for a simple Ungerboeck code.

The Ungerboeck code can be used as a plug-in replacement for the popular, uncoded, four-phase QPSK modulator. The information rate is still two bits per symbol. There is no change in the channel symbol rate, so the coded system has the same bandwidth as the uncoded QPSK system and transmits the same number of data bits per symbol. Hence, the user of the system is unaware of the presence of the code. However, the system now can run at a considerably lower E_b/N_0; a factor of four reduction in transmitted power is a representative performance improvement.

E. Multiterminal Information Networks

A multiterminal communication network consists of more than one data source, more than one data user, or more than one channel between them. Communication networks can have conflicting requirements imposed by the needs of the several terminals. Some multiterminal configurations are the multiaccess communication channel, the two-way communication channel, and the feedback communication channel.

A *multiaccess communication channel* is a single communication channel that is used by more than one user. A *communication protocol* is an agreement by which multiple users share a multiaccess communication system. Many practical channels are intrinsically multiaccess channels, but the designer elects to break them into one-way channels using a technique such as *time division* or *frequency division*. This is a simple and workable solution, but one wishes to know if there is a performance penalty and to know the structure of an optimal communication scheme.

A *two-way channel* has two terminals. Each terminal attempts to get a message across to the other terminal through the two-way channel, but the transmission in one direction interferes with the transmission in the other direction. The problem is to design the terminals to achieve high data rates in both directions simultaneously. This can be a very difficult problem if both transmitters have access to the channel output, and has been open for more than twenty years.

A *broadcast communication system* consists of a single transmitter and multiple receivers. If the same message is to be sent to all receivers, then the task of designing the communication waveform is no different than when there is a single receiver. However, if a different message is to be sent to each receiver, the problem is more complex. Conventionally, the channel is divided according to the needs of the receivers, using time-division or frequency-division signaling techniques. Time-division or frequency-division multiaccess signaling cannot achieve the capacity region of a broadcast channel. Optimum techniques are more tightly interlocked, sending a single composite waveform that is read in a different way by each receiver to obtain its own message.

A *diversity communication system* sends the same information to a user twice through two channels so that if one channel is broken, the message will still arrive. A degraded diversity system is more subtle. It sends half the message through each of two channels but in such a way that either half suffices to reconstruct a degraded copy of the message. A high-fidelity reproduction is obtained if both channels are intact; a low-fidelity reproduction is obtained if only one channel is intact. Information theory describes the structure of such diversity systems.

III. Surveillance Systems

A surveillance system collects noisy data from the environment and processes the raw data into useful data for a user. Examples are radar, sonar, radio astronomy, holography, and medical tomographic imaging. Data required by the user may be detected objects, estimated parameters of objects, or reconstructed images. Modern formulations of these problems view the data space as random and the measurements as noisy. Information theory searches for optimal and suboptimal algorithms for processing the noisy data by starting from optimality principles. In contrast, the subject of signal processing searches for practical algorithms for processing the noisy data by starting from understood processing algorithms. Sometimes the two approaches converge on the same algorithm, and sometimes there is a gap between what is achievable in theory and in practice.

Decision theory is concerned with the problem of deciding among a set of hypotheses when given a collection of imperfect measurements. *Estimation theory* is concerned with the problem of selecting the best value of a parameter from a continuum of possible values when given a collection of imperfect measurements. Estimation theory is also concerned with the selection of a best waveform from a collection of waveforms when given a collection of imperfect measurements. The estimation of the unknown parameter or waveform depends on measurements that are random variables. The quality of the estimate is limited by the quality of the measurements. These limitations can be expressed by means of information-theoretic bounds; one such bound is known as the Cramer–Rao inequality.

A. Detection of Signals

The simplest problem of decision theory, called *hypothesis testing* or *detection,* is to decide between two mutually exclusive hypotheses. In the case of a radar, the two hypotheses are called *target present* and *target absent.* In the case of signal acquisition, the two hypotheses are called *signal present* and *signal absent.* In the general case, the two hypotheses are called the *null hypothesis,* H_0, and the *alternate hypothesis,* H_1. The problem is to decide which hypothesis is correct by collecting and processing data. The data are randomly distributed with a probability distribution that depends on the true hypothesis. The set of data may actually be quite extensive, but it is enough to think of it as a simple measurement whose outcome can only be an element of a finite set of K elements called the measurement space, and indexed by k. The theory applies to arbitrary data sets simply by replacing the scalar measurement by an appropriate vector measurement.

Associated with each hypothesis is a probability distribution on the measurement space. If H_0 is true, then q_{0k} gives the probability that k will be the measurement outcome; if H_1 is true, then q_{1k} gives this probability. A simple measurement consists of an observation of a realization of the random variable, and the processing problem is to decide whether hypothesis H_0 or hypothesis H_1 is true. Every hypothesis testing rule can be described as a partition of the measurement space into two disjoint sets $\mathcal{U}_0$ and $\mathcal{U}_1 = \mathcal{U}_0^c$. If the measurement is an element of $\mathcal{U}_0$, decide that H_0 is true; if it is an element of $\mathcal{U}_1$, decide that H_1 is true.

Accepting hypothesis H_0 when H_1 actually is true is called a type I error; the probability of this event, denoted by α, is $\alpha = \sum_{k\in\mathcal{U}_0} q_{1k}$. Accepting hypothesis H_1 when H_0 actually is true is called a type II error; the probability of this event, denoted by β, is $\beta = \sum_{k\in\mathcal{U}_1} q_{0k}$. The optimum pair of decision regions can be expressed in terms of a *threshold* T and the log-likelihood ratio. The *Neyman–Pearson theorem* says that the sets

$$\mathcal{U}_0(T) = \{k \mid \log(q_{0k}/q_{1k}) \geq T\}$$

$$\mathcal{U}_1(T) = \{k \mid \log(q_{0k}/q_{1k}) < T\}$$

are an optimum family of decision rules parametrized by T in the sense that no decision rule can have type I error and type II error simultaneously better than any of these rules. The type I and type II error probabilities can be traded against each other by varying the threshold T.

B. Estimation of Parameters

The simplest estimation problem involves an unknown real parameter θ, to be determined, and a real random measurement X, with a continuous probability distribution $q(x \mid \theta)$, conditional on the parameter θ. The unknown θ must be estimated based on an observation of X. The estimate of θ given the measurement X is a function $\hat{\theta}(x)$. The estimate $\hat{\theta}$ is a random variable, because it is a function of the random variable X.

The quality of an estimator is judged by its bias $\bar{\theta} = E[\hat{\theta}(x)]$ and by its variance $\sigma_\theta^2 = E[\hat{\theta}(x) - \bar{\theta}]^2$. Intuitively, one hopes to choose the estimator $\hat{\theta}(x)$ so that its bias is zero and the variance is as small as possible. Such an estimator is called a *minimum-variance unbiased estimator*. Sometimes, however, that estimator does not exist, or another estimator has some advantage, and so another estimator is used.

The Cramer–Rao bound is a lower bound on the variance of any estimator. For an unbiased estimator of a single parameter θ, the most common form of the bound is

$$\sigma_\theta^2 \geq \left\{E\left[\frac{\partial}{\partial\theta}\log q(x \mid \theta)\right]^2\right\}^{-1}$$

Suppose that a known waveform $s(t)$ has spectrum $S(f)$ and that additive Gaussian noise has spectral density $N(f)$. The received noisy signal with an unknown time of arrival τ is

$$v(t) = s(t - \tau) + n(t)$$

The Cramer–Rao bound says that any estimator of the time of arrival satisfies

$$\sigma_\tau^2 \geq \left[\int_{-\infty}^{\infty} \frac{2\pi f|S(f)|^2}{N(f)}\,df\right]^{-1}$$

The performance of the *matched-filter estimator* comes close to the Cramer–Rao bound if the noise is white and the signal-to-noise ratio is sufficiently high. The matched-filter estimator passes $v(t)$ through a filter with impulse response $s^*(-t)$ (with some fixed delay to make it causal) and estimates τ from the location of peak of the filter output.

Similar remarks apply to the problem of estimating the frequency offset, ϕ, of an otherwise known passband waveform. The Cramer–Rao bound says that any estimator of the frequency of the carrier onto which a pulse $s(t)$ is modulated has an error variance satisfying

$$\sigma_\phi^2 \geq \left[\int_{-\infty}^{\infty} \frac{|S'(f)|^2}{N(f)}\,df\right]^{-1}$$

where $S'(f)$ is the derivative of $S(f)$. The matched-filter estimator of frequency consists of a bank of passband matched filters stepped in frequency. The filter with the largest output provides the estimate of carrier frequency. If the noise is white, and the signal-to-noise ratio is sufficiently high, the performance of the matched-filter estimator is close to the Cramer–Rao bound. This matched-filter estimator of frequency offset often can be approximated by a *phase-locked loop*.

C. Methods of Inference

Every set of data is fragmentary and can be extrapolated or interpolated only if one has a model underlying the data. For example, time sampling represents a continuous-time function by its values at a discrete set of time instants. These values can be interpolated using the Nyquist–Shannon interpolation formula provided the signal is bandlimited. By requiring the signal to satisfy such a condition, we are imposing a model onto the data that the data set by itself cannot justify. Sometimes a model of this kind may not be available; it then must be construed using the data and some general principle of inference.

The *maximum-entropy principle* of Jaynes is a principle of data reduction that says that when reducing a set of data into the form of an underlying model, one should be maximally noncommittal with respect to missing data. If one must estimate a probability distribution **q** on the data source satisfying certain known constraints on **q**, such as

$$\sum_k q_k f_k = t$$

then, of those distributions that are consistent with the constraints, one should choose as the estimate of **q** the probability distribution $\hat{\mathbf{q}}$ that has maximum entropy. When the source is continuous, the maximum-entropy principle refers to the differential entropy.

A nice example can be given for a probabilistic source with a real-valued output X whose mean and variance are known, but otherwise the probability distribution governing the source output is unknown. Then the maximum-entropy principle says that one should estimate that the probability density $q(x)$ is a Gaussian probability density with the given mean and variance because a Gaussian random variable has the largest differential entropy of a given mean and variance.

In large imaging problems, as in tomography or radio astronomy, it can be computationally expensive to find the maximum-entropy image, although good algorithms (such as the EM algorithm) are available for this purpose.

The *minimum-discrimination principle* of Kull-back is a more general principle that applies when, in addition to a set of constraints on the source probability distribution **q**, one is also given a probability distribution **p** that is a prior estimate of **q**. The principle of minimum discrimination states that, of those probability distributions that satisfy the constraints, one should choose as the new estimate that distribution $\hat{\mathbf{q}}$ that minimizes the discrimination $L(\hat{\mathbf{q}}; \mathbf{p})$. Because $L(\mathbf{p}; \mathbf{p}) = 0$, if the prior distribution **p** satisfies the constraints, then **p** itself will be chosen as the new estimate of the source probability distribution satisfying the constraints.

Neither the minimum-discrimination principle nor the maximum-entropy principle is universally accepted as a fundamental principle. If the source is a discrete source and **p** is the equiprobable distribution, the minimum-discrimination principle reduces to the maximum-entropy principle. In this sense, the principle of minimum discrimination is the more general principle.

IV. Transcription Systems

An information source produces messages by generating a sequence of symbols from a fixed alphabet called the source alphabet. The alphabet may be finite, in which case the source is called a discrete source, or the source alphabet may be continuous, such as the set of real numbers, in which case the source is called a continuous source. A source might also put out continuous functions of time.

A continuous amplitude information source can assume any one of an infinite number of amplitude values and so requires an infinite number of binary digits for its exact specification; the entropy rate is infinite. To transmit the output of a continuous information source and recover it exactly, a channel of infinite capacity is required. Because every continuous channel is perturbed by noise and therefore has a finite capacity, it is not possible to transmit the output of a continuous source over a channel and recover it exactly; there is always some distortion. A waveform source can be converted into a discrete-time source by sampling as described by the *Nyquist–Shannon sampling formula*. A continuous-amplitude source can be converted into a discrete source by quantization.

Source transcription is the task of preparing the output of the source to be represented by a commonplace stream of bits superficially displaying no trace of the characteristics of the source. This function may be broken into three subfunctions for ease of discussion. These are data compression, data compaction and data encryption.

The output of a discrete information source has an output that is a random sequence of symbols from a finite alphabet containing J symbols given by $\{a_0, a_1, \ldots, a_{J-1}\}$. An information source is said to be *memoryless* if successive symbols generated by the source are statistically independent. That is, a source is memoryless if each symbol is selected without influence from all previous symbols. If previously selected symbols influence the selection of a symbol, then the source is said to possess memory. If the selection of a symbol is influenced only by the immediately preceding symbol, the source is known as a *Markov source*.

A. Compaction of Data

Data sources such as facsimile, voice, digital recording, data tables, or word text can produce many millions or billions of bits. However, in their natural form, the data from these sources can be highly redundant. Practical data compaction codes are now available that can reduce considerably the number of bits needed to encode such sources.

A fixed-length block code for compaction of a source with J symbols encodes n source output symbols into a codeword of length k bits, where n and k are fixed. There are J^n possible source output blocks of length n, so the blocklength of a binary code must be at least $\log_2 J^n$ bits if every possible output block is to be encoded. This requires at least $\log_2 J$ code bits per source output symbol. In general, this is much greater than the source entropy rate.

A fixed-length block code can encode at the entropy rate but then must allow the possibility of an error. A block code for data compaction with rate a little above the entropy provides only $n[H(p) + \varepsilon]$ bits, so $2^{n(H+\varepsilon)}$ codewords are assigned to the "typical" source output blocks—those blocks of greatest probability. By picking n large, the probability of a nontypical—hence nonencodable—source output block can be made many orders of magnitude smaller than the probability of failure of the equipment. A fixed-length block code for source compaction must rely on this kind of reliability argument in order to encode at a rate near the entropy.

A variable-length block code encodes n source output symbols into k channel symbols, where either n or k is variable. The most common example is the *Huffman code,* for which n is fixed while k is variable and depends on the block of n symbols observed.

The variable-length codewords of a Huffman code are constructed from knowledge of the probabilities of each of the J source symbols. The construction is recursive. Given M symbols in the source alphabet, form a new source alphabet by choosing two symbols of lowest probability, say X and Y, and combining them into a new artificial symbol $\{X, Y\}$ with probability equal to the sum of the two constituent probabilities. This forms a new source with one fewer symbol. The code for the original source is obtained from a code for the artificial source by appending a 0 or a 1 to the codeword for symbol $\{X, Y\}$ to obtain the two codewords for symbols X and Y. All other symbols retain the same codeword. In turn, design a code for that artificial source using the same procedure to combine two symbols. The procedure stops when one symbol remains.

A Huffman code can be formed just as easily for blocks of length n. Simply replace the source symbols in the construction with blocks of source symbols, and replace the symbol probabilities with probabilities of blocks. By choosing a large enough n—usually an n quite small will do—the average codeword length can be made as close to the source entropy as desired, and so a nearly optimal Huffman code can be constructed.

A Huffman code is a prefix code. It needs no explicit punctuation. Successive n blocks of source symbols can be encoded one after the other and concatenated. By decoding the codewords in a first-in, first-out fashion, the source symbols are uniquely recovered.

Tree codes (both first-in first-out and last-in first-out tree codes) are also in use for source compaction. The encoding operation has a sliding structure whereby, as a few source symbols enter the encoder, a few codeword bits leave the encoder. The relationship between the number of symbols entering the encoder and the number of bits leaving it is usually variable, depending on the particular source symbols to be encoded.

A data compaction code requires a probabilistic model of the source in order to encode to near the entropy of the source. More general source compaction codes, called *universal* source codes, implicitly construct their own model of the source as they go along (assuming that past source output sequences are representative of future output sequences) and eventually encode at a rate near the entropy of whatever source they are given. The *Ziv–Lempel code* is a universal variable-to-fixed-length block code for data compaction that does not require an *a priori* source model. The technique is to find an earlier duplicate occurrence of a substring of source output symbols to be encoded and to refer back to that earlier substring. The encoder retains a copy of the raw data that has already been encoded and the decoder maintains an identical copy after it has been decoded. At each iteration, it searches for a longest prefix of the data yet waiting to be encoded within the data already encoded. A substring is encoded in three parts: a binary-encoded pointer telling where an earlier copy of the substring begins within recently encoded data; a binary-encoded number giving the length of the substring; and the value of the next source symbol. By including the next source symbol, the situation cannot degenerate into a nonencodable situation.

B. Compression of Data

The average amount of information required to describe a source output symbol is equal to the entropy of the source. Sometimes it is not convenient or practical to retain all this information. It then is no longer possible to maintain an exact reproduction of the source. An analog source has infinite entropy, so distortion must always be present when the source output is passed through a channel of finite capacity.

Data compression is the practice of intentionally reducing the information content of a data record. This should be done in such a way that the least-distorted reproduction is obtained. Information theory finds the performance of the optimum compression of a random source of data; a naive encoder will have greater distortion.

A discrete memoryless information source generates a random sequence of symbols from a finite alphabet $\{a_0, a_1, \ldots, a_{J-1}\}$, which is to be approximately described by a second alphabet, called the reproducing alphabet, often identical to the source alphabet but not always so. For example, the reproducing alphabet might consist of the union of the source alphabet and a single new element denoting "data erased."

A *distortion matrix* is a J by K matrix with nonnegative elements ρ_{jk} that specifies the distortion associated with reproducing the jth source symbol by the kth reproducing symbol. Usually the distortion in a block is defined as the arithmetic average of the distortion of each symbol of the block. This is called a *per-letter fidelity criterion*.

An important distortion matrix is the *probability-of-error* distortion matrix. For this case the alphabets are identical with $\rho_{jk} = 0$ if $j = k$ and with $\rho_{jk} = 1$ if $j \neq k$.

A source compression block code of blocklength n and size M is a set consisting of M sequences of length n of reproducing symbols. Each source output block of length n is mapped to that one of the M codewords that results in the least distortion. The entropy of the output of the data compressor is less than that of the original source and therefore can be encoded into a smaller number of bits.

Data compression is a deterministic process. The same block of source symbols always produces the same block of reproducing symbols. Nevertheless, if attention is restricted to a single source output symbol, the symbol b_k into which source symbol a_j is encoded behaves as a random variable even though the block encoding is deterministic. This random variable can be described by a transition matrix $Q_{k|j}$ describing an artificial channel that approximates the data compression. Each time the source produces symbol a_j, it is reproduced by symbol b_k with probability $Q_{k|j}$.

The source-distortion function $D(R)$ is given by

$$D(R) = \min \sum_{jk} p_j Q_{k|j} \rho_{jk}$$

where the minimum is over all probability transition matrices $\mathbf{Q}$ connecting the source alphabet and the reproducing alphabet that satisfy $I(\mathbf{p}; \mathbf{Q}) \leq R$. The definition is justified by the source compression coding theorems of information theory. Any data compression code using R bits per source symbol must provide a distortion of at least $D(R)$, and codes essentially this good exist in principle.

C. Encryption of Data

The advent of electronic mail makes the functions of privacy and authentication essential in a digital communication system because otherwise it is easy for an unauthorized receiver to electronically scan messages to extract information or to insert false information. Data encryption is the function that ensures the privacy of a digital communication system by ensuring that an eavesdropper cannot understand the message. Authentication is the function that ensures that the message originates with the authorized transmitter. Authentication can be provided by a digital signature that is impervious to forgery; this requirement leads to similarities with a cryptosystem.

Cryptosystems may be classified into two major types. The first type is the conventional cryptosystem. It requires some kind of secret key. The key provides an invertible function E_k known to the cryptosystem but hidden from the eavesdropper. Usually, the key is thought of as the index k specifying the function rather than the function itself. The message $\mathbf{d}$ is passed through the function E_k to produce the encrypted message $\mathbf{c} = E_k(\mathbf{d})$. When an authorized receiver obtains the encrypted message $\mathbf{c}$, he decrypts it using the inverse function to obtain

$$E_k^{-1}(\mathbf{c}) = E_k^{-1}(E_k(\mathbf{d})) = \mathbf{d}$$

We may regard the set of all E_k to be publicly known. The key is then the index k selecting a particular encryption function from the specified set.

The second kind of cryptosystem, the *public key cryptosystem,* is a cryptosystem in which the encryption function E_k is made public. This makes cryptographic sense only if E_k is a so-called "one-way" function. This is an invertible function with the unusual property that E_k^{-1} is not practically computable from E_k.

Bibliography

Blahut, R. E. (1987). "Principles and Practice of Information Theory." Addison-Wesley, Reading, Massachusetts.

Blahut, R. E. (1990). "Digital Transmission of Information." Addison-Wesley, Reading, Massachusetts.

Brillion, L. (1962). "Science and Information Theory," 2nd ed. Academic Press, New York.

Gallager, R. G. (1968). "Information Theory and Reliable Communication." Wiley, New York.

McEliece, R. J. (1977). "The Theory of Information and Coding." Addison-Wesley, Reading, Massachusetts.

INFRARED AND MILLIMETER ASTRONOMY

Robert D. Gehrz *University of Minnesota*
Harley A. Thronson, Jr. *University of Wyoming and Royal Observatory, Edinburgh*

GLOSSARY

Aperture synthesis: Production of high spatial resolution images by dividing the collecting area of a telescope into smaller apertures spread out in a pattern covering several baselines. In many systems, the baselines are variable.

Brown dwarf: A very cool low-mass star with insufficient mass (less than about 80 times the mass of Jupiter) to convert hydrogen into helium by nucleosynthesis as do normal stars.

Central engine: The central energy source, often of undetermined detailed physical nature, in a supernova, nova, quasi stellar object (QSO), or active galactic nucleus.

Charge-coupled device (CCD): A light-sensitive electronic device, usually consisting of very many individual elements, which can be used to "photograph" extended sources.

Cosmic background: Faint radiation at a wavelength of several millimeters that is the highly redshifted remnant of the energy released in the creation of the universe, the Big Bang.

Eddington limit: The luminosity required for radiation pressure to drive hydrogen atoms away from a star; the numerical value is 3.5×10^4 solar luminosities per solar mass.

Forbidden line emission: Emission lines from a low-density gas due to states that are collisionally de-excited at ordinary densities.

Interstellar medium (ISM): Gas and dust that permeate the space between the stars in a galaxy.

Light bucket: A telescope designed primarily for the collection of photons rather than for imaging at the diffraction limit of its aperture.

Pseudophotosphere: An optically thick shell of hot gas that emits like a blackbody.

Starburst: An extremely energetic short-lived episode of star formation. Starbursts may emit a considerable fraction of the total luminosity of the galaxy in which they occur.

Supernova, Type II: A violent explosion caused by the gravitational collapse of the iron-rich core of a massive star.

Thermonuclear runaway: An explosive nuclear burning process that takes place in a degenerate gas; explosive nucleosynthesis.

Infrared (IR) and millimeter (MM) astronomy may be defined as observational work conducted at wavelengths between 1 micron and 1 mm. This field has become particularly significant within the past five years because of data from NASA's Infrared Astronomical Satellite (IRAS), the development of large-format imaging IR array detectors, and the completion of several new facilities for observations at MM/Sub-MM wavelengths. Exciting new observational results have been obtained for comets, novae, supernovae, regions of star formation, and galaxies.

Basic concepts and advances in the new field of IR astronomy through 1985 were described by Gehrz, Grasdalen, and Hackwell in Volume 2 of the "Encyclopedia of Physical Science and

Technology'' (Paper I, 1987, Academic Press, Inc.). In this contribution, we extend the discussion presented in paper I to include results in IR and MM wave astronomy that have occurred since 1985. We have assumed that the reader has access to the material in Paper I.

I. The IRAS Survey

IRAS, launched in 1983, enabled the first comprehensive study of the IR universe. About 250,000 individual sources were quickly identified from this single survey, about a third of all objects cataloged at all wavelengths by astronomers to date. Because a large fraction of astrophysical objects (the majority of stars, dust, and cold gas, energetic ''starburst'' galaxies, objects at the edge of the material universe) emit predominantly or exclusively in the IR, analysis of IRAS survey data has been a major undertaking for astronomers during the last half of the 1980s.

Studies of the IRAS data can be distinguished by whether an IR source appears as a point source (unresolved by the satellite's optics) or as an extended object, such as a large, dusty interstellar cloud or nearby galaxy. Very many more objects are far away than are nearby, so that studies of point sources often emphasize the large-scale structure of the Milky Way galaxy or the universe. In contrast, although the number of nearby objects is much smaller, individual nearby objects appear as extended sources that can be distinguished in more spatial detail using the IRAS survey.

A. Point Sources in the IR Sky

Of the approximately 250,000 objects that appear in the IRAS Point Source Catalog, about 67% are various types of stars, and about 10% are galaxies. Analysis of these point sources has been fundamentally important because the large sample size means that the results can give a statistically accurate measure of the structure of the IR sky.

The most common stars found in the IRAS are luminous red giants, stars nearing the end of their lives, that are often ejecting dust and gas. Material lost by giants has been processed in the cores of the stars, so that ejection of the material into space is a critical stage in replenishing the interstellar medium (ISM) with material enriched in heavy elements and suitable for the formation of planets. IRAS observations allowed astronomers to estimate that these red giants inject the equivalent of about one-half the mass of our sun into the ISM each year.

A surprising result from the IRAS survey of ''normal'' stars was the discovery that some nearby stars have weak excess emission in the IR, indicative of small amounts of dust or gravel in orbit around the star. While the result does not prove that there are planets around these stars, it does suggest that solid material is found surrounding stars other than our sun. We discuss this result further in Section XI.

B. The IR Emission from Nearby Galaxies

IRAS maps of galaxies, including our own Milky Way, presented astronomers with a much clearer understanding of the importance of dust in the universe and left them with a few unsolved mysteries. Normal galaxies known to possess cool, neutral interstellar gas were shown by IRAS to be luminous sources of emission from cold (25–40 K) dust. These galaxies may emit as much as 25% of their total energy at 40–120 microns. This large fraction is a direct consequence of the high efficiency of dust for absorption of shorter-wavelength photons. Although there is vigorous debate about the details of the sources of heating of the dust, astronomers agree that visual and ultraviolet photons from many sources can all warm interstellar grains.

It is presently popular to posit starbursts as a major source of dust-heating in luminous galaxies, but light from the hundreds of billions of normal stars and from the mysterious central engines can also heat dust grains. Many of the most energetic galaxies may have resulted from recent collisions between normal galaxies, which radically alter the rate of star formation. Enigmatically, many of these superluminous galaxies appear fairly undisturbed. Some of the explanations that have been offered to explain the enormous IR luminosities of these galaxies include starbursts, massive black holes in the nuclei, high-speed collisions between dusty interstellar clouds, and extremely efficient absorption of starlight from very large numbers of stars.

II. COBE, ISO, SOFIA, and SIRTF

IR astronomy's potential to reveal the nature of the universe has barely been tapped by existing telescopes and instruments. For outside the earth's atmosphere, the performance of an instrument designed to detect IR light can be limited by the emission of the telescope itself. Thus, very cold telescopes, carrying large amounts of liquid helium, can be flown into space to work at these wavelengths. Such facilities can also observe many wavelengths that are inaccessible from even the best sites on the ground. To realize this potential, the European Space Agency (ESA) and NASA have proposed a trio of telescopes in the 1990s, and NASA has recently launched a satellite to observe the faint echo of the explosion that began space and time.

The NASA Cosmic Background Explorer (COBE) was launched in November, 1989 to study the oldest light in the cosmos, the faint MM-wavelength emission, remnant radiation from the Big Bang. COBE will determine the spatial uniformity of this emission, a parameter related to the uniformity of the primeval explosion. Non-uniformities in the Big Bang are thought to have lead to the formation of the galaxies that we see today. COBE will also test for processes that might have altered the shape of the spectrum of the remnant radiation since the Big Bang. Preliminary results from COBE, reported at the January 1990 meeting of the American Astronomical Society, show that the cosmic background radiation has a temperature of 2.735 K and that the background is surprisingly uniform in all directions. One implication of these observations is the uniformity of the early universe is difficult to reconcile with the large-scale clustering of galaxies in the present universe.

The Infrared Space Observatory (ISO), a 60-cm cooled telescope under construction by ESA for launch in mid-1993, will be the first of the next generation of space-based IR telescopes. It will carry three cameras to map the emission from the pervasive cool dust and a spectrometer to investigate the emission lines from gas. NASA has proposed two advanced IR facilities. The first is the Stratospheric Observatory for Infrared Astronomy (SOFIA), a Boeing 747 modified to carry a 2.5-m telescope to altitudes of 41,000 feet. SOFIA, to be completed by the mid-1990s will allow astronomers access to a large telescope above the atmospheric water vapor. SOFIA's large aperture will afford substantially increased light-gathering and spatial-resolving power over the smaller Kuiper Airborne Observatory (KAO). Space Infrared Telescope Facility (SIRTF) scheduled for the late 1990s will be a satellite carrying an extremely cold 80-cm telescope into orbit. SIRTF is expected to have a 5-year lifetime and will possess unprecedented sensitivity for observations of very cool objects such as brown dwarfs, or nearby planets outside our solar system. Because of their large redshifts, objects at great distances will emit much of their light at the wavelengths to which SIRTF will be most sensitive.

III. IR and Sub-Millimeter Telescopes and Arrays

Although conventional reflecting telescopes can be used for IR and Sub-MM observations, the past decade has witnessed the development of telescopes built specifically for observations at wavelengths longer than one micron. Telescopes designed to work primarily at these longer wavelengths have distinguishing characteristics. IR telescopes will usually have a large f ratio, indicating that the area covered by the instrument's optics is a small part of the sky. This serves to reduce the background radiation falling on the detector. The newer telescopes are being placed on high, very dry sites to minimize atmospheric water vapor absorption. IR astronomers have gone, literally, to the ends of the earth to find ideal observing conditions: by the end of the next decade, Antarctica may become a major astronomical complex. Some observations have already been obtained from this frozen site, particularly of the very weak emission from dust at about 15 K buried within the Milky Way's gas clouds.

While large light-gathering apertures remain a major goal of all telescope builders, the technical and financial hurdles of constructing a stable, high-precision mirror remain considerable. Consequently, astronomers have found ingenious methods to approximately duplicate the advantages of large mirrors: superior light collection ability and high angular resolution. Duplicating only the collecting area of a large telescope is relatively simple, and astronomers have been using so-called "light buckets" at many wavelengths for over a century. The more difficult problem is to duplicate the high resolving power of a large, good-quality mirror. Under ideal conditions, the smallest angle that can be measured is given by $1.22W/D$, where W is the wavelength of observation and D is the diameter of the light-collecting optics. Instead of making a single mirror of diameter D, for example, one may construct several smaller telescopes, separated by a distance D or greater. The difficulty with this method of mimicking large mirrors is that the smaller telescopes must themselves be very rigid and must not move with respect to one another by much more than a fraction of a wavelength. This criterion is technically challenging but has been successfully achieved at a number of observatories. Foremost among these "apertures synthesis" telescopes is the Very Large Array in New Mexico, working at centimeter radio wavelengths for about a decade. However, four telescope array systems (two in the United States, one in Japan, and one in Europe) are at present working at very short radio wavelengths (MM waves), almost to very long IR wavelengths, at about 1 mm. Over the next several years, some of these instruments will begin to regularly obtain high-resolution observations at about half-millimeter in wavelength, and subsequent telescope arrays are being proposed specifically to carry out regular programs of study at 300–600 microns.

At the short end of the IR spectrum, astronomers are adapting techniques developed for obtaining very high resolution data at visual wavelengths for observations at 1–10 microns. A group led by C. H. Townes at the University of California at Berkeley has constructed a variable base-line spatial interferometer operating at about 10 microns. Their instrument, consisting of a pair of telescopes mounted on very stable truck beds, can be moved to suitable sites for observing and the telescopes can be separated to duplicate the angular resolving power of a larger telescope. In the near-IR (1–3 microns), H. M. Dyck and his collaborators at the University of Wyoming are developing a fixed base-line spatial interferometer consisting of two small telescopes rigidly attached to a set of concrete pilings separated by 30 m.

IV. IR Polarimetry

IR polarimetry has, within the past few years, become a valuable technique for determining the geometries of stellar outflows, reflection nebulae, and astrophysical magnetic fields. Two sensitive new systems recently placed into operation are a far-IR polarimeter constructed for the Hawaii MM array by R. Hildebrand and a near-IR polarimeter (Minnesota IR Polarimeter; MIRP) constructed for the NASA IR Telescope Facility by T. J. Jones. Both can measure polarizations to an accuracy of a few tenths of a percent. The Wyoming IR Group pioneered imaging infrared photopolarimetry in the early 1980s, and similar studies have been conducted lately using the new near IR imaging camera (IRCAM) at the United Kingdom IR Telescope (UKIRT).

Imaging polarimetry reveals highly polarized reflection nebulae around young stars; the polarization H vectors point in the direction of the stars that illuminate the nebulae (see Fig. 1). Measurements of the far IR polarization of young stellar objects like the BNKL object in Orion show that magnetic fields are present in the outflows around these objects, and that some of the grains in the dust surrounding them must be in the form of long cylinders. Far IR polarimetry has provided similar data about particles and magnetic fields near the center of the Galaxy. MIRP has yielded new information about the structure of magnetic fields in colliding galaxies, about the structure of the interstellar magnetic field of the Galaxy, and about the ISM dust grain constituents in the direction of the Galactic Center.

V. Far-IR Lines

Many stars and galaxies emit a large fraction of their light at IR wavelengths, as does the ISM gas and dust (see Fig. 2). While the radiation from stars, dust, and galaxies is primarily continuum emission, the gaseous emission is mostly from lines or bands. ISM emits so strongly at IR wavelengths because so much of the gas is cold, with temperatures in the range of several de-

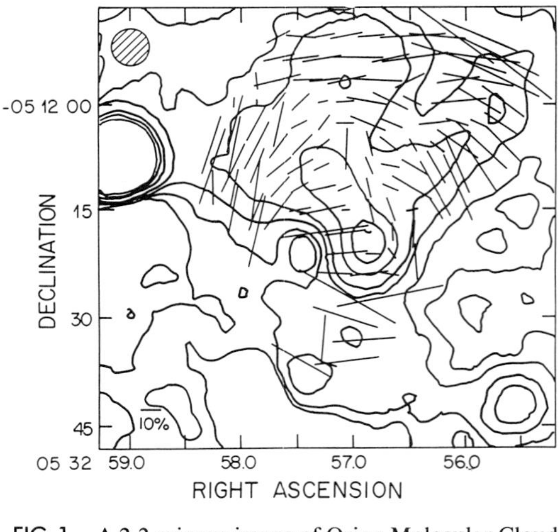

FIG. 1. A 2.2-micron image of Orion Molecular Cloud 2 (OMC-2), IRS 1, showing the direction and strength of the polarized E vector in a nebula that scatters light from a central source. [Courtesy of R. D. Gehrz, from J. J. Johnson *et al.* (1990). *Astron. J.*]

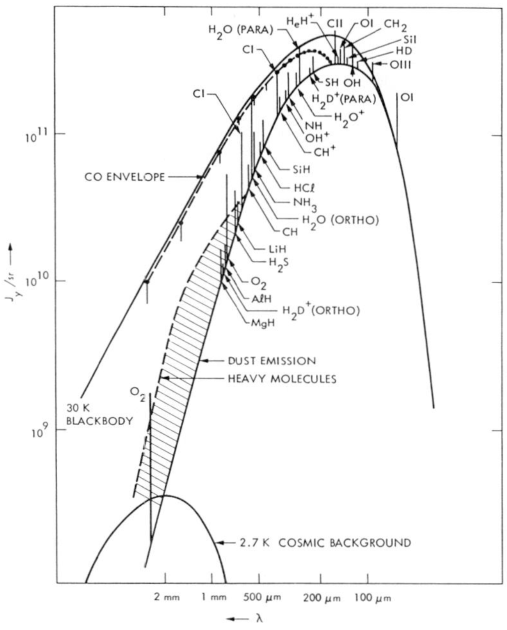

FIG. 2. A model of the gas and dust emission from a dense interstellar cloud in the Milky Way. The dust emission is shown as the smooth underlying curve, characteristic of material at a temperature of a few tens of degrees above absolute zero. The emission lines are calculated for a typical chemical abundance proposed for interstellar space. Most of this spectrum is not observable from telescopes on the ground. [Courtesy of T. G. Phillips (Caltech).]

grees above absolute zero up to a few hundred degrees. Gas at higher temperatures (1000–2000 K) emits visual light as do the stars, and even hotter ISM gas has been detected by X-ray satellites. However, in our galaxy and in a large number of other galaxies, most of the gas is cool enough to require observations at 50–200 microns. Because of strong absorption by water vapor in the earth's atmosphere, even the highest, driest mountain tops are unsuitable for regular observations at these wavelengths. Most of our information about the gas emission lines comes from observations obtained since the mid-1970s with NASA's Kuiper Airborne Observatory, a 0.9-m telescope flown to altitudes of about 13 km and above about 99% of the atmospheric water.

The most studied of the far-IR lines is the [CII] 157 micron emission. In luminous galaxies and massive, molecular clouds in the Milky Way, this line is strong in regions of intense star formation. The intense ultraviolet radiation from hot, young stars dissociates molecules and ionizes atoms within the remains of the clouds from which the stars formed.

More curious has been the discovery that [CI] 609 micron emission is very strong within interstellar gas clouds that were originally thought to be overwhelmingly molecular. Popular models for ISM chemistry predicted that all atomic carbon was either bound with oxygen in the robust CO molecule or condensed into carbon dust grains. One explanation for the surprising strength of the atomic carbon emission is that the dense molecular clouds are constructed more like a Swiss cheese with holes and cloudlets, a more complicated structure than originally proposed. In this picture, the surface area of molecular clouds for the photodissociation of CO is much greater than originally believed.

Only a handful of IR emissions from ISM molecules and atoms have been observed to date, because there is only a single telescope (the KAO) capable of obtaining spectroscopic data throughout the IR. A number of proposed space observatories (see Fig. 3 and Section II) will vastly improve our capabilities in the coming decade.

VI. Near-IR Arrays and Imaging

Until very recently, IR images had to be constructed by the time-consuming process of scanning or point-wise mapping with a single detector. Within the past few years, large-format array detectors, with several thousand individual sensitive elements (pixels), have become widely available. These detectors have been installed in imaging cameras and spectrometers at IR observatories throughout the world. Now, large areas of the sky can be "photographed" in the IR at one time, so that IR astronomers can enjoy the same advantages as astronomers working at visual wavelengths with photographic plates or charge-coupled devices (CCDs) that cover a very large area. Near-IR CCDs are constructed from semiconductors that are sensitive to IR light, but are otherwise quite similar to the CCDs used at visual wavelengths. Most of the development of these arrays came from military-related research. At longer IR wavelengths, astronomers are still generally limited to using small numbers of detectors within any instrument. This remains a serious limitation to the amount and quality of imaging data that can be collected at mid- and far-IR wavelengths.

FIG. 3. Artist's conception of an orbiting telescope to study the emission from gas in interstellar space during the mid-1990s. Most of the emission from dense gas clouds where new stars and planets are born is not detectable from telescopes on the ground. (Artwork by Ball Aerospace Corp., courtesy of G. J. Melnick.)

Figure 4, an image of the molecular cloud DR 21 taken in the light of the 2.1-micron line of molecular hydrogen, shows exciting results from the new breed of near-IR cameras. Emission from this line is caused by excitation of molecular hydrogen gas by the intense short-wavelength radiation bath from the massive hot, young stars. The entire cloud appears to be alight in the image because of the energetic star formation that permeates the cloud.

These modern photon-counting IR imaging detectors have digitized outputs that can be fed directly into powerful computers for reduction and analysis. They are, perhaps, an even greater scientific revolution than were the sensitive photographic materials that were developed for optical astronomy 75 years ago.

VII. The 3.4-Micron Hydrocarbon Emission Feature

Near-IR spectroscopy since 1985 has confirmed that hydrocarbon molecules may produce the near IR 3.1–3.4 micron emission features observed in planetary nebulae, comets, and molecular cloud cores (see Fig. 5). This emission has been attributed to stretching vibrations in C–H bonds of various hydrocarbon compounds such as polycyclic aromatic hydrocarbons (PAHs), hydrogenated amorphous carbons (HACs), and quenched carbonaceous composites (QCCs). Other emission features characteristic of hydrocarbons are found in the 6–14-micron spectra of some of these astrophysical objects. The hydrocarbon emission features have been found in only a handful of stellar objects such as novae, planetary nebulae, and a small number of carbon stars. Generally, circumstellar hydrocarbon emission is seen only in sources with radiation fields that can produce high excitation in a circumstellar nebula.

Dust in dense molecular clouds probably has a hydrocarbon grain component because the 3.2–3.4-micron and 7–14-micron emission features are found in IR spectra of HII regions, molecular cloud cores, and young stellar objects. Since

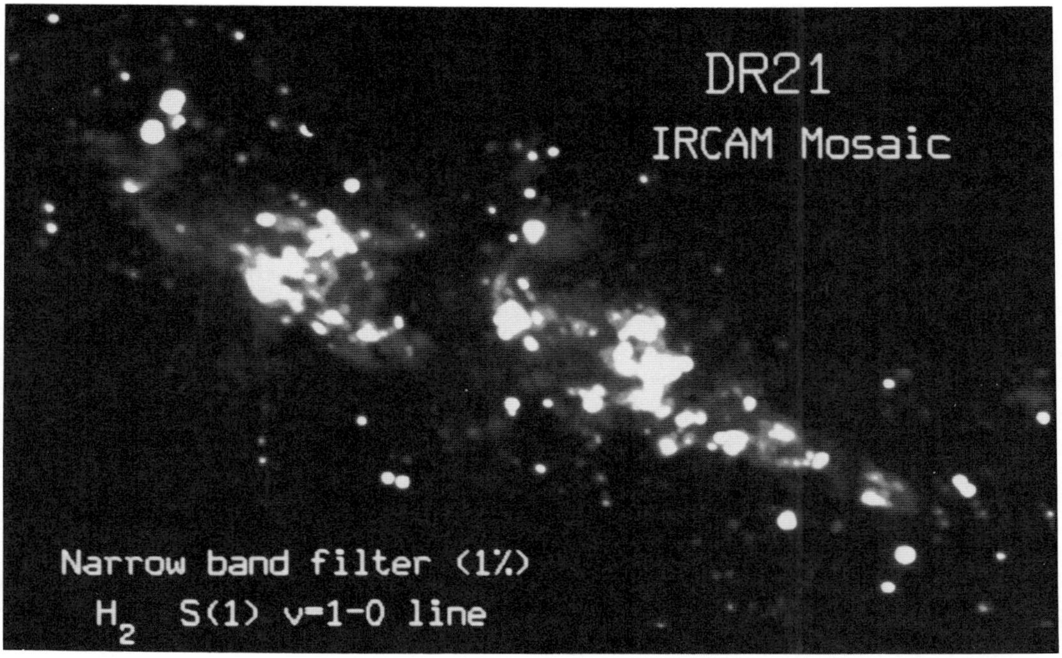

FIG. 4. Molecular hydrogen emission from the active star-forming region, DR 21. The image shows the distribution of light at 2.1 microns caused by excitation of the molecule by hot young stars that are being born throughout this source. (Courtesy of the United Kingdom Infrared Telescope Camera Group. Copyright © Russell, Berton, Garden)

these features are seldom seen in stars, the production of hydrocarbon grains and hydrocarbon mantles on stardust may be a process that is particularly efficient in the environment of dense ISM molecular clouds.

Hydrocarbon emission features in comets are especially interesting. The 3-micron emission feature in Comet Halley is substantially different in width and effective wavelength from the emission from other astrophysical sources (see Fig. 5). Since hydrocarbon materials subjected to ultraviolet radiation and gamma rays in the laboratory can be altered to change the wavelength of the near IR emission, it seems reasonable to conclude that comet grains may have been processed differently than the grains in other astrophysical sources. The physical conditions in the primitive solar system might be deduced from a detailed knowledge of the physical history of the development of comet grains.

VIII. New IR Results on Classical Novae

Circumstellar dust formation has been studied by IR observations of outbursts of classical novae. The eruption results from a thermonuclear runaway on a white dwarf accreting matter in a close binary system. The ejecta initially appear as an expanding pseudophotosphere, and free-free and line emission are observed when the gas becomes optically thin. Dust formation occurs in many novae as the ejecta cool and is characterized by rising thermal IR emission as the dust absorbs energy from the central engine. The IR emission increases as the grains grow to maximum size and then declines as the mature grains flow into the ISM. When dust shells become optically thick, the IR energy equals the outburst luminosity, showing that the central engine has a constant luminosity for a long time. Most novae produce carbon dust, but recent observations show that novae can produce every other type of astrophysical grain. Within the last four years, it has been shown that nova shells can be strongly cooled by IR fine-structure forbidden-line emission.

A. Dust Formation in Novae

The dust formation hypothesis has been confirmed for several recent novae. While most no-

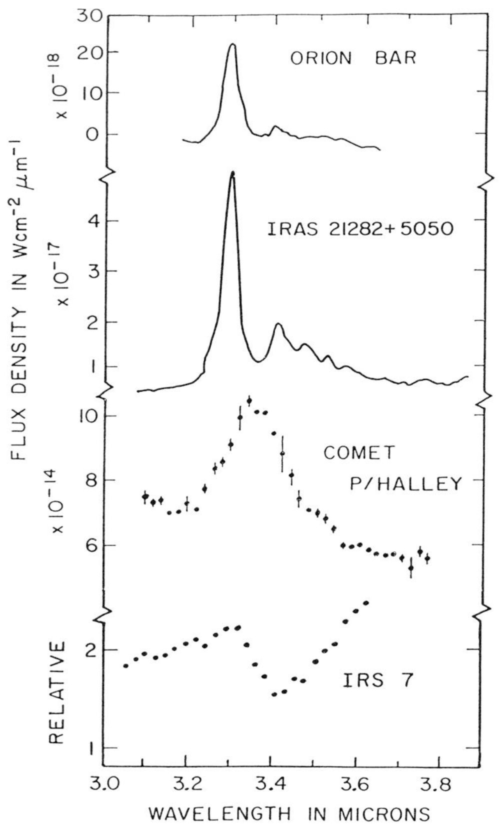

FIG. 5. High-resolution IR spectra of the 3.3–3.4-micron hydrocarbon emission bands in several objects (Orion Bar; Allamandola, Tielens, and Barker 1987, IRAS 21282 + 5050; de Muizon *et al.* 1986, and Halley; Knacke, Brook, and Joyce 1986). [Courtesy of R. D. Gehrz (1990). *In* "Proceedings of the NAS/ASUSSR Joint Workshop on Planetary Sciences" National Academy Press, Washington, D.C.]

vae form carbon dust, a few novae have formed silicates, silicon carbide, and hydrocarbons. The hard radiation from a nova's central engine can provide the radiation processing believed to be important in creating hydrocarbons from amorphous carbon. The formation of more than one type of grain has recently been recorded for at least three novae. Nova Centaurus 1986 (see Fig. 6) apparently formed carbon, silicates, and hydrocarbons. Since silicate condensation occurs in environments where $C < O$ and carbon condensation requires $C > O$, these observations apparently require significant abundance gradients within the ejecta of a single nova. One possibility is that the polar plumes and equatorial ring that are produced in the explosion have different compositions. The extraordinarily deep transitory dip in the visible light from Nova Cen 1986 (Fig. 6) suggests the formation of clumps in the ejecta.

B. IR Coronal Emission from Novae

IR spectroscopic observations of recent novae show that forbidden fine-structure lines can be strong sources of cooling in the ejecta. The strongest of these was the [Ne II] 12.8-micron emission from QU Vul. Measurements of these lines can lead to the identification of atomic and molecular species in nova ejecta, and are useful for estimating physical conditions and chemical abundances in the ejecta. The abundances give information bout nucleosynthesis in both the nova progenitor and in the thermonuclear runaway causing the eruption. While the IR transitions themselves are collisionally excited, the ionization states responsible for the transitions must be largely radiatively excited. Ionization temperatures inferred from the photoionization of the coronal states exceed 500,000–1,000,000 K. IR speckle interferometric measurements and high-resolution IR spectroscopy suggest that the coronal emission occurs far out in the ejecta rather than close to the central engine. The abundances of the optical and IR coronal species suggest that these novae result from accretion matter onto ONeMg white dwarfs that are the evolutionary endproduct of intermediate mass (10–20 solar mass) stars. Thermonuclear runaways in such systems can produce significant quantities of the radioactive isotopes ^{22}Na and ^{26}Al, which decay into ^{22}Ne (2.7 years) and ^{26}Mg (7.3×10^5 years). These materials could be trapped in grains during the dust formation phase to produce grain materials with significant overabundances of ^{22}Ne and ^{26}Mg such as have been discovered in solar system meteorites. These solar system materials could therefore have been produced in nova explosions.

C. Nova Energetics from IRAS Observations

IR observations of the energy distributions of the optically thick dust shells of novae show that the central engine maintains constant luminosity close to the Eddington limit for up to 500 days. IRAS observations of novae lead to interesting speculation on the late evolutionary stages of the eruption and on the nature of the accretion

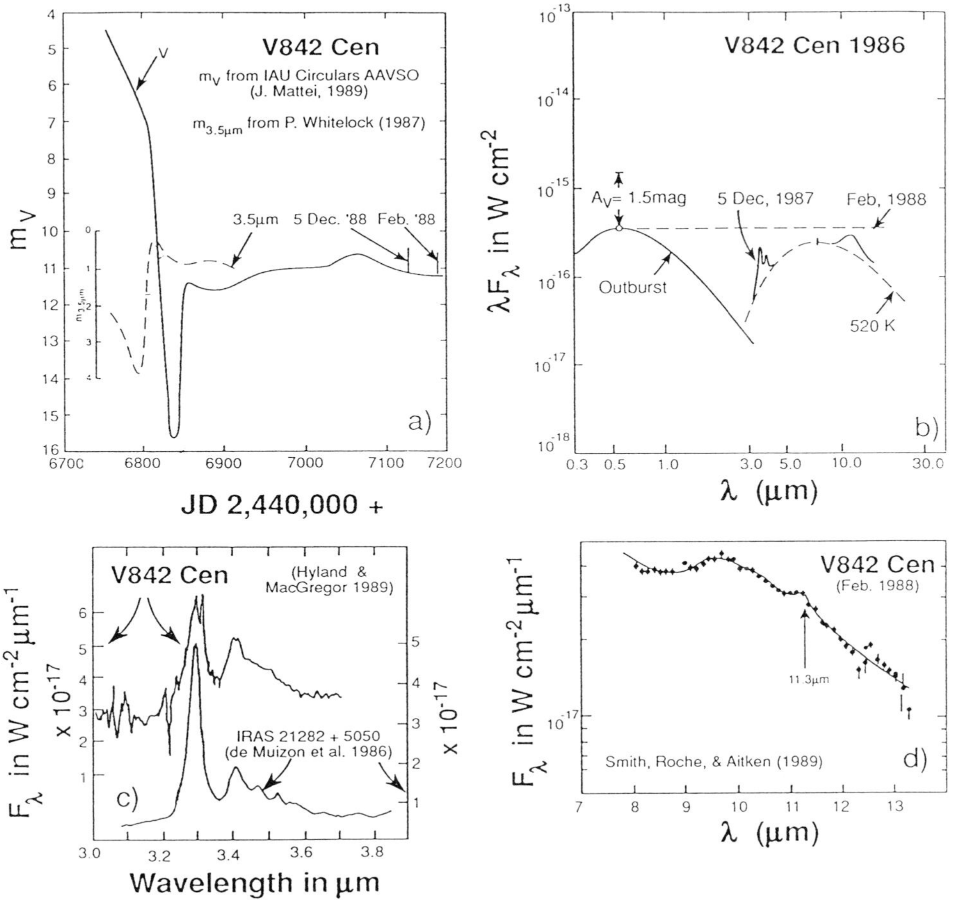

FIG. 6. The development of Nova Centaurus 1986. A deep short-lived visible minimum was accompanied by the formation of dust. Carbon and silicates cause the 7–13-micron emission feature. Emission features at 3.28, 3.4, and 11.3 microns are from hydrocarbons. [Courtesy of R. D. Gehrz (1990). *In* "The Physics of Classical Novae: Proceedings of IAU Colloqium No. 122" Kluwer, Dordrecht.]

phase. At least several old novae and nova precursors have surprisingly large far-IR luminosities, which could be due to either dust emission or fine-structure line emission. The central engine required to power this emission must be 10 to 100 times more luminous than current theories of the accretion phase would predict. Two possibilities are that the constant luminosity phase lasts for many years, and that the accretion disk radiation comes out at extreme ultraviolet (EUV) wavelengths.

IX. Supernova 1987a

Supernova 1987a in the large Magellanic Cloud, the first near-by Type II Supernova in almost 400 years, has afforded unprecedented tests of theories of the evolution and demise of massive stars. IR observations are giving fundamental new information about the nucleosynthesis in both the explosion and the progenitor star, the physical development of the ejecta, and the formation of dust in the ejecta. Recent IR spectra (see Fig. 7) show emission lines from Ar, Co, and Fe that suggest that the expanding shell is in transition from the optically thick phase to the optically thin phase. When these lines become optically thin, they can be used to estimate the abundances of the atomic species that produce them. The chemical composition of the ejecta is affected by the nucleosynthesis in both the explosion and the progenitor.

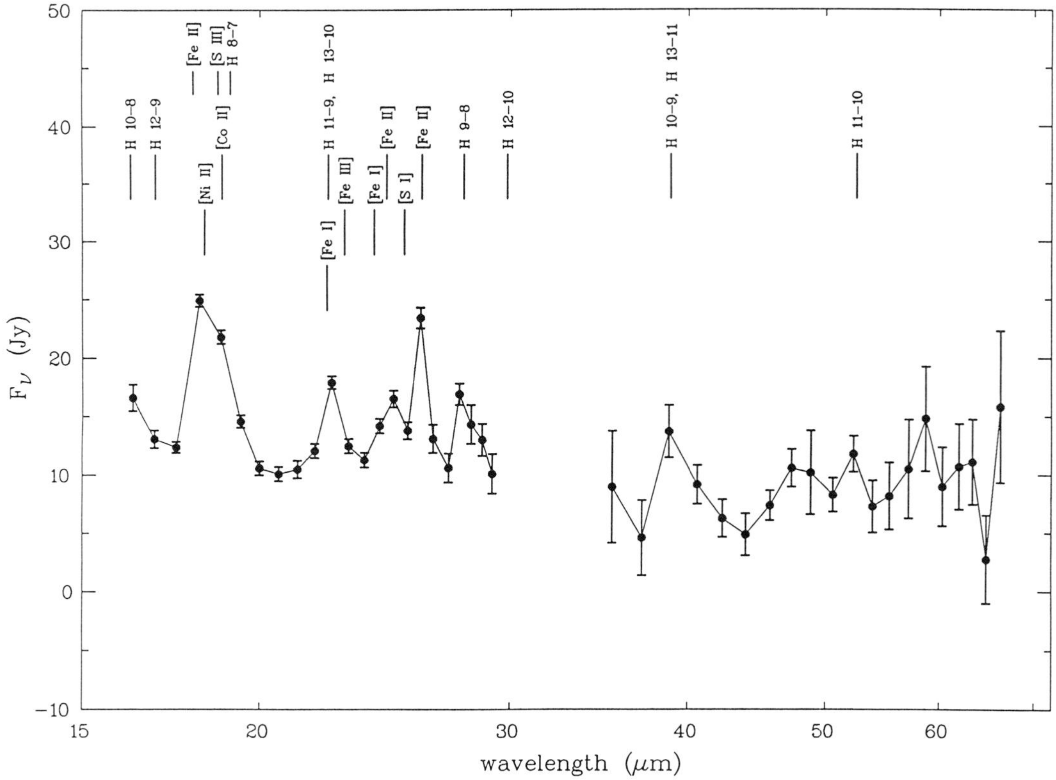

FIG. 7. The 7–60-micron spectrum of SN 1987a taken from the KAO. [Courtesy of E. Dwek, from H. Mosely *et al.* (1990). *Astrophys. J.*]

Astronomer's suspicion that dust grains can form in the ejecta of the supernova explosions has been tested by IR observations of SN 1987a. When grains form in a supernova remnant, they emit thermal IR radiation and can block the visible radiation from the central engine. The time at which dust forms depends on the velocity of the ejecta as well as on the development of the luminosity of the ejecta and central engine. Visible and IR data suggest that substantial amounts of dust had formed in SN 1987a by early 1989, two years after the eruption. These data showed that an accelerated decline in visible brightness was accompanied by a brightening in the thermal IR, and that the red wings of visible emission lines had disappeared, as if a thick dust shell were blocking our view of the far side of the ejecta. The evolution of the infrared radiation showed that radioactivity from $^{56}Co \rightarrow {}^{56}Fe$ decay, not a pulsar, was still powering the central engine as late as early 1990.

X. Recent IR Studies of Comets

Comet nuclei formed during the early stages of the evolution of the solar nebula. Studies of the material ablated during perihelion passage can provide information about the chemical and mineral history of the primitive solar system. IR observations of comet comae and dust tails show near-IR continuum emission from small carbon grains and the 10–20-micron emission features from silicate grains. Generally similar, but not identical, spectra are observed in emission from circumstellar shells and in absorption in the ISM (see Fig. 8). The silicate hypothesis appears to have been confirmed for comets by the Giotto PIA mass spectrometer results at Halley.

IR measurements of comets Halley, Encke, Wilson (1986l), and Bradfield (1987s) during their recent perihelion passages have provided interesting new information about the nature of

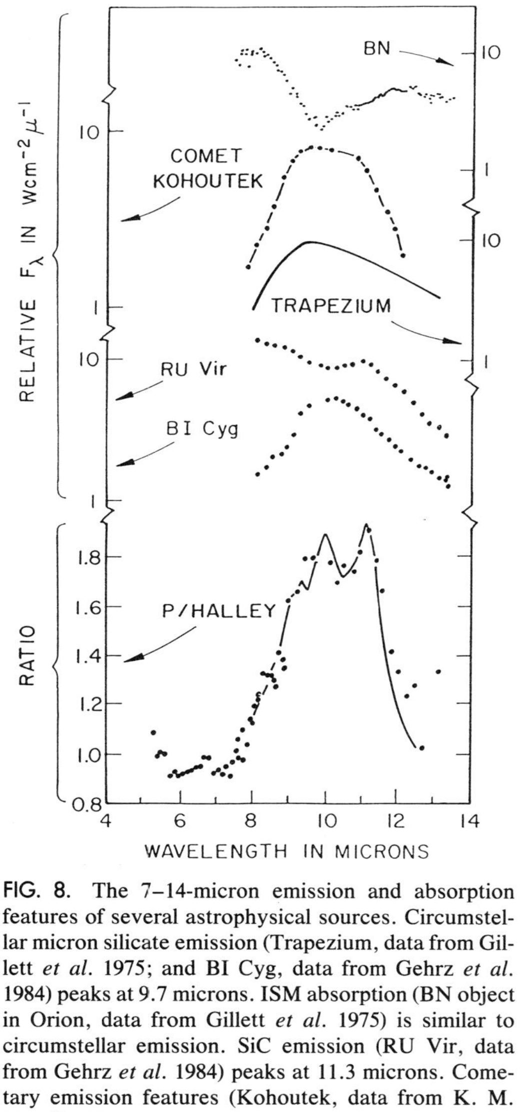

FIG. 8. The 7–14-micron emission and absorption features of several astrophysical sources. Circumstellar micron silicate emission (Trapezium, data from Gillett *et al.* 1975; and BI Cyg, data from Gehrz *et al.* 1984) peaks at 9.7 microns. ISM absorption (BN object in Orion, data from Gillett *et al.* 1975) is similar to circumstellar emission. SiC emission (RU Vir, data from Gehrz *et al.* 1984) peaks at 11.3 microns. Cometary emission features (Kohoutek, data from K. M. Merrill 1974, *Icarus* **23,** p. 566; and Halley, data from Breger *et al.* 1987) are not always like the classical astrophysical silicate feature. P/Halley's emission feature shows detailed structure. The solid-line fit to the P/Halley data is a model containing crystalline olivine and pyroxene (from Sandford and Walker 1985). [Courtesy of R. D. Gehrz (1990). *In* "Proceedings of the NAS/ASUSSR Joint Workshop on Planetary Sciences" National Academy Press, Washington, D.C.]

comet grains and nuclei. Encke's coma showed not strong silicate emission features, no near-infrared hydrocarbon emission, very little superheat, and little activity except near perihelion. These observations suggest that Encke's coma is composed primarily of large grains. In fact, Encke behaves more like an asteroid than a comet, and most of the observed IR variations for heliocentric distances outside 0.8 AU can be attributed to thermal emission from a tumbling bare nucleus. Bradfield showed jet-like coma activity like that observed on the nucleus of Halley.

IR spectra of Halley and Bradfield revealed some basic differences between comet emission features and their stellar/interstellar counterparts (Figs. 3, 8). Stellar features are broad and structureless, as expected from amorphous grains. Comet features have a structure suggesting a mixture containing crystalline silicates (olivines, pyroxene) with a trace of amorphous silicates. Halley's 3.3–3.4-micron emission feature differed substantially in width and effective wavelength from emission in other astrophysical sources. Such anomalies imply that comet grains have been subjected to high temperatures and ultraviolet radiation not experienced by circumstellar and interstellar grains.

XI. The Search for Extrasolar Planets, Planetary Materials, and Brown Dwarfs

Astronomers have long sought evidence for the existence of planets and remnants of planetary formation around other stars. Because planets are so much fainter and less massive than the stars about which they orbit, solid evidence for the existence of extrasolar planetary material has remained elusive. Increasingly sensitive IR detectors and observing schemes have provided new tests for cold circumstellar clouds and low-luminosity companions.

IRAS far-IR data show evidence for faint, extended cold circumstellar dust shells around some main sequence (MS) stars like Vega (Alpha Lyrae) and Beta Pictoris (see Fig. 9). These disk-like structures may be fossil remnants from the formation of planetary systems. Although material detected by IRAS is probably mainly small and large grains, the data do not rule out the possibility that planets are present within these disks. Higher-resolution spatial and spectral measurements are required for definitive conclusions about the mineral composition and size distribution of the grains.

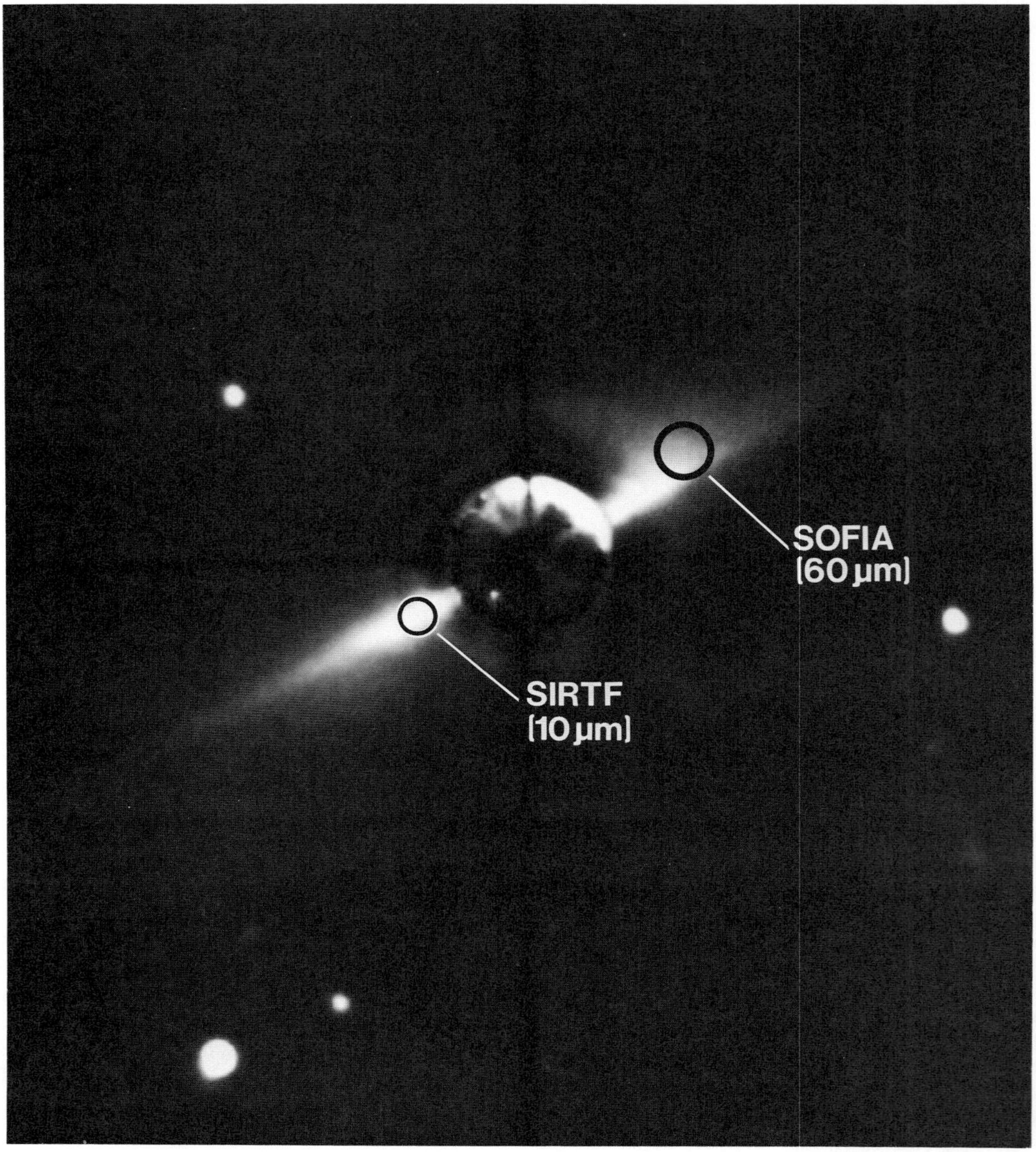

FIG. 9. A visible CCD image of the cold disk detected by IRAS around the star Beta Pictoris. [Courtesy of R. J. Terrile, from B. A. Smith and R. J. Terrile (1984). *Science* **226,** 1421.]

Small chunks of material, whether grains, bits of gravel, or even planets like the earth, are difficult to detect when they are close to stars. Therefore, astronomers have concentrated their efforts on searching for large nonstellar companions. Such objects are larger than any planet in our solar system, but are not massive enough to shine as true stars. They have been dubbed "brown dwarfs," and a small number of potential candidates have recently been reported. These objects are also very cool, when compared with normal stars such as our sun, and they emit most of their light at wavelengths longer than about 1 micron. One clever search for brown dwarfs by Benjamin Zuckerman and Eric Becklin attempted to detect excess IR emission from white dwarf stars, very hot stars that emit only modest amounts of IR light. Although a brown dwarf/white dwarf pair would be too close together to be seen as individual objects, emission from the brown dwarf would make the light from the combined system brighter in the IR than would be the case for the white dwarf alone. In a small handful of cases, they found such an excess. Other astronomers have suggested that this excess is caused by an orbiting cloud of dusty gas. Nevertheless, searching for very large numbers of white dwarfs in the sky may be a powerful technique for finding the elusive giant planets.

Other astronomers have taken very long exposures of star clusters such as the Pleiades and the Taurus Dark Cloud, arguing that large numbers of normal stars must be accompanied by the presence of large numbers of brown dwarfs or other planet-like objects. Results so far indicate a small number of very faint objects that do not seem to be normal luminous stars. Although much work needs to be done, astronomers have been surprised by the difficulty of detecting brown dwarfs, given the sensitivity of modern techniques. It may be that planetary materials, or the very large planets that we should be able to presently detect, are very much rarer than was once thought. Is this also true for small planets like the earth?

ACKNOWLEDGEMENTS

RDG is supported by NASA, the United States Air Force, the National Science Foundation, and the University of Minnesota Graduate School. HAT is supported by NASA and by the NSF's Experimental Program to Stimulate Competitive Research.

BIBLIOGRAPHY

Allamandola, L. J., and Tielens, A. G. G. M., eds. (1989). "Interstellar Dust." Kluwer Academic Publ., Dordrecht, The Netherlands.

Allamandola, L. J., Tielens, A. G. G. M., and Barker, J. R. (1987). "Infrared Absorption and Emission Characteristics of Interstellar PAHs." *In* "Interstellar Processes," (D. J. Hollenbach and H. A. Thronson, Jr., eds.), pp. 471–489. Reidel, Dordrecht, The Netherlands.

Beichman, C. A. (1987). *Annu. Rev. Astron. Astrophys.* **25,** 521.

Beichman, C. A., and Ridgeway, S. (1991). Adaptive optics and interferometry. *Physics Today* **44**(4), 48.

Gehrz, R. D. (1988). *Annu. Rev. Astron. Astrophys.* **26,** 377.

Gehrz, R. D. (1990). New infrared results for classical novae. In "Physics of Classical Novae" (A. Cassatella and R. Viotti, eds.), p. 138. Springer-Verlag, Dordrecht.

Gehrz, R. D., Grasdalen, G. L., and Hackwell, J. A. (1989). "Astronomy, Infrared." *In* "Encyclopedia of Astronomy and Astrophysics," (R. A. Meyers, ed.), p. 1. (Paper I) Academic Press, San Diego.

Gehrz, R. D., and Ney, E. P. (1990). *Publ. Nat. Acad. Sci. (U.S.A.)* **87,** 4354.

Hanner, M. S., ed. (1988). "Infrared Observations of Comets Halley and Wilson and Properties of the Grains." NASA Conference Publication 3004.

MacLean, I. (1988). "Sky and Telescope," Vol. 75, p. 254.

Soifer, B. T., Houck, J. R., and Neugebauer, G. (1987). *Annu. Rev. Astron. Astrophys.* **25,** 187.

Telesco, C. M. (1988). *Annu. Rev. Astron. Astrophys.* **26,** 343.

Wynn-Williams, C. G., and Becklin, E. E., eds. (1987). "Infrared Astronomy With Arrays." Univ. of Hawaii, Institute for Astronomy, Honolulu.

INFRARED SPECTROSCOPY

Norman B. Colthup *American Cyanamid Company*

GLOSSARY

Absorbance: Vertical coordinate used for infrared spectra that is equal to the log of the reciprocal of the sample transmittance.

Absorptivity: Constant characterizing the capacity of a sample to absorb radiation of a specific wavelength, independent of sample thickness or concentration.

Dipole moment: Magnitude of the positive or negative charge constituting a dipole, multiplied by the spacing between the charges.

Fermi resonance: Quantum mechanical interaction between close-lying energy states of a fundamental and an overtone or combination that shifts the absorption frequencies and redistributes the intensities.

Fundamental: Band in the infrared spectrum that results from a change from the vibrational ground state to the first excited vibrational state of a molecule.

Group frequency: Frequency region of the spectrum where absorption is expected when a chemical functional group such as a carbonyl is present in a molecule.

Interferometer: Device that splits radiation into two beams and then recombines them, resulting in interference that depends on the path length difference between the two beams.

Monochromator: Device that separates radiation having a single frequency from radiation having many different frequencies.

Normal coordinate: Single coordinate defined in such a way that it describes the effective amplitude of a normal mode of vibration in a molecule.

Normal mode: Vibration where each Cartesian coordinate of every atom in the molecule oscillates with the same frequency and goes through the equilibrium point at the same time; there is no molecular translation or rotation.

Oscillator: Mass or group of masses that vibrate at certain frequencies.

Overtone: Band in the infrared spectrum that results from a change from the vibrational ground state to the second or a higher vibrational state of a molecule.

Photon: Individual particle or quantum of radiation.

Transition: Change from one quantum mechanically defined energy state to another.

The infrared (IR) spectrum results from the interaction of radiation with molecular vibrations and, in gases, with molecular rotations. The spectrum itself is a plot of sample transmission of IR radiation as a function of wavelength or related units. Infrared spectroscopy is the physics that deals with the theory and interpretation of this spectrum and is one of the most popular techniques for identifying molecules. The IR spectrum can be used as a type of "fingerprint" unique to a molecule. In addition, the presence or absence of many chemical functional groups such as phenyls and carbonyls usually can be established from the spectrum. Quantitative analyses of mixtures can be obtained. Infrared spectra can be run for liquids, solids, or gases without special difficulties. Different types of spectrometers can be used, and a wide variety of sample handling techniques are available, many of which are described in this article.

I. Basic Theory

A. Electromagnetic Spectrum

Electromagnetic radiation can be characterized by its wavelength λ, its frequency ν, or its wave number $\bar{\nu}$. In the IR region the unit used for wavelength is the micrometer (μm). The frequency unit is cycles per second or hertz (Hz). The wave number unit is cycles per centimeter or reciprocal centimeters (cm^{-1}). The wave number (cm^{-1}) is the number of waves in a continuous wave sequence 1 cm long. The relationship between the units is given in Eq. (1):

$$\bar{\nu}\ (\text{cm}^{-1}) = \frac{1}{\lambda\ (\text{cm})} \qquad \bar{\nu}\ (\text{cm}^{-1}) = \frac{10^4}{\lambda\ (\mu\text{m})} \qquad (1)$$

$$\bar{\nu}\ (\text{cm}^{-1}) = \frac{\nu\ (\text{Hz})}{c\ (\text{cm/sec})}$$

From this, one can see that wave number (cm^{-1}) is equal to the reciprocal of the wavelength (cm) or is equal to 10^4 times the reciprocal of the wavelength (μm). The wave number (cm^{-1}) in a vacuum is also equal to the frequency (Hz) divided by c, the velocity of light in a vacuum given in centimeters per second. This makes the wave number proportional to the frequency.

The visible region of electromagnetic radiation extends from about 0.38 to 0.78 μm. The IR region extends from the end of the visible region at 0.78 μm to the microwave region with a wavelength of ~1 mm. The IR region is usually divided into three sections. The section used most by chemists is the mid-IR region extending from 2.5 μm, or 4000 cm^{-1}, to ~50 μm, or 200 cm^{-1}. The division at 4000 cm^{-1} is the high wave number limit for fundamental vibration absorption in the IR. The low wave number limit is more variable since it is more or less an instrumental limitation. The region between the visible and the mid-IR regions is called the near-IR region. This region of the IR has been used for many applications, especially for quantitative analysis. The region beyond ~50 μm (200 cm^{-1}) is called the far-IR region. This region is used for studying low-frequency vibrations and some molecular rotations.

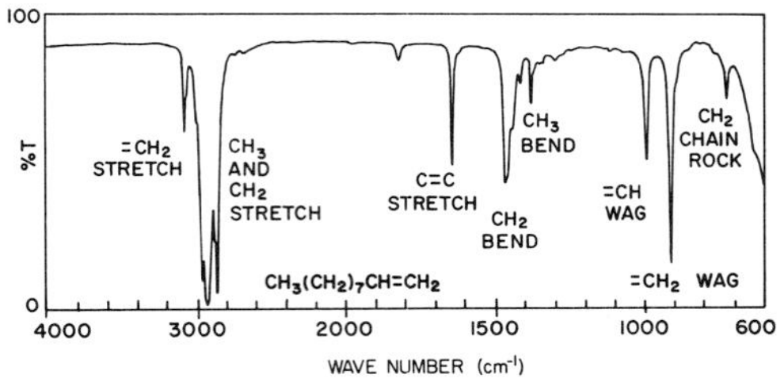

FIG. 2. Infrared spectrum of 1-decene in a 0.01-mm NaCl cell.

Electronic transitions give rise to absorption in the ultraviolet and visible regions of the spectrum, and pure rotations of gaseous molecules give rise to absorption in the far-IR and microwave regions of the spectrum. Intramolecular vibrations of molecules give rise to absorption throughout most of the IR region. [*See* ATOMIC SPECTROSCOPY; MOLECULAR OPTICAL SPECTROSCOPY.]

B. Infrared Spectra Coordinates

Some examples of IR spectra are given in Figs. 1 through 6. Chemical group vibrations associated with spectral bands are indicated. These are all liquids run in a 0.01-mm-thick NaCl cell. The horizontal coordinates for IR spectra are usually either linear with wavelength (μm) or linear with wave number (cm^{-1}) with generally a factor of 2 scale change at 2000 cm^{-1}. An advantage of the wave number scale is that the wave number of the radiation is proportional to its frequency and to photon energy, and these properties are related to the frequencies and energies of molecular vibrations.

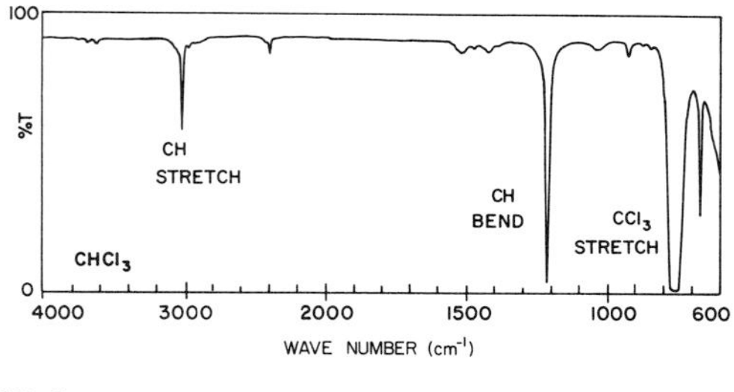

FIG. 1. Infrared spectrum of chloroform in a 0.01-mm NaCl cell.

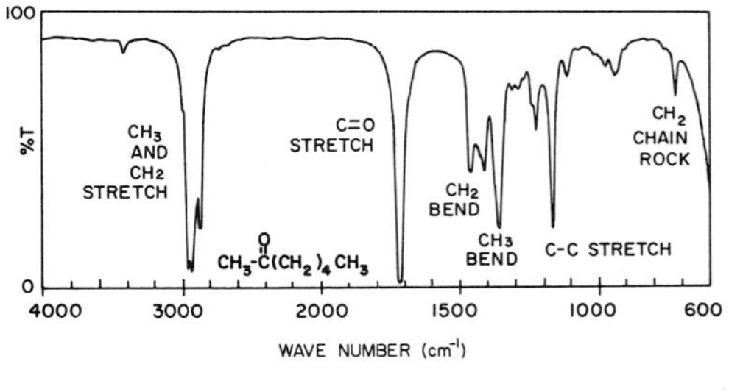

FIG. 3. Infrared spectrum of 2-heptanone in a 0.01-mm NaCl cell.

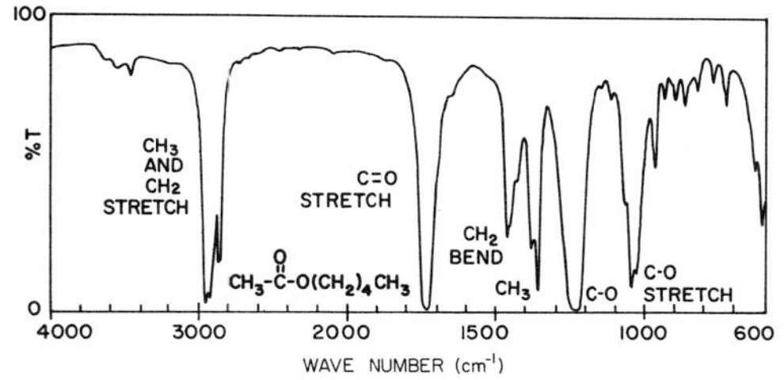

FIG. 4. Infrared spectrum of *n*-amyl acetate in a 0.01-mm NaCl cell.

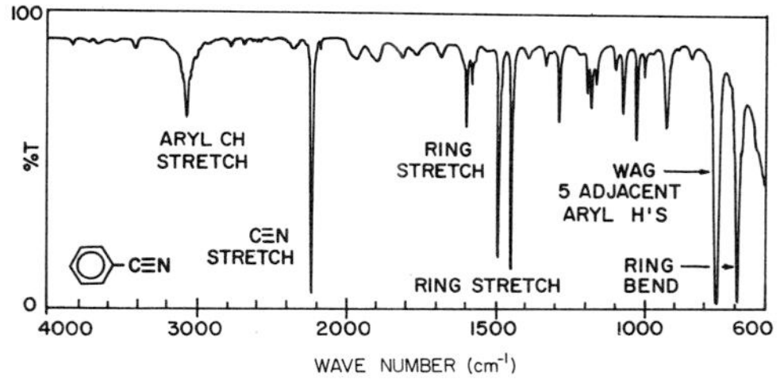

FIG. 6. Infrared spectrum of benzonitrile in a 0.01-mm NaCl cell.

The vertical coordinate in a single-beam spectrum is a measure of the intensity of the radiation of a given wave number that has passed through a sample and reached the detector. Usually, this spectrum is ratioed with another single-beam reference spectrum without a sample to give a ratioed or double-beam spectrum. The transmittance T is the intensity of the sample single-beam spectrum divided by the intensity of the reference single-beam spectrum at the same wave number. The vertical coordinate most commonly seen in an IR spectrum is linear with percent transmittance ($\%T$), which is transmittance T multiplied by 100.

Another vertical coordinate scale used increasingly is the linear absorbance scale, where absorbance A is given by the $\log_{10}$ of the transmittance reciprocal:

$$A = \log_{10}(1/T) \tag{2}$$

The advantage of an absorbance scale is that the absorbance is proportional to the product of sample thickness and concentration. This is discussed in Sec. IV,A.

C. Diatomic Vibrations

When molecular vibrations are studied, it is useful to consider the nucleus of any atom in the molecule as a mass concentrated at a single point, held in place by chemical bonds that act much like massless coil springs. The diatomic molecule is the simplest molecule type, consisting of two nuclei connected by a chemical bond formed by electrons. The electrons in a molecule move much more rapidly than the nuclei, so the electrons can quickly equilibrate into new electronic structures as the slowly moving nuclei change their spacing. This means that there is a definite potential energy for each nuclear configuration. For the diatomic molecule this is something like the potential energy of an ordinary coil spring. There is a certain equilibrium bond length where the energy is a minimum. If this length is increased or decreased, the potential energy increases and a restoring force is generated, tending to restore equilibrium. In the diatomic molecule, there is only one bond and only one vibration, that which periodically changes the length of the bond. In the harmonic oscillator approximation, the restoring force on each mass is assumed to be linearly proportional to the bond length change from the equilibrium bond length. The proportionality constant is called the force constant k. The vibrational frequency ν of the diatomic molecule can be calculated by the methods of classical mechanics, as in Eq. (3):

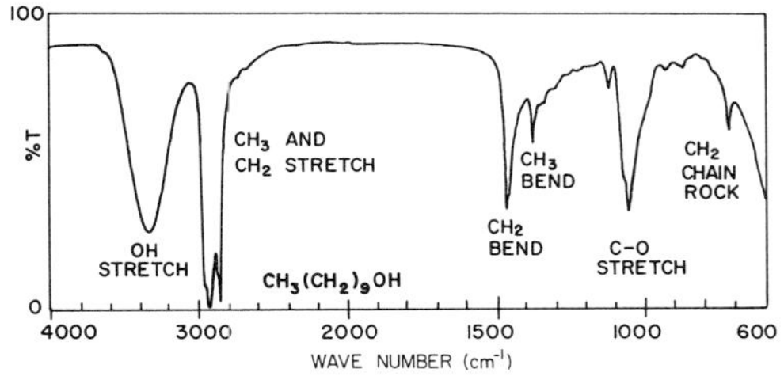

FIG. 5. Infrared spectrum of *n*-decyl alcohol in a 0.01-mm NaCl cell.

$$\nu = \frac{1}{2\pi}\left[k\left(\frac{1}{m_1} + \frac{1}{m_2}\right)\right]^{1/2} \tag{3}$$

Here ν is the vibrational frequency, m_1 and m_2 the two atomic masses, and k the force constant, namely, the restoring force on either mass divided by the bond length change from equilibrium at any time. Note that the frequency is independent of the vibrational amplitude. The masses move in a manner that keeps the center of mass stationary. If a_1/a_2 is the relative amplitude of the two masses m_1 and m_2 during the vibration, then

$$\frac{a_1}{a_2} = -\frac{m_2}{m_1} \tag{4}$$

TABLE I. Diatomic Molecules

Molecule	Wave number (cm^{-1})	Force constant (mdyne/Å)
CO	2143	18.6
NO	1876	15.5
HF	3962	8.9
HCl	2886	4.8
HBr	2559	3.8

Stretching force constants are usually expressed in millidynes per angstrom (mdyne/Å); 1 mdyne/Å equals 100 N/m, the equivalent SI unit. Masses are usually expressed in unified atomic mass units (carbon = 12). If these units are used, the wave number $\bar{\nu}$ of the radiation that has the same frequency as the molecular vibration is given by

$$\bar{\nu} = 1303 \left[k \left(\frac{1}{m_1} + \frac{1}{m_2} \right) \right]^{1/2} \quad (5)$$

Some examples of diatomic molecules that absorb in the IR are listed in Table I. Equation (5) relates the wave number of the absorption band given to the force constant and atomic masses of the molecule.

D. Polyatomic Vibrations

Polyatomic molecules have more than one vibrational frequency. The number can be calculated from the following. One atom in the molecule can move independently in three directions, the x, y, and z directions in a Cartesian coordinate system. Therefore, in a molecule with n atoms, the n atoms have $3n$ independent ways they can move. The center of mass of the molecule can move in three independent directions, x, y, and z. A nonlinear molecule can rotate in three independent ways about the x, y, and z axes, which pass through the center of mass. A linear molecule has one less degree of rotational freedom since rotation about its own axis does not displace any atoms. These translations of the center of mass and rotations can be performed with a rigid molecule and do not change its shape or size. Subtracting these motions, there remain $3n - 6$ degrees of freedom of *internal* motion for nonlinear molecules and $3n - 5$ for linear molecules. These internal degrees of freedom change the size or shape of the molecule without rotating it or translating its center of mass.

It can be shown by the methods of classical mechanics that the $3n - 6$ (or $3n - 5$) internal degrees of freedom of motion correspond to $3n - 6$ (or $3n - 5$) different normal modes of vibration. In a normal mode of vibration the Cartesian displacement coordinates of every atom change periodically, each oscillating with the same frequency and passing through the equilibrium configuration at the same time. The molecule does not translate its center of mass or rotate.

The vibrational form can be described by specifying the relative amplitudes of the Cartesian displacements of each mass (Fig. 7). The vibration can also be described in terms of the relative changes in the *internal coordinates* of the molecule, namely, changes in the bond lengths and bond angles. For example, in Fig. 7 the CO_2 molecule has two bonds; in one vibration, both bonds stretch at the same time (in-phase stretch), whereas in another vibration one bond stretches while the other bond contracts (out-of-phase stretch). There are two mutually perpendicular bending vibrations that have the same frequency.

For each normal mode of vibration, a single coordinate can be defined called a *normal coordinate*. When one normal mode of vibration is activated, one normal coordinate periodically changes in value. At the same time that the normal coordinate changes, each Cartesian displacement coordinate changes in a specified proportion (positive or negative) to the change in the normal coordinate, so that the resulting motion is a normal mode of vibration. Normal coordinates are very useful for theoretical studies of molecular vibrations.

E. Infrared Absorption

In a spectrometer, a source of IR radiation sends all IR wavelengths of interest through a

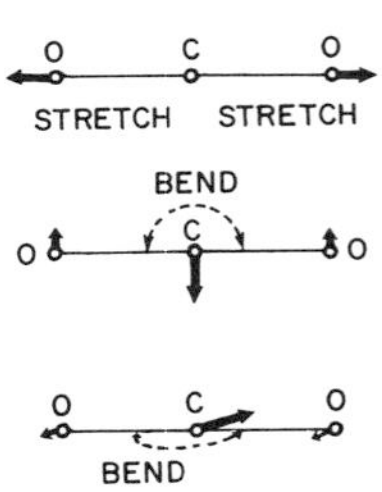

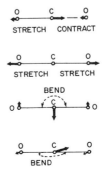

FIG. 7. Normal modes of vibration of carbon dioxide.

sample. The IR radiation causes some of the molecules to vibrate with increased amplitude, which increases the vibrational energy. The increase in vibrational energy is at the expense of radiation energy, resulting in the absorption of IR radiation at certain frequencies. The absorption frequency of a fundamental absorption band in the IR is the same as the frequency of the molecular vibration that caused the absorption. This provides a means of observing molecular vibrational frequencies that can provide a molecular "fingerprint" for identifying molecules. The frequencies can also be used to characterize internal features within the molecule that can provide information about the molecular structure.

F. Dipole Moment Change

There must-be some means by which the radiation energy can be transferred to the molecule when the molecule absorbs radiation energy. This involves the dipole moment of the molecule. A dipole consists of a positive and a negative charge of equal magnitude separated by a distance. The dipole moment is the magnitude of either charge multiplied by the spacing. Within a molecule, we can picture atoms as particles with small excess negative or positive charges, since chemical forces act to make some atoms have a slight excess or deficiency of electrons. We can picture the negative charge of the dipole as the total excess negative charge of the negative atoms concentrated at the center of the excess negative charge and can picture the positive charge of the dipole as the total excess positive charge on the positive atoms concentrated at the center of the excess positive charge. In CO_2, for example, the center of excess negative charge is between the two electronegative oxygens and the center of excess positive charge is at the relatively electropositive carbon. At equilibrium, these two charge centers coincide with zero spacing, so the dipole moment is zero.

Many molecular vibrations cause the dipole moment to change. For example, in HBr, the bromine is more electronegative than the hydrogen, so the bromine has a slight excess negative charge and the hydrogen a slight excess positive charge. During the vibration, the H–Br spacing changes and also the amount of excess charge on each atom changes, causing the dipole moment to change.

The electromagnetic radiation imposes an electric field on the molecule. This electric field exerts forces on charges, and by definition the forces on positive and negative charges are oppositely directed. The atoms with excess negative charge are pulled in one direction, while the atoms with excess positive charge are pulled in the opposite direction. These forces tend to induce a change in dipole moment. The electric field of the radiation oscillates at the radiation frequency, and this tends to induce an oscillating dipole moment in the molecule. If the radiation-induced dipole moment oscillation has the same frequency as the dipole moment oscillation resulting from a molecular vibration, then the radiation may induce the molecule to vibrate with increased amplitude. If a vibration causes no change in dipole moment, then there is no way the radiation can excite that vibration. In a homonuclear diatomic molecule such as H_2 or Br_2, the two atoms have identical excess charges (namely, zero), and the dipole moment does not change during the vibration as it is always zero. There is no way the electric field of the radiation can induce the two similar atoms to move in opposite directions as required in a vibration. The selection rule for IR absorption requires that in order to be IR-active, a molecular vibration must cause a change in dipole moment. The IR absorption intensity is proportional to the square of the change in dipole moment with respect to the change in the normal coordinate. This reflects the fact that the more the dipole moment changes during a vibration, the greater the probability that the radiation of the proper frequency can excite that vibration.

G. Symmetry and Infrared Activity

If a molecule has some symmetry, a particular vibration of that molecule may be IR-inactive; that is, the vibration will not give rise to any IR absorption. This is because the dipole moment change can be zero as a direct consequence of the symmetry.

One symmetry element is the center of symmetry. If a molecule in the equilibrium configuration has a center of symmetry, one can start at any atom and go in a straight line through the center and an equal distance beyond, where one will find another atom of identical type. An example is carbon dioxide O=C=O (see Fig. 7). Such a molecule at equilibrium would have a dipole moment of zero. The vibrationally distorted molecule where each atom has moved to the end of its displacement vector may have less symmetry than the molecule at equilibrium. One can repeat this procedure for the vibrationally distorted molecule. If it still has a center of symmetry, the vibration is said to be symmetric with respect to the center of symmetry. An example in Fig. 7 is the in-phase stretch of O═C═O, where both CO bond lengths are always equal. Such a vibration is IR-inactive since the dipole moment (which is always zero) does not change. If the vibrationally distorted molecule no longer has a center of symmetry, then the vibration is said to be antisymmetric with respect to the center of symmetry. An example in Fig. 7 is the out-of-phase stretch vibration of O═C═O, where the positive carbon is no a longer midway between the two negative oxygens. The dipole moment changes during this vibration, which is IR active.

Symmetry elements other than the center of symmetry include planes of symmetry and twofold or higher axes of symmetry. When a plane of symmetry is present, the plane can be thought of as a mirror. When each atom in the molecule is moved to the position of its mirror image, the resulting configuration is indistinguishable from the original. When a twofold axis of symmetry is present, the molecule can be rotated by half a full circle to give a configuration indistinguishable from the original. A full discussion of symmetry and group theory cannot be given here. However, molecules that do not have a center of symmetry may have IR-inactive vibrations as a consequence of these other symmetry elements. For example, the tetrahedral sulfate ion SO_4^{2-} does not have a center of symmetry, but the in-phase stretch of the four SO bonds is IR-inactive. The four negative oxygens move radially at the same time, but the symmetry requires that the center of their excess negative charge does not move relative to the more positive sulfur.

H. Quantum Mechanical Harmonic Oscillator

The simplest classical harmonic oscillator is a single mass m suspended from the ceiling by a spring that obeys Hooke's law. If the mass is pulled down a distance x from its equilibrium point, the spring length minus its length at equilibrium is x. A restoring force on the mass is generated that is proportional to the spring length change. The magnitude of the restoring force equals kx, where k is the force constant. If the mass is held stationary at this point, the potential energy PE is

$$\mathrm{PE} = \tfrac{1}{2}kx^2 \tag{6}$$

This is also the total energy for this condition since the kinetic energy is zero. If the mass is released, it moves toward the equilibrium point and the kinetic energy increases as the potential energy decreases. At equilibrium, the energy is entirely kinetic; the mass overshoots the equilibrium point and continues on until the energy is again entirely potential at maximum amplitude, and the cycle is repeated again. Throughout the vibration the total classical energy is unchanged and is

$$E = \tfrac{1}{2}kx_{\max}^2 \tag{7}$$

where $x_{\max}$ is the maximum amplitude. In a classical vibration the maximum amplitude is continuously variable since one is free to pull out the spring to any length before it is released to vibrate. This means that the energy of the classical harmonic oscillator is continuously variable and can have any value.

Oscillators the size of molecules obey the laws of quantum mechanics. The vibrational energy of the quantum mechanical harmonic oscillator is not continuously variable, but has discrete values given from quantum mechanics as

$$E = (v + \tfrac{1}{2})h\nu_o, \qquad v = 0, 1, 2, \ldots \tag{8}$$

Here E is the vibrational energy, h Planck's constant, ν_o the classical vibrational frequency of the oscillator, and v the quantum number, which can have only integer values. In the classical oscillator, the lowest possible energy is zero when there is no vibration. In the quantum mechanical oscillator, the lowest possible energy is $\tfrac{1}{2}h\nu_o$, which is not zero, so the molecule can never stop vibrating entirely. This state where $v = 0$ is called the ground vibrational state.

If the vibrational energy is to be increased, the quantum number v must be increased. When the quantum number is increased by 1, the energy change ΔE from the previous equation is

$$\Delta E = h\nu_o \tag{9}$$

A photon has an energy E given by

$$E = h\nu_p \tag{10}$$

where ν_p is the frequency of the photon. When the photon electric field frequency ν_p is equal to the classical dipole moment oscillation frequency ν_o for this vibration, the photon will have exactly the right energy (ΔE) needed to increase the vibrational quantum number by 1.

The transition when the quantum number changes by 1 is called an allowed transition in a harmonic oscillator. The most important of these is the transition where the oscillator goes from the $v = 0$ level to the $v = 1$ level. This is called the fundamental transition and is responsible for most of the strong bands in the IR spectrum. The ($v = 0 \rightarrow v = 1$) transition is much more probable than the ($v = 1 \rightarrow v = 2$) transition because at room temperature many more oscillators exist in the low-energy $v = 0$ state than in the $v = 1$ state (or higher states).

In a polyatomic molecule with $3n - 6$ different normal modes of vibration, each normal mode of vibration can be treated separately. In the harmonic oscillator approximation,

$$E = (v_1 + \tfrac{1}{2})h\nu_1 + (v_2 + \tfrac{1}{2})h\nu_2 + \cdots \quad (11)$$

where each mode has its own quantum number v and frequency ν. In the harmonic oscillator only one vibration may be excited at one time and the quantum number may change only by 1.

I. Effect of Anharmonicity

In the single-mass harmonic oscillator discussed, the restoring force is a linear function of the mass displacement and the potential energy is a squared function of the mass displacement $\frac{1}{2}kx^2$. Mechanical anharmonicity results if the restoring force is not a linear function of the mass displacement, in which case the potential energy will have higher-order terms such as cubic and quartic terms. Electrical anharmonicity results if the dipole moment change is not a linear function of the mass displacement. If either mechanical or electrical anharmonicity is present, transitions where the quantum number changes by 2 or more will no longer be forbidden in the IR spectrum. This allows overtones to appear in the spectrum. In a fundamental transition, the quantum number changes by 1 and the photon causing the transition has the same frequency as the classical dipole moment oscillation. In an overtone transition, the quantum number changes by 2 or more. The photon that has the right energy to change the quantum number by 2 has a frequency twice that of the molecular dipole moment oscillation, and in a harmonic-type vibration there will be no dipole moment component changing at this frequency. In an anharmonic vibration, the dipole moment change is complicated by the anharmonicity, and overtones are allowed in the spectrum. The overtone intensity depends on the amount of anharmonicity. Overtones are usually fairly weak.

In a harmonic oscillator, the spacing ΔE between the energy levels for $v = 0, 1, 2, \ldots$ has a constant value $h\nu$. If mechanical anharmonicity is present, the spacing is no longer exactly constant, which means that overtone frequencies will not be exactly 2, 3, or more times the frequency of the fundamental. For example, $CHCl_3$ has a CH bending fundamental band at 1216 cm^{-1} and a much weaker CH bending overtone band at 2400 cm^{-1}. A ketone has a carbonyl stretching fundamental band near 1715 cm^{-1} and a much weaker overtone band near 3410 cm^{-1}.

In polyatomic molecules, combination and difference bands are allowed when anharmonicity is present. In a combination-type transition one photon excites two different vibrations at the same time to a new excited state where both vibrational modes have nonzero quantum numbers (say, $v_1 = 1$ and $v_2 = 1$). If both quantum numbers are 1, the combination band will appear in the spectrum near the frequency sum of the two fundamentals. In a difference-type transition, the molecule that is already vibrating in an excited state for one vibration (say, $v_1 = 1$) absorbs a photon of the proper energy and changes to an excited state of a different vibration (say, $v_2 = 1$). The difference band appears at exactly the frequency difference of the two fundamentals in this case. Combination and difference bands, like overtones, are usually fairly weak.

J. Fermi Resonance

In a polyatomic molecule it may happen that an overtone energy level ($v_1 = 2$) has nearly the same energy as a fundamental energy level ($v_2 = 1$) of a completely different vibrational mode. This means that, if no perturbation occurred, an overtone absorption band would have nearly the same frequency as that of the fundamental band of a different vibration. If anharmonicity is present, the higher-order terms in the potential energy may cause perturbations between the fundamental and overtone types involved, generating new mixed energy levels. The vibration types involved should be those that can be coupled by the anharmonic potential function, which requires them to be of the same symmetry type. The perturbation can become significant when the unperturbed energy level difference is small. Combination bands, as well as overtones, can be involved in this interaction, which is called Fermi resonance.

Consider the case where the unperturbed overtone and fundamental nearly coincide. When interaction occurs, two strong bands appear in the spectrum, above and below the ex-

TABLE II. Examples of Fermi Resonance

Molecule	Wave number (cm^{-1})	Assignment
NaNCO	620	NCO bend
	(1216, 1305)[a]	(NCO in-phase stretch plus overtone of NCO bend)
	2220	NCO out-of-phase stretch
C_6H_5CHO	1392	Aldehyde CH in-plane bend
	1700	Aldehyde C=O stretch
	(2740, 2825)[a]	(Aldehyde CH stretch plus overtone of CH bend)

[a] The two bands in parentheses have nearly equal intensities, and both involve a fundamental mixed with an overtone of another vibration.

pected position of the overtone and the fundamental before interaction. Both bands involve the fundamental and both involve the overtone. The strong intensity of both bands comes from the fact that the fundamental is involved in both bands. The frequency spacing is a function of the perturbation (Table II).

If the expected frequencies of the unperturbed overtone and the interacting fundamental are not identical but are still close to one another in frequency, interaction will not be as strong as before. Two bands of unequal intensity will be seen at again somewhat wider spacing than that for the two unperturbed bands. The stronger band will be nearer the unperturbed fundamental and will involve more of the fundamental vibration. The weaker band will be nearer the unperturbed overtone and will involve more of the overtone vibration. The weaker band will still involve some fundamental vibration, however, which will cause this "overtone" band to be more intense than an unperturbed overtone.

K. Molecular Rotation

Pure rotation of molecules in the gaseous state causes absorption of radiation in the microwave region and to some extent in the far-IR region. In order for a pure rotation to absorb radiation, the rotating molecule must have a permanent dipole moment. Imagine that the dipole moment is oriented perpendicularly to the radiation electric field direction. The field exerts forces in opposite directions on the negative and positive ends of the dipole. This generates a torque, which tends to rotate the dipole moment and therefore tends to increase the rotational frequency of the molecule. If the rotational frequency increases, the rotational energy increases at the expense of the radiation energy. The rotational energy, like the vibrational energy, is not continuously variable but is quantized. Imagine a rotating linear molecule such as HCl in a certain rotational energy state with a quantum number J, which has an integer value (1, 2, 3, ...). The selection rule for pure rotation states that photon energy absorption can increase the quantum number by only 1 to the state $J + 1$. The photon that has the right energy to cause this transition has a frequency intermediate between the classical rotational frequencies for the initial (J) and the final ($J + 1$) states. Unlike the classical vibrational frequency, the classical rotational frequency of the molecule increases during the transition, and the oscillating electric field of the photon with this intermediate frequency can stay nearly synchronized with the rotating dipole moment throughout the transition. An analysis of the rotational fine structure in the spectrum may yield information about the moments of inertia of the molecule.

L. Gas-Phase Band Contours

In the vibrational spectrum the molecule usually changes from the ground vibrational state ($v = 0$) to the first excited vibrational state ($v = 1$). When the sample is in the gaseous state, the molecule may change its rotational state at the same time it changes its vibrational state. The molecule in the ground vibrational state is rotating with a certain angular momentum. When the molecule ends up at the first excited vibrational state, it may be rotating with an increased or decreased angular momentum. As a result of the rotational energy changes, rotational structure is superimposed on the vibrational band, which is referred to as a vibration–rotation band.

If the molecular moments of inertia are sufficiently low and the spectrometer has adequate resolution, rotational fine structure can be resolved in the vibration–rotation band. For larger molecules, the fine structure is usually unresolved, resulting in a broad band. The contour of the band may reveal the direction of the dipole moment change caused by the vibration. In polyatomic linear molecules such as CO_2 and acetylene, IR-active stretching and bending vibrations cause dipole moment changes parallel and perpendicular to the molecular axis, respectively. For parallel vibrations, the gas-phase band contour is a broad doublet (Fig. 8). In the low-frequency and high-frequency wings of the

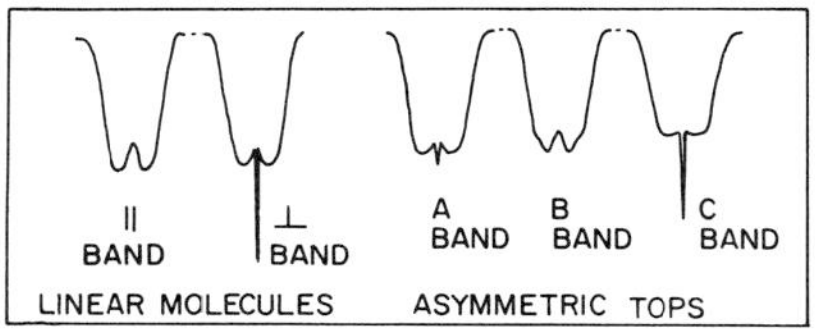

FIG. 8. Infrared spectra of gas-phase bands for linear molecules and asymmetric top molecules. Unresolved contours are shown for different types of bands. Asymmetric top molecules have different contours for different ratios of the moments of inertia. The parallel band of linear molecules and the B-type band of the asymmetric top have no central peak.

band, the rotational quantum numbers for each of the various energy states have decreased and increased by 1, respectively, during the vibrational transition. Perpendicular bands have the same broad doublet seen in the parallel bands, but a perpendicular band has an additional central peak not seen in the parallel band, where the rotational energy remains unchanged during the vibrational transition.

Tetrahedral or octahedral molecules such as CH_4 and SF_4 are called spherical tops and have three equal moments of inertia for rotation about three mutually perpendicular axes. The gas-phase contour is similar to the perpendicular band of the linear molecule, with two broad wings and a central peak for all the IR-active vibrations.

Molecules with one threefold or higher axis of symmetry such as $CHCl_3$, BF_3, and C_2H_6 are called symmetric tops. Two moments of inertia are equal and differ from the third unique moment of inertia for rotation about the axis of threefold or higher symmetry. When a vibration causes a dipole moment change parallel to the major symmetry axis, the unresolved gas-phase contour is similar to the perpendicular band of the linear molecule, a broad doublet with a central peak. When the dipole moment change is perpendicular to the major symmetry axis, the band structure is more complex and the unresolved contour depends on the relative magnitudes of the moments of inertia.

In molecules with less symmetry, the three moments of inertia are different. These are called asymmetric tops. The axes with minimum and maximum moments of inertia are called the *a* and *c* axes, respectively, and the axis with intermediate moment of inertia is called the *b* axis. Vibrations with dipole moment changes parallel to these axes are called A, B, and C bands. The unresolved gas-phase contours of A and C bands have broad, more or less symmetric wings and a sharp central peak. The B band has more or less symmetric wings, but is unique in that it has no central peak. The contours of all these bands are dependent on the relative values of the moments of inertia. If the moment of inertia for rotation about the *c* axis is relatively large, as in planar molecules, the central peak of the C band is relatively strong compared with the central peak of the A band, as seen in Fig. 8. If the dipole moment change is not exactly parallel to any of the *a*, *b*, or *c* axes, a mixed contour results.

II. Instrumentation

A. Infrared Spectrometers

Infrared spectrometers come in a variety of types but have many common features. All have a source that emits all the IR radiation of interest. These are usually various solid materials heated to incandescence by an electric current. The radiation energy distribution as a function of wavelength approaches that of a theoretical black body where the energy reaches a maximum at a wavelength (μm) equal to $2897/T$, where T is the absolute temperature (K). The operational temperature is such that the radiation energy is usually at a maximum near the short-wavelength limit of the spectrum (usually $\sim$2 μm) and decreases as the wavelength gets longer. In the far-IR region, source energy is very low.

All spectrometers must have some kind of detector. These are devices that, in one way or another, change radiation energy into an electrical signal that can be amplified and processed to yield a spectrum. Thermal detectors measure the heating effect of the radiation and respond equally to all wavelengths. Examples include thermocouples, bolometers, and pyroelectric detectors. Detectors that utilize photon energy to free bound electrons in the detector material are called photodetectors. Photodetectors, unlike thermal detectors, do not respond to all wavelengths but have a long-wavelength limit where the photon has insufficient energy to excite the electrons. One example is the photoconductive detector, in which the absorption of photon energy promotes bound electrons to free states. This results in increased electrical conduction.

In between the source and detector, the spectrometer must have some means of analyzing the radiation so that an intensity can be deduced for each wavelength resolution element. Two completely different types of devices are used, namely, monochromators and interferometers. Monochromators with gratings or prisms are used in dispersive instruments, and interferometers are used in Fourier transform instruments.

B. Grating Spectrophotometers

Most spectra seen in the literature are of the ratioed or double-beam type. A double-beam grating instrument is called a spectrophotometer. In this type of instrument the beam from the source is divided into two beams: a sample beam and a reference beam. The sample is placed in the sample beam, and the two beams are alternately passed into the monochromator through the entrance slit, usually at 13 Hz.

In a monochromator, radiation from the entrance slit goes to a paraboloidal mirror, which makes the radiation parallel. The parallel radiation goes to a diffraction grating, which consists of a reflecting surface with straight parallel grooves very closely spaced. Each of these grooves acts as an independent slitlike source of radiation, diffracting it in different directions. The radiation from the grating is focused onto the exit slit, and only radiation leaving the grating at the specific angle goes in a direction that can pass through the exit slit (Fig. 9). When radiation leaves the grating at that angle, parallel beams coming from any two adjacent grooves have traveled different distances and, for one particular wavelength of radiation, will be exactly one wavelength ahead or behind one another. This means that beams of this wavelength leaving at this angle from all the grooves will be *in phase* and show constructive interference when they converge at the exit slit. Other wavelengths will not be in phase and will show destructive interference at this angle. This is called the first order. When parallel beams coming from any two adjacent grooves are two, three, or more wavelengths ahead or behind one another, the parallel beams from all the grooves will also be in phase. These are called the second, third, or higher orders. Unwanted grating orders are removed with filters. This means that, for one grating angle, essentially monochromatic radiation leaves the monochromator toward the detector. When the grating is rotated to a slightly different angle, the path length difference for beams from adjacent grooves will be slightly different, so radiation with a slightly different wavelength will pass through the monochromator.

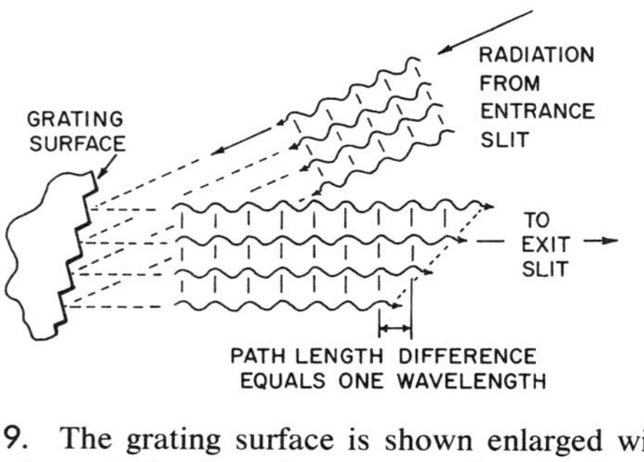

FIG. 9. The grating surface is shown enlarged with incoming radiation from the entrance slit and reflected radiation going to the exit slit. For adjacent grooves, the beams at these angles have a path length difference. When this equals one wavelength of radiation as shown, all the grooves will emit radiation of that wavelength in phase toward the exit slit.

When the spectrometer is set at a given wavelength, the sample beam and reference beam alternately pass through the monochromator and activate the detector. If the two beams do not have the same intensity because of sample absorption, an alternating signal is generated and is used to measure the percent transmission of the sample at that wavelength. The grating angle is changed, and the whole spectrum is generated wavelength by wavelength. Usually, several gratings are used for the whole spectral range, and a grating may be used in more than one order. As the wavelength increases, the slit is widened to allow more energy through to compensate for decreased source emission at long wavelengths.

C. Fourier Transform Infrared Spectrometers

In a Fourier transform infrared (FT-IR) spectrometer, there is no monochromator to disperse or separate the radiation by wavelength. Instead, a whole single-beam spectrum is generated all at once. The intensities of all of the wavelength elements are analyzed simultaneously. Since all the radiation frequencies reach the detector at the same time, there is a large signal-to-noise ratio. This is called the multiplex or Fellgett advantage and is one of the principal advantages that an FT-IR spectrometer has over a dispersive instrument. This advantage is particularly noticeable for low-energy conditions or where scale expansion is required to bring out very weak bands. There is also an advantage in that the spectrum can be recorded in less time.

The unique part of an FT-IR spectrometer is the Michelson-type interferometer (Fig. 10). Radiation from the source is made parallel and strikes a beam splitter, typically at 45°. Ideally the beam splitter transmits half the radiation striking it and reflects the other half. One type of beam splitter is a thin layer of germanium coated on an IR-transmitting support. The transmitted and reflected beams leave the beam splitter at right angles, and both strike mirrors, which return the two beams to the beam splitter. The two beams recombine at the beam splitter and show interference. The radiation leaving the beam splitter may go back to the source or may go at right angles, passing through the sample and going on to the detector.

One of the two mirrors is movable, so its distance from the beam splitter can be varied. The path length difference for the two beams in the interferometer is called the retardation and is two times the displacement of the movable mirror from the equidistant point. If a monochromatic source such as a laser is used, the radiant energy reaching the detector will vary as a cosine function of the retardation. The detector response will reach a maximum every time the retardation is an integral number of wavelengths of the radiation. At this time the beams from the two mirrors combine at the beam splitter in phase for the beam going to the detector and show constructive interference. If the movable mirror is then moved one-quarter of a wavelength of radiation, the retardation is changed by one-half of a wavelength. The beams from the two mirrors combine at the beam splitter one-half of a wavelength out of phase for the beam going to the detector and show destructive interference. The detector response as a function of the retardation is called the interferogram. The spectrum can be generated from the interferogram by a Fourier transform. The Fourier transform of a single cosine wave-type interferogram is a single wavelength, in this case that of the laser source.

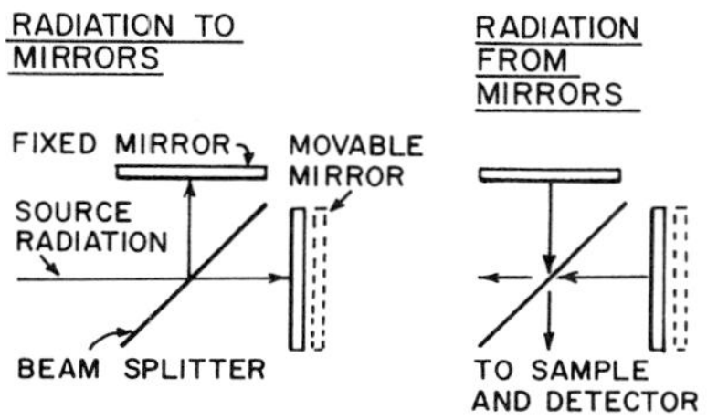

FIG. 10. Michelson-type interferometer. Left: Source radiation is transmitted and also reflected by a beam splitter to two mirrors. Right: Both mirrors reflect radiation back to the beam splitter, where interference occurs.

If a polychromatic source is used, its spectrum can be thought of as a series of closely spaced laserlike emission lines, each with its own wavelength and intensity. Each of these generates a cosine function-type interferogram. The interferogram of a polychromatic source of radiation is a summation of all the cosine functions for each of the laserlike resolution elements. An interferometer does not produce a spectrum but produces an interferogram. A computer must be used to perform the Fourier transform, which generates the spectrum from the interferogram. Once this is done, the computer is available for further processing of the spectrum.

Just one scan of the movable mirror produces a whole single-beam spectrum. However, a spectrum produced from one scan has a relatively high noise level. Usually, a number of scans are taken and signal-averaged by the computer. The noise is reduced by the square root of the number of scans. A single-beam spectrum with the sample in place is stored in the computer memory. A reference single-beam spectrum is taken without the sample and is also stored in the memory. These two single-beam spectra are ratioed by the computer to give a percent transmittance spectrum.

The computer can be used to modify the spectrum further. For example, the vertical or horizontal scale can be expanded, the background can be straightened, or a linear absorbance scale can be generated. A useful procedure is spectral subtraction whereby, for example, a solvent spectrum can be subtracted from a solution spectrum to yield the pure solute spectrum.

III. Sample Handling Techniques

A. Infrared-Transmitting Materials

One of the features of IR spectroscopy is that solids, liquids, and gases can be run without special difficulties. Usually, some sort of IR-transmitting material is needed to support or enclose the sample. Materials such as glass and quartz are useful as windows in the near-IR but even thin windows do not transmit much below 3000

cm^{-1}. The low wave number transmission limits of IR-transmitting materials are not sharply defined but depend on the window thickness. Four commonly used materials and their approximate low wave number limits are NaCl, 600 cm^{-1}; KBr, 350 cm^{-1}; CsBr, 250 cm^{-1}; and CsI, 200 cm^{-1}. These materials are all water-soluble. Water-insoluble materials and their low wave number limits include CaF_2, 1200 cm^{-1}; BaF_2, 850 cm^{-1}; Irtran-2, 700 cm^{-1}; AgCl, 350 cm^{-1}; and KRS-5 250 cm^{-1}. Irtran-2 is made of zinc sulfide an is often used for water solutions or for making films from water solution. Silver chloride is useful but is soft, deforms easily, and darkens with exposure to light. KRS-5 is thallium bromide iodide and is often used in the internal reflection technique to be discussed later. In the far-IR, high-density polyethylene transmits to as low as 30 cm^{-1} but cannot be used above 600 cm^{-1} because of its absorption.

B. Salt Polishing

Sodium chloride can be easily polished between use. The crystal is sanded flat with a fine-grade sandpaper if it is freshly cleaved, scratched, or damaged by water. Two polishing laps are prepared. There are different types, but the wet lap can be simply two thicknesses of fine nylon cloth stretched over a flat surface. The wet lap is wetted with water and sprinkled with a little fine polishing powder such as aluminum oxide or cerium oxide. This is rubbed smooth and all excess water is wiped off. The flat salt plate is rubbed about 20 strokes on the wet lap and then, without delay, is buffed about 7 strokes on the dry lap, which can be simply a layer of diaper cloth held flat. Cesium bromide can be polished the same way, but with alcohol substituted for water. The best polish comes when the lap is nearly dry.

C. Liquid Samples

The easiest samples to run on IR instrumentation are those in the liquid state. Slightly viscous samples can be simply squeezed between two polished IR-transmitting plates and run as a thin film. A typical film thickness is ~0.01 mm. If the liquid is not viscous, usually a spacer is added between the plates to keep the plates apart at the appropriate spacing. Spacer material can be metal foil or an insoluble polymeric film. Two strips roughly 10 by 2 mm can be used, for example, one on each side of the area the IR beam will pass through. These are called temporary cells and are disassembled and cleaned after each use. The thickness cannot be accurately reproduced.

Fixed cells are not disassembled after use but instead are filled, emptied, and cleaned with solvent through ports on the cell assembly. The liquid enters the leak-proof sample area between the plates through holes in the cell window. These are used for volatile liquids or when the thickness needs to be accurately known or held constant as in quantitative analysis. Many commercially available designs are used, and cells come in thickness from 0.01 to 4 mm.

If the cell windows are sufficiently flat, the cell thickness can be measured by running the IR spectrum of the empty cell and observing interference fringes in the form of percent transmission undulations. Wave number $\bar{\nu}_1$ (cm^{-1}) is read at one transmission maximum, and wave number $\bar{\nu}_2$ is read at another transmission maximum that is 1, 2, 3, or more generally n maximum away from the first. The cell thickness t is

$$t\ (\mathrm{mm}) = \frac{5n}{\bar{\nu}_1 - \bar{\nu}_2} \qquad (12)$$

Interference results because part of the beam is twice reflected inside the cell and is retarded by twice the cell thickness relative to the transmitted beam with which it interferes.

D. Gas Samples

Gas cells used for IR spectroscopy come in a variety of types. The simplest is a basic cylinder 10 cm long with IR-transmitting windows on each end. These may be cemented on or clamped in place, with vacuum-tight gaskets providing the seal. Entrance and exit tubes are provided and fitted with stopcocks. The cell is filled and emptied with a gas handling system.

The sampling chamber of most IR spectrometers is not large enough to accommodate longer cell lengths directly. However, cells of much longer path length are available that use mirrors to deflect the IR beam and to reflect it back and forth many times in the cell chamber before it leaves the cell and reenters the spectrometer. These long-path-length cells are used for detecting very small quantities of gas in pollution studies, for example.

A technique often used with FT-IR instruments is gas chromatography, or GC–FT-IR. Here the effluent from a gas chromatography column is fed through a heated light pipe with IR-transmitting windows on the ends. Source radiation passes through the cell into the FT-IR spectrometer. The gas chromatography column separates the gas-phase components and ideally sends them one by one through the light pipe, where the high speed of the FT-IR instrument is utilized to get the spectrum of each component "on the fly," so to speak.

E. Solution Spectra

The techniques for running solids in IR are quite varied. In the first case a solid can be dissolved in a suitable solvent and run as a liquid. Unfortunately, no solvent is free of absorption in the IR region and, usually, the better the solvent, the greater its absorption. This means that more than one solvent must be used to get the whole IR solution spectrum in all regions. A commonly used pair of solvents are CCl_4 above 1330 cm^{-1} and CS_2 below 1330 cm^{-1}. These can be used in cells 0.1–1 mm thick, for example, with solute concentrations in the range 10–1%. In double-beam grating spectrophotometers a cell of matching thickness containing solvent only can be put into the reference beam to compensate for the solvent bands. In FT-IR instruments, a reference solvent spectrum can be subtracted from the solution spectrum to remove solvent bands. Another common solvent for solution spectra is $CHCl_3$ often used in 0.1-mm cells with 5 to 10% solute. $CHCl_3$ has strong bands at 1216 and 757 cm^{-1}, where solute information is often lost or inadequately presented. Even water has been used as a solvent for some applications. Here the cell thickness must be kept small, as water is a very strong IR absorber. The internal reflection technique described in Sec. III,I has been successfully used for water solutions.

F. Films

Solid-state films of suitable thickness can be prepared from melts or solution. Such films are most suitable for amorphous materials, especially polymers. Crystalline films may scatter light and show nonreproducible orientation effects from special orientations of the crystal on the IR window surface. A sample can be heated between two salt plates until molten and allowed to solidify. Solutions can be put onto a plate and the solvent evaporated to form a film. This is a good technique for running water-soluble polymers, for example. Sometimes a film can be prepared on a substrate and stripped off and run as an unsupported film. If a film is too uniform in thickness, interference fringes similar to those from an empty cell may be seen, as discussed earlier. If a film is too irregular in thickness, a spectrum with a false percent transmittance will result from the fact that different parts of the beam go through sample areas with different thicknesses.

G. Mulls

One of the best techniques for running crystalline solids is the use of a mineral oil or Nujol mull. Here a few milligrams of simple are finely ground with a small amount of mineral oil to make a thick paste like cold cream, for example. The paste can be prepared with a mortar and pestle and spread between two IR-transmitting windows. A well-ground sample has a brownish color like smoke when one looks through it. Most beginners do not grind the sample well enough and use too much oil. Mineral oil has only a few bands in narrow regions. The CH stretch region between 3000 and 2800 cm^{-1} and the CH bend region at about 1460 and 1375 cm^{-1} are obscured, however. If information is needed in these regions a second mull must be prepared using a halogenated oil such as Halocarbon or Fluorolube, which contain CF_2 and CFCl groups but no CH. These have no bands from 4000 to 1300 cm^{-1} but have strong bands below 1300 cm^{-1}. Some people use the halogenated oil spectrum above 1300 cm^{-1} and the mineral oil spectrum below. In this case care must be taken to ensure that the sample thickness is the same in both preparations.

H. Potassium Bromide Disks

A very popular technique for running solids is the KBr disk technique. Here a few milligrams of sample are very finely ground and then mixed with 50 to 100 parts of dry KBr powder. The mixture is placed in a special device and compressed into a disk at high pressure. If all goes well, a transparent disk results, which is put into the spectrometer and run. Commercial KBr disk makers are available in many forms. Some are activated with wrenches or levers, while others are used with a hydraulic press. Some can be evacuated, which gives the disk transparency a longer lifetime, but this is not necessary if the disk is used promptly.

Advantages of the disk over the mull include the fact that KBr, unlike mineral oil, has no bands above 400 cm^{-1}. Also, many polymers are more easily ground in KBr. Microsamples are easier to prepare with the KBr disk. The KBr disk has disadvantages compared with the mull, however. The biggest problem is that KBr is hygroscopic, and bands from absorbed H_2O appear in the spectrum in variable amounts that depend on the technique. One never knows whether the water is in the sample or the KBr preparation. Also, spectra of KBr disks are sometimes less reproducible because of changes in sample polymorphism, which result from the preparation.

I. Internal Reflectance

Internal reflectance results when a beam of radiation inside a material of relatively high index of refraction approaches the surface between this and a material of lower index of refraction. If the angle of approach is nearly perpendicular to the surface, much of the radiation is transmitted through the surface and a little is internally reflected. As the angle of incidence gets larger with respect to the perpendicular to the surface, a certain critical angle is exceeded after which all the radiation is internally reflected and none is transmitted. However, the internally reflected beam penetrates a little into the lower index of refraction material in the form of a standing wave before it is reflected internally.

As used in IR spectroscopy, an internal reflectance plate (Fig. 11) is made of a high index of refraction material such as thallium bromide iodide. The plate is usually a few millimeters thick, and the ends are beveled to allow radiation entry at one end at an angle inside the plate. The beam is multiply internally reflected and zigzags between the surfaces until it leaves at the other end. A sample is pressed into intimate contact with the plate on one or both sides. The zigzag beam penetrates a few micrometers into the sample every time it is internally reflected from a sample area on the plate surface. The sample thickness is immaterial as long as it exceeds a few micrometers. Since the radiation penetrates the sample, sample absorption reduces the beam intensity at certain wave numbers, as in a transmission spectrum. There is one notable difference. The standing wave penetration into the sample is wavelength-dependent; the longer the wavelength of radiation, the greater is the penetration. The internal reflectance spectrum resembles a transmission spectrum where the sample thickness gets larger in direct proportion to the radiation wavelength. There are also some small index refraction effects that make the internal reflectance spectra a little different from transmission spectra, but these are minimized by keeping well away from the critical angle, where internal reflectance is no longer total.

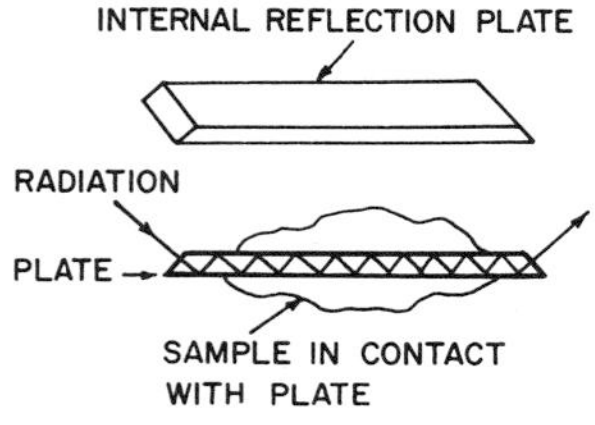

FIG. 11. Plate used for internal reflection spectroscopy. The lower drawing shows sample in contact with the plate and radiation being multiply internally reflected within the plate.

Internal reflection spectroscopy is used for obtaining the spectra of rubbery materials that are hard to grind. The rubbery material is simply pressed against the internal reflection plate and it is ready to run. Internal reflection is also used to obtain selectively the spectrum of the top few micrometers of a sample surface, where the composition may be different from that farther down. It is also good for water solutions because its controlled penetration keeps the effective sample thickness small.

J. Diffuse Reflectance

Diffuse reflectance is a technique usually used with FT-IR instruments. A powdered sample is placed in a small container, where source radiation strikes it and is diffusely reflected in various directions. This radiation is collected and measured by the spectrometer. Usually in the mid-IR region the finely powdered sample is diluted to 5 to 10% with finely powdered KBr or KCl. The spectrum is ratioed against a reference spectrum of pure powdered KBr or KCl. The ratioed spectrum is processed by a computer using a function $f(R_\infty)$ derived by Kubelka and Munk, which changes the reflectance spectrum into one resembling a linear absorbance spectrum:

$$f(R_\infty) = \frac{(1 - R_\infty)^2}{2R_\infty} = \frac{k}{s} \qquad R_\infty = \frac{R_\infty(\text{sample})}{R_\infty(\text{reference})} \tag{13}$$

Here R_∞ is the reflectance of a thick scattering layer, k the molar extinction coefficient, and s a scattering coefficient, which is a function of particle size. The spectrum is quite sensitive to particle size, which affects the radiation scattering. Spectral distortion (compared with a transmission spectrum) may occur if the particle size is not uniformly fine. Black, strongly scattering materials such as coal can be run by this technique.

IV. Quantitative Analysis

A. Beer's Law

The basic law for spectroscopic quantitative analysis is Beer's law. This shows how sample concentration is related to a measure of radiation intensity in a spectrometer. Consider a sample in solution, held in a cell of uniform thickness that transmits the monochromatic radiation of interest. Let the intensity of the radiation entering the sample be I_0 and the intensity of the radiation that has passed through the sample be I. Then the transmittance T is given by

$$T = I/I_0 \tag{14}$$

The percent transmittance (%T) is given by multiplying the transmittance T by 100. Beer's law is commonly expressed as

$$\log_{10}(I_0/I) = abc \tag{15}$$

Here (I_0/I) can be recognized as the reciprocal of the transmittance $(1/T)$. The quantity b is the cell thickness and c the sample concentration in the solution. The quantity a is called the absorptivity, which is a constant characterizing the capacity of the sample to absorb radiation. Its value varies with the wavelength or frequency of the radiation being measured and with the units used for cell thickness and sample concentration.

Beer's law is more simply expressed as

$$A = abc \tag{16}$$

where A is called the absorbance, defined as

$$A = \log_{10}(I_0/I) \quad \text{or} \quad A = \log_{10}(1/T) \tag{17}$$

If the cell thickness and the radiation wavelength are held constant, Beer's law states that the concentration is linearly proportional to the absorbance.

B. Beer's Law Deviations

In IR spectroscopy, the concentration range being measured may be large, sometimes ranging from zero to 100%. Under such circumstances, deviations from Beer's law may be observed. If the cell thickness and radiation wavelength are held constant, a plot of concentration versus absorbance should be a straight line if Beer's law holds. Two conditions are implied in the derivation of Beer's law. The first is that the radiation being measured is monochromatic. In an IR spectrometer, especially under low-resolution conditions, what is actually measured is the intensity of a narrow region of the spectrum that may be significantly wide compared with the width of the absorption band being measured. This means that the absorbance deduced is an average absorbance for a finite wavelength section of the absorption band. This can cause deviation from Beer's law. The second condition for linearity is that the sample absorptivity not change with concentration. If the concentration range is large, the sample environment may change. For example, when the concentration is low, the sample is surrounded by solvent, whereas when the concentration is high, the sample is surrounded by other sample molecules. The change in environment can cause absorptivity changes and deviations from Beer's law. When the concentration change causes hydrogen-bonding changes, deviations can be severe. If Beer's law does not hold exactly, a plot of concentration versus absorbance (for constant cell thickness and wavelength) will not be a straight line, but will have a slight curvature. For narrow concentration ranges, such a plot will be nearly linear.

C. Measurement of Absorbance

There are a variety of ways of measuring the absorbance. In a single-beam spectrum the vertical coordinate I is a measure of the source radiation intensity (at a given wavelength) attenuated by sample absorption and atmospheric carbon dioxide and water vapor absorption. A reference single-beam spectrum is run with the same instrument conditions but without the sample. Let this vertical coordinate be I_0. If the vertical coordinates of these two spectra are divided, wavelength by wavelength, a spectrum is generated where the vertical coordinate is transmittance or, when multiplied by 100, percent transmittance. This is not the percent transmittance of the chemical sample, but rather that of the whole cell assembly. In addition to the absorption of radiation by the sample, radiation can be lost by cell reflection and scattering of radiation, as well as by beam blockage by an undersized cell aperture or by beam attenuation. A background correction must be made.

If the vertical coordinate of the spectrum is linear with percent transmittance, then the percent transmittance reading at, say, the bottom of a sample band is taken to be proportional to I. The percent transmittance at the same wavelength is read for the background point, that is, where the recorder pen would be if there were no sample band. This is taken as proportional to I_0. From these values for I and I_0 the background corrected sample absorbance can be calculated as $\log_{10}(I_0/I)$.

Sometimes the vertical coordinate of the spectrum is the absorbance value rather than the percent transmittance. In this case, the absorbance reading at the band peak is corrected by subtracting the absorbance reading of the background point at the same wavelength where the recorder pen would be if there were no sample band.

D. Cell-In/Cell-Out Method

The most direct quantitative procedure is the cell-in/cell-out method. Here, a dispersive-type instrument is set at the analytical wavelength or wave number where the sample has an absorption band. The cell is filled with a nonabsorbing solvent, and its percent transmittance or absorbance value is read and used as the background point. Then the process is repeated using the same cell filled with sample plus solvent, and its percent transmittance or absorbance value is read. From these values, absorbance, corrected for background, can be calculated. If the same cell and instrument settings are used, this absorbance should be proportional to sample concentration in the solvent. The proportionality constant is evaluated by measuring standards of known concentration.

If the solvent has some absorption at the analytical wavelength or wave number, both the sample and solvent contribute to the total absorbance. Beer's law is additive; that is, the total absorbance is equal to the sum of the *abc* values for each component. The solvent should absorb less strongly than any of the solvent–sample mixtures at the analytical wavelength. In this case, the pure solvent is used for a "zero sample" or background reading as before. The absorbance of pure solvent is subtracted from the absorbance of the solution of the sample plus solvent. Because Beer's law is additive, this absorbance difference should be proportional to sample concentration when the same cell and instrument settings are used if Beer's law holds.

E. Base Line Method

A popular way to do a quantitative analysis from recorded spectra is the base line method. In this method, taking a percent transmittance or absorbance reading of the band peak is straightforward. It is the method of getting the background percent transmittance or absorbance that gives the method its name. Again, one tries to imagine where the recorder pen would be if the component being measured were not present. If one has an isolated band in a region with no other absorption, the background line is easy to draw as a line tangent to the spectral background. If one has a band that comes on the sloping side of a band of the solvent or of a major component, as in Fig. 12, one has a choice. One could try to sketch a rounded background for the "zero sample" condition and use that for the background point. This can be used but is somewhat subjective and may not be very reproducible. An alternative is to use a line tangent to the spectrum at the band wings or even connecting some more distant points. The more closely the line approaches the true background, the better, but it is not necessary that the tangent line and the true background coincide exactly. A consistent base line construction should yield a reproducible measured absorbance for a given concentration, and the absorbance should vary linearly with concentration. Again, this is calibrated with standards. One of the advantages of the method is that it can reduce or eliminate a correction for the finite background absorption

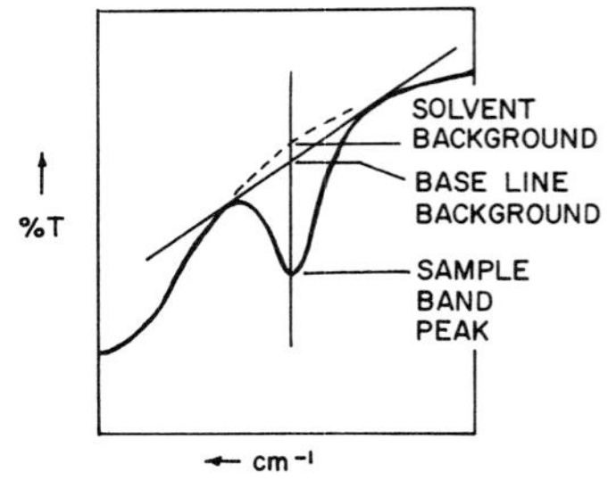

FIG. 12. Part of an infrared spectrum showing the base line construction for the base line method used in quantitative analysis.

of the solvent or major component. Some care should be taken in choosing the tangent points for the base line. These points should not be too sensitive to concentration variations of other components that may be present.

F. Ratio Methods

In most solid-state spectra, the sample film thickness and the amount of sample in a KBr disk or a Nujol mull are not known. It is still possible to do quantitative analysis by the ratio method. This is based on the fact that, in a given mixture, the absorbance ratio of any two bands in one spectrum should be independent of the sample thickness. Consider a two-component mixture, each component of which has an analytical band with no interference from the other component. The absorbance ratio for the two analytical bands is, from Beer's law,

$$\frac{A_1}{A_2} = \frac{a_1 b_1 c_1}{a_2 b_2 c_2} \quad \text{or} \quad \frac{A_1}{A_2} = \frac{a_1 c_1}{a_2 c_2} \tag{18}$$

The b values are identical and cancel since the absorbances are measured for the same sample preparation. Since a_1/a_2 is a constant, the absorbance ratio is proportional to the concentration ratio. One can also write

$$c_1 = \frac{100}{1 + c_2/c_1} \tag{19}$$

which, when multiplied out simply states that the sum of the two concentrations c_1 and c_2 is 100%. In this equation the ratio c_2/c_1 is replaced by its equivalent from the previous equation to give

$$c_1 = \frac{100}{1 + (a_1/a_2)(A_2/A_1)} \tag{20}$$

The a_1/a_2 ratio is a constant that can be determined by measuring A_2/A_1 for one standard of known concentration. Once a_1/a_2 is evaluated, the concentration c_1 of an unknown can be calculated from the absorbance ratio.

Another ratio method is the internal standard method. In this method a known amount of an internal standard material is added to the sample mixture. The internal standard is chosen so that it has no absorption at the analytical wavelength for the sample and vice versa. Again from Beer's Law, the absorbance ratio is

$$\frac{A}{A_s} = \frac{ac}{a_s c_s} \quad \text{and} \quad c = c_s \frac{a_s A}{a A_s} \tag{21}$$

where the subscript s denotes the internal standard. Here the internal standard concentration c_s is known, and the constant ratio a_s/a can be determined from one sample of known concentration, after which the concentration can be calculated from the absorbance ratio.

G. Gas State Analysis

In a quantitative analysis involving gases, the concentration term c in Beer's law is replaced by the pressure or partial pressure p of the gas being measured. Beer's law reads

$$A = abp$$

In this case, the measurement of the background absorbance is usually that of the evacuated cell or the cell filled with nonabsorbing gas such as nitrogen. There is a complication in the use of Beer's law in the vapor phase that is called pressure broadening. Not only is the absorbance of a gaseous component a function of its partial pressure; it is also a function of the total pressure. This means that the absorbance of a gaseous component with a fixed partial pressure can be changed by introducing another completely nonabsorbing gas such as nitrogen. The rotational fine structures of gas-phase bands are broadened by collisions between the molecules of the component being measured, and other gas molecules and collisions vary in frequency and severity as the pressure increases. For this reason the total pressure is often kept constant in a quantitative analysis of gases. The desired partial pressure of the gas to be analyzed is introduced into an evacuated cell. Then the total pressure is increased to a standard value such as 760 mm Hg by introducing nitrogen, for example, before measuring the absorbance.

H. Multicomponent Analysis

In the most general case for quantitative analysis, one wishes to measure several components of a mixture and there are no isolated analytical wave numbers. This means that, at the best analytical wave number for one component, the other components have finite absorption, which interferes with the measurement. Fortunately, Beer's law is additive, which means that at any given wave number in the spectrum the total absorbance A is equal to the sum of the abc values for each component. One can specify that all the measurements will be done in the same cell so the thickness is constant for the whole analysis. This means that b, the cell thickness, can be combined with a, the absorptivity, to give a new constant k, which replaces ab in Beer's law. If there are three components to be measured, three absorbance measurements are needed at three different wave numbers. The Beer's law relationships are written

$$A_1 = k_{11}c_1 + k_{12}c_2 + k_{13}c_3 \tag{22a}$$

$$A_2 = k_{21}c_1 + k_{22}c_2 + k_{23}c_3 \tag{22b}$$

$$A_3 = k_{31}c_1 + k_{32}c_2 + k_{33}c_3 \tag{22c}$$

Here A_1, A_2, and A_3 are absorbances at wave numbers 1, 2, and 3, where components 1, 2, and 3, respectively, are best measured. Three standards are prepared with known concentrations c, bracketing the desired concentration ranges for the analysis. These are all run at the first analytical wave number to give three A_1 values. Equation (22a) can then be used three times to evaluate k_{11}, k_{12}, and k_{13}. Then the same three standards can be used to evaluate the k values for the A_2 and A_3 equations. Once all the k values are known, the three equations can be used to calculate the concentrations in an unknown from the three measured absorbances. Variations of this basic Beer's law procedure have been used to reduce the labor, and computer programs can be used for repetitive analyses.

I. Integrated Band Intensities

Absorbance values of band peaks are most commonly used for quantitative analysis. However, a peak height measurement is somewhat sensitive to instrument resolution. If the resolution is reduced, a narrow-shaped band will become broader and the peak height will be reduced. The integrated intensity is a measure of the total band area, and this shows much less sensitivity to instrumental resolution. Furthermore, it has greater theoretical significance in that the integrated band intensity is a measure of the total radiation energy absorbed for this vibrational mode and it is proportional to the square of the change in dipole moment with respect to the change in the normal coordinate.

One way to characterize the band intensity is to express it as the integrated absorptivity as a function of wave number. From Beer's law the absorptivity a is equal to $A/(bc)$, which means that the integrated intensity can be expressed as the absorbance A, integrated over the whole band, divided by bc. If the spectrum of a solution is plotted with the horizontal coordinate linear with wave number $\bar{\nu}$ (cm^{-1}) and the vertical coordinate linear with absorbance A, then the band area, corrected for background and divided by bc, is the integrated intensity. If the cell length is measured in centimeters and the concentration is measured in moles per cubic centimeter, then the integrated absorptivity is in centimeters per mole. Other units have been used.

V. Group Frequencies

A. Concept of Group Frequencies

Bands at certain frequencies in the IR spectra have been related to the presence of certain functional groups in the chemical structures. For example, in the spectra of a series of unconjugated ketones, a band common to all is a strong band near 1715 cm^{-1}. This has been assigned to the stretching of the carbonyl bond and is a group frequency for unconjugated ketones. There are many other bands in these ketone spectra, which differ from molecule to molecule, especially below 1300 cm^{-1}. These are fingerprint-type bands that can be used to distinguish one ketone from another. A large body of empirical knowledge has been built up about the characteristic group frequencies, which has proved to be very useful to the chemist. The vibrations that give rise to group frequencies are those whose vibrational forms are nearly the same in a series of related molecules.

B. Vibrational Interaction

If all the bonds in a molecule vibrated separately, the diatomic vibrational frequency formula given earlier could be used to predict the whole spectrum. The fact is that bonds do not usually vibrate separately and much interaction occurs. However, interactions occur only if vibrations have the same type of symmetry. For example, in a planar molecule such as vinyl fluoride, planar vibrations do not interact with nonplanar vibrations since these have different symmetries with respect to the plane.

One type of interaction occurs when two identical bonds share a common atom. An example is the H_2O molecule, which has two OH bonds with a common oxygen atom. In the H_2O molecule, one OH bond cannot be vibrationally excited without also exciting the other identical OH bond at the same time. The second bond vibrates either in phase or out of phase with the first. In one case, both bonds stretch at the same time and contract at the same time, and in the other, one bond stretches while the other bond contracts. In the H_2O gas-phase spectra, these are observed at 3652 and 3756 cm^{-1}, respectively. Thus, the in-phase and out-of-phase vibrations do not have the same frequencies. The main reason for this is that, when the two vibrating bonds are not at the equilibrium length, both bonds exert restoring forces on the common oxygen atom. The force resultant is different for the in-phase and out-of-phase stretch vibrations, and this affects the frequencies. This is called vibrational interaction.

There are several XY_2 groups that have correlatable stretching frequencies. For example, alkane CH_2 groups have stretching vibrations that absorb near 2930 and 2850 cm^{-1}, amino NH_2 groups have stretching vibrations that absorb near 3370 and 3300 cm^{-1}, and sulfone SO_2 groups have stretching vibrations that absorb near 1300 and 1130 cm^{-1}. In each case the higher wave number involves the out-of-phase stretch and the lower wave number involves the in-phase stretch.

Consider the XYZ group where the X—Y bond and the Y—Z bond have quite *different* frequencies when unconnected. Examples include the C—O—H group in alcohols, the C—C≡N group in nitriles, and the C—S—H group in mercaptans. Here the other groups on the carbon are ignored. The XYZ group as a whole has two stretching frequencies, but the interaction is different from that for the XY_2 case. In the high-frequency vibration of the XYZ group, only the atoms of the high-frequency bond move appreciably. In the examples given, this means that when the high-frequency OH, C≡N, or SH bonds vibrate, the attached carbon hardly moves since it is attached to the high-frequency bond with a low-frequency C—O, C—C, or C—S bond. This means that the rest of the molecule does not affect the OH, C≡N, or SH vibrations mechanically very much since the nearly stationary attached carbon atom localizes the vibration. In this manner, one can see that such group vibrations as OH, C≡N, and SH are group frequencies; that is, their presence in a molecule gives rise to absorption in a predictable frequency range.

While the OH vibration is mechanically unaffected by the rest of the molecule, the OH group has a force constant that can be changed by hydrogen-bonding effects. An alcohol in dilute CCl_4 solution has a free OH band near 3640 cm^{-1}. Hydrogen bonding lowers the OH frequency and increases the bandwidth and intensity. A pure alcohol is hydrogen bonded (OH···O) and absorbs broadly and strongly near 3300 cm^{-1}.

In a ketone, the high-frequency C═O bond is connected to the rest of the molecule by two low-frequency C—C bonds. In the carbonyl vibration the two attached carbons hardly move, making the carbonyl a good group frequency, mechanically nearly independent of the rest of the molecule. The carbonyl frequency can be varied by electron donation or withdrawal effects from the attached groups, and these can shift the frequency. These effects are fairly well understood, which means that the shifts are predictable.

The CH_2, NH_2, and SO_2 groups discussed earlier are attached to the molecule by low-frequency C—C, C—N, or C—S bonds, so the attached atoms hardly move, isolating the CH_2, NH_2, and SO_2 stretching vibrations. This means that both the in-phase and out-of-phase stretching vibrations for these groups are good group frequencies, nearly independent mechanically of the rest of the molecule.

In a group such as the C═S group, the vibration is not isolated like a C═O vibration. The C═S is attached to the rest of the molecule by C—C or C—N bonds, which have nearly the *same* frequency as the C═S bond. As a result, interaction will take place and more than one vibration will involve C═S stretching.

In such groups as CH_3 and SO_3, there are three identical bonds. These interact, so the group vibrates as a whole in three different modes: an in-phase stretch and two different out-of-phase stretch vibrations. These are good group frequencies because the group is connected to the molecule with a low-frequency C—C or C—S bond. In a group such as a benzene ring there are six identical or nearly identical C—C bonds, which interact to give six different stretching modes. Some of these are group frequencies.

C. Survey of Group Frequencies

Table III contains some selected group frequencies used in qualitative analysis. Some discussion of the data follows. In the region from 4000 to 2000 cm^{-1}, various XH groups absorb. In the region from 3700 to 3100 cm^{-1}, OH groups in alcohols and phenols and water have bands. Various types of NH also absorb here, as well as acetylenic CH groups. In the region from 3100 to 3000 cm^{-1}, absorption occurs for aryl CH and

TABLE III. Selected Spectra Structure Correlations

Group[a]	Wave number region (cm^{-1})[b]	Assignment[c]
Alkanes		
R—CH_2—R	2936–2916 s	Out-of-phase str.
R—CH_2—R	2863–2843 m	In-phase str.
R—CH_2—R	1475–1450 m	CH_2 def.
—CH_2—CH_2—CH_2—CH_2—	726–722 w	In-phase rock[d]
R—CH_3	2972–2952 s	Out-of-phase str.
R—CH_3	2882–2862 m	In-phase str.
R—CH_3	1475–1450 m	Out-of-phase def.
R—CH_3	1383–1377 m	In-phase def.
$C(CH_3)_2$	1389–1381 m	Sym. in-phase def.
$C(CH_3)_2$	1372–1368 m	Antisym. in-phase def.
$C(CH_3)_3$	1401–1393 m	Sym. in-phase def.
$C(CH_3)_3$	1374–1366 s	Antisym. in-phase def.
Olefins		
C═C	1680–1630 mw	C═C str.
C═CH_2	3100–3075 w	CH_2 out-of-phase str.
R—CH═CH_2	995–985 s	Trans CH wag[e]
R—CH═CH_2	910–905 s	═CH_2 wag
R_2C═CH_2	895–885 s	═CH_2 wag
RCH═CHR (trans)	980–965 s	Trans CH wag
RCH═CHR (cis)	730–650 m	Cis CH wag
CH_2═CH—CO—OR	970–960 m	═CH_2 wag
CH_2═CH—O—R	820–810 s	═CH_2 wag
X≡Y and X═Y═Z		
C—C≡C—H	2140–2100 w	C≡C str.
C—C≡C—H	3340–3267 s	C—H str.
C—C≡N	2260–2240 m	C≡N str.
—C≡N (conjugated)	2240–2220 v	C≡N str.
S—C≡N	2170–2135 m	C≡N str.
C═C═CH_2	2000–1900 s	Out-of-phase str.
—N═C═O	2275–2263 s	Out-of-phase str.
—N═C═S	2150–2050 s	Out-of-phase str.
Aromatics		
Aromatic CH	3100–3000 w	CH str.
Aromatic ring	1620–1585 v	Ring str.
Aromatic ring	1590–1565 v	Ring str.
Aromatic ring	1525–1470 v	Ring str.
Mono and meta	710–665 s	Ring bend out of plane
Five adjacent ring H's	800–730 s	In-phase CH wag
Four adjacent ring H's	805–735 s	In-phase CH wag
Three adjacent ring H's	825–705 s	In-phase CH wag
Two adjacent ring H's	860–795 s	In-phase CH wag
Isolated ring H	935–810 s	CH wag
Carbonyls		
R—CO—R	1725–1705 s	C═O str.
Conjugated ketones	1700–1640 s	C═O str.
R—CO—H	1740–1720 s	C═O str.
Aryl—CO—H	1710–1685 s	C═O str.
R—CO—O—R	1750–1735 s	C═O str.
Conjugated esters	1735–1715 s	C═O str.
Lactone (γ)	1795–1740 s	C═O str.
—COOH (dimer)	1720–1680 s	C═O str.
—$CO_2^-Na^+$	1650–1540 s	Out-of-phase str.
—$CO_2^-Na^+$	1450–1360 m	In-phase str.

TABLE III *(Continued)*

Group[a]	Wave number region (cm^{-1})[b]	Assignment[c]
R—CO—N	1690–1630 s	C═O str.
O—CO—N	1740–1683 s	C═O str.
R—CO—Cl	1810–1795 s	C═O str.
Anhydride (noncyclic)	1825–1770 s	In-phase C═O str.
Anhydride (noncyclic)	1755–1715 ms	Out-of-phase str.
Anhydride (cyclic)	1870–1845 m	In-phase C═O str.
Anhydride (cyclic)	1800–1750 s	Out-of-phase str.
Carbonyl substituents		
CH_2—C═O	1440–1405 m	CH_2 def.
CH_3—C═O	1375–1350 ms	CH_3 in-phase def.
H—CO—R	2900–2800 w	CH str.[f]
H—CO—R	2775–2695 w	CH str.[f]
H—CO—R	1420–1370 w	CH def.
—CO—O—R	1300–1150 s	C—O str.
—CO—OH (dimer)	3000 broad m	OH str.
—CO—OH	1315–1280 s	C—O str.
—CO—NH_2	3520–3180 s	NH_2 str. (two bands)
—CO—NH_2	1635–1600 m	NH_2 def.
—CO—NH—(noncyclic)	3470–3250 m	NH str.
—CO—NH—(noncyclic)	1550–1510 m	NH def. + C—N stretch
Alcohols and ethers		
C—OH (unbonded)	3641–3593 w	OH str.
C-OH (H-bonded)	3500–3000 s	OH str.
CH_2—OH	1075–1000 s	C-O str.
R_2CH—OH	1150–1075 m	C—O str.
R_3C—OH	1210–1100 m	C—O str.
Aryl—OH	1260–1180 s	C—O str.
CH_2—O—CH_2	1140–1085 s	C—O—C out-of-phase str.
Aryl—O—CH_2	1310–1210 s	Aryl—O str.
Aryl—O—CH_2	1050–1010 m	O—CH_2 str.
Nitrogen groups		
—NH_2	3550–3330 mw	NH_2 out-of-phase str.
—NH_2	3450–3250 mm	NH_2 in-phase str.
—NH_2	1650–1590 mw	NH_2 def.
CH_2—NH—CH_2	1146–1132 m	C—N—C out-of-phase str.
Aryl—N	1330–1260 m	Aryl—N str.
C═N	1690–1630 m	C═N str.
CH_2—NO_2	1556–1545 s	NO_2 out-of-phase str.
CH_2—NO_2	1388–1368 m	NO_2 in-phase str.
Aryl—NO_2	1530–1500 s	NO_2 out-of-phase str.
Aryl—NO_2	1370–1330 m	NO_2 in-phase str.
Chlorine		
C—Cl	830–560 m	C—Cl str.
C—CH_2—CH_2—Cl (trans)	730–723 m	C—Cl str.
C—CH_2—CH_2—Cl (gauche)	649–635 m	C—Cl str.
CH_2—Cl	1300–1240 m	CH_2 wag
Sulfur		
—SH	2590–2540 w	SH str.
CH_2—S	1270–1220 m	CH_2 wag
—SO_2—	1400–1300 s	SO_2 out-of-phase str.
—SO_2—	1200–1100 s	SO_2 in-phase str.
—SO_3Na	1230–1120 s	SO_3 out-of-phase str.
—SO_3Na	1080–1025 m	SO_3 in-phase str.

(continues)

TABLE III (*Continued*)

Group[a]	Wave number region (cm^{-1})[b]	Assignment[c]
Phosphorus		
PH	2440–2275 m	PH str.
P=O	1320–1140 s	P=O str.
P—O—C	1050–970 s	P—O—C str.
Silicon		
SiH	2250–2100 s	SiH str.
Si—CH_3	1280–1255 s	CH_3 in-phase def.
Si—O—R	1110–1000 s	Si—O—C str.
Si—O—Si	1110–1000 s	Si—O—Si str.
Boron		
BH	2640–2350 s	BH str.
B···H···B	2220–1540 ms	BH str.
B—O	1380–1310 s	BO str.

[a] R is an alkane group.
[b] Wave number regions given in cm^{-1}. Relative intensities are indicated by s (strong), m (medium), w (weak), and v (variable).
[c] Abbreviations: str., stretch; def., deformation; sym., symmetric; antisym., antisymmetric.
[d] CH_2 rock is CH_2 rotation in the CH_2 plane.
[e] Wag is rotation out of the CH_2 plane or out of the aryl or olefinic plane.
[f] Fermi resonance doublet, CH stretch + CH deformation overtone.

olefinic CH. In the region from 3000 to 2800 cm^{-1}, various types of CH_3 and CH_2 groups absorb. Strongly hydrogen bonded hydrogens in acidic compounds absorb broadly in the region from 3100 to 2400 cm^{-1}. Finally, SH, BH, PH, and SiH groups absorb in the region from 2600 to 2100 cm^{-1}.

Various types of triple bonds such as nitriles and cumulated double bonds such as isocyanate groups absorb in the region from 2300 to 1900 cm^{-1}. Various types of double bonds, including C=O, C=N, and C=C absorb from 1900 to 1550 cm^{-1}. Aromatic ring vibrations absorb near 1600 and 1500 cm^{-1}.

Hydrogen bending vibrations absorb from 1600 to 700 cm^{-1}. Bending vibrations for CH_2 and CH_3 absorb from 1500 to 1350 cm^{-1}, and very useful out-of-plane CH wag vibrations in olefins and aromatics absorb from 1000 to 700 cm^{-1}. In olefins these can be used to distinguish vinyls, vinylidines, and cis and trans 1,2-disubstituted olefins. In aromatics, these bands can usually distinguish the number of adjacent aromatic hydrogens between substituents: five for monosubstituted, four for ortho, three and one for meta, and two for para.

In the range from 1400 to 900 cm^{-1} vibrations from SO_2, SO_3, P=O, and many types of C—O groups have strong bands. Usually below 1350 cm^{-1} only strong bands are interpreted since there are many bands in this region that are not group frequencies. This, of course, is only a very small sample of the large body of group frequency correlations available for qualitative analysis that can be found in IR texts.

Bibliography

Bellamy, L. J. (1975). "The Infrared Spectra of Complex Molecules," 3rd ed. Wiley, New York.

Chalmers, J. M., Mackenzie and Willis, H. A. (1984). FT-IR spectroscopy in an industrial laboratory. *Appl. Spectrosc.* **38,** 763.

Colthup, N. B., Daly, L. H. and Wilberly, S. E. (1975). "Introduction to Infrared and Raman Spectroscopy," 2nd ed. Academic Press, New York.

Crocombe, R. A., Olson, M. L., and Hill, S. L. (1987). "Computerized Quantitative Infrared Analysis," pp. 95–130. ASTM STP 934, G. L. McClure, ed. American Society for Testing and Materials, Philadelphia.

Ferraro, J. R. and Basile, L. J. (Eds.), (1978, 1979, 1982, 1985). "Fourier Transform Infrared Spectroscopy," Vol. 1–4. Academic Press, New York and Orlando.

Griffiths, P. R. (1975). "Chemical Infrared Fourier Transform Spectroscopy." Wiley, New York.

McClure, W. F. (1984). History and future prospects for near-infrared analysis. *Anal. Proc.* **21,** 485.

Pouchert, C. J. (1985). "The Aldrich Library of FT-IR Spectra," Vol. 1 and 2, The Aldrich Chemical Company, Inc., Milwaukee.

INFRARED TECHNOLOGY

W. L. Wolfe *The University of Arizona*

GLOSSARY

Detector: Device that linearly transduces optical power to an electrical signal.

Emittance: Emitted power per unit area.

Infrared: That part of the electromagnetic spectrum with wavelengths between about 1 μm and 1 mm.

Irradiance: Received power per unit area.

Optical power: Radiant energy per unit time.

Radiance: Power per unit area and solid angle.

Radiant intensity: Power per unit solid angle.

Radiometry: Science of the measurement of the amount and properties of radiation.

Sensor: Instrument, usually consisting of optics, detectors, and electronics, that gathers radiation and converts it to some other form. The form may be an image, a warning, a control signal, or other.

The electromagnetic spectrum encompasses radiation of many different kinds. It ranges from gamma rays of very high frequency and short wavelength to radio and navigation frequencies of the opposite characteristics. Infrared radiation has wavelengths just longer than visible ones. The visible spectrum, from violet to red, comprises wavelengths from about 400 to 800 nm (from 0.4 to 0.8 μm). The infrared spectrum consists of radiation from 0.8 to 1000 μm (or 1 mm). The part of the spectrum of just longer waves is called, reasonably enough, the millimeter-wave region.

Whereas most of the observed phenomena in the visible region are related to the reflection of sunlight or artificial illumination, most infrared phenomena are related to the emission of radiation from objects near room temperature. The radiation from the sun peaks in the middle of the visible spectrum. Radiation from most objects on the earth, including people, peaks at about 10 μm. Although there is copious infrared radiation from the sun, because of its distance from the earth, it is surpassed by ambient radiation at about 4 μm.

Infrared investigators have subdivided the region into the near infrared, middle infrared and far infrared, but they are inconsistent about the regions to which they apply their appellations. The divisions have been related to the transmission of the atmosphere shown in Fig. 1 and types of application. To the longwave side of the visible, the atmosphere becomes alternately transparent and opaque. The region from about 1 to 2.5 μm, which is transparent, is called by many the shortwave infrared. The transparent region from about 3 to 6 μm is called the middle infrared, and the transparent region from about 8 to 12 μm is called the far infrared. However, in space applications, there are no atmospheric limitations, so the band can extend to 20 or 30 μm. Astronomers have operated out to several hundred micrometers and called it the far infrared, and so have laboratory spectroscopists.

I. Applications

Infrared technology is used for a wide variety of industrial, military, residential, and analytical uses. The radiation is closely related to temperature and temperature changes. It can therefore be used for remote measurements of temperature and its variations with space and time. Many molecules have characteristic emission and absorption spectra. Thus, infrared techniques can be used as a sensitive tool for both qualitative and quantitative chemical analyses.

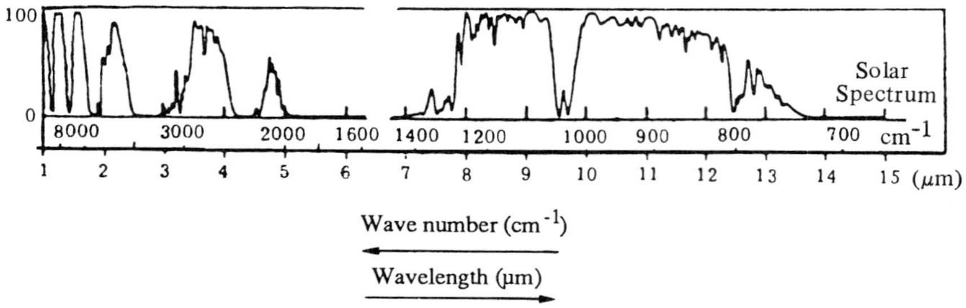

FIG. 1. Low-resolution solar spectrum from 1.0 to 15.0 μm. (Published with permission from U.S. Air Force Geophysics Laboratory.)

It is useful in astronomy for the detection of cooler stars and quasi-stellar objects, as well as for determining their spectral characteristics. Because the main products of combustion are water vapor, carbon dioxide, and carbon monoxide, and because these have significant emission bands in the infrared, several detection and surveillance schemes are predicated on infrared techniques. The evening weather pictures on television are also generated by a satellite-borne infrared system. The higher-altitude clouds are colder than the ground and therefore provide an infrared contrast.

A. Military Applications

Perhaps the most widely known military infrared instruments are the Sidewinder air-to-air missile and a satellite-borne intercontinental ballistic missile (ICBM) detection system. These are both examples of the detection of the emission from an exhaust plume or very hot engine.

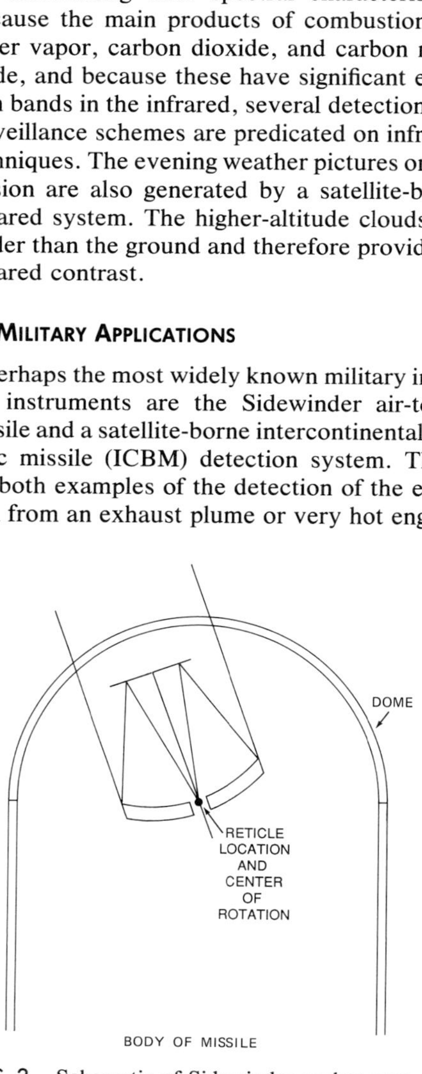

FIG. 2. Schematic of Sidewinder seeker system.

The Sidewinder missile guidance system is shown schematically in Fig. 2. A special infrared dome, made of magnesium fluoride because of its good transmission and robust physical properties, protects the optical system inside. Then an optical system consisting of a primary and secondary mirror and a set of correction lenses causes an image to focus onto a special reticle (described in the next paragraph). All the light from the reticle is refocused onto a lead sulfide detector, as shown in Fig. 3. The jet engine temperatures are about 800 K. The radiation from them passes through the atmosphere with a typical distribution like that shown in Fig. 4. It should be no surprise then that many Sidewinders fly right up the tailpipes of their intended victims. But they don't have to view the tailpipe. The jet plume, invisible to us, emits copious amounts of infrared radiation. Although it is emission from carbon dioxide that transmits through an atmosphere that contains carbon dioxide (which therefore absorbs some of the radiation), appreciable amounts still reach the missile. Thus, attacks from the side and even the front are possible.

The reticle is a very clever device that is used to modulate the radiation, to discriminate against clouds, and to provide directional information. A typical sunrise reticle is shown in Fig. 5 along with a point source of radiation on it. All

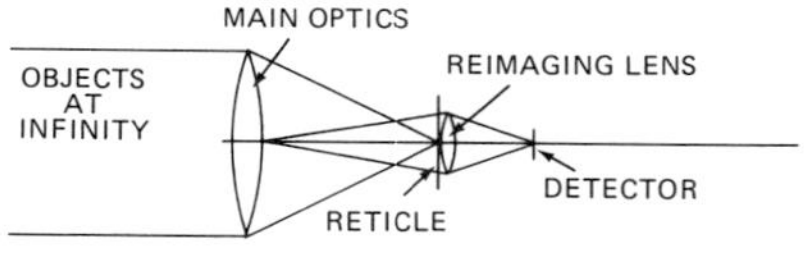

FIG. 3. Reticle optics. Light from the object at infinity (or at least a large distance) is focused on the reticle. The reimaging lens is right behind the reticle and a little larger. The main optics (lens or mirror) is focused onto the detector.

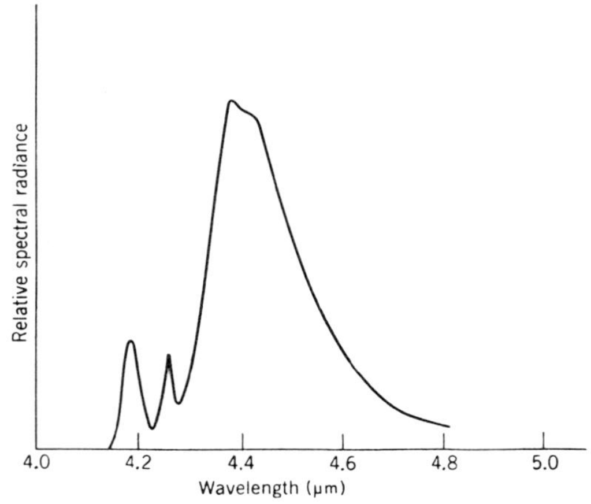

FIG. 4. The 4.4-μm emission band of carbon dioxide. (Courtesy of U.S. National Bureau of Standards.)

the light on the reticle gets to the detector. As the reticle rotates, light first gets to the detector by passing through a slot and then is prevented from doing so by the opaque blades; the detector output goes up and down in essentially a square wave. The 50% region is a reference level to establish the phase of the square wave. The pick-ups on the reticle correlate this with the coordinate system of the missile. In this way the direction of the target is established. An extended source like a sunlit cloud does not generate the same nice square wave. If the cloud is larger than two blades, very little modulation is generated because some always gets through and some is always blocked; the average is almost constant. The degree of modulation is a complicated function of the exact design of the reticle and the exact shape and orientation of the cloud.

Several other missiles have also been designed and built using these principles: the Falcon, Redeye, and Maverick among them.

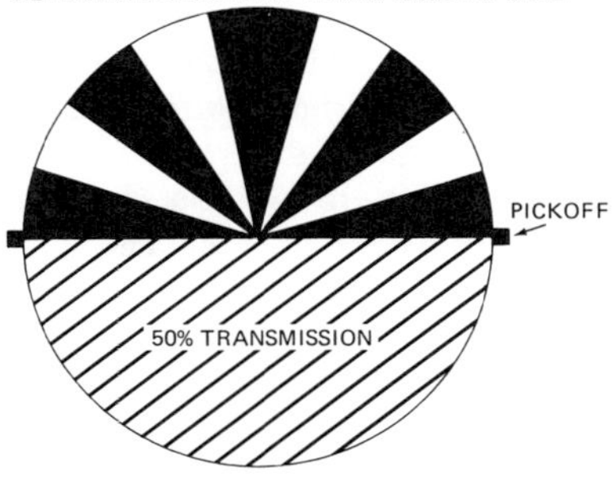

FIG. 5. Sunrise reticle.

Anyone who has ever seen the launch of a major rocket must be impressed, if not awed, by the tremendous energy of the event. Much of that energy is in the visible and infrared radiation from that enormous plume. It should be possible to detect it from enormous distances—and it is. This is the basis of a geosynchronous satellite-borne infrared detection system. Such a satellite maintains the same position with respect to a spot on the ground. In fact, it orbits about the earth at the same rate that the earth rotates about its own axis. Thus, any spot on the earth can be viewed constantly. Thus, as the missile rises above the atmosphere and the clouds, the emission from the CO_2 and H_2O bands may be sensed. The radiation is enormous, but so is the distance. If 1 kW is so emitted, then at the synchronous altitude, because of the inverse square law, the power per unit area is about 10^{-12} W m^{-2}. This is a minute amount, but as is shown in the analysis part of this article, it is detectable!

There are other ways to detect such missiles. They can be sensed in both their coasting and midcourse phase or during reentry. The missile payload and all its components come to thermal equilibrium at about 300 K. This is an equilibration due to radiation interchange with the earth at about the same temperature. It is reasonable to approximate such a payload as being a black body with a cross section of about 1 m^2. The detection of such an object is also difficult but under certain conditions is possible. If the path from the sensor, assumed to be above the atmosphere, to the missile has a space background, the detectors can be very sensitive.

The use of night-vision infrared systems received much attention during the Vietnam War and continues to do so. Although the equipment is more complicated than a normal black-and-white television set, it operates in much the same way. However, it senses the emitted thermal radiation from the scene. This permits the viewing of people in relatively thick foliage, driving at night without illumination, and viewing of targets and obstructions in the road or forest. Figure 6 shows an ordinary view and an infrared view in the daytime of a soldier hiding in the forest. The same concepts can lead to the detection of land mines, although the physical phenomena are much more subtle. The detections and false alarms are therefore somewhat less satisfactory than for the night-vision work. Perimeter defense can be based on either passive or active systems. A light-beam barrier is

FIG. 6. Two views of a soldier in the woods. The top view is a normal, visible photograph; the bottom is an infrared image.

set up around the perimeter of the area to be detected. Anything warm that passes through the field of view of the passive system triggers the alarm. Similarly, anything that passes through the active infrared beam triggers the alarm. As is usually the case, the setting of the trigger is critical, and even so there are a few things like animals and blowing branches that can fool the system.

For every measure there seems to be a countermeasure. Infrared systems are also used to detect the planes that attack with air-to-air missiles like Sidewinders. By techniques described later, they scan a certain field of view behind the plane, searching for other planes. The launch of a missile is accompanied by the rocket plume, and a variety of means can be used to differentiate the flash from the many other glints and highlights from the natural background.

B. Medical Applications

There are two main types of medical applications of infrared techniques. These are thermography, or thermal imaging, and chemical diagnostics. The former is based on infrared imaging techniques that can sense temperature differences on the order of 0.1 K. These apparent temperature patterns have been used for the early determination of breast cancer, the delineation of the boundary of healthy versus necrotic tissue in severe burns, and the location of the cause of circulatory deficiencies and sinus obstructions. It can provide a dramatic demonstration of the way in which cigarette smoking decreases peripheral circulation. The technique has also been used to contribute to the analysis of malingerers claiming back problems! Infrared techniques in the medical laboratory are largely confined to spectrophotometry, a technique for measuring the percentage composition of specific solutes like sugar in the blood.

The use of infrared imagery for cancer diagnosis was first investigated in the late 1950s. Pathology in the breast, either a benign or malignant tumor, causes a local heating and increase in temperature. This increase diffuses to the surface of the skin and causes a local increase in surface temperature. Diagnosticians have mainly used asymmetries in the left–right pattern of a chest for diagnosis. The method depends, therefore, upon heating from pathology, thermal diffusivity, a skin that radiates completely, and symmetry. Unfortunately, not all of these conditions apply well enough in a sufficient number of cases. This promising, noninvasive technique has been found to provide a higher false-alarm rate and lower detection of true cancer than acceptable. It is true that many of the detected "cancers" turned out to be other anomalies. Thus the invasive technique of X-ray imagery is still the chosen one.

The skin is essentially black in the infrared. It is blacker in the region of 8–12 μm than in 3–5 μm. The 8–12 μm region has been the spectrum of choice, since the temperature differences are more apparent and any reflections from the environment are minimized. Thus, it is possible to do a good job of temperature measurement. However, the small lack of blackness (or emissivity) has led to the development of other techniques.

One exploratory technique promises to provide a better measure of temperature difference and to better define the areas of pathology. It is a three-color technique, using passive detection in the regions 3–5 μm, and 8–12 μm, while illuminating the patient with 0.9-μm radiation. The ratio of the signal at 3–5 μm to that at 8–12 μm is generated electronically. Then differences in the ratio from spatial point to spatial point are independent of the emissivity difference from point to point. In fact, the signal difference is related directly to temperature difference unless the *ratio* of the emissivity in 3–5 μm to that in 8–12 μm changes from point to point. The skin is relatively transparent at about 0.9 μm. Thus, illumination and consequent imagery at that wavelength provide a reasonable view of the venous pattern. When overlayed on the other imagery, a better picture of the location of pathology should be obtained.

Figure 7 shows high-resolution imagery of a man with an obstructed nasal passage. Note the circular scan pattern. Figure 8 shows before and after operation pictures of a man with circulatory problems in the leg. Figure 9 shows a similar thermogram of the hand of a man before and after a drag on a cigarette. The imagery has been converted so that higher temperatures are represented by red and low temperatures by blue, with yellows and greens intermediate.

C. Meteorology

Global patterns of weather can now be photographed in essentially real time. The U.S. government Environmental Sciences and Services Agency (ESSA) has orbited two satellites in geosynchronous, equatorial orbits, the Geosynchronous Orbiting Environmental Sensing (GOES) satellites. Each satellite has a visible and infrared spin-scanner (the VISSR). Its function is to take an infrared and visible picture of the entire projected disc of the earth that it can see. An outline drawing of the optical system is shown in Fig. 10. A Ritchey Chretien telescope is mounted on a satellite that spins at a constant rate. There is a mercury cadmium telluride detector at one focal plane, and via a beamsplitter there is an array of photodiodes for visible sens-

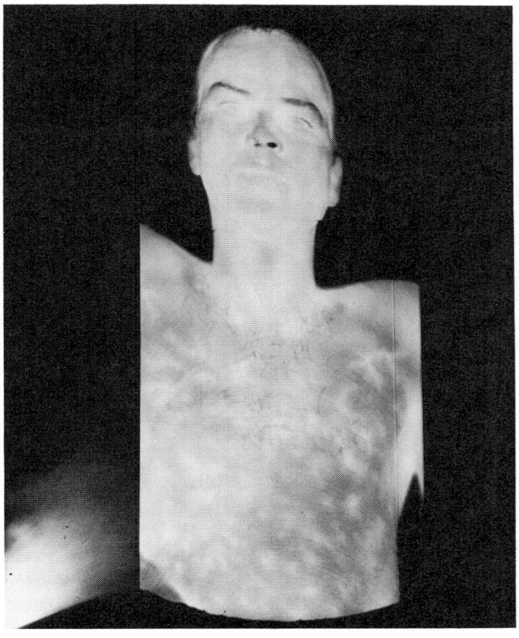

FIG. 7. Infrared image of a man with nasal obstruction. Note the circular scan pattern.

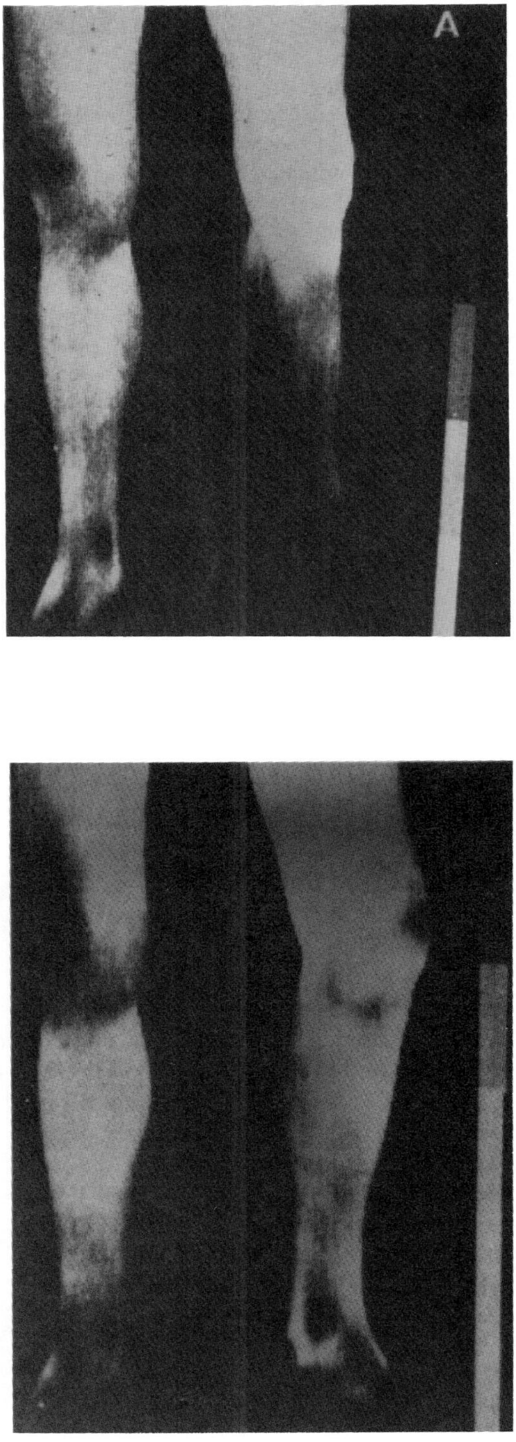

FIG. 8. Before (top) and after (bottom) pictures of a man with circulatory problems in the leg. The top picture shows a cold left leg below the knee; the bottom picture shows the corrected, normal situation.

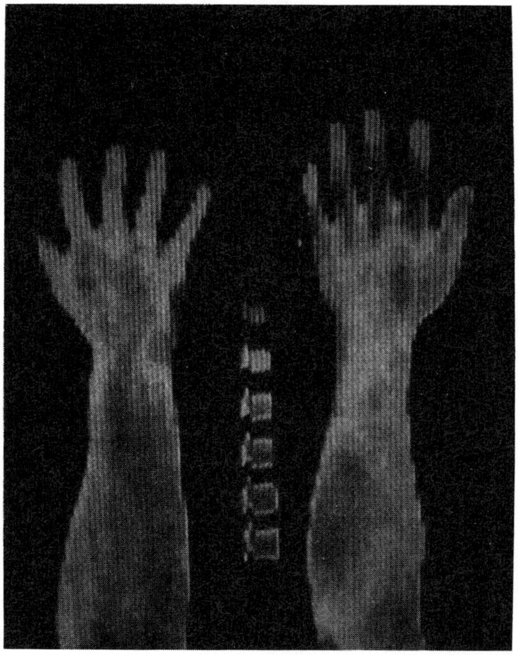

FIG. 9. The hand of a smoker: on the left, before a drag; on the right, minutes after the drag. Note the marked decrease in circulation.

ing. As the satellite spins, the image of the detector scans a line on the earth. At each point it receives radiation from either the earth or the top of a cloud. The flat mirror tilts, little by little, to increase or decrease the radius of the circle until the entire disc is covered. The contrasts in the imagery are related almost directly to temperature differences. The clouds are high and at about 240 K. The earth is at about 275–315 K. Both the clouds and the ground have emissivities close to unity. The spectral region is 10.5–12.5 μm. The detector is cooled to a temperature of 90 K by a radiation cooler, a device that couples the cold of space to the detector by an appropriate radiative cooler design. Some of the imagery even shows the relative cold of the mountain ranges compared to the warmth of the lowlands. A particularly good example of this is the Mogollon Rim in Arizona (of Zane Grey fame) that runs diagonally across the northeastern portion of that state [*See* REMOTE SENSING TECHNIQUES.]

A more complicated weather sensor comes under the general heading of sounder. Some of the experimental, not operational, satellites of the TIROS and NIMBUS series have had such sounders used for sensing the vertical temperature profile of the atmosphere. The technique is based on the fact that carbon dioxide is the same percentage ratio of the total composition of the atmosphere at all altitudes; this is called a constant mixing ratio. It also has an emissivity that varies with wavelength from about zero at 10 μm to about 100% at 16 μm for any appreciable amount of the gas. An infrared instrument with about five spectral channels arranged from

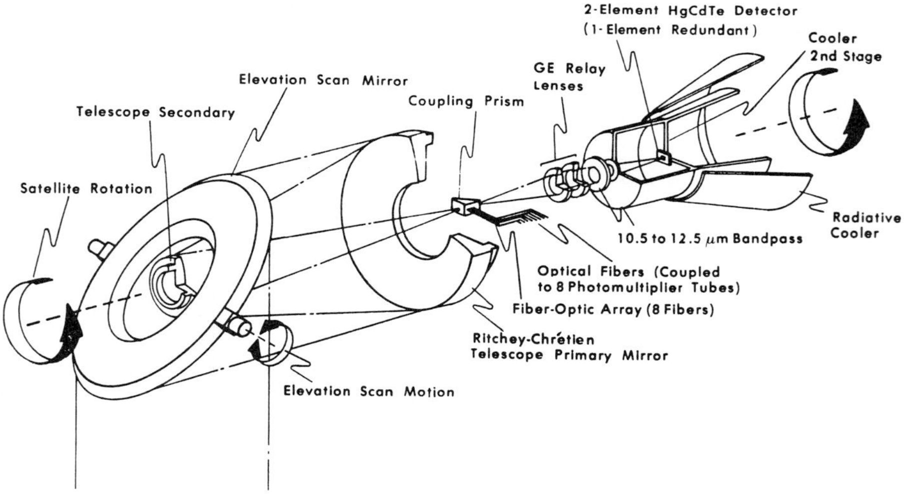

FIG. 10. Visible–infrared spin-scan radiometer (VISSR). [Reprinted with permission from Due, C. T. (1982). "An IRIA State of the Art Report: Optical Mechanical, Active/Passive Imaging Systems, Vol. II. Environmental Research Institute of Michigan, Ann Arbor, Mich. Copyright 1982 Environmental Research Institute of Michigan.]

about 11 μm to about 16 μm then probes the radiation of the atmosphere to different depths. Since the emissivity is so high at 16 μm, only the top of the atmosphere is sensed by the 16-μm channel. The 11-μm channel senses radiation from all altitudes down to some fairly low height. Based on theoretical models of radiation from such radiative paths, the temperature profile can be unravelled. This is a somewhat delicate problem called an inverse problem. Given the result, how was it caused? Various iterative techniques have been used to solve it; various analyses have been carried out to determine the optimum number of spectral bands and their location, and several different types of instruments have been flown. The results are that vertical profiles with altitude resolution of about 1 km and temperature resolution of about 1 K have been accomplished. Radiosonde techniques were used for the verification of these profiles.

Another sounding technique is called LIDAR (laser identification and ranging). This is an active technique, similar to radar. A laser pulse is generated and transmitted outward. The light is scattered back from the atmosphere. A time-gated detector senses the return. Since it is not active immediately after the generation of the pulse, the detector is not "blinded" by the backscatter from the mirror. In fact, since it is only active for a very brief period of time, it senses the return from only a small portion of the atmosphere at a specific range. Light travels about 33 cm in 1 nsec; thus, segments of the atmosphere about 1 m in depth can be probed this way. The use of several wavelengths permits a limited amount of constituent identification.

D. Other Applications

One of the relatively old and reliable applications of a very simple infrared system is the railroad car "hot box" detector. Sometimes in the course of the thousands of miles of travel, the journal box of a railroad car starts to overheat. This is usually due to improper maintenance, but other causes are possible. A fairly simple, effective, and inexpensive technique is the use of a small infrared optical system set up near the track and viewing at the height of the journal boxes. It has a small-angle, horizontal field of view. As trains pass by, it sees wheels and journal boxes. It must differentiate because wheels are hot. A certain sophistication is needed in this counting. A threshold level is set, and boxes above this level are deemed in trouble. The sensor is coordinated with the communications system of the railroad, and warning is given in the proper place.

At least two different types of burglar detections are accomplished by infrared methods. The first and most straightforward is beam interruption. A small infrared source, usually an emitting diode, is coupled to a lens to form a beam. The output is modulated at frequencies near 1 kHz to distinguish it from ambient radiation. The beam can be very narrow or in a fan geometry, but it is arranged so that an intruder is likely to pass through it, either on entry or in going to valuables. Small infrared photodetectors sense the beam and are programmed to give an alarm only if they no longer sense it. The infrared beam, of course, is invisible to the naked eye and is therefore less likely to be discovered by an intruder than a visible one, or the various types of electrical intrusion detection apparatus. The wavelength of operation of such systems is approximately 1 μm.

There are also purely passive infrared intrusion-detection systems. These take advantage of the radiant emission of a human being. They can be mounted in the corner of a room, and their field of view is arranged such that a large fraction of the room is encompassed in the field. This is possible optically since only coarse resolution is required; no imaging is performed. Any high-frequency variation in the received infrared signal is detected. This is accomplished, of course, by proper shaping of the temporal bandpass of the electronics, allowing no dc to pass. Although the face and hands and any other warm parts of the intruder may represent only a very small fraction of the total radiation received, the sensitivity of such systems allows detection to be made. Needless to say, the user should see to it that there will be no swinging doors or blowing curtains that may cause false alarms.

One technique utilizes a set of Fresnel lenses embossed in transparent plastic. These focus radiation from different portions of the field of view onto a thermal detector. The detector is ac coupled to the electronics so that only changes are sensed. Such sensors are used as door openers, arrival detectors, and intrusion alarms.

II. Infrared Astronomy

Infrared astronomy is a large and burgeoning field. The central theme is the sensing of temperature. Although it is impossible to measure true temperature, the phenomena that are measured relate closely enough to be of real value. An infrared instrument, usually a spectrometer, is placed at the focus of an appropriate telescope. Spectral analyses of the outputs give the temperature information. Some fascinating discoveries have been made. Jupiter is at a higher temperature than its equilibrium with the sun would dictate. It may be that compressional forces from its very large size cause this. The star Vega has what is termed an infrared excess. It has more infrared radiation than a single black-body curve would indicate. The infrared astronomical satellite (IRAS) found that this was due to a lower-temperature surround, a collection of matter around Vega at a lower temperature. This could be planets or incipient planets. The infrared measurements on many stars help to establish their temperatures and therefore assist in their classification. One of the more recent experiments, using very-long-wavelength radiation, is the search for the 3 K black-body radiation background. The Big Bang theory says that the creation of the universe generated an enormous high-temperature radiation field. It has since cooled and expanded until now it is a 3 K field at the outer edges of the universe. [*See* ASTRONOMY, INFRARED.]

III. Radiometry

Infrared sources can be categorized in several ways: equilibrium and nonequilibrium, natural and artificial, and continuous or discontinuous in wavelength or time. Equilibrium radiators are those in thermal equilibrium with their surroundings. Their maximum power per unit area is dictated by the Planck radiation law,

$$M_\lambda = c_1\lambda^{-5}[\exp(c_2/\lambda T) - 1]^{-1}$$

where M_λ is the power per unit area and wavelength; c_1 the first radiation constant, and equals c_2, the second radiation constant, 1.4388 cm K; λ is the wavelength; and T the absolute temperature.

The total power radiated over all wavelengths is given by the Stefan–Boltzmann Law,

$$M = \int_0^\infty M_\lambda \, d\lambda = \sigma T^4$$

where σ is the Stefan–Boltzmann constant and is equal to $5.67 \times 10^{-8}\ \mathrm{m}^{-2}\ \mathrm{K}^{-4}$. Nonequilibrium radiators are lasers. Only perfect radiators emit according to the Planck equation. They are often called black bodies because they absorb as well as they emit. A perfect radiator is a perfect absorber and is therefore black. The emissivity of a body is the ratio of its radiant emittance to that of a black body. If a body's emissivity is independent of wavelength but less than one, the body is said to be gray. If the emissivity varies smoothly with wavelength, the body is said to be colored but still a continuous emitter. Many solids may be described this way. Most gasses have highly structured emissivities with large regions of no emission and regions in which there are sharp lines of emission. As long as they are equilibrium radiators, however, the Planck curve dictates the maximum power per unit area at any wavelength. The wavelengths of emission are dictated by the characteristic motions of charges. Materials with free electrons are essentially continuous radiators because the electrons are accelerated. Most dielectrics have bound charges that oscillate according to the reduced mass and binding strength of the constituent molecules. These frequencies in fact give spectral fingerprints to all materials and make possible the whole field of spectroscopy. [*See* RADIOMETRY; MOLECULAR OPTICAL SPECTROSCOPY; LASERS.]

A. Radiometric Nomenclature

In order to take into account the various spatial distributions involved, several radiometric quantities have been defined. The fundamental one is radiance; it is the power per unit projected area and solid angle. The symbol approved by the international committee on illumination (C.I.E.) is L. Thus

$$L = \partial^2 P/\cos\theta \, \partial A \, \partial\Omega$$

where P is the power, A the area, and Ω the solid angle.

Radiance is equivalent to what is called brightness or luminance for visible radiation. Some workers call it intensity or specific intensity. Radiant emittance or radiant exitance is the emitted power per unit area and is the integral over solid angle of radiance. Irradiance or incidance is the equivalent physical quantity for received radiation. Some workers call *this* intensity. The integral of radiance over area is intensity (in this scheme of nomenclature). It is usually used to describe radiation from subresolution sources. Other schemes have been proposed. Jones has suggested, based on the fact that the terms are based solely on geometric concepts, that the basic terms be sterance, incidance, exitance, and intensity. The terms are then modified appropriately. Radiance becomes radiant sterance; irradiance is radiant incidance; emittance is radiant exitance, and radiant intensity is radiant intensity. Other modifiers like "visible" and "photon" could also be used. Nicodemis proposed the word "areance" to encompass exitance and incidance, and pointance in place of intensity. Geist and Zalewski put forth the so-called Chinese restaurant scheme. In this, an array of modifiers is chosen for each term. The first scheme of nomenclature described here comes closest to being accepted by usage. However, there is no unanimity of names and symbols in this field. Great care is sometimes necessary in reading the literature.

B. Radiative Transfer

In a medium of refractive index n in which there is no absorption or scattering, the basic power transfer is given by

$$dP = (L/n^2)dA_1 \cos \theta_1 \, dA_2 \cos \theta_2/R^2$$

A differential amount of power dP is radiated from a differential element of area dA_1 to a similar one dA_2 at a distance R. The angles are the angles between the direction of radiation and the surface normals. In general, during an integration over the surface the distance R varies, but for a remote source R may be considered a constant, and both angles may be considered zero. If, in addition, n is 1, then the simplified equation is transferred to a total and simplified form

$$P = LA_1A_2/R^2$$

If the source is subresolution, the radiance and its area should be replaced by intensity,

$$P = IA_2/R^2$$

The irradiance is

$$E = I/R^2$$

This is the classic form of the inverse square law. The intercontinental rocket example can be treated with it. If the radiant intensity of the rocket at launch is one megawatt per steradian (10^6 W sr^{-1}), then at a distance of 2000 km the

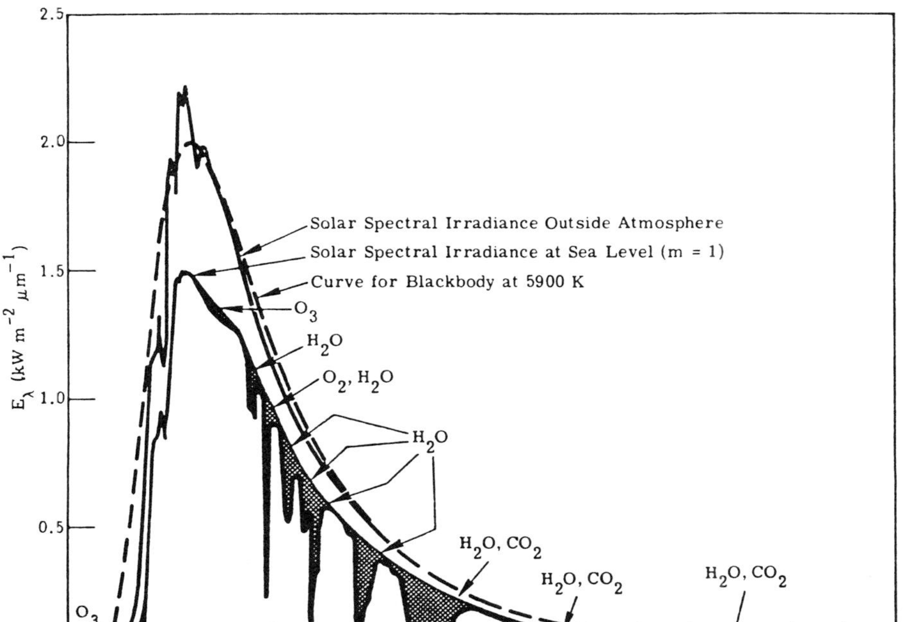

FIG. 11. Spectral distribution curves related to the sun. The shaded areas indicate absorption at sea level due to the atmospheric constituents shown. [From Wolfe, W. L., and Zissis, G. J. (1986). "The Infrared Handbook." The Office of Naval Research, LC 77-90786; ISBN 0-9603590-1-X, revised edition.]

irradiance is

$$E = 10^6 \text{ W sr}^{-1}/(2 \times 10^6)^2 \text{ m}^2$$
$$= 2.5 \times 10^{-7} \text{ W m}^{-2}$$

Even for a source of only(!) one-tenth this amount, the irradiance is detectable with reasonable size optics.

C. Characteristics of Some Natural Sources

The sun may be characterized as a black body with a temperature of 5900 K—at least in the infrared. Its peak radiation, according to the displacement law, is then at 0.5 μm. The radiance is given by the Planck equation. The irradiance at the earth is less, because of the great distance. It may be calculated by multiplying the radiance by the solid angle of the sun. This gives the solar spectral irradiance, the value at the top of the atmosphere. Figure 11 shows this calculated value, measured values, and values for solar radiation through the atmosphere.

The earth may be considered a black body at about 300 K. This, of course, is a function of the local temperature and the exact material. Most materials are relatively black in the infrared. Figure 12 shows some representative data of various soils, indicating an emissivity of about 90% throughout most of the infrared region.

The moon is a reflection of the sun. It has a reflectivity that is almost independent of both angle and wavelength; it has a visual magnitude −12.2. The hot side of the moon, illuminated by the sun, reaches a temperature of about 400 K, while the cold side goes as low as 150 K.

People are essentially blackbodies in the infrared. They have emissivity values within a few percent of 100%. People of different races are indistinguishable beyond about 2 μm.

Very many human-made objects are painted. Characteristics of most paints are that they have an emissivity of about 10% and are almost featureless beyond a few micrometers.

IV. Infrared Optical Materials

In the visible, almost all lenses and windows are made of glass. Unfortunately, glass becomes opaque at about 1.5–2.0 μm. Other materials must be used. These range from large, artificially grown crystals of common table salt to small, artificial and natural diamonds. There are almost 50 different refractive materials used for infrared instrumentation. They may be divided for descriptive purposes into crystals, glasses, compacts, and plastics. Usually, the longer the wavelength of application, the more difficult the attainment of an appropriate material. [*See* GLASS.]

Table I shows the properties of most of the important materials used for infrared instrumentation. They are listed essentially in order of increasing wavelength utility. The top three materials—fused silica, sapphire, and rutile—are hard, strong, and have high melting temperatures, but they are useful only to about 3 μm. Fused silica is glasslike; the others are crystals. Calcium aluminate, arsenic sulfur, and chalcogenide glasses are all used. The first-named is useful to about 6 μm, and great care must be used to keep water out of it. Arsenic–sulfur

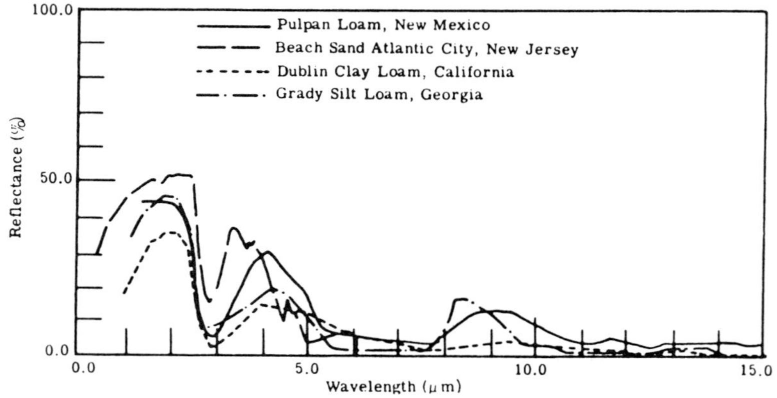

FIG. 12. Representative spectral reflectance. [Reprinted with permission from Condit, H. R. (1970). The spectral reflectance of American soils, *Photogramm, Eng.*, **36**. Copyright 1970 *Photogramm. Eng.*]

TABLE I. Useful Properties of Important Infrared Materials

Material	Spectral range (μm)	Refractive index	Density (g/ml)	Strength (10^6 psi)	Melting temperature (K)	Specific heat	Thermal expansion (10^{-6}/K)
SiO_2	0.2–5	1.5	2.2	10.6	1983	0.22	0.5
Al_2O_3	0.2–5	1.7	4.0	50	2300	0.18	6.7
TiO_2	0.5–5	2.4	4.3		2100	0.17	9
MgO	0.25–5	1.7	3.6	36	3073	0.21	11
Irtrans:							
1 MgF_2	1–8	1.3	3.2		1528		11
2 CdS	1–12	2.2	4.1		2103		7
3 CaF_2	1–8	1.4	3.2		1692		20
4 ZnSe	1–12	2.4	5.3		1788		8
5 MgO	1–8	1.5	3.6		3220		12
Ge	2–12	4.0	5.3	14.9	1109	0.07	5.75
Si	1–12	3.5	2.3	19	1693	0.17	4.2
CdS	0.5–15	2.4	4.1		1560		4.2
ZnSe	0.5–24	2.4	5.3		1790		
KCl	0.2–15	1.5	2.0		1049	0.16	36
As_2S_3	0.6–15	2.4	3.2	2.3	483		25
NaCl	0.2–20	1.5	2.2	5.8	1074	0.20	44
BaF_2	0.3–15	1.4	4.8	7.7	1553		18
LiF	0.2–20	1.3	2.7	9.4	1143	0.37	37
KRS-5	0.6–40	2.4	7.4				
TPX	1–200	1.3					
Polyethylene	1–12	1.3					
Styrofoam	50–300						
Diamond	0.3–80	2.4					

glass is also called arsenic trisulfide glass, but is really part of an arsenic–sulfur glass system. For that reason it can be inhomogeneous in both transmission and index. The general class of chalcogenide glasses consists of arsenic, sulfur, selenium, tellurium, and germanium in various amounts. Both of these latter glasses are good to about 12 μm but have lower softening points and are weaker than the materials previously discussed.

The Irtran materials were developed by Eastman Kodak; they are hot-pressed compounds that can be formed to some extent in disks and bowls and other shapes. In addition to the basic properties of the materials, these compounds scatter light to some degree. The saving grace is that infrared radiation, being of longer wavelength than visible, is scattered less. Thus the materials are quite useful.

Germanium, silicon, zinc selenide, and zinc sulfide are all semiconducting materials. The first two are usually available in either single-crystal or polycrystalline form. Their high refractive index values and low refractive dispersion make them useful as lens materials. The zinc compounds have been grown by chemical vapor deposition and are available in disks of about 50 cm diameter (or smaller). All of these semiconductors suffer a loss of transmission at elevated temperatures. Germanium is the worst; its critical temperature is 125°C. The others gradually deteriorate at about 300°C. Silicon and germanium are completely opaque in the visible; they look like metals.

The remaining materials are somewhat special. Lithium and barium fluoride can both be used fairly far into the infrared (and the ultraviolet), but they suffer from thermal shock. Vigorous polishing of lithium fluoride may cause it to crack! Materials like potassium iodide, potassium bromide, sodium chloride, and silver chloride have all been used, and sometimes are still used, for special applications. They have relatively long wavelength transmission, but they are soft, weak, easily attacked by various chemicals including water, and are toxic to some degree. Polyethylene can only be used in thin sheets, but may be useful as a sealing membrane for protecting the other materials from moisture. Finally, diamond, with all its wonderful properties, is only available in small sizes and is expensive.

There are two aspects to mirrors: the mirror blank and the coating. Blanks should have a high strength-to-weight ratio, be stable with time and temperature, and take a good polish. The classical materials have been Pyrex, fused silica, and low-expansion silica variations. Metallic mirror blanks are generally aluminum and beryllium. Most mirrors can be light weighted either by removing material from the back in an appropriate pattern or by fusing a thin plate to a structure of the general form of an egg crate. The glassy mirrors take a better polish. Beryllium has the highest strength-to-weight ratio. The special glasses have zero expansion (at a designated temperature). The metal mirrors can be made part of an optical-bench structure and can be self-compensating for temperature changes.

Mirror coatings are usually metallic, but for some special applications narrow-band multilayer, dielective coatings are used. In the infrared, all the metallic coatings have reflectivities greater than 95% (when they are clean). Gold has the highest and is not chemically attacked. Aluminum tends to form a very thin oxide and is not as reflective. Silver lies between the two in both characteristics.

V. Optical Systems

Optical systems are used to form or relay an image or to increase the collection of radiation from a subresolution source. The systems may consist entirely of lenses or of mirrors, or they may be a combination of both. In principle they have the same characteristics, foibles, and advantages as do optical systems for the visible—or any other spectral region. The features that are endemic to the infrared are the requirements for very wide spectral coverage and the peculiarities of the refractive materials. Also, because there are no high-performance infrared television tubes for all regions of the spectrum, optical–mechanical scanning systems are a necessity. [*See* OPTICAL SYSTEMS DESIGN.]

The lens systems used follow very closely the designs for the visible—singlets, doublets, Gausses, Tessars, etc. The only real differences are the color corrections and the shapes that result from the different index-of-refraction values.

The mirror systems consist of singles, doubles, and triples—as in the visible. An important variation that seems to be characteristic of infrared designs is the eccentric pupil design.

Single mirrors have the shapes of spheres, parabaloids, or ellipsoids. The spheres are used if resolution requirements are not too great. Paraboloids are used for imaging objects at infinity, and ellipsoids are used for near objects. A convex hyperboloid combined with a paraboloid is probably the most frequently used two-mirror system; it is called a Cassegrain. If a concave ellipsoid is used, the system is called a Gregorian. A Cassegrain with two general aspheric surfaces is better than a standard Cassegrain, and is called a Ritchey Chretien. All of the above have perfect on-axis imagery as a result of the geometry of their surfaces. To attain good imagery over a wide field, other designs are used. Foremost among the wide angle systems is the Schmidt. It consists of a spherical mirror with its aperture stop at its center of curvature and a corrector plate in the same position. The stop at this position insures that all rays are on axis. The corrector plate reduces spherical aberration. Such a system can provide 50-μrad imagery over 20° full fields.

The two-mirror systems all provide an accessible focal plane behind the primary, but they require struts or spiders to hold the secondary in place. A relatively new class of designs might be described as eccentric pupil three-mirror devices. A section of a full circular mirror, somewhat less than half the diameter, is used for each of three mirrors. By this stratagem, the secondary is not in the incoming beam. It is not necessary to use three mirrors, but practice has shown that the extra correction provided by the third mirror is useful and sometimes necessary. Linear fields up to 20° with resolution on the order of 50 urad may be obtained.

An optical system with a small field of view can cover a larger field if the small field is scanned over the large field by some optical–mechanical mechanism. This may be as simple as a large, flat mirror that oscillates or rotates. The optical system may be mounted on a gimbal that has a programmed scan. Two of the popular ways are a polygon scanner and a pair of rotating prisms, shown in Fig. 13.

A. Detectors

Infrared detectors transduce a radiant signal into an electrical one. It is useful to think of the input signal in terms of power and in terms of a

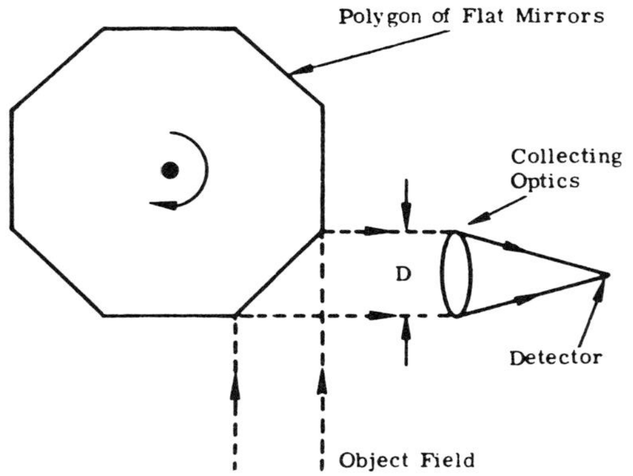

(a)

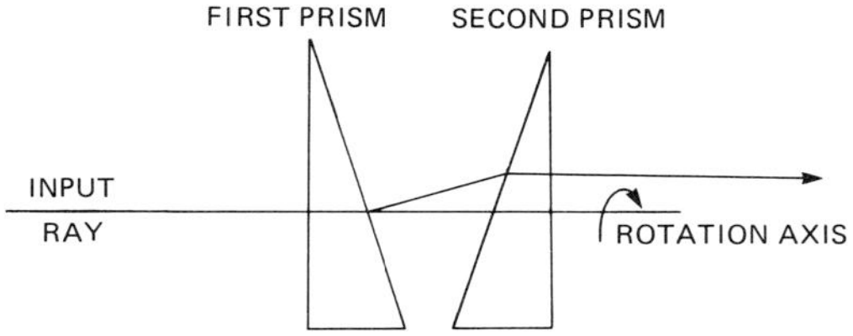

(b)

FIG. 13. (a) An exterior-mirror polygon scanner. (b) Rotating prisms.

photon rate. The detectors typically take an average of the signal over a length of time from about 1 nsec to about 1 msec. Thus it is not possible to measure any signal variations at the rate of either the optical or infrared frequency. The electrical signal is usually proportional to the average power or photon rate or of the time integral of them—over the integration time. An important exception to this direct detection process is optical heterodyning, which will be discussed separately.

Direct detectors can be categorized as photon detectors or thermal detectors, and they can also be separated into single, or elemental, detectors and imaging detectors. It is appropriate to discuss elemental detectors first, as they are simpler. Both thermal and photon detectors can also be described in terms of the physical processes by which they do detection.

This section then covers in order the following: elemental thermal detectors, elemental photon detectors, areal thermal detectors, and areal photon detectors (principally arrays).

1. Elemental Thermal Detectors

Most of these detectors are based on the fact that incident radiant power heats a detector and increases its temperature. Some property of the detector is dependent on temperature. Bolometers depend on the change of resistance with temperature. Thermocouples and thermopiles depend on the change of electrical potential between two dissimilar materials with temperature, called the Seebeck affect. Pyroelectric detectors depend on the change of internal electric polarization with the change in temperature, and Golay cells utilize the expansion of gas with increasing temperature.

Each one of these depends on the basic thermal interaction between the incident radiation the detector and its heat sink. The temperature increase T as a function of frequency ω is given by

$$|T(\omega)| = aRP(\omega)/\sqrt{1 + \omega^2\tau^2}$$

where a is the detector absorptance, R the thermal resistance of the detector, $P(\omega)$ the frequency spectrum of the input power, ω the radian frequency, and τ a time constant. The time constant is given by RC where C is the thermal capacitance. The thermal capacitance is the specific heat C_p times the mass M of the detector. The thermal resistance is the reciprocal of the thermal conductance, which in turn is the thermal conductivity times the cross-sectional area divided by the length of the element that connects to the thermal sink. The result, cast in this form, is similar to that of a single time-constant electrical circuit. The absorptance specifies the fraction of incident power that is absorbed and converted to heat. So the temperature rise is proportional to it. A high thermal resistance ensures that most of the absorbed power remains in the detector, rather than being conducted to the thermal sink. Therefore the temperature increase is proportional to it. The response time is slow if the resistance is high, because the detector does not readily release its heat. If the detector is large or has a large specific heat (or both), then the time constant RC is large because it takes more energy to heat a larger mass, or one with a larger heat capacity. The dc response RP is independent of this storage phenomenon. The high-frequency response is independent of the thermal resistance, but it decreases linearly with frequency.

These detectors are usually operated in simple voltage-divider networks, as shown in Fig. 14.

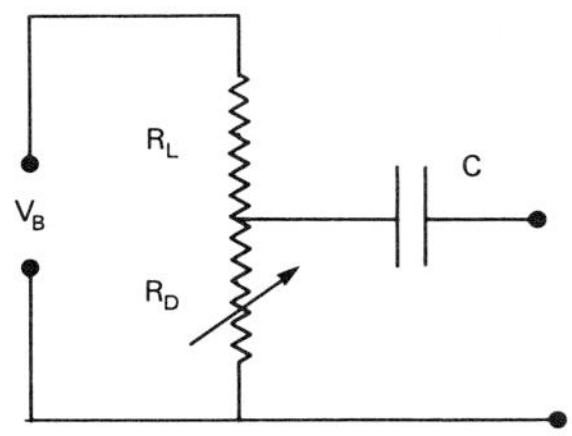

FIG. 14. Detector network; V_B is a dc bias voltage, R_L a load resistance, and R_D the variable detector resistance. The detector is connected to the preamplifier through the capacitor C.

The signal is routed through a capacitor so that only alternating signals are passed to the amplifier. The final equation for the output voltage of this circuit is

$$v = R_L \, dR_D \, V_B/(R_L + R_D)^2$$

Thus, using the earlier result,

$$v = \frac{R_L V_B}{(R_L + R_D)^2} \frac{aPR_D}{\sqrt{1 + \omega^2 \tau^2}}$$

This is the basic equation that describes the operation of bolometers. For the generation of good signal, the detector resistance, bias voltage absorptance, and temperature coefficient of resistance should all be high. The load resistance should be matched to the detector resistance. These considerations have ignored the presence of noise.

Much of the work on bolometers has gone into the search for materials with high values of temperature change of resistance. Early work was done on metals and carbon; later, semiconductors of two specific types were tried; and some work was done on superconductors, which surely have a very large change in resistance as they cross the transition temperature from conductor to superconductor. The work has been driven by two different applications. One was by the astronomers and spectroscopists who were interested in the far infrared (around 100 μm) and could accept unusual logistic problems in their laboratories—operation near absolute zero, for instance. The other was the group of industrial instrumentalists who searched for room-temperature, convenient detectors for railroad-car hot-box detectors, satellite horizon sensors, and thermographic cameras for medical and industrial diagnostics.

2. Photon Detectors

These detectors, which have an output that is proportional to the rate or total number of incident photons, are also called photodetectors. The essence of their operation is the absorption of a photon and the resultant creation of a hole–electron pair. The output signal is then dependent on whether a resistance, a change in photodiode operation, or a motion in a magnetic field is sensed. The fundamental operation may be understood by imagining the process in a crystal of pure germanium or silicon. Each of these is a cubic crystal with a valence of four. This consists of atomic sites surrounded by a collection of electrons. In the outermost shell reside four electrons. These are bound to the nucleus by electrostatic forces, with shielding from the other, inner electron shells. Thus they are not held very tightly. In fact, about 1 eV is enough energy to cause them to escape from their host atom and roam free in the lattice, buffeted by various thermal and mechanical motions. In terms of solid-state theory, this electron has made a transition from the valence band to the conduction band. It is a free electron and can contribute to the flow of electrons. This process is also known as the internal photoelectric effect by analogy with the more familiar photoeffect, in which electrons are freed from a photosurface into a vacuum and accelerated to an anode by application of an electric field. The current is proportional to the number of carriers generated per unit time, and they in turn are proportional to the number of photons incident per unit time with energy above the binding energy. The proportionality constant is called the quantum efficiency.

The equation for the increase in free photoelectrons can be written

$$N = \eta A E_p - N/\tau$$

where η is the quantum efficiency, A the detection area, E_p the number of incident photons per second per unit area, and τ the recombination time. This says simply that the rate of increase of photoelectrons is the generation rate minus the recombination rate. There are different types of recombination with different time constants that need to be considered in the detailed design of infrared photoconductors. A solution of this simple differential equation is

$$N(\omega) = \eta \tau A E_p/(1 + j\omega)$$

This is the same rolloff characteristic as for bolometric thermal detectors. The quantum efficiency corresponds to the absorptance, and AE_p, the total photon rate, corresponds to the input power. This detector is also used in a voltage-divider network, and the essence of detection is the change in resistance. The change in this case is directly related to the change in the number of free electrons through the conductivity equation

$$\sigma = nqv/E = Nqv/EV$$

where σ is the conductivity, n the number of photoelectrons per unit volume, V the volume, q the electronic charge, v the electron velocity, and E the electric field strength.

The change in resistance is related to the change in conductivity by

$$R = l/\sigma A$$

where l is the length and A the cross-sectional area.

These can all be combined to obtain the expression for the response of an infrared photoconductive detector.

A second important type of infrared photodetector is the diode detector. These are used frequently in the visible as detectors and in many circuit elements. The I–V (current–voltage) curve is shown in Fig. 15. When the diode has forward bias applied, the current flows easily and increases exponentially until saturation. When it is backbiased, not much current flows and the (negative) current changes very little with increasing negative bias. The relationship is described by the Ebers–Moll equation,

$$I = I_0[\exp(qV/kT) - 1]$$

where I is the current, I_0 the zero-bias current, V the bias voltage, k the Boltzmann constant, and T the diode temperature. When infrared radiation illuminates the diode, additional carriers are

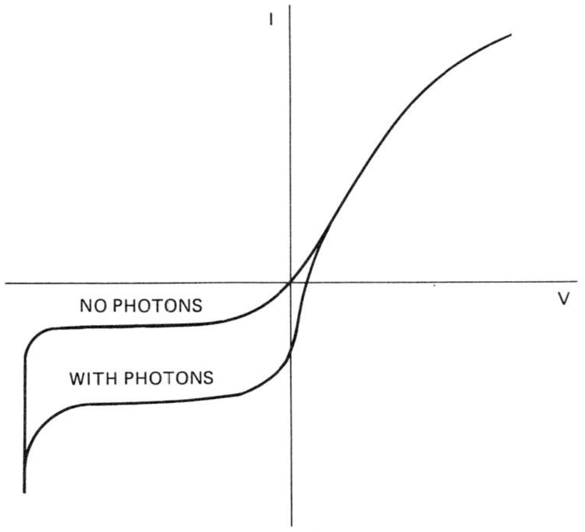

FIG. 15. Photodiode current–voltage (I–V) curves.

available to participate in current flow, as shown by the lower curve in Fig. 15. This current is given by

$$I = \eta q N$$

The expression is easy to understand. The photon rate N is converted to a photoelectron rate by the quantum efficiency, and the electronic charge converts this to a true electronic current. Diodes are generally faster than are photoconductors, because the generation of carriers and other interactions all occur in the tiny region near the junction.

B. Detector Descriptions

It has become customary in infrared technology to describe detectors in terms of a figure of merit called specific detectivity or dee star. The latter appellation comes from the symbol for it, namely D^*. It is defined as

$$D^*_\lambda = \sqrt{AB}\ \mathrm{SNR}/P_\lambda$$

It is the signal-to-noise ratio SNR per unit incident power P (in watts) for a detector that has an area A of 1 cm and a bandwidth B of 1 Hz. The units of D^* are cm $\mathrm{Hz}^{1/2}$ W^{-1}. These normalizations are based on the assumptions that the noise has a flat frequency spectrum and is proportional to the square root of the detector area. If the latter assumption is not true, the detector is often described by its noise equivalent power (NEP). This is defined as

$$\mathrm{NEP} = P/B^{1/2}\mathrm{SNR}$$

The NEP is the signal power that gives an output signal equal to the noise in a 1-Hz bandwidth; it may also be described as the power that gives a signal-to-noise ratio of 1 in that bandwidth. It has the units W $\mathrm{Hz}^{-1/2}$ (watts per root Hertz). Another use of NEP entails the noise in the frequency bandwidth of interest:

$$\mathrm{NEP} = P/\mathrm{SNR}$$

Then the units are watts.

All of these summary figures of merit may be for quasimonochromatic radiation or total radiation. In the first case, the D^* is called a spectral D^* and is written $D^*(\lambda, f, B)$, where the parameters within the parentheses are the wavelength of the radiation, the frequency at which the radiation was measured, and the frequency bandwidth (which must be 1 Hz). Most good infrared detectors are photon limited under reasonable conditions. Thus, some additional information about the background photon flux is obligatory.

Most thermal detectors operated at room temperature have D^* values ranging from 10^8 to 10^9 cm $Hz^{1/2}$ W^{-1} and time constants as fast as 1 msec. Pyroelectric detectors have a wide range of values and can be described generally as having an NEP that increases by an order of magnitude as the frequency response increases by three orders of magnitude. They are therefore useful as detectors of relatively high-power, high-frequency laser radiation.

Thermal detectors, used for astronomical and laboratory purposes, are operated within a few degrees of absolute zero. Usually, these detectors are not describable by a specific detectivity. They do have very low (good) NEP values on the order of 10^{-18} W $Hz^{-1/2}$ and time constants approaching seconds.

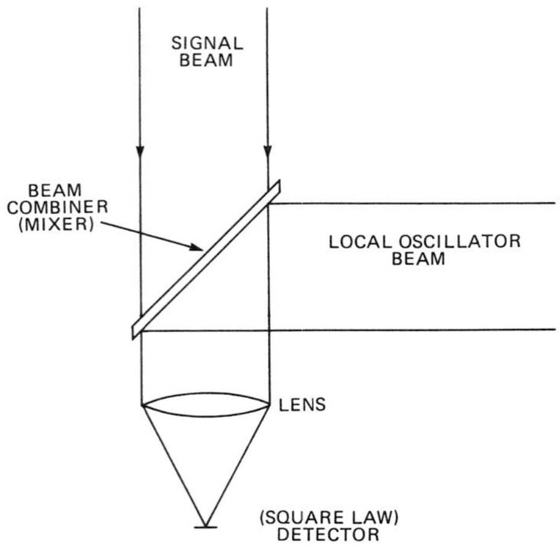

FIG. 16. Heterodyne geometry. Both beams could be convergent as they strike the beam combine, but they must emerge coincident.

C. Heterodyne Detection

This technique, used in radio broadcasting for years, is relatively new to infrared and optical technology. When two waves of different frequencies impinge on a square-law detector, the output consists of a dc term as well as sum and difference frequencies. Thus, as shown in Fig. 16, two quasimonochromatic beams are combined with a beamsplitter (in this case a beam combiner) and made to illuminate an ordinary detector with approximately the same geometry (same size, some convergence). If the power of the signal beam is P_s, that of the local oscillator beam P_{lo}, and the difference frequency ω_d, then the output signal is

$$V_s = P_s P_{lo} \cos \omega_d$$

The dc and sum frequency terms have been ignored, as they are usually filtered out by the electronics. Usually the signal power is weak and the local oscillator power is relatively strong. It is clear the output signal will be increased by increasing the local oscillator power. This is done to insure that the detector will be photon-noise limited. The electronics are tuned to a narrow frequency centered on the optical difference frequency.

This is a very sensitive detection technique; equivalent D^* values of approximately 10^{20} have been achieved. It requires detectors of high quantum efficiency, but their noises are relatively unimportant. Only signals of narrow spectral bandwidth can be utilized, but the spectrum can be swept by tuning the electrical filter. Heterodyne detection has been used in experimental devices for communication, laser radar, and astronomical observations.

Bibliography

Johnson, R. B., and Wolfe, W. L. (1986). "Selected Papers on Infrared Design." SPIE Vol. 513, Bellingham, Wash. LC 85-062041, ISBN 0-89252-548-7.

Wolfe, W. L., and Zissis, G. J. (1986). "The Infrared Handbook. The Office of Naval Research, LC 77-90786, ISBN 0-9603590-1-X, revised edition.

INTEGRAL EQUATIONS

Ram P. Kanwal *Pennsylvania State University*

Glossary

Cauchy representation: Representation of a function $f(z)$:

$$F(z) = \frac{1}{2\pi i} \int_C \frac{f(\zeta)}{\zeta - z} \, d\zeta$$

where z and ζ are points in the complex plane $\mathbb{C}$ while C is a contour in $\mathbb{C}$.

Compact operator: Operator that transforms any bounded set in a Hilbert space onto a precompact set.

Eigenvalue: Complex numbers λ_n of the integral equation $g(x) = \lambda \int_a^b K(x, y) g(y) \, dy$.

Eigenfunctions: Nonzero solutions $g_n(x)$ of the integral equation $g(x) = \lambda \int_a^b K(x, y) g(y) \, dy$.

Fredholm alternative: Alternative that specifies the conditions under which a linear integral equation can have a unique solution.

Green's function: Kernel obtained when a differential operator is inverted into an integral operator.

Hermitian kernel: Kernel $K(x, y)$ if $K(x, y) = \overline{K(y, x)}$, where bar indicates complex conjugate.

Hilbert–Schmidt theory: Theory pertaining to the series expansion of a function $f(x)$ which can be represented in the form $\int_a^b K(x, y) h(y) \, dy$.

Kernel: Function $K(x, y)$ occurring under the integral sign of the integral equation $\phi(x) g(x) = f(x) + \lambda \int_a^b K(x, y) F\{y, g(y)\} \, dy$.

Neumann series: Series obtained by solving the integral equation by successive approximations.

Riemann–Hilbert problem: Conversion of a singular integral equation with Cauchy kernel into an algebraic equation in terms of the boundary values of the function.

Separable kernel: Kernel $K(x, y) = \sum_{i=1}^n a_i(x) b_i(y)$; also called degenerate.

Singular integral equation: Equation in which either the kernel in the integral equation is singular or one or both of the limits of integration are infinite.

Integral equations are equations in which the unknown function appears under the integral sign. They arise in the quest for the integral representation formulas for the solution of a differential operator so as to include the boundary and initial conditions. They also arise naturally in describing phenomena by models which require summation over space and time. Among the integral equations which have received the most attention are the Fredholm- and Volterra-type equations. In the study of singular integral equations, the prominent ones are the Abel, Cauchy, and Carleman type.

I. Definitions, Classification, and Notation

An integral equation is a functional equation in which the unknown variable $g(x)$ appears under the integral sign. A general example of an integral equation is

$$\phi(x)g(x) = f(x) + \lambda \int_a^b F\{x, y; g(y)\}\, dy \qquad a \le x \le b \quad (1)$$

where $\phi(x)$, $f(x)$, and $F\{x, y, g(y)\}$ are known functions and $g(x)$ is to be evaluated. The quantity λ is a complex parameter. When $F\{x, y, g(y)\} = K(x, y)g(y)$, Eq. (1) becomes a *linear* integral equation:

$$\phi(x)g(x) = f(x) + \lambda \int_a^b K(x, y)g(y)\, dy \qquad a \le x \le b \quad (2)$$

where $K(x, y)$ is called a kernel. Four special cases of Eq. (2) are extensively studied. In the *Fredholm* integral equation of *the first kind* $\phi(x) = 0$, and in his equation of the *second kind* $\phi(x) = 1$; in both cases a and b are constants. The *Volterra integral equations* of the first and second kinds are like the corresponding Fredholm integral equations except that now $b = x$. If $f(x) = 0$ in either case, the equation is called homogeneous.

A nonlinear integral equation may occur in the form (1) or the function $f\{x, y, g(y)\}$ may have the form $K(x, y)F(y, g(y))$ where $F(y, g(y))$ is nonlinear in $g(y)$.

When one or both limits of integration become infinite or when the kernel becomes infinite at one or more points within the range of integration, the integral equation is called *singular*.

We shall mainly deal with functions which are either continuous or integrable or square integrable. A function $g(x)$ is square integrable if $\int_a^b |g(x)|^2\, dx < \infty$, and is called an $\mathcal{L}_2$ function. The kernel $K(x, y)$ is an $\mathcal{L}_2$ function if

$$\int_a^b |K(x, y)|^2\, dx < \infty$$

$$\int_a^b |K(x, y)|^2\, dy < \infty \qquad (3)$$

$$\int_a^b \int_a^b |K(x, y)|^2\, dx\, dy < \infty$$

We shall use the inner product (or scalar product) notation

$$\langle \phi, \psi \rangle = \int_a^b \phi(x)\bar{\psi}(x)\, dx \qquad (4)$$

where the bar indicates complex conjugate. The functions ϕ and ψ are orthogonal if $\langle \phi, \psi \rangle = 0$. The norm of the function ϕ is $\|\phi\| = (\langle \phi, \phi \rangle)^{1/2}$. If $\|\phi\| = 1$, then ϕ is called *normalized*. In terms of this norm the famous Cauchy–Schwarz inequality can be written as

$$|\langle \phi, \psi \rangle| \le \|\phi\|\,\|\psi\| \qquad (5)$$

while the Minkowski inequality is

$$\|\phi + \psi\| \le \|\phi\| + \|\psi\| \qquad (6)$$

NOTATION. We shall sometimes write the right-hand side of Eq. (2) as $f + \lambda K g$ and call K the *Fredholm operator*. Furthermore, for Fredholm integral equations it will be assumed that the range of integration is a to b unless the contrary is stated. The limits a and b will be omitted.

II. The Method of Successive Approximations

Our aim is to solve the inhomogeneous Fredholm integral equation

$$g(x) = f(x) + \lambda \int K(x, y)g(y)\, dy \qquad (7)$$

where we assume that $f(x)$ and $K(x, y)$ are in the space $\mathcal{L}_2[a, b]$, by Picard's method of successive approximations. The method is based on choosing the first approximation as $g_0(x) = f(x)$. This is substituted into Eq. (7) under the integral sign to obtain the second approximation and the process is then repeated. This results in the sequence

$$\begin{aligned} g_0(x) &= f(x) \\ g_1(x) &= f(x) + \lambda \int K(x, y)g_0(y)\, dy \\ &\;\vdots \\ g_m(x) &= f(x) + \lambda \int K(x, y)g_{m-1}(y)\, dy \end{aligned} \qquad (8)$$

The analysis is facilitated when we utilize the iterated kernels defined as

$$\begin{aligned} K_1(x, y) &= K(x, y) \\ K_2(x, y) &= \int K(x, s)K_1(s, y)\, ds \\ &\;\vdots \\ K_m(x, y) &= \int K(x, s)K_{m-1}(s, y)\, ds \end{aligned} \qquad (9)$$

It can be proved that $K_{m+n}(x, y) = \int K_m(x, s)K_n(s, y)\, ds$. Thereby, we can express the mth approximation in (8) as

$$g_m(x) = f(x) + \lambda \int \left[\sum_{n=1}^{m} \lambda^{n-1} K_n(x, y) \right] f(y)\, dy \tag{10}$$

When we let $m \to \infty$, we obtain formally the so-called *Neumann series*

$$g(x) = \lim_{m\to\infty} g_m(x)$$

$$= f(x) + \sum_{m=1}^{\infty} \lambda^m \int K_m(x, y) f(y)\, dy \tag{11}$$

In order to examine the convergence of this series, we apply the Cauchy–Schwarz inequality (5) to the general term $\int K_m(x, y) f(y)\, dy$ and get

$$\left| \int K_m(x, y) f(y)\, dy \right|^2$$

$$\leq \left(\int |K_m(x, y)|^2\, dy \right) \int |f(y)|^2\, dy \tag{12}$$

Let us denote the norm $\|f\|$ as D and the upper bound of the integral $\int |K_m(x, y)|^2\, dy$ as C_m^2, so that relation (12) becomes

$$\left| \int K_m(x, y) f(y)\, dy \right|^2 \leq C_m^2 D^2 \tag{13}$$

We can connect the estimate C_m^2 with C_{m-1}^2 by applying the Cauchy–Schwarz inequality to relation (9) and then integrating with respect to y so that $\int |K_m(x, y)|^2\, dy \leq B^2 C_{m-1}^2$ where $B^2 = \int\int |K(x, y)|^2\, dx\, dy$. Continuing this process we get the relation $C_m^2 \leq B^{2m-2} C_1^2$. Substituting it in (13) we arrive at the inequality

$$\left| \int K_m(x, y) f(y)\, dy \right|^2 < C_1^2 D^2 B^{2m-2} \tag{14}$$

This means that the infinite series (11) converges faster than the geometric series with common ratio $|\lambda| B$. Thus, if $|\lambda| B < 1$, the Neumann series converges uniformly and absolutely. Fortunately, the condition $|\lambda| B < 1$ also assures us that solution (11) is unique as can be easily proved. In view of the uniform convergence of series (11) we can change the order of integration and summation in it and write it as

$$g(x) = f(x) + \lambda \int \Gamma(x, y; \lambda) f(y)\, dy \tag{15}$$

where $\Gamma(x, y; \lambda) = \sum_{m=1}^{\infty} \lambda^{m-1} K_m(x, y)$ is called the *resolvent kernel*. This series is also convergent at least for $|\lambda| B < 1$. Indeed, the resolvent kernel is an analytic function of λ, regular at least inside the circle $|\lambda| B < 1$. From the uniqueness of the solution it can be proved that the resolvent kernel is unique.

A few remarks are in order:

1. We can start with any other suitable function for the first approximation $g_0(s)$.
2. The Neumann series, in general, cannot be summed in closed form.
3. The solution of Eq. (7) may exist even if $|\lambda| B > 1$.

The same iterative scheme is applicable to the Volterra integral equation of the second kind:

$$g(x) = f(x) + \lambda \int_a^x K(x, y) g(y)\, dy \tag{16}$$

In this case the formulas corresponding to (11) and (15) are

$$g(x) = f(x) + \sum_{m=1}^{\infty} \lambda^m \int_a^x K_m(x, y) f(y)\, dy \tag{17}$$

and

$$g(x) = f(x) + \lambda \int_a^x \Gamma(x, y; \lambda) f(y)\, dy \tag{18}$$

where the iterated kernel $K_m(x, y)$ satisfies the recurrence formula $K_m(x, y) = \int_y^x K(x, s) K_{m-1}(s, y)\, ds$, with $K_1(x, y) = K(x, y)$ as before. The resolvent kernel is given by the same formula as given previously and is an entire function of λ for any given (x, y).

III. The Fredholm Alternative

Let us consider the inhomogeneous Fredholm integral equation of the second kind

$$g(x) = f(x) + \lambda \int K(x, y) g(y)\, dy \tag{19}$$

when the kernel is *degenerate* (*separable*) (i.e., $K(x, y) = \sum_{k=1}^{n} a_k(x) b_k(y)$, where $a_k(x)$ and $b_k(y)$, $k = 1, \ldots, n$, are linearly independent functions). Thus, Eq. (19) becomes

$$g(x) = f(x) + \lambda \sum_{k=1}^{n} a_k(x) \int b_k(y) g(y)\, dy \tag{20}$$

where we have exchanged summation with integration. It emerges that the technique of solving Eq. (20) depends on the choice of the complex parameter λ and on the constants c_k defined as

$$c_k = \int b_k(y) g(y)\, dy \tag{21}$$

which are unknown because $g(y)$ is so. Thereby, Eq. (20) takes the algebraic form

$$g(x) = f(x) + \lambda \sum_{k=1}^{n} c_k a_k(x) \tag{22}$$

Next, we multiply both sides of (22) by $b_i(x)$ and integrate from a to b so that we have a set of linear algebraic equations

$$c_i = f_i + \lambda \sum_{k=1}^{n} a_{ik} c_k, \qquad i = 1, 2, \ldots, n \tag{23}$$

where

$$f_i = \int b_i(x) f(x)\, dx$$
$$a_{ik} = \int b_i(x) a_k(x)\, dx \tag{24}$$

Let us write the algebraic system (23) in the matrix form

$$(\mathbf{I} - \lambda \mathbf{A})\mathbf{c} = \mathbf{f} \tag{25}$$

where $\mathbf{I}$ is the identity matrix of order n, $\mathbf{A}$ is the matrix a_{ik}, while $\mathbf{c}$ and $\mathbf{f}$ are column matrices.

The determinant $D(\lambda)$ of the algebraic system (23) is

$$D(\lambda) = \begin{vmatrix} 1 - \lambda a_{11} & -\lambda a_{12} & \cdots & -\lambda a_{1n} \\ -\lambda a_{21} & 1 - \lambda a_{22} & \cdots & -\lambda a_{2n} \\ \vdots & & & \\ -\lambda a_{n1} & -\lambda a_{n2} & \cdots & 1 - \lambda a_{nn} \end{vmatrix} \tag{26}$$

which is a polynomial of degree at most n in λ. Note that $D(\lambda)$ is not identically zero because when $\lambda = 0$, it reduces to unity. Accordingly, for all values of λ for which $D(\lambda) \neq 0$, the algebraic system (25) and thereby integral equation (19) has a unique solution. On the other hand, for all values of λ for which $D(\lambda) = 0$, algebraic system (25), and with it integral equation (19), is either insoluble or has an infinite number of solutions. We discuss both these cases.

The Case $D(\lambda) \neq 0$. In this case the algebraic system (25) has only one solution given by Cramer's rule

$$c_k = \left(\frac{D_{1k}f_1 + \cdots + D_{hk}f_h + \cdots + D_{nk}f_n}{D(\lambda)}\right)$$
$$k = 1, 2, \ldots, n \tag{27}$$

where D_{hk} denotes the cofactor of the (h, k)th element of the determinant (26). When we substitute (27) in (22) we obtain the unique solution

$$g(x) = f(x) + \lambda \frac{\sum_{j=1}^{n} \sum_{k=1}^{n} D_{jk} f_j a_k(x)}{D(\lambda)}$$
$$= f(x) + \frac{\lambda}{D(\lambda)}$$
$$\times \int \left\{ \sum_{j=1}^{n} \sum_{k=1}^{n} D_{jk} b_j(y) a_k(x) \right\} f(y)\, dy \tag{28}$$

where we have used relation (24). This expression can be put in an elegant form if we introduce the determinant

$$D(x, y; \lambda) = \begin{vmatrix} 0 & -a_1(x) & -a_2(x) & \cdots & -a_n(x) \\ b_1(y) & 1 - \lambda a_{11} & -\lambda a_{12} & \cdots & -\lambda a_{1n} \\ b_2(y) & -\lambda a_{21} & 1 - \lambda a_{22} & \cdots & -\lambda a_{2n} \\ \vdots & & & & \\ b_n(y) & -\lambda a_{n1} & -\lambda a_{n2} & \cdots & 1 - \lambda a_{nn} \end{vmatrix} \tag{29}$$

which is called the *Fredholm minor*. Then Eq. (28) takes the form

$$g(x) = f(x) + \lambda \int \Gamma(x, y; \lambda) f(y)\, dy \tag{30a}$$

where the resolvent kernel Γ is the ratio of two determinants, that is,

$$\Gamma(x, y; \lambda) = D(x, y; \lambda)/D(\lambda)$$
$$= \frac{1}{D(\lambda)} \sum_{j=1}^{n} \sum_{k=1}^{n} D_{jk} b_j(y) a_k(x) \tag{30b}$$

It is clear from the above analysis that if we start with the homogeneous integral equation

$$g(x) = \lambda \int K(x, y) g(y)\, dy \tag{31}$$

we shall obtain the homogeneous algebraic system

$$(\mathbf{I} - \lambda \mathbf{A})\mathbf{c} = 0 \tag{32}$$

When $D(\lambda) \neq 0$, this algebraic system and the homogeneous integral equation (31) have only the trivial solutions.

The Case $D(\lambda) = 0$. In this case the algebraic system (32) and hence the homogeneous integral equation (31) may have either no solution or infinitely many solutions. To examine these possibilities it is necessary to discuss the subject of eigenvalues and eigenfunctions of the homogeneous problem (31). Strictly speaking we should write it as $\int K(x, y)g(y)\,dy = \omega g(x)$ for ω to be an eigenvalue, but in the theory of integral equations it has become customary to call the parameter $\lambda \neq 0$, for which the homogeneous equation (31) has a nontrivial solution, its eigenvalue. The corresponding solution $g(x)$ is called the eigenfunction of the operator K. From the above analysis it follows that the eigenvalues of (31) are the solutions of the polynomial $|\mathbf{I} - \lambda\mathbf{A}| = 0$. There may exist more than one eigenfunction corresponding to a specific eigenvalue. Let us denote the number r of such eigenfunctions as g_{i1}, g_{i2}, ..., g_{ir} corresponding to the eigenvalue λ_i. The number r is called the *index* of the eigenvalue λ_i (it is also called the *geometric* multiplicity of λ_i while the *algebraic* multiplicity m means that $D(\lambda) = 0$ has m equal roots). We know from linear algebra that if p is the rank of the determinant $D(\lambda_i) = |\mathbf{I} - \lambda_i\mathbf{A}|$, then $r = n - p$. If $r = 1$, λ_i is called a simple eigenvalue. Let us assume that the eigenfunctions g_{i1}, ..., g_{ir} have been normalized (i.e., $\|g_{ij}\| = 1$ for $j = 1, \ldots, r$). Then to each eigenvalue λ_i of index $r = n - p$, there corresponds a solution $g_i(x)$ of the homogeneous integral equation (31) of the form $g_i(x) = \sum_{k=1}^{r} \alpha_k g_{ik}(x)$, where α_k are arbitrary constants.

For studying the case when the inhomogeneous integral equation (19) has a solution even when $D(\lambda) = 0$, we need the integral equation

$$\psi(x) = f(x) + \lambda \int \overline{K(y, x)}\psi(y)\,dy \tag{33}$$

which is called the *transpose* (or *adjoint*) of Eq. (19) which is then the transpose of Eq. (33). For the separable kernel $K(x, y)$ as considered in this section, the transpose kernel is $\overline{K(y, x)} = \sum_{k=1}^{n} \overline{a_k(y)b_k(x)}$. When we follow the same steps that we followed for integral equation (19) we find that the transposed integral equation (33) leads to the algebraic system $(\mathbf{I} - \bar{\lambda}\bar{\mathbf{A}}^{\mathrm{T}})\mathbf{c} = \mathbf{f}$, where $\mathbf{A}^{\mathrm{T}}$ stands for the transpose of $\mathbf{A}$ while c_k and f_k are now defined as

$$\begin{aligned} c_k &= \int \overline{a_k(y)}\psi(y)\,dy \\ f_k &= \int \overline{a_k(y)}f(y)\,dy \end{aligned} \tag{34}$$

respectively. Clearly, the determinant of this algebraic system is $\overline{D(\bar{\lambda})}$. Accordingly, the transposed integral equation (33) also possesses a unique solution whenever (19) does. Also, the eigenvalues of the homogeneous part of Eq. (33), that is,

$$\psi(x) = \lambda \int \overline{K(y, x)}\psi(y)\,dy \tag{35}$$

are the complex conjugates of those for (31). The eigenvectors of the homogeneous system $(\mathbf{I} - \lambda\bar{\mathbf{A}}^{\mathrm{T}})\mathbf{c} = 0$, are, in general, different from the corresponding eigenvectors of system (32). The same applies to the eigenfunctions of the transposed integral equation (35). Because the geometric multiplicity r of λ_i for (31) is the same as that of $\bar{\lambda}_i$ for (35), the number of linearly independent eigenfunctions of the transposed equation (35) corresponding to $\bar{\lambda}_i$ are also r in number, say, ψ_{i1}, ψ_{i2}, ..., ψ_{ir} which we assume to be normalized. Accordingly, any solution $\psi_i(x)$ of (35) corresponding to the eigenvalue λ_i is of the form $\psi_i(x) = \sum_{k=1}^{n} \beta_k\psi_{ik}(x)$, where β_i are arbitrary constants. Incidentally, it can be easily proved that the eigenfunctions $g(x)$ and $\psi(x)$ corresponding to eigenvalues λ_1 and $\bar{\lambda}_2$ ($\lambda_1 \neq \lambda_2$) of the homogeneous integral equation (31) and its transpose (35) respectively, are orthogonal.

This analysis is sufficient for us to prove that the necessary and sufficient condition for Eq. (19) to have a solution for $\lambda = \lambda_i$, a root of $D(\lambda) = 0$, is that $f(x)$ be orthogonal to the r eigenfunctions ψ_{ij}, $j = 1, \ldots, r$, of the transposed equation (35). The necessary part follows from the fact that if Eq. (19) for $\lambda = \lambda_i$ admits a certain solution $g(x)$, then

$$\begin{aligned} &\int f(x)\overline{\psi_{ij}(x)}\,dx \\ &\quad= \int g(x)\overline{\psi_{ij}(x)}\,dx \\ &\qquad - \lambda_i \int \overline{\psi_{ij}(x)}\,dx \int K(x, y)g(y)\,dy \\ &\quad= \int g(x)\overline{\psi_{ij}}(x)\,dx \\ &\qquad - \left(\lambda_i \int \overline{g(y)}\,dy \int \overline{K(x, y)}\psi_{ij}(x)\,dx\right) \\ &\quad= 0 \end{aligned}$$

because $\bar{\lambda}_i$ and $\psi_{ij}(x)$ are an eigenvalue and a corresponding eigenfunction of (35). For the proof of the sufficiency, we appeal to the corresponding condition of orthogonality for the linear algebraic system which assures us that the inhomogeneous system (25) reduces to only $n - r$ independent equations (i.e., the rank of the matrix $(I - \lambda\mathbf{A})$ is exactly $p = n - r$ and therefore the system $(\mathbf{I} - \lambda\mathbf{A})\mathbf{c} = \mathbf{f}$ is soluble). Substituting this value of $\mathbf{c}$ in (22) we have the required solution of (19).

This analysis is true for a general integrable kernel. Fredholm gave three theorems in this connection and they bear his name. These theorems are of great importance in general discussion but are of little use in constructing closed form solutions or obtaining solutions numerically. Fredholm's first theorem gives the same formula as (30a) where the resolvent kernel is

$$\Gamma(x, y; \lambda) = D(x, y; \lambda)/D(\lambda), \qquad D(\lambda) \neq 0 \quad (36)$$

which is a meromorphic function of the complex variable λ, being the ratio of two entire functions $D(x, y; \lambda)$ and $D(\lambda)$ which are given by suitable Fredholm series of form similar to (30b). The other two theorems discuss the case $D(\lambda) = 0$ for a general kernel. The discussion given above and these three theorems add up to the following important result.

The Fredholm Alternative Theorem. For a fixed λ, either the integral equation (19) possesses one and only one solution $g(x)$ for integrable functions $f(x)$ and $K(x, y)$ (in particular the solution $g(x) = 0$ for the homogeneous equation (31)), or the homogeneous equation (31) possesses a finite number r of linearly independent solutions $g_{ij}, j = 1, \ldots, r$, with respect to the eigenvalue $\lambda = \lambda_i$. In the first case, the transposed inhomogeneous equation (33) also possesses a unique solution. In the second case, the transposed homogeneous equation (35) also has r linearly independent solutions $\psi_{ij}(x), j = 1, \ldots, r$, corresponding to the eigenvalues λ_i; and the inhomogeneous integral equation (19) has a solution if and only if the given function $f(x)$ is orthogonal to all the eigenfunctions $\psi_{ij}(x)$. In this case the general solution of the integral equation (19) is determined only up to an additive linear combination $\sum_{j=1}^{r} \alpha_j g_{ij}(x)$.

IV. The Fredholm Operator

We have observed in Section I that the Fredholm operator $Kg(x) = \int K(x, y)g(y)\, dy$ is linear (i.e., $K(\alpha g_1 + \beta g_2) = \alpha K g_1 + \beta K g_2$, where α and β are arbitrary complex numbers). In this section we study some general results for this operator. For this purpose we consider a linear space of an infinite dimension with inner product defined by (4) (i.e., $\langle f, g\rangle = \int f(x)\bar{g}(x)\, dx$). This inner product is a complex number and satisfies the following axioms:

(a) $\langle f, f\rangle = 0$ iff $f = 0$.
(b) $\langle \alpha f_1 + \beta f_2, g\rangle = \alpha\langle f_1, g\rangle + \beta\langle f_2, g\rangle$.
(c) $\langle f, g\rangle = \overline{\langle g, f\rangle}$.

The norm $\|f\|$ defined by (4) generates the natural metric $d(f, g) = \|f - g\|$. Furthermore, we have the Cauchy–Schwarz and Minkowski inequalities as given by (5) and (6), respectively.

An important concept in the study of metric spaces is that of completeness. A metric space is called complete if every Cauchy sequence of functions in this space is a convergent sequence (i.e., the limit is in this space). A *Hilbert space* H is an inner product linear space that is complete in its natural metric. An important example is the space of square integrable functions on the interval $[a, b]$. It is denoted as $\mathcal{L}_2[a, b]$, called $\mathcal{L}_2$ space in the sequel.

An operator K is called *bounded* if there exists a constant $M > 0$, such that $\|Kg\| \le M\|g\|$ for all $g \in \mathcal{L}_2$. We can prove that the Fredholm operator with an $\mathcal{L}_2$ kernel is bounded by starting with the relation $f = Kg$. Then by using the Cauchy–Schwarz inequality we have

$$|f(x)|^2 = \left|\int K(x, y)g(y)\right|^2 dy$$

$$\le \int |K(x, y)|^2\, dy \int |g(y)|^2\, dy$$

Integrating both sides of this relation we find that $\|f\| = \|Kg\| \le \|g\| \left[\int\int |K(x, y)|^2\, dx\, dy\right]^{1/2}$ and we have established the boundedness of K. The norm $\|K\|$ of an operator K is defined as

$$\|K\| = \sup(\|Kg\|/\|g\|) \qquad (37a)$$

or

$$\|K\| = (\sup\|Kg\|;\ \|g\| = 1) \qquad (37b)$$

The operator K is called continuous in a Hilbert space if whenever $\{g_n\}$ is a sequence in the domain of K with limit g, then $Kg_n \to Kg$. A linear operator is continuous if it is bounded and conversely.

A set S is called precompact if a convergent subsequence can be extracted from any sequence of elements in S. A bounded linear operator K is called compact if it transforms any bounded set in H onto a precompact set. Any bounded operator K, whose range is finite-dimensional, is compact because it transforms a bounded set in H into a bounded finite-dimensional set which is necessarily precompact. Many interesting integral operators are compact. For instance, if the Hilbert space is $\mathcal{L}_2$ space and $K(x, y)$ is a degenerate kernel $\sum_{i=1}^{n} a_i(x)b_i(y)$, then K is a compact operator. This follows by observing that

$$Kg = \int \left[\sum_{i=1}^{n} a_i(x)b_i(y)g(y)\right] dy$$

$$= \sum_{i=1}^{n} c_i a_i(x)$$

(i.e., the range of K is a finite-dimensional subspace of $\mathcal{L}_2$). Furthermore,

$$\|Kg\| = \left\|\sum_{i=1}^{n} c_i a_i(x)\right\| \le \sum_{i=1}^{n} |c_i| \|a_i\|$$

$$\le \sum_{i=1}^{n} \|a_i\| \int |b_i(y)| |g_i(y)| \, dy$$

Finally, by applying the Cauchy–Schwarz inequality we have $\|Kg\| \le M\|g\|$, where $M = \sum_{i=1}^{n} \|a_i\| \|b_i\|$. Accordingly, K is a bounded linear operator with finite-dimensional range and hence it is compact.

The following property of compact operators will prove useful in the next section. Let K be a compact operator on the Hilbert space H, and L be a bounded operator. Then both KL and LK are compact operators. To prove this property for the case of LK we let $\{f_n\}$ be a uniformly bounded sequence in H. Since K is compact it contains a subsequence $\{f_{n'}\}$ such that $\|LKf_{n'} - LKf_{m'}\| \le \|L\| \|Kf_{n'} - Kf_{m'}\|$. This means that $\{LKf_n\}$ is also a Cauchy sequence. In the case of KL, we observe that if $\{f_n\}$ is uniformly bounded, and L is bounded, then $\{Lf_n\}$ is also uniformly bounded. The compactness of K now assures us that there exists a subsequence $\{KLf_{n'}\}$ which is a Cauchy sequence. Thus, KL is also compact. As a particular case we find that if K is compact then so is K^2.

There are many interesting results regarding the compact operators. Some of them are as follows.

1. If $\{K_n\}$ is a sequence of compact operators on a Hilbert space H, such that for some K we have $\lim_{n\to\infty} \|K - K_n\| = 0$, then K is compact.
2. If $K(x, y)$ is continuous for all $a \le x, y \le b$ then K is a compact operator on $\mathcal{L}_2[a, b]$.
3. An $\mathcal{L}_2$ kernel K (i.e., $\int\int |K(x, y)|^2 \, dx \, dy < \infty$) is a compact operator.

V. Hermitian Kernels and the Hilbert–Schmidt Theory

Let us now consider a technique quite different from the Neumann and Fredholm series. This technique is based on considering the eigenvalues and eigenfunctions of the homogeneous integral equation with *Hermitian* kernel (i.e., $K(x, y) = \overline{K(y, x)}$ (then K is called the Hermitian operator). For real K it becomes $K(x, y) = K(y, x)$ (i.e., a symmetric kernel). We shall restrict ourselves to the Hilbert space $\mathcal{L}_2$ of square integrable functions and will benefit from the concepts of the previous section. Because

$$\begin{aligned} \langle K\phi, \psi\rangle &= \int \bar{\psi}(x) \left[\int K(x, y)\phi(y) \, dy\right] dx \\ &= \int \phi(y) \left[\int K(x, y)\bar{\psi}(x) \, dx\right] dy \\ &= \int \phi(x) \left[\int K(y, x)\bar{\psi}(y) \, dy\right] dx \\ &= \langle \phi, \bar{K}\psi\rangle \end{aligned} \tag{38}$$

the operator $\bar{K}(y, x)$ is called the *adjoint* operator. When K is Hermitian, this result becomes $\langle K\phi, \psi\rangle = \langle \phi, K\psi\rangle$ (i.e., K is *selfadjoint*). On the other hand, $\langle K\phi, \phi\rangle = \overline{\langle \phi, K\phi\rangle}$. Combining these two results we observe that the inner product $\langle K\phi, \phi\rangle$ is always real and the converse is also true.

Systems of orthogonal functions play an important role in this section so we give a brief account here. A finite or an infinite set $\{\phi_k\}$ is said to be an orthogonal set if $\langle \phi_i, \phi_j\rangle = 0$, $i \ne j$. If none of the elements of this set is zero vector, it is said to be a proper orthogonal set. A set is orthonormal if $\langle \phi_i, \phi_j\rangle = \delta_{ij}$, where δ_{ij} is the Kronecker delta which is zero for $i \ne j$ and 1 if $i = j$. As defined in Section I, a function ϕ for which $\|\phi\| = 1$ is said to be normalized. Given a finite or a countably infinite independent set of functions $\{\psi_n\}$, we can replace them by an equivalent set $\{\phi_n\}$ which is orthonormal. This is achieved by the so-called *Gram–Schmidt* procedure:

$$\phi_1 = \frac{\psi_1}{\|\psi_1\|}$$

$$\phi_1 = \frac{\psi_2 - \langle \psi_2, \phi_1\rangle \phi_1}{\|\psi_2 - \langle \psi_2, \phi_1\rangle \phi_1\|}$$

$$\vdots$$

$$\phi_n = \frac{\psi_n - \sum_{i=1}^{n-1} \langle \psi_n, \phi_i\rangle \phi_i}{\|\psi_n - \sum_{i=1}^{n-1} \langle \psi_n, \phi_i\rangle \phi_i\|}$$

as is easily verified. In case we are given a set of orthogonal functions then we can convert it into an orthonormal set simply by dividing each function by its norm.

Starting from an arbitrary orthonormal system we can construct the theory of Fourier series on the same lines as the trigonometric series. This is achieved if we attempt to find the best approximation of an arbitrary function $\psi(x)$ in terms of a linear combination of an orthonormal set $\{\phi_n\}$.

By this we mean that we choose the coefficients $\alpha_1, \alpha_2, \ldots, \alpha_n$ in order to minimize

$$\|\psi - \sum_{i=1}^{n} \alpha_i\phi_i\|^2 = \|\psi\|^2 + \sum_{i=1}^{n} |\langle\psi, \phi_i\rangle - \alpha_i|^2 - \sum_{i=1}^{n} |\langle\psi, \phi_i\rangle|^2 \tag{39}$$

Clearly, the minimum is achieved by setting $\alpha_i = \langle\psi, \phi_i\rangle = a_i$ (say), which are called the Fourier coefficients of ψ relative to the orthonormal system $\{\phi_n\}$. Then (39) becomes

$$\|\psi - \sum_{i=1}^{n} \alpha_i\phi_i\|^2 = \|\psi\|^2 - \sum_{i=1}^{n} |a_i|^2$$

from which it follows that $\sum_{i=1}^{n} |a_i|^2 \leq \|\psi\|^2$. For an infinite set $\{\phi_n\}$ this inequality is

$$\sum_{i=1}^{\infty} |a_i|^2 \leq \|\psi\|^2 \tag{40}$$

which is called the *Bessel inequality*. If an orthonormal system of functions can be found in $\mathscr{L}_2$ space such that its every element can be represented linearly in terms of this system, it is called an *orthonormal basis*. Thus, we have $\psi = \sum_i \langle\psi, \phi_i\rangle\phi_i = \sum_i a_i\phi_i$. From this relation we readily derive the Parseval identity:

$$\|\psi\|^2 = \sum_{i=1}^{\infty} |\langle\psi, \phi_i\rangle|^2$$

Incidentally, if $\|\psi - \sum_{i=1}^{n} \alpha_i\phi_i\| \to 0$ as $n \to \infty$, then ψ is said to *converge in the mean* to the series $\sum_{i=1}^{\infty} \alpha_i\phi_i$. The reason for this terminology is that the norm entails the integration of the square of the function.

We are now ready to discuss the solutions of the integral equation $\lambda K\phi = \phi$. We take $K(x, y)$ to be a Hermitian kernel so that, in view of relation (38) K is self-adjoint. As such, this operator has some very interesting properties as we establish below.

Property 1. *Existence of an eigenvalue.* If the Hermitian kernel is also an $\mathscr{L}_2$ function then at least one of the quantities $\pm(\|K\|)^{-1}$, where this norm is defined by (37), must be an eigenvalue of $\lambda Kf = f$.

Proof. Because K is a Hermitian kernel, it is self-adjoint because of (38), and being an $\mathscr{L}_2$ function it is compact as mentioned in the previous section. Accordingly, we consider a sequence $\{f_n\}$ such that $\|f_n\| = 1$ and $\|Kf_n\|$ converges to $\|K\|$. Note that

$$\begin{aligned} 0 &\leq \|K^2f_n - \|Kf_n\|^2f_n\|^2 \\ &= \|K^2f_n\|^2 - 2\|Kf_n\|^2\langle K^2f_n, f_n\rangle + \|Kf_n\|^4 \\ &= \|K^2f_n\|^2 - \|Kf_n\|^4 \end{aligned}$$

But $\|Kf_n\|$ converges to $\|K\|$, so that $\lim_{n\to\infty} \|K^2f_n - \|Kf_n\|^2f_n\| = 0$. In this relation we can use the fact that K^2 being the product of compact operators is compact and, therefore, we can extract a subsequence $\{f_{n'}\}$ from $\{f_n\}$ so that $\{K^2f_{n'}\}$ converges to a function, say $\|K\|^2g$. Thus $\lim_{n\to\infty} \|\,\|K^2\|g - \|K\|^2f_{n'}\| = 0$, so that $\{f_{n'}\}$ converges to g and $K^2g = \|K\|^2g$. But this means that $((\|K\|)^{-1}K - 1)((\|K\|)^{-1}K + 1)g = 0$ and the result follows.

As mentioned in Section III, an eigenvalue is simple if there is only one corresponding eigenfunction, otherwise the eigenvalue is called degenerate. The spectrum of K is the set of all eigenvalues, in view of the above-mentioned property we find that the *spectrum of a Hermitian kernel is never empty.*

Property 2. *The eigenvalues of a Hermitian operator K are all real.*

Proof. Suppose $\lambda K\phi = \phi$. Then by taking the inner product of this relation with ϕ, we have $\lambda\langle K\phi, \phi\rangle = \|\phi\|^2$ or $\lambda = \|\phi\|^2/\langle K\phi, \phi\rangle$. As already observed $\langle K\phi, \phi\rangle$ is real for a Hermitian kernel. The quantity $\|\phi\|^2$ is also real. Thus λ is real.

Property 3. *All eigenfunctions of a Hermitian operator K corresponding to distinct eigenvalues are orthogonal.*

Proof. Let ϕ_1 and ϕ_2 be the eigenfunctions corresponding respectively, to the distinct eigenvalues λ_1 and λ_2. Then we have $\lambda_1 K\phi_1 = \phi_1$ and $\lambda_2 K\phi_2 = \phi_2$ so that $\langle K\phi_1, \phi_2\rangle = \lambda_1^{-1}\langle\phi_1, \phi_2\rangle$ and also $\langle K\phi_1, \phi_2\rangle = \langle\phi_1, K\phi_2\rangle = \lambda_2^{-1}\langle\phi_1, \phi_2\rangle$. Thus $\lambda_2\langle\phi_1, \phi_2\rangle = \lambda_1\langle\phi_1, \phi_2\rangle$. Since $\lambda_1 \neq \lambda_2$, we find that $\langle\phi_1, \phi_2\rangle = 0$, as desired.

Property 4. *The multiplicity of any nonzero eigenvalue is finite for every Hermitian operator K with $\mathscr{L}_2$ kernel.*

Proof. Let the functions $\phi_{1\lambda}(x), \phi_{2\lambda}(x), \ldots, \phi_{n\lambda}(x), \ldots$ be the linearly independent eigenfunctions which correspond to a nonzero eigenvalue λ. We appeal to the Gram–Schmidt process and then find linear combinations of these functions which form an orthonormal system $\{u_{k\lambda}(x)\}$. Their complex conjugate functions $\{\overline{u_{k\lambda}(x)}\}$ also form an orthonormal system. Let the function $K(x, y)$ with fixed x be written as $K(x, y) \sim \sum_i a_i$

$\overline{u_{i\lambda}}(y)$, where $a_i = \int K(x, y)u_{i\lambda}(y)\, dy = u_{i\lambda}(x)/\lambda$. By applying the Bessel inequality (40) to this series, we have $\int |K(x, y)|^2\, dy \geq \Sigma_i (\lambda^{-1})^2 |u_{i\lambda}(x)|^2$, which, when integrated, yields the inequality

$$\int\int |K(x, y)|^2\, dx\, dy \geq \sum_i (\lambda^{-1})^2 = \frac{m}{\lambda^2}$$

where m is the multiplicity of λ. But K is an $\mathscr{L}_2$ kernel so the left-hand side of this relation is finite. It follows that m is finite.

Property 5. *The sequence of eigenfunctions of a Hermitian kernel K can be made orthonormal.*

Proof. Suppose that, corresponding to a certain eigenvalue, there are m linearly independent eigenfunctions. Because K is a linear operator, every linear combination of these functions is also an eigenfunction. Thus, by the Gram–Schmidt procedure, we can get an equivalent number of eigenfunctions which are orthonormal. On the other hand, for distinct eigenvalues, the corresponding eigenfunctions are orthogonal and can be readily normalized. Combining these two parts we have established the required property.

Property 6. *The eigenvalues of a Hermitian operator K with $\mathscr{L}_2$ kernel form a finite or an infinite sequence $\{\lambda_n\}$ with no finite limit point.* Furthermore, if we include each eigenvalue in the sequence a number of times equal to its algebraic multiplicity, then

$$\sum_{n=1}^{\infty} (\lambda_n^{-1})^2 \leq \int\int |K(x, y)|^2\, dx\, dy$$

The proof of this property can be presented by a slight extension of the arguments given in the analysis of Property 4.

Property 7. *The set of eigenvalues of the nth iterated kernel coincide with the set of nth powers of the eigenvalues of the kernel K(x, y).*

Proof. Let λ be an eigenvalue of K with corresponding eigenfunction $\phi(x)$ so that $(I - \lambda K)\phi = 0$, where I is the identity operator. The result of operating on both sides of this equation with the operator $(I + \lambda K)$ yields $(I - \lambda^2 K^2)\phi = 0$, or

$$\phi(x) - \lambda^2 \int K_2(x, y)\phi(y)\, dy = 0$$

which proves that λ^2 is an eigenvalue of the kernel $K_2(x, y)$. Conversely, if λ^2 is an eigenvalue $K_2(x, y)$, with $\phi(x)$ as its corresponding eigenfunction $\phi(x)$, we have

$$(I - \lambda^2 K^2)\phi = 0$$

or

$$(I - \lambda K)(I + \lambda K)\phi = 0$$

If λ is an eigenvalue of K this equation is satisfied and we have established the property for $n = 2$. Otherwise, we set $[(I + \lambda K)]\phi(x) = \mathscr{X}(x)$ so that the above equation becomes $(I - \lambda K)\mathscr{X}(x) = 0$. Since we have assumed that λ is not an eigenvalue of K, it follows that $\mathscr{X}(x) \equiv 0$. This means that $(I + \lambda K)\phi = 0$, or $-\lambda$ is an eigenvalue and we have again proved our result for $n = 2$. The general result follows by continuing this process.

In the next stage we wish to expand a nonzero Hermitian kernel in terms of its eigenfunctions. It may have a finite or infinite number of real eigenvalues. We order them in the sequence $\lambda_1, \lambda_2, \ldots, \lambda_n, \ldots$ in such a way that

1. Each eigenvalue is repeated as many times as its multiplicity, and
2. we enumerate these eigenvalues in an order which corresponds to their absolute values (i.e., $0 < |\lambda_1| \leq |\lambda_2| \leq \cdots \leq |\lambda_n| \leq |\lambda_{n+1}| \leq \cdots$).

Let $\phi_1(x), \phi_2(x), \ldots, \phi_n(x), \ldots$ be the sequence of corresponding orthonormalized eigenfunctions which are arranged in such a way that they are no longer repeated and are linearly independent in each group corresponding to the same eigenvalue. Thus to each eigenvalue λ_k there corresponds just one eigenfunction $\phi_k(x)$. We shall have this ordering in mind in the sequel.

Property 1 has assured us that a nonzero Hermitian kernel always has a finite, nonzero lowest eigenvalue λ_1. Let ϕ_1 be the corresponding eigenfunction. Now we remove this eigenvalue from the spectrum of K by defining the truncated kernel $K^{(2)}(x, y)$:

$$K^{(2)}(x, y) = K(x, y) - (\phi_1(x)\bar{\phi}_1(y)/\lambda_1)$$

which is also Hermitian. If $K^{(2)}(x, y)$ is nonzero then let λ_2 be its lowest eigenvalue with corresponding eigenfunction $\phi_2(x)$. Because

$$K^{(2)}\phi_1 = K\phi_1 - (\phi_1(x)/\lambda_1) \int \phi_1(y)\phi_1(y)\, dy = 0$$

we observe that $\phi_1 \neq \phi_2$ even if $\lambda_1 = \lambda_2$. Similarly, the third truncated Hermitian kernel is

$$K^{(3)}(x, y) = K^{(2)}(x, y) - \phi_2(x)\frac{\overline{\phi_2(y)}}{\lambda_2}$$

$$= K(x, y) - \sum_{k=1}^{2} \frac{\phi_k(x)\overline{\phi_k(y)}}{\lambda_k}$$

Continuing this process we have

$$K^{(n+1)}(x, y) = K(x, y) - \sum_{k=1}^{n} \frac{\phi_k(x)\overline{\phi_k(y)}}{\lambda_k} \tag{41}$$

which yields the $(n + 1)$th lowest eigenvalue and the corresponding eigenfunction $\phi_{n+1}(x)$. Thereby we find that either this process terminates after n steps (i.e., $K^{(n+1)}(x, y) = 0$), and the kernel $K(x, y)$ is a degenerate kernel $\sum_{k=1}^{n}(\phi_k(x)\overline{\phi_k(y)}/\lambda_k)$, or the process can be continued indefinitely and there are an infinite number of eigenvalues and eigenfunctions so that

$$K(x, y) = \sum_{k=1}^{\infty} \frac{\phi_k(x)\overline{\phi_k(y)}}{\lambda_k} \tag{42}$$

This is called the bilinear form of the kernel. Recall that we meet a similar situation for a Hermitian matrix **A**. Indeed, by transforming to an orthonormal basis of the vector space consisting of the eigenvectors of **A** we can transform it to a diagonal matrix.

From the bilinear form (42) we derive a useful inequality. Let the sequence $\{\phi_k(x)\}$ be all the eigenfunctions of a Hermitian $\mathscr{L}_2$ kernel $K(x, y)$ with $\{\lambda_k\}$ as the corresponding eigenvalues as described and arranged in the above analysis. Then the series

$$\sum_{n=1}^{\infty} \frac{|\phi_n(x)|^2}{\lambda_n^2} < C_1^2 \tag{43}$$

where C_1^2 is an upper bound of the integral $\int |K(x, y)|^2\, dy$. The proof follows by observing that the Fourier coefficients a_n of the function $K(x, y)$ with fixed x, with respect to the orthonormal system $\overline{\phi_n(y)}$ are $a_n = \langle K(x, y), \overline{\phi_n(y)}\rangle = \phi_n(x)/\lambda_n$. Substituting these values of a_n in the Bessel inequality (40) we derive (43).

The eigenfunctions do not have to form a complete set in order to represent the functions in $\mathscr{L}_2$. Indeed, any function which can be written as "sourcewise" in terms of the kernel K (i.e., any function $f = Kh$) can be expanded in a series of the eigenfunctions of K. This is not surprising because integration smooths out irregularities or if the functions f, K, and h are represented by the series, then the convergence of the series representing f will be better than that of the series representing K and h. This important concept for a Hermitian kernel is embodied in the

Hilbert–Schmidt theorem. If $f(x)$ can be written in the form

$$f(x) = \int K(x, y)h(y)\, dy \tag{44}$$

where K and h are in $\mathscr{L}_2$ space, then $f(x)$ can be expanded in an absolutely and uniformly convergent Fourier series with respect to the orthonormal system of eigenfunctions of K, that is,

$$f(x) = \sum_{n=1}^{\infty} f_n\phi_n(x), \quad f_n = \langle f, \phi_n\rangle \tag{45a}$$

The Fourier coefficients f_n are related to the corresponding coefficients h_n of $h(x)$ as

$$f_n = h_n/\lambda_n = \langle h, \phi_n\rangle/\lambda_n \tag{45b}$$

and λ_n are the eigenvalues of K.

Proof. The Fourier coefficients of the function $f(x)$ with respect to the orthonormal system $\{\phi_n(x)\}$ are

$$\begin{aligned} f_n &= \langle f, \phi_n\rangle = \langle Kh, \phi_n\rangle = \langle h, K\phi_n\rangle \\ &= \langle h, \phi_n\rangle/\lambda_n = h_n/\lambda_n \end{aligned}$$

because K is self-adjoint and $\lambda_n K\phi_n = \phi_n$. Accordingly, we can write the correspondence

$$f(x) \sim \sum_{n=1}^{\infty} f_n\phi_n(x) = \sum_{n=1}^{\infty} \frac{h_n\phi_n(x)}{\lambda_n} \tag{46}$$

The estimate of the remainder term for this series is

$$\begin{aligned} \left|\sum_{k=n+1}^{n+p} h_k \frac{\phi_k(x)}{\lambda_k}\right|^2 &\le \sum_{k=n+1}^{n+p} h_k^2 \sum_{k=n+1}^{n+p} \frac{|\phi_k(x)|^2}{\lambda_k^2} \\ &\le \sum_{k=n+1}^{n+p} h_k^2 \sum_{k=1}^{\infty} \frac{|\phi_k^2(x)|}{\lambda_k^2} \end{aligned} \tag{47}$$

Now the series $\sum_{k=1}^{\infty}|\phi_k^2(x)|/\lambda_k^2$ is bounded in view of relation (43) while the partial sum $\sum_{k=n+1}^{n+p} h_k^2$ can be made arbitrarily small because $h(x) \in \mathscr{L}_2$ and, as such, the series $\sum_{k=1}^{\infty} h_k^2$ is convergent. Thus, the estimate (47) can be made arbitrarily small so that series (46) converges absolutely and uniformly. Next, we show that this series converges to $f(x)$ in the mean and for this purpose we denote its partial sum as $\psi_n(x) = \sum_{m=1}^{n}(h_m/\lambda_m)\phi_m(x)$ and estimate the value $\|f(x) - \psi_n(x)\|$. Because

$$f(x) - \psi_n(x) = Kh - \sum_{m=1}^{n} \frac{h_m}{\lambda_m}\phi_m(x) = K^{(n+1)}h$$

where K^{n+1} is the truncated kernel (41), we find that

$$\begin{aligned} \|f(x) - \psi_n(x)\|^2 &= \|K^{(n+1)}h\|^2 \\ &= \langle K^{(n+1)}h, K^{(n+1)}h\rangle \\ &= \langle h, K^{(n+1)}K^{(n+1)}h\rangle \\ &= \langle h, K_2^{(n+1)}h\rangle \end{aligned} \tag{48}$$

in view of the self-adjointness of the kernel $K^{(n+1)}$ and the relation $K^{(n+1)}K^{(n+1)} = K_2^{(n+1)}$. Now we use Property 7 for the Hermitian kernels and find that the least eigenvalue of the kernel $K_2^{(n+1)}$ is λ_{n+1}^2. On the other hand, Property 1 implies that

$$1/\lambda_{n+1}^2 = \sup\|K^{(n+1)}h\|^2/\|h\|^2$$
$$= \sup(\langle h, K_2^{(n+1)}h\rangle)/\|h\|^2$$

Combining it with (48) we get $\|f(x) - \psi_n(x)\|^2 \leq \|h\|^2/\lambda_{n+1}^2$. Because $\lambda_{n+1} \to \infty$, we have proved that $\|f(x) - \psi_n(x)\| \to 0$ as $n \to \infty$.

In order to prove that $f = \psi$, where ψ is the series with partial sum ψ_n, we use the Minkowski inequality (6) and get $\|f - \psi\| \leq \|f - \psi_n\| + \|\psi_n - \psi\|$. The first term on the right-handside of this inequality tends to zero as proved above. Because series (47) converges uniformly, the second term can be made as small as we want (i.e., given an arbitrarily small and positive ε we can find n large enough that $|\psi_n - \psi| < \varepsilon$). One integration then yields $\|\psi_n - \psi\| < \varepsilon(b - a)^{1/2}$ and we have proved the result.

Let us now use the foregoing theorem for solving the inhomogeneous Fredholm integral equation of the second kind:

$$g(x) = f(x) + \lambda \int K(x, y)g(y)\, dy \tag{49}$$

with a Hermitian $\mathcal{L}_2$ kernel. First, we assume that λ is not an eigenvalue of K. Because $g(x) - f(x)$ in this equation has the integral representation of the form (44) we expand both $g(x)$ and $f(x)$ in terms of the eigenfunctions $\phi_n(x)$ given by the homogeneous equation $\phi_n(x) = \lambda_n \int K(x, y)\phi_n(y)\, dy$. Accordingly, we set

$$g(x) = \sum_{n=1}^{\infty} g_n\phi_n(x), \quad f(x) = \sum_{n=1}^{\infty} f_n\phi_n(x) \tag{50}$$

where $g_n = \langle g, \phi_n\rangle$ is unknown and $f_n = \langle f, \phi_n\rangle$ is known. Substituting these expansions in (49) we obtain

$$\sum_{n=1}^{\infty} g_n\phi_n(x) = \sum_{n=1}^{\infty} f_n\phi_n(x) + \lambda\int K(x, y) \sum_{n=1}^{\infty} g_n\phi_n(y)\, dy \tag{51}$$

In view of the uniform convergence of the expansion, we can interchange the order of integration and summation, and get

$$\sum_{n=1}^{\infty} g_n\phi_n(x) = \sum_{n=1}^{\infty} f_n\phi_n(x) + \lambda \sum_{n=1}^{\infty} \frac{g_n\phi_n(x)}{\lambda_n} \tag{52}$$

Now we multiply both sides of (52) by $\overline{\phi_k(x)}$ and integrate from a to b and appeal to the orthogonality of the eigenfunctions and obtain

$$g_k = f_k + (\lambda/\lambda_k)g_k \tag{53a}$$

or

$$g_k = f_k + (\lambda/(\lambda_k - \lambda))f_k \tag{53b}$$

Substitution of (53) into (50) leads us to the required solution

$$g(x) = \sum_{n=1}^{\infty} \left(f_n + \frac{\lambda}{(\lambda_n - \lambda)} f_n\right) \phi_n(x)$$
$$= f(x) + \lambda \sum_{n=1}^{\infty} \int \frac{\phi_n(x)\overline{\phi_n(y)}}{(\lambda_n - \lambda)} f(y)\, dy$$
$$= f(x) + \lambda \int \Gamma(x, y; \lambda)f(y)\, dy \tag{54}$$

where the resolvent kernel $\Gamma(x, y; \lambda)$ is expressed by the series

$$\Gamma(x, y; \lambda) = \sum_{n=1}^{\infty} \frac{\phi_n(x)\overline{\phi_n(y)}}{\lambda_n - \lambda} \tag{55}$$

and we have again interchanged the integration and summation. It follows from expression (55) that the singular points of the resolvent kernel Γ corresponding to a Hermitian $\mathcal{L}_2$ kernel are simple poles and every pole is an eigenvalue of the kernel.

In the event that λ in Eq. (49) is equal to one of the eigenvalues, say, λ_p of K, solution (55) becomes infinite. To remedy it we return to relation (53) which for $k = p$ becomes $g_p = f_p + g_p$. Thus, g_p is arbitrary and $f_p = 0$. This implies that $\int f(x)\phi_p(x)\, dx = 0$ (i.e., $f(x)$ is orthogonal to the eigenfunction $\phi_p(x)$). If this is not the case, we have no solution. If λ_p has the algebraic multiplicity m, then there are m coefficients g_p which are arbitrary and $f(x)$ is orthogonal to all these m functions.

Integral equations arise in the process of inverting ordinary and partial differential operators. In the quest for the representation formula for the solutions of these operators so as to include the initial or boundary values in it, we arrive at integral equations. In the process there arises the theory of Green's functions which are symmetric and become the kernels of the integral equations. If they are not symmetric, then they can be symmetrized. We illustrate these concepts with the help of the Sturm–Liouville differential operator

$$L = -\frac{d}{dx}\left\{p(x)\frac{d}{dx}\right\} + q(x)$$

where $p(x)$ and $q(x)$ are continuous in the interval $[a, b]$ and in addition $p(x)$ has a continuous derivative and does not vanish in this interval. We discuss two kinds of equations, that is,

$$Ly = f(x), \quad a \le x \le b \tag{56}$$

and

$$Ly - \lambda r(x) y = 0 \tag{57}$$

where $f(x)$ and $r(x)$ are given functions. The function $r(x)$ is continuous and nonnegative in $[a, b]$. Each of these equations is subject to the boundary conditions

$$\begin{aligned} \alpha_1 y(a) + \alpha_2 y'(a) &= 0 \\ \beta_1 y(b) + \beta_2 y'(b) &= 0 \end{aligned} \tag{58}$$

Let us assume that it is not possible to obtain a nonzero solution of system (57) and (58) for the case $\lambda = 0$ (this means that there is no eigenfunction corresponding to the eigenvalue $\lambda = 0$). Accordingly, we assume that a function ϕ_1 satisfies the boundary condition $(58)_1$: $\alpha_1 \phi_1(a) + \alpha_2 \phi_1'(a) = 0$ and another function ϕ_2 (independent of ϕ_1) satisfies the boundary condition $(58)_2$: $\beta_1 \phi_2(b) + \beta_2 \phi_2'(b) = 0$. This amounts to solving two initial value problems, namely, $L\phi_1 = 0$, $\phi_1(a) = -\alpha_2$, $\phi_1'(a) = \alpha_1$ and $L\phi_2 = 0$, $\phi_2(b) = -\beta_2$, $\phi_2'(b) = \beta_1$. With the help of these two linearly independent solutions ϕ_1 and ϕ_2 we use the method of variation of parameters and assume the solution of the inhomogeneous equation (56) as

$$y(x) = C_1(x)\phi_1(x) + C_2(x)\phi_2(x) \tag{59}$$

where C_1 and C_2 must be found from the relations

$$C_1'(x)\phi_1(x) + C_2'(x)\phi_2(x) = 0 \tag{60a}$$

$$C_1'(x)\phi_1'(x) + C_2'(x)\phi_2'(x) = -f(x)/p(x) \tag{60b}$$

We need one more relation for ϕ_1 and ϕ_2 to facilitate the solution of (56). This is found from the fact that ϕ_1 and ϕ_2 are two linearly independent solutions of the homogeneous equation $Ly = 0$. As such

$$\begin{aligned} 0 &= \phi_2 L\phi_1 - \phi_1 L\phi_2 \\ &= -\phi_2 \frac{d}{dx}\left(p \frac{d\phi_1}{dx}\right) + \phi_1 \frac{d}{dx}\left(p \frac{d\phi_2}{dx}\right) \\ &= -\frac{d}{dx}\left\{p\left(\phi_2 \frac{d\phi_1}{dx} - \phi_1 \frac{d\phi_2}{dx}\right)\right\} \end{aligned}$$

so that the quantity within the braces is a constant. Inasmuch as ϕ_1 and ϕ_2 can be determined up to a constant factor, we can choose this expression to be

$$p\left(\phi_2 \frac{d\phi_1}{dx} - \phi_1 \frac{d\phi_2}{dx}\right) = -1 \tag{61}$$

From relations (60) and (61) we find that $C_1'(x) = -\phi_2(x) f(x)$ and $C_2'(x) = \phi_1(x) f(x)$. Thus

$$C_1(x) = \int_x^b \phi_2(\xi) f(\xi)\, d\xi$$

$$C_2(x) = \int_a^x \phi_1(\xi) f(\xi)\, d\xi$$

with convenient constants of integration. Substituting these values in (59) we arrive at the solution

$$\begin{aligned} y(x) &= \phi_1(x) \int_x^b \phi_2(\xi) f(\xi)\, d\xi \\ &\quad + \phi_2(x) \int_a^x \phi_1(\xi) f(\xi)\, d\xi \\ &= \int_a^b G(x, \xi) f(\xi)\, d\xi \end{aligned} \tag{62}$$

where the function

$$G(x, \xi) = \begin{cases} \phi_1(\xi)\phi_2(x), & \xi \le x \\ \phi_1(x)\phi_2(\xi), & \xi \ge x \end{cases} \tag{63}$$

is called the Green's function of this boundary value problem. It can be written in an elegant form by defining the regions

$$x_< = \min(x, \xi) = \begin{cases} x, & a \le x \le \xi \\ \xi, & \xi \le x \le b \end{cases}$$

$$x_> = \max(x, \xi) = \begin{cases} \xi, & a \le x \le \xi \\ x, & \xi \le x \le b \end{cases}$$

Then $G(x, \xi) = \phi_1(x_<)\phi_2(x_>)$.

Finally, we attend to Eq. (57) whose solution follows from (62) to be

$$y(x) = \lambda \int r(\xi) G(x, \xi) y(\xi)\, d\xi \tag{64}$$

This is an integral equation with kernel $r(\xi)G(x, \xi)$. Although this kernel is not symmetric, it can be symmetrized by setting $[r(x)]^{1/2} y(x) = g(x)$ and defining the symmetric kernel $K(x, y) = G(x, \xi)[r(x)]^{1/2}[r(\xi)]^{1/2}$. Then (64) becomes the integral equation

$$g(x) = \lambda \int K(x, y) g(y)\, dy \tag{65}$$

If there was a term on the right-hand side of (57) we would have arrived at an inhomogeneous integral equation of the second kind. Incidentally, it can be readily verified that Eq. (64) satisfies the given boundary conditions. The case when $\lambda = 0$ has a nonzero eigenfunction can be handled by a slight extension of the foregoing arguments.

The theory of Green's functions as derived above can be displayed very elegantly with the help of the Dirac delta function and other generalized functions.

VI. Singular Integral Equations on the Real Line

An integral equation is said to be singular either if the kernel is singular within the range of integration or if one or both limits of integration are infinite. In this section we study some famous singular integral equations. They arise very frequently in various branches of physics and engineering. No general theory is available for these equations but methods are available for solving some special cases. We start with the Abel integral equation

A. The Abel Integral Equation

This equation is

$$f(x) = \int_a^x \frac{g(y)}{(x-y)^\alpha}\,dy, \qquad 0 < \alpha < 1 \quad (66)$$

To solve it we multiply both sides of this equation by $dx/(u-x)^{1-\alpha}$ and integrate with respect to x from a to u so that we have

$$\int_a^u \frac{f(x)\,dx}{(u-x)^{1-\alpha}} = \int_a^u \frac{dx}{(u-x)^{1-\alpha}} \int_a^x \frac{g(y)\,dy}{(x-y)^\alpha}$$

When we change the order of integration on the right-hand side of this equation we have

$$\int_a^u \frac{f(x)\,dx}{(u-x)^{1-\alpha}} = \int_a^u g(y)\,dy \int_y^u \frac{dx}{(u-x)^{1-\alpha}(x-y)^\alpha} \quad (67)$$

Next, we set $t = (u-x)/(u-y)$ in the second integral so that

$$\int_y^u (u-x)^{\alpha-1}(x-y)^{-\alpha}\,dx = \int_0^1 t^{\alpha-1}(1-t)^{-\alpha}\,dt = \frac{\pi}{\sin \alpha\pi}$$

where we have used the value of the Eulerian beta function $B(\alpha, 1-\alpha) = \pi \csc \alpha\pi$. Thus relation (67) becomes

$$\frac{\sin \alpha\pi}{\pi} \int_a^u \frac{f(x)\,dx}{(u-x)^{1-\alpha}} = \int_a^u g(y)\,dy \quad (68)$$

Differentiation of this relation finally yields the solution

$$g(y) = \frac{\sin \alpha\pi}{\pi} \frac{d}{dy}\left[\int_a^y \frac{f(x)}{(y-x)^{1-\alpha}}\,dx\right] \quad (69)$$

Similarly, the solution of the integral equation

$$\int_s^b \frac{g(y)}{(y-x)^\alpha}\,dy = f(s), \qquad 0 < \alpha < 1 \quad (70)$$

is

$$g(y) = -\frac{\sin \alpha\pi}{\pi} \frac{d}{dy}\left[\int_y^b \frac{f(x)}{(x-y)^{1-\alpha}}\,dx\right] \quad (71)$$

There are many related integral equations which can be solved by similar steps. For instance, the solution of the integral equation

$$f(x) = \int_a^x \frac{g(y)\,dy}{[h(x)-h(y)]^\alpha}, \qquad 0 < \alpha < 1 \quad (72)$$

where the function $h(x)$ is strictly increasing differentiable function with nonzero $h'(x)$ over some interval $a \le x \le b$, is

$$g(y) = \frac{\sin \alpha\pi}{\pi} \frac{d}{dy}\left[\int_a^y \frac{h'(u)f(u)\,du}{[h(y)-h(u)]^{1-\alpha}}\right] \quad (73)$$

Similarly, the solution of the integral equation

$$f(x) = \int_x^b \frac{g(y)\,dy}{[h(y)-h(x)]^\alpha}, \qquad 0 < \alpha < 1 \quad (74)$$

is

$$g(y) = -\frac{\sin \alpha\pi}{\pi} \frac{d}{dy}\left[\int_y^b \frac{h'(u)f(u)\,du}{[h(u)-h(y)]^{1-\alpha}}\right] \quad (75)$$

These relations remain valid when $a \to -\infty$ and $b \to \infty$.

B. The Cauchy Integral Equation

The equation

$$g(x) = f(x) + \lambda \int_0^1 \frac{g(y)\,dy}{y-x} \quad (76)$$

is the inhomogeneous Cauchy integral equation. Here the integral is the Cauchy principal value. To solve this equation we appeal to the identity

$$\int_0^u \frac{dy}{(u-y)^{\alpha-1}y^\alpha(y-x)} = \begin{cases} \dfrac{\pi \cot \alpha\pi}{(u-x)^{1-\alpha}x^\alpha}, & 0 < x < u \\[2ex] \dfrac{-\pi \csc \alpha\pi}{(x-u)^{1-\alpha}x^\alpha}, & u < x \end{cases} \quad (77)$$

and then define the function $\phi(x, u)$ as

$$\phi(x, u) = \frac{1}{(u-x)^{1-\alpha}x^\alpha}, \qquad 0 < x < u \quad (78)$$

where α is such that $-\pi \cot \alpha\pi = (1/\lambda)$. Then $\phi(x, u)$ is the solution of the integral equation

$$-\lambda \int_0^u \frac{\phi(y, u)}{y - x}\, dy = \phi(x, u), \qquad 0 < x < u \tag{79}$$

while

$$\int_0^u \frac{\phi(y, u)}{y - x}\, dy = -\frac{\pi \csc \alpha\pi}{(x - u)^{1-\alpha} x^{\alpha}}, \qquad u < x \tag{80}$$

When we multiply (76) by x we get

$$\lambda \int_0^1 \frac{y g(y)\, dy}{y - x} = x g(x) - x f(x) + c \tag{81}$$

where $c = \lambda \int_0^1 g(y)\, dy$. Next, we multiply both sides of (81) by $\phi(x, u)$ as defined by (78), integrate from 0 to u and change the order of integration. The result is

$$\begin{aligned} &-\lambda \int_0^u y g(y)\, dy \int_0^u \frac{\phi(x, u)\, dx}{x - y} \\ &-\lambda \int_u^1 y g(y)\, dy \int_0^u \frac{\phi(x, u)\, dx}{x - y} \\ &= \int_0^u x g(x) \phi(x, u)\, dx \\ &\quad - \int_0^u x f(x) \phi(x, u)\, dx + c \int_0^u \phi(x, u)\, dx \end{aligned}$$

With the help of relations (79) and (80) and the fact that $\int_0^u \phi(x, u)\, dx = \pi \csc \alpha\pi$, the above relation becomes

$$\begin{aligned} &\lambda\pi \csc \alpha\pi \int_u^1 \frac{y^{1-\alpha} g(y)}{(y - u)^{1-\alpha}}\, dy \\ &= -\int_0^u x f(x) \phi(x, u)\, dx + c\pi \csc \alpha\pi \end{aligned} \tag{82}$$

This is an Abel-type integral equation whose solution is found from the previous analysis to be

$$\begin{aligned} \lambda y^{1-\alpha} g(y) = {} & \frac{\sin^2 \alpha\pi}{\pi^2} \frac{d}{dy} \\ & \times \left[\int_y^1 \int_0^u (u - y)^{-\alpha} \right. \\ & \left. \times (u - x)^{\alpha-1} x^{1-\alpha} f(x)\, dx\, dy \right] \\ & + \frac{c \sin \alpha\pi}{\pi (1 - y)^{\alpha}} \end{aligned} \tag{83}$$

Now we use the relation $-\pi \cot \alpha\pi = 1/\lambda$ and do a little algebraic manipulation and obtain the required solution as

$$\begin{aligned} g(x) = {} & -\frac{f(x)}{1 + \pi^2\lambda^2} + \frac{\lambda}{(1 + \pi^2\lambda^2) x^{1-\alpha} (1 - x)^{\alpha}} \\ & \times \int_0^1 \frac{(1 - y)^{\alpha} y^{1-\alpha} f(y)\, dy}{y - x} \\ & + \frac{c}{x^{1-\alpha} (1 - x)^{\alpha} \sqrt{1 + \pi^2\lambda^2}} \end{aligned} \tag{84}$$

Finally, we set $y = (y' - a)/(b - a)$, and find from the above analysis that the solution of the integral equation

$$g(x) = f(x) + \lambda \int_a^b \frac{g(y)\, dy}{y - x} \tag{85}$$

is

$$\begin{aligned} g(x) = {} & -\frac{f(x)}{1 + \pi^2\lambda^2} \\ & + \frac{\lambda}{(1 + \pi^2\lambda^2)(x - a)^{1-\alpha} (b - x)^{\alpha}} \\ & \times \int_a^b \frac{(b - y)^{\alpha} (y - a)^{1-\alpha} f(y)\, dy}{y - x} \\ & + \frac{c}{(x - a)^{1-\alpha} (b - x)^{\alpha}} \end{aligned} \tag{86}$$

where c is an arbitrary constant.

The solution of the Cauchy-type integral equation of the first kind:

$$\int_a^b \frac{g(y)\, dy}{y - x} = f(x), \qquad a < x < b \tag{87}$$

can be obtained with a very similar analysis and is

$$\begin{aligned} g(x) = {} & \frac{1}{\pi^2 \sqrt{(x - a)(b - x)}} \\ & \times \left[\int_a^b \frac{\sqrt{(y - a)(b - y)}}{x - y} f(y)\, dy + \pi c \right] \end{aligned} \tag{88}$$

In particular, when $a = -1$, $b = 1$, it follows that the solution of the *airfoil equation*

$$\frac{1}{\pi} \int_{-1}^1 \frac{g(y)\, dy}{y - x} = f(x), \qquad -1 < x < 1 \tag{89}$$

is

$$\begin{aligned} g(x) = {} & \frac{1}{\pi \sqrt{1 - x^2}} \int_{-1}^1 \frac{\sqrt{(1 - y^2)} f(y)}{x - y}\, dy \\ & + \frac{c}{\sqrt{1 - x^2}} \end{aligned} \tag{90}$$

C. Singular Integral Equations with a Logarithmic Kernel

We start with the integral equation

$$\int_{-1}^{1} \ln|x-y| g_0(y)\, dy = 1, \qquad -1 < x < 1 \tag{91}$$

By setting $x = \cos\alpha$, $y = \cos\beta$, Eq. (91) becomes

$$\int_0^{\pi} \ln|\cos\alpha - \cos\beta| G(\beta)\, d\beta = 1, \quad 0 < \alpha < \pi \tag{92}$$

where $G(\beta) = g_0(\cos\beta)\sin\beta$. Let us now expand $G(\beta)$ as $G(\beta) = \sum_{n=0}^{\infty} b_n \cos n\beta$ and use the summation formula

$$\ln|\cos\alpha - \cos\beta| = -\ln 2 - 2\sum_{n=1}^{\infty} \frac{\cos n\alpha \cos n\beta}{n} \tag{93}$$

Then relation (92) becomes

$$\int_0^{\pi}\left[-\ln 2 - 2\sum_{n=1}^{\infty}\frac{\cos n\alpha\cos n\beta}{n}\right] \times \left[\sum_{m=0}^{\infty} b_m \cos m\beta\right] d\beta = 1$$

from which it follows, due to orthogonality of cosine functions, that

$$-\pi b_0 \ln 2 - \sum_{n=1}^{\infty} \pi b_n \frac{\cos n\alpha}{n} = 1$$

Thus, $b_0 = -(1/(\pi \ln 2))$, $b_n = 0$, $n \geq 1$, and we find that the solution of Eq. (91) is

$$g_0(y) = -\frac{1}{\pi \ln 2}\frac{1}{\sqrt{1-y^2}} \tag{94}$$

In passing we observe that by substituting solution (94) in (91) we have the useful identity

$$\int_{-1}^{1} \frac{\ln|x-y|}{(1-y^2)^{1/2}}\, dy = -\pi \ln 2, \qquad -1 < x < 1 \tag{95}$$

Next, we consider the integral equation

$$\int_{-1}^{1} \ln|x-y| g(y)\, dy = f(x), \qquad -1 < x < 1 \tag{96}$$

Differentiation with respect to x gives

$$\int_{-1}^{1} \frac{g(y)}{x-y}\, dy = f'(x), \qquad -1 < x < 1$$

whose solution follows from (90) to be

$$g(x) = \frac{1}{\pi^2}\int_{-1}^{1}\left[\frac{1-y^2}{1-x^2}\right]^{1/2}\frac{f'(y)}{y-x}\, dy + \frac{C}{\pi\sqrt{1-x^2}} \tag{97}$$

where $C = \int_{-1}^{1} g(y)\, dy$. To find the constant C, we multiply (96) by $1/\sqrt{(1-x^2)}$ and integrate it with respect to x from -1 to 1 and change the order of integration. The result is

$$\int_{-1}^{1} g(y)\, dy \int_{-1}^{1} \frac{\ln|x-y|}{(1-x^2)^{1/2}}\, dx = \int_{-1}^{1}\frac{f(x)}{(1-x^2)^{1/2}}\, dx$$

which, in view of identity (95), becomes

$$(-\pi \ln 2)C = \int_{-1}^{1}\frac{f(x)}{(1-x^2)^{1/2}}\, dx$$

Thus

$$C = -\frac{1}{\pi \ln 2}\int_{-1}^{1}\frac{f(x)}{(1-x^2)^{1/2}}\, dx$$

which when substituted in (97) yields the solution

$$g(x) = \frac{1}{\pi^2}\int_{-1}^{1}\left(\frac{1-y^2}{1-x^2}\right)^{1/2}\frac{f'(y)}{y-x}\, dx - \frac{1}{\pi^2 \ln 2(1-x^2)^{1/2}} \times \int_{-1}^{1}\frac{f(y)}{(1-y^2)^{1/2}}\, dy \tag{98}$$

Various other forms of integral equations with logarithmic kernels can be solved in a similar fashion.

VII. The Cauchy Kernel and the Riemann–Hilbert Problem

For the study of the singular equations in the complex plane $\mathbb{C}$, we require a few important results from the analysis of a complex variable. We present some of these concepts needed for the Cauchy kernel. Let C be a simple, smooth, and closed curve in the complex z plane endowed with the counterclockwise orientation.

The complement $\mathbb{C}\backslash C$ consists of two parts, one interior (bounded) part S_+ and the other exterior part S_-. A function $F(z)$ defined and analytic in the complement $\mathbb{C}\backslash C$ is called a *sectionally analytic* function with discontinuity contour C. Let $f(\zeta)$ be a continuous function defined for $\zeta \in C$. The Cauchy (or analytic) representation of f is the sectionally analytic function

$$F(z) = F\{f(\zeta); z\} = \frac{1}{2\pi i} \int_C \frac{f(\zeta)\, d\zeta}{\zeta - z}, \qquad z \in \mathbb{C}\backslash C \tag{99}$$

The boundary values $F_\pm(\omega)$ of this function on both sides of C satisfy the Plemelj relations

$$\begin{aligned} F_+(\omega) &= \frac{1}{2} f(\omega) - \frac{i}{2} H(f) \\ F_-(\omega) &= -\frac{1}{2} f(\omega) - \frac{i}{2} H(f) \end{aligned} \tag{100}$$

where $H(f) = (1/\pi) \int_C (f(\zeta)/(\zeta - \omega))\, d\zeta$, $\omega \in C$, is called the Hilbert transform of f. Solving (100) for f and $H(f)$ we get

$$\begin{aligned} f &= F_+ - F_- = [F] \\ H(f) &= \frac{1}{\pi} \int_C \frac{f(\zeta)}{\zeta - \omega}\, d\zeta = i(F_+ + F_-) \end{aligned} \tag{101}$$

where $[F]$ is called the jump of F across C.

Now let $\Phi_1(\zeta)$ and $\Phi_2(\zeta)$ be two continuous functions defined on C. The Riemann–Hilbert problem is to find the sectionally analytic function $Y(z)$ defined on $\mathbb{C}\backslash C$ whose boundary values satisfy

$$\Phi_1(\zeta) Y_+(\zeta) - \Phi_2(\zeta) Y_-(\zeta) = \Psi(\zeta) \tag{102}$$

where $\Psi(\zeta)$ is a function given on C. We assume that Φ_1 and Φ_2 never vanish on C. It is called the normality condition. When we divide both sides of the above equation by $\Phi_1(\zeta)$ we get

$$Y_+(\zeta) = \Phi(\zeta) Y_-(\zeta) + \psi(\zeta) \tag{103}$$

where $\Phi = \Phi_2/\Phi_1$ and $\psi = \Psi/\Phi_1$. When $\psi = 0$, Eq. (103) becomes the homogeneous Riemann–Hilbert problem

$$X_+(\zeta) = \Phi(\zeta) X_-(\zeta) \tag{104}$$

To solve (103) we first reduce it to the simple form

$$W_+(\zeta) = W_-(\zeta) + \psi(\zeta) \tag{105}$$

which is obtained from (103) by taking $\Phi(\zeta) = 1$ because the solution of (105) is known to have the analytic representation

$$W(z) = F\{\psi(\zeta); z\} = \frac{1}{2\pi i} \int_C \frac{\psi(\zeta)\, d\zeta}{\zeta - z} \tag{106}$$

where we have appealed to definition (99). We first solve the homogeneous Riemann–Hilbert problem (104). For this purpose we take the logarithm of both sides of (104), and get

$$\ln X_+(\zeta) = \ln X_-(\zeta) + \ln \Phi(\zeta) \tag{107}$$

where we assume, for the time being, that $\ln \Phi(\zeta)$ is single valued on C. A particular solution of (107) is given by the analytic representation

$$\ln X(z) = F\{\ln \Phi(\zeta); z\} = \frac{1}{2\pi i} \int_C \frac{\ln \Phi(\zeta)\, d\zeta}{\zeta - z} \tag{108}$$

or $X(z) = e^{F\{\ln \Phi(\zeta); z\}}$, which is a sectionally analytic function that never vanishes on $\mathbb{C}\backslash C$ and whose boundary values satisfy (104) because

$$\begin{aligned} \frac{X_+(\zeta)}{X_-(\zeta)} &= \exp[F_+\{\ln \Phi(\omega); \zeta\} \\ &\quad - F_-\{\ln \Phi(\omega); \zeta\}] \\ &= \exp[\ln \Phi(\zeta)] = \Phi(\zeta) \end{aligned}$$

Note that this basic solution is normal because $X(\infty) = 1$. Now, if $Y(z)$ is any other solution of the homogeneous problem (104) then the function $Y(z)/X(z)$, which is known to be analytic on $\mathbb{C}\backslash C$, is also analytic on C because its jump across C vanishes:

$$\left[\frac{Y}{X}\right]_+ - \left[\frac{Y}{X}\right]_- = \frac{\Phi Y_-}{\Phi X_-} - \frac{Y_-}{X_-} = 0$$

Thus, Y/X is an entire function and the most general solution of the homogeneous Riemann–Hilbert problem is $Y(z) = P(z)X(z)$ where $P(z)$ is an entire function. It is called the fundamental solution of the Riemann–Hilbert problem (fundamental in the sense that all other solutions can be obtained from it in a suitable way).

Let us now consider the case when $\ln \Phi(\zeta)$ is multiple valued on C and introduce the number k

$$k = \frac{1}{2\pi i} \Delta_c(\ln \Phi(\zeta)) = \frac{1}{2\pi} \Delta_c(\arg \ln \Phi(\zeta)) \tag{109}$$

where $\Delta_c(f(\zeta))$ denotes the increment of the function $f(\zeta)$ when the curve C is transversed in the positive direction. Thus, k is the index of the point $z = 0$ with respect to the curve C', the image of the curve C under the function $\Phi(\zeta)$. The number k, which is always an integer, is called the *index* of the Riemann–Hilbert problem.

Let $Y(z)$ be a solution of the homogeneous Riemann–Hilbert problem (104); we define the sectionally analytic function $\tilde{Y}(z)$ as

$$\begin{aligned} \tilde{Y}(z) &= Y(z), \qquad z \in S_+ \\ \tilde{Y}(z) &= (z - z_0)^k Y(z), \qquad z \in S_- \end{aligned} \tag{110}$$

Thus, $\tilde{Y}(z)$ satisfies the following boundary value problem where z_0 is an arbitrary point of S_+:

$$\begin{aligned} \tilde{Y}_+(\zeta) &= \Phi_0(\zeta)\tilde{Y}_-(\zeta), \\ \Phi_0(\zeta) &= (z - z_0)^{-k}\Phi(\zeta) \end{aligned} \tag{111}$$

Thereby $\ln \Phi_0(\zeta)$ has become single valued and we can apply the previous analysis to conclude that the solution of (111) is $\tilde{Y}(z) = P(z)\tilde{X}(z)$, where $P(z)$ is a polynomial and where $\tilde{X}(z) = \exp[F(\ln \Phi_0(\zeta); z)]$ is the fundamental solution. Then it follows from (110) that the solutions of (104) are of the form $Y(z) = P(z)X(z)$ where $P(z)$ is an arbitrary polynomial and where the fundamental solution $X(z)$ is given by

$$X(z) = \exp\left[\frac{1}{2\pi i}\int_C \frac{\ln \Phi_0(\zeta)\, d\zeta}{\zeta - z}\right], \qquad z \in S_+ \tag{112a}$$

$$X(z) = (z - z_0)^{-k} \exp\left[\frac{1}{2\pi i}\int_C \frac{\ln \Phi_0(\zeta)\, d\zeta}{\zeta - z}\right] \qquad z \in S_- \tag{112b}$$

Once a fundamental solution of the Riemann–Hilbert problem has been obtained, we can solve the inhomogeneous problem (103) as follows. Let $X(z)$ be a fundamental solution and let $Y(z)$ be a solution of (103) which we can write as

$$\frac{Y_+}{X_+} = \frac{Y_-}{X_-} + \frac{\psi}{X_+} \tag{113}$$

because $\Phi = X_+/X_-$. The solution of this equation with polynomial behavior at $z = \infty$ is

$$\frac{Y(z)}{X(z)} = P(z) + F\left\{\frac{\psi(\zeta)}{X_+(\zeta)}; z\right\}$$

Thus

$$Y(z) = P(z)X(z) + X(z)F\left\{\frac{\psi(\zeta)}{X_+(\zeta)}; z\right\} \tag{114}$$

This formula gives the solution of the Riemann–Hilbert problem with polynomial behavior at $z = \infty$. For obtaining the solutions that vanish at $z = \infty$, it is necessary to consider the sign of the index k. When $k \geq 0$, (114) will be a solution provided the degree of P does not exceed $k - 1$. When $k < 0$, however, for the solution to vanish at $z = \infty$, the polynomial $P(z)$ should vanish and so should the coefficients $\alpha_1, \alpha_2, \ldots, \alpha_{-k}$ of the Taylor expansion

$$F\left\{\frac{f(\zeta)}{X_+(\zeta)}; z\right\} = \frac{\alpha_1}{z} + \frac{\alpha_2}{z^2} + \cdots \quad \text{at} \quad z = \infty$$

We are now ready to solve one of the most important singular integral equations, namely, the Carleman integral equation:

$$a(\zeta)g(\zeta) + \frac{b(\zeta)}{\pi i}\oint_C \frac{g(\omega)}{\omega - \zeta}\, d\omega = f(\zeta) \tag{115}$$

over a closed contour C, where $a(\zeta)$, $b(\zeta)$, and $f(\zeta)$ are given functions on C subject to the normality condition $a^2(\zeta) - b^2(\zeta) \neq 0$. To solve this equation we appeal to the analytic representation

$$G(z) = \frac{1}{2\pi i}\oint_C \frac{g(\omega)\, d\omega}{\omega - z} \tag{116}$$

of the unknown function $g(\zeta)$. Next, we substitute the Plemelj formulas (100) in (115) and get

$$G_+(\zeta) = \Phi(\zeta)G_-(\zeta) + \psi(\zeta) \tag{117}$$

where

$$\Phi(\zeta) = \frac{a(\zeta) - b(\zeta)}{a(\zeta) + b(\zeta)}, \qquad \psi(\zeta) = \frac{f(\zeta)}{a(\zeta) + b(\zeta)} \tag{118}$$

Thus, we have the Riemann–Hilbert problem (117) to solve. For this purpose we consider the index (109) and then define the fundamental solution (112). Now

$$\begin{aligned} X_+(\zeta) &= \exp\{F_+[\ln[\Phi(\omega)(\omega - z_0)^{-k}]; \zeta\} \\ &= \exp\{\tfrac{1}{2}\ln[\Phi(\zeta)(\zeta - z_0)^{-k}] + \gamma(\zeta)\} \\ &= \sqrt{\Phi(\zeta)}e^{\gamma(\zeta)}/(\zeta - z_0)^{k/2} \end{aligned} \tag{119}$$

where

$$\gamma(\zeta) = \frac{1}{2\pi i}\oint_C \frac{\ln[\Phi(\omega)(\omega - z_0)^{-k}]}{\omega - \zeta}\, d\omega \tag{120}$$

Similarly,

$$X_-(\zeta) = e^{\gamma(\zeta)}/\sqrt{\Phi(\zeta)}(\zeta - z_0)^{k/2} \tag{121}$$

If $k \geq 0$, the solution of the Riemann–Hilbert problem (117) is given as

$$G(z) = X(z)P(z) + X(z)F\left\{\frac{f(\zeta)}{(a(\zeta) + b(\zeta))X_+(\zeta)}; z\right\} \tag{122}$$

where $P(z)$ is a polynomial of degree $(k - 1)$ at most. If $k < 0$, the solution is

$$G(z) = X(z)F\left\{\frac{f(\zeta)}{(a(\zeta) + b(\zeta))X_+(\zeta)}; z\right\} \tag{123}$$

provided

$$\oint_C \{(f(\zeta)\zeta^j/(a(\zeta) + b(\zeta))X_+(\zeta))\}\, d\zeta = 0$$

for

$$0 \le j \le -k - 1.$$

Because

$$\begin{aligned}(a(\zeta) &+ b(\zeta))X_+(\zeta)\\ &= (a(\zeta) + b(\zeta))\sqrt{\Phi(\zeta)}\,(\zeta - z_0)^{-k/2}e^{\gamma(\zeta)}\\ &= \sqrt{a^2(\zeta) - b^2(\zeta)}\,(\zeta - z_0)^{-k/2}e^{\gamma(\zeta)}\end{aligned}$$

it follows by using the Plemelj formula $g(\zeta) = G_+(\zeta) - G_-(\zeta)$, and relations (119), (121), and (123) that the solution of the integral equation (115) is

$$\begin{aligned}g(\zeta) &= \frac{a(\zeta)f(\zeta)}{a^2(\zeta) - b^2(\zeta)}\\ &\quad - \frac{e^{\gamma(\zeta)}(\zeta - z_0)^{-k/2}b(\zeta)}{\sqrt{a^2(\zeta) - b^2(\zeta)}\,\pi i}\\ &\quad \times \oint_C \frac{f(\omega)e^{-\gamma(\omega)}(\omega - z_0)^{k/2}\, d\omega}{\sqrt{a^2(\omega) - b^2(\omega)}\,(\omega - \zeta)}\,\omega \qquad (124)\end{aligned}$$

so long as $k < 0$ and

$$\oint_C \frac{f(\omega)e^{\gamma(\omega)}(\omega - z_0)^{k/2}\omega^j}{\sqrt{a^2(\omega) - b^2(\omega)}}\, d\omega = 0$$

$$0 \le j \le -k - 1 \qquad (125)$$

Similarly, when $k \ge 0$ the solution becomes

$$\begin{aligned}g(\zeta) &= \frac{a(\zeta)f(\zeta)}{a^2(\zeta) - b^2(\zeta)}\\ &\quad - \frac{e^{\gamma(\zeta)}(\zeta - z_0)^{-k/2}b(\zeta)}{\sqrt{a^2(\zeta) - b^2(\zeta)}\,\pi i}\\ &\quad \times \left[\oint_C \frac{f(\omega)e^{-\gamma(\omega)}(\omega - z_0)^{k/2}\, d\omega}{\sqrt{a^2(\omega) - b^2(\omega)}\,(\omega - \zeta)} + P(\zeta)\right]\end{aligned} \qquad (126)$$

where $P(\zeta)$ is a polynomial whose degree does not exceed $k - 1$.

For the special case when a and b are constants. Eq. (115) reduces to the Cauchy integral equation

$$ag(\zeta) + \frac{b}{\pi i}\oint_C \frac{g(\omega)}{\omega - \zeta}\, d\omega = f(\zeta) \qquad (127)$$

while its solution follows by observing that $k = 0$, and Φ and γ are constants. Thus, we appeal to relation (126) and find the solution to be

$$g(\zeta) = \frac{af(\zeta)}{a^2 - b^2} - \frac{b}{(a^2 - b^2)\pi i}\oint_C \frac{f(\omega)\, d\omega}{\omega - \zeta} \qquad (128)$$

VIII. Nonlinear Integral Equations

Let us finally present an elementary discussion of nonlinear integral equations. Because there are no analytic techniques by which these equations are solved, their treatment is available on ad hoc basis. A nonlinear Fredholm integral equation is of the form

$$g(x) = f(x) + \lambda \int F\{x, y, g(y)\}\, dy \qquad (129)$$

where both x and y lie in the domain (a, b) and we have omitted the limits a, b of integration as in the previous discussion. Equation (129) is called an *Uryson* equation. Perhaps the most important particular case is the *Hammerstein* equation:

$$g(x) = f(x) + \lambda \int K(x, y)F(y, g(y))\, dy \qquad (130)$$

These nonlinear integral equations are being presently studied by modern numerical methods. We shall limit ourselves to giving the iterative scheme for solving the general case (129). This scheme is similar to the one given for the linear case in Section II. For this purpose we impose the following conditions on the functions occurring in this equation. We assume that $f(x)$ is continuous in (a, b). The function $F(x, y, g(y))$ is continuous with respect to x and y in the rectangle $a \le x, y \le b$ and satisfies the Lipschitz condition with respect to $g(y)$ (i.e., $|F\{x, y, g_1(y)\} - F\{x, y, g_2(y)\}| \le L|g_1(y) - g_2(y)|$), where L is a positive constant. The continuity of F with respect to x and y assures that $|F\{x, y, g(y)\}| < M$ for bounded $g(y)$, where M is a positive constant.

Now we follow the iterative technique as given in Section II and set the first approximation for $g(x)$ to be $g^{(0)}(x) = f(x)$ and subsequent ones as

$$g^{(n)}(x) = f(x) + \lambda \int F\{x, y, g^{(n-1)}(y)\}\, dy$$

$$n \ge 1 \qquad (131)$$

Because

$$g^{(n)}(x) = \sum_{k=1}^{n} \{g^{(k)}(x) - g^{(k-1)}(x)\} + g^{(0)}(x)$$

the convergence of the sequence $g^{(n)}(x)$ is equivalent to the convergence of the series whose kth term is $(g^{(k)}(x) - g^{(k-1)}(x))$. To examine the convergence of this series we set

$$\begin{aligned}g^{(1)}(x) - g^{(0)}(x) &= \lambda \int F(x, y, f(x))\\ &= \phi(x)\end{aligned}$$

as $g^{(0)}(x) = f(x)$, and assume that $|\phi(x)| < A$, a constant. Then we find that

$$\begin{aligned} |g^{(k)}(x) - g^{(k-1)}(x)| &= |\lambda| \left| \int F\{x, y, g^{(k-1)}(y)\} - F\{x, y, g^{(k-2)}(y)\}\, dy \right| \\ &\le |\lambda| \int |F\{x, y, g^{(k-1)}(y)\} - F\{x, y, g^{(k-2)}(y)\}|\, dy \\ &\le |\lambda| L \int |g^{(k-1)}(y) - g^{(k-2)}(y)|\, dy \\ &\le \cdots \le [|\lambda| L(b - a)]^{k-1} A \end{aligned}$$

Thus, if $|\lambda| L(b - a) < 1$, the series will be absolutely and uniformly convergent and $g^{(n)}(x)$ will tend to a function $g(x)$ which will be the solution of Eq. (129).

To prove the uniqueness of the solution, we let $g(x)$ and $h(x)$ be two solutions. Then the value of the difference $\psi(x) = g(x) - h(x)$ is

$$\psi(x) = \lambda \int [F\{x, y, g(y)\} - F\{x, y, h(y)\}]\, dy$$

When we denote by $\psi_{\max}$, the maximum value of $\psi(x)$ in (a, b) and appeal to the Lipschitz continuity of F, we find that

$$|\psi(x)| < |\lambda| \int |\psi(y)\, dy| \le |\lambda| L(b - a)\psi_{\max}(x)$$

which means that $\psi_{\max} \le |\lambda| L(b - a)\psi_{\max}$. But $|\lambda| L(b - a) < 1$, so we have $\psi_{\max} = 0$ and the uniqueness of the solution is proved.

Let us now consider the nonlinear Volterra integral equation

$$g(x) = f(x) + \lambda \int_0^x F\{x, y, g(y)\}\, dy \qquad (132)$$

with the same conditions on the function $f(x)$ and $F\{x, y, g(y)\}$ as given above. The iterative scheme again yields the sequence $g^{(0)}(x) = f(x)$ and

$$g^{(n)}(x) = f(x) + \lambda \int_0^x F\{x, y, g^{(n-1)}(y)\}\, dy \qquad n \ge 1 \qquad (133)$$

and its convergence is equivalent to that of the series whose kth term is $g^{(k)}(x) - g^{(k-1)}(x)$. To study this convergence we observe that

$$\begin{aligned} g^{(1)}(x) - g^{(0)}(x) &= \lambda \int_0^x F\{x, y, f(y)\}\, dy \\ &\le |\lambda| \int_0^x |F\{x, y, f(y)\}|\, dy \\ &\le |\lambda| \int_0^x M\, dy = M|\lambda| x \qquad (134) \end{aligned}$$

Then from (133) it follows that

$$\begin{aligned} |g^{(k)}(x) - g^{(k-1)}(x)| &= |\lambda| \left| \int_0^x F\{x, y, g^{(k-1)}(y)\} - F\{x, y, g^{(k-2)}(y)\}\, dy \right| \\ &\le |\lambda| \int_0^x L|g^{(k-1)}(y) - g^{(k-2)}(y)|\, dy \\ &\le \cdots \le \frac{(L|\lambda|\,|x|)^k}{k!} M \qquad (135) \end{aligned}$$

But the last term in (135) is the kth term of the power series for $M \exp\{L|\lambda|\,|x|\}$, so that the series $g^{(0)}(x) + \sum_{k=1}^{\infty} \{g^{(k)}(x) - g^{(k-1)}(x)\}$ is absolutely and uniformly convergent for all values of λ and its sum $\lim_{n\to\infty} g^{(n)}(x)$ is the solution of the integral equation (132). The uniqueness of this solution can be proved by a slight extension of the arguments presented above for the Fredholm case.

IX. A Taylor Expansion Technique

In the previous analysis we have presented the Neumann and Hilbert-Schmidt expansion techniques for solving the integral equations. Recently, it has been discovered that both the linear and nonlinear integral equations can also be solved with the help of the Taylor series. To present the basic ideas of this method, we consider the Fredholm integral equation of the second kind

$$g(x) = f(x) + \int_a^b K(x, y) g(y)\, dy \qquad (136)$$

and differentiate it n times with respect to x so that we have

$$g^{(n)}(x) = f^{(n)}(x) + \int_a^b \frac{\partial^n K(x, y)}{\partial x^n} g(y)\, dy.$$

For $x = 0$, the above relation becomes

$$g^{(n)}(0) = f^{(n)}(0) + \int_a^b \left.\frac{\partial^n K(x, y)}{\partial x^n}\right|_{x=0} g(y)\, dy. \qquad (137)$$

When we substitute the Taylor series

$$g(y) = \sum_{m=0}^{\infty} \frac{1}{m!} g^{(m)}(0) y^m \qquad (138)$$

for $g(y)$ in (137) we get

$$g^{(n)}(0) = f^{(n)}(0) + \int_a^b \frac{\partial^n K(x, y)}{\partial x^n}\bigg|_{x=0} \left(\sum_{m=0}^{\infty} \frac{1}{m!} g^{(m)}(0)y^m\right] dy. \quad (139)$$

Next, we set

$$T_{mn} = \frac{1}{m!} \int_a^b \frac{\partial^n K(x, y)}{\partial x^n}\bigg|_{x=0} y^m \, dy \quad (140)$$

in (139) and obtain

$$g^{(n)}(0) = f^{(n)}(0) + \sum_{m=0}^{\infty} T_{mn} g^{(m)}(0), \quad (141)$$

$n = 0, 1, 2, 3, \ldots$. Accordingly, the evaluation of the solution $g(x)$ of integral equation (136) reduces to solving the above infinite system of algebraic equations for the Taylor coefficients $g^m(0)$. This is achieved by truncating this system in a suitable manner so that we get a determinate system at every step. Thus, we get an approximate solution to the desired order of accuracy. For instance, let us take (i) $n = 0$, $m = 1$, (ii) $n = 1$, $m = 1$; (iii) $n = 2$, $m = 2$, in (141) so that we get the determinate system of three equations

$$(T_{00} - 1)g(0) + T_{01}g^{(1)}(0) = -f(0) \quad (142a)$$

$$T_{10}g(0) + (T_{11} - 1)g^{(1)}(0) = -f^{(1)}(0) \quad (142b)$$

$$T_{20}g(0) + T_{21}g^{(1)}(0) + (T_{22} - 1)g^{(2)}(0) = -f^{(2)}(0) \quad (142c)$$

Equations (142a) and (142b) yield the values of $g(0)$ and $g^{(1)}(0)$, which when substituted in (142c), give the value of $g^{(2)}(0)$. Thus, we obtain the solution $g(x)$ to $O(x^2)$.

The elegance of the method lies in the fact that frequently we get an exact solution of an integral equation. We illustrate this point with the help of the integral equation

$$g(x) = (x + 1)^2 + \int_{-1}^{1} (xy + x^2y^2)g(y)\, dy. \quad (143)$$

Accordingly, $f(x) = (x + 1)^2$, $K(x, y) = xy + x^2y^2$, and we have

$$f(0) = 1, \quad f^{(1)}(0) = 2, \quad f^{(2)}(0) = 2$$

$$T_{00} = 0, \quad T_{01} = 0, \quad T_{10} = 0, \quad T_{11} = \frac{2}{3}$$

$$T_{20} = \frac{4}{3}, \quad T_{21} = 0, \quad T_{22} = \frac{2}{5}$$

When we substitute these values in Eq. (142) and solve for the first three Taylor coefficients of $g(x)$, we get

$$g(0) = 1, \quad g^{(1)}(0) = 6, \quad g^{(2)}(0) = \frac{50}{9}.$$

Thus, we have

$$g(x) = 1 + 6x + \frac{25}{9}x^2,$$

which happens to be the exact solution of Eq. (143).

BIBLIOGRAPHY

Anderson, R. S., and Dehovg, F. R. (1980). "Application and Numerical Solution of Integral Equations." Noordhoff, Alphen aan den Rijn, Holland.

Cochran, J. A. (1972). "The Analysis of Linear Integral Equations." McGraw-Hill, New York.

Estrada, R., and Kanwal, R. P. (1985). Distributional solutions of singular integral equations. *J. Integral Equations* **8**, 41–65.

Estrada, R., and Kanwal, R. P. (1987). The Carleman-type singular integral equations. *SIAM Rev.* **29**, 263–290.

Hochstadt, H. (1973). "Integral Equations." Wiley, New York.

Jerry, A. J. (1985). "Introduction to Integral Equations with Applications." Dekker, New York.

Kanwal, R. P. (1971). "Linear Integral Equations." Academic Press, New York.

Kanwal, R. P., and Liu, K. C. (1989). A Taylor expansion approach for solving integral equations. *Int. J. Math. Educ. Sci. Tech.* **20**, 411–414.

Muskhelishvili, N. I. (1953). "Singular Integral Equations." Noordhoff, Groningen, Holland.

Peters, A. S. (1968). Abel's equation and the Cauchy integral equation. *Comm. Pure Appl. Math.* **21**, 51–65.

Zabreyko, R. P. *et al.* (1975). "Integral Equations." Noordhoff, Leyden, Holland.

INTEGRAL FAST REACTOR (NUCLEAR ENGINEERING)

J. C. Courtney *Louisiana State University*
M. J. Lineberry *Argonne National Laboratory*

Glossary

Actinide elements: Elements with atomic numbers equal to 90 or more. These are the elements that can undergo nuclear fission in reactors.

Burnup: Amount of nuclear fuel consumed. It may be expressed in terms of atom percent or the amount of energy produced per mass of fuel inserted into the reactor.

Cladding: Structural material that surrounds the nuclear fuel rods in a reactor core. Its functions are to contain fission and activation products formed in the fuel and to protect the fuel from chemical attack by the primary coolant.

Core: Region of the reactor that sustains the nuclear fission chain reaction. In fast reactors, it is also called the driver region.

Fuel cycle: All operations that are required to obtain nuclear fuel from natural resources, to fission it, and to dispose of waste products in an environmentally acceptable manner. A closed fuel cycle includes recycle of unfissioned uranium and plutonium found in spent fuel to fabricate fresh nuclear fuel assemblies.

Primary coolant system: Flow path of coolant fluid through the core of the nuclear reactor.

Reprocessing: Chemical separation of the elements found in spent fuel. Actinides may be refabricated into fresh fuel to be recycled to a reactor core.

Safeguards: All measures taken to prevent the diversion of radioactive materials, especially the actinide elements, to unauthorized uses.

Spent fuel: Nuclear fuel that is removed from a reactor core or blanket. It contains fission and activation products as well as unconsumed heavy elements.

Transuranic waste: Unwanted radioactive materials with atomic numbers greater than that of uranium (92). These materials are of concern because of their long half-lives and the potential for ingestion.

The integral fast reactor (IFR) is an advanced form of nuclear technology that has been pursued formally since 1984. Much of the base technology for the IFR is rooted in development programs dating back about three decades. The reactor itself has features that assure reliable removal of heat under any credible condition; such a design is said to possess inherent safety characteristics. Significant improvements in the nuclear fuel cycle are also being developed. An innovative pyrometallurgical technique for reprocessing spent fuel would replace the more conventional aqueous process. The objective of the IFR development program is to demonstrate the feasibility of the concept addressing both real and perceived problems of the current forms of nuclear technology.

I. Role of Nuclear Energy

Growth in the number of today's light water reactors (LWRs) is stalled throughout most of the world. No new plants have been ordered in the United States since 1978, and many earlier orders have been cancelled. Nevertheless, nuclear energy today supplies almost one-sixth of the U.S. electrical generation. The fraction is much higher in some countries, notably France where reactors supply more than two-thirds of all electrical needs. Without new orders, U.S. reactor deployment will reach a plateau of about 120 plants in the next few years. Without major changes in the institutional climate, the number may not increase.

At the same time, there is a wealth of opinion that nuclear energy retains a fundamental importance to the economic growth of the industrialized nations. The correlation of growth in domestic output with growth in electrical energy consumption is remarkably consistent. The Gross National Product (GNP) and consumption of energy from electrical and nonelectrical sources are plotted in Fig. 1. Data are normalized to their 1970 values. The correlation between GNP and electrical consumption is remarkably consistent, even during the tumultuous energy upheavals of the 1970s. Nonelectrical usage of energy is little different today than two decades ago. The message seems clear: economic growth is accompanied by increases in electrical consumption, at least in the recent past.

Supporting growth in electrical energy supply, in order to sustain economic growth, is therefore understandably imperative for all the industrialized nations. Large expansion in the market share of any of today's electrical energy technologies raises problems of one kind or another. With LWRs the concerns are cost, public perception of safety, and disposal of nuclear waste. With coal, concerns exist about the health and environmental impacts associated with mining and burning of coal. With natural gas or oil, the concern is depletion of the world's natural resources and political stability in some supplier nations. The Iraqi takeover of Kuwait in 1990 illustrates this problem. With more exotic energy approaches, the problems are cost, or even more fundamentally, technological feasibility.

Focusing on the nuclear energy options, perhaps changes will occur or solutions can be found that will enable LWR deployment to grow once again. Meanwhile, development of entirely new nuclear reactor technologies is occurring. The IFR is one of these, and, in the United States it is the most promising as well as the main advanced reactor technology under development.

II. Characteristics of the Reactor

A. Neutron Energy and Reaction Rates

The term "fast reactor" refers to the average speed of the neutrons that cause energy-produc-

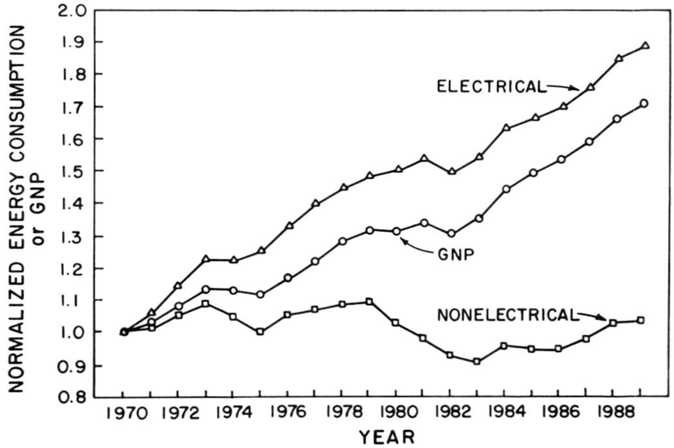

FIG. 1. Energy consumption and GNP between 1970 and 1989. [Information on GNP is from the Economic Report of the President, transmitted to Congress February 1990, House Document No. 101–121; Energy consumption data are given in the Annual Energy Review 1989 and Monthly Energy Review July 1990 published by the U.S. Department of Energy's Energy Information Administration.]

ing fission reactions. These events in turn release energy in the form of heat and more high-energy neutrons. If light-nuclei materials (such as the hydrogen contained in water) are prevalent, neutron–nuclei scattering collisions very quickly reduce the emitted neutron energies to fractions of an electron volt. If, on the other hand, few light nuclei exist within the reactor, neutrons collide only with much more massive nuclei and retain much of their few-million-electron-volt energy gained during fission. Light-nuclei materials are avoided in fast reactors by using molten sodium in place of water as the coolant. [*See* NUCLEAR FUEL CYCLES; NUCLEAR POWER REACTORS.]

A very important feature of fast reactors is that the much higher energy neutrons increase the average number of neutrons released in each fission event. Some of these neutrons are absorbed in ^{238}U and convert it to ^{239}Pu, an excellent nuclear fuel. While this process occurs to some extent in all reactors, the extra neutrons released in fast reactors produce more ^{239}Pu at a given power level in a given time than in any other reactor type. In fast reactors, it is possible to convert ^{238}U to ^{239}Pu faster than the initial charge of fuel is consumed in sustaining the fission process. Thus there can be a net gain of ^{239}Pu, which might be used to fuel additional reactors. This is called the breeding process. While ^{238}U is not an efficient nuclear fuel, it is the most abundant form of uranium. Conversion of ^{238}U to ^{239}Pu takes advantage of the vast worldwide resources of this material and makes them available for energy production. Enough ^{238}U exists in the United States that, if it were converted to ^{239}Pu, it could supply all our electrical needs for thousands of years. This energy supply potential has been the principal underlying rationale for development of sodium-cooled fast reactors.

The energy supply potential of fast reactors was known long ago. The concept was championed by Walter Zinn, who, as the first Director of Argonne National Laboratory, led the development of the Experimental Breeder Reactor-I (EBR-I). In 1951, it became the first nuclear reactor of any kind of generate electricity. Since then fast reactors have been under development in many nations. But even after nearly four decades of development, fast reactors, too, have their problems. While some have operated very reliably, others have not. Moreover, in their present form, fast reactors are even more costly than LWRs.

The IFR concept incorporates the features of fast reactors that have proven advantageous, but new features are also being developed. The IFR employs a new metallic form of fuel rather than the more conventional oxide fuels. The reactor core, coolant pumps, and intermediate heat exchanger are submerged in a large pool of liquid sodium coolant. Chemical separation of the actinide elements from the spent fuel, their reconstitution into fresh fuel, and handling of the waste products are based on a new high-temperature technique called the pyroprocess. The word integral in the IFR acronym refers to one siting option for the facilities needed to close the fuel cycle. Fast reactors must have a closed fuel cycle to be economic, and thus periodic reprocessing and recycling of actinides and disposal of associated waste are required. The new fuel cycle technology of the IFR is such that it may be economical and advantageous to have the fuel cycle facility on the same site and thus integrated with the reactors. Conversely, centralized siting of fuel cycle facilities serving several IFRs may also be the path chosen. These and other features combine to provide a form of nuclear technology with enhanced safety characteristics and potentially lower cost.

B. Metal Fuel

The current generation of reactors use a uranium dioxide (UO_2) ceramic fuel or a mixture of uranium and plutonium dioxides. These fuels perform very reliably, but a new metallic fuel is being developed for the IFR because it offers significant advantages. Most importantly, the thermal conductivity of metal fuel is about a factor of 10 higher than that of an oxide, thereby enhancing reactor safety characteristics. Also, metal fuel is necessary to implement the compact and simple fuel reprocessing technique described later. Yet to realize these potential advantages, metal fuel performance in the core of a reactor must be as good or better than oxide fuel.

A primary figure of merit for any nuclear fuel is how much energy can be extracted before it must be removed from the reactor. Practically all reactors use fuel in the form of a heavy element compound (e.g., UO_2) sealed inside a metal cladding. The cladding retains the radioactive products that result from fission and forms one of several barriers to the release of these materials to the environment. As energy is extracted from a fuel rod, those fission products that are in gaseous form slowly pressurize the cladding. Fission products retained in the fuel material cause it to swell and slowly increase mechanical stresses within the cladding. Also, the fast neutrons gradually change the metallurgical properties of the cladding. Eventually, mechanisms such as these cause the cladding to crack and release at least the gaseous fission products into the coolant system. While this is not in itself a safety problem, it does remove an important barrier that retains the fission products. In practice, essentially all reactors are operated so that the fuel is removed before cladding breach is likely to occur.

The energy extracted is measured by burnup, which can be expressed as the fraction of uranium and plutonium actually consumed, relative to that initially present in the fuel. High burnup is desirable in all reactors. In most reactors fuel removal and replacement requires the reactor to be taken out of service for at least-several days; the higher the burnup that can be achieved, the less frequently this must be done. In closed fuel cycles where fuel is reprocessed and recycled back to the reactor, high-burnup implies less fuel must be processed each year. Even in once-through fuel cycles in which discharged fuel is simple stored, achieving high burnup means less new fuel has to be supplied to refuel the reactor. Hence, high burnup increases the revenue produced by the reactor and reduces the plant operating cost.

Oxide fuels in fast reactors now reach burnups on the order of 10%, although this limit is still being increased. Burnup values in this range, and perhaps as high as 15%, are the goals set for the metal fuel being developed for the IFR program.

The metal fuel for the IFR is an alloy of uranium and zirconium, or uranium–plutonium–zirconium. In 1985 these alloys were first introduced into the Experimental Breeder Reactor-II (EBR-II), an experimental sodium-cooled reactor in Idaho that serves as a prototype for the IFR that would be needed for commercial operation, it has the same general features. This prototype, which is the follow-on to EBR-I, began operation in 1964. Since then EBR-II has served as one of the world's most reliable sodium-cooled reactor test facilities. By early 1991, EBR-II had been fueled for some time with the specific metal alloys of the IFR. Several thousand fuel rods have been used in the reactor without cladding breach, and burnups on the order of 15% have been achieved routinely. Burnups of this magnitude imply that fuel can be left in the reactor for about 3 yr before reprocessing is required.

Precisely the same physical phenomenon that makes sodium-cooled fast reactors better producers of ^{239}Pu gives metal fuel a superior conversion potential than any other fuel type. The oxygen present in oxide fuel compounds are relatively light nuclei, which provide energy loss mechanism during scattering that is not present with metals. With metal-fueled fast reactors it is possible to gain enough plutonium in about 10 years to provide the initial fuel inventory for a completely new reactor core. The importance of rapid breeding depends on the rate at which the reactors are being deployed. To match the deployment rate, reactor core design can be tailored to produce more or less plutonium, even to the degree of generating only enough plutonium to be self-sustaining. With metallic fuel, there is maximum flexibility to vary fuel breeding at essentially any time in order to match deployment.

C. Sodium Coolant

The physical properties of sodium make it the ideal coolant for fast reactors such as the IFR. It has the relatively high atomic weight needed to keep neutrons from losing much energy in collisions. Sodium has excellent heat transfer properties. Its high thermal conductivity and specific heat allows efficient removal of heat from the surface of the cladding. A low melting point (98°C or 208°F), high boiling point (899°C or 1650°F), and low vapor pressure are further advantages. The high boiling point and low vapor pressure mean that pressurization of the primary system in order to maintain coolant in a liquid state is not required. The low vapor pressure also means that the primary coolant systems of sodium-cooled reactors can be operated at pressures determined by pumping requirements, typically less than 1 MPa (150 psia). The lower the primary system pressure, the less likely that radioactive materials would escape from the core in the event of an accident.

Sodium's reasonable viscosity and density coupled with its high specific heat allow efficient heat removal with a minimum of power required for pumps, but more importantly these same properties promote natural convective flow. Natural convection is desirable because it provides a completely passive means (i.e., no actuators have to function and no operator action is required) to remove heat from the decay of fission products. This can be assured even if the main coolant pumps are shut off or damaged in an accident.

Sodium is chemically compatible with stainless steels at elevated temperatures. Corrosion of stainless steels is negligible even at sodium temperatures in excess of 538°C (1000°F). Present fuel designs are based on sodium temperatures between 340°C (644°F) at the inlet to the core and 500°C (932°F) at the outlet from the core.

The IFR reactor core and all components of the primary coolant system, including a sodium-to-sodium intermediate heat exchanger (IHX), are contained in a large tank of sodium. The arrangement of the EBR-II primary system is shown in Fig. 2. This design has a large thermal inertia; that is, the sodium surrounding the nuclear fuel and the IHX acts as an efficient heat sink. Sodium on the secondary side of the IHX does not pass through the reactor core so it does not become radioactive. The secondary sodium serves as a heat sink for energy produced in the reactor; it is circulated to a sodium-to-water heat exchanger located outside the reactor building. Steam produced in this unit may be superheated before it is sent to the turbine generator to produce electrical power. Higher temperature steam can be obtained from sodium-cooled reactors than from water-cooled reactors; thus the thermodynamic efficiency of the turbine is greater for the IFR. Experience at EBR-II since 1964 indicates that failure rates of sodium–water heat exchangers are low and consequences of leakage events are minor.

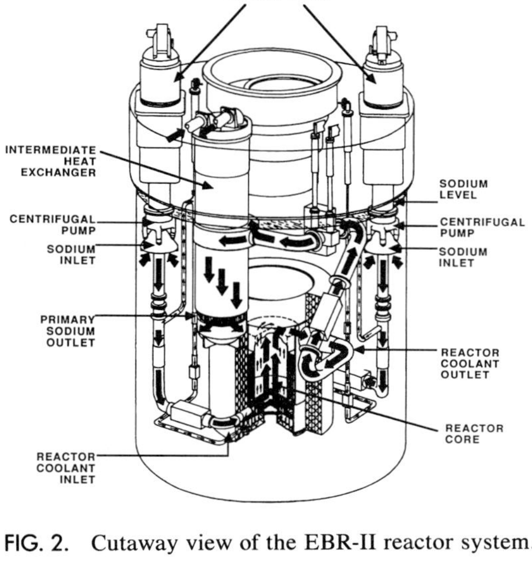

FIG. 2. Cutaway view of the EBR-II reactor system.

Of all the fission products, radioisotopes of iodine are considered to be the most hazardous. Liquid sodium and iodine vapor combine readily to form a solid, sodium iodide. Sodium is present inside the fuel cladding to maximize the heat transfer from the metal fuel slug to the cladding and then to the coolant. Iodine released from the fuel is trapped as a solid within the cladding. Even if the cladding were to fail in an accident, the sodium in the pool would capture the iodine. Other chemically active fission products such as cesium are also retained in the sodium coolant. Hence, even an incredible accident that severely damages many fuel rods would have minor radiological consequences outside of the primary coolant system. Current planning for response to power reactor accidents requires resources to evacuate an area defined by a radius of 10 miles from the plant. With an IFR, this distance might be reduced to 3 miles or less because of the improved retention of fission product nuclides, especially iodine, within the fuel and primary cooling system of the reactor.

D. Safety Characteristics

The large pool of sodium coolant and the thermal properties of metal fuel yield important new safety characteristics for the IFR. These characteristics have been demonstrated in an extensive series of tests in the EBR-II reactor. The EBR-II is a small but complete power plant; it has a maximum thermal power of 62 MW. Heat is transferred to a turbine generator that supplies about 20 MW of electricity to a commercial transmission and distribution grid. Thus, tests in EBR-II simulate conditions that might be expected in systems developed for future commercial deployment.

The most impressive of these tests involved a deliberate loss of coolant flow without manual or automatic reactor shutdown. This has long been thought to be among the most serious of possible reactor accidents. If this unlikely event were to occur in an LWR, the cladding would begin to oxidize rapidly and the fuel would start to melt. With FBR-II at full power, and the automatic shutdown systems disabled, operators were instructed to shut off electrical power to the primary coolant system pumps and to take no further corrective action. After loss of power, the pumps began slowing down with mechanical inertia providing some rotation for about 100 sec until complete stoppage. Figure 3 presents the sodium temperature at the reactor outlet versus time after pump electrical interruption.

After the pump stopped, flow was continued by natural convective circulation and supplemented by a small battery-operated electromagnetic auxiliary pump. The peak temperature was well below the boiling point of sodium and dropped rapidly about 60 sec into the transient. If the small auxiliary pump had been turned off, the peak temperature was predicted to be only 17°C (30°F) higher. After a few minutes the system was stable at roughly the same temperatures as encountered in normal operation. Heat from the core was removed by natural circulation and this system state could have been maintained indefinitely. The agreement between calculations and measurements suggests that the important factors governing passive power reduction and coupled natural convective heat removal are well understood. Peak temperatures reached were not high enough to prevent an immediate restart of the reactor, and within 5 hr the reactor was back at full power ready for the next test.

This second test involved stopping the flow of sodium in the secondary side of the intermediate heat exchanger (IHX), depriving the primary coolant system of its heat sink. This, too, was done without automatic reactor shutdown and again no operator action was permitted. Sodium temperatures in the primary coolant system before and after shutting down the flow of the secondary coolant are shown versus time in Fig. 4. The peak reactor outlet sodium temperatures were rapidly reduced to levels lower than their normal full power values, and transient overtemperatures were negligible.

The benign results of these two tests reflect the ability of the primary sodium pool to absorb large amounts of energy with only a modest rise in temperature and the high thermal conductivity of the metal fuel. Because the sodium pool thermal inertia and the fuel thermal conductivity are intrinsic properties of the system and cannot fail, the safety characteristics observed are inherent to this reactor design.

The results of these tests and other analyses and experiments suggest that sodium-cooled, pool-type reactors with metallic fuels do not need complicated back-up systems for emergency shutdown and post-shutdown heat removal. Consequently they may have major cost savings compared to the current generation of power reactors. The relatively low temperatures throughout the core even under abnormal conditions imply that a large measure of safety is inherent in the basic design of the IFR. Furthermore, analysis has shown that these EBR-II results are typical of what would be expected in larger IFR-type fast reactors. Predictions of temperatures by computer simulation of conditions within the primary coolant system matched closely the tests results observed in EBR-II. This indicates that the mathematical models and input data used are appropriate to predict the thermal behavior of different IFR designs under a variety of normal and abnormal conditions.

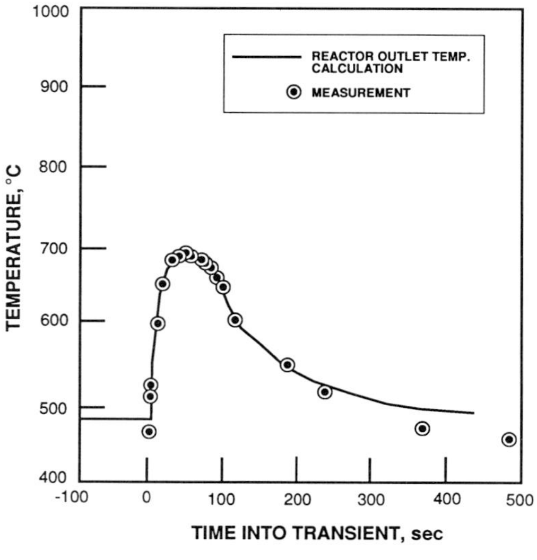

FIG. 3. Temperature response of EBR-II to a loss of primary coolant flow without a reactor scram.

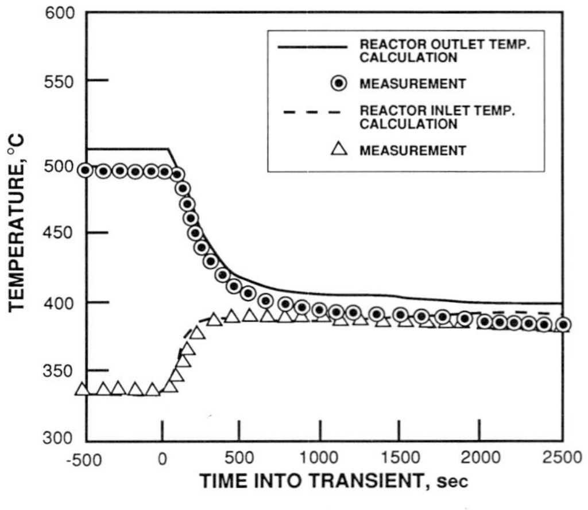

FIG. 4. Temperature response of EBR-II to a loss of secondary IHX coolant flow.

III. Fuel Reprocessing

A. Fuel Cycle-Requirements

One of the major differences between fast reactors and LWRs is the enrichment of fuel or fraction of the uranium that is ^{235}U. At high neutron energies, cross sections for fission are low, so fast reactors must use fuel that has more ^{235}U or ^{239}Pu nuclei per unit volume. Typical enrichments of large fast reactors are about 20% compared to an average of about 3% for LWRs. When discharged from the reactor because the burnup limit has been reached, fast reactor fuel enrichment is about 15%, whereas LWR fuel at discharge is perhaps 1.5%. Because of the small amount of ^{235}U and ^{239}Pu present in spent LWR fuel, reprocessing to recover these valuable materials is not economically imperative. For fast reactors, however, there is no economic option other than reprocessing the fuel to recover ^{239}Pu and ^{235}U and to put them back into the reactor in the form of new fuel.

Reprocessing of LWR fuel is nonetheless being done now in other countries. Large commercial-scale facilities exist in France and are now being expanded. Similar facilities are currently under construction in Great Britain. Japan is planning to begin operation of a commercial-scale plant in the mid-1990s, which will replace a smaller plant now in service. These national commitments to reprocess spent fuel from LWRs may be based either on the desire to recycle fuel back to the reactors or on waste management criteria. Separation of radioactive materials by their level of activity, half-life, and potential for environmental damage increases the efficiency of nuclear waste management. Regardless of the motivation, in each of these countries fuel cycle facilities will exist that presumably could be used in their fast reactor development programs.

In the United States reprocessing and recycling of LWR fuel were projected to begin in the 1970s, and a large facility was constructed at Barnwell, South Carolina. This plant was approaching completion in 1977 when President Carter banned reprocessing in the United States because of concern over the proliferation of nuclear weapons. Although the ban was lifted by President Reagan in 1981, there has been no resumption of activity at the Barnwell site. The prevalent view is that, in the light of the current situation, reprocessing would not be economically viable in the United States.

The traditional view has been that reprocessing of fast reactor fuel, which with its higher enrichment and burnup is somewhat more difficult, would follow LWR reprocessing. The technology and perhaps some of the facilities used in the LWR fuel cycle were viewed as necessary preludes to fast reactor reprocessing. Conventional reprocessing is done with the PUREX (for plutonium–uranium extraction) process. PUREX is a solvent extraction process in which the oxide fuel is first dissolved in nitric acid. Plutonium and uranium are separated from the fission products in a multistage chemical extraction process that employs selective distribution of elements between aqueous and organic phases. Inherent in PUREX plants are large economies of scale. They are thought to be most cost effective when sized to serve 30 to 50 LWRs. A plant of this capacity would cost several billion dollars.

A key problem in bringing fast reactors to deployment status in the United States is the absence of existing PUREX facilities. No matter how successful the fast reactor development program, the deployment of these reactors will begin at a slow rate, and after the first few years only a small number could be expected. Yet even the first one will require a reprocessing and fuel fabrication facility. With the economies of scale inherent in PUREX and in fabrication facilities for oxide fuel, a small facility would have high unit costs (dollars per kilogram of fuel processed), while a large initial facility would have a large capital cost and idle capacity during its early years. Thus, without LWR reprocessing facilities on which to build and which might be modified to serve the initial fast reactor plants, deployment of the latter is severely hindered.

B. Integral Fast Reactor Fuel Cycle

In the IFR program, the basic fuel cycle processes are much different than PUREX. Fuel remains a high-density metal throughout the process. Separation of uranium and plutonium from fission products, and fabrication into new fuel takes place in a small number of high-temperature operations. This has been termed pyrometallurgical (for high-temperature metal) processing, or more simply, pyroprocessing. Because of the small number of steps involved in the pyroprocess and the high density of the fuel in process, the amount and size of the equipment and the size of the facility needed to conduct fuel cycle operations is much reduced.

The pyroprocess has the potential to be economic even at a size sufficient to serve one or a small number of reactors. If this can be demonstrated, a unique U.S. hurdle to fast reactor deployment will be overcome.

The main process steps are illustrated in Fig. 5. A fuel assembly consisting of some 200 or more fuel rods with cladding intact is introduced for processing into a remotely operated, shielded room called a hot cell. The assembly is taken apart, and the structural components (everything except the fuel rods themselves) are removed and discarded as waste. The rods are passed through a shear and chopped into short pieces. The chopped segments are placed into an electrorefiner at 500°C that both dissolves the uranium–plutonium–zirconium from the cladding and electrolytically separates the uranium and plutonium from zirconium and the fission products.

In the IFR process electrorefining is to be used for the first time to reprocess nuclear fuel. It is a common process used in industry to purify a number of metals such as copper and nickle. The electrorefiner anode consists of the impure metal fuel that is dissolved in molten cadmium. Purified fuel (uranium and plutonium) is then electrolytically deposited at the cathode, while the impurities remain in solution within the electrorefining vessel.

A schematic of the IFR, electrorefining process is shown in Fig. 6. The device itself is a steel vessel about 1 m in diameter and 1 to 2 m high. Chopped fuel dissolves slowly in the liquid cadmium anode, which is maintained at about 500°C. At the appropriate cell voltage, uranium or an uranium–plutonium mixture is deposited on a solid metal cathode or into a liquid cadmium cathode. The vast majority of fission products are left in either the cadmium anode or the electrolyte, although small concentrations of some fission products do electrotransport to the cathodes.

When the solid cathode is used, the chemical thermodynamics are such that uranium will transport almost exclusively (i.e., without plutonium). Alternatively, uranium and plutonium can be electrotransported together into a liquid cadmium cathode where they are deposited as a metal precipitate and an intermetallic compound ($PuCd_6$), respectively. In this way, uranium in the form of ^{238}U can be cycled back to the reactor to produce more plutonium, while the uranium–plutonium mixture can be returned to fission and produce the heat that is converted to electrical power. Interestingly, the thermodynamic properties of this process make it impossible to produce a pure plutonium product, and all the fuel produced contains sufficient fission products to require special remote handling procedures and make unauthorized uses difficult.

The cathodes that result from electrorefining are processed to remove entrained electrolyte and/or cadmium. In either case, this step involves raising the temperature of the cathode product in a furnace to a temperature (700 to 900°C) that dissociates the cadmium intermetallic compound and vaporizing the cadmium for collection elsewhere or to a temperature that vaporizes the entrained electrolyte salt (~1100°C).

After mixing the desired weights of uranium and/or plutonium for new fuel rods, raw fuel slugs are produced by injection casting, a process similar to that used routinely in the manufacture of many plastic products. The raw fuel slugs are then removed from molds, sheared to the correct length, and inspected to confirm acceptable composition and quality. Acceptable

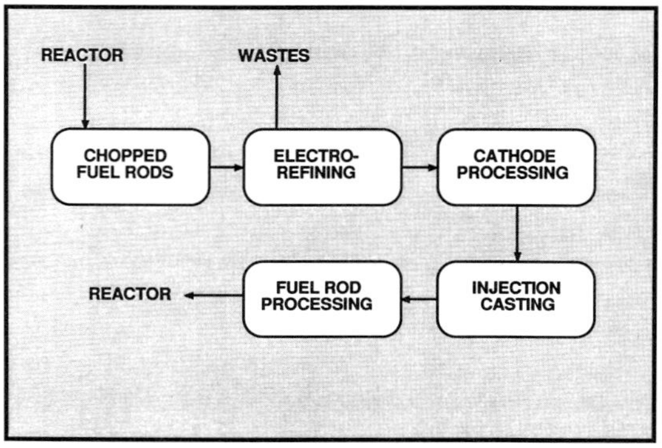

FIG. 5. Block diagram of the major steps in pyrometallurgical fuel cycle.

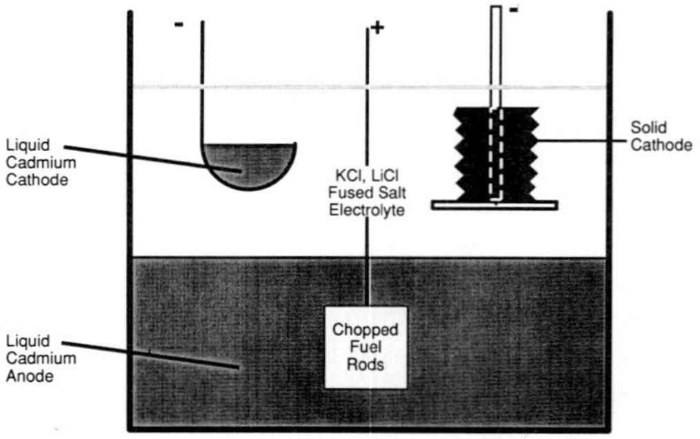

FIG. 6. Schematic diagram of the electrorefining process.

fuel slugs are inserted into new cladding material and seal welded, and new assemblies are fabricated from these finished fuel rods and returned to the reactor.

C. Waste Treatment

Pyroprocessing offers the possibility of separating four minor actinides, ^{237}Np, ^{240}Pu, ^{241}Am, and ^{243}Am, from the rest of the waste stream. These four long-lived alpha-emitters dictate the confinement period for radioactive waste generated by processing spent fuel. If these nuclides are recovered and recycled in an IFR, they can be fissioned efficiently by the high-energy neutron spectrum, thus generating energy and converting them into much shorter-lived fission products. By significantly reducing or eliminating these four minor actinides, the confinement time criteria for geological waste repositories can be made much less severe. Since the separation of Np, Pu, and Am occurs naturally in the IFR pyroprocess, a logical extension of this technology is the treatment of spent fuel from light water power reactors. If this can be accomplished at a reasonable cost, the management of high-level waste from all nuclear fuel cycles could be simplified.

The IFR process does not produce high-level radioactive liquid wastes. Also, fission gases are more easily handled. Four nuclides usually found in gaseous form, ^{3}H, ^{14}C, ^{85}Kr, and ^{129}I, are of great environmental concern because of their long half-lives and mobility in the biosphere. In the pyrometallurgical process, ^{129}I is trapped as a halide salt in the electrorefiner electrolyte rather than being released as a gas. The ^{14}C also remains as a solid and is dissolved in the electrorefiner anode cadimum rather than being oxidized to CO_2 to be recovered by gas treatment systems. Both ^{3}H and ^{85}Kr are released from the fuel during chopping and electrorefining. These gases will be collected from the process cell argon atmosphere by purification systems and stored within the facility. Mixture of fission gases with corrosive vapors (a significant design problem for PUREX plants) is not a factor in design of these systems. [*See* RADIOACTIVE WASTES.]

The principal IFR process wastes are from the electrorefiner. The molten salt will be discharged from the electrorefining cells and converted to a nontransuranic waste by extraction of residual actinides into a Cd–Li alloy. Most of the transuranic-contaminated, high-level process wastes are from the electrorefiner anode or the salt treatment process. If they are not separated and recycled, they will be contained in a copper alloy matrix and encapsulated in corrosion-resistant metal containers for deep geologic disposal. Volumes of the IFR wastes from the pyrochemical process have been estimated and compared with those from the PUREX process. The two processes produce about the same volumes of high- and intermediate-level wastes, but the pyroprocess produces less low-level waste.

A hot cell complex at Argonne's site at the Idaho National Engineering Laboratory is being modified to serve as a demonstration fuel cycle facility. When completed, all the operations necessary to process spent fuel and reconstitute fresh fuel assemblies for EBR-II will take place in a single building adjacent to the reactor. This relatively small but complete demonstration of both reactor and fuel cycle IFR technology may set the stage in the mid-1990s for a larger scale prototype plant.

D. Security and Safeguards

Any fuel processing method should have features that prevent unauthorized diversion of the nuclear fuel (particularly actinide elements that could be used to produce nuclear weapons) from its intended application. In the IFR process, the fuel is either in the reactor or is contained within heavy shielding throughout all of the fuel cycle including the reprocessing, storage, and refabrication steps. At no time is there any human contact with the materials that must be secured. This is because the pyrometallurgical technique does not remove all the fission products from the reprocessed fuel. This small carryover of residual fission products does not affect fuel performance, but makes the reconstituted fuel so radioactive that it must be shielded and handled remotely. These impurities and the fact that the process does not separate plutonium from uranium make the fuel materials less desirable for nuclear weapons use. Anyone wishing to make unauthorized use of IFR fuel would need a special shield for diversion of the materials and access to a remotely operated facility capable of the complex steps required to purify the heavy metals for use in nuclear weapons.

If the colocation option for the reactor and fuel cycle facility is chosen, no off-site transfers of nuclear materials are required after the delivery of fuel for the first core and blanket. This greatly reduces the potential for diversion of materials through hijacking of shipments. Plutonium transport outside of the reactor and reprocessing facility site could be totally eliminated if the option of uranium startup for the reactor were chosen and all of the plutonium was produced, reprocessed, and fissioned at the same location.

Bibliography

Chang, Y. I. (1989). The integral fast reactor. *Nucl. Technol.* **88,** 129.

Lineberry, M. J., and Phipps, R. D. (1987). A demonstration facility for the IFR fuel cycle. *Proc. Nucl. Fuel Reprocess. Waste Management Conf. Fr. Nucl. Soc.* **1,** 153.

Planchon, H. P., Jr., Golden, G. H., and Sackett, J. I. (1987). Demonstration of passive safety features in EBR-II. *Proc. Am. Power Conf.* **49,** 529.

Planchon, H. P., Jr., Sackett, J. I., Golden, G. H., and Sevy, R. H. (1987). Implications of the EBR-II inherent safety demonstration test. *Nucl. Eng. Des.* **101,** 75.

Stevenson, C. E. (1987). "The EBR-II Fuel Cycle Story." Amer. Nuclear Soc., LaGrange Park, Illinois.

Till, C. E., Chang, Y. I., and Lineberry, M. J. (1990). The integral fast reactor. *Proc. 7th Pacific Basin Nuclear Conf.,* San Diego, Calif. *Trans. Am. Nucl. Soc.* **61** (Supplement 1), 449.

INTEGRATED CIRCUIT MANUFACTURE

Peter Sukanek *University of Mississippi*
William R. Wilcox *Clarkson University*
James G. Ryan *IBM*

GLOSSARY

Acceptor: Impurity in a semiconductor that accepts conduction electrons to become ionized and produce holes. When the acceptor ion concentration exceeds the donor ion concentration, the material is called *p*-type.

Amorphous solid: Solid possessing no long-range order (i.e., a glass).

Carrier lifetime: Mean time between the formation of excess charge carriers (holes or electrons) and their recombination.

Compound semiconductor: Semiconductor which is a chemical compound. These are often classified by the groups in the periodic table from which the elements come, such as III-V (e.g., GaAs) or II-VI (e.g., HgCdTe).

Crystal: Solid material with a regular, repeating, three dimensional order.

Dislocation: Line defect in a crystal. An edge dislocation is the defect bounding a partial plane of material inserted into the lattice. A screw dislocation is visualized by cutting part way through a crystal and shearing one half with respect to another.

Donor: Impurity that donates conduction electrons to the semiconductor, producing *n*-type material when present in excess.

Dopant: Intentionally added impurity in a semiconductor which increases its electrical conductivity. For silicon, the dopants are boron (to make it *p*-type) and phosphorus, arsenic, or antimony (to make it *n*-type).

Epitaxy: Two crystals in intimate atomic contact having a preferred crystallographic orientation between them. Also commonly, but incorrectly, used to denote deposition of a film on a substrate.

Integrated circuit (IC): Complex electrical circuit consisting of many transistors, diodes, capacitors, and resistors designed either to perform a logic operation or to store bits of data. When the IC is contained on a semiconductor substrate, it is called monolithic; when it is a combination of individual devices (sometimes with monolithic ICs) bonded to an insulating substrate, it is called a hybrid circuit.

Interstitial: Atom in a crystal at a site other than a lattice site.

Kerf: Cut made through a solid body.

Latch up: Mode of IC failure in which the circuit ceases to function or self-destructs.

Parasitic capacitance: Additional capacitance in a transistor caused by interaction with a semiconducting substrate, thereby reducing the switching speed of the device.

***p–n* junction:** Boundary in a semiconductor between a region containing an excess number of holes (*p*-type) and a region containing an excess number of electrons (*n*-type).

Point defect: Imperfection at a point in a crystal lattice caused, for example, by a missing atom on a lattice site or by an interstitial atom.

Stacking fault: Region in a crystal where the normal stacking sequence of atomic planes has been violated. In silicon this typically consists of extra disks of (111) planes inserted in the lattice, bounded by a partial dislocation.

Substitutional: Impurity atom in a crystal residing on a lattice site.

Superlattice: Crystal lattice in which the composition changes dramatically and periodically in each atomic plane (e.g., GaAs–AlAs).

Via: Hole cut through an insulator to permit contact of one level of metal to another.

Very large-scale integration (VLSI): IC with approximately 10^5–10^8 devices.

Integrated circuits (ICs) are electronic devices consisting of transistors, diodes, capacitors, and resistors made and interconnected on a single solid substrate material. ICs are used primarily for logic operations or for memory. In very large or ultra large scale integration (VLSI-ULSI), hundreds of thousands to hundreds of millions of these electronic devices are interconnected on a chip of solid typically measuring a centimeter on each side. While the vast majority of ICs are made from single-crystal silicon, a small percentage is made from gallium arsenide and other compound semiconductors from groups III and V, as well as from groups II and VI. Research is underway on use of polycrystalline materials. The methods currently used to fabricate or manufacture IC chips from single crystal silicon are outlined. However, most of the techniques are applicable to compound semiconductors as well. IC fabrication is a very competitive business, and the technology is evolving rapidly. The common thread is the trend to smaller dimensions, necessitating lower processing temperatures, shorter processing times, new materials, new techniques, and scrupulous attention to cleanliness, in terms of both particulates and impurities in process chemicals.

I. Introduction

Fabrication of IC chips from single-crystal silicon wafers is a multistep process requiring care, cleanliness, and precision at each step. In the crystal, *p–n* junctions, capacitors, and resistors are produced by the controlled introduction of dopant atoms by ion implantation, epitaxial growth, or diffusion. Electrode, insulator, contact regions, and conductors are formed in or deposited on the crystal. These steps are not performed simultaneously; they must be repeated several times in the various levels of the production sequence.

As a very simple example of the fabrication of a single device in a silicon crystal, consider the steps required to make the *n*-type, enhancement-mode, metal oxide semiconductor field effect transistor (MOSFET) illustrated in Fig. 1. This device is normally "off"; no current can flow between the source and the drain. When a positive potential is supplied to the metal gate, electrons are attracted to and holes are repelled from the silicon–silicon dioxide interface below the gate. When the gate potential is sufficiently large, the electron concentration exceeds the hole concentration, and so a layer near the surface is inverted to *n*-type. Current can then flow between the source and the drain if a potential difference is applied between them. For a given drain-source voltage, the larger the gate potential, the larger the current flow until a saturation point is reached.

The fabrication sequence for this MOSFET is illustrated in Fig. 2. First, the surface is oxidized to produce a protective layer of silicon dioxide. An organic, photosensitive material called a photoresist is deposited on the oxide. The solubility of this organic material is altered by exposure to radiation. The surface is then irradiated in a particular pattern to expose the resist. After the soluble portion of the resist is dissolved in a developer, the resulting pattern is transferred to the underlying oxide layer in an etching operation. The organic material on top of the oxide must resist the etchant. The result is the A level, and its purpose is to define the source and drain regions in the semiconductor. The exposed silicon is doped with an *n*-type material such as phosphorus in a diffusion or ion implantation process. Another layer of oxide is then grown on the silicon. In the second, or B, level the gate and contact regions are defined. Again, a photoresist layer is deposited on the oxide, irradiated, developed, and the exposed oxide etched away. A thin, dense, high-purity oxide is formed in the exposed regions. At level C the contact regions are exposed. A layer of metal, usually aluminum or an aluminum mixture, is deposited. A final mask level serves to define the source and the drain contacts as well as the gate elec-

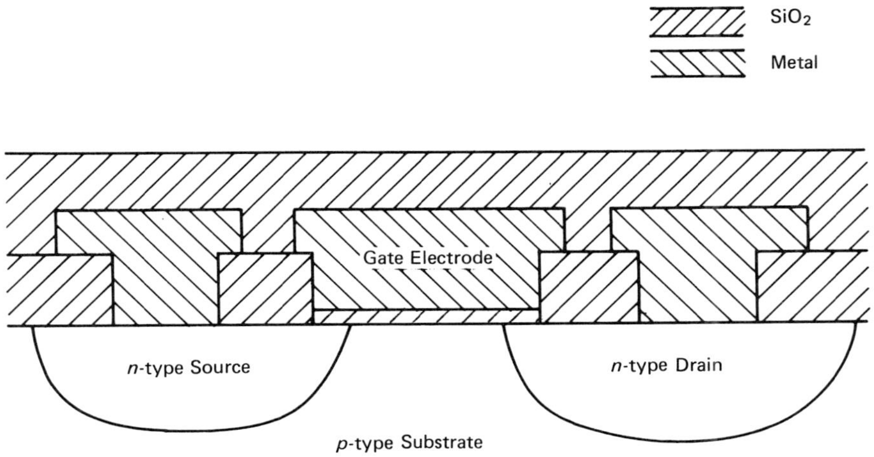

FIG. 1. Schematic diagram of enhancement mode MOSFET. Dimensions are not to scale.

trode. A passivating layer of insulating material is deposited to protect the device and isolate it from other metal lines.

This simple example required four levels; modern integrated circuits are processed through as many as 15 to 20 levels and require several hundred separate processing steps. Aluminum gate electrodes are typically not used. Rather, doped polycrystalline silicon (polysilicon or poly) or metal silicides have replaced them. In most applications, two or more insulating layers of different materials are employed.

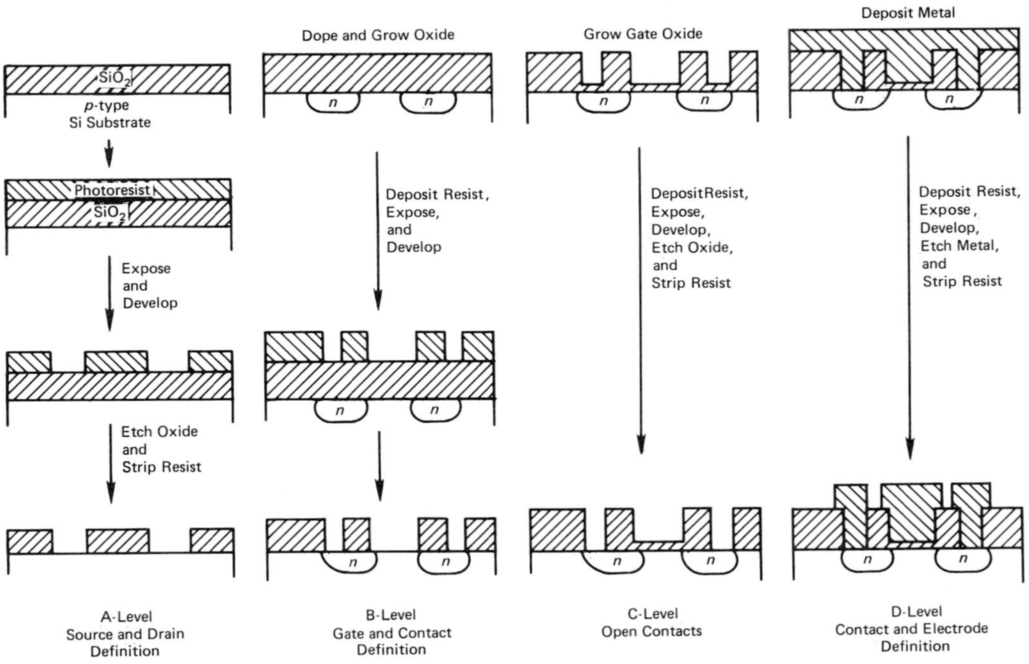

FIG. 2. Four processing levels required in the production of the MOSFET shown in Fig. 1. Any real process involves the production of tens or hundreds of millions of devices in a chip at one time, with tens or hundreds of chips on a wafer. Dimensions are not to scale.

Multiple metal lines are employed, one stacked above another. Special precautions must be taken to isolate one device from an adjacent one. The smallest image size or "groundrule" is currently in the half to subhalf micrometer range, a size approximately one-fiftieth the diameter of human hair. Consequently, the ability to overlay one level on a previous one must be controlled to much less than 0.1 μm.

It is important to realize that the same operations described above are taking place almost simultaneously all over the silicon wafer. Literally millions of these field effect transistors (FETs) are made at locations determined by the pattern of irradiating the resist material. In addition, a number of different devices (diodes, *p*-type MOSFETs, capacitors, etc) are fabricated in each integrated circuit. Some processing steps for these devices might coincide with those for the FETs, while other devices would require additional levels. Several dozen to several hundred integrated chips, in most cases all of them identical, are simultaneously made on a wafer of single crystal silicon.

In the following sections, each of these various processing steps is examined in more detail.

II. Production of Semiconductor-Grade Silicon: Sand to Wafers

Elemental silicon is produced by heating a powdered mixture of carbon and silica (SiO_2 from quartz sand or crystals) in a carbon arc furnace. Biproducts include carbon monoxide (CO) and silicon carbide (SiC). The silicon powder produced is metallurgical grade (MG), and is used in large quantities for alloying with iron in steel production. MG silicon contains many impurities and must be purified before it can be used for IC fabrication.

The most common method of producing semiconductor-grade (SG) silicon from MG silicon is the Siemens process. In a fluidized bed at about 1100°C, MG silicon powder is reacted with HCl gas to produce trichlorosilane ($SiHCl_3$), with other chlorinated silanes as biproducts. The $SiHCl_3$ is purified by distillation and then reacted with H_2 over an electrically heated silicon rod to deposit SG silicon. The purified silanes are also used for deposition of single crystal and polycrystalline silicon films in IC fabrication, as described in Section VIII.

An alternate technology for the production of SG silicon is the Komatsu silane process. Here, MG silicon powder is reacted with H_2 and silicon tetrachloride ($SiCl_4$) in a fluidized bed to produce SiH_2Cl_2 and other silanes. The gas mixture is catalytically reacted to $SiCl_4$ and SiH_4. After distillation, the $SiCl_4$ is recycled to the initial reactor and the impurities are discarded. The purified SiH_4 is pyrolized in a fluidized bed to give SG silicon powder. The H_2 byproduct is also recycled. The impurity content of the SG silicon from the silane process is somewhat less than that from the standard trichlorosilane process, with boron and phosphorus concentrations on the order of 0.01 and 0.06 ppb, respectively.

About 80% of the SG silicon is converted into single crystal ingots by the Czochralski (CZ) technique (sometimes called "crystal pulling" or the "Teal-Little method"). Some SG silicon is formed into solid rods and used for floating zone melting crystal growth (float zoning).

In Czochralski growth, a silicon melt is formed in a fused silica (quartz) crucible, as shown in Fig. 3. Surrounding the crucible are typically a graphite crucible support, a graphite resistance heater, thermal insulation, and a water-cooled stainless steel container. A long thin seed is cut from a previous crystal. Its end is dipped into the melt and melted back. The heater temperature is reduced to cause growth, and the seed is slowly withdrawn, with rotation. The crystal diameter is at first decreased to a few millimeters to reduce thermal stresses and allow any dislocations present to grow out. Then thermal conditions are adjusted to bring the crystal out to its desired diameter. The entire operation is performed in an inert atmosphere, usually argon or helium, at reduced pressure. The largest sized wafer in production use today is 200 mm, usually referred to as "8 in.," although wafers as large as 300 mm ("12 in."),

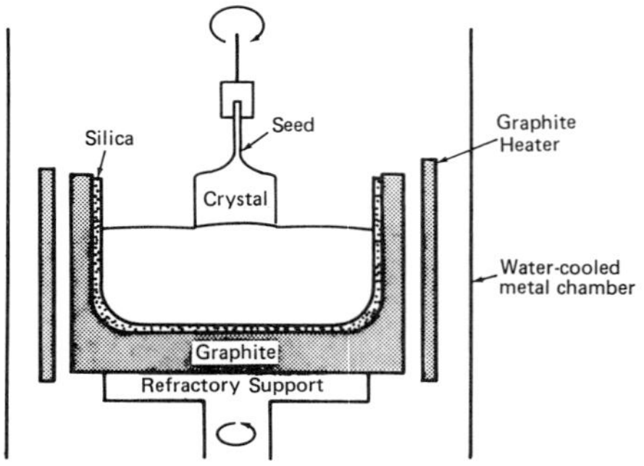

FIG. 3. Schematic diagram of the Czochralski crystal growth apparatus.

completely dislocation free, have been grown. Crystals of both <100> and <111> orientation are available.

Higher purity crystals are available from float zoned silicon, although the maximum commercially available diameter is 5 in. In the float zone process, the bottom end of a polysilicon rod is brought into contact with an O-shaped radio frequency coil with an internal diameter much less than the rod (referred to as a "needle-eye" heater coil). The rf field induces eddy currents in the silicon, which melts, flows down through the "needle-eye" onto a seed crystal below the coil, and solidifies. The heater traverses the entire rod. Since the melt is not in contact with a crucible, the impurity content of the wafers is determined solely by that of the starting material. Such high purity is required by silicon infrared detectors and by high voltage–high power rectifiers and thyristors.

After growth, the cylindrical crystal is centerless-ground to remove irregularities and to reach the desired diameter. Flats to identify orientation and doping and sometimes alignment grooves for lithography are also ground onto the sides of the ingots. The ingots are then sliced "bologna-style" into wafers. For this, an inside-diameter diamond saw is used, in which cutting is carried out at the inside surface of the ring-shaped blade. (The usual outside-diameter saw causes larger kerf losses because the blade must be thicker for mechanical rigidity.) The wafers are chemical-mechanically lapped to a very flat damage-free surface by use of colloidal silica particles in a gentle etchant liquid such as hypochlorite in water. After cleaning to remove both organics and inorganics, the wafers are shipped to the semiconductor fabrication plant. The final cost is on the order of \$0.20 to \$1.00 per cm^2 and depends on doping level, diameter, impurity content specifications, surface treatment, etc.

There are several important defects that can occur in CZ crystals. Figure 4 shows one type of dislocation in a silicon lattice. (This diamond lattice is common to silicon and other semiconductors.)

Dislocations are deleterious for several reasons. They make it easy for wafers to bow or warp under the thermal stress caused by inserting and removing wafers from hot furnaces in oxidation, diffusion, and hot-wall chemical vapor deposition. Warpage beyond a small amount can make lithographic operations difficult. In severe cases, the wafers can even shatter. Diffusion of impurities tends to be faster down dislocation cores, causing irregular p–n junctions, which ruins device performance. Because there is a compressive stress on one side of the dislocation and tension on the other side, impurities are attracted to these regions. Transition metal impurities, for example, can occupy the dislocation core after heating and cooling. Such decorated dislocations are harmful to device performance if they occur within a transistor. On the other hand, if the dislocations are on the back side of the wafer, far from the devices, they serve to attract ("getter") harmful impurities and increase the minority carrier lifetime.

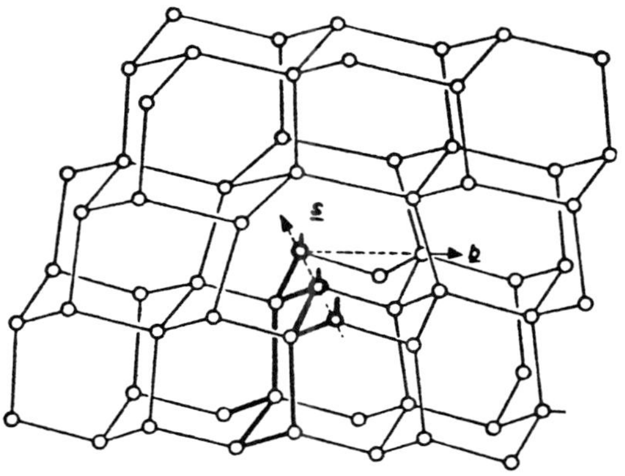

FIG. 4. One type of dislocation in silicon.

The impurity concentration in CZ crystals oscillates along their length. These striations occur because the growth rate oscillates as the crystal is rotated and pulled in a nonuniform temperature field. More importantly, there are large convection patterns in the silicon melt during CZ growth caused by the crystal and crucible rotations and by buoyancy. This convective flow leads to nonuniformities in both the axial and the radial directions. Recent work has shown that they may be greatly reduced by applying an external magnetic field to the crucible. Because the melt is conductive, the external field increases the effective viscosity of the fluid, decreasing convection.

Stacking faults in the crystal are generated because the equilibrium concentration of interstitial silicon atoms decreases rapidly as the temperature falls after growth. If dislocations are present, they absorb excess interstitials. In the absence of dislocations, the interstitials cluster together to form tiny (111) disks. The stacking faults form in a swirl pattern across the wafer and are revealed by certain crystallographic etches.

Oxygen is present in large quantities in CZ silicon because the silica crucible dissolves in the melt. Magnetic melt stabilization reduces the amount of oxygen impurities since the reduction in convection reduces the dissolution rate of the crucible. Again, the solubility of oxygen in the crystal decreases rapidly as the temperature falls after growth. Small oxygen concentrations and short times at high temperature yield oxygen clusters, which strengthen the silicon and reduce warpage problems because of solution hardening. High oxygen concentrations and long annealing times yield oxide precipitates, which punch out dislocations and increase warpage. Warpage is a minimum at oxygen concentrations of 20 to 25 ppm. With proper heat treatment, the oxygen atoms diffuse out from the surface, where devices are to be formed, and precipitate only in the bulk of the silicon. These precipitates act as internal getters for harmful impurities and increase the excess-carrier lifetime. It is common practice to supply wafers which have been processed in this manner.

Carbon is also present in silicon. It comes from contamination of the SG silicon itself, from organic contaminants in the furnace and its components, from reaction of the silica crucible with its graphite support to produce CO and CO_2, and from reaction of the SiO evaporating from the melt with the hot graphite also to produce CO and CO_2. Carbon enhances oxide precipitation and swirl formation. When the concentration in the melt becomes large, SiC particles may form and cause the silicon to develop dislocations and new grains. In Czochralski growth, the carbon content is controlled to the parts per million range by operating at a partial vacuum, 4 to 750 Torr.

Compound semiconductors, such as gallium arsenide (GaAs) and cadmium telluride (CdTe), are often grown by the horizontal Bridgman (HB) technique. A polycrystalline material is placed inside a horizontal tube or boat with a seed crystal at one end. The boat is sealed to prevent the evaporation of one of the components. (The vapor pressure of As over GaAs at its melting point is 1 atm.) An external heater slowly traverses and melts the poly feed, which then crystallizes onto the seed. Crystals produced in this way are D-shaped and are contaminated by the boat material.

Round, single crystal wafers of III–V semiconductors have been made by the high pressure, liquid encapsulated Czochralski method. Ga and As are heated in a boron nitride crucible with a tightly fitting boric oxide (B_2O_3) cover. The cover melts at about 400°C, reducing As evaporation. Crystal growth proceeds in the same way as described above for silicon, with an As overpressure of 20 atm. Much higher purity crystals are obtained by this method compared with the Bridgman method.

III. Oxidation

An oxide (or other dielectric) can serve many functions in IC fabrication and in the completed IC. It can provide a barrier to diffusion, ion implantation, or epitaxial growth. It can act as a gate dielectric for a field effect transistor or help protect the completed device from contamination by the environment. Such dielectric layers can be formed either by reaction of the solid with the surrounding gas or by chemical vapor deposition.

Several types of insulating films may be grown on a silicon surface, including silicon dioxide (SiO_2), silicon nitride (Si_3N_4), and silicon oxynitride. Silicon is oxidized either in nominally dry oxygen or in oxygen containing a large amount of water vapor. Growth occurs at the oxide–silicon interface. That is, the silicon atoms in the oxide are immobile while oxidizing species diffuse through the oxide to react at the silicon surface. One reason silicon is the major semiconductor in use today is the ease with which a stable, adherent oxide is formed. For silicon, the properties of "thermal oxide" formed by oxidation are superior to deposited oxide. Silicon nitride can be grown by exposing silicon to ammonia at approximately 1100°C, but the reaction is self-limiting at a few nanometers. Oxynitride growth is achieved by exposing SiO_2 to ammonia at approximately 1100°C. The growth of silicon nitride and silicon oxynitride by direct nitridation are not as commonly used as oxidation; therefore, we confine our discussion here to the thermal oxidation of silicon.

Both the diffusion and the surface reaction influence the oxidation rate, with the surface reaction being rate controlling at low temperatures and for short times. Oxidation rate increases when either the diffusivity of the oxidant or the surface reaction rate (or both) increase. Process conditions causing an increase in both diffusion and surface reaction include the use of wet oxygen rather than dry oxygen, the presence of HCl in the oxidizing ambient, increasing the pressure of the oxidant, and heavy substrate doping. The surface reaction is also sensitive to the crystallographic orientation of the substrate. The oxide growth rate is higher for crystal planes with higher silicon atom density [e.g., {111} > {100}].

The dielectric properties of oxide grown in dry oxygen are superior to that grown in the presence of water vapor, presumably because of the presence of OH groups and a corresponding reduction in the number of covalently bonded bridging oxygen atoms. When the water content is suddenly changed, the oxidation rate and the oxide properties change within minutes to those appropriate to the new water content. Consequently, oxidations are usually begun with wet oxygen to give a high rate. The water is turned off a few minutes before the end of the oxidation period to yield good dielectric properties.

After oxidation, the silicon atoms plus the oxygen atoms occupy more than twice the volume occupied by the same number of silicon atoms before oxidation. That is, oxidation moves the silicon atoms farther apart. This has several important consequences. First of all, the expansion can create stresses in the oxide if the surface of the crystal is not planar because of prior patterning steps. Second, if a portion of the surface is covered, for example by a polycrystalline silicon or silicide gate with oxide under it, the gate is forced up at the edges because oxidation occurs only there. (Oxidizing species can diffuse only for short distances under the gate.) Third, to create the additional space between silicon atoms in the oxide, silicon atoms are injected as interstitials into the silicon crystal and vacancies in the lattice are consumed at the surface.

Another defect that can result from oxidation and other high temperature processes is warpage. Warpage is caused by thermal stress during insertion and withdrawal of the wafers from a hot furnace and by formation of films on only one side of the wafer. The warpage problem increases with increased insertion or removal rate, increased wafer diameter, decreased wafer thickness, increased furnace temperature, and increased amount of oxygen precipitates in the silicon.

The fluxes of interstitials into and vacancies out of the silicon during oxidation in turn manifest themselves in several ways. Because the equilibrium point defect (i.e., vacancies and interstitials) concentration increases with doping of both acceptors and donors, the interfacial reaction rate for oxidation increases with impurity doping. The interstitial flux into the silicon causes an increase in diffusion rate for many impurities. If sufficiently large, the interstitial flux causes stacking faults to form and to grow. At the lower oxidation temperatures becoming common today, however, the interstitial flux can be weak enough that stacking faults emit interstitials and shrink.

Oxides may be characterized by many different methods, but optical and electrical characterization are the most popular. Optical characterization may be done by methods as simple as using film color as an indicator of film thickness and quality or by using instrumental methods such as ellipsometry. An ellipsometer is used to measure the reflection of monochromatic polarized light from a transparent film such as SiO_2 in order to determine film thickness and index of refraction. Electrical characterization is used to investigate charges existing inside the oxide and at its interfaces with the semiconductor and metal electrodes. These charges cause bending of the valence and conduction bands in the adjacent semiconductor, altering device performance. Many of the charges are fixed and are fairly reproducible, permitting the device designer to compensate for them. However, some are mobile and nonreproducible, moving with time under the influence of both applied and internal fields. This causes erratic and drifting device characteristics, leading both to yield problems and to premature failure.

The primary source of mobile charges in silicon oxide is sodium ions, although lithium and potassium ions also may contribute. Sodium is ubiquitous, being present in ordinary developers, solvents, and materials, and spread widely by human beings unless great care is exercised. Avoiding sodium contaminating before, during, and after oxidation requires constant vigilance.

IV. Lithography

The objective of the lithographic operations is to place a pattern in a radiation sensitive material called a resist. This pattern is then transferred to the underlying substrate in an etching or implantation operation. The substrate may be an insulating layer, a metal, or the semiconductor itself. This section discusses resist materials, processing, and exposure technologies.

A resist is a material whose solubility changes on exposure to radiation. Consequently, resists may be classified by the kind of material (organic or inorganic), the solubility change (more or less soluble), and the wavelength or source of radiation used (ultraviolet, electron beam, X ray, or ion beam). A resist must satisfy a number of requirements, many of which are often conflicting. Two important requirements are (1) the resist must have a high sensitivity to radiation, so that it can be quickly exposed allowing large wafer throughput; and (2) that it have a large contrast; that is, the difference in solubility between the exposed and the unexposed areas should be large. Of course, it should "resist" the etchant used when the pattern is transferred to the substrate.

A *positive* resist becomes *more* soluble after exposure; a *negative* resist becomes *less* soluble. Figure 5 illustrates this behavior. The differences in solubility are brought about by radiation-induced chemical changes in the resist during the exposure. In a positive organic resist, the radiation can either lower the molecular weight of the material (if the radiation is sufficiently energetic) or bring about a reaction which turns a dissolution inhibitor into a dissolution accelerator. In a negative organic resist, the radiation leads to an increase in the molecular weight. Positive organic resists sensitive to ultraviolet radiation in the 436 to 365 nm region are the most popular materials in use at this writing for VLSI fabrication.

A typical UV-negative resist is a solution of a polymer resin and a photoactive compound (PAC). The PAC absorbs UV radiation and forms chemical links between the resin molecules. The result is a highly cross-linked "gel" with an extremely high molecular weight. When placed in a solvent, the unexposed resist dissolves, but the exposed material cannot. However, in traditional negative resists, the solvent

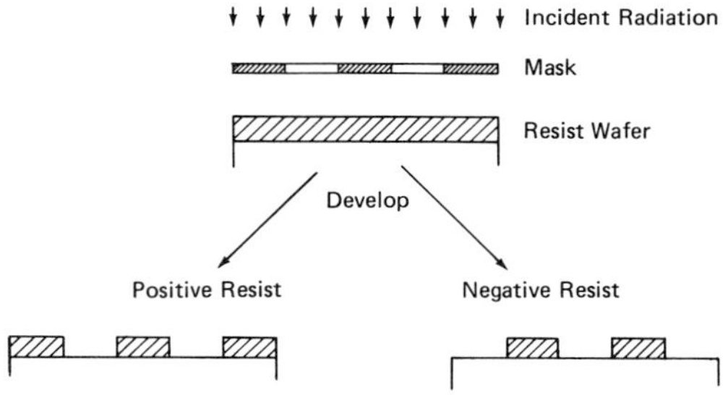

FIG. 5. The behavior of positive and negative resists. After exposure a positive resist is more soluble in the developer; a negative resist is less soluble.

can diffuse into the gel and swell it. This swelling limits the application of these negative resists to situations where the desired line widths are greater than about 5 μm. Typical UV positive resists are solutions of a resin and photoactive compound in an organic solvent. The PAC performs two functions. Unexposed, it acts as a dissolution inhibitor, reducing the solubility of the resin in the basic developer. Exposed, it reacts with water present in the resist to form an organic acid which greatly increases the dissolution rate.

Resist materials formulated for shorter wavelength, more energetic radiation are traditionally solutions of a high molecular weight polymer. These shorter wavelengths include deep ultraviolet (250 nm or less), electron beams, X rays, and ion beams. The incident radiation is absorbed directly by the polymer, which then undergoes either a scission reaction or a cross-linking reaction. Scissions produce low molecular weight products which are easily removed in a solvent. Cross-linking increases the molecular weight and reduces the solubility. In either case it is desirable to start with a polymer of high molecular weight and narrow molecular weight distribution to ensure high sensitivity and uniformity of response.

The processes involved with coating, exposing, developing, and removing a resist from a substrate are complex and are critical in many cases, especially when the images to be printed in the resist are about 1 μm or less. Upon initial receipt, the wafer is first cleaned in a sulfuric-nitric acid or sulfuric-peroxide bath and then exposed to an oxygen plasma or ultraviolet light source to remove any organic material. Such rigorous cleaning is usually impossible for wafers that have already undergone some processing. The surface is treated with an adhesion promoter such as hexamethyldisilazane (HMDS) to prevent resist from lifting during lithographic processing. Thin, uniform coatings of resist are obtained by spin coating. Here the filtered liquid resist is poured onto the wafer, which is then spun at 2000 to 6000 rpm. The film thickness, which is on the order of 1 μm, increases with fluid viscosity and solvent evaporation rate and decreases with the spin speed. The wafers are baked at a temperature of between 70 and 100°C to evaporate some of the solvents remaining after the spin and to increase resist adhesion. After the bake, the wafers are exposed and developed, sometimes with an intervening, postexposure bake. The sensitivity and contrast of a resist are functions of the resist type and chemical composition as well as the processing conditions, such as the developer temperature and develop time.

At this point the wafer is ready for the next processing step, which usually involves transferring the resist pattern to the substrate. In some processes where the wafer is exposed to relatively high temperatures or a severe environment, such as in metal etching or ion implantation, the wafers are first "hard" baked to temperatures in the range of 130 to 200°C. At these temperatures, typical positive resists undergo a number of chemical reactions which increase their molecular weight and decrease their solubility. At the same time, the increased temperature can reduce the viscosity of the resist before these reactions take place. Some deformation of the resist pattern, called resist "reflow," can occur.

In the exposure step the resist surface is illuminated with radiation. In many cases, a broad beam of the radiation passes through a physical mask, illuminating some areas of the wafer and not others. (The processes required to produce a mask are discussed below.) The various types of exposure can be distinguished based on the distance between the wafer and the mask. In contact printing, the mask and resist surfaces are in intimate contact. Near contact or proximity printing is characterized by a mask-resist separation on the order of 1 to 10 wavelengths. In projection printing there is a large separation between the two. Diffraction, or the ability to "concentrate" light at a point, is often the limiting factor in obtaining fine patterns. If a sufficiently narrow beam of radiation can be produced, the desired pattern can be written directly on the wafer surface. In this case the "mask" is a set of positioning instructions for the beam which have been stored in a computer. Such direct write systems are possible with electron or ion beams only.

Projection printing is the method most commonly used in the production of ICs where the minimum image size is 3 μm or less. Two different types of systems are available: reflection printing systems, which employ mirrors to direct the light, and refraction systems, which use lenses. In both types of exposure devices, the feature size is directly proportional to the wavelength of light used and inversely proportional to the numerical aperture (NA) of the optical system. For many resists, the proportionality factor is about 0.8. The numerical aperture is a measure of the light-gathering power of the system. When the system is in a gaseous medium, the NA is equal to the reciprocal of twice the f-number of the optics. The reflection projection systems currently available typically have a small NA. The throughput of the systems is usually fairly large, on the order of one hundred 150 mm wafers per hour. Refraction printers, on the other hand, can have a fairly high NA. The lens system allows the mask size to be reduced on the wafer surface. Commercially available refraction printers have mask size to chip size ratios of 1 : 1 to 10 : 1. The mask image is stepped across the wafer surface and can be refocused at each step to accommodate wafer bowing (warpage). These devices are usually called "wafer steppers" or "step-and-repeat" tools. The most common source of light is a high pressure mercury arc lamp. However, the newest steppers employ an excimer laser operating at 248 nm in the deep ultraviolet.

The minimum size of the images or critical dimension that can be produced in the resist depends on a number of parameters in the exposure step. In addition to the wavelength of light and the numerical aperture of the exposure system, there are the intensity of the radiation, wavelength spread, the spatial divergence of the beam, the nature of the substrate, the amount of scattering from the underside of the mask, the size and shape of the images in the mask, and the proximity of the images to each other. All of these factors are coupled with the resist properties and processing conditions discussed above.

The required critical dimension shrinks with each generation of IC. Table I summarizes the present and projected approximate critical dimensions required for different generation dynamic random access memory (DRAM) chips. Chip size is given in megabits (M), the number of binary digits the chip can store. An indication of the exposure wavelength and numerical aper-

TABLE I. Critical Dimensions (CD) and Lithography Conditions in Memory Chips

DRAM	CD (μm)	Wavelength (nm)	NA	DOF (μm)
1 M	1.0	436	0.42	2.47
4 M	0.7	365	0.42	2.07
16 M	0.5	248	0.42	1.41
64 M	0.35	193	0.42	1.09
256 M	0.25	193	0.60	0.54

ture (NA) of the exposure tool are also included, together with the depth of focus (DOF).

The wavelength region typically encountered with ultraviolet radiation is approximately 450 to 200 nm. A 20,000 eV electron beam, on the other hand, has an effective wavelength of only 0.06 nm. Diffraction effects are negligible. While it is possible to achieve much finer linewidths with e-beams, scattering in the resist precludes reaching the diffraction limit. Both projection and direct-write e-beam systems are used. The former is in many ways similar to the refraction projection system discussed above. The "lenses" are magnets which direct and focus the beam. In direct-write systems, the electron beam, which can be either round or shaped, is used much as a pencil to draw out the pattern on the resist. While conceptually simple, this type of system requires large computer support to store the pattern and direct the beam. In addition, it is slow. However, it is a common method of making the photomasks used for optical projection printing.

Diffraction and scattering effects are eliminated when an X-ray source is used. In addition, dust and other particles which may be present are transparent to the radiation. Unfortunately, resist materials are also somewhat transparent, decreasing their sensitivity. Since X-ray optics are not available, exposure must be performed with the mask in close proximity to the resist and with a 1 : 1 mask. The mechanical problems associated with proximity printing are the same as with ultraviolet light: it is difficult to obtain a constant, uniform separation between the wafer and the mask across the entire area of the wafer, especially if it is bowed as a result of previous processing. Obtaining high contrast masks is another area of concern in this wavelength region. A gold pattern on a boron nitride substrate is one type that has been employed. It is also difficult to obtain small size, high intensity sources. Synchrotron radiation from electron storage rings is currently being investigated for this application. Despite these problems, it is widely believed that X-ray lithography will be the successor to optical methods.

A final source of radiation for lithographic operations is ion beams. As with electron beams, ion beams can be used either in a projection system or in a direct-write mode. Spot sizes on the order of 0.1 μm have been claimed, and there is little scattering in the resist film to cause an increase in the linewidth. In addition, organic resist materials are usually an order of magnitude more sensitive to ion beams than to electron beams. A final significant advantage of focused ion beams is that they allow "resistless" processing at some levels. That is, the ions can be directly implanted into the substrate only in those areas where they are desired.

With the exception of the direct-write systems possible with electron and ion beams, a physical mask is required for all types of lithography. The mask must be made of a substrate which is transparent to the radiation, and a pattern of some opaque material is formed on this substrate. Since the quality of the resist images is determined by the quality of the mask, a mask set for a product represents a significant investment of time and money.

For UV lithography, the mask substrate is glass, usually fused silica (quartz glass). The opaque coating can be chromium or silicon dioxide. The first step in the mask making process is the creation of a "reticle," which is the desired pattern at 5 to 20 times the final size. In the past when image sizes were large, the reticle was made by photographically reducing a mechanically drawn plot of the pattern. As the size of images has decreased, the technology involved with creating a reticle has become more complex. The method most often used currently is a direct-write e-beam system which draws the pattern in the resist at about 10 times the final chip size. This pattern is then etched into the opaque material underneath. The final 1X photomask, if required, is created in a step-and-repeat operation using the reticle as the mask. If the wafers are to be exposed in a reduction stepper, the mask can be made directly by the e-beam.

Mask making for e-beam, X-ray, and ion-beam lithography requires different processes, each with different problems. Since electron beams interact strongly with matter, the transparent parts of an e-beam mask must be free of all material. Thus, the masks are usually suspended metal foils with holes cut in them. For ion beams, (110) silicon has been used as the mask substrate since fairly large channels exist in this crystalline direction.

As the wavelength of the exposing radiation decreases and the numerical aperture of the lithographic system increases, the depth of focus (DOF) of the system decreases. The depth of focus is an approximate distance from the focal plane in which acceptable images are formed; as the distance from the focal plane increases, the image becomes more and more blurry. Sharp images require that both the top and bottom of the resist layer are within the DOF. This can create a problem for lithography, especially if the resist is deposited on substrates which are not flat but have some topography from previous processing. There have been several approaches to planarizing substrates for subsequent lithography. One is to deposit an intermediate layer, usually an organic material, which is planarized by surface tension forces. The time required to planarize decreases as the viscosity of the material decreases, as its thickness increases, and as the distance between substrate features also decreases. Because of this last factor, artificial, nonfunctional features are sometimes placed on the wafer referred to as a planarization block mask. Another technique is to deposit an inorganic layer, such as silicon dioxide or silicon nitride, and then mechanically grind or lap the wafers as described in Section II.

V. Etching

The purpose of etching is to transfer to the underlying layer the pattern formed in the resist by lithography. This pattern transfer can be accomplished in a solvent liquid or in a reactive gas. These methods are referred to as wet etching and dry etching, respectively. In addition to the etching environment, etching can be classified according to the shape of the etched profiles. In isotropic etching, the etch rate is the same in the lateral as the downward direction. The sidewalls are in the shape of a segment of a circle. If the etch rate depends on direction, the etching is said to be anisotropic, or directional. The most anisotropic type of etch gives vertical sidewalls; here, the etch rate in the lateral direction is zero. Either type of etch profiles may be desired, depending on the application. In order to ensure good coverage of the etched regions in a subsequent film deposition process, an isotropic or close to isotropic profile is desired. This would be the case, for example, when contact holes are being etched in an insulator. Vertical sidewalls are desired, on the other hand, when the opened regions must be in close proximity to each other. Isotropic and vertical etch profiles are illustrated in Fig. 6. The figure also shows how these profiles change after a 100% overetch, that is, after the wafers are left in the reactive environment for twice the time required to etch the film. Isotropic etching clearly leads to a loss of image resolution during overetch. To account for film thickness and etch rate variations in any real process, some overetching is always required.

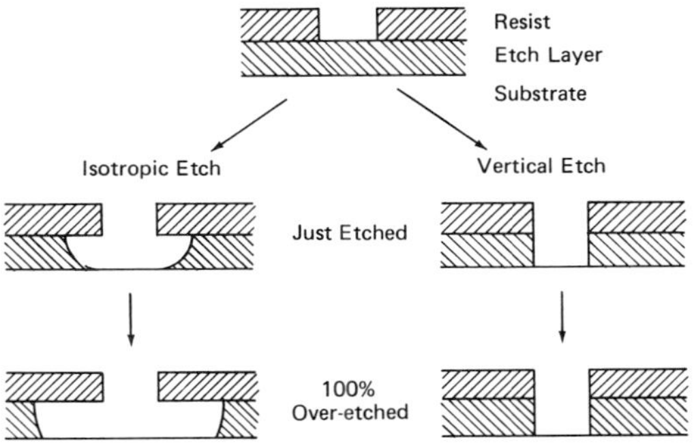

FIG. 6. Comparison between isotropic and vertical etching profiles and the effect of a 100% overetch on the profiles. The sketches assume that neither the resist nor the substrate are attacked by the etchant.

Wet etching is usually isotropic, although anisotropic etchants are available for some crystalline materials. The etch rates depend on the film doping, the temperature and concentration of the etchant, and the degree of agitation of the liquid.

The most common application of wet etching is to open or to clean contact holes in silicon dioxide. This is usually accomplished in a buffered hydrofluoric acid (HF) solution. Isotropic silicon etching is performed in a mixture of nitric and hydrofluoric acids. The {110} planes in silicon are preferentially dissolved in aqueous potassium hydroxide, while hydrazine preferentially dissolves the {111} planes. Hot phosphoric acid is an etchant for silicon nitride and some of the metal silicides. Many organic resists can be removed by typical organic solvents. However, if the resist is cross-linked or has undergone a high temperature bake, a much stronger oxidizing solvent is used. Hot sulfuric–nitric acid mixtures, or mixtures of sulfuric acid and hydrogen peroxide (Caro's acid or "piranha") have been used.

The use of wet etching in the electronics industry is decreasing and is rapidly being replaced by plasma etching. This has several benefits: (1) it is generally cleaner than wet etching, (2) the inlet gases are safer to use, (3) operation is safer, and (4) the effluent is easier to clean and dispose of. The major benefit of plasma etching, however, is the ability to obtain directional profiles with relatively high etch rates.

As the word is used in the electronics industry, a *plasma* is a reactive gas environment formed from a relatively unreactive gas in a high frequency electric field. The reactive species in the gas include ions and free radicals (atoms or groups of atoms containing unpaired electrons). At any temperature there are always some ions and radicals in a gas as a result of dissociation reactions. As the temperature of the gas increases, the equilibrium concentrations of these species also increase. To obtain a concentration that is large enough to cause measurable etch rates in an otherwise unreactive gas, the temperature would have to be prohibitively high. For example, temperatures at the melting point of silicon (1412°C) are required to cause a significant concentration of oxygen atoms in O_2. In a plasma, however, the temperature that would be measured by a thermocouple is approximately room temperature. For this reason, these plasmas are sometimes referred to as "cold" plasmas or, more properly, glow discharges.

The reactive species in a glow discharge are generated by collisional processes in the gas. In the presence of an electric field, positive ions are accelerated toward the cathode. Electrons and negative ions are accelerated toward the anode. These ions and electrons collide with other gas molecules, generating more ions and electrons, dissociating stable molecules into reactive radicals, and exciting gaseous species into higher energy states. When these excited species relax to the ground state, they emit a photon whose energy is characteristic of the particular species and excited state. If the photon is in the visible part of the spectrum, the gas "glows." This is how neon lights work.

A glow discharge is not at equilibrium. The translational temperature of a gas is a measure of the kinetic energy or speed of the gas molecules. Since the uncharged species are not accelerated in the electric field, their translational temperature is relatively low. On the other hand, the electrons and ions are accelerated in the field, and so their translational temperatures are higher. Indeed, in high frequency discharges the electronic temperature is ~30,000 K; the ion temperatures are much lower since the higher mass of the ions prevents them from following the field as closely as the electrons. The discharge produces a "solution" of reactive species (the ions and radicals) in an unreactive diluent (the unreacted gas molecules). The concentration of radicals is quite high, perhaps 30–50%, while that of the ions is low, approximately 0.1%.

In principle, a glow discharge can be formed in a dc electric field. In practice, a radio frequency (rf) or microwave field is employed. This allows the use of an insulator such as an oxide-covered silicon wafer as one of the electrodes. In addition, high frequency fields can sustain the discharge at lower gas pressures than dc fields. The frequency most often used is 13.56 MHz, although frequencies in the 50 to 500 kHz range, and as high as 2.45 GHz, are also used. Because the ions are so massive, they cannot respond as well as the electrons to the rapid changes in the field. In a time averaged sense, the powered electrode acts as the cathode and undergoes continuous bombardment by the positive ions. The grounded electrode acts as the anode and is bombarded by negative ions. Because of the requirement of electrical neutrality and the presence of free electrons, there are more positive ions than negative ions. Therefore, the cathode receives more ions than the anode. In general, as the excitation frequency increases, the flux of ions to the surface increases, and the ion energy decreases. The most important parameter in determining etch isotropy is ion bombardment.

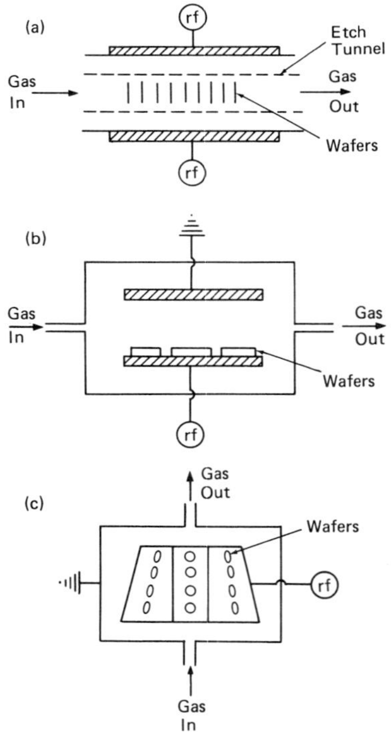

FIG. 7. Plasma etching reactor geometries: (a) barrel or tunnel reactor, (b) parallel plate reactor, and (c) hexode reactor. In the parallel plate geometry, either or both plates may be powered. Ion bombardment of the wafers occurs when they are on the powered electrode.

Several reactor configurations have been used, as illustrated in Fig. 7. In the barrel or tunnel configuration, the wafers are loaded into boats similar to those used in oxidation furnaces. The boat is placed inside a quartz tube, and the plasma is generated in the gas inside the tube using external electrodes. In many cases, a metal mesh etch tunnel (Farraday cage) is placed inside the quartz tube, with the wafer boat resting on the metal cage. This cage serves to eliminate ion bombardment of the wafers. In the parallel plate reactor system, the wafers are placed on either the grounded or the powered electrode, with the other electrode directly above them. Some of these systems can accommodate several wafers on the electrode. In others, only one wafer is etched at a time to reduce wafer-to-wafer variation. If the wafers are placed on the powered electrode, they undergo ion bombardment in addition to being exposed to the reactive radicals. This type of etch is usually referred to as reactive ion etch (RIE). With the wafers on the grounded electrode, there is little ion impingement, and the process is often referred to simply as plasma etching. Finally, it is possible to power both electrodes and thereby adjust the energy with which the ions strike the surface. This configuration is called triode etching. A final reactor geometry is referred to as a hexode. The wafers are placed on a hexagonally shaped cathode, with four or five wafers per side. The inside wall of the bell-jar cover forms the grounded anode.

A wide variety of materials can be etched in a glow discharge. The inlet gas must be so chosen that the radicals formed in the plasma react with the substrate to form a product which is volatile at the ambient temperature and pressure in the plasma. For silicon dioxide the most common etch gas is CF_4 and mixtures of it with oxygen or hydrogen, although a number of other gases have been employed, such as SF_6 and NF_3. For silicon and silicon nitride, CF_4–O_2 mixtures are used. For aluminum, chlorine-containing etch gases such as Cl_2 and CCl_4 are employed because aluminum fluoride is not volatile. To remove organic material, an oxygen plasma is used.

By properly choosing the plasma conditions it is possible to obtain a variety of etch profiles, from isotropic to vertical. Ions play a major role in this process. In general, vertical etching is possible only when the ions impinge normal to the surface. The ions appear either to influence the desorption of the products, or to create reactive sites on the surface. The former is sometimes referred to as the "surface inhibitor mechanism of anisotropy," and the latter, "surface damage induced anisotropy." In either event the etch rate in the vertical direction is larger than that in the lateral direction in which there is a negligible ion flux. The degree of isotropy is affected by a number of parameters, including the gas pressure, the amount of substrate to be etched (the "loading"), the discharge frequency, the bias voltage on the wafer, and the etch gas itself.

Any method of increasing the energy or the directionality of the ions increases the extent of anisotropy. Increasing the pressure increases the concentration of reactive species, but the increased number of collisions decreases the ion directionality, and the etch becomes more isotropic. Similarly, increasing the discharge frequency increases the ion concentration but reduces the energy, again making the etch more isotropic. High energy ions affect the electrical properties of the substrate as well as the etch rate. In magnetron etching, the plasma is confined in a magnetic field to increase its ionization efficiency without increasing the ion energy. In this way, the etch rate is increased without sacrificing directionality or increasing the substrate damage. Electron cyclotron resonance (ECR) is a related technique which also increases the number of ions and reactive species. In some techniques, the plasma is generated in a location remote from the wafers to be etched, and ion energy is controlled by extracting and accelerating them through a grid.

The etch rate is a function of a number of variables. The gas composition is often used to control the etch selectivity (that is, the ratio of the film to substrate etch rate), as well as the etch rate itself. For example, in etching silicon dioxide on top of silicon, it is desirable to have a large etch rate of the oxide as well as a large ratio of oxide to silicon etch rates so that the attack on the underlying silicon is minimized during any overetch that may be required. The addition of H_2 to CF_4 greatly reduces the etch rate of silicon but has a small effect on the etch rate of SiO_2. Similarly, the addition of oxygen to CF_4 increases the etch rate of silicon, but has little effect on that of silicon dioxide. In addition to the inlet gas composition, etch rates depend on the loading, rf power and frequency, gas pressure, and flow rate.

Plasma etching offers the potential of full automation of the etch process by monitoring the emissions from the plasma. As mentioned previously in this section, one of the myriad reactions occurring in the plasma is the excitation of gas species to upper electronic states. These excitations are almost always accompanied by relaxations in which photons are emitted at particular energies. By monitoring the emission at an appropriate wavelength, it is possible to determine when the etching reactions are completed and thereby avoid etching the substrate. For example, when etching aluminum in a chlorine plasma, disappearance of the AlCl emission at about 260 nm indicates that aluminum is no longer being attacked. In addition to monitoring the end point, recent work on low temperature (~100°C) plasma etching has indicated the possibility of removing material one atomic layer at a time. Such a technique, which gives the ultimate in control, is referred to a "digital etching."

Plasmas are used in several ways in the electronics industry in addition to etching. Plasma-enhanced chemical vapor deposition (PECVD) allows deposition of a film at lower temperature than is possible in conventional CVD (see Section VIII). Plasmas are also used in sputter etching and deposition, in which atoms sputtered off the cathode by noble gas ions are deposited on a substrate (see Section X).

VI. Diffusion

The transistors in an integrated circuit consist of small regions doped with different amounts of various impurities to produce *p–n* junctions. There are several ways in which a desired local variation in impurity content can be produced: by ion implantation, by growth of a new layer of crystal doped differently from the substrate, and by diffusion of an impurity.

Imagine that we have a wafer of silicon doped uniformly with boron at a concentration of 10^{16} boron atoms/cm^3 of silicon. Boron is an acceptor, making the silicon *p*-type. To produce a *p–n* junction we can diffuse a donor impurity such as phosphorus in from the surface by heating the silicon in a gas containing elemental phosphorus or a phosphorus compound. The *p–n* junction is the surface where the ionized boron and phosphorus concentrations are equal. If the boron concentration remains at its original value of 10^{16}/cm^3 throughout the crystal, then the *p–n* junction is at the point where the phosphorus concentration is also 10^{16}/cm^3. The spatial distribution of two impurities near the *p–n* junction determines the electrical characteristics of the device.

Diffusion is carried out in resistance-heated tube furnaces like those used for oxidation. Usually a gaseous diffusion source is passed through the tube. Typical gases are BBr_3, B_2H_6, PH_3, AsH_3, $POCl_3$, $B(CH_3O)_3$, BCl_3, PBr_3, and Sb_3Cl_5 in a carrier gas such as H_2, He, or O_2. Alternatively, wafers may be sealed in an ampoule with a diffusion source, a liquid diffusant may be painted or spun on the wafers, or a solid source may be used from which the impurity evaporates. Usually O_2 is used as a carrier gas so that oxidation takes place at the same time as impurity diffusion, thereby simultaneously preparing the wafers for the next lithographic step. The presence of oxygen also prevents halide diffusion sources from roughening the surface of the silicon.

If the diffusion coefficient D for the impurity in the silicon is constant, if the concentration C_s of impurity at the surface of the wafer is constant, if the impurity diffuses in along the entire surface, and if the diffusion time t is too short to permit the impurity to diffuse to the other side of the wafer, then the variation of impurity concentration C with distance x into the substrate is given by

$$C = C_0 + (C_s - C_0)\ \mathrm{erfc}(x/2(Dt)^{1/2}) \quad (1)$$

where C_0 is the initial concentration of that impurity in the crystal and erfc is the complementary error function, tabulated in many mathematics handbooks.

Often, a high surface concentration C_s is undesirable. One way of lowering it is to use a lower partial pressure of the diffusion source in the furnace. However, it is often more convenient to use a two-step process, a predeposition followed by a drive-in. The diffusion source is present during the short predeposition but not during the long drive-in step. If the product of the drive-in time t_d and the diffusion coefficient D_d during drive-in is much larger than that for predeposition, $D_p t_p$, and if no impurity either enters or leaves the silicon during the drive-in, then at the end the final impurity concentration at any depth is given by

$$C = (2C_{s,p}/\pi)(D_p t_p/D_d t_d)^{1/2} \exp(-x^2/4D_d t_d) \quad (2)$$

where $C_{s,p}$ is the surface concentration during predeposition. This is a Gaussian distribution.

Equations (1) and (2) incorporate many assumptions that are usually not entirely true in practice. Diffusion usually takes place through holes cut in a mask, so that C depends on lateral position as well as on depth. Except for very low C_s with no oxidation, D is not constant. It varies with C, with x, with the presence of other impurities and defects, and is altered when chemical reactions such as oxidation, nitridation, and silicide formation take place at the silicon surface. In addition, some impurities segregate preferentially to the oxide while others prefer the silicon, causing large changes in C_s if oxidation is also taking place during drive-in. Consequently, numerical methods are required for more accurate prediction of diffusion. Even then, uncertainties remain so that some empirical fine-tuning of diffusion conditions is required to achieve desired concentration profiles.

Three diffusion mechanisms are thought to be important in silicon, although debate on the details continues. In the vacancy mechanism a substitutional atom moves to an adjacent empty lattice site (a vacancy). Antimony diffusion in silicon is believed to occur primarily through a vacancy mechanism. In the interstitial mechanism an atom moves interstitially (in between the lattice sites). Many metallic elements such as nickel, copper, and iron are transported through silicon by interstitial diffusion. In the interstitial-kick mechanism, a substitutional atom jumps into an interstitial position, moves interstitially for some distance, and then kicks another substitutional atom off a lattice site and occupies it. Phosphorus diffusion in silicon is an example of the interstitial-kick mechanism. Substitutional impurities appear to be able to form impurity-point defect pairs which diffuse together. Some impurities, such as gold, are thought to diffuse by two mechanisms simultaneously, leading to complex behavior.

When an impurity moves by a single mechanism we find

$$D = D_0 \exp(-E/kT) \qquad (3)$$

where D_0 is a constant, E is an activation energy, k is Boltzmann's constant, and T is absolute temperature. Thus, log D versus $1/T$ plots yield straight lines, as shown in Fig. 8. Interstitial impurities that form no bonds with the silicon atoms, such as Li, Cu, and Fe, have the highest diffusion coefficients in Si with the least temperature dependence (least E). Interstitial atoms such as O, that chemically bond to neighboring Si atoms have a diffusion coefficient 3 to 4 orders of magnitude lower and a much larger E value than the interstitials because chemical bonds must be broken before they can move.

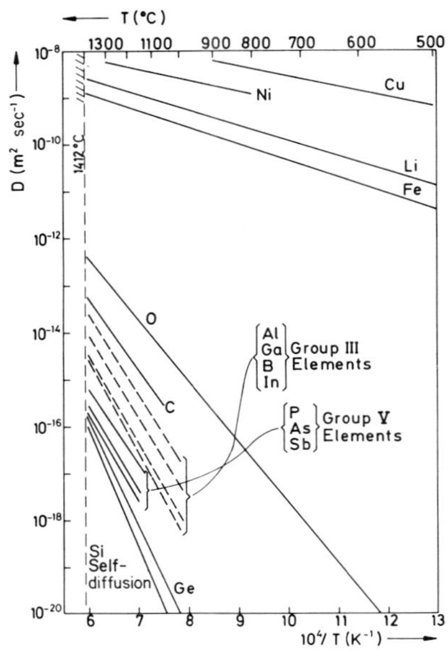

FIG. 8. Diffusion coefficients for very low impurity concentrations in single-crystal dislocation-free silicon. [Data from Frank, W., Gosele, U., Mehrer, M., and Seeger, A., (1984). *In* Nowick, A. S., and Murch, G. (Eds.), "Diffusion in Solids II," Academic Press, Orlando, Fla.]

Substitutional impurities move slower still because not only must they break chemical bonds to move but they also must move via vacancies or must kick another atom from a lattice site.

Diffused areas are characterized both electrically and chemically. Electrical characterization is performed by making resistance measurements on diffused areas. The measured resistances are then compared to standards in order to determine the amount of dopant that is electrically active. The chemical concentration of dopant may be determined by secondary ion mass spectrometry (SIMS), where a doped region is bombarded by a primary ion beam that knocks secondary ions from the doped sample. The secondary ions are then mass analyzed in order to determine the sample composition. A comparison of the electrically active and chemical concentrations is useful for investigations of dopant precipitation phenomena and for evaluation of the effect of heat treatments of dopants.

VII. Ion Implantation and Annealing

Ion implantation is an alternative to diffusion to create doped regions. A source of the dopant is vaporized and ionized, and the positive ions are accelerated to high energies in an electric field. The resulting beam is directed at the wafers. In all cases, the high energy ions damage the crystal as they are slowed down by interactions with the lattice. In addition, many of the implanted ions do not reside on a substitutional location. Hence, an annealing step is required to electrically activate the implanted ions and to remove the damage from the crystal. During implantations, electrical neutrality is achieved by conduction through the wafer, or, in the case of high dose implants, by simultaneous scanning with an electron beam. In this section, implant systems, implant profiles, and various annealing methods are discussed.

Ion implantation has several advantages over diffusion. It is much easier to control both the amount and purity of dopant delivered to the wafer and the depth and profile of the dopant atoms. Ion implantation is performed at much lower temperatures than diffusion and can accommodate a wide variety of possible dopants. The low temperature makes it possible to use resist as an implant mask, thus potentially eliminating one process step. The major disadvantage of ion implantation is that annealing is required afterwards, although several implants can be annealed at the same time. In addition, it is impossible to grow an oxide at the same time as the implantation proceeds, so no "automatic" passivation is possible (unlike diffusion in an oxidizing atmosphere). However, an implantation can take the place of the predeposition step in diffusion. A high temperature step then serves to anneal any damage as well as to drive in the dopant.

A typical ion implanter can be divided into four parts: an ion source, an accelerator, a mass analyzer to remove impurities, and a delivery system. Ionization can be achieved in several ways. In electron impact ionization, a gas containing the dopant is supplied directly or is generated by evaporation of a solid. An electron beam then impinges on the gas to ionize it. The positive ions (in most cases) are extracted from the gas with an electrode. The extracted beam is accelerated in an electric field to energies on the order of 5 to 500 keV. High energy boron implanters are capable of delivering up to 3 MeV. In these systems, negative boron atoms are extracted from the source and accelerated to about 1 MeV. Three electrons are stripped from each atom in a nitrogen bath, and the resulting B^{2+} ions are accelerated away from the high voltage.

A number of ions of different species and charge are always present in the beam. The particular species and charge desired are separated from the others by applying a magnetic field at right angles to the beam. Each ion follows a characteristic trajectory in the field, depending on its mass and charge. The beam may be focused using other magnets. Typical beam spot sizes for implanters range from 0.01 to 10 cm. To ensure a uniform dose, either the beam is scanned over the wafer surface or the wafers are scanned across the beam, or both. The implant may be performed in a batch mode, where many wafers are processed at once, or in a serial mode, where the wafers are fed to the implanter one at a time.

While the desired atomic species can be selected through the use of the magnetic field, there is still the possibility of contamination during an implant. The major sources are sputtered metal atoms from the implanter caused by the impact of high energy ions, cross contamination arising from using the same implanter for different dopants, and outgassing of a photoresist implant mask. This latter problem can be eliminated by a hard bake of the resist before entry into the implanter.

When the ion beam strikes the wafer, its kinetic energy is transformed into heat, which can cause the wafer to reach temperatures of several hundred degrees Celsius. This increased temperature can lead to localized regions of self-annealing on the wafer. If the heat is not effectively removed, significant variations in as-implanted dopant activation are observed. In addition, if temperature gradients exist across the wafer, the extent of the damage created by the implant can vary across the wafer, also influencing its electrical properties.

In a similar fashion, electrostatic charging of the wafer surface can lead to significant variations in the amount of ions different regions receive. This is especially a problem when the wafers are masked by an insulating film such as SiO_2. In this case, the flux must be significantly reduced, or the wafer surface must be continuously neutralized by a flood of electrons.

If the ion beam is directed onto an amorphous substrate, the concentration profile of the implanted dopant is gaussian. The ion concentration at any location depends on the surface dose, which in turn is directly related to the beam area and current, both measurable quantities. Typical beam currents are on the order of 1 to 10 mA. The mean distance into the wafer is called the projected range, and its standard deviation, the straggle. The gaussian nature of the implant profile extends to the regions around the mask edge. Close to the edge, the dopant concentration starts to decrease. The standard deviation in this lateral direction is called the transverse straggle and is slightly less than the straggle. The projected range, straggle, and transverse straggle all increase with increasing beam energy and with decreasing ion size. These values also depend on the substrate, decreasing with increasing substrate density. For 100 keV implants into silicon, 99.5% of the boron atoms are within 0.5 μm of the surface, whereas for antimony the distance is 0.09 μm. A knowledge of the range and straggle variation with ion, energy, and substrate allows the determination of the mask thickness required to stop, say, 99.99% of the incoming ions. Silicon oxide and nitride, as well as resist, are used as implant masks.

As the ions enter the mask material, they can knock some of the mask atoms into the substrate. This is known as the recoil phenomenon. The depth and amount of the recoiled atoms depend on the energy and size of the incident ions, as well as on the thickness of the mask. Recoiled oxygen resulting from implants through a thin oxide layer is a particular problem. These oxygen atoms can initiate dislocations, act as gettering sites, and reduce the after-anneal carrier concentration.

When the ions enter the wafer, they lose energy to the silicon lattice and eventually stop by interacting with the electrons around the lattice atoms and with the atomic nuclei. The former is referred to as electronic stopping, and the latter as nuclear stopping. It is the nuclear stopping events which lead to crystal damage by kicking the substrate atoms out of their lattice positions. If the displacement occurs with sufficient energy, further recoil-type damage can be created deeper in the crystal. Low atomic mass implants create a different type of disordered region than heavy atoms. The light atoms such as boron are initially slowed by electronic interactions. When sufficient energy has been lost, nuclear stopping predominates. Thus, the disordered region is comparatively deep. In an implant with heavier phosphorus or arsenic atoms, nuclear interactions and the resulting crystal damage occur closer to the surface, and the recoiled atoms continue the damage farther into the crystal.

Sometimes the scattered ions may become "channeled" into a $\langle 110 \rangle$ direction of the lattice. There are large spaces in this direction, allowing the implanted ions sufficient room to travel relatively long distances without stopping. This phenomenon is more likely to occur when the lattice is relatively undamaged, that is, along the tail of the distribution or at low doses. If tight control of the implant profile is required, the crystal is sometimes damaged by silicon atoms before the dopant implant. This creates an amorphous surface region and avoids channeling.

Another method for reducing channeling is to tilt and twist the surface of the wafer relative to the incident ion beam. When mounted in this manner, the wafers no longer present an ordered surface to the incident beam but one that is more random. Variations in the amount of warpage or bow in the wafers, the flex in the mounting mechanism, and in the incident ion beam angle lead to variations in the extent of channeling across the wafers.

An annealing step is always required after an implantation. The wafers are heated to relatively high temperatures, not only to repair the damaged crystal, but also to activate the dopant atoms, since they often do not stop on substitutional locations. The higher the temperature of the annealing step, the greater the recovery of the crystal. Two types of annealing behavior are distinguished, depending on the extent of crystal damage. If the implant created an amorphous layer, the anneal causes regrowth of the crystal through the mechanism of solid phase epitaxy. If there is a region of partial disorder, caused, for example, by a low dose implant, the point defects and dislocations are more difficult to eliminate.

At ~1100°C, the carrier lifetimes are completely restored, but there is still some residual crystal damage. In many cases, heating to high temperature is prohibited by other factors. At temperatures over 500°C there is significant dissolution of silicon into any metallic aluminum that may be present; the aluminum melts at 660°C. In addition, there can be considerable diffusion of the implanted atoms at high annealing temperatures.

In addition to furnace annealing, lasers and incoherent light sources have been used. In laser annealing, an infrared or ultraviolet laser is scanned across the surface of the wafer. If the laser has sufficient energy it melts the surface of the crystal. With a pulsed laser the liquid refreezes so rapidly that little diffusion occurs, yet the annealing is complete. With continuous wave lasers, no melting occurs. The energy is sufficient to activate the implanted atoms, but the heating and cooling is sufficiently rapid to preclude diffusion. However, large thermal stresses are set up in the wafer when localized regions are heated to high temperature. This can result in the formation of dislocations. Indeed, backside damaging with a laser has been used as a means of gettering impurities. An alternative to the laser is to use an incoherent light source. These are high power arc lamps which heat the silicon wafer to 1100–1200°C in approximately 10 sec. These have the advantage of treating the entire wafer at once, increasing throughput, and reducing the thermal stress.

Ion implantation has been used to create silicon-on-insulator (SOI) structure. Buried layers of silicon dioxide or silicon nitride have been made by deep implants of oxygen or nitrogen. If the dose is sufficiently high, a region of SiO_2 or Si_3N_4 is formed several micrometers below the surface after heat treatment. Wafers with buried oxide layers made in this way are commercially available.

VIII. Chemical Vapor Deposition

Chemical vapor deposition (CVD) refers to deposition of a film on a solid substrate by chemical reaction of a gas. In CVD one may obtain a single crystal layer, a polycrystalline material, or an amorphous material. The form produced depends primarily on the substrate, the deposition rate, and the temperature. At high temperatures and low deposition rates on a clean single crystal substrate, the atoms produced by the chemical reaction have sufficient time and surface mobility to move around the surface of the substrate and find low energy sites. A single crystal film results unless the mismatch between substrate and film crystal lattices is too large. As the temperature is decreased or the deposition rate is increased, the adsorbed atoms have less opportunity to find a low energy site before being covered by more atoms. Nucleation of new grains occurs to produce a polycrystalline material. With continued decreases in temperature or increases in growth rate, the grain size becomes smaller and smaller until adsorbed atoms are not able to move at all before they are buried. An amorphous layer results.

CVD is used to grow single crystal silicon films, polycrystalline silicon (poly) gate electrodes on oxide, phospho-silicate glass (PSG) layers to getter impurities, silicon nitride and oxide as masks and as dielectrics, various conductors such as metals and metal silicides as gate electrodes and interconnect lines, and so on.

Often, a film may be deposited by more than one method. Silicon can, for example, be deposited by any one of the following reactions:

$$SiH_4 \rightarrow Si + 2H_2$$

$$SiH_2Cl_2 \rightarrow Si + 2HCl$$

$$SiHCl_3 + H_2 \rightarrow Si + 3HCl$$

Silicon dioxide may be deposited using many different reactant gases and reactor conditions. Relatively high temperatures are used when high quality oxides with good insulating properties are required. Low temperature oxides may be used in applications where compatibility with low melting point materials is required or in masking applications where insulator quality is not the primary concern.

The impurities previously listed as diffusion sources can be added to the gas stream to produce doped polycrystalline silicon and oxide layers. Silicon compounds can be reacted with ammonia to produce silicon nitride and with nitrous oxide, to form silicon oxide. Metals can be deposited using metal halide or organometallic sources. Some materials may be selectively deposited only on areas of a substrate that chemically interact with the source gas. For example, in "selective tungsten" technology, the substrate Si reduces the WF_6 source gas, whereas SiO_2 does not. This difference allows tungsten to be deposited only on exposed silicon. After the silicon is buried under the tungsten film, the tungsten metal itself promotes tungsten deposition only over the already deposited tungsten.

CVD may be carried out either in a hot-wall or a cold-wall reactor. A hot-wall reactor is substantially the same as those used for diffusion and for oxidation. The wafers are stacked in a slotted quartz holder but usually farther apart than in oxidation and in diffusion to allow transport of reactants in between the wafers and transport of products out. The disadvantage of a hot-wall technique is that deposition occurs on the tube walls as well, necessitating occasional cleaning to avoid flaking off of these deposits. The yield is also reduced by deposition on the walls.

In a cold-wall CVD reactor the wafers are usually placed on graphite, which is heated by induction heating. A water-cooled coil wrapped around the outside of the glass wall carries high frequency current that induces current to flow in the graphite susceptor, and the electrical resistance of the graphite causes it to heat up. Typically the graphite is in the shape of a vertical barrel with flat, slightly inclined walls inside a glass bell jar. The wafers are laid in circular depressions machined in the walls of the graphite susceptor. Alternatively, radiant energy can be used to heat the wafers. Because the glass container walls are cool, little or no deposition takes place on them. The primary limitation in cold-wall CVD is the small number of wafers that are processed in each run.

In recent years, low pressure CVD (LPCVD) has become popular for hot-wall processing. At atmospheric pressure the wafers must be widely separated to allow reactants to diffuse into the spaces between them in order to ensure uniform deposition rates across each wafer. By lowering the pressure to a few torr or less, the mean free path of the gas molecules increases to several centimeters, allowing up to several hundred wafers to be processed in each run.

In general the CVD rate increases as the reactant partial pressures in the gas increase, the product partial pressures decrease, the temperature increases, and the flow rate through the reactor increases. The deposition is a multistep process, involving chemical reactions in the gas, chemical reactions at the deposition surface, diffusive and convective mass transfer in the gas, and diffusion on the surface. The chemical reactions are much more temperature dependent than the diffusion steps. Consequently, at low temperatures the deposition rate is reaction controlled, with the logarithm of the deposition rate usually varying linearly with $1/T$, as shown in Fig. 9. At high temperatures the rate is mass

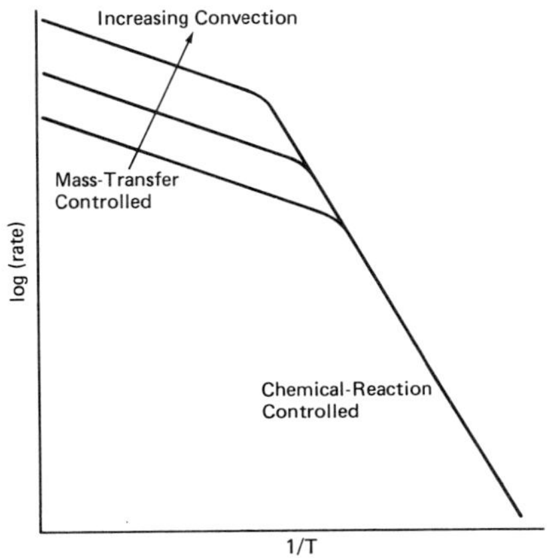

FIG. 9. Chemical vapor deposition rate as a function of temperature.

transport controlled, with log rate vs. $1/T$ having a much smaller slope than for the reaction-controlled portion and with the rate increasing with increasing convection in the gas.

The use of a plasma to etch materials was described in Section V. A plasma may also be used to accelerate chemical vapor deposition, so that it can be carried out at lower temperatures. This is called "plasma-enhanced CVD," or PECVD. The primary difference between etching and PECVD is the composition of the gas. Thus, for example, it is possible to deposit an amorphous film from silane (SiH_4) on any substrate down even to room temperature. Unlike the silicon film deposited at 800°C, the film deposited at room temperature contains roughly as many atoms of hydrogen as of silicon. That is, it is a silicon hydride, from which solar cells can be fabricated but not yet integrated circuits.

A high-intensity light may also be used to enhance CVD. This is called photon-assisted CVD or PACVD. The incident photons may act both to heat the substrate and to cause photochemical reactions. If a laser is used as a light source, the deposition may be localized to the neighborhood of the beam. The beam may be moved directly to write lines on a substrate. However, additional development is required in order to fabricate submicrometer structures; therefore, the primary application may be in printed circuit boards and hybrids, rather than for integrated circuits.

IX. Epitaxy

Epitaxy is a crystallographic term meaning that the crystal lattices of two substances in contact with one another have a preferred orientation to one another. Epitaxial growth may be achieved either by chemical vapor deposition (as described in Section VIII) or by techniques using molecular beams or the growth of layers from solution. Examples of epitaxial growth include the formation of a single crystal silicon film with one doping level on a single crystal silicon substrate with other doping and single crystal silicon deposition on a sapphire substrate (SOS).

Two techniques have grown popular for III–V film deposition and may yet prove useful in silicon devices. These are molecular beam epitaxial growth (MBE) and liquid phase epitaxial growth (LPE). In MBE the wafer is placed in a very high vacuum, such that the mean free path of gaseous molecules is much longer than the size of the chamber. A source of one type of desired atoms is placed in a chamber with a small hole aimed at the wafer, producing an atomic beam. The use of several such sources can be used to produce doped layers, compounds, and very rapid changes in composition of the grown layers (e.g., superlattices).

Liquid phase epitaxy is really growth of layers from a solution. As practiced with the III–V compounds, a wafer is placed on a graphite slider which is moved to place the wafer in contact with a solution contained in a graphite cavity. Lowering the temperature below the equilibrium value (the solubility) causes growth to occur. Layers of different composition can be grown on top of one another by moving the wafer from one solution composition to another.

Silicon on insulator (SOI) is under intense development as a means of avoiding parasitic capacitance and latch-up. Some SOI structures may also permit three-dimensional integrated circuits to be fabricated. One form of SOI in present use is silicon-on-sapphire (SOS). An epitaxial silicon film is grown by CVD on a single-crystal sapphire (Al_2O_3) wafer. Each device is formed in a silicon island produced by etching away the silicon around it down to the sapphire substrate. Sapphire is an electrical insulator but a good thermal conductor.

Current SOI effort is concentrated on growth of single or large-grained silicon on top of a thin insulator, usually oxide, on top of a silicon wafer. Many techniques for accomplishing this are under development. One method is to cut periodic holes in the insulator and do CVD under conditions such that nucleation of silicon does not occur on the bare insulator. Silicon grows epitaxially from the substrate up through the holes and then spreads laterally over the surface of the insulator.

Another method for SOI is to use CVD to deposit polycrystalline silicon on the insulator, melt the poly layer, and cause it to refreeze. Surface tension tends to cause the molten silicon to ball up, and so the poly layer is usually covered by a thin layer of oxide or nitride, completing a four-layer sandwich as shown in Fig. 10. One technique used is to first cut holes in the bottom oxide, so that the polysilicon is in contact with the substrate. Then when the poly layer is melted and refrozen, growth can take place from the substrate up through the holes to produce a single crystal layer. Alternatively, a laser can be used to melt a narrow zone in the poly and move it slowly along the surface.

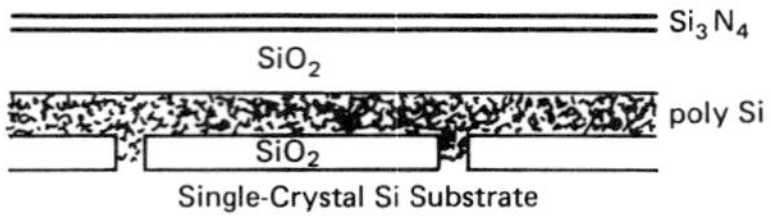

FIG. 10. One method of producing SOI. The poly layer is melted by heating it from above; it is then refrozen.

Another SOI technique is to ion implant a heavy dose of oxygen or nitrogen atoms deep into a silicon wafer. Annealing causes a silicon oxide or nitride layer to form within the wafer, isolating the surface layer of silicon from the substrate.

X. Metallization and Contacts

Conductors must be deposited and patterned on an integrated circuit to act as gate electrodes in FETs, connect devices together on a chip, and allow the chip to be connected to the outside world. In modern ICs, several layers of metals are used to allow for increased density of components on the chip as well as to decrease the signal path, increasing the device speed. A variety of pure metals (Al, Cu, Au, Cr, Ti, W, Pb, Sn), alloys (Al-Cu, TiW), and compounds (metal silicides and nitrides) are used as conductors in integrated circuits. Ideally, they should satisfy a number of requirements, many of which are conflicting. They should be highly conductive, easily deposited, corrosion resistant, readily etched, stable, capable of withstanding high temperature, and adherent to the substrate.

The most common uses for metals in ICs are for contact materials and interconnects. Commonly used contact materials include silicides, Ti, Cr, and Ta. A contact material should be capable of reducing native oxides on the substrate in order to ensure reproducible contact. Contact layers are usually the first layer in a multilayer metallization and therefore must exhibit excellent adhesion to the substrate. The most common interconnect metal currently in use for ICs is aluminum or mixtures of aluminum with silicon and/or copper. Copper is often the interconnect of choice for many packaging applications. Polycrystalline silicon alone or with a metal silicide is often used as a gate electrode because, unlike aluminum, it can be heated to high temperatures without adverse effects on the silicon substrate. Tungsten metallizations are also used in applications where refractory properties are required or in situations where step coverage or hole filling is needed.

Two types of metal–semiconductor contacts are possible, rectifying and ohmic. The rectifying contact, also called a Schottky diode, can be incorporated in the device design as an active circuit element. The metal acts as an infinite source of holes and electrons. Consequently, when the metal and semiconductor are brought together, a *p–n* junction forms at the interface. As with any diode, current flows in one direction only. Rectifying behavior can be eliminated by heavily doping the semiconductor in the contact region before metallization. The result is called an ohmic contact, which allows current to flow easily in both directions.

Metals are deposited by several methods, the primary ones being chemical vapor deposition and physical vapor deposition (PVD) (i.e., evaporation and sputtering). Film growth by CVD is discussed in Section VIII. Tungsten, deposited using a mixture of WF_6 and H_2, is one example. Physical vapor deposition is perhaps the most popular group of deposition methods. In evaporation, a source of the metal to be deposited is heated at low pressure, 10^{-6} Torr or less. Evaporation sources may be heated by resistance, rf induction, or by electron beam methods. A low pressure is required to reduce surface contamination as well as to allow the metal to evaporate. Even at a millionth of a torr, ambient gas species impinge on the substrate at a rate of about 1 monolayer/sec. This can be a significant source of contamination in some applications. As in CVD, the morphology and properties of the deposited film depend on the substrate temperature and the rate at which the evaporated atoms strike the surface.

Sputter deposition is performed in a glow discharge, usually at a higher pressure than in plasma etching, about 0.001–0.1 Torr. In most cases, the gas is one of the noble gases, argon being the most popular. The material to be deposited, called the target, is placed on the cathode. The plasma-generated positive ions strike the surface with sufficient energy to remove, or sputter, target atoms. These atoms deposit all over the inside of the chamber, including the substrate which usually forms the anode. Cathode bias, target temperature, gas species, and pressure control the sputter rate. Substrate bias and temperature control the film morphology and deposition rate. Sputtering may also be performed in a reactive ambient such as a mixture of argon and nitrogen. For example, sputtering titanium with nitrogen gas leads to a titanium nitride film.

Various problems have been observed with the multilevel metallization used in ICs, including step coverage, hillocks, silicon solubility, and atomic migration due to mechanical or electrical stress. Most metallization problems have been addressed by materials or structural changes (or both). Poor step coverage is often observed with PVD films. Step coverage problems have been addressed by minimizing topography and using processes such as CVD that provide improved step coverage. Hillocks are protrusions from the metallization that are caused by differences in thermal expansion coefficient between the metal film and Si substrate. The addition of alloying elements such as Cu and multilayer metallizations have lessened the susceptibility to hillock formation. The origin of the silicon solubility problem is that when heated, the silicon in the contact regions dissolves in the aluminum and diffuses along the metal line. Upon cooling, the silicon precipitates. Etch pits are formed in the underlying silicon and become filled with aluminum, causing a metal to substrate short circuit. One way to minimize this problem is to use a silicon–aluminum mixture for metallization. However, since the solubility increases with increasing temperature, there is always some dissolution and precipitation of the silicon when the temperature varies. There is a practical upper limit of about 500°C on wafers when aluminum is present. A second method of reducing the solubility is to introduce one or more "barrier layers" between the silicon and the aluminum. Both silicides and titanium–tungsten mixtures have been used for this purpose.

Electromigration defects are observed during reliability stressing. As current flows through the thin aluminum lines, it causes atom migration along the grain boundaries. Small variations in the line thickness are amplified, resulting in voids, or holes, in the metal lines. The atoms which leave the void areas pile up to form hillocks of metal. Eventually, the consequence is an open or a short circuit and device failure. One method of minimizing electromigration is to incorporate small amounts of copper into the aluminum. The copper apparently "plugs up" the grain boundaries, reducing the migration. Stress migration is similar to electromigration, with the exception that the driving force is mechanical stress, not current. Alloying with copper also reduces the susceptibility to stress migration.

When multiple layers of metals are used, the different levels are connected by holes (vias) formed through interlevel dielectric materials. These insulation regions can be inorganic materials like silicon dioxide or silicon nitride, an organic material, or combinations of these. The most popular class of organic insulators is polyimide. Several different kinds of polyimides are available, but all are characterized by being insoluble, stable to relatively high temperatures (about 400°C), and impervious to water vapor. In most cases, the polymer is dispensed as a solution of polyamic acid, spin coated on the wafer, and cured to allow the imidization reaction to proceed. In addition to its desirable physical properties, the spin coated polyimide is more planar than typical inorganic materials.

XI. Packaging

After chip fabrication is complete, the chip must be packaged. Packaging seves to protect the chip from the outside world and allows electrical connection to it. The packaging sequence includes testing and dicing (wafer is cut into chips); electrically "good" chips are then electrically connected to the package and encapsulated.

First, the backside of the chip is electrically connected to the packaging substrate with either a conductive polymeric material or by a metal bond. The connections to the device side of the chip are usually made in one of three ways. Wire bonding is the most commonly used technique. A gold or aluminum wire is thermocompression or thermosonically bonded to the last level of metal on the chip. The other end is attached to the electrical circuits on the package substrate. Wire bonding is a low cost technique, but one drawback is that the density of chip pads that can be bonded is limited.

A second interconnection method is known as tape automated bonding. A gold or copper bump is formed on the chip and then plated copper beams are thermocompression bonded to all the bumps on the chip simultaneously. The copper beams are supported on tape that is fed from a reel. After the bond to the bumped chip is made, the tape plus chip combination is collected on a second reel, where it will wait until ready for bonding to the package substrate and separation from the tape frame. Tape automated bonding offers a higher pad density than wire bonding but somewhat costs more. The third bonding option is the "flip-chip" technology. Solder balls are formed on the chip bonding sites. The chip is turned face down so that the solder balls are in direct contact with metal pads on the package substrate. The solder is then heated in order to bond with the substrate pads. The "flip-chip" technology offers a high pad density, and pad designs are not limited to the chip periphery, as in wire bonding and tape automated bonding.

After the interconnection operations are completed, the packages are encapsulated to protect them from the environment. The encapsulation technology depends upon the application. Chips may be hermetically sealed for high reliability applications, whereas a plastic encapsulant may be used for low cost applications. Many different package shapes are also available. Issues such as cost, performance, reliability, size and shape, and ability to dissipate heat help in determining the package type.

XII. Reliability

In order to ensure that reliable devices have been produced by the IC manufacturing process, a sampling of chips is tested. Because the failure rate due to wear under normal use conditions is expected to be quite low, accelerated testing must be done. Failure characteristics may be studied in relatively short times by increasing temperature, voltage, current, and humidity above normal use conditions. Thermal cycling from a low temperature to a high temperature is also used in order to test the mechanical integrity of the chip and package.

Reliability tests often combine several accelerating factors, with each test directed toward understanding a particular failure mode. Voltage–temperature stresses are used to investigate the effect of mobile ionic species in oxides. High applied electric fields combined with temperature are used to study dielectric breakdown and charge injection. Voltage, temperature, and humidity are used to accelerate and detect corrosion of chip and package metallizations. Corrosion in ICs is often caused by processing residues or contaminants such as chlorine ions. High current densities combined with high temperatures are used to evaluate electromigration. High temperature and high intrinsic stresses are used as the accelerating factors for stress migration (Section X). Repeated thermal cycling simulates device turn on and also storage conditions. Wiring and dielectrics are stressed by differences in thermal expansion coefficients during thermal cycling. The data generated by such stresses are used to improve device processing and ensure product reliability.

Bibliography

Colclaser, Roy A. (1980). Microelectronics: Processing and Device Design. Wiley, New York.

Elliott, David J. (1982). Integrated Circuit Fabrication Technology. McGraw-Hill, New York.

Ghandhi, Sorab K. (1983). VLSI Fabrication Principles. Wiley–Interscience, New York.

Lee, H. H. (1990). "Fundamentals of Microelectronics Processing." McGraw-Hill, New York.

Mayer, J. W., and Lau, S. S. (1990). "Electronic Materials Science for Integrated Circuits in Si and GaAs." Macmillan, New York.

Ravi, K. V. (1981). Imperfections and Impurities in Semiconductor Silicon. Wiley–Interscience, New York.

Sze, S. M. (ed.) (1988). VLSI Technology. McGraw-Hill, New York.

INTEGRATED CIRCUIT TESTING

D. Michael Miller *University of Victoria, Canada*

GLOSSARY

Aliasing: In BIST, the effect where the act of compacting test response data to a manageable size results in identical responses for a faulty circuit and a good circuit.

Built-in self-test (BIST): Testing strategy in which the generation of the test vectors and the analysis of the response to applying them are integral parts of the circuit under test.

Design for testability (DFT): Any circuit design strategy intended to enhance the testability of the circuit.

Error model: Abstraction in which physical failures are viewed in terms of the distribution of errors in the test response data rather than in terms of the detailed circuit itself.

Fault simulation: Extension of normal circuit simulation techniques to include the modeling of faults.

Logic fault model: Mathematical abstraction of the effect of a physical failure used as the basis for the algorithmic identification of test vectors and for the analysis of the effectiveness of testing methods.

Physical failure: Physical defect in an integrated circuit that causes it to behave abnormally.

Test set: Set of test vectors selected to ascertain the correct behavior of a circuit relative to a particular set of faults.

Test vector: Input pattern to be used in testing a circuit together with the expected response.

Integrated circuits are subject to a variety of physical failures. In this article, the concern is for testing methods designed to assure correct functional behavior. Testing operational characteristics, such as timing delay and power consumption, will not be direct concern. The methods presented are classed as behavioral or functional tests.

A functional test is based on analysis of a design at some level of abstraction, for example, the gate level. Such a test may detect design errors that occur at a lower level of abstraction, for example, the transistor or mask level, but it cannot detect design errors made at the level upon which the test is based or at a higher level, for instance, the register transfer level.

Functional tests can be classified as external or internal depending on whether the mechanism for applying the tests and observing the results in separate or an integral part of the circuit under test. Completely internal testing is most commonly referred to as the built-in self-test. External testing is always off line, that is, it is conducted outside the normal operation of the circuit. Built-in self-testing may be off line or on line. In the latter case, often referred to as concurrent testing, testing the operation of the circuit is an integral part of its normal operation.

I. Fault Models

Physical failures in an integrated circuit arise from physical defects, such as broken or shorted conducting paths. Detailed analysis of potential failures is thus a very complex and technology dependent activity. To simplify matters, and to permit a mathematical or algorithmic treatment of the problem, functional testing is based on a logical fault model, which is an abstraction of the effects of physical failures. The quality of a test, of course, depends on how realistically the

ENCYCLOPEDIA OF PHYSICAL SCIENCE
AND TECHNOLOGY, VOL. 8

model represents the functional misbehavior resulting from a physical fault. [*See* INTEGRATED CIRCUIT MANUFACTURE.]

A. The Stuck-at Model

The single stuck-at fault model assumes that a physical failure corresponds to one line in the circuit being stuck-at logic 0 or at logic 1. The attraction of this model is its relative simplicity, and for this reason it is the model most often used. The functional behavior of a faulty circuit is readily determined from the functional description of the fault-free circuit. In addition, the number of potential faults grows linearly with the number of lines in the circuit—a circuit with t lines has $2t$ potential single stuck-at faults.

The model can be extended to the multiple stuck-at case, but here a circuit with t lines has $3^t - 1$ potential faults. Such a large number of faults is impractical for exhaustive analysis and the multiple stuck-at model has thus been of mostly theoretical interest.

B. The Bridging Model

The bridging fault model is intended to reflect the behavior resulting from a short between two conducting paths in a circuit. It is assumed that the presence of such a short results in a hard-wired *and* or *or* function, the choice depending on the technology in which the circuit is implemented. Increasing circuit density has heightened the potential and the concern for such shorts.

A major difficulty in dealing with bridging faults is the fact that such a fault may introduce a feedback path into what should be a combinational block of logic and the faulty block becomes sequential. In this case, a sequence of tests may be required to detect the fault.

C. The Stuck-Open Model

Metal-oxide semiconductor (MOS) technology exhibits a failure mechanism not covered by the stuck-at or bridging fault models. For simplicity, only the complementary MOS (CMOS) case is considered. Figure 1 shows the block structure of a fully complemented CMOS combinational cell. For any input pattern, there should be a conducting path through the network of p-fets or the network of n-fets. If a transistor fails so that it can never conduct, it is then possible that for certain input patterns there will

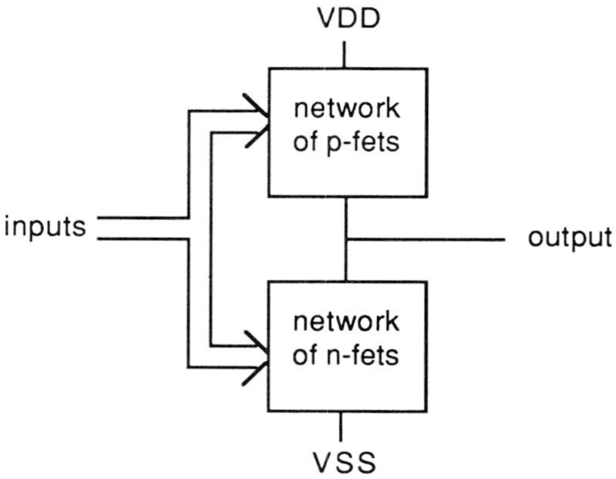

FIG. 1. Structure of a combinational CMOS cell.

not be a conducting path in either block of transistors. In this case, the output is floating. However, the output of the cell is driving some capacitance load, and for some period of time, that load will hold the previous output value. A memory affect had thus been introduced into a combinational circuit. The stuck-open fault model captures this behavior.

A stuck-open fault indices sequential behavior, so detecting such a fault requires two test patterns be applied. The first must step up the circuit to the opposite value to that expected for the second. For example, to detect an n-fet stuck open, a test is applied to set the output to 1 followed by a test that depends on the n-fet in question to change the output to a 0. If the output remains at 1 for the second test, a stuck-open fault exists.

D. Faults in Programmable Logic Arrays

Programmable logic arrays (PLAs) also give rise to failures not covered by the conventional stuck-at model. Figure 2 is a logical abstraction of a PLA. The functionality of the PLA is determined by the connections made at grid points in the AND and the OR plane. Physically, these connections are realized by n-fet transistors and the PLA implements *nor–nor* two-level realizations with inverted inputs and outputs. Each column of the AND plane implements a product term, while each row of the OR plane combines certain product terms to form a sum-of-products realization of one of the output functions.

A cross-point fault is caused by an extra or a missing connection. In the AND plane, an extra connection decreases the size of the term realized by the product line and is therefore referred

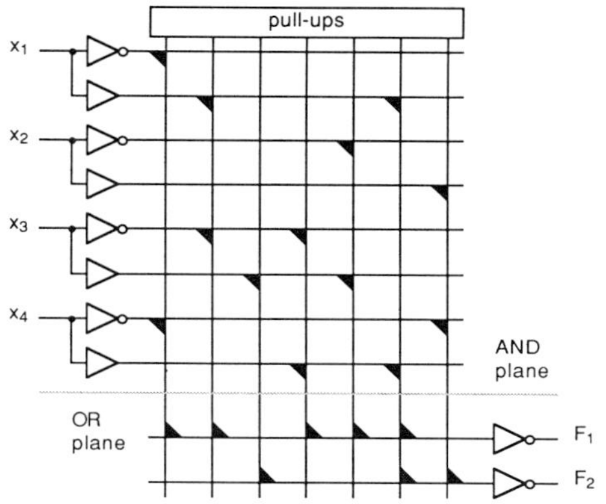

FIG. 2. Logical abstraction of a PLA realizing $F_1 = x_1x_4 + \bar{x}_1x_3 + x_3\bar{x}_4 + x_2\bar{x}_3 + \bar{x}_1\bar{x}_4$ and $F_2 = \bar{x}_3 + \bar{x}_1\bar{x}_4 + \bar{x}_2x_4$.

to as a shrinkage fault. A missing connection in this plane causes an increase in the size of the product term and is called a growth fault. For the OR plane, an extra connection causes a product term to appear erroneously in an output function, while a missing connection causes the product term not to appear in an output function in which it should. These faults are thus termed appearance and disappearance faults, respectively.

II. The Test Set Approach

To fully appreciate recent developments, it is necessary to have some knowledge of the conventional approach to circuit testing. This section considers combinational logic only. Section III considers certain methods that permit the application of combinational testing strategies to sequential circuits.

The first step in test generation for combinational circuits is to develop a fault dictionary for the circuit in question. This is typically done based upon a gate level description with single stuck-at faults as the target fault set. While the other fault models are not usually explicitly considered in constructing the test, experience has shown that a robust single stuck-at fault test set will often provide good coverage of the other types of faults as well.

The number of single stuck-at faults that must be explicitly considered can be reduced by applying fault equivalence and fault dominance. The former means that only one of a set of functionally equivalent faults need be explicitly considered. The latter means that no fault need be considered if it can be shown that the set of tests for that fault is a subset of the set of tests for some other fault.

It should be noted that fault equivalence and fault dominance do not apply to exclusive-OR gates, and hence, generating tests for circuits containing these elements can be more complex than for circuits that do not.

Once the collapsed set of faults has been determined, the next step is to identify test vectors that detect these faults. The objective is to find a test set such that for every target fault at least one of the test vectors will yield a different result in the presence of the fault than it does for the fault-free circuit. Hence, by applying the test set and comparing the observed results to those expected, any fault in the target set of faults, and all equivalent and dominating faults, will be detected.

A number of algorithms have been devised for the automated generation of test sets. The D algorithm, developed by J. P. Roth at IBM in the 1960s, is perhaps the best known. Others, such as PODEM and FAN, build on Roth's ideas and are more efficient. However, it is worth noting that test generation has been shown to belong to the class of nondeterministic polynomial problems. Known algorithms for this class of problem have time complexity that is exponential in the size of the problem. In the case of test generation, the known algorithms become impractical as the number of gates becomes large.

Fault simulation is an important part of the test set generation process. In one common approach, a fault is selected and an algorithmic method is used to find a test vector that covers that fault. Fault simulation is then used to determine the full list of faults, from the target fault class, which are covered by the vector. All these faults are marked as covered, and the process continues by selecting some as yet uncovered fault to be used in generating the next vector.

In another scenario, a test vector is selected at random, and fault simulation is used to determine what faults are covered. Another vector is randomly selected, and the fault simulation is repeated. This process is repeated to build up a test set. It stops when full fault coverage, or some reasonable fraction thereof, is achieved.

Fault simulation is also very important in assessing the effectiveness of other test methods. For example, various methods for built-in self-tests are described in some detail in Section IV. While there are now some analytical results that estimate the performance of these methods, fault simulation is the only sure way to accurately assess the effectiveness of one of these techniques with respect to a specific circuit.

III. Design for Testability

The vast majority of research into the identification of test sets has been restricted to combinational circuits. It is possible to extend many methods to the case of a sequential circuit, but the combinatorics of the problem explode and such extensions have proven to be of little practical interest.

The sequential circuit testing problem can be overcome by designing the circuit so that it can be reconfigured and treated as combinational at testing time. This general approach has come to be known as design for testability (DFT). Such methods have the advantage that the complex problem of testing a sequential circuit is reduced to the more tractable problem of explicitly testing only the combinational parts of the circuit. The memory elements are implicitly tested since they are used in applying the tests to the combinational blocks. However, the methods also have disadvantages. The sequential circuit cannot be tested at its normal operating speed—it takes time to load, apply, and analyze the results of the combinational test vectors. Also, there is an area overhead penalty since the necessity for configuration at testing time makes the memory elements in the sequential circuit more complex.

Increased circuit density has permitted a corresponding increase in the complexity of the functionality of an integrated circuit. As the functionality increases relative to the number of chip pins, it becomes more difficult to test the circuit since its internals are less visible to the outside world. DFT technique solve this problem by arranging at test time that the memory elements can all be loaded or observed from one or possibly two pins.

A. Scan Design

Figure 3 illustrates the general DFT approach, known as scan design. In the scheme shown, a pin is required to input test vectors (scan in) and a second is required to observe the response (scan out). These could be multiplexed. Control is required to select between the normal operating and test modes. This usually takes the form of one or more additional clocks. The pin overhead for these techniques is thus not very high. This is an important aspect since chip pins are a very valuable resource.

The key aspect of scan design is that, at test time, the memory elements of the circuit are configured into a shift register (the scan path) such that test vectors and the results of applying them can be shifted in and out of the chip. The general approach to scan-path-based testing of a circuit is as follows:

1. switch to shift register mode and check the shift register operation by shifting in and out an alternating sequence of 0's and 1's;
2. scan the initial test vector into the shift register using the special control clocks;
3. return to normal mode and apply the test using the normal operation clocks;
4. return to shift mode and shift out the response to the test while simultaneously shifting in the next test vector;
5. return to step (3) as required.

Control of the circuit mode is accomplished external to the chip under test and in most schemes simply involves applying certain clocks in specific sequences. Testing of a chip in this way requires a circuit tester cognizant of the specific DFT architecture being employed.

Scan path techniques were first introduced in the late 1960s, but level sensitive scan design (LSSD), introduced by Eichelberger and Williams in 1977, is likely the best known DFT technique. It is IBM's discipline for structural DFT and has been used in many IBM systems.

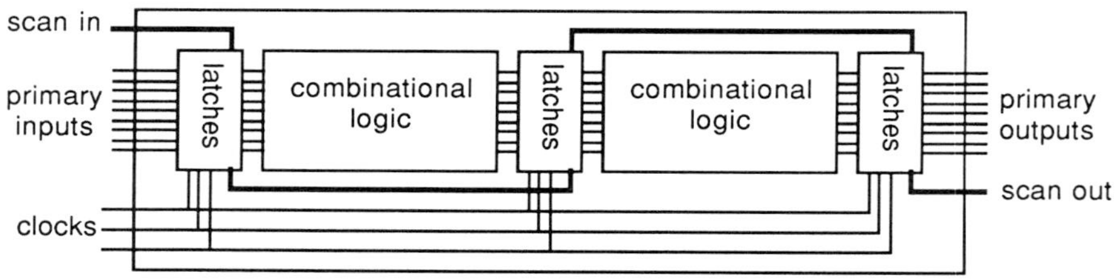

FIG. 3. General architecture of a scan path design.

For this approach, a logic circuit is considered level sensitive if, and only if, the steady-state response to any allowable input change is independent of the delays in the circuit. The objective is to obtain circuits that are insensitive to ac parametric variations. The key to designing such circuits is a level sensitive memory element free of race and hazard conditions. The memory element must also support reconfiguration to a scan path. The extended latch used in the LSSD scheme is shown in Fig. 4.

To achieve testability, LSSD designers must follow certain guidelines. Clearly, all internal storage must be made up of hazard-free polarity hold latches, and these latches must be organized into one or more scan paths. Clocks cannot be gated and can only be used to control latches and not as data to the latches. Two or more nonoverlapping clocks must be employed. There are a number of rules about how the clocks are to be used and as to how latches may interact directly or indirectly. These rules are required to ensure race-free operation of the circuit.

The primary advantage of LSSD is that it supports scan path testing and therefore permits a sequential circuit to be treated as combinational during test. Another advantage is that ac testing, test generation, and fault simulation are all simplified because correct operation of the circuit is nearly independent of its ac characteristics and because there are no hazards or races to contend with. The primary disadvantage is the added complexity of the LSSD latch, which is 2 to 3 times more complex than a simple latch. Overheads of 4–20% have been reported. The variation arises from the degree to which the designer incorporates the L_2 latches into the system function. For a circuit designed in the double latch

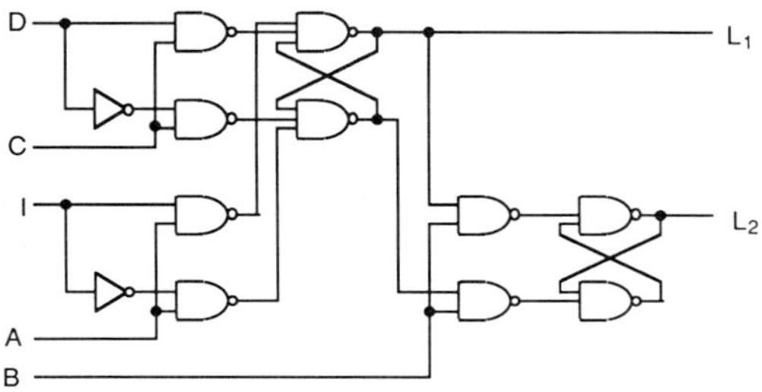

FIG. 4. LSSD polarity hold shift register latch. [From Eichelberger, E., and Williams, T. W. (1977). A logic design structure for LSI testability. *Proc. IEEE Des. Automation Conf., 14th,* pp. 462–468. Copyright © 1977 by IEEE.]

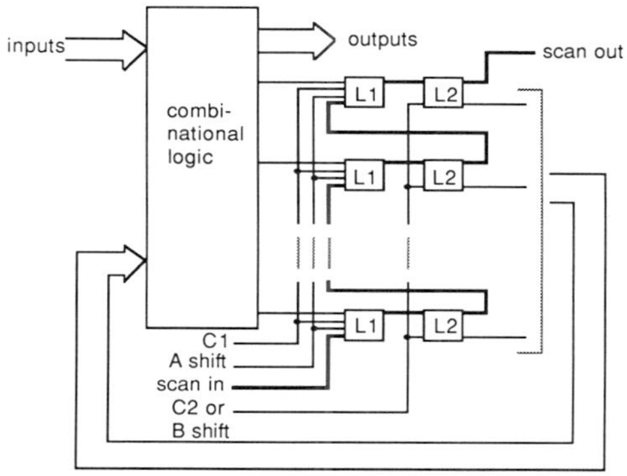

FIG. 5. General architecture for a double latch LSSD. [From Eichelberger, E., and Williams, T. W. (1977). A logic design structure for LSI testability. *Proc. IEEE Des. Automation Conf., 14th,* pp. 462–468. Copyright © 1977 by IEEE.]

mode (see Fig. 5), both the L_1 and the L_2 latches appear in the system path. For the single latch designs, the L_2 latches are only used in the scan path and must therefore be considered part of the DFT overhead.

Numerous other scan path architectures have been suggested. Many are variations or enhancements of LSSD. Others provide more flexibility. Random access scan, for example, provides a direct access path to each internal system latch, thereby enhancing its controllability and observability. There is a relatively high overhead, however, of about 3 to 4 gates per latch as well as 2 address decoders and an output AND tree used in achieving the random access capability. The pin overhead is between 10 and 20 but can be reduced to about 6 by using a serially loaded address counter.

DFT techniques offer solutions to the problem of testing sequential circuits and to the problem of making the internals of a circuit visible at the external pins. However, there is a time penalty since the tests and the results of applying them must be serially scanned on and off the chip. A very practical difficulty is that many commercial chip testers typically do not have sufficient memory depth behind a pin to properly support scan-path-based testing techniques. As a result, testing time is increased even further and control of the testing process is more complex than it need be.

The most significant drawback to the DFT approach is that an appropriate set of test vectors must still be determined. Indeed, scan path methods mean that combinational testing strategies must now be applicable to much larger circuits than was the case in the past.

IV. Built-in Self-Test

A built-in self-test (BIST) technique, as the term implies, incorporates all facets of the testing process into the chip under test. Since chip pins are a critical resource in a VLSI design, BIST approaches attempt to limit the additional pins required to implement the test. Typically, one pin is required to select between the normal and test modes, and a second is required to deliver the pass/fail result of the test. Test vector generation and response data collection and validation are incorporated into the chip. Primary criteria for any BIST technique are that the area overhead of the test circuitry be low and there should be no significant degradation in the performance of the circuit in its normal operating mode.

As in DFT approaches, the problem of testing a sequential circuit is reduced to that of testing a combinational circuit. In this case, the latches of the sequential circuit are tested as they are used to generate appropriate test vectors and to collect the response to these vectors. The collected response is usually compacted to a signature consisting of a few bits. This signature is compared on chip to the result expected to produce a simple pass/fail result. Figure 6 shows the general scenario of a BIST.

The key problem with BIST techniques is that the compaction of the response data implies a loss of information, and there is some chance that a faulty circuit may produce the expected good signature. This phenomenon is known as aliasing.

A. BIST Test Vector Generators

Suppose a BIST is to be applied to an n-input combinational block. Some number of test vectors must be applied. One approach would be to use a test set generation program to identify a test set for a particular fault class, such as all single stuck-at faults. The difficulty of this approach relative to a BIST is there is typically no economical method to store and apply the test set chip. The fundamental philosophy of a BIST requires the vectors as in LSSD is not appropriate.

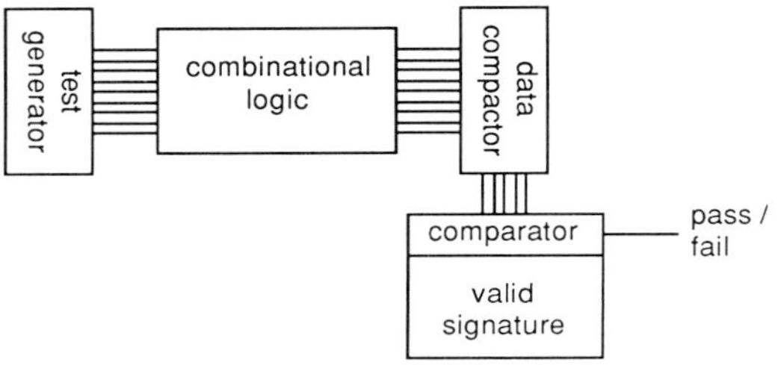

FIG. 6. General structure of a BIST.

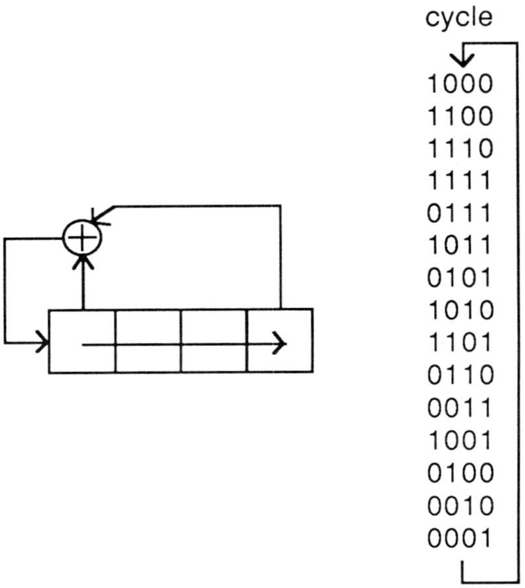

FIG. 7. An autonomous LFSR implementing $x^4 + x + 1$.

What is needed is a method, economical in both space and time, for generating the test vectors as they are required. For a combinational block with up to 20 inputs, it is reasonable to consider applying all possible input conditions as test vectors. This is referred to as exhaustive testing. At the relatively slow rate of 1 MHz, a 20-input combinational block can be exhaustively tested in about 1 sec. The test vector generator in this case can be a counter or, in fact, any n-bit register that can be made to cycle through the complete set of 2^n patterns.

An autonomous linear feedback shift register (LFSR) is the most popular choice of generator because of the relatively low overhead. Figure 7 shows a 4-bit LFSR that generates a cycle of 15 patterns (0000 is excluded). Such a register can be modified to include the all-zeros state by the addition of a small number of gates, but this is not usually necessary to achieve reasonable fault coverage since it is very seldom that all zeros is an essential test vector, that is, the only vector that detects some fault.

The behavior of an LFSR can be described as a polynomial over the Galois field GF(2). For example, the register in Fig. 7 corresponds to the polynomial $x^4 + x + 1$ (in these polynomials summation is modulo 2). Certain such polynomials are termed primitive, and it has been shown that an autonomous LFSR has the maximal cycle length of $2^n - 1$ if, and only if, the corresponding polynomial is primitive. Tables of primitive polynomials are available for all degrees up to 100 and more, so identifying an appropriate LFSR to be used as a BIST test generator is straightforward. Such tables can be found in any good reference on algebraic coding theory or on error correcting codes.

An LFSR consists of a set of latches or flip-flops and some number of exclusive-OR gates [exclusive-OR is the additive operator over GF(2)]. In a BIST design, the LFSR required for test generation is formed by reconfiguring certain memory elements required for the normal operation of the sequential circuit under test. The area overhead involved is that required for the exclusive-OR gates, the feedback path in the register, and the control logic required to select between the normal and BIST modes of operation.

Exhaustive testing may be prohibitive. In this case, the LFSR-based test generator may be used to produce a test sequence with less than $2^n - 1$ vectors, and the test is referred to as pseudorandom. It is well known that an LFSR is a poor pseudorandom number generator. Despite this, it has been found to be reasonably effective as a generator in pseudorandom testing.

B. BIST Response Data Compaction

Applying BIST can result in a considerable amount of response data. For example, exhaustive testing of a 20-input, 16-output, combinational circuit produces on the order of 16 million bits of response data. The standard BIST strategy is to compact this data to a signature consisting of a fairly small number of bits. For a multiple output circuit, the signature usually has one bit per output since the signature register is just a reconfiguration of those elements used to store the circuit outputs during normal operation of the chip. Note that in much of the BIST literature, the term compression is used rather than compaction. This is not strictly correct since compression implies no loss of data, which is not the case here.

Various data compactors have been proposed for BIST schemes. Those based on LFSRs are most common. Figure 8 shows examples of such compactors for both the single and multiple output cases. It has been generally accepted since the inception of BIST in the late 1970s that an LFSR corresponding to a primitive polynomial makes the best data compactor. This is discussed in more detail in Section IV, C, on aliasing.

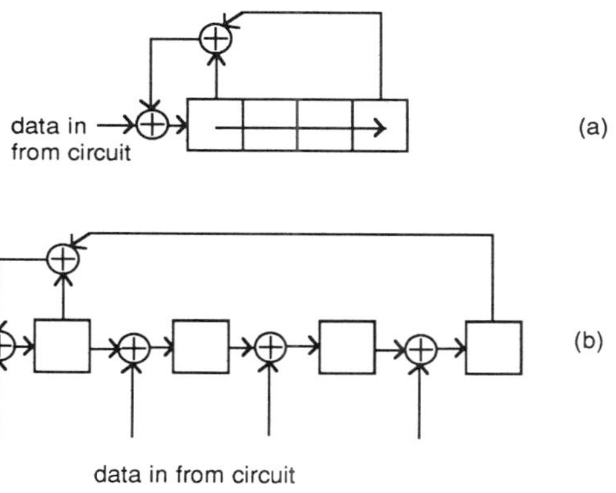

FIG. 8. LFSR-based data compactors: (a) single input and (b) multiple input.

A typical sequential circuit architecture has blocks of combinational logic interleaved with registers. In such an architecture, applying BIST requires that a particular register be configured as a generator when testing one block and as a compactor when testing another. In addition, there must be some mechanism for initializing the register and for observing its contents.

Built-in logic block observation (BILBO) is an approach in which all the necessary functions are incorporated in a single register design. A typical BILBO register is shown in Fig. 9. As shown, two control bits (B_1 and B_2) are used to select the appropriate operation for the register as follows:

1. $B_1 = 1, B_2 = 1$: normal operation with each Z_i connected to Q_i through a latch;
2. $B_1 = 0, B_2 = 0$: a scan path with input scan in, output scan out;
3. $B_1 = 1, B_2 = 0$: a multiple input data compactor based on $x^4 + x + 1$ (note that the circuit outputs are inverted upon entering the compactor);
4. $B_1 = 0, B_2 = 1$: an LFSR test vector generator based on $x^4 + x + 1$.

C. Aliasing in BIST

Since the response data is being compacted to significantly fewer bits, the probability that a faulty circuit will produce the good signature,

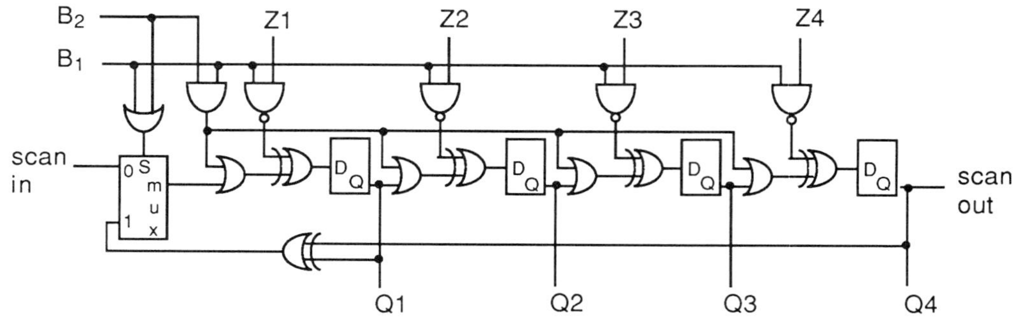

FIG. 9. BILBO register based on $x^4 + x + 1$.

and thus go undetected, is of major concern. At first glance, one would assume that the probability of such an aliasing effect for a k-bit signature should be $1/2^k$, that is, all but 1 of the possible 2^k signature values denote a fault. This is, of course, only the case if all signature values are equally likely.

The fault models described earlier are of little assistance in the formal analysis of aliasing. Rather, an error model is required that estimates the distribution of a fault's effect throughout the response data. Several have been suggested in the literature. One recent model that has proven to be effective is the equally probable error model. In this model, it is assumed that there is a fixed probability p that a response bit will be in error, independent of all other bits. This means there is a fixed probability of an error pattern with a given weight (the weight is the number of bits in error) and this probability is a function of p.

The equally probable error model is a good assumption in terms of evaluating the global behavior of a data compactor rather than its behavior relative to a particular circuit. If a particular circuit is to be considered, the probability that any bit in the response data is in error can be predicted through fault simulation rather than assuming this value is constant over all bits. This is very costly computation, but it is justified if assessing the likelihood of aliasing is deemed to be of particular importance.

Recently, T. W. Williams and his colleagues at IBM have shown that under the equally probable error model, assuming constant error probability, data compactors based on primitive polynomials perform much better than those based on nonprimitive polynomials. They have also shown that, for a k-bit register based on a primitive polynomial, the probability of aliasing as a function of the length of the input sequence is asymptotic to the intuitive value $1/2^k$. It is widely believed that this carries over to multiple input compactors, but at this point it has not been formally proven.

The data stream produced by a faulty circuit is $\hat{\mathbf{D}} = \mathbf{D} \oplus \mathbf{E}$, where $\mathbf{D}$ is the data stream produced by the fault-free circuit and $\mathbf{E}$ is a binary vector with 1's wherever $\hat{\mathbf{D}}$ is in error. Let $\sigma(\mathbf{X})$ denote the signature resulting from applying the compactor in question to a data stream $\mathbf{X}$. Because of the linearity of the compactor, it is easily shown that aliasing occurs if, and only if, $\sigma(\mathbf{E}) = \mathbf{0}$. Hence, we can ignore $\mathbf{D}$ and consider $\mathbf{E}$ as the input to the compactor.

Williams'analysis is based on a simple Markov model of the behavior of the compactor. A k-bit compactor has 2^k states $s_0, s_1, \ldots, s_{2^k-1}$. Let s_0 denote the all-zero state of the register. Further, let $\pi(s_i, t)$ denote the probability the compactor is in state s_i after processing t bits from the incoming data stream. Each state s_i has two predecessor states s_i^0 and s_i^1, depending on whether the input to the data compactor is 0 or 1. Let p_t be the probability the tth bit of data presented to the data compactor is in error. Hence,

$$\pi(s_i, t) = p_t\pi(s_i^1, t-1) + (1 - p_t)\pi(s_i^0, t-1) \quad (1)$$

To begin,

$$\begin{aligned} \pi(s_i, 0) &= 1 \qquad \text{for } i = 0 \\ &= 0 \qquad \text{for all } i \neq 0 \end{aligned} \quad (2)$$

Given Eq. (2) and iteratively applying Eq. (1) for $t = 1, 2, 3, \ldots$, one can compute the probability the compactor will be in any particular state after any number of bits. Note that it is straightforward to do this computation, but it can be rather costly if k is large.

The probability of aliasing for an m-bit data stream is

$$\mathrm{pr}(m) = \pi(s_0, m) - \prod_{t=1}^{m} (1 - p_t) \qquad (3)$$

The product termin Eq. (3) is the probability that aft er m bits, the compactor has never left state s_0. In Williams' work, and for the graphs presented in Figs. 10 and 11, $p_t = p$, a fixed value, for all t. In this case, the probability of aliasing is

$$\mathrm{pr}(m) = \pi(s_0, m) - (1 - p)^m \qquad (4)$$

Figures 10 and 11 are graphs of the probability of aliasing for a single input data compactor based on the polynomial $x^{16} + x^{12} + x^9 + x^7 + 1$ for two values of p. This polynomial is of interest since it is the basis for the signature analysis method developed by the Hewlett-Packard company for board level testing. Both graphs are asymptotic to $1/2^{16}$. These graphs are illustrative of the behavior of compactors based on primitive polynomials. Nonprimitive polynomials exhibit much more erratic behavior and their aliasing performance is frequently not asymptotic to $1/2^k$.

Williams has shown analytically that the behavior illustrated in Fig. 11 is consistent for data

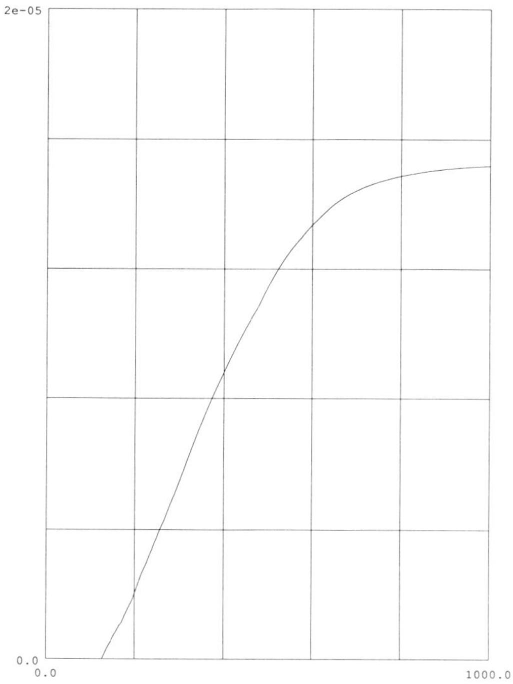

FIG. 11. Probability of aliasing versus input sequence length for $x^{16} + x^{12} + x^9 + x^7 + 1$ with $p = 0.01$.

compactors based on primitive polynomials for $p \leq 0.5$. Since it is reasonable to assume that p will indeed, on average, be less than 0.5, this is an important result. It confirms the widely reported empirical evidence that an LFSR-based BIST is an effective integrated circuit testing technique.

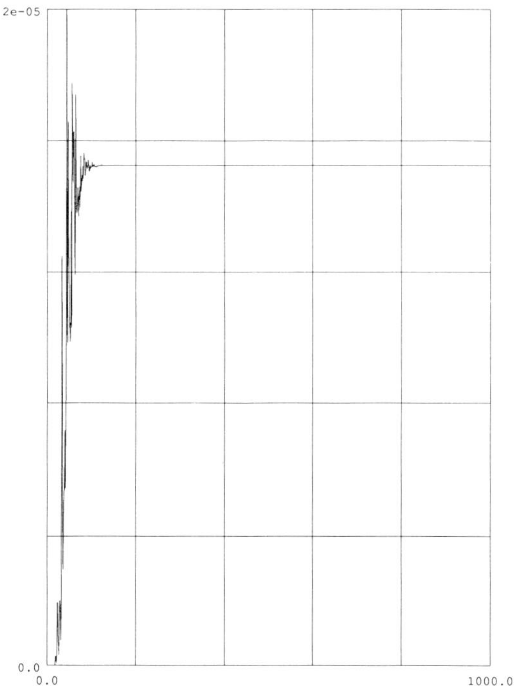

FIG. 10. Probability of aliasing versus input sequence length for $x^{16} + x^{12} + x^9 + x^7 + 1$ with $p = 0.9$.

The computational procedure just described can theoretically be extended to the case of a multiple input data compactor, but the resulting procedure is unwieldy since for a k-input register each state has 2^k predecessor states. A typical register has 16 or more inputs, so on the order of 2^{16} computations would be required for each value of t. Progress in assessing the aliasing of multiple input LFSR-based data compactors awaits further theoretical development.

D. Cellular-Automata-Based BIST

LFSR-based techniques are predominant in the BIST literature because of their relative simplicity and their effectiveness. However, there are certain drawbacks. The overhead costs of BIST techniques are unavoidable—it takes area to incorporate testing on the chip. LFSR-based schemes can cause problems at chip layout time because of the feedback paths in the test vector generators and in the data compactors. Such problems can largely be avoided by good cell design, but there can be unavoidable performance penalties.

The most serious problem is the fact that LFSRs are not very good pseudorandom number generators. This stems from the shifting of data from one position to the next, which means that the value of a bit is perfectly correlated to the value of its neighbor one time step earlier. Such correlation is contrary to the notion of randomness. Indeed, LFSR-based pseudorandom number generators fail badly when standard random number tests are applied.

An LFSR generator can be designed with the exclusive-OR gates between register cells rather than on the feedback path. This partially solves the problem but not for all bit positions.

Another class of pseudorandom number generators conducive to hardware implementation has recently been considered by various researchers. These generators are one-dimensional cellular automata (CA) in which each cell communicates only with its nearest neighbors. The behavior of a cell is given by a rule that specifies the new value of the cell (s_i^+) in terms of the current values of its neighbors (s_{i-1}, s_{i+1}) and possibly the current value of the cell itself (s_i). The cell operation is thus a three-variable function, and the rules can be conveniently identified by the decimal number whose binary representation corresponds to the truth vector of that function. For example,

$$\text{rule 90:} \quad s_i^+ = s_{i-1} \oplus s_{i+1}$$

$$\text{rule 150:} \quad s_i^+ = s_{i-1} \oplus s_i \oplus s_{i+1}$$

Figure 12 shows a 4-bit register made up of rule 90 and 150 cells. As shown, it has a cycle length of 15 ($2^4 - 1$). Extensive testing has shown that CA pseudorandom number generators perform better than their LFSR counterparts. The reason is, except for a rule 90 cell at an end of the register, the value of a cell is a combination of previous values and not simply a value shifted in from a neighboring cell. The bit-to-bit position correlation of the LFSR is thus not present in cellular automata generators. Of course, this advantage does not come for free since earth cell is more complex than in the LFSR. On the other hand, there is no global feedback path.

CA pseudorandom number generators were developed for other purposes, but the BIST is a

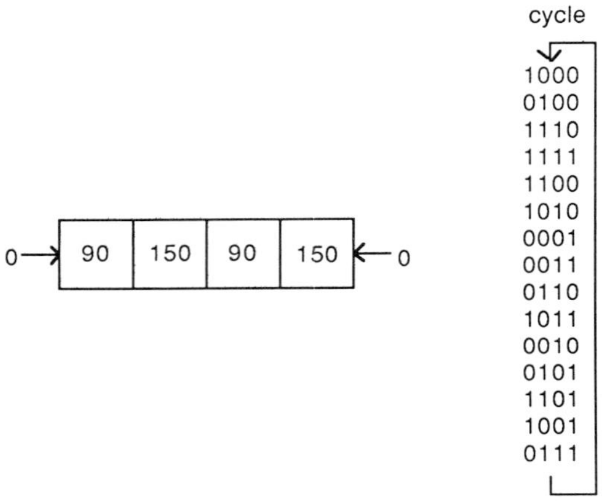

FIG. 12. Autonomous 4-bit hybrid 90/150 CA register.

rather obvious application. Their superior randomness properties can be of significant benefit. For example, consider the two-input CMOS *nand* cell in Fig. 13. Detection of transistor X stuck open requires the application of two test patterns (1, 1) and (1, 0) to (A, B). However, this sequence cannot be generated by an LFSR if the cell driving A is shifted into the cell driving B. A CA generator can, of course, generate the required patterns.

This is not a pathological case since it is reasonable to expect that a *nand* gate combining primary inputs could be fed by adjacent register cells. It is also indicative of the difficulties that arise in more complex situations.

CA registers can also be used as data compactors in a BIST. The single input case is accomplished by connecting the input in place of the 0 at one end of the register. For the multiple output case, the basic rules can be extended to

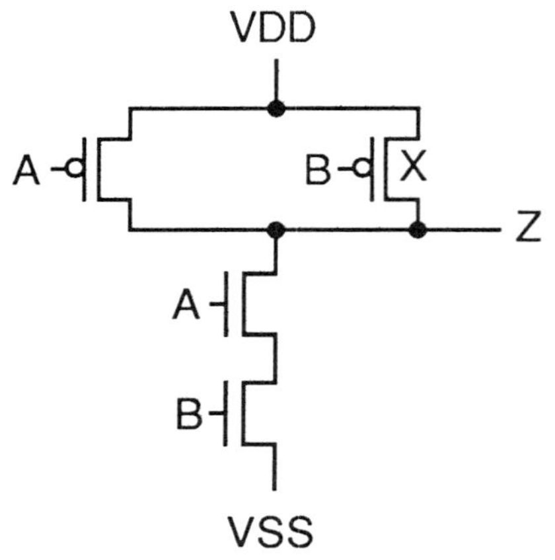

FIG. 13. A 2-input CMOS *nand* cell.

incorporate the circuit outputs (Z_i) in calculating cell values, for example,

$$\text{rule } 90^*: \quad s_i^+ = s_{i-1} \oplus s_{i+1} \oplus Z_i$$

$$\text{rule } 150^*: \quad s_i^+ = s_{i-1} \oplus s_i \oplus s_{i-1} \oplus Z_i$$

The BILBO concept (Fig. 9) can be readily adapted to the CA case, a strategy that has been termed cellular automata logic block observation.

As indicated, analysis of the behavior of LFSRs is based upon the theory of polynomials over the Galois field GF(2). Until recently, no such theoretical underpinning has existed for CA registers. Recent research at the University of Victoria has disclosed the isomorphism between LFSRs based upon primitive polynomials and rule 90/150 CA registers. In summary, this research shows that the two types of registers are implementations of linear finite state machines and provides methods for transforming between an LFSR and a CA that implement the same machine. This provides a direct connection between rule 90/150 CA registers and primitive polynomials. For example, the HP polynomial $x^{16} + x^{12} + x^9 + x^7 + 1$ is implemented by a CA register with cell pattern 1010000000111001, where a 0 denotes a rule 90 cell and a 1 denotes a rule 150 cell.

This research has also shown that, for a single input case, the aliasing behaviors of an LFSR and an isomorphic CA register are identical. The procedure for computing the aliasing probability described previously is readily extended to the CA case.

As for LFSRs, analysis of the aliasing behavior of multiple input CA-based data compactors is an open area. However, one very significant point can be immediately noted. Consider the situation in Fig. 14, which shows two circuit outputs fed in the conventional way into a multiple input LFSR data compactor. Suppose a fault in the circuit presents itself as an error at output z_i at time t and as the same polarity error at output z_{i+1} at time $t + 1$. Clearly, the errors cancel and

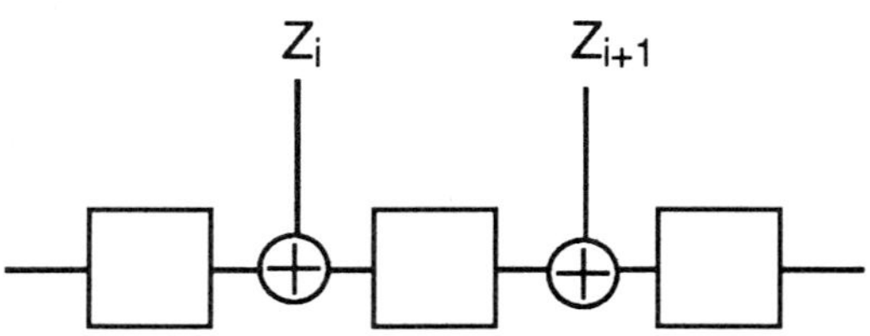

FIG. 14. Portion of a multiple input LFSR data compactor.

the fault will go undetected. It is very easy to construct an actual circuit exhibiting this phenomenon. Arithmetic circuits are particularly vulnerable.

The situation described does not occur as easily in the CA case since the first error to be seen is distributed in both directions through the register. It is far more difficult to construct a realistic circuit in which the fault will be masked because of error effects canceling each other.

The CA approach clearly has certain advantages over the LFSR approach to a BIST. However, there is a higher earea overhead because of the larger number of exclusive-OR operations required. Neither approach can be said to be universally superior to the other. Each should be considered when a BIST is to be used in a design, and the choice made should be based upon the particular situation.

V. Testing Programmable Logic Arrays

Section IV presented the approaches to a BIST for combinational logic with no assumptions about how the logic is implemented. The high degree of structure of a PLA allows for special testing strategies not applicable to unstructured (random) logic.

In Fujiwara's approach to the design of an easily testable PLA, extra logic and extra rows and columns are added to the PLA, as shown in Fig. 15. The shift register is used to select a column (product term) in the AND plane. Each column is "anded" with the complement of the corresponding shift register cell (recall that and AND plane actually implements the *nor* operation). An extra product term is added so that each row of the AND plane has an odd number of connections. Similarly, an extra row is added to the OR plane so that each column in that plane has an odd number of connections. Two extra control lines are added to permit disabling of the primary inputs and their complements. Finally, two exclusive-OR parity cascades are added.

The augmented PLA has the following properties.

1. The shift register can be used to select an arbitrary column of the AND plane by setting a 0 in the selected column and a 1 in all others.
2. The primary inputs and the control lines C_1 and C_2 can be configured to sensitize precisely one row of the PLA.

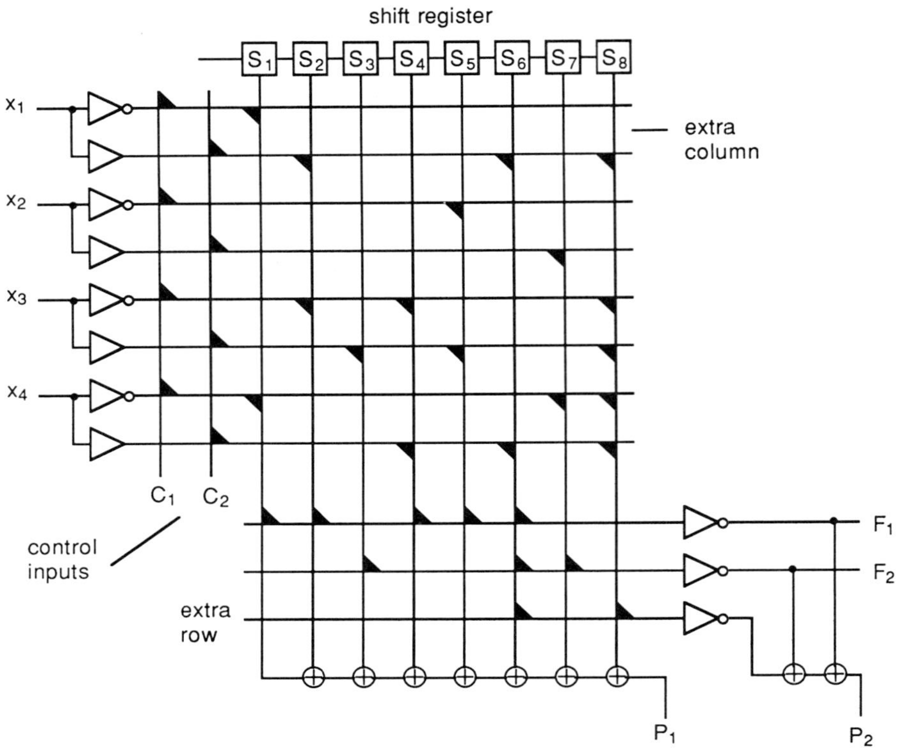

FIG. 15. PLA of Fig. 3 augmented for testability.

3. The cascade of exclusive-OR gates below the OR plane can be used as a parity checker to detect any odd weight errors that propagate to it.

4. The cascade of exclusive-OR gates to the right of the OR plane can be used to detect odd weight errors that originate in the OR plane.

Based on these properties, the augmented PLA is tested by the universal test set shown in Table I. A PLA with n inputs and m product terms prior to augmentation requires a total of $2(n + m) + 3$ tests. The test set is termed universal since it applies to any PLA augmented, as shown in Fig. 15, regardless of the functionality of the PLA. It has been shown that this test set detects all stuck-at faults in the shift register, as well as all single stuck-at and cross-point faults in the remainder of the PLA. This method can be extended to multiple faults, but it becomes unwieldy since each column must be observed independently. They cannot be combined with an exclusive-OR cascade, as in Fig. 15. In addition, the number of tests required becomes $2n(m + 1) + m + 3$.

The advantages of this scheme and those like

TABLE I. PLA Universal Test Set[a]

	$X_1 \ldots X_i \ldots X_n$	C_1	C_2	$S_1 \ldots S_j \ldots S_{m+1}$	P_1	P_2
I^1	0............0	1	0	1............1	0	0
I_j^2, $1 \le j \le m + 1$	0............0	1	0	1......0......1	1	1
I_j^3, $1 \le j \le m + 1$	1............1	0	1	1......0......1	1	1
I_j^4, $1 \le i \le n$	1......0......1	0	1	0............0	β	—
I_j^5, $1 \le i \le n$	0......1......0	1	0	0............0	β	—

[a] Notes: n is the number of inputs in the unaugmented PLA; m is the number of product terms in the unaugmented PLA; $\beta = 0$ if m is even and $\beta = 1$ if m is odd; and a dash indicates a 0 or 1 may be chosen arbitrarily.

it are clear. The PLA is tested with a functionally independent test set. For single faults, the response to the tests is also functionally independent. For multiple faults, the responses to the tests are not functionally independent, however, but they can be easily derived from the PLA. The amount of extra hardware required is not high and grows only linearly as the size of the PLA increases. Very high fault coverage is achieved. The method is appropriate for a BIST, since for single faults, both the tests and their responses are functionally independent. Finally, the method is applicable to high-density PLAs, including those that incorporate folding.

VI. Remarks

The DFT and BIST techniques presented in this review are illustrative of the current state of the art in integrated circuit testing. It is clear there is no universal panacea to the testing problem and that designers must be fully aware of a variety of approaches. Determining the most appropriate test methodology to apply is a major design decision. Indeed, that is the most significant change that has occurred in integrated circuit testing. With the conventional test set approach, testing was viewed as somewhat of an afterthought, something to be attended to once the functional design was completed. Complexity has forced testing into the design process as a motivating factor in the initial choice of design methodology and system architecture.

Computer-aided design (CAD) tools in support of testing are still in their infancy. They tend to be stand alone and somewhat disjoint of tools in support of design. The next few years will undoubtedly see significant steps forward on this front, with tools in support of the DFT and BIST becoming central components in integrated CAD packages. The clear goal is for the testing issues to become integral and automatic, relieving the designer from detailed considerations. Hand-crafted scan paths and BIST generators and compactors will hopefully go the way of manual placement and routing. Adoption of a good testing strategy will only be achieved when the CAD system does most of the work for the designer, leaving him or her to concentrate on the functionality of the design in hand.

Bibliography

Bardell, P. H., McAnney, W. H., and Savir, J. (1987). "Built-In Test for VLSI: Pseudorandom Techniques." Wiley, New York.

Breuer, M. A., and Friedman, A. D. (1976). "Diagnosis and Reliable Design of Digital Systems." Computer Science Press, Rockville, Maryland.

Fujiwara, H. (1985). "Logic Testing and Design for Testability." MIT Press, Cambridge, Massachusetts.

McCluskey, E. J. (1986). "Logic Design Principles: with Emphasis on Testable Semicustom Circuits." Prentice-Hall, Englewood Cliffs, New Jersey.

Miller, D. M., ed. (1987). "Developments in Integrated Circuit Testing." Academic Press, London.

Roth, J. P. (1980). "Computer Logic, Testing and Verification." Computer Science Press, Rockville, Maryland.

Williams, T. W., ed. (1986). "VLSI Testing," Vol. 5 of "Advances in CAD for VLSI" (T. Ohtsuki, ed.). Elsevier, Amsterdam.

INTELLIGENT CONTROL

A. Meystel *Drexel University*

GLOSSARY

Attention (scope of): Subset of available information to be concentrated upon at a given level of resolution. Within the scope of attention all objects are considered at a higher resolution.

Autonomous robots: Robots that are supposed to operate with no (or minimal) human involvement in a variety of complicated situations. Autonomous operation is possible only using functions similar to human functions of cognition and perception.

Joint planning/control process: Control process performed in nested hierarchical controllers. Rough control at the top levels can be considered "planning." Its time scale does not allow for description of dynamic processes. Control processes described at lower resolution levels gradually acquire more and more dynamics. The process at the very bottom is usually a real-time control process.

Multiresolutional representation (or nested hierarchical model): System of representation that contains a number of levels with gradually increasing resolution the top down. The top level presents a very coarse model which is being gradually refined during the user's communication with lower levels.

Nested hierarchical controller: Controller using nested hierarchical model of world representation. It contains as many loops as the model has levels of resolution. Each loop is working as an independent closed-loop controller. The consistency of representation should be maintained during the process of control.

Redundant systems: Systems with analytical or linguistical description containing "excessive" information. In fact, this information enables intelligent controllers to provide more adequate operation.

We shall address a new area of systems engineering endeavor, which is perceived as an intersection of artificial intelligence (AI), operation research, and control theory, and which is actively spurred and stimulated by the advances in computer science (see Fig. 1).

Control theory is a comparatively young scientific discipline, which aimed first toward "regulation" and stable operation of machines, then toward providing stable and accurate operation of arbitrary dynamical systems with feedback, and finally toward providing required functioning of any preassigned object of control including machines in a variety of environments, man-machine systems, and even human teams, economical systems. In the latter, incarnation control theory was understood to be a tool of much more broad conceptual entities such as general theory of systems and cybernetics. [*See* CONTROL SYSTEMS FEEDBACK: CONTROL SYSTEMS, IDENTIFICATION.]

Control theory turned out to be more viable (and fundable) than these general conceptual entities, primarily because the community of specialists in control theory was always associating themselves with a well-established mathematical apparatus of differential and integral calculi (later enhanced by methodology of linear algebra and other domains of mathematics), and with a concrete customer who understood this mathematical apparatus (and/or believed in it).

ENCYCLOPEDIA OF PHYSICAL SCIENCE
AND TECHNOLOGY, VOL. 8

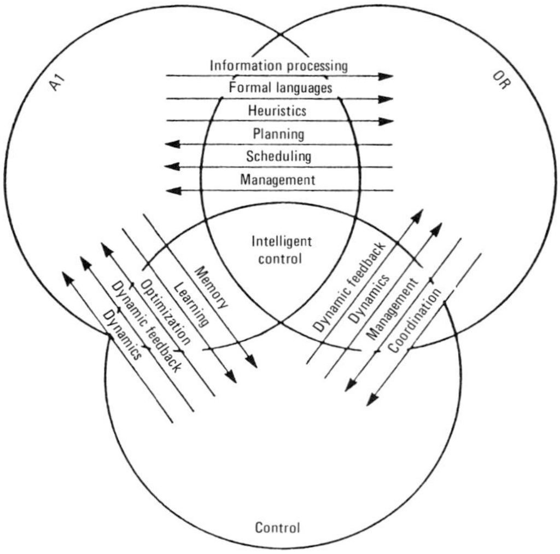

FIG. 1. Intelligent control as a part of its scientific paradigm. [From G. N. Saridis, (1985). Foundations of the theories of intelligent controls, *in* "Proceedings of the IEEE Workshop on Intelligent Control." Troy, New York. Copyright © 1985 by IEEE.]

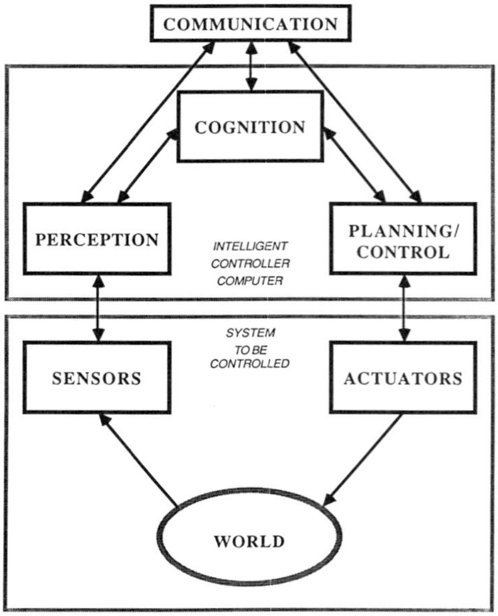

FIG. 2. Closed loop of a typical intelligent controller.

And yet there was always a definite dissatisfaction with the results and orientation of the control theory.

Conventional control is dealing with a broad variety of problems in a spectrum of devices, starting with a speed regulators in the early steam engines and ending with stabilizing a goal-oriented group of the spacecrafts. However, the following problems are unequivocally considered to be difficult for solving in the paradigm of conventional control theory:

1. Optimum control of nonlinear systems.
2. Optimum control of stochastic systems.
3. Control of 6DOF multilink manipulators.
4. Control of redundant systems.
5. Control of autonomous robots.
6. Control of systems with multisensor feedback information.
7. On-line control of systems with incomplete initial knowledge of the model and/or of the environment.
8. Control of systems under human supervision.

All of these systems need a loop that would contain the intelligent means capable of dealing with a number of complicated problems: perception for organizing a diversified information set coming from a multiplicity of sensors, knowledge base for enabling the system not only to interpret the results of perception but also to put them in a perspective necessary for determining strategies and policies of future operation as well as to submit all necessary information for planning/control processes, planner/controller to generate proper control sequences, and so on (Fig. 2).

For a long period of time, the specialists in the area of control had a general feeling that there was a need in formulating the difference between the two important entities: the first one is a so-called control theory (conventional control theory), or theory of automatic control, and the second the secont elusive entity, which is always around and differs drastically from the conventional control theory. This second entity tends to utilize the unconventional approaches and tends to expand out of the domain of integral and differential calculi into a number of other domains starting with automata theory and ending in linguistics, fuzzy sets, neural networks, and so on.

I. Solving Control Problems: New Paradigm Is Required

A. Conventional Control

A paradigm of conventional control theory treats subjects of interest in a view of a particular part of their behavior: which can be represented by the apparatus of differential and integral calculi, theory of differential equations, linear algebra, and vector analysis. This is the way of formulating the problem in the theory of conventional control. It starts with a definition of a system.

Definition. A system Σ, $\Delta \supset \Sigma$ is a mathematical structure $(T, X, U, \Omega, Y, \Gamma, \phi, \eta)$ defined by the following axioms.

Axiom 1. Existence. There exists a given time set T, a state set X, a set of input values U, a nonempty set of acceptable input functions (or command sequence, or control)

$$\Omega = \{\omega: T \rightarrow U\}$$

a set of output values Y, and a set of output functions

$$\Gamma = \{\gamma: T \rightarrow Y\}$$

Axiom 2. Direction of time. T is an ordered subset of the reals.

Axiom 3. Organization. There exists a state-transition function (or trajectory of motion, or solution curve)

$$\phi: T \times T \times X \times \Omega \rightarrow X$$

whose value is the state $t \in T$ resulting at time $t \in T$ from the initial state (or event) $x = x(\tau)$ at the initial time $\tau \in T$ under the action of the input $\omega \in \Omega$. This function has the following properties:

(a) Direction of time. Function ϕ is defined for all $t \geq \tau$, but not necessarily for all $t < \tau$.

(b) Consistency. Function $\phi(t; \tau, x, \omega) = x$ for all $t \in T$, all $x \in X$, and all $\omega \in \Omega$.

(c) Nested concatenation, or composition. For any $t_1 < t_2 < t_3$ the following holds

$$\phi(t_3; t_1, x, \omega) = \phi(t_3; t_2, \phi(t_2; t_1, x, \omega), \omega)$$

for all $x \in X$ and for all $\omega \in \Omega$.

(d) Causality. If $\omega_1, \omega_2 \in \Omega$ and $\omega_1 = \omega_2$ then $\phi(t; \tau, x, \omega_1) = \phi(t; \tau, x, \omega_2)$.

Axiom 4. Transfer function mapping. There exists a map $\eta: T \times X \rightarrow Y$, which defines the output $y(t) = \eta(t, x(t))$.

Several generations of control scientists turned out to be captured within the rigid cage of this model of the reality. One can see immediately that a very strict structure is required from the beginning in which the sets of input, output, and states are clearly separated and given in advance. No negotiation is presumed as a part of the future control operation, no overlapping among the sets is presumed. The system does not contain any notion of goal of operation as a part of the structure. However, this might not be required at this stage: it does have the set for control, but we have not yet discussed how this set will be applied.

In reality, we are interested in defining the state-transition function not only after but also before the definite moment in time ($t \geq \tau$). Otherwise the problems and prediction are difficult to solve, which are the most important problems in the domain of contemporary real systems to be controlled.

Axioms 1–3 imply that the time scale of the system should be preselected. Another way of dealing with the system model can be introduced that does not require the time scale of the system to be displayed. Interestingly enough, there is a tacit presumption that this concatenation [see property (c)] should be unique, which is an extremely rigid requirement. It actually excludes from consideration all redundant systems where a multiplicity of concatenations can be found.

This set of definitions and axioms is usually supplemented by a demand of stationarity, linearity, and smoothness. Properties of the state transition function lead to the following theorem. Every system Δ with a state-transition function as previously defined and with the norm $\|\omega\| = \sup\|u(t)\|$ has a transition function in a form

$$dx/dt = f(t, x, \pi^t\omega)$$

where operator π^t is a mapping $\Omega \rightarrow$ U is derived from $\omega \rightarrow u(t) = \omega(t)$. The suggestion to select π^t in a form π^t: $\omega \rightarrow (u(t), u'(t), \ldots, u^{(n)}(t))$ is rejected, which furtherly narrows down the domain of systems under consideration. In the case of a smooth, linear, finite-dimension case, the transition function obeys the simplified relations. (The simplification is determined by selecting norms of the corresponding spaces with no derivatives of the time functions for controls. Only now we are coming to realize that this expectation might be quite right, we are dealing now with the systems that need a norm based on all set of $u(t), u'(t), \ldots, u^{(n)}(t)$.

$$dx/dt = F(t)x + G(t)u(t), \quad y = H(t)x(t),$$

where $F(t)$ and $G(t)$ are parts of the expression $f(t, u, u(t)) = F(t)x + G(t)\, u(t)$, $H(t)$ is a mapping $T \rightarrow \{p \times n \text{ matrices}\}$, which is obtained from

$$y(t) = \eta(t, x(t)) = H(t)x(t)$$

$T = R^1$, and X, U are normed spaces, $F(t)$ is a mapping F: $T \rightarrow \{n \times n \text{ matrices}\}$, $G(t)$ is a mapping $G: T \rightarrow \{n \times m \text{ matrices}\}$, n is a dimensionality of states $x \in R^n$, m is a dimensionality of controls $u \in R^m$, p is a dimensionality of outputs $y \in R^p$. Proper adjustments and modifications are being made for a variety of cases: discrete systems, systems with nonvarying parameters, etc.

The control law in conventional control is defined as mapping $k: T \times X \rightarrow U$, which puts in correspondence $x(t)$ and $u(t)$ for each moment of time. So, in this formulation we do not define how the control law corresponds to any of the control requirements. The standard problem of control is defined as follows: for each event from the set of initial events (t_0, x_0) the control should be determined $u(\cdot)$, which transforms this initial event into the goal set, and minimizes the cost functional simultaneously.

Another definition of a control problem has a clear reference to the conventional control theory. The control problem is recommended to be divided into the following steps: (1) establishing of a set of performance; (2) writing down the performance specifications; (3) formulating a model of the system in a form of a set of differential equations; (4) using conventional control theory find the performance of the original system, and if it does not satisfy the list of requirements, then cascade or feedback compensation must be added to improve the response; and (5) using modern control theory approach assign the entire eigenstructure, or the necessary structure is to be designed to minimize the specified performance index (which is understood as a quadratic performance index). In general, one can easily find that there is a surprising lack of uniformity in the existing views on control problem.

The following definition of control law can be considered consistent with the practice of control: control of a process implies driving the process to effectively attain a prespecified goal. One can see that the notion of goal is included in this definition.

B. Issues of Dissatisfaction with the Conventional Control Theory

We can see that the latter definition does not say anything about the system, or its model. This is a remarkable fact! Indeed, the system per se is out of the scope of our interest. The body of conventional control offers a model of a system, and then proposed methods of dealing with this formal body within the boundaries of the model selected. The user is more interested in the theory of control, which would be invariant of the model of system. What we are interested in (together with the user) is, in fact, a process under consideration, and a goal we must drive this process toward.

Given the above example of a classical approach to control problems, the following issues characteristic for the conventional control theory can be focused upon.

(a) Model is considered to be the source of the theories for problem solving, not vice versa. ("Let us take the existing mathematical theory, and let us see what are the resembling control problems—this is the business of control theory.") As a result, one can take a book in control theory and not be able to tell it from the book on the theory of differential equations, on linear algebra, or on the theory of linear operators.

(b) The problems of control are being formulated and solved not to the extent of the need of the user, but to the extent of intrinsic capabilities of the existing analytical and computational apparatus. ("This is what I can do, and I really do not care whether this contrivance can solve your real problem or not.") The researchers in control area do not want to deal with the so-called ill-posed problems. Luckily, the theory of ill-posed problems has appeared about regularization of a class of problems in the area of linear operators. After this the word "ill-posed problem" is understood as a scientific term in the theory of linear operators. In the meantime, all of the real problems of control are actually ill-posed problems no matter what kind of mathematical model was offered for their solution.

(c) Formulation of the control problem is considered to be a prerogative of the "control person," and not a result of the dialog between the "user" and the "control person." ("How can I talk to him when he cannot identify his electronic carburetor neither with rings nor with ideals?") Thus, the technical requirements and their negotiation is not considered to be a part of solving the problem of control. Dealing with the "natural" cost functions is considered to be outside of the control theory. Eventually, the reality of existing cost functions is usually not negotiated, and the designers of control systems often live in the imaginary world of minimization of doubtful (although solvable) quadratic forms. Optimum controllers are traditionally considered to the degree of minimizing the average quadratic error. Time minimization is not considered to be an attractive problem. In general, optimization problems are carefully avoided.

(d) Planning is not considered to be a part of control problem and is left out to the AI people (or to the user). ("You plan, I will control the motion along with your plan.") One can find mentioning of planning primarily in the papers on dynamic programming, which makes the dynamic programming even more connected to the corresponding AI methodologies (such as search). Other areas of control theory prefer somebody external to plan the motion trajectory in advance (preferably, off line). Then, the results of planning are considered a part of control-problem formulation. In the meantime, the intrinsic linkage between planning and control is perceived in all control problems. Planning per se is considered to be an intrinsic AI topic; it seems to be more linguistically inclined, and treats subjects that are being omitted from the classical paradigm of conventional control theory. Formulating of what is the goal of the operation seems to be among the topics attractive for AI specialist. Cost function is a topic of focusing within the operation research (OR) theory. Search algorithms with heuristics are developed by specialists in AI and OR. The only light expansion in the search processes and "planning" is known within the theory of dynamic programming.

(e) Problems of dealing with information are out of the scope of the existing control theory. ("Everything should arrive to me in the form of parameters, variables, or controls—no matter what you should do to get it!") It was a substantial innovative move when K.-S. Fu started openly talking about the control systems with recognition in the loop. Processes of recognition can affect the control processes drastically since the vocabulary of the controller may depend on the recognition results.

(f) Adaptive and learning systems, neural networks, and other imitations of brain processes, fuzzy controllers, linguistic controllers, fractal dimension in control, and so on. ("In my time, 'fuzzy system' meant failure!") This list starts with items that are accepted to be a part of control theory, and expands toward much more esoteric areas that are needed in contemporary controllers, generated by this need, and yet cannot be considered legitimate tools of control theory. Some of these topics are taken care of outside of the control discipline. For example, if probabilistic processes with insufficient knowledge of probabilistic characteristics are present within the system, then the dynamics of controlled motion, conditions of stability for such a motion, and minimization of the average quadratic error of such a motion cannot be done legitimately by the control theory methods. So people use these methods illegitimately. Or apply a number of new techniques starting with woo-doo methods and ending with a very bright interesting ideas deserving to be considered seriously.

II. Intelligent Control: New Theoretical Paradigm Is Emerging

A. Many Ways in which the Control Problem May Be Attacked

Control theory focused traditionally on control system (CS), which is supposed to provide operation of a plant (PL) satisfying some requirements (see Fig. 3). CS is meant to exist separately from PL, and the flow of controls U is presumed to be generated by CS as something that can be interpreted as a "feedforward" control (FW). External "feedback" (EFB) was to be designed as the ultimate result of the efforts of a control engineer involved in the process of creation of CS. This was the case in the beginning. Very soon however, it was understood that the plant in turn affects the control system as a kind of internal feedback (IFB). The necessity to constantly explicate plant during the process of control design brought to conclusion that PL should be represented as a part of CS, and "to design the controller" means "to design the feedback." Sure, the exosystem (EXO) affected both of them. So, instead of concentrating on

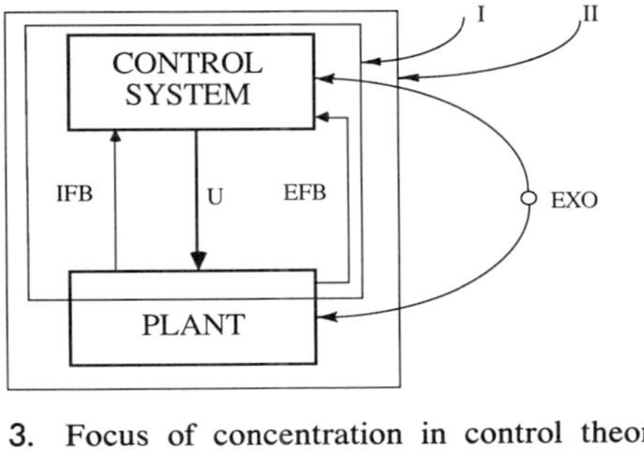

FIG. 3. Focus of concentration in control theory. [From A. Meystel (1987). Intelligent control: highlights and shadows, *in* "Proceedings of the IEEE International Symposium on Intelligent Control." Philadelphia, Pennsylvania. Copyright © 1987 by IEEE.]

(I), the control engineers went on with analysis and design of the whole combination (II).

The system is usually decomposed into a plant and a controller. The convenience of DI model (i.e., a model based on premises and apparatus of differential and integral calculi), obtained as a result of this decomposition, is paid for by tremendous loss of information. In AI methodology, even mathematically unstructured information can be retained within the logical or linguistical (or similar to those) systems of representation. However, the elegance and strength of integral/differential models can hardly be utilized within AI framework in a direct way.

The apparatus of differential and integral calculi (DIC) was a powerful tool that has virtually predetermined the system of representation. Although any problem was initially formulated in a language of technological application (LTA), the whole bulk of LTA knowledge (negotiated initially with a user) could not be utilized in the problem-solving process because of the constraints imposed by the DIC language, which is always less diversified than LTA language. So, it became a tradition that any set of technical requirements to the future CS as well as a description of the reality of PL were translated first from the "language of the engineer," or LTA representation, to the lingo of DIC representation. After the problem was solved within DIC representation, the solution ought to be translated back to the realworld language. This process of consecutive translation of the situation from one language into another language is shown in Fig. 4.

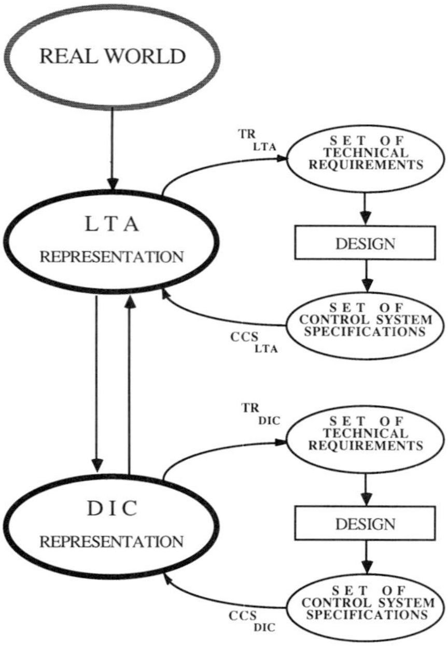

FIG. 4. Design based on two different representations. [From A. Meystel (1987). Intelligent control: highlights and shadows, *in* "Proceedings of the IEEE International Symposium on Intelligent Control." Philadelphia, Pennsylvania. Copyright © 1987 by IEEE.]

Undoubtedly, the following inclusion holds: $TR_{LTA} \supset TR_{DIC}$, which determines the same situation with representations of the output of the design process $CSS_{LTA} \supset CSS_{DIC}$. Certainly, one also would have to comply with the fact of reality that DIC techniques could resolve only problems that are limited compared to that one needed to be solved. Thus, the following way has become customary in control theory: not those problems to be solved were usually attempted but those that is possible to solve within the DIC language. Several decades of this situation led to the exponentially increasing number of various solutions obtained within DIC representation for various problems. However, the actual number of solutions assuming a translation into LTA representation is not as impressive. All LTA activities were done by the users.

In the meantime, a variety of technologies appeared demanding from control systems built on the LTA representation that they must not be abridged by the process of mapping the set of technical requirements from LTA representation into DIC representation. These technologies include intelligent machines and robots, systems of flexible and integrated manufacturing, autonomous devices including autonomous mobile systems, intelligent systems of control and communication like C^3I (even not to talk about SDI and similar to it). All of these systems are equipped by a multiplicity of sensors (including vision), and have to operate with no human involvement. The problem of translating everything into the paradigm of DIC language seemed to be a formidable one. There was a practical necessity of using anything available: in this case, the LTA representation. The LTA technologies are supported by a powerful engineering tool: computer that is now being understood in a broader context than just support for computations (Fig. 5).

Even taking the limited subset of robots as an example, one can easily understand that DIC representation cannot be satisfactory for the problems that arise in this area. Indeed, it is well

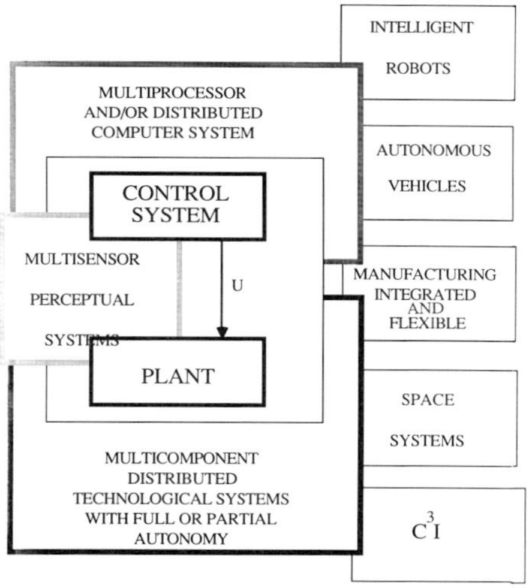

FIG. 5. New technological paradigm. [From A. Meystel (1987). Intelligent control: highlights and shadows, *in* "Proceedings of the IEEE International Symposium on Intelligent Control." Philadelphia, Pennsylvania. Copyright © 1987 by IEEE.]

known how cumbersome the complete system of linear deterministic differential equations is, written for a rigid 6DOF multilink manipulator, and how doubtful the effort to solve this system is (since the model of manipulator is severely simplified, all its parameters are not, and cannot be known accurately, nonlinearities and coupling are neglected, errors are magnified by the process of solution, and so on).

B. Complexity of a System To Be Controlled

The plant system PL is being driven by CS with the help of a multiple (in a general case) set of actuators A, under the condition of uncertainty of PL and A parameters (which are known only partially). Since each of the actuators can be associated with a "subsystem" or a "subassembly" of the system, a hierarchical or similar decomposition of the overall system is expected (Fig. 6). After the decomposition is completed, the lower levels contain too much information for using in the design of the higher levels. Talking about "parameters" presumes the existence of some model (a mathematical one, usually, in DIC representation), which might be not the case. The knowledge of PL explicated from the LTA-representation is frequently presented in such a way that the resulting PL-model in DIC representation turns out often to be quite rudimentary, or, at least, too simplistic. Adaptive controllers seemed to be a good solution; however, they also tried to squeeze the richness of the system into a DIC structure of the primary nonadaptive controller. This is why sophisticated users turned toward the AI models: production systems do not required to make any model simplification.

The rest of the knowledge (if one does not want to lose it) can be taken care of using the available AI methods: linguistic representations, production systems, etc. The uncertainties cannot be judged on using the existing probabilistic models since the information does not exist for building such models. A new information about the PL parameters should be obtained during the plant operation, thus the discovery of the new plant models is expected as a part of control procedure. The variety of the expected operation modes should be taken in account, and the processes of operation under all possible conditions must be taken in consideration. Even for a simple multilink manipulator, one cannot easily answer the question what is the "best" case of operation, what is the "worst" case, and whether there is any hypothetical "average" case that could be accepted as a "design" case.

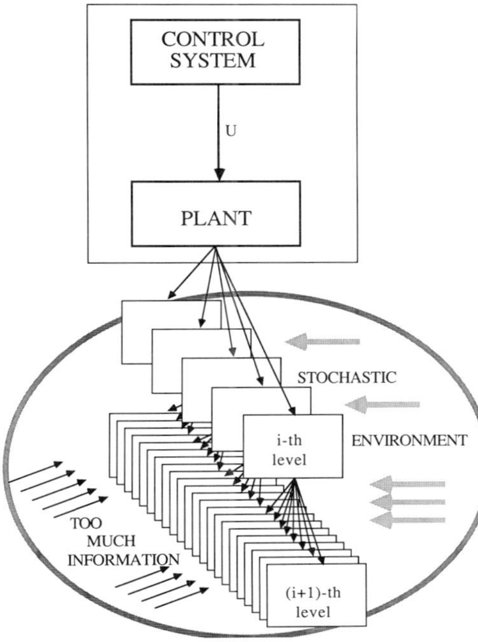

FIG. 6. Hierarchical decomposition of the system. [From A. Meystel (1987). Intelligent control: highlights and shadows, *in* "Proceedings of the IEEE International Symposium on Intelligent Control." Philadelphia, Pennsylvania, Copyright © 1987 by IEEE.]

EXO is becoming a part of PL. On the other hand, it is clear that this multilink manipulator has one goal of operation, and yet it should be controlled by a multiplicity of controller since it has many actuators. Thus, multiactuation is becoming an important issue in the intelligent control problem.

C. Exosystem and Multiactuation as Parts of the Overall Problem

Information about EXO often cannot be given in the beginning, this information should be recognized within the reality of EXO, and after recognition, it should be dealt with properly. This information contains facts of different importance (resolution?), and they should be processed in a different way: some of them should be focused on, some of them should not, and they can be considered in a generalized manner as a part of more general entity unifying a variety of facts. Thus, the idea emerges of studying the reality of EXO under different resolutions depending on our interest in the details. Surely, the consistency is to be provided for the overall system using the different parts of EXO considered under different resolutions.

The easiest way of providing this consistency is to consider the EXO as a hierarchy of decomposition in parts or resolutional hierarchy, which happens to be the same (this concept coincides with the frame concept in AI). This is how the perceptual subsystem delivers the EXO to the controller. The hierarchy of EXO appears in a way that is quite similar to the way in which the hierarchy of PL appears: the bulk of the information (knowledge?) about the world, or the world description should be decomposed (tessellated) into a hierarchical resolutional set of parts (Fig. 7). The mechanism of the new knowledge acquisition is provided by a system of multiple sensors, their signals must be integrated in order to enrich our knowledge of EXO, in other words EXO should be constantly perceived. Perception of EXO should be considered a part of normal system operation, thus learning is a natural procedure that requires recognition of familiar features and objects as well as discovery of unfamiliar entities and concepts.

On the other hand, since most of the systems are multiactuator systems, their actuators must be assigned individual controllers, and each of them should be dealt with as an individual control system within its scope of attention. At the same time, all this multiactuator system can be

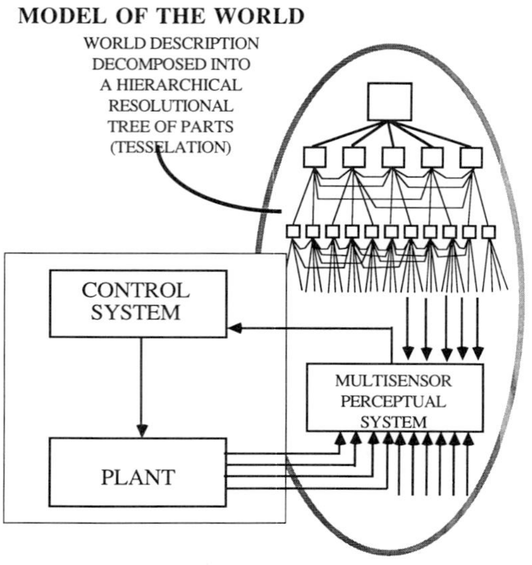

FIG. 7. Multisensor perceptual system and its inner knowledge representation. [From A. Meystel (1987). Intelligent control: highlights and shadows, *in* "Proceedings of the IEEE International Symposium on Intelligent Control." Philadelphia, Pennsylvania. Copyright © 1987 by IEEE.]

considered as an object of control: a single system is supposed to coordinate the activities of the multiple controllers subsystems. A separate controller is supposed to submit to the coordinator a control assignment that is obtained at a higher level of the control hierarchy (lower level of resolution) and deal with the objects, parameters, variables, and controls formulated at a higher level of generality.

Thus, we came to the hierarchically intelligent controller, which has organization, coordination, and hardware control levels (see Fig. 8) as described by G. Saridis. The organization level accepts and interprets the input commands and related feedback from the system, defines the tasks to be executed, and segments it into subtasks in their appropriate order of execution. At the organization level appropriate translation and decision schemata linguistically implement the desirable functions. The coordination level receives instructions from the organizer and feedback information for each subtask to be executed and coordinates execution at the lowest level. The lowest level control process usually involves the execution of a certain motion and requires, besides the knowledge of the mathematical model of the process, the assignment of end conditions and a performance criterion (cost function) defined by the coordinator.

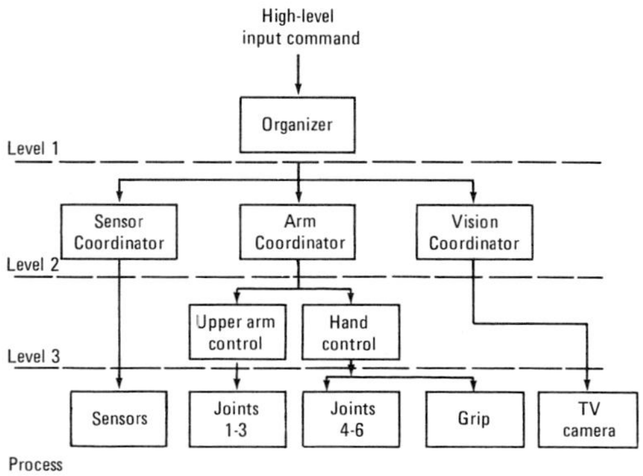

FIG. 8. Hierarchical intelligent control system. [From G. N. Saridis (1985). Foundations of the theories of intelligent controls, *in* "Proceedings of the IEEE Workshop on Intelligent Control." Troy, New York. Copyright © 1985 by IEEE.]

D. Problem Formulation Is also a Part of the Control Problem

Finally, it is a rule, not an exception, that the task is posed imprecisely, that the description of many functions to be provided by a control system is incomplete, and the expected situations of the operation are given to a control engineer by the user in an approximate way. In many cases it is determined by the very fact of impossibility to transfer the knowledge of a user to the designer (control engineer). In many cases it is determined by intractability of the problem as it seems to the user. The control engineer is designing the substantial part of the future system (starting with task formulation and ending with actuators operation).

However, often this control engineer is not familiar with the context of operation. A long time ago, it was understood that the design of the control process is a trade-off with the parameters of the system. Later it became clear that it is a trade-off with the model as well as the actual structure of the system. It is becoming clear now that the trade-off includes the processes of task formulation. Moreover, the negotiation of the task set is the part of design. We can expect that in the future systems, the continuous process of task negotiation will be a part of the control system (Fig. 9).

E. Intelligent Controller

Consider all of the above factors together, and the concept of intelligent controller emerges as a combination of (1) methodology of a hybrid sys-

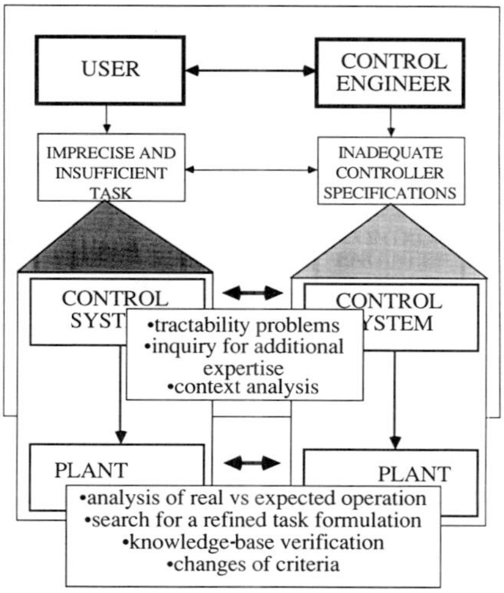

FIG. 9. Structure of the user-control engineer negotiations. [From A. Meystel (1987). Intelligent control: highlights and shadows, *in* "Proceedings of the IEEE International Symposium on Intelligent Control." Philadelphia, Pennsylvania. Copyright © 1987 by IEEE.]

tem with DIC/LTA representation, (2) hierarchical model of imprecise and incomplete plant, (3) hierarchical and incomplete knowledge of the exosystem delivered by multiple sensors and reorganized constantly in the process of learning, and (4) task negotiation as a part of control system as well as control process (see Fig. 10). A number of techniques is devised and developed for this particular paradigm of consideration: theory of hierarchical control, entropy methods for hierarchical controller design, principle of increasing precision with decreasing intelligence, etc. A number of results is potentially applicable within this paradigm: theory of team control and theory of fuzzy sets and systems. Many developments of control theory are directed for use in control systems: learning and self-organizing systems, neural networks, knowledge-based, linguistical, and cognitive controllers.

F. New Discipline: Intelligent Control

1. Blend of the Disciplines: Control Theory, Artificial Intelligence, and Operation Research

So, how is it possible to control the motion and, more generally, the development of any kind of system, independent of their complexity,

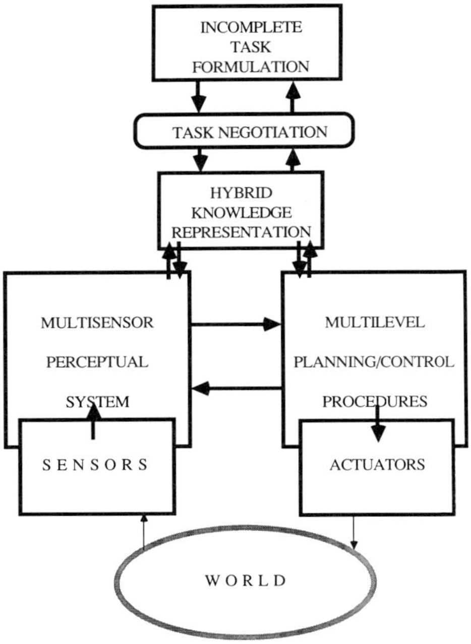

FIG. 10. Structure of intelligent controller. [From A. Meystel (1987). Intelligent control: highlights and shadows, *in* "Proceedings of the IEEE International Symposium on Intelligent Control." Philadelphia, Pennsylvania. Copyright © 1987 by IEEE.]

of our capability of separating it from the environment and localizing it, of the context, of the forms of knowledge available, and the methods for its representation? One cannot do it using the control theory solely. Its tools, yet powerful, do not see beyond the myopic constraints self-imposed by the designer and hidden within the mechanism of DIC representation.

One cannot do it using artificial intelligence theory (is there any?): AI surrenders when time-dependent dynamic processes are involved. It fences itself from the ideas of stability, controllability, and others. Both control theory and AI cannot operate out of the OR paradigm: its queues and game situations are typical for the variety of applications. Intelligent control intends to fuse these three disciplines together when required. The alloy seems to be powerful and flexible.

Intelligent control, as a discipline, is expected to provide generalization of the existing control disciplines on the basis of (1) combined analysis of the plant and its control criteria, with the system of goals and metagoals that determine the process of negotiations through the overall design procedure; (2) processes of multisensor operation with information (knowledge) integration and recognition in the loop; (3) man-machine cooperative activities, including imitation and substitution of the human operator; and (4) computer structures representing the above-mentioned elements.

Here we arrive to the shadows of the situation in the area of intelligent control. None of the elements mentioned are supported by substantial research and analysis. There is no established terminology identifiable with the area of intelligent control. The word "intelligent" is used in a variety of contexts with different nuances of meaning, which contributes to confusion in a number of cases. There is a tremendous inertia of following the conventional recommendations and views that are hindering the development of intelligent control ideas and methods.

A new area of the system science, intelligent control, is emerging at the intersection of number of important scientific disciplines: automatic control, artificial intelligence, and operation research. Interest in this discipline appeared about a decade ago; however, the "birthdate" of intelligent control can be alluded to as the date of the first meeting of scientists interested in intelligent control (Troy, New York, 1985). This meeting testified the existence of substantial interest to this phenomenon. At the first meeting, the principles of the intelligent control as a discipline were put together. After the first meeting, the IEEE Technical Committee on Intelligent Control was organized. About two hundred IEEE members entered the new committee. An interesting discussion was in the progress, dedicated to the definition of the intelligent control as well as to the possible syllabus of a courses on intelligent control. At the second meeting, the discussions continued, which demonstrated a growth in the interest to the new emerging discipline (Philadelphia, 1987). The second meeting derived from the principles obtained at the first approaches, some specifics, and highlighted many of the future perspectives. This meeting had more sponsors and broader participation (only the United States was at the first meeting; Europe, Japan, and other developing countries were at the second meeting). The third international conference (Washington, D.C., 1988) is to demonstrate a number of conventions in terminology as being accepted by most of the participants (several hundred scientists became members of the Technical Committee).

2. Dealing with Knowledge: A Distinctive Trait of Intelligent Control

Knowledge can be defined as the function of removing uncertainty in the operation of an intelligent machine. G. Saridis proposed to measure knowledge by the entropy, and to use the rate of knowledge as a measure of intelligence of the machine. The following rates are of importance: throughput, blockage, coordination, internal decision, and noise. Knowledge requires taking care of the following activities: perception, representation, cognition, reasoning, and decision making (including planning/control).

One of the most powerful ideas of intelligent control is the idea of a direct link between the organization of knowledge and the structure of intelligent controller. In the conventional control theory knowledge is involved in the structure of the controller and in the processes of control only implicitly. We are not yet used to working with this matter—knowledge. And yet, we can foresee the drastic changes in the design and control methodologies linked with knowledge as a control agent.

This is why the research in the area of intelligent control is organized around two major topics linked with knowledge: (1) knowledge implementation—structures of intelligent control systems and (2) knowledge evaluation—observations and computations in intelligent control.

The process of removing uncertainty in the execution of various tasks can be characterized by precision. Since the value of precision is limited at each hierarchical level, the control hierarchy can be always associated with the resolutional hierarchy. Resolution of knowledge representation strongly affects all subsystems of the system shown in Fig. 10.

G. The Structure and the Subjects of Intelligent Control Theory

The word "intelligent control" was coined by the late K.-S. Fu, who dedicated the last decade of his life to the research and analysis of various aspects of the nonconventional control systems. The definition of intelligent control appeared initially in *Self-Organizing Control of Sochastic Systems* by G. Saridis, where the property of intelligence was linked with the capability of a system to expose a variety of features that traditionally were out of the scope of specialists in conventional control theory: decision making, games, image recognition, adaptation to the uncertain media, self-organization, and planning and scheduling of operations. Even the very process of control problem formulation is visualized in an unconventional way: no preferred mathematical model is presumed, most of the information is presented in a descriptive manner, and the initial assumptions are being challenged during the whole process of problem solving, and then during the process of control.

It also became clear that any actual advances in AI, robotics, and, speaking generally, intelligent machines can be achieved only on the basis of control application of particular AI methods in robots and other intelligent machines. The same ideas are valid for CAD-CAM, large-space systems, flexible manufacturing, unmanned systems, telepresence devices, and autonomous vehicles. During the 1970s, the extensive development of new technologies based on computer application and linked with robotics and integrated manufacturing in industry, intelligent warfare and C^3I in military systems, space technologies, etc., generated a number of new extensions for the area of intelligent control. By fusing the multisensor outputs, employing the visual feedback, and observing different parts of the same process at different levels of control hierarchy, all these things brought to creation of a new type of controllers: controllers with recognition in the loop.

After the term "recognition" is accepted, the other terms become accepted, the most important of them is knowledge. It becomes clear that a closed mathematical model should not be the basis of analysis and synthesis of control systems and processes but instead a system of world representation based on a broader knowledge of the operation to be performed, and the context of the performance. Now, the structure of the intelligent controller as an object of analysis of the theory of Intelligent Control (Figs. 2, 8, and 10).

Multiple advantages of semiotic systems of world representation gave birth to a new type of control systems: systems with linguistical control. From controlling by numbers, linguistical controllers evolved to control by concepts. An advanced type of learning processes (namely, conceptual learning linked with creation of new concepts) has attracted attention of specialists in learning, and stimulated interest to utilization of learning properties in controllers.

A strong link between intelligent control and operation research theory was obvious at the stage of appearance of systems with adaptive control and self-organization. Now, when the rule-based and other knowledge-based controllers indicated that the production systems, given thorough treatment in the area of artificial intelligence, become a legitimate part of computer-based controllers, the merger of all of them (AI, OR, and Control Theory) seems unavoidable within the framework of the theory of intelligent control.

Synthesis of the theory of intelligent control is not expected to be just a mechanical gathering and combining all of the related theoretical "gadgets" from the literature. The number of forgotten or overlooked ideas can fertilize the existing theories with new properties. For example, the problem of negation is becoming increasingly important in the systems of knowledge representation for intelligent control. The "power of veto" can be understood in a sense different from a trivial logical negation. (Interestingly enough, the use of the generalized negation is considered to be one of the major stages in the process of appearance of intelligence in humans.)

The appearance of this new discipline is not being met with cheers by everybody. It is well known that many of AI, OR, and control specialists are not leaning toward any merger among these disciplines. It seems much easier to build a theory around the model than to build a model to satisfy the conclusions from the theory. However, it is now clear that this merger is an unavoidable one, since the results of this merger are long awaited in robotics, integrated manufacturing, computer-aided design, and many other areas.

Intelligent control does not aim toward incremental development of a definite formal tool, like it happened in the theory of conventional control, which is developing all possible implications from the theory of differential and integral equations, and is doing this in a rigid consistent manner. The goal of intelligent control is rather to achieve as more adequate satisfaction of real requirements in real environment by the help of consistent blending of a variety of scientific formal theories and methods previously belonging to different scientific domain. It is an expectation that the scientific consistency of intelligent control as a discipline will be provided by a consistency of the functioning system for which the problem has been solved, so to speak, consistency on a metalevel of its representation.

III. Major Theoretical Issues of the Intelligent Control Theory

A. Ill-Posedness of Real Problems

The problems of control in reality are usually ill-posed. Ill-posed problems arise almost always when experimental data are to be used to construct a model of reality. Assume that the model of the system is expected to be constructed in the form $Au = f$, $f \in F$, where A: $D_A \supset U \rightarrow F$ is an operator with a nonempty domain of definition D_A, in a metric space U, with a range in a metric space F. The ill-posed problem is on hand when the conditions of solvability, uniqueness, and stability are not satisfied. (Solvability requires that the range of the value Q_A of the operator A coincide with F; uniqueness requires that the equality $Au_1 = Au_2$ for any $u_1, u_2 \in D_A$ should imply the equality $u_1 = u_2$; and the stability condition requires that the inverse operator A^{-1} be continuous on F. An important class of ill-posed problems is generated by random errors in the input information, or by a stochastic nature of the source of information. Well posedness is achieved by using a concept of narrowing of the region of definition of the primary operator. The problem is said to be well posed if (1) it is known *a priori* a solution u of the problem, which belongs to the specified set M, $D_A \supset M$, and the solution u is unique in the class M and (2) infinitely small variations of the solution u correspond to infinitely small variations of the right side f in ($Au = f$) retaining the solution in the class M.

The regularization method of the ill-posed problems is based on the idea that the minimum deviations of the f values can be stabilized by using some auxiliary nonnegative functional satisfying some additional parametric conditions. These ideas are important since they attract our attention to the processes in the vicinity of the solution. It means that the model in the vicinity can be different from the model in the large. This in turn implies a powerful conclusion about nested set of models (since the consideration about a couple vicinity model–model in the large can be repeated recursively).

B. Nested Models of the Information Acquisition, Estimation, Identification, Representation, and Control

It is tempting to consider this nested set of models to be a phenomenon of a general type that is linked with the general laws of efficient information processing in the systems with limited computer power. Any methodology of successive approximation suggests a need in using nested representation system with consecutive refinement of the resolution of information top down. The advantages of successive approximation were focused upon in early R. Bellman's works as related to the control problems with limited storage.

A class of dynamic systems is being successfully solved by using so-called multigrid methods. Nested hierarchical representation of information with its consecutive retrieval properties (top-down estimation, identification, and control) is becoming commonplace in information systems and data bases. It seems that the models of scattering in the estimation theory are kindred to the general framework of nested hierarchical models of representation, information acquisition, estimation, identification, and control. One can expect that merger between these methods with multiple time-scale analysis is inevitable.

However, this conceptual scheme is not appropriate within the structure of conventional control theory. Obviously, the upper levels of the nested hierarchy with their low resolution of state representation and slower time scales coincide with activities typical for dynamicless planning with its vague results and approximate recommendations. Clearly, the lower the level is, the higher is the accuracy and the faster is the time scale (i.e., the more dynamical model is being considered). This gradual change from the planning processes toward the real-time control is becoming more and more clear to the researchers and control engineers.

C. Nested Hierarchy of Control Loops

Given the previous considerations, one can transform the loop shown in Fig. 10 into the nested hierarchy of control loops (see Fig. 11). This is a phenomenon that can help us consider planning/control as a joint recursive process, and to build all other algorithm of dealing with information and knowledge in a similar manner. One can see that while the loops are independent control wise, they are linked together within the vertical structures of representation for perception, knowledge organization, and planning/control correspondingly. This vertical linkage serves to provide consistency of the overall controller operation. In the conventional

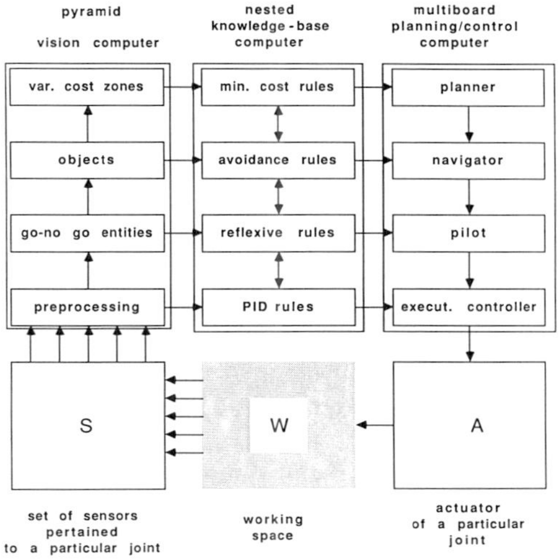

FIG. 11. Nested multiloop structure.

controller, the flow of control information is never coordinated with similar processes at other levels of resolution (from above and from below) as well as at the other time scales.

It was demonstrated that nested hierarchy of knowledge (which is organized according to the degree of certainty and belief) implies a nested hierarchy of decision-making processes. This leads to a similar nested hierarchical structure of a controller. Nested hierarchical controller turned out to be successful for the first efforts in the area of autonomous robotics. Three-level NHC with a module based on planner–navitator–pilot system is currently employed in several versions of mobile autonomous robots. However, no nested control loops were introduced at that time, and the key significance of processing at different resolutions at each hierarchical level is not completely understood.

The multiresolutional loops of the controller shown in Fig. 11 can be considered as an entity ("intelligent module"). This entity is built on two interrelated knowledge bases: one, carrying the entity-relationships structure of the world representation and the other, defining planning/control operations on this structure.

D. Negotiation of Cost Function among the Loops

One of the first approaches proposed for decision-making processes on nested hierarchical structures was by Y. C. Ho and K.-C. Chu, employing, in certain cases, the dynamic problem to an equivalent static team decision problem, and that for LQG cases in particular, the optimal control problem can be expressed as a linear function of the observed data. T. Yoshikava has demonstrated that in a discrete time system with N control stations, the (partially) nested information structure of Y. C. Ho and K.-C. Chu can be represented as one-step-delay-sharing information structure, and the algorithm of dynamic programming (DP) is applicable. DP seems to be the most appropriate and perspective method because of the following considerations:

1. Most of the systems we are dealing with, in the intelligent control area, are sustantially nonlinear, coupled, and cumbersome ones: off-line precomputation of table look-up would be expected for control of such a system.
2. DP as a graph search allows for enhancement by a number of heuristical methods that are intended to make the algorithms more computationally efficient.

Selection of the proper system of cost functionals is becoming important. We do not have too many cost assignment strategies on hand that can be considered "tractable" and confirmed by substantial experience of broad application. One of the possible alternatives is the strategy of cost assignment in which the total cost of the node selection ("feasibility of the node expansion") C_f is divided in two parts:

$$C_f = C_g + C_h$$

where C_g is the cost from the initial node to the one of the sets of generated nodes candidates, and C_h is an evaluation of the cost from the node candidate to the goal.

When no additional information is available, one should determine the minimum possible value of distance between the candidate node and the goal, using the accepted metric of the space of the search. This strategy leads efficiently to the optimum solution. Another strategy is known from the Stackelberg games as "leader–follower" strategy. Its recommendations coincide with the heuristic of A^*-algorithm: the upper bound of the minimum cost should be selected for comparison of alternatives. In a nested hierarchy these recommendation determines the envelope of independent decision making.

The nested resolutional (by generalization) world representation (e.g., category of "knowledge" C_{gk}) corresponds to the nested resolutional (by attention) world representation (e.g., category of "knowledge" C_{ak}) as follows

$$\begin{array}{ccccccc} \cdots \supset & C_{gk,i-1} & \supset & C_{gk,i} & \supset & C_{gk,i+1} & \supset \cdots \\ & \downarrow & & \downarrow & & \downarrow & \\ \cdots \subset & C_{ak,i-1} & \subset & C_{ak,i} & \subset & C_{ak,i+1} & \subset \cdots \end{array}$$

which is the major basis of nested decision-making processes on these hierarchies. A rule of ordering the decisions follows on the basis of nesting and the policy of decision making. Given a nested world representation

$$S_1 \supset S_2 \supset S_3 \supset \cdots \supset S_i$$

and a set of cost functionals for these representations, based on common policy of decision making, the set of decisions will constitute a nested hierarchy

$$D_p(S_1) \supset D_p(S_2) \supset D_pS_3) \supset \cdots \supset D_p(S_i)$$

E. Planning in the Loop

1. Planning

Traditionally considered to be a process that is performed separately from the process of control. This is acceptable for the vast multiplicity of systems where planning can be performed off line, and the process of control can be initiated given a set of highly generalized units of knowledge together with a number of unchangeable goals. By lowering the level of generalization and keeping the certainty and belief in the required limits of the level resolution, we can build in a hierarchy of nested planning processes. In this hierarchy, the desirable trajectory determined at the higher level arrives to the lower level as a fuzzy envelope of operation (FEO). The new planning is being done within FEO at a higher resolution.

This decoupling of the decision-making upper levels (or off-line stages) from the lower levels of decision making and immediate performance (or on-line stages) is probably the most characteristical property for distinguishing the planning stages from the control stages of operation as well as distinguishing the corresponding subsystems or any device where constant human involvement is presumed. This decoupling does not take place in intelligent control system: planning and control are the inseparable parts of the unified HNC. The levels of planning and control are connected together by the intermediate level of decision making dealing with processes that have to use knowledge at a definite level of generalization and yet after processes of updating are completed.

2. Attention-Driven Planning

This means that at this intermediate level, the results of the ongoing motion affect the results of generalization (since the system of "perception" initiates processes of information updating). We name planning processes navigation per se at the level of "planning-control" subsystem where the results of real-time updating are becoming crucial for the results of planning. The nested hierarchy of perception does not require having any hierarchy of sensors although this does not preclude any acceptable hardware solution. Nested hierarchy at the stage of preprocessing is being viewed as a result of sequential zooming operation or, in other words, operation of the focusing of attention. Zooming must be based on focusing of attention; otherwise, the constraint of the limited computing power would not be satisfied. (One can see that this concept can be interpreted within the framework of existing theories of image organization (and interpretation.)

The processes of planning should be performed at the level as well as all together, where they should constitute a nested hierarchy of mutually consistent results. The whole problem must be solved based on a new set of premises pertaining to knowledge-based motion, control of autonomous systems, and using other means of solution. The new premises generate the new promises, and the new strategies of planning for a hierarchical nested intelligent module can be devised within the structure of intelligent controller.

Planning processes are understood as processes of determining the desirable motion goals and/or trajectories (with increased precision at lower levels of planning) without actually moving. Thus, planning is expected to generate the input to the control system in the form of a description of the state (or the sequence of states) to be achieved during the operation. This means that the system of planning must actually predict the motion trajectory, which should be admissible and, at the same time, should provide the desirable value of the cost function.

3. Joint Planning/Control Process

This also means that the input for control system is to be determined as a result of planning. Finally, it means that in the autonomous control system planning and control should be considered as a hierarchically joint knowledge-based process (and/or system) because of their intrinsic interactive character and mutual influence. This principle of planning/control inseparability is totally consistent with existing theory and practice of design and implementation of hierarchical intelligent systems.

All of the planning-control levels of the mechanism of knowledge-based navigation interact vertically via recursion of the algorithms of sequential production providing sequential refinement top down and correctional replanning bottom up. Functioning of the hierarchical production systems of perception and planning control is supported by vertical interaction of levels in the "knowledge base" via aggregation and decomposition based on preassigned values of resolution per level. So, the thesaurus as well as context exist as a result of internal processes of self-organization within the body of knowledge.

On the contrary, the two couples of subsystems (perception-knowledge base and knowledge-base–planning/control) (shown in Fig. 10) are being viewed in the theory of intelligent control, as vertical nested knowledge processing hierarchies with horizontal interaction per level. Indeed, all new knowledge acquired should be organized; the list of primitives in operation must be verified and updated. This procedure is being done at a horizontal level as well as exercising the algorithms of control. In the latter case, the map of the world as well as the list of rules to deal with this map are becoming an object of heuristic discretization and search.

4. Prediction

On the other hand, the prediction should be obtained before the actual motion starts, and information on the world at this stage is usually incomplete. Thus, the contingencies must be contemplated based on construction of plausible situations for which the uncertain variables and parameters should be estimated. Synthesis of contingencies is done more efficiently if the zones of state space are eliminated where the search should not be done. Most of these zones are determined by constraints and the dynamic model of intelligent control system. Interestingly enough, the dynamic models should be different for different levels of intelligent controller: the higher is the level of nested hierarchy, the lower the influence of the dynamic processes linked with motion.

5. Contingencies

Clearly, the role of control subsystem is presumed to be a compensatory one, so that the uncertainties of the initial information, and the inconsistencies of the cost-function formulation could not diminish the expectations about the desirable results of motion conveyed to the control system in the form of the plausible situations. The specifics of any intermediate stage between the planning and control (here it has been traditionally named "navigator") are reflected in the specifics of dealing with the knowledge base, which is being constantly updated at this level.

The contingency motion trajectories, which are obtained as a result of planning (and subsequently, as a result of navigation), must be considered as a set of alternative tasks for control, and are to be given as an input to the controller. Thus, the better the result of planning (i.e., the better the uncertainties have been handled at the stage of planning and the closer the preplanned trajectory is to the potential optimum control trajectory), the easier the compensatory role of the conventional controller, which is presumed to be at the bottom of the planning-control hierarchy.

F. Perception Stratified by Resolution

In the subsystem *P* (perception) the information mapped from the world is being stored and organized. The process of organization presumes the process of recursive generalization: the "whole" at the input in *P* is many times stratified by resolution.

"Phaneron" is the array of information that is coming into *P* from the whole multiplicity of sensors. (The term "phaneron" was introduced by C. S. Pierce for the totality of information that can be called phenomenal world.) Phaneron is not structured at the moment of arrival, but it should be recognized and identified within the "entity-relational" knowledge structure. These processes are broadly discussed in literature, and the importance of such phenomena as "attention" and "resolution" was emphasized many times in literature on computer vision.

Separation in levels appeared to be a natural phenomenon linked with the properties of attention and its intrinsical links with the process of generalization. In fact, generalization is required to provide the efficiency of computing resources use and allocation, and attention is one of its tools. Thus, the new class labels, which are created by the process of generalization, are being considered as new primitives of the upper level of world representation. This rule, the class labels of the lower level are considered as primitives for the higher level, is one of the laws of the mechanism of nested hierarchy.

The results of this identification (a snapshot of the world) contain information, part of which can be different in the previous snapshot and part will not change (e.g., about relations among objects and/or their properties). Thus, the identification can be done only in the context (i.e., in constant interaction with another body of information) ("thesaural knowledge base"). This affects the set of preprocessing procedures, which are being separated from the rest of the intelligent module primarily because of the first experience of manufacturing of the computer vision systems. Simultaneously, with the process of finding phaneron structure (or image interpretation), the problem of proper allocation of the information contained within phaneron should be done.

G. Nested Dynamic Programming

The principle of optimality of Bellman can be stated as follows for stochastic problems: at any time whatever the present information and past decisions, the remaining decisions must constitute an optimal policy with regard to the current information set. Y. Bar-Shalom (1981) has shown that in the case of incompletely observed Markov process, stochastic dynamic programming can be applied. The sequence of "planning–navigating–piloting (or guidance)–actuator control (or execution)" appears as a direct result of nested hierarchical search in the structure of information under consideration. The method of nested dynamic programming (NDP) follows from the commutative diagrams and analysis given by A. Meystel. He states that the optimum control should be found by consecutive top-down and bottom-up procedures, based on the following rules.

Rule 1. NDP should be performed first at the most generalized level of information system with complete (available) world representation.

This will obviously lead to a very fuzzy solution from the view of the lowest level of system ("actuator"). However, this enables substantial advantages later: the substantial part of the world will be excluded later from consideration at the lower levels.

$$
\begin{array}{llllllll}
\overset{fa}{(m_1 \in M_1)} & \underset{fa}{\overset{g}{\supseteq}} & \overset{fa}{(m_2 \in M_2)} & \underset{fa}{\overset{g}{\supseteq}} \cdots \underset{fa}{\overset{g}{\supseteq}} & \overset{fa}{(m_{i-1} \in M_{i-1})} & \underset{fa}{\overset{g}{\supseteq}} & \overset{fa}{(m_i \in M_i)} & \text{(line 1)} \\
\downarrow & & & & \downarrow & & \downarrow & \\
\mathrm{NDP}(J_1, M_1) = m_1, & & & & \mathrm{NDP}(J_{i-1}, M_{i-1}) = m_{i-1}, & & \mathrm{NDP}(J_i, M_i) = m_i & \text{(line 2)} \\
\downarrow & & & & \downarrow & & \downarrow & \\
\text{output} & & & & \mathrm{CH}(m_{i-1}) = M_{i-2} & & \mathrm{CH}(m_i) = M_{i-1} & \\
\downarrow & & & & \downarrow & & \downarrow & \\
\text{controller} & & & & (i-2)\text{th} & & (i-1)\text{th} & \text{levels}
\end{array}
$$

Rule 2. NDP is being performed consecutively level after level top down. The subspace of the search at each of the consecutive lower levels is constrained by the solution at the preceding upper level recomputed to the resolution of the next lower level.

The area, which for the upper level is considered as the optimum solution, is considered at the lower level as the stripe (zone) of independent decision making. However, due to the additional information that appears at a given level during the performance, the optimum solution of the lower level may require to seek beyond the envelope of independent decision making. Rule 3 is to be applied in this case.

Rule 3. When during the actual motion, due to the new information, the optimum trajectory determined at a given level must violate the assigned boundaries, this new information should be submitted to the upper level (proper generalization must be performed, and the information structure must be updated). This generates a new top-down NDP process.

Rule 4. When the arrival of the new information is bounded (e.g., by a "limit of vision"), then the recursion of nested process of planning is being done with consecutive process of subgoals creation.

The nested hierarchy of maps $\{m_i\}$, $i = 1, 2, \ldots$, is the input for planning/control system. Actually, this nested hierarchy is being generated in the process of interaction between the subsystems M and C. This process of interaction is demonstrated in the algorithm above.

Line 1 shows two nested hierarchies: one of them by generalization (of maps $\{M_i\}$) and another by focus of attention (of maps $\{m_i\}$). Hierarchy of sets is obtained from the hierarchy of sets by applying NDP algorithm per level (line 2). In order to do this, a nested hierarchy is added to the nested hierarchy. In order to compute a set, the results of applying NDP per level, are enhanced up to the meaningful consistent map partition; one of possible algorithms for this is "convex hull." So this system is closed-loop level to level top down, and after convergence, the system of controller commands is obtained.

Levels of the control algorithm constitute the nested hierarchy of the "team players," which is using at each level the initial scope constraints and cost functional defined by the upper level and then submits the results of computation to the lower level.

BIBLIOGRAPHY

Bellman, R. (1961). Successive approximations and computer storage problems in ordinary differential equations, *Commun. ACM,* **4**(4).

Fedotov, A. M. (1982). "Linear Ill-Posed Problems with Random Errors in the Input Information." Publ. Nauka. Cib. Affiliation, Novosibirsk (in Russian).

Fu, K. S. (1969). Learning control systems, *in* "Advances in Information System Science" (J. T. Tou, ed.). Plenum Press, New York.

Fu, K. S. (1971). Learning control systems and intelligent control systems: An intersection of artificial intelligence and automatic control, *IEEE Trans. Autom. Conrol* **AC-16.**

Fu, R. S. (1970). Learning control systems—review and outlook, *IEEE Trans. Autom. Control* **AC-15.**

Graham, J. H., and Saridis, G. N. (1982). Linguistic design structures for hierarchical systems, *IEEE Trans. Systems Man Cybernetics* **SMC-12**(3).

Hadamard, J. (1902). Sur les problemes aux derivees partieliesphysique, *Bull. Univ. Princeton* **13,** 49–52.

Ho, Y. C., and Chu, K.-C. (1972). Team decision theory and information structures in optimal control problems, Parts 1 and 2, *IEEE Trans. Autom. Control* **AC-17**(1).

Ho, Y. C., and Chu, K.-C. (1973). On the equivalence of information structures in static and dynamic teams, *IEEE Trans. Autom. Control* **AC-18,** 187–188.

Ho, Y. C., and Chu, K.-C. (1974). Information structure in dynamic multi-person control problems, *Automatica* **10,** 341–345.

Meinardus, G. (1967). "Approximation of Functions: Theory and Numerical Methods." Springer-Verlag, Berlin and New York.

Meystel, A. (1983). Intelligent control of a multiactuator systems, *in* "IFAC Information Control Problems in Manufacturing Technology 1982 (D. E. Hardt, ed.). Pergamon, Oxford and New York.

Meystel, A. (1985). Intelligent control: Issues and perspectives, *Proc. IEEE Symp. Intelligent Control, Troy, New York.*

Meystel, A. (1986). Knowledge-based controller for intelligent mobile robots, *in* "Artificial Intelligence and Man-Machine Systems" (H. Winter, ed.) Lecture Notes in Control and Information Systems, Vol. 80. Springer-Verlag, Berlin and New York.

Meystel, A. (1986). Planning in a hierarchical nested controller for autonomous robots, *Proc. 25th IEEE Conf. Decision Control, Athens, Greece.*

Meystel, A. (1987). Nested hierarchical intelligent module for automatic generation of control strategies, *in* "Languages for Sensor-Based Control in Robotics" (U. Rembold and K. Hormann, eds.), NATO ASI Series, Vol. 29. Springer-Verlag, Berlin and New York.

Saridis, G. N. (1977). "Self-Organizing Control of Stochastic Systems." Marcel Dekker, New York.

Saridis, G. N. (1979). Toward the realization of intelligent controls, *Proc. IEEE* **67**(8).

Saridis, G. N. (1983). Intelligent robotic control, *IEEE Trans. Autom. Control* **AC-28**(5).

Saridis, G. N. (1985). An integrated theory of intelligent machines by expressing the control performance as entropy, *Control-Theory Adv. Tech.* **1**(2).

Saridis, G. N. (1985). Intelligent control for robotics and advanced automation, *in* "Advances in Automation and Robotics," Vol. 1. JAI Press, Greenwich, Connecticut.

Saridis, G. N. (1985). Foundations of the theory of intelligent controls, *Proc. IEEE Symp. Intelligent Control, Troy, New York.*

Saridis, G. N. (1987). Knowledge implementation: Structures of intelligent control systems, *Proc. IEEE Symp. Intelligent Control, Philadelphia, Pennsylvania.*

Saridis, G. N., and Lee, C.-S. G. (1979). An approximation theory of optimal control for trainable manipulators, *IEEE Trans. Systems Man Cybernetics* **SMC-9.**

Saridis, G. N., Graham, J., and Lee, G. (1979). An integrated syntactic approach, and suboptimal control for manipulators and prostheses, *Proc. 18th CDC, Ft. Lauderdale.*

INTELLIGENT NETWORKS: ARCHITECTURE AND IMPLICATIONS

Syed V. Ahamed *City University of New York*
Victor B. Lawrence *AT&T Bell Laboratories*

Glossary

B (bearer) channel: Information bearing channel that provides a transparent digital path between one access point of the network and another. In the context of an integrated services digital network, and B channel has been standardized at 64,000 bits/sec.

Carrier serving area: Designation of a particular geographic area whose communication needs can be served by a carrier system between a central distribution point within the geographic area and an exchange facility.

Carrier system: System for modulating a periodic carrier signal with the information of one or more channels to be able to transmit the combined signal over any specific transmission medium.

Channel: Logical connection between any two points in the network to exchange information. For the channel user, the exact physical path or the type of information carrying media is inconsequential. For the network, the physical and the logical address of the channel play an important role. The network may allocate, switch, reallocate, monitor, transfer, multiplex, or accomplish any function to convey the user information optimally.

Circuit switching: Mode of interconnecting logical channels between nodes of the network, maintaining the digital transparency for the duration of the use, and finally releasing the channels to return to their idle state.

Common channel signaling system (CCS): Standardized and universal signaling and communications interface for numerous nodes (such as SCPs, SSPs, and STPs) to query and respond within the CCS control network. The CCS7 (common channel signaling system number 7) is the most widely accepted and versatile system. In the INs, the transactions capabilities applications protocol (TCAP) level of the CCS7 is used.

D (delta) channel: Supporting channel that carries out-of-band signaling information-bearing B channels. At basic rate ISDN the D channel is standardized at 16,000 bits per second, and at all other rates the D channel is at 64,000 bits per second.

Digital hierarchy: Ordering of the various lower capacity local channels that permits easy multiplexing and demultiplexing to and from higher capacity long-distance channels.

Electronic switching systems (ESS): Integrated facilities for switching channels within the network by electronic devices operated by stored program. Intelligent network switches also perform administrative, interfacing, and service functions for the local and remote switching modules, various networks, and carrier systems.

Functional components (FCs): Components that permit the easy introduction of new services in the IN/1+ and IN/2 environments by being modular in their functionality. They are capable of being executed in the interpreter mode by the service logic interpreter (SLI) to build new service quickly and efficiently. For example, an FC such as JOIN connects a new line to an existing call, and the new number is conferenced into the existing telephone path.

Intelligent network/1: One of the first intelligent networks evolved to support the simpler services such as the 800 service (in the United States or the 130 service in Germany), or the call card validation service. Very simple predetermined service functions may be provided by this class of networks. Users do not have an option to program and configure the network in this rudimentary IN.

Intelligent network/1+ and /2: Newer intelligent network configurations suggested by Bell Communications Research (Bellcore) in the United States. Developed to provide rapid and easy introduction of new network services through the 1990s. The FCs resident in SCPs, SSPs, or even the IPs may be used to provide fast, inexpensive, and short-term network services in these newer networks. Some of the newer features possible by the FC concept have already been introduced in United States.

Intelligent peripherals (IPs): Peripheral support devices that are computer driven programmable systems that enhance the network services such as speech recognition, synthesis, announcements, and voice messaging. They are controlled by SCPs or SSPs in the network and add another dimension of specialized services that the network can provide to the end users.

Network intelligence: Network capacity to adaptively switch, seek, monitor, and interconnect the information bearing channels, information sources, and information users.

Network services: Class of customer services provided by the intelligent networks above and beyond those readily available from conventional networks, such as the standard telephone network.

Node: Physical location or logical address in the network at which specific network functions, such as switching, relaying, tapping, and monitoring, can be performed.

Packet: Fixed and maximum length unit of information (data or control) that is sent from a source to a destination. A packet may be a totally independent unit of communication with all the routing information necessary for transmission. A packet may also be one of a series of packets en route to the destination. The entire series will then complete the communication function across a preestablished path. The packet contents may be data or the control information to establish and inform the features of the path.

Packet switching: Mode of relaying information in a packet form with complete identification for the packet to reach its final destination and for the network to complete the transmittal, recovery, billing, and other associated network functions.

Service control points (SCPs): Nodes in the CCS7 network that provide responses to the queries from the users. These are introduced and activated to communicate with the STPs in the CCS7 network. By and large, in the earlier IN versions such as the 800 network, the responses are stored in an active and well managed data base. The response to the user query is a quick look up in the on-line data base in the SCPs. In the more recent SCPs for later versions of INs (such as IN/1+ and IN/2), new software support of the service logic interpreter is added to find responses by executing the functional components (FCs) associated with the service demanded by the user. Service validation function can also be accomplished in the SCPs.

Service management systems (SMSs): Systems that provide the management and the updating of the data bases in the SCPs. Data and statistics may be provided to the querying node. The administration of the data bases for maintenance and introduction of services is accomplished via the SMSs that communicate with the SCP via the dedicated BX.25 link.

Service transfer points (STPs): Nodes embedded in the CCS7 signaling network, switch (or transfers) signaling messages from the SSPs and SCPs. Standard communication interface permits easy access from most of the SSPs and SCPs in the CCS7 network. Switch manufacturers also make the STPs.

Service switching points (SSPs): Nodes that permit easy access points between the network and the users. A node has a specialized software environment to recognize the service conditions demanded by the users. It forwards the request for further instructions to the STPs. It also receives the response to the request and completes the service request by the user.

Stored program control: Capacity to control the network functions by programs or microcode generated and stored as software or utilities.

Subscriber loop carrier: Carrier system used in the loop plant of existing telephone network that is used to carry numerous telephone conversations between an exchange and a remote terminal. Such carrier systems are used in relatively few countries and are not universally prevalent.

Time division multiplexing: Concept of allocating finite time slots to individual channels and thus share a high-speed digital medium among two or more low-speed users.

Vendor services: Services provided by source of information to the customers at no additional cost or for a fee. The network then communicates the information necessary to complete the transaction.

Universal information services network (UISN): Adaptive and intelligent services network proposed by AT&T to provide a wide variety of universal information services. A large variety of features are proposed. Some of the existing services are the 911 (Public Emergency), 900 (Televoting), and virtual private network (VPN). Most of these functions revolve around the existing circuit switches already in the local and regional offices. Typically, the UISN also has SSPs, STPs, SCPs, IPs, off-network nodes (ONNs with their functionality being akin to that of IPs and VFNs), and service creation environments (SCEs). This network uses a transport tier and an enriched service tier in the service software architecture of the UISN.

Vendor feature nodes (VFNs): Nodes extraneous to the network that are owned and operated by third party service subscribers. They can provide special services such as polling or opinion surveys. These nodes can reach the network users and interact to provide special services to them. The general communication link is to the SSPs via a subset of the CCS7 messages so as not to disrupt the normal network functions or the network control messages.

An information society has started to emerge. The availability of the right information at the

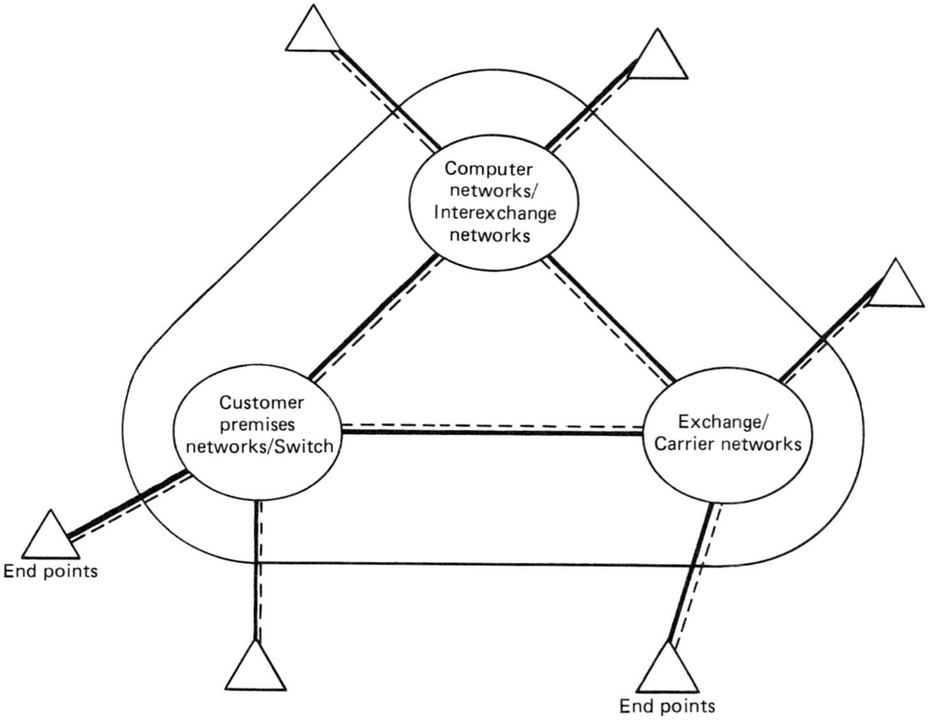

FIG. 1. Conceptual representation of an IN: data, ——; control, ----.

right time becomes the necessity for survival and excellence. In view of providing key information to a very large community of users with quick access to and dependability of the computer systems, the telecommunications scientists have conceptualized global information networks. These networks are preprogrammed to be adaptive, algorithmic, resourceful, responsive, and intelligent.

Intelligent networks (IN) are defined as the carriers of information with distinct algorithmic adaptation. In the context of hardware, intelligence resides in the customized integrated circuit chips, their sophisticated layout, and their interconnections. In the context of software, intelligence is coded as programs, utilities, or modules. It may reside in the active memories of computers during the execution phase. In the context of firmware, intelligence is microcoded into the control memories of the monitoring computers. Thus, the basic computers (the hardware, the software, and the firmware), which control, monitor, and process the information, become an integral part of intelligent networks. The flow of the information takes place over appropriate channels within the network and also within a diversity of participating networks, as shown in Fig. 1. These channels are dynamically assigned, switched, and reallocated to carry the information from node to node. The facilities that actually switch channels may be central offices, switching centers, private branch exchanges, or even satellites that relay information. The actual transport of the information is carried out over transmission facilities of the network. Such facilities may span a small laboratory or a nation or the whole world. The size of the network or its geographical expanse is inconsequential to its nature. The four essential building blocks (see Fig. 2) of any intelligent network become the interface for the flow of information in and out of the network, the monitoring computers, the switching systems, and the associated transmission facilities.

Large amounts of intelligence are encompassed in the conventional analogue networks, such as the plain old telephone service (POTS) network. However, in more recent context, intelligent networks refer only to digital networks, even though there are a large number of analogue components that exist within the network. Analogue information over fragmented time in-

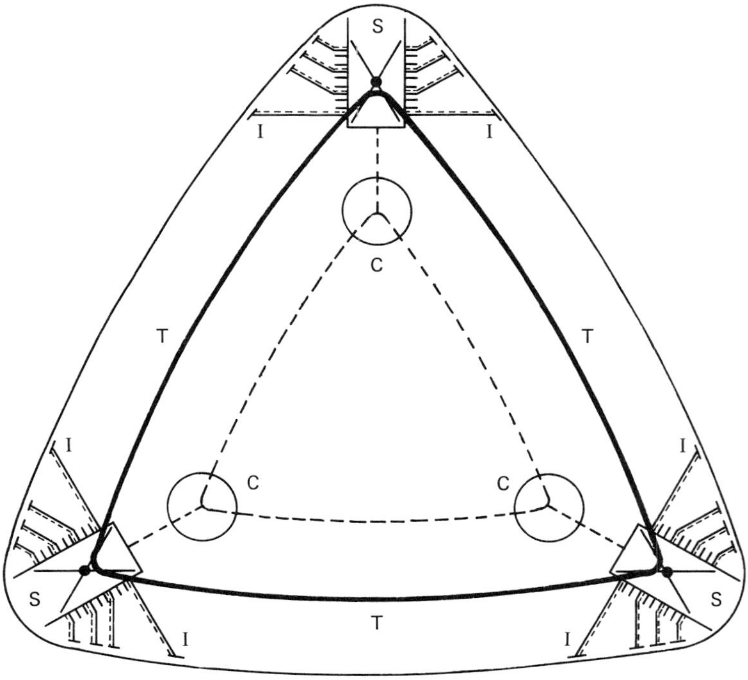

FIG. 2. Building blocks of an IN showing the flow of control and data: data, ____; control, -------; c, controlling computers; S, switches; I, network interfaces; T, transmission path and facilities.

tervals gives the networks the capacity to regroup the information transmitted throughout the network as digital information. Thus, analogue information may be digitized, individual bits may be transmitted as analogue data with very low error rates (such as one bit in ten million bits). The digital information may be recovered and reconstituted as the original analogue data. The integrity of the information is thus very high since a great majority of the network functionality takes place in the digital domain. Analogue information such as voice and wave forms may be communicated freely throughout the networks after initial digitization.

I. Basic Concepts

The capacity to adapt to the extensive and dynamic network conditions is a requirement of intelligent networks. The network environment may change because of a large number of internal and external conditions. The network may become overloaded or faulty; it may experience switching delays or inadequate standby channel capacity or any other network condition. Further, the user of the source and the destination of the information may lead to extraneous searching before the right information is conveyed to the customer. It is here that the built-in algorithmic intelligence should monitor the network performance without the user or operator or any other human intervention. In essence, the network adaptively responds to the commands that control and execute the entire range of communications functions.

Intelligent networks perform in two distinct directions. First, they have to actively process information to respond to the queries of the user. Second, they have to adapt and fulfill the switching and transmission requirements to convey information from its source to its destination, wherever either one may be geographically or logically located within the network. The network intelligence can thus be grouped into its information processing aspect and its switching and transmission aspect. In Fig. 3, the functional organization of an intelligent network is depicted.

A. Information Processing Aspects

Networks are designed to serve a large number of users with a large number of queries, seeking a wide variety of answers. The queries may be in-depth or peripheral, they may have constraints and modifiers, they may seek solu-

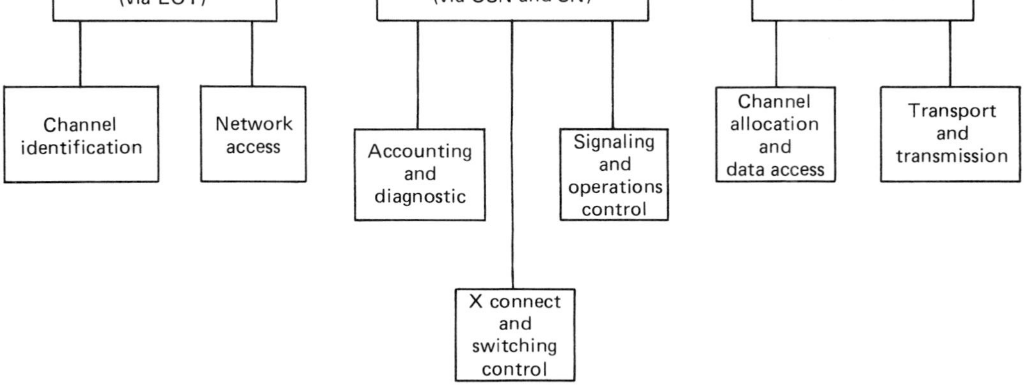

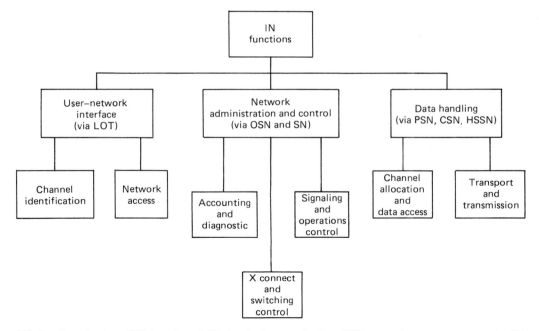

FIG. 3. Organization of IN functions: LOT, local office termination; OSN, operations systems network; SN, signaling network; PSN, packet switched network; HSSN, high-speed switched network; CSN, circuit switched network.

tions and modify the subsequent queries depending upon the previous answers, etc. For this reason, the network functions require a certain amount of sophistication to comprehend the query, seek the answer, and convey the right answer to the right user within a reasonable amount of time.

The front-end processor of the computers which handle the user queries needs natural language processing capabilities. The software for processing natural language queries would exist at the user network interface shown in Fig. 3. Such processors have embedded elaborate rules of grammar to comprehend a complex query. Next, the information sought needs to be identified and accessed. The information may be available locally within the local data base environment of the computer handling the user query or may be available elsewhere in the network. In the former case, a search within the local data base is initiated. In the latter case, a query is dispatched to another node where the answer is available. Information that is supplied to the customer through a public domain intelligent network (PDIN) may be from an information vendor. Such information vendors are abundant. For example, a hospital may be searching for an organ donor. In this case, a national data base with a list of donors may be maintained by a private facility, which dispenses its information for a fee. In this case, the user would incur a cost in receiving the information. The network has to determine the appropriate information needed by both parties (the customer and the vendor) so that the transaction may take place.

Such transactions have to be monitored by the unattended network via its own follow-up sequence of programs. The functions of locating the information sought by the user, the choice of the programs to execute the network functions, etc., become the software environment that drives these networks.

Thus, the nature of intelligence required in the networks to handle information access and retrieval, the comprehension of the user query, and the integration of the steps necessary in the procurement of the information sought become necessary subfunctions of an IN. Concepts evolved from formal language theory provide the software tools to comprehend the user queries. Concepts evolved from knowledge engineering provide software tools to tackle the retrieval, the design, and the fabrication of the answers sought by the users.

B. Switching and Transmission Aspects

The switching of information-bearing channels is essential in order to use a specific channel to perform a variety of service functions for the customer for a finite length of time. Switches perform in three distinct ways (see Fig. 4). First, the channel may be circuit switched, that is, switched by the network and allocated to a certain user for as long as the user may need it. Second, the channel may be packet switched, that is, the information may be packetized and dispatched to the appropriate destination, either as an individual packet or as a series of packets in an appropriate sequence to complete an informational transaction. Third, the switching may be performed by the channel itself; in this case, the information is known to be channel switched. The third type of switching generally occurs in private networks, and the customer (private branch exchange, PBX) exchange carries out the localized switching. In the first and second cases, the external network has the option to choose and switch between various channels, depending upon the availability, type of service, and source and destination of information. This calls for intricately designed switching systems, which are discussed in Section VI.

The transmission of the information also needs intelligence. The network can choose between a large number of paths and circuits. The network conditions strongly influence the path selected. These paths may be quite physical, such as a pair of wires, or they may be one or more channels multiplexed over one physical media, such as a wire pair, a coaxial cable, an optical fiber, a digital radio circuit, or any viable medium for data transmission.

Fortunately, a large number of adaptive algorithms have been developed during the evolution of the conventional telephone network. The newer and truly sophisticated networks offer a new breed of intelligence. The capacity to incrementally modify the network at the customer command would be impossible by the older POTS network hardware and its rudimentary software. The choice of the path may also satisfy certain other user-defined constraints, such as minimal cost, minimal delay, and low error. The path routing intelligence is handled by a different layer of the widely accepted network model (see Section IV). Processing of address information for communication also needs certain specialized capabilities. For example, the intelligence to wake up an idle channel and to

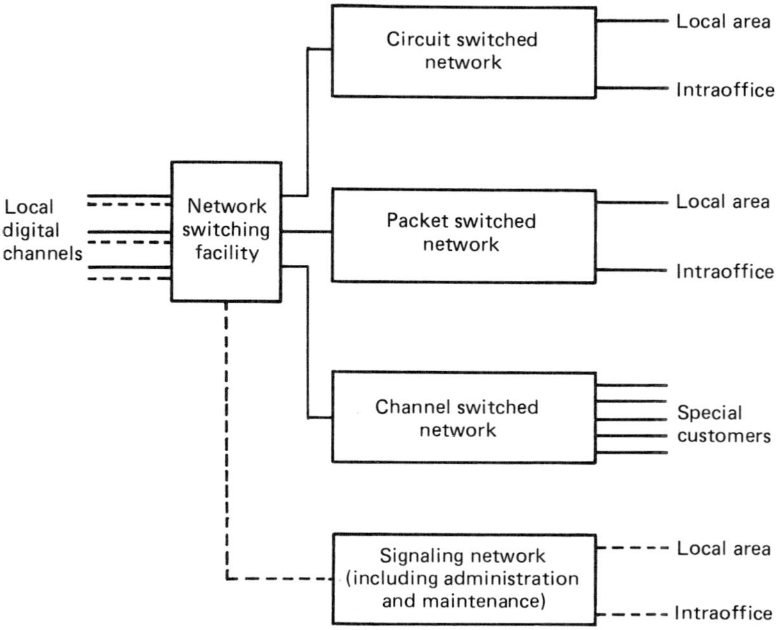

FIG. 4. Integration of various networks for the transport of data (via the circuit switched network, packet switched network, and channel switched network) and for the flow of control (via the signaling network.) Data, ____; control, -------.

test it before the actual communication needs very different procedures than those for cost minimization. Thus, it becomes necessary to classify the types of intelligence necessary for the smooth, error-free transmission of information. Functioning of these networks without chaos becomes a fundamental requirement in light of the possible faulty conditions that can

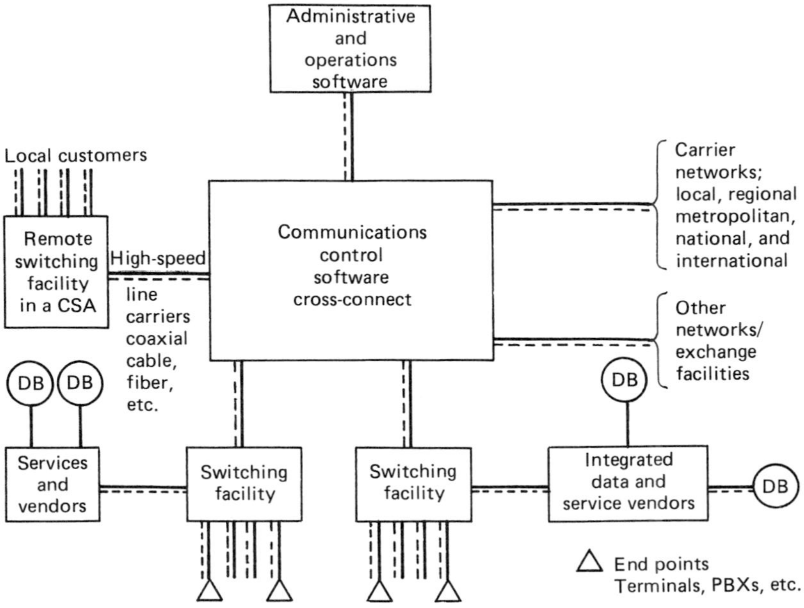

FIG. 5. Architectural layout of an exchange facility for an IN (CSA, carrier serving area; DB, data base) Data, ____; control, -------.

exist in the network, the transmission, and the associated control computers.

Intelligent networks have widely dispersed intelligence modules (software routines, microcoded read only memories, programmable read only memories) and information modules (data bases). It becomes necessary to provide access to the right module at the right time. Hence, some of the questions addressed by the network architects pertain to the types of networks and their environments, local and global intelligence, local and global data bases, and accessibility in the communications, interfaces, sources, and destinations of the information communicated. In Fig. 5, a typical layout of an exchange facility within an IN is depicted. This leads to the architectural issues which govern the network design.

II. Intelligent Network Components

A. Basic Components

Intelligent networks consist of sources and destinations of information, network nodes, transmission facilities, and networks to control the switching and transmission through the network. The need for a common channel signaling network to support and control the information-bearing channels has been recently recognized, and most intelligent networks have this additional network component in their architecture. These controlling networks adopt out-of-band signaling. It should be recognized that this mode of signaling (as opposed to in-band signaling) is only one of the possible ways to control intelligent networks.

B. Data Sources and Destinations

Customers, vendor data bases, billing systems, public domain information banks, and any information storage or handling facility are data sources, provided they can be interfaced with the network. The sources of intelligence, such as programs, routines, and modules, also become part of the control information. This information may reside as data bases, programs, or operating systems for the interconnected computers within the network. However, the difference between information that passes through the network and the information to control and monitor the flow of customer information remains fundamental. Such a difference also exists in computer systems. The flow of data signals is distinct from the flow of the control signals within the computer architecture.

C. Network Nodes

Nodes of an IN perform a wider variety of sophisticated functions in comparison with the functions of the nodes within the telephone or computer network. Nodes may be designed as one of four types: (1) nodes in which no through data traffic is permitted (e.g., the end office or a computer port); (2) nodes through which only through traffic is advised (e.g., a satellite relay station or a digital repeater bank); (3) nodes through which both through and terminal traffic are allowed (e.g., a metropolitan switching office that forwards information to other nodes and has spare capacity and links terminating at a local area customers); and (4) nodes where numerous links meet to permit local and global exchanges of channels and where local and through traffic is permitted. See Fig. 6 for the distribution of these nodes in a typically mountainous region of a national network.

In addition to the switching of information-bearing channels, a typical node in a PDIN manages and controls the flow of information in context of the services it is providing. Vendor

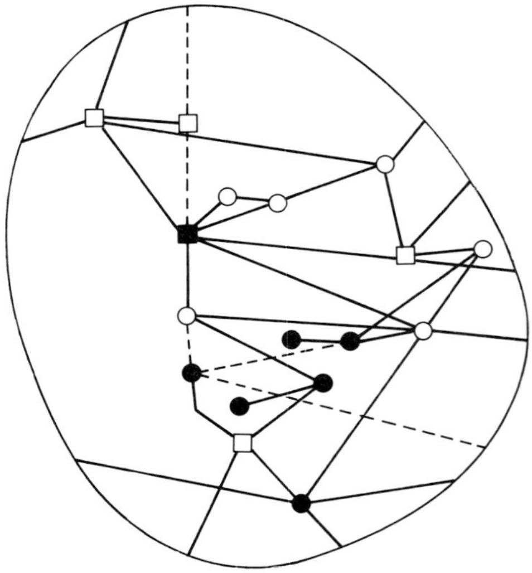

FIG. 6. Common types of nodes and links within a regional network. High-capacity coaxial carrier systems, ____; radio links (depending upon the terrain), -------; solid circle, no through traffic (e.g., end office in a small town); open circle, only through traffic (e.g., a repeater station); open square, through and terminal traffic; and solid square, through traffic switching and switching facility for local traffic.

services need the correct querying, retrieval, and follow up. Administrative, maintenance, and billing information is appropriately exchanged. Diagnostics are administered and follow-up operator actions are communicated. In the context of the integrated services digital network (ISDN), the nodes serve to manage the B channels. As presented earlier, the control and signaling information for switched channels is received on the D channel or in the appropriate X.25 protocol for the packet switched channels. The network control module responds to this information and acts to establish the digital connectivity of the B channels via the switching or the connection control module. Further, the node may be called upon to send signaling information to the next ISDN central office regarding the activated and active B channels.

The node also provides access to the information vendors to supply the necessary information to the network users. It serves to alert the office administration and management network regarding the call progress, charges, rates, billing information, etc. The node can serve as a gateway office by providing access to other networks, such as packet switched or private networks. Very specialized interfacing functions and, thus, resident modules are necessary to permit a dependable flow of voice, data, or video signals through the node. Diagnostic and maintenance functions are also undertaken by nodes to check out the network modules and their functionality. In case the gateway office serves numerous countries, the node functions to send control signals to access foreign networks through the international signaling interface.

In the United States, where the subscriber loop carrier systems (see glossary), private networks, and carrier serving areas (see glossary) are plentiful, the nodes of the intelligent networks serve as a greater diversity of functions. Private network interfacing calls for certain specialized functions from the node. Such functions are individually tailored to the specific node or the central office. The more recent electronic switching systems (ESS, see glossary) have made such customization possible by the modular hardware and software approach used by the ESS architecture designers. In pursuing a modular approach, these nodes are divided to pursue four basic functions. First, the interfacing with a 4-wire or 2-wire digital subscriber loop at any one of the basic or wide-band ISDN rates is accomplished by the peripheral switching modules. Second, the switching function for the numerous data channels is carried out by the main switching modules within the node for the local traffic or the call is forwarded via the interexchange carrier network and the interoffice signaling network. Third, the localized communications between the various switching modules is carried out by the communications module that provides a cross-connect facility between the switching modules. Finally, the office administration and network diagnostic and routine housekeeping functions are carried out by the administrative module (see Fig. 5).

D. Transmission Facilities

Digital information may be transmitted over any number of physical media. As shown in Fig. 7, the line coder, the transmit filter, the channel media (with or without repeaters), the regenerator, and the line decoder constitute an entire digital facility. In the regional, national, and global networks, a large number of digital carrier systems are in place.

Metallic media has been used extensively to carry digital data in most of the local, metropolitan, and regional networks. Transmission rates depend upon the distances and the coding techniques used. Local loops to the subscribers can carry data effectively at the basic access rate of 144 kb/sec. The line rate can be as high as 192 kb/sec. With the proposed 2B1Q (2 binary bits converted to 1 quaternary level) code with refined digital echo cancellation techniques, the line rate can approach 1 Mb/sec over the shorter loops that span the carrier serving area (CSA) location and subscribers at a maximum distance of 12,000 ft. The T1 carrier facility carries digital information at 1.544 Mb/sec extremely dependably. Digital carriers at the T1C rate (3.152 Mb/sec in the United States) and at the DS2 rates (6.312 Mb/sec in United States and 8.448 Mb/sec in Europe) are also readily available.

Other rates for digital transmission facilities are 44.736 Mb/sec in the United States and 34.368 Mb/sec in Europe. The physical media at this DS3 rate are usually light-wave transmission facilities and free space with the 11-GHz digital radio carrier facilities. Higher bit rates at 274.176 Mb/sec (United States) and 139.264 Mb/sec (Europe) are also in service. The intelligent networks can be interfaced with some or all of these digital carrier systems, depending upon the type of the node and its switching facility. These data rates are derived from the digital hi-

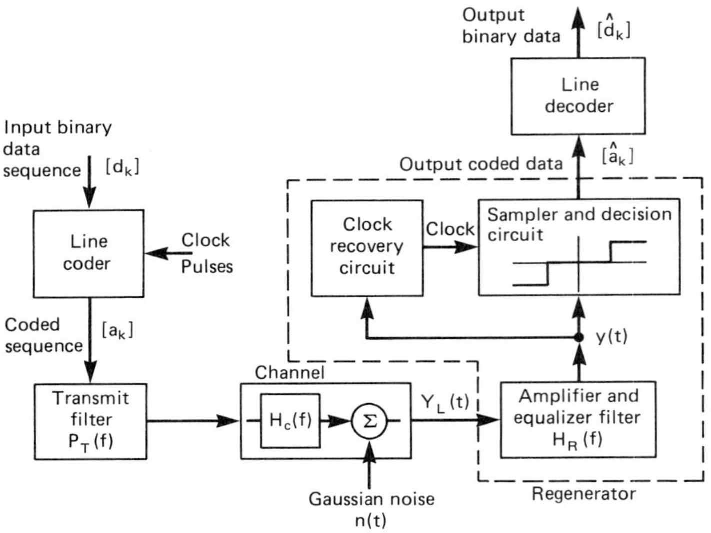

FIG. 7. A typical digital transmission facility for an IN. [From Miller, M. J., and Ahamed, S. V. (1987, 1988)].

erarchies of the different countries around the world.

These carrier systems are used in context of the intelligent networks to carry digital information over any given distance from one node to the next. The switching and transmission facility does not constitute an intelligent network unless it is architecturally controlled by its own control packets or its control network.

III. Architectural Considerations—an Overview

A. Network Architecture and Computer Architecture

Network architecture has evolved from computer architecture. The functionality of the digital network influences its architecture. Networks have immensely distributed processing, memory, administrative, and data-base capabilities. Conventional computer architecture addresses issues pertaining to the hardware modules (central processors, memories, input/output processors, and their bus structures). Priviledged instructions available to the operating system and the basic utility programs perform the start-up and core functions that monitor the functionality of the computer system. The PDINs are continuously active and have to be functional under far more stringent conditions. The monitoring and fault tolerance of networks is more crucial in the public domain. Hence, their architecture reflects these additional features.

Network architecture addresses a far wider spectrum of issues. For the participating computers with any IN, the hardware, their localized privileged instructions, the local software modules, and priority instructions become localized issues. On a global basis, network architecture addresses the issues dealing with the communication between the various nodes (which may be of various types, see Section II,C), the channel capacities, the data bases available and their access, the types of interface, and the compatibility and control of the network layers functions (see Section IV) and the channel banks (which separate out the channels and lead them to the appropriate destinations). Fortunately, considerable standardization has taken place in the terminology and design of network structure and the associated protocols by the International Telegraph and Telephone Consultative Committee (CCITT).

Information and intelligence from the external environment is received from network users via the standardized network interfaces. Typically the CCITT requirements on these interfaces permit most networks to be able to communicate with most devices and digital systems. Information is communicated through the networks to the appropriate destination(s) based upon the collective and derived intelligence from the users and from the network itself. The user information coupled with the network resident intelligence provides enough secondary or processed information to control the generic network functions which serve the user. The network intelligence implements the global commands of the user in a manner consistent and coherent with the design of that appropriate network. Hence, at the device and usage level, considerable attention is necessary to make the particular network perform according to user needs. For this reason, different sets of data bases, interfaces, components, and their interconnections are evolving to facilitate consistent network functioning for the present and for the future. Certain architectural standards have been formulated, and at least five basic building blocks of intelligent networks have been identified and discussed in Section IV. From the study of the components and their architecture, it becomes evident that the boundaries of the components and their location are less important than their interconnection and sequentiality of their modular functions. In this section we discuss some of the important topological arrangements of the INs.

IN architecture attempts to use as much of the existing network as possible with the supporting IN core network to facilitate the enhanced functionality. The IN core network has at least three nodes at the SSPs, STPs, and SCPs. Any number of peripherals may be added and identified for the particular environment and/or application at hand.

The IN core network connects the SSPs, STPs, and SCPs by common channel signaling number 7 (CSS7) links. SSPs detect special service requirements of the particular call. These SSPs have the CCS7 facilities to query a data base located in the SCP via the transaction capabilities applications part (TCAP) of the CCS7 protocol. These SSPs also receive service calls from other lower level central offices and may link and support various vendor feature nodes (VFNs), intelligent peripherals (IPs), operation support system (OSS), and interexchange carriers (ICs).

The signal transfer point facilitates the communication between SSPs and SCPs. The transfer takes place to dispatch the query to the right SCP for quick response. This communication takes place via the CSS7 links. The functions of the STP may be controlled by the resident signaling engineering and administration system (sometimes referred to as SEAS).

The SCP acts primarily as an end point of the CCS network to find the answers to queries from the various SSPs. These answers are generally in the form of data crucial for the completion of the service requested. Data are typically retrieved from a highly organized operational data base resident in the SCPs. The main hardware component of the SCP is a powerful specialized computer that handles the numerous SCP functions in parallel and in real time. The SCPs are also generally interconnected through the IN core packet switching capability. Depending upon the requirements, it is also feasible to interconnect the packet switch of the various SCPs to the packet switch public data network (PSPDN).

The service management systems serve the SCP (or SCPs) to which they are connected via the X.25 or BX.25 links. The functioning of the SCP is managed and streamlined by the SMS. It is also feasible to extend the range of SMS to communicate with numerous SCPs. The communication link is localized and distinct from the IN core network which may service a larger number of SCPs, STPs, and SSPs.

The intelligent peripherals are used in the provision of enhanced services such as end user data base information, announcements, voice messaging, and speech synthesizing and recognition. Economics plays a major role in the design and selection of IPs. These can serve a number of users or even a number of SSPs and perform a number of functions. The IPs may be accessed via a circuit switch or even a packet switch. Response time is crucial in the deployment and sharing of IPs in the network. ISDN services may also call upon the IP's support functions, if the local network architecture permits the interconnection.

IV. Specialized and Architectural Components

In the global context of designing and building intelligent networks, it is desirable to consider five basic functional building blocks in most intelligent networks. These blocks can be considered as information processing systems in their own right but in the network context play a cooperative role in making the networks perform smoothly and dependably. It is necessary to consider the still evolving hardware, software, and firmware structure of these five generic components. The configuration and the supporting information structure of these five components can vary considerably from one network to another, one vendor to another, and from one major application to another. For instance, the

Regional Bell Operating Companies' (RBOC) expectations of IN/1 (the 800 network) and the IN/2 (see Section IV) differ considerably but undergo a transitory stage via the IN/1+ network. The deployment of the various components can be significantly different. The software variations in IN/1, IN/1+, and IN/2 are truly remarkable. The implementation of American Telephone and Telegraph's Universal Services Intelligent Network (USIN) to support the national network functions is considerably different from the RBOC's IN series networks that support the regional network and data-base functions. In this section we present these components from a global point of view. (Such differences and functionalities are presented in great detail by Ahamed and Lawrence, 1992.)

A. Bellcore Intelligent Networks (N/1, IN/1+, IN/2, IN/?)

Bell Communication Research views intelligent networks as evolutionary, thus facilitating the slow migration of the networks in the public domain. The Regional Bell Operating Companies around the United States have taken three distinct steps (IN/1, IN/1+, and IN/2) in the last few years (see Weber, 1980; Bellcore, 1986, 1987). These three architectures are presented in Figs. 8, 9, and 10, respectively. Considerable collaboration in the phased introduction of these networks is essential to maintain uniformity and consistency of services throughout the nation and the globe. Vendors from all nations participate in supplying the network's components, in-

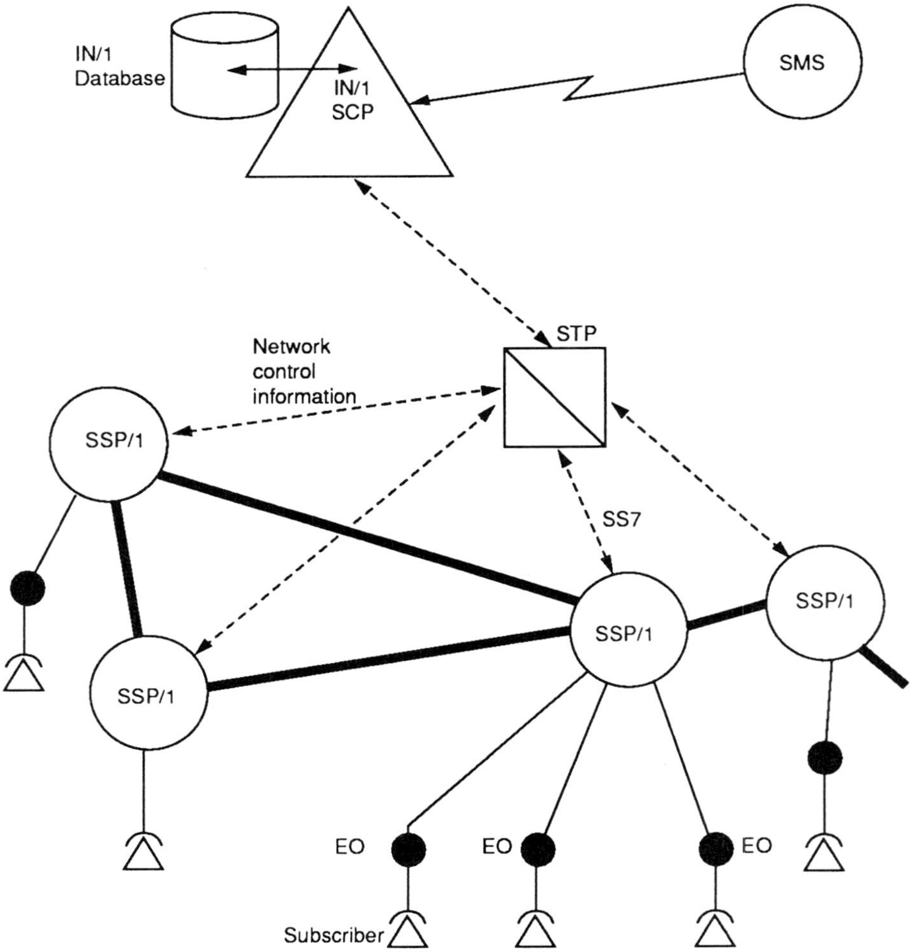

FIG. 8. Typical architecture of IN/1. SCP, service control point; SMS, service management system; STP, service transfer point; SSP/1, service switching point for IN/1.

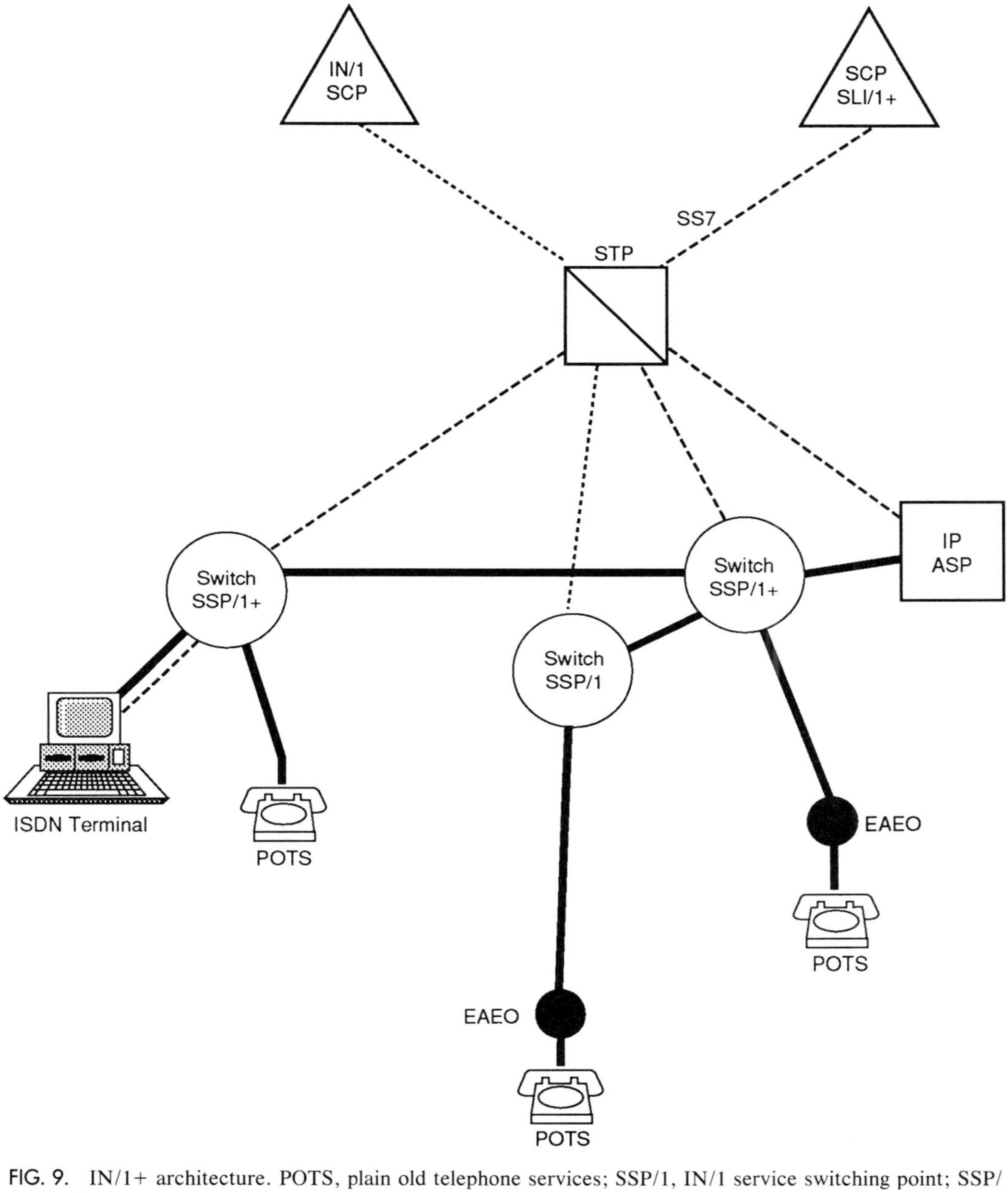

FIG. 9. IN/1+ architecture. POTS, plain old telephone services; SSP/1, IN/1 service switching point; SSP/1+, IN/1+ service switching point; STP, signal transfer point; IP, intelligent peripheral; ASP, adjunct service point; SCP, service control point; SLI, service logic interpreter; EAEO, equal access end office; ISDN, integrated service digital network. Solid line, information (data) path; dashed line, IN/1+ queries; dotted line, IN/1 queries.

terfaces, and software modules. To maintain any semblance of order over the next decade CCITT and ANSI publishes the requirements. Most networks tend to adhere to these standards and introduce network such as the 800 network as it is deployed in the United States. This network meets all the requirements of the first version of public domain intelligent network (IN/1). Newer advanced intelligent networks, sometimes referred to as AINs have been conceived, and their architecture has been analyzed in detail.

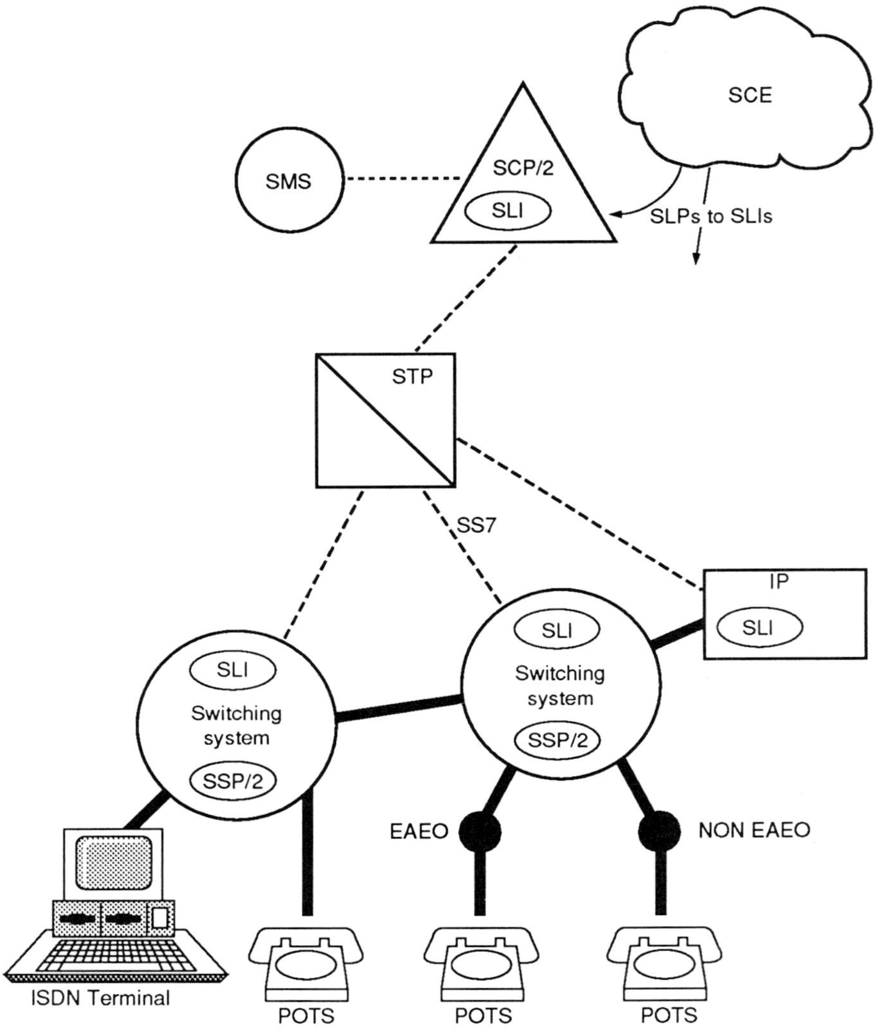

FIG. 10. IN/2 architecture. SSP/2, service switching point for IN/2; STP, service transfer point; SCP/2, service control point for IN/2; SMS, service management systems; IP, intelligent peripheral; SCE, service creation environment; SS7, signaling system 7; SLI, service logic interpreter; ISDN, integrated services digital network; EAEO, equal access end office; POTS, plain old telephone service; SLPs, service logic problems. Dashed line, signaling; sold line, transport; dotted line, operations.

In the United States, major network standards, definitions, and functional devices with certain generic and interface requirements have been introduced in the past few years. Three such networks IN/1, IN/1$^+$, and IN/2 are commonly accepted for phased introduction over through the 1990s. The rest of this section is dedicated to the building blocks of these networks.

Figure 8 depicts the architecture of a first level IN, referred to as IN/1 or the 800 network. There are four basic components of IN/1 as it exists in the United States. This network meets the three requirements (SPC, CCISS, and some service independence) to be classified as intelligent. The building blocks of IN/1 are service switching points (SSPs), service control point (SCP), service management system (SMS), and signal transfer points (STPs). One SMS may serve numerous SCPs, and one SCP may serve numerous SSPs. The flexibility is depicted in Fig. 11.

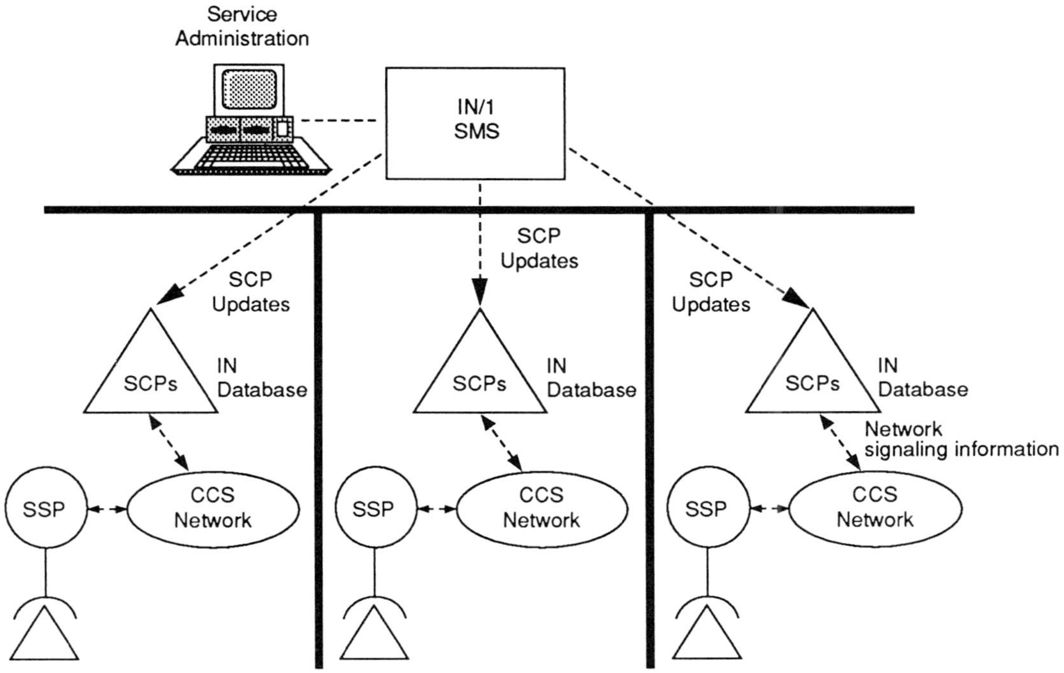

FIG. 11. Interaction between SSP, SCP, and SMS of IN/1.

The architecture of this network was aimed toward introducing newer service capabilities. The software building blocks of this network's SSPs, SCP, and SMS were designed and assembled to permit the customers to use new specific services (800, weather, time of day, etc.) on a widespread basis in real time. The introduction of newer services is still a problem because the software modules are specific to each service and have to be developed for each new service introduced. The service capabilities are also limited.

1. Service Switching Point (SSP)

Service Switching Points are physical or logical entities generally located at or in close proximity to the switching systems that contain call processing software.[1] There are two aspects of the SSP: the physical switch that performs the switching function and the logical software module that resides within the switch, forcing the execution of the SSP functions. The term SSP is sometimes used to refer to both the physical and logical modules and a certain amount of caution is necessary in the interpretation of the term. The switching system which hosts the SSP may be an end office or a tandem switching facility. Generally, an access tandem houses the SSP and may receive 800 calls from other ESS central offices, step by step switching systems, or even cross-bar offices. The access tandem housing the SSPs use common channel signaling (CSS) to facilitate interoffice signaling and also have the facilities to use interexchange carriers (ICs). The service switching points react to the specific triggers from the customers. In response, the SSPs send out queries to a service control point within the network. Generally, these switching points can be viewed as highly efficient and dependable data-base systems that react to user input such as the 800 number. In general, the user input can be a specific service request such as to bill the call to an alternate number or construct a private virtual network. When the SCP responds to the query from the SSP, the SSP can instruct the switching system

[1] Call processing software monitors the completion of the individual steps necessary to complete any call through the network. Typical steps for a circuit switched voice call are accept the complete sequence of digits, complete ringing connection, supply ringing signals by alerting called and calling party, detect response from called party, disconnect the ringing path, establish voice path, await hang-up by either party, disconnect the voice path, release the connection.

to complete the call attempted by the user (such as connecting to the 800 service number, or permit an alternate billing, or offer a private network connection). The call processing software of the switching system is thus invoked to complete the call.

The user information is relayed between the customers and the SSP's via the voice facilities of the network. The queries to the SCP are passed via the inter office signaling system (SS7) and made via CCS network consisting of highly dependable packet switches. These switches are called Signal Transfer Points which perform context dependent signal transfer within the network.

2. Service Control Point (SCP)

The service control point is a physical or a virtual node within the intelligent network containing the active data base of customer records. This data base is actively queried from the SSPs within the network to seek and obtain service completion information. Hence, the optimal and effective management and utilization of this critical and valuable data base becomes the key to real time seek-and-obtain the critical service completion information.

Certain sophistication in the hardware and software hierarchy is essential to make the SCP handle the high volume (several million calls per hour) and diversity (depending upon the types of services and subservices provided) in the information sought from the SCP. In a sense, in its design the SCP should be considered a highly efficient parallel processor, data storage–retrieval computer system. The input and output processing needs special attention. The environment in which the SCP operates is relatively well defined, and its functional requirements are clearly delineated. Thus, the hardware design assures consistency with the operational environment (STP, SMS, STP, and SSP), the type of processing accomplished (data-base functions, their updating, their security, error recovery, duplication, etc.), and the interfaces with the other network components (SS7 network, other signaling networks, with service management systems, alarm and security systems, etc.).

a. Hardware Aspects of the SCP. Four major hardware components constitute an SCP. First, an elaborate and highly dependable mass storage system (typically large capacity disk drives and disk controllers) make up the database storage. Second, a bank of parallel processors with their own dedicated memory blocks serve to access the bulk storage within the SCP and also communicate with the input/output devices of the data base. Third, a series of front-end processors preprocess the queries received via the SS7 network or any similar compatible network with a well specified protocol. Finally, a series of BX.25 front-end processors to receive service management information from the SMS and interface for maintenance, security, and operations of the SCP completes the major hardware components.

It is important to note that any computer hardware architecture with the optimally distributed bus structure can adequately perform the SCP functions. However certain architectures (such as parallel processor, multi bus systems) are more suitable. In the interest of high dependability expected from the SCP, duplication of hardware and buses enhances the confidence level on the functioning of these special purpose computer systems. Typically the downtime on the SCP is under three minutes a year, and the wait time in call completion demands both redundancy and speed from the SCP.

b. Software Aspects. There are two groups of software structures in the SCP. The first group deals with the functioning of the SCP as a coherent computational entity which serves the hierarchical function of the SCP in the intelligent network architecture. The second group deals with the applications that the intelligent network (which hosts the SCP) is equipped to handle. The architectural configuration of an SCP functional software consists of five major modules. First, the service network interface (SNI) receives the signaling information from the CCS7 and other signaling systems querying the SCP and passes the information for further response from the SCP. This major and perhaps the most optimally coded group of software routines serve to interface the SSP queries.

Second, the support system interface (SSI) provides a software interface for the service management functions to be handled via the SMS. Network management control and customer record entry and updates are handled via this interface.

Third, the observation window for the SCP operating personnel into the operations, functions, and maintenance of the SCP is provided by operations subsystem (OS). This interface between the personnel and the SCP responds to a system console that monitors the flow of data and information between the SCP components.

Fourth, the node manager (NM) subsystem fulfills the start-up and shutdown procedures of the SCP. Service continuity and early fault detection and some possible rerouting are the critical requirement of the NM subsystem. This software subsystem assures the customer data-base entries and updates without service disruption. The multitasking and load sharing of numerous CPUs within the SCP are also managed by the NM. In effect, the NM in the SCP environment performs many of the functions similar to the operating system functions (resource utilization, traffic management, load handling, I/O control, backup procedure, crash aversion, system bootup/shutdown, etc.) in a computer system environment.

Finally, the node administration (NA) subsystem permits efficient and optimal data-base functions and provides for the necessary backup of data bases. This function is of considerable importance in the SCP functions in light of the duplicated data bases for fault tolerance and service dependability (less than 3 min a year).

c. Applications Software and Application Associated Software. In a broad application framework, the SCP functions can be summarized as validation of the caller to call, the address translation of the called party (from a lookup data base, if it is necessary), and finally, identification of the carrier authorized to carry the call. The generic capability of the SCP can be tailored to serve a much wider variety of special voice services or applications. However, a majority of the SCP's implemented in the United States serve these three major applications.

In the United States, a few of the regional Bell Operating Companies have targeted three varieties of special services. Typical of these services that are being offered and which are being planned consist of 800 data-base services, alternate billing service, and private virtual networks. Other services in the IN/1 environment can be added by including special purpose routines (or software modules) directed towards the new service.

3. Service Management System (SMS)

The SMS function is intricately tied in with the functions of the SCP. In fact, the SMS is an off-line support facility to enter customer data into the SCP's data bases. It is also used to enter the call-processing software into the SCP. The SMS communicates with the SCP through interface cards to process the BX.25 protocol used for communication between SMS and SCP. The service management systems also need a series of front-end processors to tie in with the dual buses which provide data paths between the SCP's other front-end processors and the SCP's bank of central processor units. Generally, these front-end processors may be implemented by deploying microcomputer chips with appropriate interfaces.

In the IN/1 framework, new SMS modules are necessary for each of the new IN/1 services to be added. The SMS supports the SCPs. The SCPs in turn perform three major applications/services in the United States [800 data base service, the alternate billing service (ABS), and private virtual network (PVN) service]. To further group the software in the SMS environment, three groups of SMS software (SMS/800 for the 800 services, data base administration system, or DBAS, for the alternate billing service, and SMS/PVN for the private virtual network) have emerged for the IN/1 or the first generic intelligent network.

A certain amount of standardization and uniformity is desirable among the software modules for these three well accepted IN/1 services. The number of SCPs in the IN/1 can start to increase as the number of individual service providers starts to increase since each provider can have an individual SCP. However, if the SCPs of each of the service providers have to respond in a consistent way, then the SMSs that drive the SCP have to be functionally transparent. For this reason, certain standard forms of SMS/800, DBAS, and SMS/PVN have been attempted in the United States for IN/1 for the RBOCs and for the Bell Client Companies (BCCs).

It is also apparent from the functionality and the suggested architectures of more sophisticated networks (such as IN/1+ and IN/2) to be deployed during early to mid-nineties, the SMS design philosophy will need considerable reorientation because of the enhanced service independence concept weaved into the working of such newer networks.

4. Signal Transfer Point (STP)

The signal transfer points are packet switches to transfer query signals and the response signals between SSPs and SCPs. These signal transfer points are distributed within the common channel signaling (CCS) network. The STPs contain the translation information necessary to forward the data-base queries from the service switching points (SSPs) to the appropriate service control points (SCPs). Traditionally, the CCS network works in the packet switched environments, and the STPs constitute the highly reliable packet switches in the CCS network.

The querying central offices may consist of a wide variety of digital and analogue switches. The minimum configuration of the analogue switch to communicate with the STP is that it be a stored program controlled switch with a digital adjunct associated with it for common channel signaling capability. The digital switches may be all digital or remote from the digital switches, such as a CSA serving point having CCS capability.

The STP also needs some rudimentary database support for performing optimal signal transfer and selecting the appropriate service control point. With appropriate software support, the STPs in the CCS, these packet switches relay the control information in CCISS 7 signaling format throughout the network and respond to SSP queries and relay responses.

B. AT&T's Universal Services Intelligent Network

The five major functional entities in the proposed USIN are: the service switching point (SSP), the signal transfer point (STP), the service control point (SCP), the off-network node (ONN) or the intelligent peripheral (IP), and the service management system (SMS). As will be appreciated further in this section and the next section, these components or entities perform very much like any other special purpose and highly sophisticated computer systems. Being programmable at the operating system level through the special instruction level, they can perform intelligent functions in a localized geographical area for the Bell Regional Operating Companies in the United States or on a national basis for major carriers and long distance transport facilities of America Telephone and Telegraph Company. In fact, any level of adaptation of an IN can be built for any amount of geographical coverage.

Service switching point (SSP) and service creation environment (SCE) work together at the universal services nodes (USN) within the UIS network. The transport service of the UIS network would be monitored by the enriched service layer derived by the coordinated functions of SSP and SCE. Typically, the USIN would contain the service transfer point (STP), the service control point (SCP), and service management systems (SMS) and work in conjunction with any other intelligent peripheral (IP) or the off-network nodes (ONN) as they exist within the framework of the intelligent networks proposed by the RBOCS.

Various service control points (SCPs) sense a unique set of circumstances at a switch that queries a data base. Functions such as routing control, digit collection, billing and recording, and network management commands take place here at the switch which caused the SCP to query the data base. This data base contains a wide variety of network service information. Typical examples of the data bases are line information data base, Bell Operating Company 800 data base, and business services data base.

Various service switching points (SSPs) which provide basic access and switching facility within the network will also communicate with the CCS 7 network. They respond in completing the original command from the switch or the new commands after querying the data base.

Tandem access offices (TAOs) would provide the exchange of (data base, network, and/or service) information to distant locations via interexchange carriers.

This architecture of the new breed of intelligent networks makes the provision of service totally independent of the type of service being provided. The transport of relevant information is the prime objective of ingrained network intelligence. Most of these features are incorporated in the INs initiated after 1988–89.

The proposed architecture of the public switched networks to facilitate universal information services (UIS) makes this network intelligent and adaptive. The proposed network to implement these concepts has been incorporated in the universal information services network (UISN). The UISN is a feature-rich environment existing in the context modern INs. This environment can blend any combination of services (voice, data, video/image) with maximum convenience and economy. Network capabilities are optimally used to meet customer requirements. The architecture of this network is expected to be realized with the existing technology over the next few years.

The services that INs can provide include the existing 911 (public emergency) service, virtual private networks, automatic calling card, and the 900 (televoting) service. These services can be performed in the public switched networks and in private networks. They can be performed at a local and regional level or at a national and international level.

1. Service Switching Points in UISN

SSPs have been integrated with the major switching systems built by AT&T. The SSP of the Advanced 800 network is built from the electronic switching system 4ESS introduced by AT&T. The SSP of the DDSN deployed by British Telecom during the late 1980s is derived from the AT&T 5ESS switch. This switch also incorporates the STP for the DDSN.

This software module responds to the trigger condition existing within the network as the IN services become necessary. The call handling information is sought out from the service control point (SCP) via the service transfer point in the network at the universal services node. The functionality of the components is akin to the functionality of components in the RBOC's intelligent networks.

2. Signal Transfer Point in UISN

The request for service is provided by the CCISS signals to appropriate service/information providers. These signals calling for such services/information have to reach the appropriate data bases distributed within the network. The signal transfer point (STP) is a switch to forward the signals in real time and generate the response from the data bases in service control points. The STP of the Advanced 800 service is a stand-alone switch which functions in conjunction with the 4ESS.

3. Service Control Point in UISN

The service control point of the IN has two major components. First, the service logic module provides the capacity to interpret the type of service requested and the type of resources (such as data bases) to be tapped. Second, the data base(s) in the SCP contain updated information/resources to complete the request received by the SCP. These data bases can be simple tables or a collection of extremely complex data structures, depending upon the type of service/information sought by the requisitioner.

4. Off-Network Node or the Intelligent Peripheral in UISN

The type of services that an IN can provide can be highly specialized. All of these services may or may not be in the legal jurisdiction of the network owners to provide. To supplement the network services and enhance the attractiveness to the users, outside vendors may offer these services or support functions. The information/service can again be highly variable, ranging from language translation or voice recognition to delivering recorded messages or digit collection based upon the multifrequency tones received at the ONN or IP. In the UISN, the ONN is a remotely located device or module and the IP is network resident.

5. Service Management System in the UISN

New network service creation and data-base maintenance and updating call for considerable software effort. The service management system provides an authorized and efficient entry point for such network service creation and data-base maintenance.

These five basic elements used in UISN are essentially the same as those in the RBOC's IN/1+ and IN/2. The flexibility offered by the elements makes them serve as IN components in national environments, in regional, or even in private corporate network environments.

The architecture of the UISN is viewed broadly in terms of the elements, the individual functions and their management, and the cooperative functioning of the individual elements. A hierarchy with three levels is foreseen. At the lowest level reside the five essential elements of the network. At the intermediate level are the collections of local management of each of these elements and their individual functions. At the top level is foreseen the management of the cooperative roles of each of these elements to constitute a universal intelligent network. This hierarchy for the management of the network (in its entirety) is classified as the universal network management architecture (UNMA).

6. Two Tier Services Architecture in UISN

Two major service tiers exist in the provision of the universal information services (UIS) via AT&T's universal services network. The upper enriched services tier is atop the transport services tier. These two tiers drive digital information through the media between the universal network nodes. The enriched services of the UIN are partially realized by universal operating system (UOS). The UOS has access to the SSP and the SCE, also operating in conjunction with the digital switch (5ESS or 4ESS). The UOS also provides increasing customer control of the network. These three modules (UOS, SSP, and SCE) together provide an enriched service environment for the UISN. These services may be activated at any of the nodes in the UISN. The transport services offered by the media facilitate the realization of the lower level open system interconnection model (OSI, discussed in Section VI). The enriched services are capable of providing an adaptive admixture of the upper level functions of the OSI model.

7. The Enriched Services Tier of the UISN

Newer services are supported by the enriched services tier. Applications which need specialized implementation and service switching functions are accessed at this level. The universal operating system, which is also a part of this tier, performs network management functions. Typical of these functions are customer control, cost effectiveness, network problem and fault management self-healing diagnostics, and fault correction and service functions.

8. The Transport Tier of the USIN

Four levels are foreseen in the evolutionary model of this network. Partitioning, multiplexing, dropping, adding, and cross-connecting take place within this tier. Fiber optic transmission media are seen to be an ideal environment to implement the transport tier. As ISDN becomes more common, the transport tier can facilitate the ease of the basic channel functions listed above. Basic rate, primary rate, and broadband ISDN are all expected to become substantial beneficiaries of the transport tier controlling the mass capacity digital pipes in the national network environment. The subchannel facility becomes insidious to the functioning of this tier in the UISN. It is foreseen that the transmission media can become a well controlled resource in the USN environment by having a transport tier between the enriched services tier and the extremely large capacity national and international digital pipes of the near future.

9. Customer Interface for USIN

Customer access to the USIN is provided via standardized universal ports. The imminence of ISDN, broadband ISDN, and local high speed (fiber and T1) networks requires very general interface with UIN. It is foreseen that standard data and signal paths are both necessary at these universal ports. The new technologies (fiberonics, multigigabit fiber transmission, and switching, software and ultra large scale integration) at the customer premise equipment and also in the network can be gracefully integrated in the network performance by adherence to the interface requirements at the universal ports.

V. Network Types

Public domain networks and totally private networks constitute the extremes of network ownership and thus its organization and management. Whereas there is considerable freedom in the architecture and operation of the private network, the public domain networks' architecture and operation tend to be standardized and streamlined (see Section IV). In the discussion presented here, acknowledged international standards are used in context to the PDIN, especially for the ISDN.

In a broad and general sense, signaling is essential to the functionality of any IN. In the context of ISDN the signaling is carried out by the standard CCS7 network adopted in the United States and Europe. This network uses the out of band information (i.e., the information on the D channel) to control and signal the various switches to complete and monitor the B channels. Figure 13 depicts the role of the signaling and control of the information-bearing B channels. This network becomes essential in the circuit switched context because the B channels provide transparent end-to-end digital connectivity for the network users. If and when a transition to the packet mode is to occur, the CCS information is used to provide the transition and vice versa.

There are two major architectural variations in the networks used in the public domain. First, in the switched architectures (connection orientation), there are five stages for data transfer through a switched channel. The sequence may be summarized as follows: an idle channel is identified and tagged, a connection is established, the data are transferred, the channel is released, and the channel resumes to be idle again. This sequence of stages closely parallels the well-established network steps in a typical voice call, which follows the network functions (call setup, alert, connect, disconnect, and release). In the context of the ISDN, the information necessary to accomplish these individual steps is incorporated in the CCITT Q.930/931 protocol at the network layer and used over the D channel to set up the B channel.

Second, in the packet switched architectures (connectionless orientation), a packet of information is assembled with its own address so that it can be forwarded to its destination. The packet may transit through any number of nodes until it reaches its destination. The exact physical routing is not known, but the innate functioning of the participating nodes through the network assures the correct transmission of the packet. (In many ways the packet can be compared to a letter dropped in a mailing system, which assures the delivery of the letter to the right destination.) In the context of packet switching, CCITT has specified the widely accepted X.25, X.75, X.28, and X.29 protocol at the network layer (see Section IV).

The two architectures can work cooperatively, and one of the objectives of the intelligent network switches and their nodes is to assure the compatibility of the two major network ideologies. Hence, there are differences in functioning but not in integration toward being one intelligent network in the public domain. Concepts culminating in the present standardization and implementation of the IN and the ISDN have initiated the evolution of intelligent networks.

A third supporting network that has emerged because of the need to control and monitor the flow of information is called the common channel signaling (CCS) network.

Private and semiprivate networks (sometimes called channel switched networks) may also use the standard components and the associated interfaces. Generally, private branch exchanges (PBXs), private and dedicated lines, and digital distribution facilities with any amount of computerized information handling capacity may be encountered in private (intelligent) networks. These networks are emerging with great amounts of sophistication and intelligence. Typically, such networks are found in the scientific community (e.g., National Science Foundation's NSFNET, Defense Advanced Research Projects Agency's ARPANET, and Carnegie Mellon and Bell of Pennsylvania's Metropolitan Campus Network (MCN). Other examples from industry (e.g., VLSI vendors' networks) and national laboratories (e.g., Lawrence Livermoore National Laboratory's private network for its 12,000 employees, spanning 500 buildings) also prevail.

The French have also introduced the Biarritz network capable of performing a wide range of intelligent functions such as home video library, home shopping, video games, on-line videotex, encyclopedia, and graphic services. Other national intelligent networks are increasing through the year 2000. For the rest of the discussion, we refer to the evolution of the ISDN in Section VII.

Another emerging network in the competitive telecommunication environment is the private virtual network (PVN). In this type of network the user retains a certain amount of control and management of his own PVN. It is tailored to the specific needs of the business by using the resources of the RBOCs in the United States and the services offered by the interexchange carriers (ICs). The user pays for the resources and the RBOC assures their availability. The physical allocation of channels or resources is thus not committed to the user on a permanent basis. Currently the leased lines may be used for voice (private tie lines), data (leased 1200–9600 kb/sec lines), high speed data (leased 56 or 64 kb/sec lines), and broad-band data.

This type of option has become feasible only because of programmed switching through the network, and the topology of the PVN can be thus modified. It offers certain attractive features to the users, RBOCs, and the ICs. The user pays for the resources used with their availability to the entire company network and retains multiple location access to the PVN. The RBOCs retain their market share, they pass the management responsibility to the user, and investment in new technology is shared among numerous users. The ICs benefit because of the increased use of their carrier services.

Area-wide centrex (AWC) offers users some of the private exchange features via a central office. Though not truly intelligent, some interesting features such as centralized number plan, abbreviated dialing, call forwarding, and conference calls already exist in centrex systems. These features of any centrex system are extended to many exchanges in AWC. The CCS7 is activated in this network, and the application program tailored to the specific AWC translates the dialed number to the actual number according defined numbering plan for that service subscriber. The target number and the service logic instructions for handling the call are forwarded to the service switching point via the CCS7 network. The signal transfer point also participates in this transfer to the service switching point. The protocol used in this transfer between the

SCP and the SSP is the transaction capabilities application part of the CCS7 protocol.

A. Evolution of Phased Intelligence in American Public Switched Networks

1. Bellcore's View

The prolonged divestiture of the Bell System (1982 through 1984) was effective during the prime evolutionary period (1980 through the present) of the intelligent networks. Hence, the origin of the seminal concepts can be traced back to the predivestiture Bell System of the early 1980s. Some of the techniques were specifically evolved toward bringing the newer services to local telephone customers. Such facilities and plans correctly fell under the jurisdiction of the Bell Operating Companies and are implemented at the Region's level. Some of these services were introduced by the individual RBOCs, and the concepts leading to refined intelligent networks to serve the RBOCs were evolved at Bellcore (Bell Communications Research). It is here that the concepts leading to IN/1, IN/1+, and IN/2 were developed.

One of the key functions of the intelligent network also took place in 1984. The custom local area signaling services (CLASS) actually perform the intelligent functions in the SPC based #1ESS central offices by being able to selectively reject calls, auto recall, or callback service. Once again, the CCIS capability to relay the called party and the caller information was used by programs stored in the central offices to force intelligent network response. Call-related information could be exchanged between central offices via the CCIS 6 extended message capabilities, thus providing an automatic number identification (ANI) feature between switches.

The growth of preconceived algorithmic intelligence into communication network fields has been steady. In 1985, software defined network service (SDNS) was introduced. This service permitted many private network owners to take advantage of the more dramatic advances taking place in the switched network operations yet enabled them to keep the advantage of their prorated network. The virtual network defined by software commands permits private network owners such as corporations to use their own network in virtual cooperation with the switched public network.

The business and/or residence custom services also introduced in 1985 permit user to use the generic programs embedded in the central offices. With access and option to exercise these powerful central office routines (such as computer system utility routines with appropriate input data) provide the customer with centrex, custom calling, and electronic tandem switching capabilities.

Numerous developments in other directions such as billing and authorization also facilitated the commercial viability of the newly enhanced intelligent functions. While the network may functionally respond to signals and codes forwarded by the central offices and users, the collection of tolls and revenues for the service provided is also crucial. To facilitate this aspect, the validation of billing information was provided by authorization in the data-base administration systems distributed within the network. This facility, initially introduced for the 800 calls in 1981, also paved the way for other services such as calling card services. The human (operator) intelligence in handling the queries and call processing was gradually replaced by the programs. These programs queried the distributed data bases for authorization to connect and process calls by algorithmically decoding the long strings of digits to the called numbers through the networks.

The concept of call routing was also introduced as far back as 1981. The CCIS 6 provided the 800 service facility to respond to these calls by matching the location of the user with the nearest or most logical service provider. Intermediate data bases to provide the routing information were distributed throughout the network. Thus, the functions of obtaining the appropriate authorization, call routing, switching, and finally billing where all streamlined into one programmed and streamlined network operation.

The introduction of common channel signaling system 7 (CSS 7) by C-CITT permitted the eventual integration of the numerous facilities under one common conceptual and architectural umbrella. By and large, this CSS 7 becomes central in streamlining the flow of information between three basic modules, SCP (service control point), SSP (service switching point), and the TAO (tandem access office) of most intelligent networks.

2. AT&T's View

In communication networks, the direction of intelligence is highly pointed toward being functional in real time with efficacy and optimality.

In a sense, the most primitive telephone networks had these characteristics in their era. Human intelligence and discretion was freely supplemented to make and break the communication paths. Electromechanical and Stowger-type systems, although major innovations of their time, lacked programmed intelligence.

However, AT&T's introduction of the first electronic switching system (#1ESS) with its stored program control (SPC) in 1965 brought conventional programmed intelligence (or simply programs) to the telephone networks. There were three phases for the introduction of the #1ESS in the network. First, the local office switch was introduced in 1965 in Succasunna, New Jersey. Second, the tandem switch capable of interconnecting numerous local offices was introduced in 1968 at Nashville, Tennessee. Finally, the toll office (or switch) capable of reaching a much wider toll area was introduced in 1971.

Next, the introduction of the common channel interoffice signaling (CCIS) used a signaling protocol based upon the CCITT signaling system 6 recommendation in the long distance portion of the network in 1976. The tests during this time were limited to the #4A toll crossbar office with its own electronic translator system in Madison, Wisconsin, and #4 electronic switching system (ESS) in Chicago, Illinois. But in principle this facilitated the network to respond as a single information transfer entity throughout the nation, provided the signal transfer points could be adequately distributed. This service also paved the way to making the network service independent and provided the flow of information and low rate data, provided the band width requirements were met.

The CCIS signaling facility needs the basic intelligence embedded in the central offices to respond to signals received from other central offices to complete the call and follow out the usual connect, ring, hold, disconnect functions. It also paved the path toward the next set of sophisticated direct services dialing (DSD) that the network could accomplish. The DSD service as introduced in 1984 provided the flexibility for the networks to perform numerous other functions and services.

The introduction of the national 800 services in 1967 and the international 800 services in 1984 also needs specific mention since a unified capability was being forged. In addition to the usual communication functions that the networks need to accomplish, these services also performed the specific task of translating user requests for services and connections to network command by accessing a network control point embedded within the network itself. Thus, more and more of the functions were being automated and programmed to bring the conventional intelligence or adaptability within the network.

More recently, an extension to the widely used switched capability prevalent in the United States, a feature-rich service environment, universal information service (UIS) has been proposed. Most of the features of the intelligent networks, such as virtual private network, 911 public emergency service, automatic calling card, and televoting (900) services, can be included in the UIS. The user's need for critical, accurate, and quick access information to enhance productivity are addressed in the design of the network. The blending of voice, data, video, and image services will become available in this environment.

The current architectures proposed by the Regional Bell Operating Companies are conducive to the evolution of the UIS concepts, which closely parallel the IN/1, IN/1+, and IN/2 concepts. Whereas the RBOC's initial goal is to operate effectively within the regions and work cooperatively with the surrounding regions, the longer distance transportation services provided by the information carriers can also be enriched. The transport services that utilize a vast variety of media to communicate information will be enhanced by UIS. Integration of digital services as it is evolving with the ISDN will interface with the various intelligent networks by virtue of the more widely accepted common channel interoffice signaling system CCISS 7 and via the ISDN Q.931 protocol virtually in place in the various networks.

Service switching point (SSP) and service creation environment (SCE) work together at the universal services nodes (USN) within the UIS network. The transport service of the UIS network would be monitored by the enriched service layer derived by the coordinated functions of SSP and SCE. Typically, the USN would contain the service transfer point (STP), the service control point (SCP), and service management systems (SMS) and work in conjunction with any other intelligent peripheral (IP) or the off-network nodes (ONN) as they exist within the framework of the intelligent networks proposed by the RBOCs.

B. The Near Term Public Domain Intelligent Networks

1. Bellcore's View

The 800 services network represents the first generation of a public domain network. Being functional and well received in the public domain, it provides the three basic features of most INs. First, stored program control of switches and nodes is used to provide a software-controlled environment. Second, the interoffice signaling is accomplished by common channel signaling system (CCIS 6 and/or 7). Third, some of the service independence features (such as transfer of control and connection control) can be or have been incorporated.

Compared to the potential and capabilities (as they are understood in the late 1980s) of these networks, the 800 service is truly a first generation IN. Architecturally, the 800 network uses five of the seven building blocks that make networks truly flexible and intelligent.

The 800 network uses service control point (SCP/1; the /1 indicates that it refers to IN/1 for all the building blocks) extensively. The SCP architecture and data may be duplicated throughout the country. The data are all managed and maintained by a single services management system (SMS/1). Since the features of the 800 network are not completely evolved throughout the country, the SMS/1 may be used to control one or several SCPs. Updates and modifications can be carried out using simple protocols for the SCPs.

Alternate billing service (ABS) and private virtual network (PVN) are additional IN features evolved for the RBOCs. These networks and their specialized features make newer services available more quickly, more economically, and on a more customized basis. The incorporation of INs into the switching environment, together with ISDN in the customer and business environment, has become more and more realizable to make the IN services available to the network users.

Customized local area special services (CLASS) is a feature that is already established by RBOCs. These services offered can be some or a few of the services that the local environments can support. Typically, eleven services are offered as a group of these special services are listed as follows: automatic callback, automatic recall, caller number delivery to the called party, caller number blockage to the called party, customer originating trace, distinctive ringing/call waiting screening list, selective call forwarding, selective call forwarding screening list, selective call rejection, selective call rejection list, and who called me?

2. AT&T's View

In the IN/1+, the use of intelligent peripherals to interface the intelligence networks of the American Regional Holding Companies and/or other intelligent nodes is provisioned. Service independence, faster feature introduction, and standard node interfaces at various switching centers will also be the features of this IN environment. This facility is expected to be in operation during early 1990s. By the mid-1990s the universal information service intelligent network 2 (UIS/IN-2) is proposed. Voice, visual, and computer data transport is the ultimate goal of this network. Independence from the origin and destination and the timing of information is a willful objective of this network. The implementation of this policy permits interfacing with any third party vendor/user node as off-network node (ONN). In an effort to provide enriched services to the customers, most intelligent peripherals, tandem access offices, and SCPs for IN-2 will be able to function in a service creation environment in which services, concepts, and offerings may be quickly and easily tested before fully introducing them in the marketplace.

Localized network control information may be derived for user (provided the authorization exists) or the network management programs. This permits the use of software-defined network functions and configuration. Such services become extremely feasible, and they could be made for a short duration and immediately available.

VI. ISO Model and Intelligent Networks

The open system interconnect (OSI) standard (International Standard 7498) proposed by the International Organization for Standardization (ISO) and the identical CCITT recommendation (Recommendation X.200) are internationally accepted. Most networks follow these standards closely for the ease of interconnection to other networks and the flexibility of using different product vendors and standard software modules to work with these products. A conceptual representation of the OSI environment is shown in Fig. 12.

A. Layers of the OSI Model

Germane to the OSI concept are the seven layers for its implementation. The individual layers, shown in Table I, perform very specific functions to maintain the network coherent functions. The intelligence (hardware, software, firmware) to perform the various functions at any one of the layers has to be provided in specific or common devices that perform these necessary functions.

The top three layers are specific to the users of the data and information services of the network. The fourth layer, dealing with the transportation of data that is very critical in matching the user specific requirements to the network function becomes a liasion between the network service users and the network service providers. The lower three layers are specific to the actual network providing the network services.

In the application layer (AP), the intelligence modules assure the user that the service provided is consistent with the type of application. In the presentation layer (PRL), the intelligence modules interpret the information exchanged between the AP and the network. The communication syntax is appropriately negotiated, chosen, and translated. In the sessions layer (SL), the intelligence modules bind and unbind various users and their applications into logical units for dispatch and recovery to and from the network during a session. In the transport layer (TL), the modules control the end-to-end information exchange with the required degree of reliability. In the network layer (NL), the intelligence modules provide, maintain, and terminate the connections in a switched environment of the end systems. Routing and addressing information is also provided by these modules. The input and the interface to these modules is from the TL and does not depend upon the lower two levels (DL and PHL) of the network. Because of the need to carry out very critical functions, most intelligent networks follow the CCITT recommendations for the interface and modularity of the functions. In the data link layer (DL), the modules perform the error-free transmission of

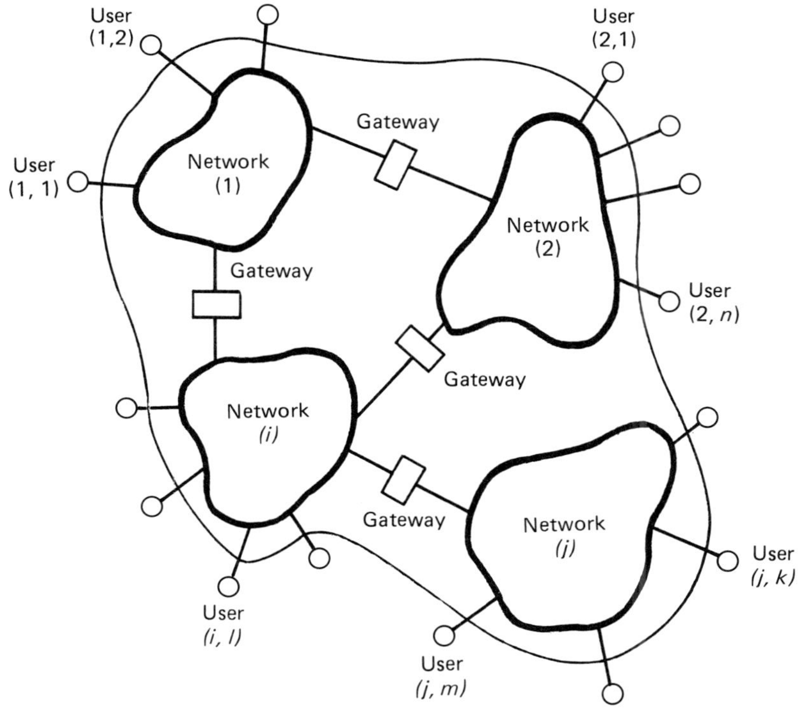

FIG. 12. A conceptual representation of the open system interconnect (OSI) environment.

TABLE I. The Open System Interconnect Model

OSI layer	Type of functional intelligence[a]
Application	AL: Facility to serve the end user. Provision of the distributed information service. Communication management between the AL and PRL. Service to the user, the application (SASE), and the group of applications (CASE) served. Authentication of user IDs, destination IDs, authority to exchange information. Determination of service quality from the lower layers. Data integrity, error recovery, and file transfers are also assured. (See ISO DIS 8649, protocol ISO 8640, CCITT X.400 message handling system.)
Presentation	PRL: Assures the delivery of information to the end users in a form that is usable and understood. The information content (semantic) is retained, even though the presentation format and language (syntax) can be altered to suit the source(s) and destination(s) of the information. (See ISO 8824 for abstract syntax notation ASN.1, and ISO 8825 for encoding, CCITT X.409.)
Session	SL: Provision of transfer data and to transfer control in an organized and synchronized manner. User may define the degree of control and synchronization that the session layer will provide. (See CCITT X.215, ISO 8326; X.225, ISO X.8327, T.62.)
Transport	TL: Selection of network service. Evaluation of the need for multiplexing. Selection of the functions from the lower layers. Optimal data size decisions. Mapping of transport addresses to network addresses or the end-point users and negotiated. Data flow regulation between the end users. Segmentation and concatenation. Error detection and its recovery. (See ISO 8072, CCITT X.214; ISO 8073, ISO DIS 8602-connectionless, CCITT X.224.)
Network	NL: Establish, maintain, and terminate switched connections. Addressing and routing functions. Service TL, independent of DL and PHL. (a) Connection: network connection, data transfer, optional expedited data and receipt transfers, reset, and connection release. (b) Connectionless: UNITDATA. (See ISO 8348, CCITT X.213; protocols CCITT X.25, 1984, packet, ISO DP 8878 with X.25 for connection oriented network service; ISO 8473 for connectionless internetworking; CCITT Q.930/Q.931 ISDN.)
Data link	DL: Synchronization/framing, error detection and recovery, and flow control for information transmitted over the physical link. (See ISO DIS 8886, 1745, 2111, 2628, 2629; CCITT X.212, X.21 for basic mode; ISO 3309, 4335, 6159, 6256; CCITT X.25, X.75, X.71 for HDLC; CCITT Q.920/Q.921 for ISDN.)
Physical	PHL: Activation, maintenance, and deactivation of the physical connection. The electrical and mechanical characteristics for physical interface and the transmission media. (See ISO 2110, CCITT V.24, V.28 or EIA RS-232-C, also EIA RS-449, CCITT X.21, V.35; EIA RS-422A, CCITT V.11, X.27 for balanced voltage; EIA RS-423A, CCITT V.10, X.26 for unbalanced voltage; CCITT I.430 for (2B + D) ISDN and CCITT I.431 for 24 B or 30 B channels.)

[a] The nature and amount of intelligence required at each level and the established standards for specifications and protocol.

bits. Two basic functions, synchronization of the data streams and error control, are essential at this layer. In the physical layer (PHL), the intelligence modules provide the functional and procedural steps to activate, maintain, and deactivate the physical connection. Both the electrical and mechanical characteristics of the interface with the external transmission media are considered by this layer.

It is important to note the intelligence modules may be in the form of software, hardware, or firmware. The actual form of these modules is unimportant as long as the functions are dependably carried through at the various layers of any IN. The standards established by CCITT in unison with ISO and those accredited by the Accredited Standards Committee (ASC) of the American National Standards Institute (ANSI) have been crucial in establishing the functions of different layers for the open systems interconnect facilities for most of the intelligent networks. The standards specify the information and the functions at each of the seven layers of the OSI reference model. If the designers of any particular network architecture decide to follow these standards, the distribution of the intelligence in the network also get firmly distributed for the control and monitoring of the network functions. The distribution of these functions is better established for the lower three layers (network, data link, and physical). The guidelines are summarized as follows. For the packet mode, the X.25 protocol is the CCITT standard at layer 3. This protocol is implemented together with link access protocol for the B channel (LAPB) at layer 2, the data link. The X.25 protocol at layer 3 is implemented with link access protocol for the D channel (LAPD) at the second layer. For the switched mode, the Q.931 standard has been established at layer 3 between the user and the exchange network interface. At layer 2, the data link layer, LAPD format is used again to carry the control information to the network call control module. This information is carried by the D channel to facilitate the network in serving the associated B channels. Typically, the Q.931 call setup message has very specific information (e.g., caller identification), the B channel service desired, the B channel identification, and the destination address. The call control network module uses this information to monitor the call setup for the B channel. The D channel message changes if the user wishes to disconnect the B channel, and the network control module responds accordingly.

The OSI layered structure also facilitates the segregation of the functions performed by individual layers. The intelligence required to perform the functions within any one layer can be localized to the hardware and software particular to that layer. The protocols that facilitate the transfer of information between the lower layers of the OSI model are undergoing standardization. The protocols at the lowest (physical) layer have been established and documented.

B. X.25 Packet Switched Network Standard

The best known standard for interfacing with the network is based upon CCITT recommendation X.25 in 1980 and revised in 1984. It spans the lower three layers of the seven-layer OSI network model and permits full network layer service by the network services vendors throughout the globe. The recommendations of 1980 (X.25 version) have been widely accepted and deployed by most network services vendors. The latter recommendations of 1984 (X.25 versions) are being rapidly implemented.

The OSI standard (or the CCITT X.200 recommendation) permits any layer to communicate with a corresponding layer at any other node in the network. The BX.25 protocol is used in the IN-core network for interoffice signaling for the intelligent services. The BX.25 version is specially modified for the RBOC environment.

VII. Example of an Intelligent Network

A. INs and ISDN

Intelligent networks can be configured in numerous ways. For this reason, owners of private networks can fine-tune the interconnections and their architectural arrangements of the five basic components to be ideally suited to the application. However, public networks have a longer life, use standardized interfaces, and serve a wide variety of network users. For national and international usage, certain standards exist. For instance, Bellcore technical advisories and generic requirements insist that the architecture follow the IN/1, IN/1+, or IN/2 specifications. Since the vendors would like to be able to sell to these RBOCs, they make their SSPs, SCPs, and STPs consistent with the RBOCs requirements. However, the intelligent networks in different countries can differ significantly. For this reason, the IN hardware and software are not identical throughout the globe. One of the ways major vendors of the IN nodes are adapting to the varying needs is to have different software utilities for different countries. Specially prominent is the situation when an American vendor of ESSs approaches the European market or vice versa.

In Sections II and III, the component and architectural details of IN/1 were discussed. Networks similar in complexity and architecture to the IN/1 are the GNS (green number service as it is sometimes referred to in Europe), the (alternate billing service (ABS), when the caller can bill the call to an alternate number or to an account associated with a calling card number), emergency response service (ERS), versions I and II, private virtual network (PVN), types 1, 2, and 3, and area wide centrex (AWC) systems. All these networks have the SSP to STP, STP to SCP, forward and backward signaling links that communicate the data for call completion, and to this extent the parent architectural blueprints of the traditional IN/1 can be modified to suit the specialized requirements of other networks. In this section we present some of major differences between IN/1 and IN/2. IN/1+ should be considered as a transition phase between IN/1 and IN/2, even though this transition can be prolonged and expensive because of the extensive RBOC networking already in place.

When a service is requested in IN/2, the SSP has some facility to complete the service locally. The triggers in the SSP/2 (the service switching points for IN/2) activate an SSP/2 to STP/2 communication whenever the SCP/2 data-base information is necessary to complete the service requested. Some basic and repeated functionality, such as add/drop lines, are incorporated in all SSPs and SCPs. The other major difference occurs with the presence of the service logic interpreter in the SCP/2. The service programmed in SCPs may be downloaded to other SSPs. Newer services can be introduced and discontinued more economically and rapidly. New service creation can be far less expensive. User programmability at SCP or SMS provides some amount of network control and the creation of private virtual networks. However, since IN/2 is still to be introduced and widely utilized, we limit the further discussion of this network and discuss the more widely accepted intelligent and integrated services digital network (ISDN).

The variety of the functions offered by the mature ISDN are both intelligent and adaptive. For this reason, the proposed ISDN architecture and administration can be adapted to any IN. In more highly specialized private networks (such as industrial, corporate, scientific, military, and governmental), the methodology for implementation may be tailored to suit and serve the priorities of the individual network. The basic concepts for the design and management prevail in most INs. Another example of the PDINs is the 800 network, which incorporates call management data-base facilities. Flexible networks and private virtual networks offer customer control on the configuration of the network for call forwarding, vendor selection, and other local modifications to the network, which influence customer activity. Such intelligent networks are regularly offered by the Bell Operating Companies in the United States. American Telephone and Telegraph Co. is in the process of installing its worldwide intelligent network, which is capable of carrying out most of the intelligent functions discussed here.

B. Basic Rate ISDN

ISDN basic access consists of providing the customer with two circuit or packet switched B channels at 64 kb/sec and one D channel at 16 kb/sec. The two B channels provide bidirectional digital connectivity, that is, the facility to see and use a clear transparent digital channel at 64 kb/sec bearing the information that the user wishes to communicate between the digital device and the distant customer. The two B channels may be individually and independently switched and provide digital communication with any other customer or source in the network. Voice, data, or video may be transmitted as digital information over the B channel. Initially, the circuit switched B channel will provide 56 kb/sec throughput capacity, and eventually it will provide the full 64 kb/sec capacity. The packet switched B channel will provide a maximum throughput of 48 kb/sec at a line rate of 64 kb/sec, (Layer 2—LAPB, subscriber digital line carrier or SDLC).

The D channel serves a variety of functions (see Fig. 13), including signaling and control information across the interface between the network and the customer. This signaling and control information manages the information-carrying B channels. This signaling is done out of band from the B channels, thus facilitating the B channels to be clear and transparent. Further, the control of the B channels via the D channel facilitates robust distributed processing across the ISDN interface. Displaying the call origination address, call transfer, call forwarding information, connected address, etc., would be facilitated by the D channel. Call progress information, such as idle, dial, alert, and connect, will also be carried by this channel. Finally, the signal information identifies the type of tone being applied to the B channel. These tones are necessary to alert the digital facility at the end of the connection. These tones may also differ or be interchanged by the network or the user terminal.

The D channel may also serve two other functions: telemetry and low-capacity packet switched transport. The services included in the telemetry type of capabilities consist of burglar and fire alarms, energy management, and emergency services. For the low-capacity packet switched transport, the maximum throughput rate is limited to 9.6 kb/sec at a line rate of 16 kb/sec.

C. Broadband ISDN

A variety of higher rates are also available in the context of the ISDN. In North America, the H_0, H_{11}, and H_{12} channels support clear access

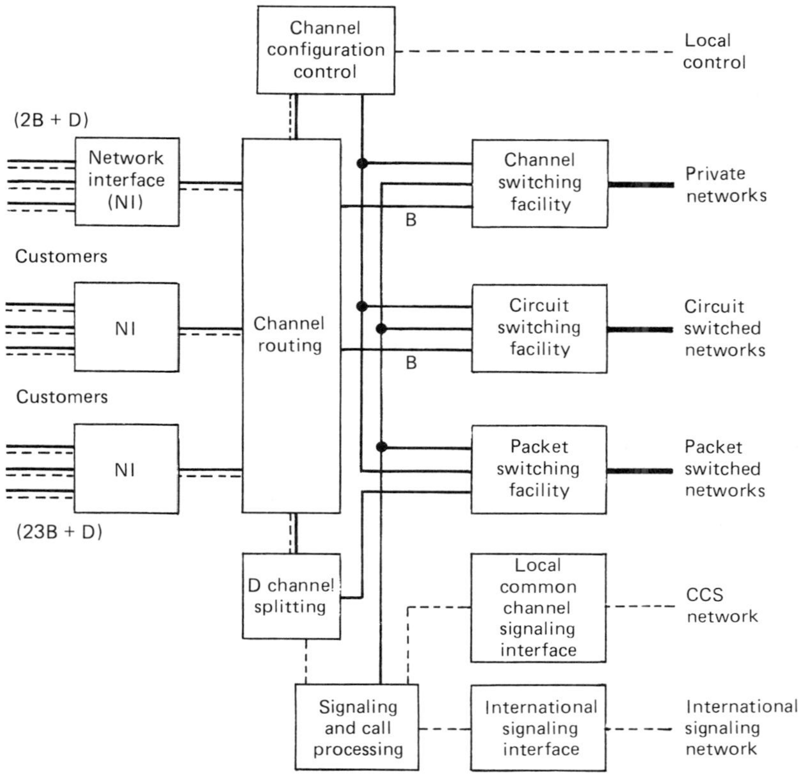

FIG. 13. Architecture of a gateway node showing the need for a common channel signaling network to control and monitor the B channels via the D channel in context of the ISDN environment.

at 384, 1536, and 1920 kb/sec, respectively. A separate D channel is used for signaling (control and maintenance). These channels may be circuit switched or packet switched.

In North America and Japan, the ISDN primary access takes place at (23B + D) rate. In Europe, the rate is (30B + D) at the primary rate interface (PRI). At this interface, the D channel is at 64 kb/sec. The single D channel can carry signaling information for as many as 40 B channels. The D channel protocol is defined by CCITT Q.921 specification or LAPD (local access protocol for D channel). This protocol is used for signaling and information transfer. It is similar to the protocol defined for packet data in the X.25 (LAPB). However, it allows for more than one logical link between end points because of the difference in the nature of the D channel information as opposed to the nature of the B channel information, which is targeted to one end point. In instances where the D channel carries X.25 data together with signaling, the LAPD protocol is used (at the data link layer, i.e., layer 2 of the 7-layer ISO model) for both logical channels—one reserved for signaling and one for X.25 data. At the network layer (i.e., layer 3), the protocol reverts to X.25 for the packet switched data and to CCITT Q.931 protocol for the signaling.

D. Rates and User Characterization

The use of the intelligent network capacities differs widely among the categories of users. Businesses (ranging from very large to small) are expected to use a large proportion of the services and features offered by intelligent networks. Hence, the higher rates are generally intended for the larger businesses for their interactive and batch modes of data transport needs, large-scale data-base access, and machine and intelligent terminal access of the network. Interfacing with the business's private networks and the digital PBXs will also become necessary at the higher network rates.

The lower standard for accessing the network at the basic rate is intended for small businesses and the residential market. The type of network and vendor services are of a different category in this sector. Home information, computers, vending, electronic directories, demand news, facsimile, low-rate video, etc., are expected to become standard features offered by the newer intelligent networks as the information society becomes better established. For most of these services, the basic (lower, 2B + D) rate is expected to suffice.

Wide-band access at a higher bit rate for specialized customers for large, high-speed data is also envisioned. Metropolitan area networks (MANs) with specialized and dispersed computational facilities may call for one intelligent network interfacing with another intelligent network. These types of high-capacity intelligent networks have been installed around scattered campuses and the nation by academic institutions and the National Science Foundation. The emergence of the optical DS3 using high-speed synchronous optical fiber networks (SONET) with data rates in excess of 2 Gb/sec will bring about the truly integrated optical switching and transmission in the architecture of intelligent networks.

VIII. Intelligent Network Switches

The switching function is essential to the functioning of an intelligent and dispersed network. The same physical medium has to perform a large variety of functions, such as carrying voice, data, and video information from any other location bidirectionally. It must also be able to monitor the network response by program or by user interaction and seek and respond with the appropriate responses to system and user queries. Packets of information have to be switched within the network to appropriate modules that can respond to the appropriate user or network commands. Hence, the architecture of a dispersed intelligent network is not complete without an intricate fabric of remotely controlled switching elements.

A. Switching Facilities

In this context, switching of digital information takes place in three types of switches: channel (private), digital (circuit), and packet. The B channel information, and any X.25 packet in the D channel, generally flows through these switches. The control and signaling information in the D channel, which supports the various B channels, flows into the common channel signaling facilities. It is here that most of the intelligence and control reside in the intelligent networks. The signaling information to and from the customers, vendors, networks, etc., converges in these facilities and gets intelligently interpreted to interconnect the bearer channels and dispatch appropriate commands and control information throughout the network.

At the information gateway (typically an ISDN office) interfacing the intelligent network with the customer terminal, the D channel information is separated from the B channel information so that the individual B channels that are served can be individually controlled and signaled. The signaling and call processing information is generated and dispatched to the common channeling signaling interface. This control information flows through a common channel signaling network to the appropriate gateway (another ISDN office) where other functions, such as call setup, call completion, and call monitoring, take place. The B channels are set up for the flow of information between the customers, vendors, service providers, etc.

As is usual in the architecture of computer systems, the flow of control information is separated out from the flow of data. In intelligent networks, the concept is carried through by separating out the common channel signaling facilities from the switching facilities. The concept of distributed processing becomes applicable in the intelligent information networks, as it is in distributed computing networks. To implement the entire system, enormous amounts of software modules and algorithmic steps become essential. For this reason, the use of stored program control (SPC) becomes necessary. Fortunately, over the past three decades, the switching and the computing technologies have been synergetic. Most of the SPC concepts in computing have been implemented in the electronic switching systems (ESS).

B. Electronic Switching in Intelligent Networks

Over the past decade, more and more of the telephone switching environments have been under the control of stored programs residing within the realm of ESS. These switching systems are controlled by intricate software modules exactly as any other sophisticated computer. The reprogramming of these switching systems is relatively straightforward in light of the requirements of the intelligent functions expected from the network. For the circuit switching part of the facility, the existing #1ESS (introduced in 1965 to local switching and to toll switching in 1970) and #1AESS (introduced in 1976 to local switching) have the basic switching capacity to switch and be programmed accordingly. However, the common channel signaling aspects need to be upgraded to accommodate the intelligent network functions, especially those of the ISDN. The flexible and highly programmable digital switches are key components in the distributed and intelligent networks.

In North America, the introduction of the more sophisticated ESS facilities (#5ESS) by AT&T and DMS-100 by Northern Telecom is also a major step in the realization of intelligent network switching nodes. Numerous other switches like GTD-5 EAX by GTE, Siemens EWSD, Ericsson AXE, NEC NEAX 61A, and Alcatel E10-FIVE are also contenders for the evolving INs, SSPs, and STPs.

The modular hardware and software building blocks in the 5ESS permit the option to customize these switching systems to perform the flexible and programmable functions with inherent mechanized intelligence. These switches can function as independent switches or in conjunction with other switches such as 1 ESS or the 1A ESS. Massive parallel processing is invoked to process many thousands of calls simultaneously. The switch also distributes the processing in three major generic hardware modules: the administrative module (AM), the communications module (CM), and the one or more localized or remote switching modules (SM).

The AM handles the administration, operation, and maintenance functions for the global switch. The processing is handled by active/standby dual 3B20D processing facility. These two processing systems function in perfect time and functional synchronism to be able to monitor and act as duplicates to prevent data loss under fault conditions. Call processing and time slot allocation takes place in this module. Functions to support call processing include maintenance under suspicious hardware performance, diagnostic administration and control, software recovery and initialization, and limited extent fault recovery and error detection.

The CM acts as an intelligent communications intermediary between the AM and SM(s) of the global switch. Information forwarded consists of call-processing and administrative data messages. The format for the exchange conforms to the CCITT X.25 recommendation for the data link layer packet switch protocol. The medium for the packet communication facility consists of two network control and timing (NCT) fiber light guide links. Each of the two links carries serial data at 32.768 Mb/sec partitioned into 256 time slots or channels, thus offering 512 channels between the modules. The architecture of the CM is highly evolved and specialized for the communication function it serves. Parallelism between multiplicity of processors makes space division feasible. Allocation of finite time slots make time division feasible. The resulting fabric of allocation of space and time is implemented by the time-space-time (TST) architecture.

The SM performs as the first stage switching device and provides the trunk and line terminations for various lines and trunks. In addition, it provides for initial call processing. Numerous analogue and digital trunks may terminate at the SM, at different rates (up to 10 of T1 at 1.544 Mb/sec, up to 16 at 2.048 Mb/sec), and in addition subscriber loop carrier systems such as SLC-40, SLC-96, and fiber SLC systems may also terminate at the SM. Each information-bearing time slot is identified and mapped in an appropriate TST slot of the CM for completing the circuit switched connection.

The 5ESS duplex 3B20 (3B20D) computer system in the switch is operated under a duplex multienvironment real-time (DMERT) operating system which is also referred to as the Unix real-time reliable (RTR) system. C programming language is supported to program the software modules of the 5ESS switch. Most of the recently introduced switches such as the 5ESS also meet the CCITT requirements for the (2B + D), (23B + D), and the (30B + D) rate interfaces for basic and primary rate ISDN.

In Europe, the steady evolution of the switching systems (Ericsson, AXE10) for intelligent network functions has been well along its way since 1984. The modularity for customization and for CCITT signaling system No. 7, which facilitates the customer services integrated in the network functions, has been incorporated into the newer switching systems being built in Europe. These switches also provide for the (2B + D), (23B + D), and (30B + D) rates. The current versions of the Siemens switching systems (EWSD) have the complete provision to be modified with additional software to serve as the SSPs in most of the evolving INs. Most of the software and hardware modifications have been standardized to accommodate the CCS7 protocol. This adaptation of the traditional EWSD environment to serve as an STP with specialized signal connection control part (SCCP level 4 of CCS7 protocol) is also standard. The SCP functions are not switching intensive, and for this reason any electronic data processing vendors or even standard computing systems with front-end processors for CCS7 protocol conversion, SCCP and TCAP software, mode managers, and SMS interface and its application software will function as a standard SCP.

IX. Trends in Intelligent Networks

Public domain intelligent networks can only evolve because of the massive capital expense necessary to standardize, design, and construct national and international networks. Small, private networks with any reasonable amount of sophistication can be built with existing technology. Between these two extremes lie a group of specialized, high-capacity, sophisticated networks, which can be classified as highly intelligent in their own right. Typical examples of these are military, industrial, computer, campus, and private networks. However, if one specifies the public domain networks, their vendors, services, and specialized features, a few general remarks may be made.

The PDINs invariably have to employ the most economical of the possible modes for data switching and transmission. The well established concept of stored program control of electronic switching has been implemented by most of the major vendors for digital switches. There is a rapid trend to replace the electromechanical switches by digital switches. The analogue switches are being replaced more slowly because of the continued demand for the POTS by a majority of the rural and suburban customers.

The impact of optical switching will have its own effect on the switching functions of the intelligent networks. Optical switching holds enormous potential for speed of and access to the time division multiplexing of the various channels. Integrated optoelectronics offers features that the SPC switching systems accomplish now with the programmable software modules. Typical functions that can be performed are customized services, selected data-base access, the interface with the packet switched networks, common channel control interface, fiber-optic media, and the large number of digital carrier systems that are in use.

Optical media for the transmission of high-speed digital information exert other major forces that shape the access possible in the PDIN environment. Optical fiber and optical communication systems are being introduced in most digital networks. The flexibility, economy, and rate of transmission (up to 1.7 Gb/sec with 20-mile repeaters and 295 Mb/sec overseas intercontinental ranges) make these systems "move" gigabits with extreme flexibility and accuracy. Recently, on-off keying techniques in the fiber transmission environment have reported optical rates of 8 Gb/sec over 68.3 km with 0.5 dB eye closure under experimental conditions as far back as 1986. The effects of attenuation and dispersion have been reduced dramatically with the high quality glass in the fiber. Under similar conditions, the eye closure with a noise margin of 0.4 dB for avalanche photo diodes (APD gain of 8, k factor of 0.4, and darkcurrent of 10 nA) is still expected to be about 1 dB. Coupled with high speed optical transmission, optical switching facility, and optical computing techniques, the intelligent networks will enter their next generation. Recently AT&T Bell Laboratories has tested 33 Gb/sec optical links.

Information vendors play a critical role in supplying customer information via the network. There is a definite need for these vendors to seek and supply information from their own data bases. The queries can be complex and also in a natural language. For this reason, the front-end processors of the vendor data-base systems need the recently introduced natural language processors.

In summary, the three emerging technologies (transmission, switching, and data-base) unified into one composite science of network architecture are modifying the course of IN evolution. At the present time, intelligent networks are in the stages of conceptual evolution that computers were during the sixties. The impact of very large scale integration (VLSI) was felt by the computing industry. Some very positive events, such as massive mainframes, chip computers, computer graphics, and artificial intelligence, were yet to occur. Intelligent networks will find their direction from the growth of ISDN, massive database technology for information vendors, optical switching, integrated optical transmission, integrated computing and switching in the communications arena, and worldwide standardization of signals and protocols. Software and knowledge engineering will also facilitate the final implementation of the global, public domain intelligent networks.

X. Social Impact of Intelligent Networks

Intelligent networks have been evolving for the past three decades. The process was slow during the sixties and seventies but gathered considerable momentum during the eighties. The economic slump of the late eighties dampened the growth and full impact but provided the socioeconomically elite of modern society the intelligent and sophisticated tools to access, derive, and perhaps manipulate sensitive information throughout the globe. It is apparent that intelligence in networks is deeply seated in service driven networks, and such networks will emerge at an alarming rate to service the demands from the society. The explosive trends in the computational fields which indeed compliment the intelligent processing of the control data to channel the information in the telecommunication network catalyzes the power and the potential of the networks.

National economies that permit and encourage the growth of intelligent networks have already demonstrated social, business, educational, and technological sophistication. Communication facilities exist in varying degrees of switching capacity, bandwidth, and networking capability. The impact of these networks can be extrapolated in at least three sectors of the economy (business/industrial, educational, and public).

First, in the business/industrial sector, the expansion of innovative devices (microprocessor-based toys, VLSI chips, HDTV, intelligent automobiles, etc.) and services (CLASS services, FAX and telecopying, slow motion video frame phones, cellular phones, and expert alert systems, etc. is becoming increasingly evident. Networks serve as the foundation for data bases and the communications that drive the regional and distributed industries. For this reason, the combined effect of networks and computers upon our knowledge worker is expected to be as profound as the effect of the automobile upon our industrial worker.

Second, in the educational sector, the networks already have a threefold impact. First, the quality of research has become excellent due to quick access to fellow workers of data bases and up-to-the second results of other researchers. Second, networked classrooms disseminate quality instruction widely and inexpensively. A single classroom can extend over a country or the globe. Student interaction and access permit synergy in creative solutions of academic and research problems. Lastly, the presence of networked terminals incubates the concept of remote data-base access. Emerging intelligent network techniques and technology find a home in the young minds of undergraduate students. A network-literate generation has already begun to surface.

Third, in the public domain, networks offer speed, accuracy, conformation, and a well documented chain of information sources and authority, thus cutting down bureaucratic delays and frustrations. Next, the data-base access and decision support systems offer critical information and artificially intelligent methodologies in making the most systemized decisions for many problems in the public sector. However, the user intelligence has to be matched with the network intelligence. Poor collaboration between these two can lead to catastrophic decisions often based upon humanly ill-reasoned logic or, for that matter, misquoted machine retrieval systems. Our political arena provides ample examples of such imbalances in the caliber of "miscommunication" between the leader and the supporting human–machine environment. Networks only enhance such error modes.

There is another disconcerting feature of these networks. Easy worldwide data base access with totally accurate and nearly instantaneous response at affordable prices brings home a new sense of power that the knowledge society has promised in the 1990s. The misuse of such power in the social context is as probable as the misuse of nuclear power in the political context. The personal and social damage which can result from such misuse can be devastating. Networks are insensitive to the type of information they carry. Pornographic information is served the same way and with the same accuracy and resolution as banking and military information.

The social impact of such an opportunity offered to a few individuals capable of exploiting the opportunity for individual gains can sometimes contradict the social norm. Such cases have become disconcertingly frequent (e.g., the Morris scandal, insider stock market information, Securities and Exchange Commission leaks) via access to computer files and sophisticated networks. In some instances, the actions of the offending individuals can be prosecuted in the courts. However, the pace of opportunity to exploit and steal individual fortunes outstrips the pace of the judicial system to incorporate new laws to arm the public defenders. Hence, at this time a few intelligent network users can outsmart the networks and get away with it due to the differential in the capacity of the judicial system to keep up with the laws to prevent the abuse of a very intelligent information tool of the society.

The access and use of this information depends only upon the users. Networks, driven by the economics of the service they provide, will serve some finite fraction of the society and provide them with information objectionable to the social norms of society. To some extent, one can look back to the days when chemical products were being developed for medical use. Now, unfortunately, the same technology can be misused to provide drugs that some societies cannot eradicate. Other examples, such as chemicals, nuclear materials, and missiles used in warfare, also exist. It appears that the social and personal impact of networks will not be without a certain amount of undesirable side effects. Lazy schoolchildren can network the solutions manuals, compulsive gamblers can become instantly bankrupt, sensitive technology can be profitably encrypted and exported for personal gain. However, free society takes these risks in introducing any new product such as automobiles, computers, facsimile, and now intelligent networks. The societies which are importing or evolving intelligent networks have embraced both the desirable and undesirable features of INs. The question that lingers is how and when the INs will mature in the information age.

Bibliography

Ahamed, S. V. (1982). Simulation and design studies of the digital subscriber line. *Bell Syst. Techn. J.* **61,** 1003–1077.

Ahamed, S. V. (1987). Social impact of intelligent telecommunications network. *Proceedings of the Pacific Telecommunication Conference, 1987.* Vol. 9, pp. 407–414.

Ahamed, S. V., and Lawrence, V. B. "Intelligent Networks and Modern Communication Systems." To be published in 1992.

Beaty, A., Jr. (1989). The evolution to intelligent network. *Telecommunications* February 1989.

Bell Telephone Laboratories (1982). "Transmission Systems for Communications." Western Electric Company, Winston-Salem, North Carolina.

Bell Communications Research, Bellcore Special Report, SR-NPL-000444, (Plan for Second Generation of the Intelligent Network), 1986; Bellcore TR-TSY-000064 (SSP's), 1986; Bellcore SR-TSY-000782 (SSP/2), 1987; Bellcore SR-TSY-00778, (SLI), 1987; Bellcore, TA-TSY-000462, (SSP Capabilities for PVN services), 1987; Bellcore, TA-TSY-000460, (BSDB, SCP Application for PVN services), 1987; Also see Bellcore ST-NPL-00002 (ISDN System Planning), 1986; etc.

Miller, M. J., and Ahamed, S. V. (1987). "Digital Transmission Systems and Networks, Vol. I: Principles." Computer Science Press, Rockville, Maryland.

Miller, M. J., and Ahamed, S. V. (1988). "Digital Transmission Systems and Networks, Vol. II: Applications." Computer Science Press, Rockville, Maryland.

Weber, R. P. (1980). "Data Processing Communication Call Processing Method." U.S. Patent 4,192,860, March 4, 1980.

INTERACTING BOSON MODEL (NUCLEAR PHYSICS)

Bruce R. Barrett and Philip Halse *University of Arizona*

GLOSSARY

Atomic weight or nuclear mass number (A): Integer equal to the sum of the number of protons Z and neutrons N.

Boson: Particle possessing integer angular momentum (or spin) and satisfying Bose–Einstein statistics (that is, symmetric under particle interchange).

Fermion: Particle possessing half-odd-integer angular momentum (or spin) and satisfying Fermi–Dirac statistics (that is, antisymmetric under particle interchange) and thereby the Pauli exclusion principle.

Isospin: Vector operator relating to the charge of particles. For the nucleon, the total isospin is $T = \frac{1}{2}$, and the third component is $T_3 = +\frac{1}{2}$ for the proton and $T_3 = -\frac{1}{2}$ for the neutron.

Parity: Symmetry of a wave function under inversion of the coordinate system: $r \rightarrow -\mathbf{r}$. The wave function either remains unchanged (even or + parity) or changes sign (odd or − parity).

Seniority (v): Integer equal to the number of nucleons in a nucleus not coupled pairwise to zero.

For over 30 years, nuclear structure physics has been dominated by two models, the single-particle shell model, developed by Maria Goeppert-Mayer and J. H. D. Jensen, and the collective model, developed by Aage Bohr and Ben Mottelson. The shell model is successful in explaining the so-called magic numbers (or closed shell values) for protons and neutrons that lead to highly stable nuclei. It is also able to describe the properties of light nuclei and of nuclei near closed shells. However, because of the large number of possible states, shell-model calculations for medium-mass and heavy mass nuclei away from closed shells are prohibitively difficult. On the other hand, the collective model is phenomenologically successful in treating the nucleus as a liquid drop, whose excitations are taken to arise from rotations and small oscillations about an equilibrium shape, with the modes corresponding to quadrupole (angular momentum two) deformations dominating. On quantization, this model can be expressed in terms of angular-momentum-two phonons (that is, bosons). [*See* NUCLEAR PHYSICS.]

Although considerable effort has been made to unite these two models since their development, these investigations have met with only partial success. In 1974, Akito Arima and Francesco Iachello introduced a new model, the interacting boson model (IBM), which is an algebraic model and offers the real possibility of providing the missing link between the single-particle shell model and the collective model, in that it contains features of both. Although the IBM was first developed for medium-mass to heavy mass nuclei with an even number of protons and an even number of neutrons (so-called even–even nuclei), it has now been extended to describe odd-mass nuclei (even–odd and odd–even nuclei) and odd–odd nuclei, the latter being the most difficult to understand. For historical as well as practical reasons, the IBM for even–even nuclei will be described first.

I. Description of the Model

The shell model treats the nucleus as a system of neutrons and protons interacting through the strong interaction. Neutrons and protons are collectively referred to as nucleons and are fermions, because they have an intrinsic spin angular momentum of one-half. As fermions, they satisfy Fermi–Dirac statistics and obey the Pauli exclusion principle, which states that no two fermions can occupy the same state in the same system, that is, they cannot have the same set of classifying quantum numbers. The Pauli exclusion principle leads to the filling of shells (or levels) produced by the mean field of the nucleons. As in atoms, the filling of a shell leads to a highly stable structure, with all the angular momenta of the nucleons in the shell summing up to zero. In the shell model, such structures are assumed to be inert, and nuclear properties are described in terms of the remaining nucleons (that is, the valence nucleons) moving outside the closed shells.

When two alike nucleons occur outside a closed shell, it is observed that their angular momenta couple to zero in the nuclear state of lowest energy, that is, the ground state. In fact, it is found empirically that the ground-state angular momenta (J) of all even–even nuclei are zero. The physical explanation of this result is the short range of the attractive strong interaction, that is, oppositely aligned angular momenta of the alike nucleons produce maximum overlap of the nucleons' wave functions and so the largest interaction. By similar reasoning, the next lowest energy states of the two alike nucleons are $J = 2$, then $J = 4$, etc. Figure 1 shows the relative strength of the alike-nucleon interaction versus the total angular momentum J of the nucleons. For two alike nucleons in the same level, only even total angular momenta can occur because of the Pauli exclusion principle, which requires their total wave function to be antisymmetric under particle interchange. The above empirical observation suggests that building blocks of nucleon pairs of angular momentum zero and two may play an important role in determining low-lying nuclear properties. A system of fermion pairs is symmetric under the interchange of any two pairs. Consequently, such

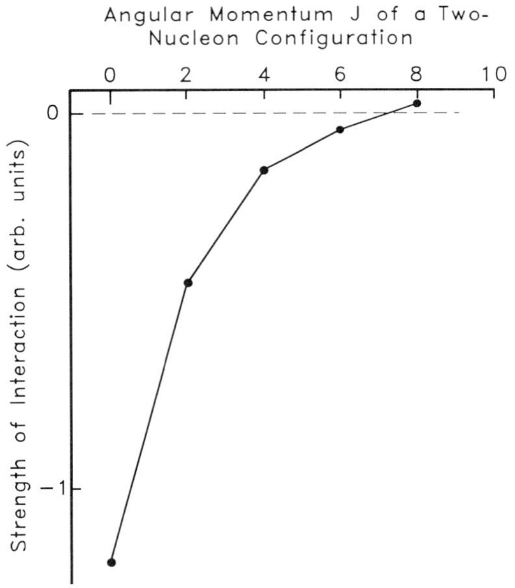

FIG. 1. Strength of the two-alike nucleon interaction versus the total angular momentum J (taken from an analysis of pairs in a $j = \frac{9}{2}$ level).

pairs are boson-like objects. These observations, together with the known phenomenological usefulness of angular-momentum-two bosons in the geometrical model, provide the motivation for the IBM.

The basic assumption of the IBM is that an even–even nucleus of N_p valence protons and N_n valence neutrons in the shell model can be treated as a system of $n_p = N_p/2$ valence proton bosons and $n_n = N_n/2$ valence neutron bosons, each having angular momentum zero or two. For reasons related to the naming of angular momenta in atomic physics, the angular-momentum-zero bosons are called s bosons, and those with angular momentum two are called d bosons. Since the number of bosons is directly related to the number of valence nucleons, the number of IBM bosons is strictly conserved. The neutron bosons can be in s states (their number given by n_{sn}) or d states (their number given by n_{dn}), such that $n_n = n_{sn} + n_{dn}$, with a similar relation for the protons. This relationship is indicated in Fig. 2. It is assumed that bosons of higher angular momenta, for example, g bosons of angular momentum four, are less probable, because the corresponding fermion pairs are less tightly bound, for the reason given earlier (see Fig. 1).

The IBM is a model, instead of a theory, because it is known that the nucleus is made up of

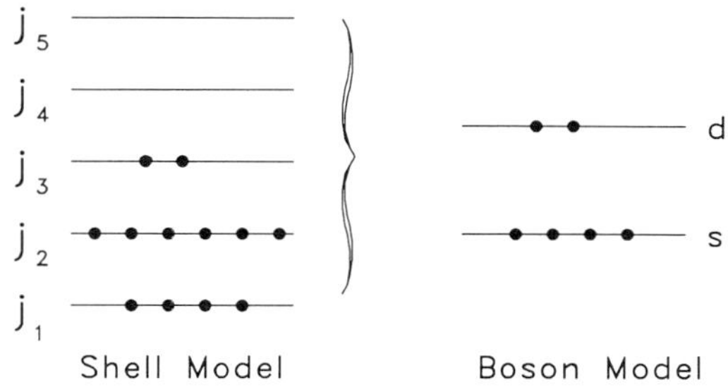

FIG. 2. Example of the truncation in the number of levels and the number of particles involved in replacing the shell-model problem by the IBM problem. The 12 nucleons in 5 shell-model levels (left-hand side) become 6 bosons in 2 levels, *s* or *d* (right-hand side). In reality, the boson configuration shown would correspond to a superposition of many shell-model configurations.

fermions and not bosons. However, the IBM can be a successful phenomenological model without defining or understanding the fermionic structure of the bosons. At the present time, the exact nature of this underlying structure is not known. Attempts to associate a microscopic structure with the IBM bosons will be discussed in Section VIII.

By building the valence structure of the nucleus from *s* and *d* bosons, one gains a twofold truncation of the shell-model problem. First, the bosons exist in only two states, *s* and *d*, while the fermions may occupy several single-particle levels with various large angular momentum values, and second, the number of interacting particles is cut in half, as shown in Fig. 2. This double truncation can reduce a shell-model problem involving 10^{12} or 10^{14} states to a boson problem in 10^2 or 10^3, which can be easily handled on a computer. Thus, it is noted that the interacting boson model is actually a shell model for bosons, but it is much simpler to apply to heavier mass nuclei.

II. Interacting Boson Model-1 (IBM-1)

The original version of the IBM does not distinguish between proton and neutron bosons; there are simply $(n_p + n_n)$ *s* and *d* valence bosons. This form of the model is referred to as the IBM-1. If one assumes that only one-body and two-body terms are important in describing the interactions among the bosons, one can easily write down a boson Hamiltonian involving all possible interactions to this order. This empirical Hamiltonian contains nine independent terms, only six of which are needed to define a spectrum for each value of N. The strength parameters of these terms can be easily determined by fitting experimental data for a given nucleus, a procedure also often used in shell-model calculations.

In their early papers, Arima and Iachello noted that the IBM-1 Hamiltonian possesses three symmetry limits, which could be related to geometrical descriptions in the collective model. Physicists feel that symmetries in nature are very fundamental, since they are often related to conserved quantities and basic principles. In the case of the IBM, the largest symmetry is the unitary group in six dimensions, U(6). The six dimensions come from the one *s* boson and the five possible states of the *d* boson [that is, the five possible orientations of its angular momentum ($J = 2$) along a given axis]. [*See* Encyclopedia article GROUP THEORY.]

This overall U(6) symmetry for the *s* and *d* bosons can be broken in three distinct ways that contain the conserved rotation group SO(3), giving rise to three dynamical symmetry chains, as indicated in Eq. (1):

$$\begin{aligned} &U(6) \supset U(5) \supset SO(5) \supset SO(3) \\ &U(6) \supset SU(3) \supset SO(3) \\ &U(6) \supset SO(6) \supset SO(5) \supset SO(3) \end{aligned} \tag{1}$$

A dynamical symmetry comes from breaking the larger symmetry by the Casimir operators of groups making up one of the subgroup chains in Eq. (1). The nuclear-physics phenomenology corresponding to the U(5) and SU(3) chains was already known. The U(5) chain is related to a spherical vibrator, while the SU(3) chain displays aspects of rotational motion. Figure 3 shows the spectrum of a nucleus exhibiting

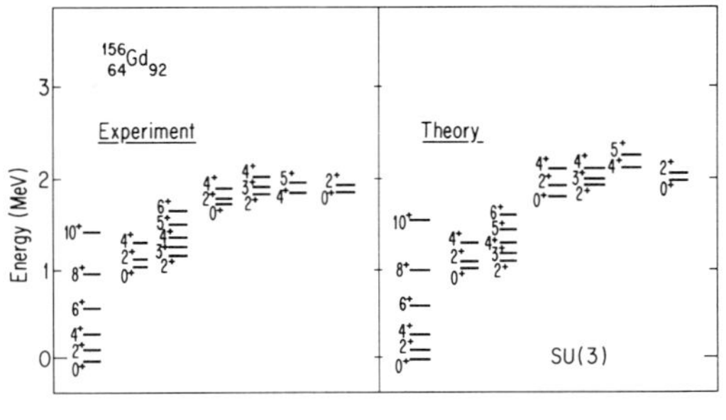

FIG. 3. Comparison of the experimental spectrum of $^{156}_{64}Gd$ (experiment) with that corresponding to the SU(3) limit of the IBM-1 (theory). Each energy level is labeled by the value of the total angular momentum J.

SU(3)-like structure. The SO(6) chain was a new prediction, which was later verified by experiment and shown to represent what are known as γ-soft or γ-unstable nuclei. In these symmetry limits, exact analytical solutions can be obtained to the IBM-1 Hamiltonian. Moreover, the general IBM-1 formalism provides numerical solutions for cases between the symmetry limits, known as transitional nuclei. [*See* GROUP THEORY, APPLIED.]

III. Neutron–Proton Interacting Boson Model (IBM-2)

The key feature missing from the IBM-1 approach is the relationship of the bosons to the underlying fermionic structure of the shell model. The work of Igal Talmi has shown the importance of the interaction between valence protons and valence neutrons in producing nuclear deformations. For this reason, the IBM was later expanded to treat separately the proton boson and neutron boson degrees of freedom. This proton–neutron interacting boson model is known as the IBM-2. A completely general one- and two-body IBM-2 Hamiltonian would contain 30 independent terms, so it is usually simplified to basically two components, a term that splits the energies of the s and d bosons, related to the pairing interaction (see Section I), and a quadrupole–quadrupole interaction between the proton bosons and the neutron bosons. The latter term is the lowest order interaction that can mix states containing different numbers of s bosons and d bosons, thought to be appropriate for nuclear deformation. The parameters of the IBM-2 Hamiltonian have been determined for a wide range of medium-mass to heavy mass nuclei, mainly in the rare-earth region, and the model has enjoyed considerable success in describing the low-lying properties of these nuclei.

Because the IBM-2 contains separately proton and neutron boson degrees of freedom, it yields not only states that are totally symmetric in both the charge and sd spaces (corresponding to the IBM-1 solutions), but also states of mixed symmetry in both spaces. These mixed symmetry states in the IBM-2 lead to predictions regarding new forms of collective motion. The degree of symmetry of the IBM-2 states can be classified according to a quantity known as F-spin, which treats the proton and neutron bosons as two charge states of a single particle in the same way that the isospin T treats protons and neutrons as two charge states of one particle, the nucleon. The states of maximum F-spin are totally symmetric and correspond to the IBM-1 states. States with F-spin less than the maximal value are of mixed symmetry and are believed to lie higher in energy as their F-spin value decreases. There has been considerable interest in the last few years in detecting experimentally the first set of mixed symmetry (or F maximal minus one) states. For highly deformed nuclei, these mixed symmetry states should have a signature of angular momentum one and parity plus with a strong magnetic-dipole gamma transition to the ground state. Numerous states with these properties have now been observed in rare-earth nuclei, supporting this prediction of the IBM-2. These states are being studied in detail in order to ascertain what new information they can tell us about nuclear structure, and candidates for other types of mixed symmetry states are being sought in other mass regions.

IV. IBM-3 and IBM-4

In most medium-mass to heavy mass nuclei, the protons and neutrons fill different major shells. In this mass region, the nuclear interaction strongly favors the proton–proton and neutron–neutron like pairs instead of pairs of neutron–proton structure. In light nuclei (mass number A less than 100), the protons and neutrons often fill the same shells. In such cases, it is equally likely to form pairs constructed from a proton and a neutron. A neutron–proton pair can be either symmetric or antisymmetric in its charge state T. The symmetric neutron–proton state has the same structure as the proton–proton and neutron–neutron pairs, so that together they form a triplet of equivalent states. The interacting boson model constructed from these three bosons is called the IBM-3. If the antisymmetric neutron–proton charge state is included as a fourth boson, one obtains the IBM-4. The IBM-3 and IBM-4 were developed by J. P. Elliott *et al.* and have been successfully applied to light nuclei, mainly for $18 \leq A \leq 46$.

For nuclei where they are appropriate, the inclusion of proton–neutron bosons allows the IBM-3 and IBM-4 to describe odd–odd nuclei and β-decay, which cannot be done with the IBM-2.

V. Interacting Boson–Fermion Model

The empirical success of the IBM for even–even nuclei encouraged its developers to expand it to odd–even and even–odd nuclei by the addition of one fermion. This odd-A version is known as the interacting boson fermion model or IBFM. The IBFM Hamiltonian contains a boson term, a fermion term, and a third term representing the interaction (or coupling) between the bosons and fermion. As in the IBM, the IBFM can be discussed in symmetry limits, as in Eq. (1), in which the odd fermion is coupled to the valence bosons in either the U(5), SU(3), or SO(6) limits. The different limits can be related to particular cases in the collective model, such as the strong-coupling or weak-coupling limits.

The addition of an odd fermion greatly increases the number of possible parameters in this model; the number of possible states also greatly increases. For these reasons, the IBFM has been applied mainly to special cases, such as a nucleon in a single j level or in several j levels with the imposition of some boson–fermion symmetry (see Section VI). This model has recently been used for studies of β-decay between odd–even and even–odd nuclei.

VI. Boson–Fermion Symmetries

In 1980, Iachello observed that in certain cases new symmetries, corresponding to simultaneous transformations of the boson and fermion systems, can be introduced. This is possible if some groups in the fermion classification (that is, group chain) coincide with some groups in the boson classification [see Eq. (1)]. Combined bose–fermi groups can then be introduced corresponding to particular couplings of the bosons and fermions.

It was, of course, known that the conservation of the total angular momentum requires the combined system to be invariant under the total angular momentum operator (the sum of parts acting on the bosons and on the fermions), generating $SO^{BF}(3)$. But it was found that spectra are often closer to those associated with combining the larger groups in Eq. (1), such as SO(6), with their fermion counterparts, implying the conservation of less well-understood quantities.

Figure 4 illustrates the spectrum of an odd-A nucleus related by such a bose–fermi symmetry to the spectrum of its even–even neighbor. It was claimed that cases such as those shown in Fig. 4 are examples of supersymmetric structure in nuclei. However, supersymmetry conventionally refers to a description involving a superalgebra, which is an algebra containing operators that transform bosons into fermions and vice versa. In fact, the cases and examples given then and in later work are for bose–fermi symmetries rather than true supersymmetries. Nevertheless, the fact that the properties of certain neighboring even–even and odd-A nuclei can be related by the same group-theoretical chains and the same Hamiltonian is of significant interest and provides new insight into the structure of complex nuclei. Present investigations regarding high-spin superdeformed bands indicate that superdeformed bands in certain neighboring even–even and odd-A nuclei may prove to be the best examples of bose–fermi symmetries in nuclei. Recent work with superalgebras indicates that examples of real supersymmetries may exist in nuclei.

VII. Other Extensions of the IBM

By its basic assumptions, the IBM is a model for low-excitation nuclear structure. For this reason, a number of expanded versions have

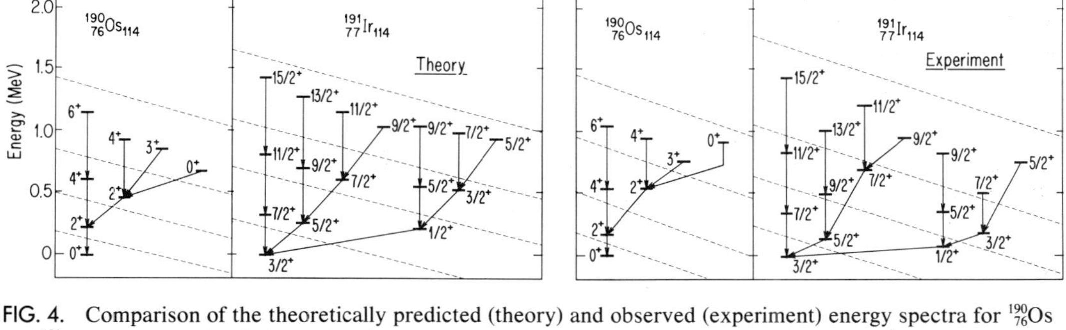

FIG. 4. Comparison of the theoretically predicted (theory) and observed (experiment) energy spectra for $^{190}_{76}$Os and $^{191}_{77}$Ir, as an example of a bose–fermi symmetry in nuclei. Each energy level is labeled by the value of the total angular momentum J. The dashed lines enclose levels of the same symmetry. The solid lines indicate levels between which strong electromagnetic radiation occurs.

been developed, so as to describe other nuclear properties. Angular momentum one (p) and three (f) bosons have been introduced to explain negative parity states in nuclei, and aligned pairs coupled to large values of the angular momentum have been used to describe high-spin states. Procedures have also been developed for treating configuration mixing in nuclei, such as the mixing between vibrational-like and rotational-like states.

VIII. Microscopic Interpretations of the IBM

The success of this formalism involving rather abstract bosons suggests that they might represent real objects within the nucleus, in particular that they may be interpreted in terms of the valence protons and neutrons of the shell model (Section I). Investigations of this possibility make up the largest single area of research arising from the IBM.

Since a pair of fermions is bosonlike (a similarity which improves as the number of fermion states increases), a natural proposal is that the s and d bosons are modeling pairs of nucleons coupled to angular momentum 0 and 2 denoted as S and D, respectively; indeed, this idea was used to motivate our discussion of the IBM and is commonly seen as part of the IBM per se. However, concluding that the validity of this interpretation follows from the equality of statistics and angular momentum alone would be a non sequitur. Moreover, many other situations are possible, such as the bosons representing quartets of nucleons (IBM results are generally not very sensitive to the number of bosons), or even having no interpretation of the bosons singly, necessitating a more complicated many-boson–many-nucleon correspondence.

In fact, there can be no automatic answer to the question of what the bosons represent, since their interpretation must depend on the phenomena they are used to describe. For instance, s and d bosons could in principle be used to describe the giant quadrupole resonance; any shell model interpretation of such bosons would have to be very different from one designed to reflect the description of low-energy phenomena with which the model is associated in practice.

Nevertheless, as described above, an interpretation of the bosons as fermion pairs is almost always the basic postulate of such investigations. It is apparent that the structure of the pairs associated with the bosons must be collective in nature, because of the transition from the nucleon shell model space to the collective-pair space is already a significant truncation.

Most attempts to develop a microscopic interpretation have centered around a search for the appropriate collective pairs in the fermion (that is, nucleon) space to be mapped onto (that is, related with) the bosons. This is indicated schematically in Fig. 5. Here, the large circle represents the full fermion shell model space, which is then truncated to the subspace constructed using the S ($J = 0$) and D ($J = 2$) pairs. Then, some subset, 2, restricted for computational reasons to consist of only those states with a small number of D pairs, is associated through mapping (represented by label 3) to the corresponding set of states, 4, in the boson space and used to determine the boson operators, corresponding to those of interest in the shell model.

One prescription for the collective fermion pairs is to solve the shell-model problem for two alike nucleons for $J = 0$ and $J = 2$ and to equate the lowest $J = 0$ eigenstate with the collective S pair and the lowest $J = 2$ eigenstate with the collective D pair. This procedure follows ideas suggested by I. Talmi regarding his work on generalized seniority. Other procedures have been proposed for constructing the collective fermion states to be associated with the IBM states, but there is no general agreement regarding an ideal choice.

However, the impossibility of performing shell model calculations for heavy nuclei (Section I), itself a rationale for use of the IBM,

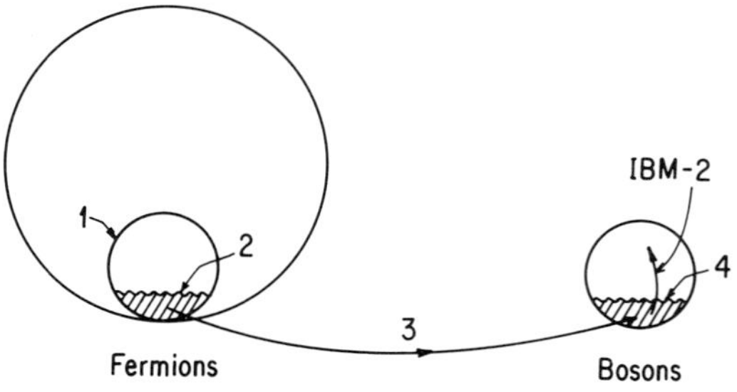

FIG. 5. Pictorial description of one microscopic IBM procedure. The full fermion space (large circle) is truncated to an S and D collective-pair space, 1. An appropriate subset, 2, is associated through the mapping (represented by label 3) to the corresponding states, 4, in the boson space. The IBM-2 interaction can now be computed microscopically, completing the boson picture.

means that the validity of the pair interpretation cannot be definitively tested. It simply is not known whether the many-pair condensate analogues of the many-boson IBM states would indeed allow a reasonable approximation to the shell model eigenstates, nor whether the shell model operators mentioned above would in fact reproduce the data. As discussed above, the shell model interpretation of the bosons must be appropriate for the levels the IBM is used to model: for instance, the interpretation for a description of all the low-energy rotational bands of ^{156}Gd (Fig. 3.) would be different from that appropriate for a description of the first, fourth, and fifth bands only. (For example, if the strength of the interaction in the theoretical boson calculations were increased by around 50%, then the second and third model bands obtained would correspond to the fourth and fifth bands in the experiment, while the observed second and third bands would have no IBM counterparts). A possible failure of the *SD* pair interpretation is then apparent in exact calculations for lighter nuclei, where it is found that the many-pair states describe only some of the levels that the IBM would be used to model. A similar conclusion has been obtained in an approximate calculation for ^{156}Gd itself. If this situation does indeed persist in heavy nuclei, it would have to be concluded that the simple interpretation of the bosons as pairs is inconsistent with the use of the IBM to model all the collective low-energy levels, as is invariably the case (Fig. 3).

There is much controversy in this area, which only further research can resolve. A truly valid shell model interpretation of the elegantly simple IBM would reveal a correspondingly simple latent structure amid the complexity of realistic shell model calculations.

Bibliography

Arima, A., and Iachello, F. (1984). "Advances in Nuclear Physics" (J. W. Negele and E. Vogt, eds.), Vol. 13. Plenum, New York.

Barrett, B. R. (1984). "Nucleon–Nucleon Interaction and Nuclear Many-Body Problems" (S. S. Wu and T. T. S. Kuo, eds.). World Scientific, Singapore.

Casten, R. F., and Feng, D. H. (1984). Nuclear dynamical supersymmetry. *In* "Physics Today," Vol. 37. American Institute of Physics. New York.

Casten, R. F., and Warner, D. D. (1988). The interacting boson approximation. *In* "Reviews of Modern Physics," Vol. 60. The American Physical Society, New York.

Dieperink, A. E. L., and Wenes, G. (1985). "Annual Review of Nuclear and Particle Science," Vol. 35. Annual Review Inc., Palo Alto, California.

Iachello, F., and Arima, A. (1987). "The Interacting Boson Model." Cambridge Univ. Press, London and New York.

Iachello, F., and Talmi, I. (1987). Shell-model foundation of the interacting boson model. *In* "Reviews of Modern Physics," Vol. 59. The American Physical Society, New York.

Iachello, F., and Van Isacker, P. (1990). "The Interacting Boson-Fermion Model." Cambridge University Press, London and New York.

Scholten, O. (1985). "Progress in Particle and Nuclear Physics," Vol. 14. Pergamon, Oxford.

INTERNAL COMBUSTION ENGINES

Charles L. Proctor, II *University of Florida*

GLOSSARY

Adiabatic process: Process in which heat energy is neither supplied to a system nor rejected from it.

Air–fuel ratio: Mass of air divided by mass of fuel in a mixture.

Air-standard cycle: Idealized cycle in which the working fluid is only air, the air acts as an ideal gas, combustion processes are replaced by reversible heat transfer processes, and the exhaust–intake process is replaced by a reversible heat rejection process that returns the air of the cycle to the original intake condition.

Carnot efficiency: Maximum attainable thermal efficiency of any engine.

Homogeneous mixture: Mixture of air and fuel in which the fuel is vaporized and the air and fuel are thoroughly mixed such that the air–fuel characteristics are the same throughout the mixture.

Ignition limits: Range of air–fuel ratios in which an air–fuel mixture will ignite and support combustion.

Isentropic process: Theoretical process that has no heat transfer, friction, or irreversibilities.

Specific enthalpy: Thermodynamic property of a substance defined as the sum of its specific internal energy and the product of its pressure and specific volume.

Specific heat at constant pressure: Rate of change of specific enthalpy with respect to temperature while at constant pressure.

Specific heat at constant volume: Rate of change of specific internal energy with respect to temperature while at constant volume.

Specific-heat ratio: Specific heat at constant pressure divided by specific heat at constant volume.

Specific internal energy: Property of a substance that represents the energy state of the substance divided by the mass being considered. For an ideal gas, specific internal energy is a function of temperature only.

Specific volume: Volume divided by the mass contained within the volume.

Stoichiometric mixture: Air–fuel mixture that contains exactly the amount of oxygen necessary to oxidize carbon of the fuel to carbon dioxide and hydrogen of the fuel to water, leaving no excess oxygen or fuel in the combustion products.

Thermal efficiency: Ratio of net work output to total energy input.

Internal combustion (IC) engines characterize devices that use the media of combustion (i.e., air–fuel mixture and products of combustion) as the working fluid in the engine. Examples of such engines include the gasoline or spark ignition (SI) engine, the diesel engine, and the gas turbine engine. Engines such as these are the most broadly applied and widely used power-generating devices currently in existence. The four-stroke gasoline-powered homogeneous-charge spark ignition (SI) engine is the most common IC engine by virtue of its tremendous success as the prime mover in the transportation industry.

I. Overview

In 1900, the production of steam engine (external combustion engine) and battery-powered (electric motor) automobiles outnumbered that of automobiles with SI engines. Within 40 years, however, virtually all cars were powered by SI engines. As late as 1930, most trains were powered by steam engines. Today, steam engines are a curiosity, and diesel engines power modern rail systems. The IC engine has always been the mainstay of the aeronautics industry through the use of SI engines and gas turbine engines. The aircraft gas turbine, in particular, has become the prime mover of the aeronautics industry due to the range, speed, and passenger comfort it provides. The gas turbine is also finding increased application as a power source in trains, ships, trucks, and buses.

Although steam generation units still produce far more electricity than IC devices, the IC engine is a vital component in handling peak load situations and emergency power production. Gas turbines are used in electric power grids for peak load periods due to their rapid startup characteristics and high power output capabilities. Diesel engines and SI engines are often used as on-site or portable electrical power units.

In addition to larger engines, IC engines power motorcycles, lawn mowers, chain saws, and devices as small as model airplanes. This versatility, along with favorable investment and operational costs, is why the IC engine finds widespread use in contemporary energy production.

II. Categories

Internal combustion engines can be divided into two categories: continuous-combustion engines and intermittent-combustion engines. The continuous-combustion engine is characterized by a steady flow of fuel and air into the engine and a stable flame maintained within the engine. Gas turbine engines exemplify the continuous-combustion engine. The intermittent-combustion engine is characterized by periodic ignition of fuel and air. Commonly referred to as reciprocating engines, these devices process discrete volumes of air and fuel in a cyclic manner. Gasoline piston engines and diesel engines are examples of this group.

III. Theoretical Analysis

All IC engines can be characterized by a series of thermodynamic events. In the continuous-combustion engine these events occur simultaneously as air and fuel flow steadily into the engine. In the intermittent-combustion engine, events occur in succession and are repeated for each full cycle of the engine.

The thermodynamic events for IC engines are (1) intake of air or air–fuel mixture; (2) compression of air or air–fuel mixture; (3) combustion of air and fuel, resulting in an increase in the temperature of the reacted air–fuel mixture; (4) extraction of work from the heated combustion products by expansion; and (5) exhaust of combustion products. These thermodynamic events will now be examined for the three most common cycles in commercially successful IC engines. These cycles are (1) the Otto cycle, typical of SI engines; (2) the Diesel cycle, typical of diesel engines; and (3) the Brayton cycle, typical of gas turbine engines. The air-standard cycle, however, must first be defined.

A. Air-Standard Cycle

Actual processes occurring in IC engines are very complex; consequently, a common tool for the analysis of IC engines is the air-standard cycle. Modeling a real engine with a simplified process permits examination of the influence of only the major operating variables on engine performance. Although numerical values calculated from such models provide only a qualitative representation of the actual process, they do provide important analytical information.

The air-standard cycle is an idealized cycle founded on the following approximations: (1) The working fluid throughout the cycle is only air; (2) the air acts as an ideal gas; (3) combustion processes are replaced by well-defined heat addition processes; and (4) the exhaust process is replaced by a heat rejection process that returns the air of the cycle to intake conditions. Since air is assumed to be an ideal, or perfect, gas, constant values of specific heat at constant volume and pressure are frequently assumed.

Since performance is a primary consideration in the evaluation of an engine, a necessary parameter for examining engines is thermal efficiency. Thermal efficiency η_{th} is defined as the ratio of net work output of an engine to total heat input:

$$\eta_{th} = (\text{net work output})/(\text{total heat input}) \quad (1)$$

When maximum attainable thermal efficiency of an engine is being considered, comparison to the Carnot efficiency is made. The Carnot efficiency $\eta_{\text{th, Carnot}}$ represents the maximum attainable thermal efficiency of any engine. It is determined by the equation

$$\eta_{\text{th, Carnot}} = 1 - \frac{\text{sink temperature}}{\text{source temperature}} \tag{2}$$

The sink temperature is the temperature of the environment surrounding the engine, and the source temperature is the peak temperature in the cycle.

In order for a real engine to approach the Carnot efficiency it must be thermally and mechanically reversible (i.e., free of large temperature gradients and friction). It is not feasible to build an engine whose processes duplicate the Carnot cycle. Engines more closely modeled by other cycles, such as the Otto cycle, Diesel cycle, and Brayton cycle, whose efficiencies are less than the Carnot cycle, are commonly used. Nevertheless, the Carnot efficiency is ultimately the ideal thermal efficiency to strive toward.

Before we examine the basic cycle characteristics of SI, diesel, and gas turbine cycles, it is necessary to introduce nomenclature common to these cycles.

B. Nomenclature

The study of IC engines involves the use of specific hardware components and defined parameters. For the gas turbine engine these components are diffusers, compressors, combustors, turbines, and nozzles. The application of these components to gas turbine engines will be described in Section III,E. The parameter needed to develop this cycle is the pressure ratio r_p. The pressure ratio is defined as the ratio of the exhaust pressure of a compressor to its inlet pressure.

Several terms unique to reciprocating engines must be defined before these cycles can be examined. In reciprocating devices using a piston–cylinder arrangement, terms are defined by the size, location, and motion of the piston within the cylinder (Fig. 1). The inner diameter of the cylinder is referred to as bore. When the piston is at its farthest location from the cylinder head, it is at bottom dead center and the gas within the cylinder occupies its maximum volume of the cycle (VBDC). When the piston is located closest to the cylinder head, it is at top dead center. At this time the gas volume is at the cycle minimum and is called the clearance volume (VTDC). The distance the piston head travels from bottom dead center to top dead center is the stroke. The volume displaced as the piston travels from bottom dead center to top dead center is the displacement volume. The clearance volume is often referred to in terms of percent clearance, or clearance volume divided by displacement volume. The compression ratio r of a reciprocating engine is defined by the volume within the cylinder at bottom dead center divided by the volume at top dead center.

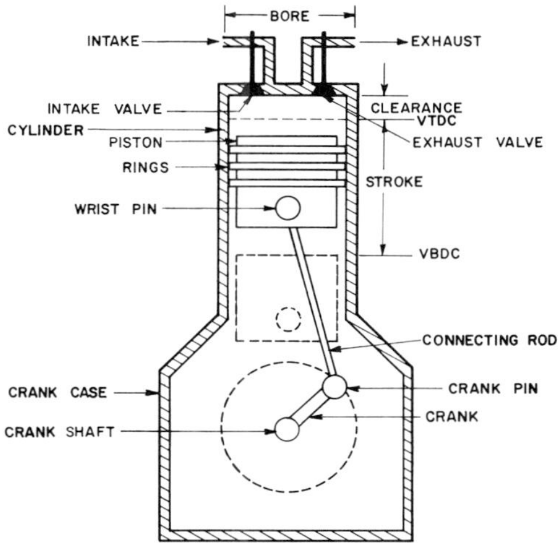

FIG. 1. Piston–cylinder nomenclature.

C. Air-Standard Otto Cycle

The Otto cycle is the theoretical cycle of interest when one is considering reciprocating SI engines. The four-stroke Otto cycle is made up of the following four internally reversible processes: 1–2, isentropic compression; 2–3, constant-volume heat addition; 3–4, isentropic expansion; and 4–1, constant-volume heat rejection.

The actual exhaust and intake stroke has been replaced by process 4–1, as described in Section IV,A. Representation of the Otto cycle on a pressure–volume (PV) diagram and temperature–entropy (TS) diagram is provided in Fig. 2.

Thermodynamic analysis of the Otto cycle produces a simple relationship among the thermal efficiency of the Otto cycle $\eta_{\text{th, Otto}}$, compression ratio r, and specific-heat ratio k:

$$\eta_{\text{th, Otto}} = 1 - (1/r^{k-1}) \tag{3}$$

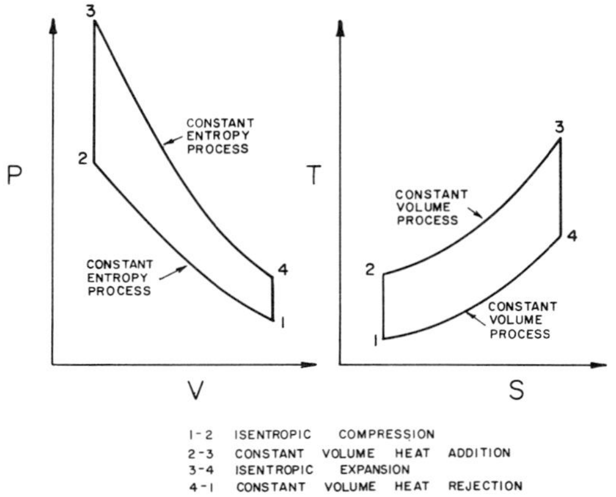

FIG. 2. Process diagrams for the Otto cycle.

The influence of compression ratio and specific-heat ratio on the thermal efficiency of the Otto cycle is shown in Fig. 3. For a given specific-heat ratio, thermal efficiency increases dramatically with increasing compression ratio at low values of r. Beyond $r = 10$, however, thermal efficiency curves flatten out, and the benefit of operating at higher and higher compression ratios lessens. In practice, the working fluid in the SI engine is an air–fuel mixture during the compression process. This places practical limits on the compression ratio due to preignition of hydrocarbon fuels commonly used in SI engines. Consequently, conventional SI engines are seldom designed with compression ratios greater than 10. This factor will be fully addressed in Section IV,A.

The various curves for the specific-heat ratio k show that thermal efficiency decreases with decreasing k. A practical consideration to be addressed at this point is the realistic selection of values of k. Maximum k is realized when the working fluid is monatomic; however, no IC engine can work with an inert gas. In practice, the nitrogen in the air used in the engine limits k to less than 1.4, and the fuels used in IC engines react to form carbon dioxide, water, and other heavier hydrocarbon molecules, which further reduces k. A commonly selected value of k is 1.4 for the compression stroke and 1.3 for the expansion stroke.

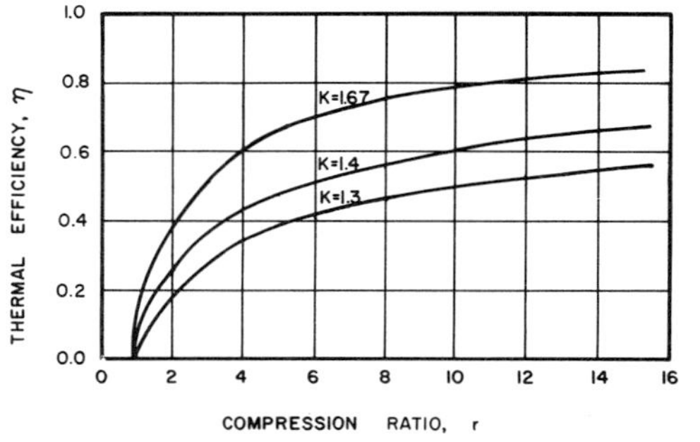

FIG. 3. Influence of compression ratio and specific-heat ratio on thermal efficiency of the Otto cycle.

D. Air-Standard Diesel Cycle

The Diesel cycle models the processes occurring in diesel engines. The diesel engine, unlike the SI engine, which uses an energy source (i.e., spark plug) to initiate combustion, begins its cycle only with air in the cylinder and injects fuel into the cylinder after the compression process. The Diesel cycle uses the increased temperature of the gas after the compression process to ignite the fuel spray entering the engine (fuel injection and combustion are analyzed in Section V). Thus, the Diesel cycle differs from the Otto cycle in the method of heat addition. Instead of constant-volume heat addition, the Diesel cycle uses constant-pressure heat addition. As such, the Diesel cycle is defined as follows: 1–2, isentropic compression; 2–3, constant-pressure heat addition; 3–4, isentropic expansion; and 4–1, constant-volume heat rejection.

The heat addition in the Diesel cycle is controlled by fuel injection, as defined by the cutoff ratio r_c. In the ideal Diesel cycle, heat addition (i.e., fuel injection) begins at top dead center and continues as process 2–3. When heat addition ends at state 3, as indicated in Fig. 4, volume V_3 is established. The cutoff ratio is then

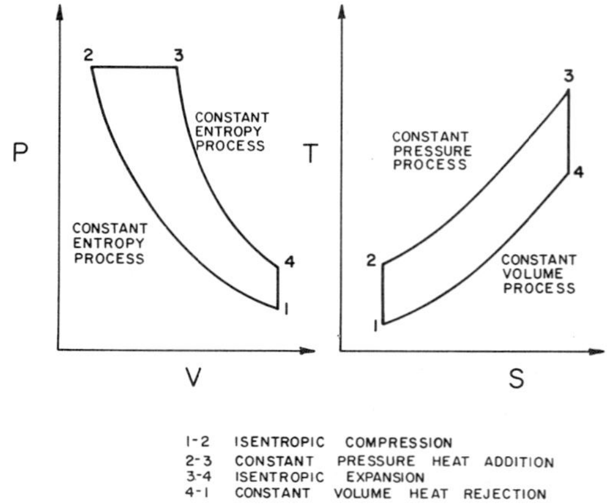

FIG. 4. Process diagrams for the Diesel cycle.

defined as V_3 divided by VTDC. Thermodynamic analysis of the Diesel cycle results in an equation for thermal efficiency of the form

$$\eta_{\text{th, Diesel}} = 1 - \frac{1}{r^{k-1}}\left(\frac{r_c^{k-1}}{k(r_c - 1)}\right) \tag{4}$$

Here, $\eta_{\text{th, Diesel}}$ is the thermal efficiency of the Diesel cycle, r the compression ratio, k the specific-heat ratio, and r_c the cutoff ratio defined above.

Analytically, it is important to note that the term preceding the parentheses corresponds to the final term in the Otto cycle thermal efficiency equation and that the term in the parentheses is always greater than 1. Consequently, for any given compression ratio, except in the limit when the cutoff ratio is zero (i.e., no heat addition to the Diesel cycle), the Otto cycle is theoretically more efficient than the Diesel cycle. The cutoff ratio severely reduces the thermal efficiency of the Diesel cycle as its value increases (Fig. 5). Consequently, engine manufacturers of modern diesel engines attempt to design and operate engines such that much of the heat addition occurs at or near constant volume (Otto cycle), thus minimizing heat addition at constant pressure and reducing the cutoff ratio.

E. Air-Standard Brayton Cycle

The Brayton cycle models the processes occurring in simple gas turbine power cycles. The basic thermodynamic processes characteristic of the Brayton cycle also model those found in thrust engines. Because the Brayton cycle represents a continuous-combustion device, separate regions of the engine serve single thermodynamic functions; this is unlike the intermittent-combustion cycles, in which all thermodynamic processes occur in a piston–cylinder device.

In a simple gas turbine engine arrangement, air is drawn into a compressor, where a pressure increase occurs. The compressor output airstream enters a combustor; fuel is injected into the air, and combustion takes place. The heated combustion products enter a gas turbine and are expanded, producing work. The work necessary to operate the compressor is extracted from the total work output of the turbine; the remainder is available as the net work output of the engine. The Brayton cycle models this cycle by the following processes: 1–2, isentropic compression; 2–3, constant-pressure heat addition; 3–4, isentropic expansion; and 4–1, constant-pressure heat rejection.

The Brayton cycle is represented on pressure–volume and temperature–entropy diagrams in Fig. 6. For this simple configuration the pressure ratio defined earlier represents the high pressure in the cycle divided by the low pressure in the cycle. A thermodynamic analysis of this cycle in the absence of significant kinetic energy change results in the thermal efficiency equation,

$$\eta_{\text{th, Brayton}} = 1 - 1/r_p^{(k-1)/k} \tag{5}$$

where $\eta_{\text{th, Brayton}}$ is the thermal efficiency of the Brayton cycle, r_p the pressure ratio, and k the specific-heat ratio. The effect of pressure ratio and specific-heat ratio on thermal efficiency is presented in Fig. 7.

Since the exhaust temperature of this cycle is well above ambient conditions, a significant improvement in the basic Brayton cycle can be realized by the addition of a heat exchanger, or regenerator, that extracts energy from the ex-

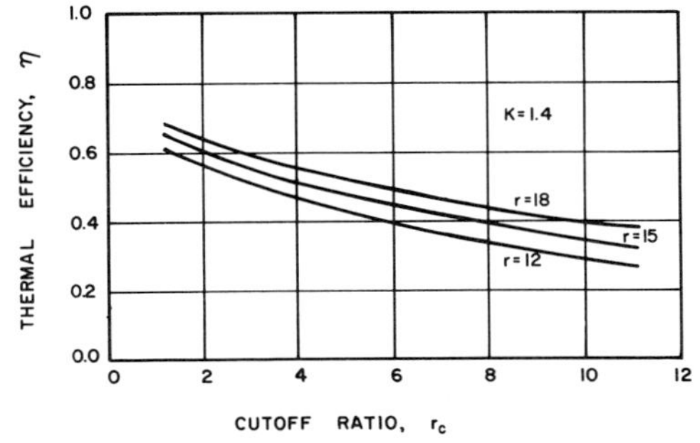

FIG. 5. Influence of cutoff ratio on thermal efficiency of the Diesel cycle.

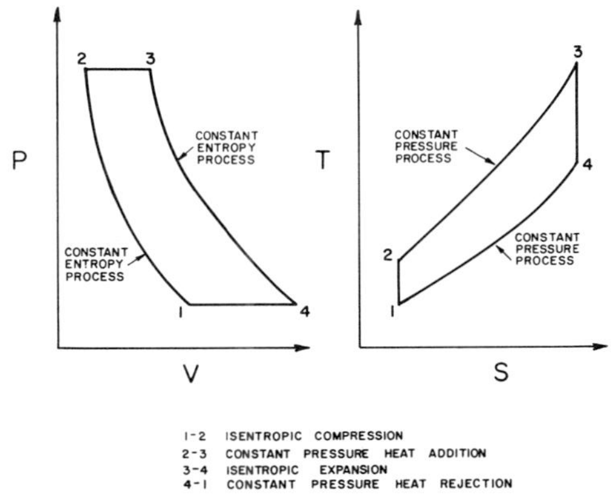

FIG. 6. Process diagrams for the Brayton cycle.

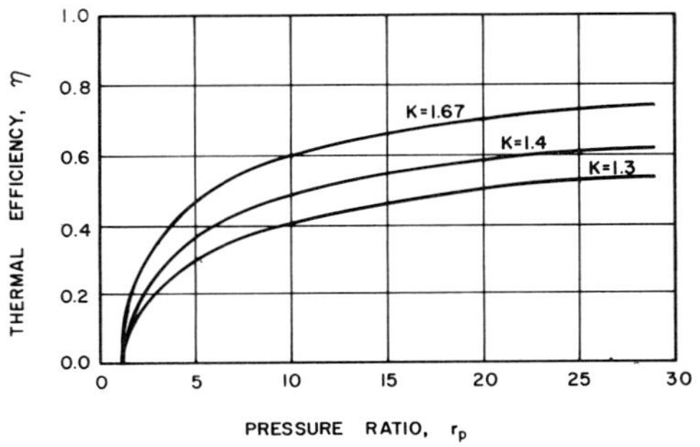

FIG. 7. Influence of pressure ratio and specific-heat ratio on thermal efficiency of the Brayton cycle.

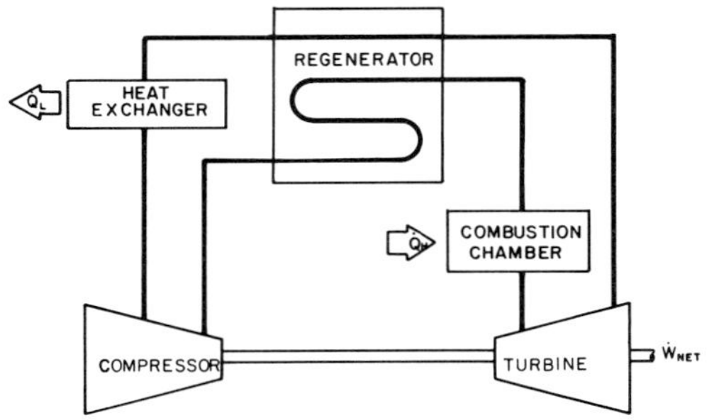

FIG. 8. Schematic of gas turbine with regeneration.

haust stream of the turbine and preheats the inlet air to the combustor. A schematic of this concept is shown in Fig. 8. The corresponding temperature–entropy diagram is provided in Fig. 9. The addition of high-effectiveness regenerators (i.e., efficient heat exchangers) may someday make the gas turbine a competitive automotive engine (see Section VI).

Thrust engines have the same fundamental thermodynamic process diagram as the Brayton cycle; however, since these engines operate at high velocities relative to ambient air, a diffuser placed before the compressor takes advantage of the kinetic energy of incoming air to increase the static pressure of the airflow before entering the compressor. Thus, less energy is required from the turbine to compress the air to a given pressure. Since no shaft work is required of a thrust engine, except that needed to run the compressor, the exhaust of the turbine is run through a nozzle, where it is accelerated and produces thrust. [*See* GAS-TURBINE POWER PLANTS.]

IV. Spark Ignition Engine

The ideal Otto cycle provides information necessary for the basic understanding of SI engines; however, it severely oversimplifies the actual components of and the process occurring in SI engines.

There are fundamentally two types of SI engine: four-stroke and two-stroke. The four-stroke engine is the most common because of its tremendous success as the prime mover in the automobile industry. Many of the basic engine components and processes of the four-stroke engine are common to the two-stroke engine (i.e., air–fuel mixture preparation, spark ignition, flame propagation, pollutant formation, and optional engine modification). These common features are described in the following subsection.

A. Four-Stroke Engine

Spark ignition engines range from single-cylinder engines to those with 12 or more cylinders.

Even though the thermodynamic processes occurring in the SI engine can be ideally represented by the Otto cycle, actual operation requires combustion instead of the idealized heat addition process. The need to intake air–fuel mixture and exhaust combustion products requires the inclusion of an exhaust–intake piston stroke (Fig. 10). Also, several mechanical components are necessary to produce the thermodynamic conditions necessary for cyclic operation of the engine.

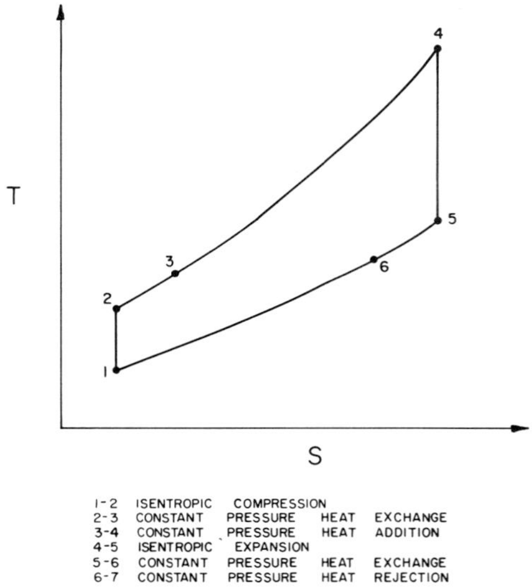

FIG. 9. Process diagram for the Brayton cycle with regeneration.

The combustion process occurring in the SI engine relies on controlled ignition of the air–fuel mixture, rapid flame propagation away from the point of ignition, and complete combustion of the fuel within the cylinder.

Controlled ignition of the air–fuel mixture results from the electrical discharge commonly produced by a spark plug located in the clearance volume. For ignition to occur, the air–fuel mixture must be within the air–fuel ignition limits of the fuel, and enough energy must be provided by the spark to generate a flame front in the mixture. Seldom is insufficient energy produced by conventional spark plugs. The ignition limits for SI fuels, however, are relatively narrow. Thus, good control of the air–fuel ratio of a mixture is vital.

Ignition is timed relative to the piston reaching top dead center during the compression stroke. Theoretically, combustion in the four-stroke engine takes place at constant volume when the piston is at top dead center; however, combustion of the air and fuel in the cylinder requires a finite amount of time. Advancing the spark, that is, electrical discharge from the spark plug before the piston reaches top dead center, allows more time for combustion to occur before the cylinder begins the expansion stroke, and the combustion process is retarded.

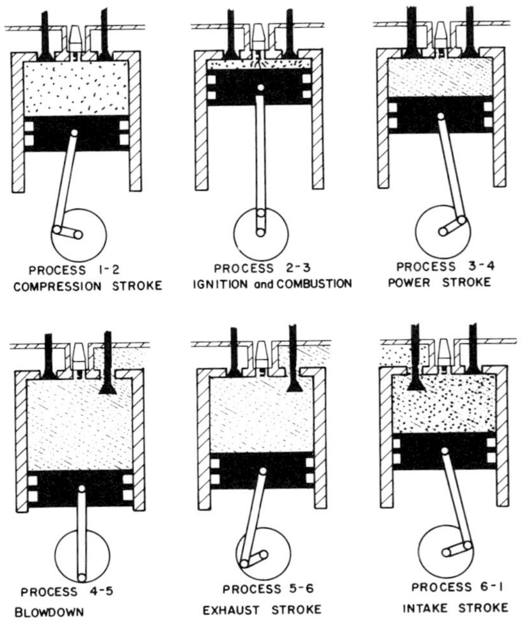

FIG. 10. Engine schematic of four-stroke spark ignition engine.

Uncontrolled ignition—engine knock—results from detonation of the air–fuel mixture before complete combustion of the air–fuel mixture has occurred. Usually, uncontrolled ignition, or autoignition, takes place during the expansion stroke. Uncontrolled ignition generates compression and expansion waves throughout the mixture. This disrupts uniform flame spread in the cylinder. Engine knock results from autoignition or variation of the speed of the flame front. Spark ignition engines usually operate fuel-lean of the stoichiometric mixture (i.e., with more air than is necessary for a chemically correct mixture). Since the autoignition temperature decreases as the air–fuel ratio approaches stoichiometric (i.e., lower temperatures after the compression stroke will result in ignition of the air–fuel mixture without requiring a spark for ignition), changing the metering of the fuel can produce knock.

The temperature at which autoignition will occur is also a function of the octane rating of the fuel used. Higher-octane fuels inhibit knock and permit engines to operate at greater air–fuel densities at a given air–fuel ratio. Consequently, the maximum usable compression ratio of an engine design is limited by the intended fuel to be used. Theoretical analysis indicates improved cycle efficiency with increased compression ratio, but the autoignition characteristics of an air–fuel mixture place a practical constraint on this design parameter.

The flame in a cylinder under controlled ignition moves away from the spark location with a spherical flame front. This process can be well characterized with a pressure–time diagram (Fig. 11A). However, if autoignition occurs, flame propagation is disrupted and the engine does not operate as designed (Fig. 11B).

The emissions of primary concern for spark ignition engines using conventional hydrocarbon fuels are carbon monoxide (CO), nitrogen oxides (NO_x), and hydrocarbons (HC), sometimes referred to as unburned hydrocarbons (UHC). Significant emissions reductions have occurred since the 1960s as the direct result of government regulation (Figs. 12, 13, and 14).

The first great strides in reducing carbon monoxide emissions from the 1960 uncontrolled levels came from designing newer engines to operate fuel lean; however, this did not reduce CO levels to the desired near-zero limit. Modern SI engines achieve very low CO emissions (levels on the order of parts per million), by near stoi-

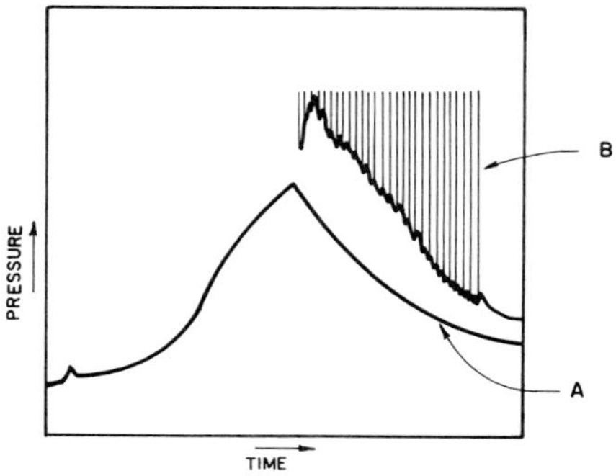

FIG. 11. Pressure–time diagram for spark ignition engine. (A) Normal operation; (B) autoignition.

chiometric operation and catalytic exhaust gas treatment.

Nitric oxides emissions in SI engines typically result from thermal, or high temperature, oxidation of nitrogen that is present in the air used by the engine. Since this process is highly temperature dependent, control of combustion temperature through exhaust gas recirculation (EGR) has permitted limited success in controlling NO_x emissions. Based on available technology, it appears the only solutions to NO_x emissions control are the three-way and dual catalysts. Note must be made that NO_x emissions control is one of the most difficult problems faced by any combustion designer when the oxidizing material is air. Even in the case of "clean" burning fuels such as hydrogen or natural gas, NO_x can be easily, and most often, unavoidably generated.

Hydrocarbon pollutant emissions in SI engines result from incomplete combustion and from hydrocarbon vapors that escape from the engine. Modern engines recirculate vapors to the fuel preparation system for burning in the engine. Products of incomplete combustion, however, can be controlled only by engine design modification or exhaust gas cleaning.

It is generally believed that products of incomplete combustion are produced from a variety of sources. When the flame front approaches the cylinder walls and the piston face, the flame is quenched because of heat transfer to those surfaces. Crevices around the top piston ring, the spark plug, valves, and cylinder gasket trap fuel which is released during the exhaust stroke. Some fuel may be absorbed in oil or combustion deposit layers and later released during the exhaust stroke. In poorly designed or operated engines, incomplete combustion may result when the flame does not progress sufficiently through

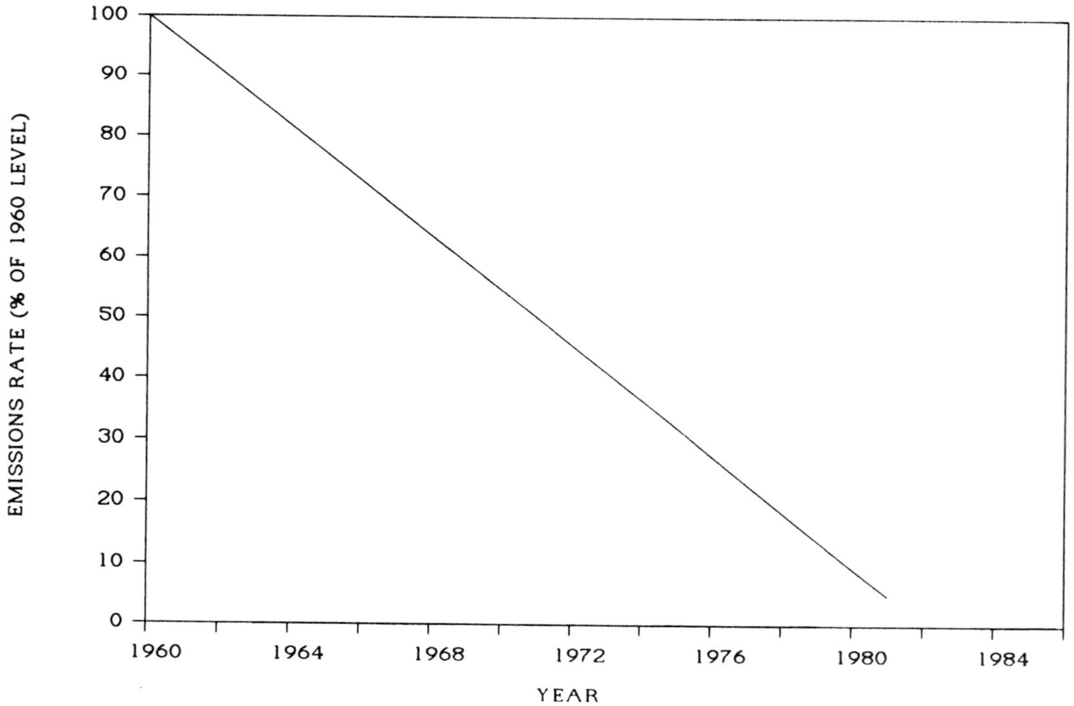

FIG. 12. Carbon monoxide emissions.

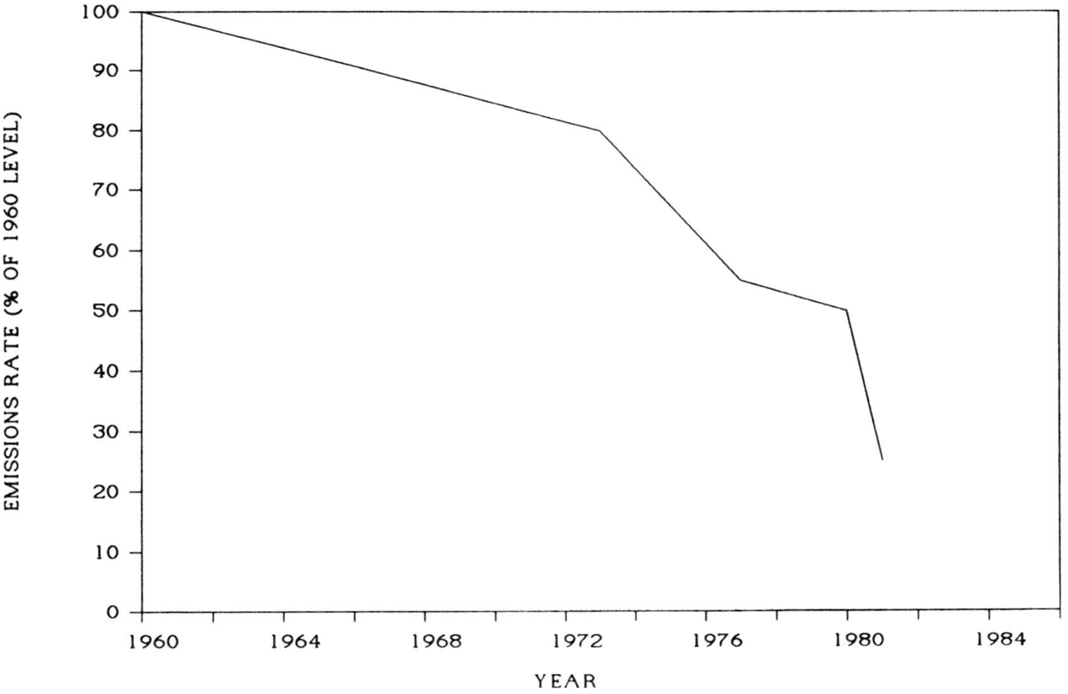

FIG. 13. Nitrogen oxides emissions.

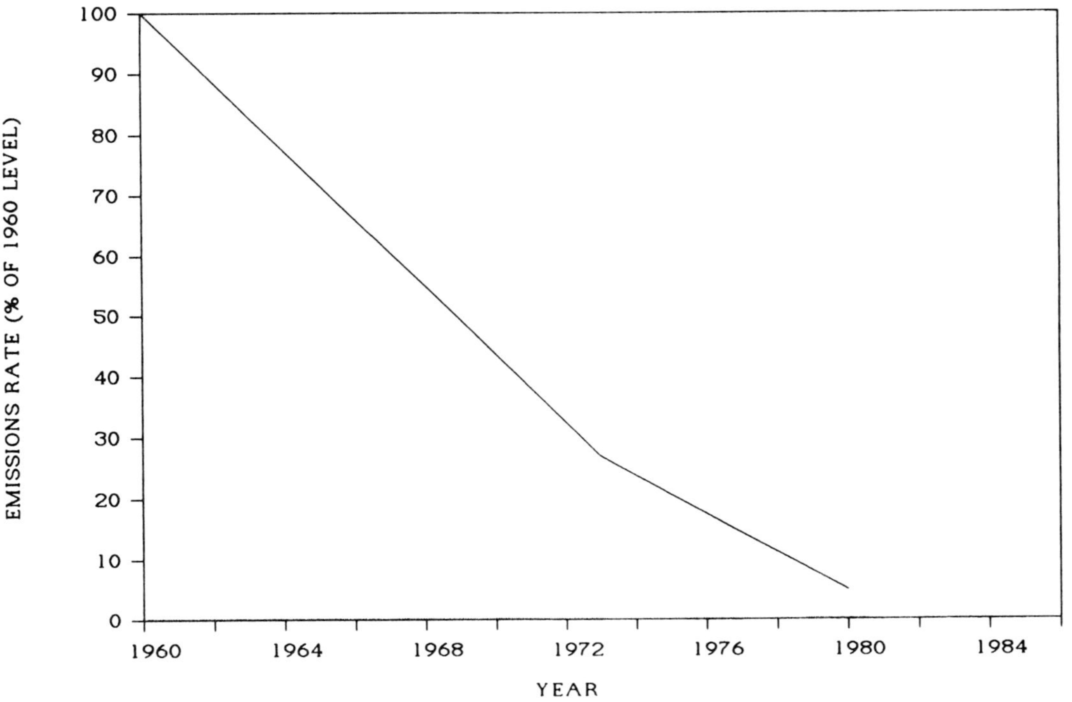

FIG. 14. Hydrocarbons emissions.

the air–fuel mixture volume before the expansion stroke begins. Increasing the air–fuel ratio of a mixture decreases its flame speed and can result in incomplete combustion. Increasing the turbulence levels of the air–fuel mixture during the compression stroke will enhance flame speed and reduce the time necessary for the flame to traverse the cylinder from the ignition point. This is accomplished in the engine design phase by promoting swirl and squish in the cylinder. Swirl is induced by tangential intake of air–fuel mixture during the intake stroke either by shrouding the intake valve or by using a swirl port. Varying piston and cylinder head design can promote squish. As the piston moves to top dead center, squish results as gases rush inward from the rapidly decreasing outer volume of the cylinder toward a main clearance volume usually near the centerline of the cylinder.

A typical pressure–volume process diagram for a conventional SI engine is presented in Fig. 15. States similar to those of the Otto cycle are noted as 1 through 4. The area created by the clockwise loop represents the work produced by the power part of the cycle. The amount of work produced (i.e., the area of the loop) is controlled by the heat release of the air–fuel mixture in the cylinder at state 1. Since air–fuel mixture intake is a controlling parameter in the SI engine and combustion results in products of combustion that must be expelled from the cylinder in order to repeat the cycle, necessary modifications to the Otto cycle are now explained.

At state 4, in an air–fuel cycle, products of combustion are contained in the cylinder with the piston at bottom dead center. An exhaust valve is opened in the cylinder head, resulting in blowdown of pressure (4–5). The piston then moves to top dead center, exhausting combustion products in the displacement volume (5–6). Since the exhaust gas must escape through a valve, the pressure within the cylinder exceeds ambient pressure. Furthermore, not all the gas within the cylinder is purged; the combustion products in the clearance volume remain. At top dead center, the exhaust valve closes and the intake valve opens. Unreacted air–fuel mixture is drawn into the cylinder. As the piston returns to bottom dead center (6–1), the intake valve acts as a throttle, and the pressure in the cylinder is less than the supply pressure provided by the air–fuel preparation system. Control of the supply pressure controls the total air–fuel mixture drawn into the cylinder and consequently the work generated by the subsequent cycle.

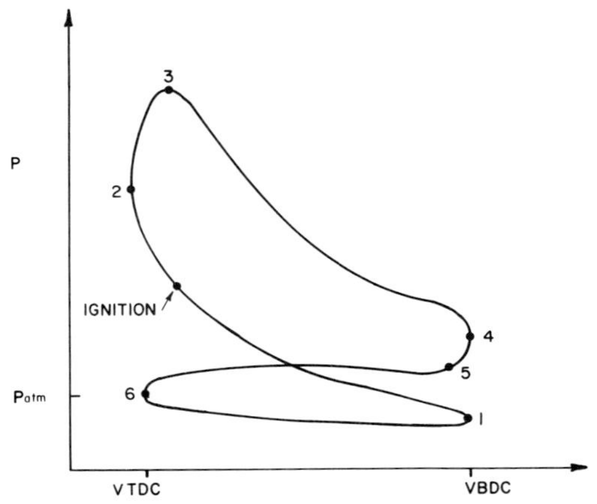

FIG. 15. Process diagram for four-stroke spark ignition engine.

Because the gas exchange loop (5–6–1) generates a counterclockwise process on a pressure–volume coordinate diagram, pumping work is required to effect this piston stroke; thus, it is a negative work component of the overall cycle. In practice, SI engines must operate between full power and idle. This requires that the power output of the engine vary by approximately an order of magnitude. In conventional engines (i.e., homogeneous-charge SI engines) the air–fuel ratio of the intake mixture must remain nearly constant at ~14.7 for commercial gasoline. This, in effect, precludes control of the work generated by the engine through variation of the air–fuel ratio. As such, limiting the intake of the air–fuel mixture is the only control of cycle output. Unfortunately, throttling the intake air–fuel mixture generates large pumping losses; at idle, pumping work becomes a major contributor to engine inefficiency.

The limited variability of air–fuel mixtures in conventional homogeneous-charge SI engines results not from the ability to generate such mixtures but rather from mixture ignition problems. To avoid pumping losses due to throttling the intake air–fuel mixture when operating engines at partial load, attempts are constantly being made to design engines to operate fuel-lean (i.e., to reduce the fuel charge within the cylinder for a given mixture density). Two techniques are generally employed to produce fuel-lean mixtures in homogeneous-charge SI engines. In Europe the "lean-burn" engine operates with air–fuel mixtures containing excess air; however, the promulgation of nitrogen oxide emission standards in the United States resulted in the broad use of reducing catalysts to manage NO_x emissions from automobile engines. Because the catalyst is ineffective in oxygen-containing environments, the lean-burn engine cannot be used in conjunction with this technique of NO_x control. Consequently, a technique called diluent combustion is used to increase the effective air–fuel ratio in these engines. Diluent-combustion engines use recirculated exhaust gas, as opposed to excess air, to reduce the fuel charge within the engine.

In the homogeneous-charge SI engine air–fuel preparation is accomplished through carburetion or intake manifold injection. Both systems meter the fuel flow relative to the airflow delivered to the engine. Although the air–fuel ratio for SI engine operation is near stoichiometric, in most engines a slightly fuel-rich mixture is provided at idle, where power and airflow are low, to compensate for large dilution from product gas left from the exhaust stroke. When airflow is large at high power output, a fuel-rich mixture is generated to ensure good combustion. For cruise conditions, the air–fuel ratio is increased and exhaust gas recirculation is used to improve engine efficiency.

Both carburetion and intake manifold injection provide adequate preparation of the air–fuel mixture. Manifold fuel injection, however, ensures more even distribution of fuel in multicylinder engines.

In aircraft carburetors, provisions are made to adjust fuel metering manually to compensate for changes in ambient air pressure and temperature with altitude. Sophisticated fuel injection systems for both automotive and aeronautical engines often use oxygen sensors in the exhaust system to adjust fuel metering for optimum performance.

A less common form of fuel preparation is cylinder head injection. Used primarily in experimental stratified-charge engines, this technique requires high fuel pressure for direct fuel injection during the compression stroke.

Attempts to operate the SI engine at very fuel-lean conditions have led to the development of stratified-charge engines. Three examples of this engine concept are divided-chamber stratified-charge, axially stratified-charge, and direct-injection stratified-charge engines (Fig. 16). Since air–fuel mixtures can be ignited only within well-defined air–fuel ratio limits, the stratified-charge engine produces a region of near stoichiometric conditions at the spark plug tip and very fuel-lean mixtures elsewhere in the cylinder. For example, a prechamber is used in the divided-chamber design to create a region for ignition. Once the flame is established, it can propagate into the fuel-lean mixture in the main chamber. In the axially stratified-charge engine, control of fuel injection timing during the intake stroke results in nearly-stoichiometric mixtures at the top of the cylinder and overall fuel-lean conditions within the cylinder. Controlled fuel injection during the compression stroke produces the ignitable mixture near the spark plug in the direct-injection stratified-charge engine.

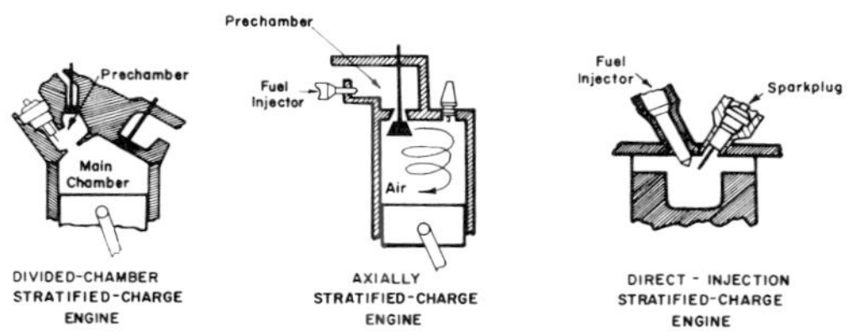

FIG. 16. Stratified-charge engine design concepts.

B. Two-Stroke Engine

Two-stroke engines differ from four-stroke engines in the method of air–fuel mixture intake and combustion product exhaust. A schematic of a typical two-stroke engine is shown in Fig. 17. Instead of intake and exhaust valves, the two-stroke engine uses pressure check valves and cylinder wall ports that are covered and uncovered by movement of the piston. In the two-stroke engine, both the volume above the piston and that below it are used in gas transfer engine operation. Operation without mechanically controlled valve movement permits the two-cycle engine to operate at higher speeds than four-stroke engines of comparable size.

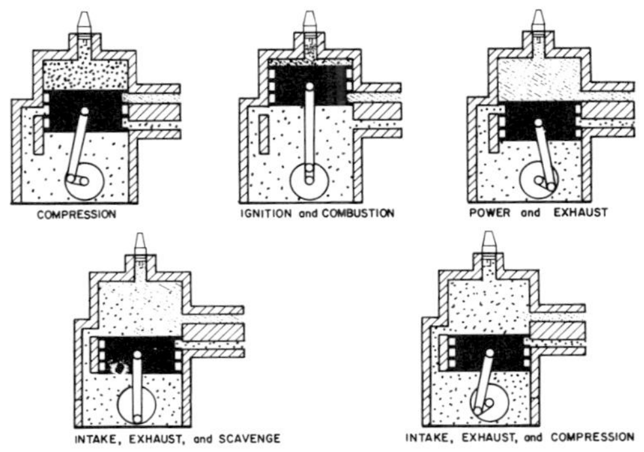

FIG. 17. Engine schematic of two-stroke spark ignition engine.

Recent developments have resulted in the manufacture of rotary two-stroke SI engines. The rotary engine differs from the conventional piston–cylinder engine in basic design (Fig. 18). Unlike the piston–cylinder engine, in which the thermodynamic process takes place in a volume defined by the cylinder head and piston of each cylinder, the rotary engine forces gases into different regions of the engine designed specifically for intake, compression, combustion, expansion, and exhaust. The fundamental thermodynamic processes are nevertheless the same for both forms of two-stroke engine.

V. Diesel Engine

The diesel engine, also known as the compression ignition engine, differs from the four-stroke SI engine in the technique used to introduce the fuel and, as a consequence, the combustion process. The overall cycle is four-stroke (i.e., intake, compression, expansion, and exhaust), but unlike spark ignition, in which an air–fuel mixture is drawn into the cylinder during the intake stroke, only air is brought into the cylinder during the intake stroke of the diesel engine. During the compression stroke the pressure and temperature of the air are increased by the compression process. By design, the temperature of the air during the compression process is greater than the autoignition temperature of the fuel intended for use. Liquid fuel is introduced by injection into the cylinder when the piston is passing near top dead center. At this point in the cycle the fuel autoignites as it enters the cylinder and burns as a diffusion flame.

This method of fuel introduction results in two very important advantages over techniques used in the SI engine. First, since only air is in the cylinder during compression, uncontrolled ignition is not a factor. Consequently, very high compression ratios can be used to promote high cycle efficiencies. In practice, high compression ratios are necessary to produce compressed-air temperatures greater than the autoignition temperature of the fuel used. Second, the fuel injected into the cylinder begins to burn as it enters the hot compressed gases within the cylinder. Thus, the diesel engine does not require a discrete ignition source, such as a spark plug. This allows the engine to operate over a very wide range of air–fuel ratios independent of ignition limit requirements. Furthermore, only the fuel needed to generate the work required during any given cycle of the engine is injected. Since fuel injection controls the work generated by the engine and not the amount of air–fuel mixture throttled into the engine as with SI engines, it is not necessary to throttle the air drawn into the diesel engine. This all but eliminates throttling losses in the diesel engine. Thus, throttling losses do not degrade the efficiency of the engine at partial load as they do with the SI engine.

Diesel engine exhaust emissions concerns are primarily hydrocarbon emissions, particulate emissions, nitric oxides emissions, and odor emissions. Carbon monoxide is seldom a problem since overall air–fuel ratios are quite large and partial oxidation of unburned fuel in the exhaust is small.

Hydrocarbon and particulate emissions have been linked to poor fuel spray injector design, fuel injector dribble, and excessive cylinder wall wetting by fuel during injection. However, no clear understanding of HC and particulate formation and subsequent emission exists. Consequently, diesel engines will continue to be plagued by these emission for the foreseeable future.

Nitric oxides emissions are a major problem for diesel engines. Because local combustion temperatures in diesel engines are virtually impossible to control, NO_x will continue to be an emissions problem in conventional diesel engines.

The odorous constituents of diesel exhaust are typically high-molecular-weight partially oxidized hydrocarbons. Unfortunately, knowing generally what they are has done nothing to help in preventing their formation in the diesel engine combustion process. As the result of attempts to

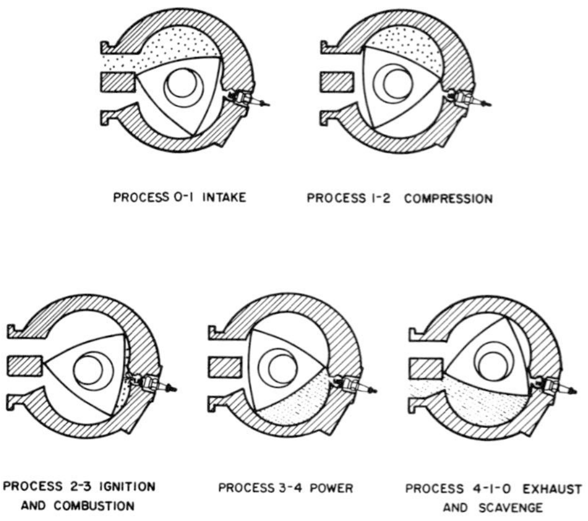

FIG. 18. Schematic of the rotary engine cycle.

reduce hydrocarbon and particulate emissions, some success has been achieved in reducing the odor of diesel exhaust; however, the generation of diesel exhaust odor remains relatively unexplained.

Supercharging is used with both SI and diesel engines to increase the initial pressure in the cylinder at the beginning of the compression stroke. This makes it possible for an SI engine of a given size to accept a greater air–fuel charge than would be possible with only atmospheric pressure driving the system. The diesel engine can also develop a greater energy output when supercharged. Supercharging can be accomplished by compressors driven by exhaust gas (turbocharging) or directly by the crankshaft (supercharging).

VI. Gas Turbine Engine

The gas turbine engine is recognized for its relative mechanical simplicity and its capacity to use a broad spectrum of fuels. In practice, the efficiency of gas turbine engines is lower than both SI and diesel engines; however, the excellent power–weight ratio of gas turbine engines can be effectively exploited. Gas turbine engines often power transportable water pumps used by fire departments, helicopters, and propeller-driven aircraft. Because gas turbine engines operate most efficiently at constant output speed (i.e., constant rpm), they have not performed well as power units in automobiles and other devices requiring variable-speed shaft output. If continuously variable transmissions become available, the regenerative gas turbine engine may become an important component of the transportation industry. For gas turbine engines operating at constant rpm, power output is controlled by fuel flow into the engine. The performance of gas turbine engines is affected by compressor efficiency, turbine efficiency, pressure ratio, peak cycle temperature, and combustion efficiency. Compressor and turbine efficiencies are continuously increasing through better design and manufacturing techniques, but little room is left for improvement. Increasing the pressure ratio can significantly improve the efficiency of an engine, but in order to retain sufficient power output, an increase in pressure ratio must be accompanied by an increase in maximum cycle temperature.

Conventional gas turbine engines operate at pressure ratios as high as 30 : 1 and as low as 1.3 : 1. This parameter is determined by design and limited by manufacturing capabilities. Experimental compressors have pressure ratios exceeding 50 : 1 with acceptable efficiencies. Cycle temperature is limited by the maximum allowable turbine inlet temperature, the pattern factor produced by the combustor, and the cooling requirements of the combustor liner.

Turbine materials and design establish the maximum gas temperature allowable to the turbine. The exhaust temperature profile (pattern factor) of the combustor is not uniform. Consequently, the average temperature of the gas entering the turbine is less than the peak temperature in the gas stream. The greater the temperature range in these gases, the worse is the pattern factor. The worse the pattern factor, the lower must be the average temperature entering the turbine to avoid damaging the turbine.

Since combustion in gas turbine engines is a steady process, the flame must be isolated from combustor materials by regions of "cold" air (air having temperatures much lower than the flame temperature, e.g., 800 K). This is done by protecting the combustor liner with air introduced through slots in the liner. This is not an extensive problem because far greater amounts of air are used to dilute hot combustion products to temperature values acceptable to the turbine. Gas turbine engines typically operate at air–fuel ratios of 60 : 1 or more. Combustion, however, takes place as a swirl-stabilized diffusion flame.

There are three basic types of combustor: can combustor, can annular combustor, and annular combustor. Can combustors are used in very small or very simple engines. Can annular combustors are used in very large engines (combustor diameters greater than 2 m). Annular combustors are found in the most advanced engines and are used with axial compressors and turbines. Although in simpler designs pressure-atomizing nozzles are used to inject fuel into the combustor, advanced designs use the air-blast atomizing nozzle.

Thrust engines are gas turbine engines that follow the same thermodynamic processes as the gas turbine engine, but instead of generating shaft power output, the thrust engine exhausts the hot combustion gases through a nozzle to generate thrust. The turbine of the thrust engine need only generate enough power through expansion of hot, high-pressure combustion gases to operate the compressor. Since this leaves the gases at greater than ambient pressure, they are expanded through a nozzle in which this excess pressure is converted to kinetic energy.

Thrust engines are capable of exhausting gas at supersonic speeds; consequently, they are important for the design of high-speed aircraft.

VII. Analysis for the Future

The greatest application of IC engines is in the area of transportation. Within this group, the automotive industry is the largest producer of IC engines, and it is in this area that a tremendous impact can be made in the future. Research is continually being undertaken to evaluate alternative engines for use in automobiles, but results consistently prove the SI engine to be superior. The SI engine has been capable of meeting pollution emissions standards established by the government and the fuel economy demands of consumers. Although industry is constantly looking for alternative engines, it will take significant advances in diesel and gas turbine engine technology (especially in pollutant emissions control) to displace the SI engine.

Current engine enhancements taking place with the SI engine are multivalve cylinders and improved turbochargers. As ceramic materials improve, the low-heat-rejection (LHR) diesel engine may contend for some share in the heavy-duty engine market.

The SI engine is undergoing significant improvement with the development of stratified-charge engines. As well as improving fuel economy, these engines may offer a solution to the NO_x emissions problems of current homogeneous-charge SI engines.

The diesel engine should remain the workhorse of heavy equipment devices; however, as improvements are made in fuel economy, the gas turbine may come to share this market.

The gas turbine engine will remain the engine of choice in the aeronautics industry. No other engine can be expected to displace the thrust engine, and in most circumstances, the gas turbine has replaced piston engines except in smaller aircraft. Rotary SI engines, however, are being seriously considered for some aeronautical applications.

Bibliography

Bryant, L. (1966, 1967). "The Invention of the Internal Combustion Engine Technology and Culture," Vol. 7, No. 2; Vol. 8, No. 2.

Campbell, A. S. (1979). "Thermodynamic Analysis of Combustion Engines." Wiley, New York.

Ferguson, C. (1985). "Internal Combustion Engines: Applied Thermo Sciences." Wiley, New York.

Heywood, J. (to be published.) "Internal Combustion Engine Fundamentals." McGraw-Hill, New York.

Lebebvre, A. W. (1983). "Gas Turbine Combustion." McGraw-Hill, New York.

Lichty, L. C. (1967). "Combustion Engine Processes." McGraw-Hill, New York.

Obert, E. F. (1974). "Internal Combustion Engines and Air Pollution." Intext Education, New York.

Patterson, D. J., and Henein, N. A. (1972). "Emissions from Combustion Engines and Their Control." Ann Arbor Science, Ann Arbor, Michigan.

Taylor, C. F. (1977). "The Internal Combustion Engine in Theory and Practice," 2 vols. MIT Press, Cambridge, Massachusetts.

INTERSTELLAR MATTER

Donald G. York *University of Chicago*

GLOSSARY

Absorption: Removal of energy by atoms, molecules, or solids from a beam of radiation, with re-emission at wavelengths other than the absorbing wavelength.

Cosmic rays: Atomic nuclei or electrons accelerated to energies of more than 1 MeV by unknown processes.

Dissociation: Break up of a molecule into smaller molecules or atoms.

Emission: Process whereby excited energy states in atoms and molecules produce radiation as electrons within the particles relax to lower energy states.

Galaxy: Aggregate of stars (numbered 10^6–10^{12}) gravitationally bound in orbits typically 10 kpc in size.

Intercloud medium: Space and material between the interstellar clouds, generally thought of as the largest volume in the interstellar medium.

Interstellar clouds: Condensations in the interstellar medium of various densities and temperatures, typically several parsecs to several tens of parsecs in size.

Interstellar medium: Space between the stars and the dust, gas, and fields that fill it.

Ionization: Removal of electrons from atoms or molecules by any of several processes.

Nucleosynthesis: Formation of heavy elements from lighter elements through fusion.

Parsec: Measure of distance, equal to 3×10^{18} cm or about 3 light-years.

Polarization: Preferential rather than random alignment of the electric vector of incoming radiation.

Recombination: Capture of an electron by a charged atomic nucleus or molecule.

Scattering: Redirection of light without changing its wavelength.

Shock front: Pressure discontinuity within which low-energy particles are accelerated and ionized or dissociated.

As far as we know, galaxies can be regarded as the main building blocks of the Universe. They are the central feature in modern astronomical research, all other fields being aimed at understanding where they came from and what goes on within them. The galaxies we can see are made up of stars, but the largest part of the volume of the galaxies is filled with dust and gas—the most pure vacuum in nature, save only the space between the galaxies themselves. By mass, the interstellar material accounts for about 10% of our galaxy. The space between the stars is referred to as the interstellar medium. According to modern theories, the existence of a visible galaxy as an active, star-forming entity depends upon the passage of atoms made in stars out into this medium. The processes that occur therein are thought to lead to formation of new generations of stars.

The detailed process of removal of atoms from stars and their aggregation into condensing clouds that form new stars in interstellar space is complex. The elaboration of the process is a major thrust in modern astronomical research. We attempt here to describe, from an empirical point of view, what is known about the interstellar medium and the central role played by the gas and dust found there in the unfolding of the larger story of the life, birth, and death of gal-

ENCYCLOPEDIA OF PHYSICAL SCIENCE
AND TECHNOLOGY, VOL. 8

axies. Following an overview, the article proceeds to describe the environment of interstellar space, the physical processes thought to be important, and the diagnostic techniques used in the field. The central ideas on the nature of the interstellar medium are then summarized. Near the end of the article, the particular details of the region near the sun are generalized to elaborate on areas of research on interstellar material in other galaxies and to discuss the cosmological importance of interstellar medium research.

I. The Interstellar Medium—An Overview

A. Clouds

The interstellar medium in our galaxy contains four readily detectable components, three of which are described in terms of clouds of atoms and molecules. The brightest components are the so called HII regions, regions of ionized hydrogen that emit radiation when the protons (H^+) and electrons recombine. The regions are constantly re-ionized by radiation from nearby stars. They are readily visible near stars with temperatures above 30,000 K (O stars). The Great Nebula in Orion, around the multiple star θ Orionis, is the best-known example of the HII region because it is visible to the naked eye.

The second component consists of dark clouds that are very cold and emit no visible radiation, but do emit far infrared (100-μm) and millimeter molecular line radiation. Absorption of background star light by dust in these clouds is responsible for the dark bands along the Milky Way in Scorpio and in Cygnus (the Cygnus rift) and for the famous dark spot in the southern sky known as the Coal Sack. [*See* ASTRONOMY, INFRARED]

A third component, detectable only with sophisticated instrumentation, consists of diffuse clouds. These are lower in mass than either HII regions or dark clouds and are warmer than dark clouds but are not warm enough to emit significant radiation. They contain too little dust to cause discernible extinction to the human eye.

B. The Intercloud Medium

A fourth component, only recently appreciated, is a very hot phase, with $T \sim 10^6$ K, thought to fill much of the void between the stars. This phase has been detected only indirectly, and its direct detection represents the most important frontier in the field. Gas with $T \sim 3 \times 10^5$ K (detected in the form of OVI or O^{+5}) is ubiquitous and is thought to imply the presence of the hotter 10^6-K material. Soft X-rays detected from gas near the Sun may arise in the 10^6-K gas. X rays from supernovae remnants at 10^7 K are easily detectable. As these remnants expand and cool, they should produce large cavities at 10^6 K.

Figure 1 illustrates the location of interstellar gas of various types, in a schematic spiral galaxy, seen from above.

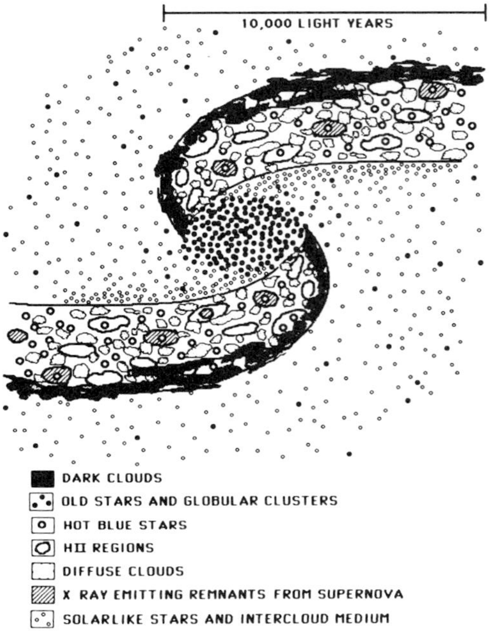

FIG. 1. Relative location, within the spiral arms of a galaxy, of various types of interstellar material.

II. Physical Environment in Interstellar Space

A. Galactic Radiation Field

Interstellar gas is ionized by radiation from many sources. The dominant source of high-energy photons, capable of ionizing hydrogen ($E >$ 13.6 eV) is the O and B stars ($T > 10^4$ K). These stars primarily reside in spiral arms, but they produce a diffuse source of radiation with the spectral shape of a 25,000-K black body and an energy density of about 1 eV/cm^3 (equivalent to the radiation detected from a single B1 star at a distance of about 30 light-years). Since the hottest, most massive stars form in groups, there are local maxima in this radiation field, discernible by the copious emission of HII regions. [*See* STAR CLUSTERS; STELLAR STRUCTURE AND EVOLUTION.]

The only place unaffected by this pervasive field is the interior of dark clouds. Hydrogen atoms at the exterior of clouds shield interior atoms from the high-energy photons ($E > 13.6$ eV, the ionization potential of HI), but lower-energy photons may penetrate. However, in the dark clouds, dust at the exterior provides a continuous opacity source, and so even visible light cannot penetrate.

Other sources of radiation include white dwarfs, hot cores of dying stars, and, of course, normal stars like the sun. The first two sources produce high-energy photons, but not in copious amounts. Normal stars produce an important source of photons only at $\lambda > 4000$ Å.

While X-ray sources permeate space, the X rays themselves have little measurable effect on interstellar clouds. X rays probably serve to warm and ionize cloud edges and to produce traces of high-ionization material.

Supernovae from time to time provide radiation bursts of great intensity, but, except perhaps in the distant halo, these have little global effect. (The mechanical impact of the blast wave from the explosion, on the other hand, is very important, as discussed later.) [*See* SUPERNOVAE.]

B. Magnetic Field

A weak magnetic field exists in space, though its scale length and degree of order are uncertain. The strength is roughly 10^{-6} G. The field was originally discerned when it was discovered that light from stars is linearly polarized ($\sim 1\%$). From star to star the polarization changes only slowly in strength and direction, suggesting that the polarizing source is not localized to the vicinity of the stars, but rather is interstellar in origin. It is thought that the field aligns small solid particles, which in turn lead to polarization of starlight. Since many elements are kept mostly ionized by the radiation field in space, the magnetic field constrains the motion of the gas (ions) and may be responsible for some leakage of gas from the galaxy.

C. Cosmic Rays

Very high energy particles (10^6–10^{21}eV) penetrate most of interstellar space. In the dark clouds, where ionizing photons do not penetrate, collisions between atoms and cosmic rays provide the only source of ions. Cosmic rays probably provide the basis of much of the chemistry in dark clouds, since, except for H_2, the molecules seen are the result of molecule–ion exchange reactions. Collisions between cosmic rays and atoms are thought to produce most of the observed lithium, beryllium, and boron through spallation. The energy density of cosmic rays is about 1 eV/cm^3, similar to that of stellar photons. Cosmic rays interact with atoms, leading to pion production. These decay to γ rays. The diffuse glow of γ rays throughout the galactic disk is accounted for by this process. [*See* COSMIC RADIATION.]

D. Cosmic Background Radiation

Light from other galaxies, from distant quasars, and even from the primordial radiation has a measurable impact on the interstellar medium. There are about 400 photons/cm^3 (or about 1 eV/cm^3, since $\lambda \sim 1$ mm) in our galaxy from the radiation bath of the Big Bang, now cooled to 2.71 K. At the remote parts of the galaxy, the integrated light of the extragalactic nebulae at 5000 Å, and of the distant quasars at $E > 13.6$ eV ($\lambda < 912$ Å) is comparable to galactic sources of such radiation.

E. Mechanical Energy Input

Stars, in the course of their evolution, propel particles into space, often at thousands of kilometers per second. These may come from small stellar flares; from massive dumps of the envelope of one star onto a binary companion, leading to an explosion (novae or supernovae); from winds driven by, among other things, radiation pressure, especially in the hottest stars; or from detonation of stellar interiors, leading to supernovae. These particle flows generate pressure on the interstellar clouds, which in regions of massive stars and supernovae, substantially heats the gas and reshapes the clouds. The random motion of interstellar clouds is largely the result of the constant stirring caused by supernovae.

III. Physical Processes

A. Absorption and Emission of Radiation

Up to a point the physics of interstellar clouds is easy to ascertain. Atoms and simple molecules are easy to detect spectroscopically. Various effects lead to excitation or ionization of atoms and molecules. The extremely low densities (10^{-3}–10^5 particles/cm^3), and the resulting great distances between atoms (millimeters to meters), means they seldom interact. When they do, the restoring radiative processes are usually fast enough that the atoms return spontaneously to their original energy states. The net result is quantized emission that is detectable at earth. The strength and wavelength of the emission can be used to discern the density, temperature, abundance, velocity, and physical environment of the emitting region.

The same physics implies that most atoms and molecules are in their ground electronic state, with very few of the higher energy states populated by electrons. Hence, when light from a given star is intercepted by an atom, only a very restricted band of photons corresponds to an energy that the atom can absorb. In these few cases, the absorption is followed immediately by return of the electron, excited by the absorbed photon, to its original state, and subsequent re-emission of an identical photon. There is only a tiny chance that the re-emitted photon will have exactly the same path of travel as the one originally absorbed. To an observer using proper equipment, it appears that a photon has been removed from the beam. Since there are 10^{10}–10^{21} atoms in a 1-cm^2 column toward typical stars, the many repetitions of the absorption/re-emission process leave a notch in the spectrum, called an "absorption line," because of the appearance of the features as seen in a spectrograph—dark lines across the bright continuous spectrum of a star. The absorption line strengths can be used to measure the physical conditions of the absorbing region. [*See* STELLAR SPECTROSCOPY.]

B. Formation and Destruction of Molecules

In the densest regions (10–10^5 atoms/cm^3), molecules are known to exist in their lowest electronic states. The most abundant molecule, H_2, is thought to be formed on the surfaces of grains, small-sized (<1-μm) particles discussed later. Neutral hydrogen and molecular hydrogen are ionized by cosmic rays (see preceding discussion) as are other species such as neutral oxygen. A complicated chain of reactions (ion–molecular reactions) then ensues, since molecules and ions exchange electronic charge at rapid rates under the conditions present in interstellar clouds. Neutral molecules are then formed by recombination of ionized molecules and ambient electrons.

Some molecules are too abundant to be formed in the reaction scheme noted (such as ammonia, NH_3). Perhaps formation on grains is important in such cases. While the production of H_2 on grains can be generalized, production of other molecules cannot be predicted without specific knowledge of the makeup of the grains, which we now lack (see later discussion).

Some molecules may be formed in diffuse clouds by shock-triggered processes. Molecules are destroyed by chemical reactions (to make other molecules) or by radiation. In general, the higher the photodestruction cross section of a molecule, the more deeply it will be buried (in an equilibrium between destruction and formation processes) in the denser regions of clouds.

The most ubiquitous molecules are H_2 and CO (10^{-5}–0.5 molecules per H atom). Two- and three-atom molecules are common (e.g., CH, CN, HCN, HCO^+, with 10^{-13} to 10^{-8} molecules per H atom). The most massive molecule now known is $HC_{11}N$. However, there is speculation that molecules as large as C_{60} may be present in large numbers. Because the nature of grains is poorly understood, it is possible that some observations that require small grains could be accounted for by large molecules (see later discussion).

C. Ionization and Recombination

Atoms and molecules in clouds are infrequently hit by photons or particles (atoms, molecules, or grains). When sufficient energy exists in the collision, an electron may be removed (ionization), producing a positively charged particle. Coulomb attraction between these particles and free electrons leads to recombination, reinstating the original state of charge. Recombination may be due to an excited state of the neutral species. Subsequent decay of the electron to the ground state, through the quantized energy levels of the neutral atom or molecule, leads to emission of photons. The best-known examples are the Balmer lines of hydrogen seen in recombination from HII regions, the strongest of which is the Hα line at 6563 Å, that leads to the red appearance of some emission nebulae in color photographs. Sometimes the recombination process leads to population of atoms in "forbidden" states not formally permitted to be populated by absorption from the ground state because of quantum mechanical selection rules. These states are normally suppressed by collisional de-excitation in laboratory gases, but at the densities encountered in space ($<10^4$ ions/cm^3), radiative decay occurs before collisional de-excitation can occur. The best-known cases are the oxygen forbidden lines, particularly $\lambda 5007$ of O^{+2}, that gives a greenish appearance to some nebulae.

D. Shock Fronts

Discontinuities in pressure occur in the interstellar medium, caused by explosions of stars, for instance. Propagation of such a pressure shock through the medium, into clouds in particular, leads to observable consequences. Shocks propagating at velocities above 300 km sec^{-1} randomly thermalize the gas impinged upon to temperatures above 10^6 K, where cooling by radiation of a gas with cosmic or solar abundance is inefficient. Such shocks are referred to as adiabatic and lead to growth of large cavities of hot, ionized gas, transparent to radiation of most wavelengths. Eventually, particularly when a dense cloud is hit by a shock, the shock speed is reduced; hence it thermalizes gas to a lower temperature, and cooling is more important. The radiation that cools the gas is just the recombination radiation discussed earlier. Thus, if a supernovae explosion occurs in a low-density region containing higher-density (hence cooler) clouds, the propagating shock wave will lead to observable radiation from cooling just where the clouds are. Supernovae remnants, such as the famous Vela or the Cygnus Loop, are thus largely filamentary to patchy in visible light due to recombination radiation from cloud edges.

E. Dust Scattering

Several observations of stars indicate the presence of dust particles in space. The first and chief indication of their presence, historically, is that stars of the same temperature (based on stellar spectra) have different colors. In general, fainter, more distant stars are redder. Some clouds have so much dust they extinguish all background stars at $\lambda < 2$ μm.

Models that try to account for the detailed features of the reddening suggest the existence of silicate grains, and perhaps some graphite grains. Sizes range from 100 Å to 1000 Å (0.01–0.1 μm) with perhaps a core of silicates and a mantle or outer shell of amorphous ices. Such grains could produce extinction by direct scattering into directions away from the line of sight of the observer, by pure absorption in the bulk of the grains (with reradiation into longer wavelengths) and by interference of refracted and scattered radiation on the observer's side of the grains. Such grains, if irregular in shape, can be aligned by the interstellar magnetic field, leading to polarization of starlight.

F. Grain Formation and Destruction

Since the exact makeup of the grains is unknown, it is not clear how they form. Specific models for grain makeup allow one to pose questions as to how certain types of grains might form. For instance, cool stars are known to expand and contract periodically (over periods of months). At the maximum expansion, the outer envelopes reach temperatures below 1300 K. At the relevant densities, solid particles can condense out of the gas. The content of the grains depends on the composition of the stellar atmospheres, but the atmospheres seem varied enough to produce, in separate stars, silicate- and carbon-based cores. Such grains may be separated from the infalling, warming gas during the contraction of the atmosphere by radiation pressure, depending upon residual electric charge on the grains.

Subsequently, grains may grow directly in interstellar clouds. In this case, small-grain cores (or perhaps large molecules) must serve as seeds for growth of the remainder of the grain by adhesion of atoms, ions, and molecules with which the seed grains collide. The type of grains formed would then depend on the charge on the grains and the charge on various ions and on the solid-state properties of the grain surface and of monolayers that build up on it.

G. Heating and Cooling of the Gas

Cooling processes in interstellar gas can be directly observed because cooling is mainly through line radiation. Diffuse clouds are cooled mainly by radiation from upper fine structure levels of species such as C^+, which are excited by collisions of atomic or ionic species with electrons, neutral hydrogen, hydrogen ions, or H_2. In dense clouds, this process is important in atoms such as carbon. In hot, ionized regions (HII regions, $T \sim 10^4$ K) recombination radiation of H^0 and O^+ carries away energy from the gas, whereas at temperatures of 10^5 K (shocks in supernova remnants) recombination and subsequent radiation from forbidden levels of O^{+2} and other multiply ionized species dominates.

Heating of the interstellar gas is poorly understood. The heating sources observable (X rays, cosmic rays, exothermic molecular reactions) are inadequate to explain the directly observed cooling rates, given the temperatures observed in diffuse clouds ($T \sim 100$ K). The prime candidate for the primary heating mechanism is photoelectron emission from grains caused by normal starlight at $\lambda \lesssim 3000$ Å striking very small grains.

Heating of dense molecular clouds ($T \sim 10$ K) is also uncertain. Obvious gas phase processes appear to be inadequate. An additional possibility in such clouds is that star formation activity (directly by infrared radiation or indirectly by winds or shocks caused by forming stars) heats the clouds. Localized shocked regions with $T \sim 25$ K have now been directly observed in dense molecular clouds through emission from rotationally and vibrationally excited H_2.

IV. Diagnostic Techniques

A. Neutral Hydrogen Emission

The spin of the nucleus (proton) of hydrogen and the electron can be parallel or antiparallel. This fact splits the ground state of hydrogen into two levels so close together that the populations are normally in equilibrium. In practice this means that the higher energy state is more frequently population and that the resulting emission, in spite of its low probability, yields a detectable emission at $\lambda = 21$ cm. In many cases, when the column density in each cloud (or velocity component) is not too high, the power detected at 21 cm is directly proportional to the number of hydrogen atoms on the line of sight of the main lobe of the radiation pattern of the radio telescope. The total number of atoms is generally expressed as a column density N_{HI} in units of atoms per square centimeter. The detection is not dependent on the *volume* density of the gas (denoted as n_{HI} atoms/cm^3) and yields no direct information on the distance of the emitting atoms: all atoms in the velocity range to which the receiver channel is sensitive are counted. Generally, the local expansion of the universe removes atoms not in our galaxy from the receiver frequency by Doppler shifting their 21-cm emission to longer wavelengths.

B. Molecular Emission

Molecules, while generally in the ground electronic state, are excited by collisional or radiative processes to higher rotational and vibration levels. Of the some 40 molecular species known in interstellar clouds, most are detected in the millimeter wavelength region through rotational excitation. Hydrogen has been detected in rotational and vibrational emission and may be detectable in electronic emission (fluorescence).

If the mechanism populating the higher level of a transition is known, the emission strength gives some information about the mechanism. For instance, if emission from several different upper levels of a molecule is detectable, the relative population of the states can be determined. Given molecular constants and the temperature, the density of hydrogen can be determined if excitation is by collisional processes.

There are several unidentified emission features in the near infrared that are apparently related to interstellar material, some of which have been attributed to molecules in the solid phase or to polycyclic aromatic hydrocarbons. Identification of these features is being actively pursured in several laboratories.

C. Atomic Emission

Recombination lines and forbidden emission lines of atoms allow determination of abundances, densities, and temperatures in HII regions. Optical telescopes provide the main data for these lines. Eventually, fine structure emission in the infrared will give us detailed abundance data inside molecular clouds. Such data are currently available only for selected regions.

D. Atomic and Molecular Absorption

Absorption lines, already explained, are used to derive column densities of many species. Because of collisional de-excitation mechanisms, H_2CO is seen in absorption against the microwave cosmic background of only 3 K. Twenty-one–centimeter radiation is absorbed by H atoms in the lowest hyperfine state against background radio continuum sources. Resonance absorption lines of molecules such as C_2, H_2, CN, and CH^+ are seen in the optical and ultraviolet spectral regions. Resonance (ground-state) transitions of most of the first 30 elements in atomic or ionic form are seen as optical or ultraviolet absorption against stellar continuum spectra. In special circumstances, the degree of absorption is related linearly to the number of atoms leading to derived column densities (particles per square centimeter) to be compared with corresponding values of N for hydrogen. The ratio $N(X)/N(HI)$ gives an abundance of the species X, though in practice several ionization states of a species X must be accounted for. Conversely, some ions of heavy elements may be detected when hydrogen is ionized (HI unobservable), and the number of ionized hydrogen atoms must be accounted for (using, for instance, knowledge of the electron density and the intensity of the Balmer recombination radiation).

When ratios $N(X)/N(HI)$ are available for clouds, they are frequently referred to solar abundance ratios. If there are 1/10 as many atoms of a certain kind per H atom as found in the sun, the element is said to be depleted by a factor of 10 in interstellar space.

E. X-Ray Emission and Absorption

X-ray absorption lines have not yet been detected from the hot gas mentioned earlier. While this is one of the most important measurements to be done in the study of interstellar material, it awaits the arrival of a new generation of very large X-ray telescopes. X-ray absorption edges have been detected, but these are contaminated by circumstellar absorption in the X-ray source itself, with little possibility of the velocity distinction possible in resonance absorption lines.

X-ray emission arises from radiative recombination and collisional excitation followed by radiative decay. Broad band X-ray emission from interstellar gas at 0.1 to 1-keV energies has been detected, but no high-quality spectra are yet available of the resolved emission lines from the hot gas. Such measurements are extremely important because the large hydrogen column densities at distances >100–200 pc absorb such soft X-ray photons. Any detections will thus refer only to very nearby gas, which can therefore be studied without confusion from more distant emission. Broadband X-ray emission at higher energies from the diffuse hot gas cannot yet be separated from a possible continuum from distant QSOs and Seyfert Galaxies.

Higher-energy (>1-keV) X-ray lines and continuum have been detected from supernova remnants and from very hot ($T \sim 10^7$ K) gas falling into distant clusters of galaxies.

F. γ-Ray Emission

As noted earlier, cosmic rays interact with interstellar clouds to produce γ rays. A knowledge of the distribution of interstellar clouds and of the observed distribution of diffuse γ radiation may lead to a detailed knowledge of the distribution of cosmic rays in the galaxy. Our current knowledge is based largely on the cosmic rays detected directly at one point in the galaxy (earth).

V. Properties of the Interstellar Clouds

Given the many possibilities for detection of radiation emitted or modified by interstellar gas, astronomers have pieced together a picture of the interstellar medium. In many cases, the details of the physical processes are vague. In most cases, detailed three-dimensional models cannot be constructed or are very model dependent. On the other hand, in some cases, sufficient knowledge exists to learn about other areas of astrophysics from direct observations. The example of the cosmic-ray distribution has already been given. Others are mentioned subsequently.

Interstellar clouds are complex aggregates of gas at certain velocities, typically moving at ± 6 to 20 km sec^{-1} with respect to galactic rotation, itself $\sim$250 km sec^{-1} over most of the galaxy. Each cloud is a complex mixture of a volume of gas in a near pressure equilibrium and of isolated regions affected by transient pressure shocks or radiation pulses from star formation or from supernova explosions. Clouds are visible in optical, UV, or X-ray emission (or continuum scattering) when they happen to be close to hot stars and are otherwise detectable in absorption (molecules or atoms) or emission from low-lying excited levels ($\gtrsim$0.01 eV) or from thermal emission of the grains in the clouds.

A. Temperatures

Molecular clouds are as cold as 10 K. Diffuse clouds are typically 100 K. HII regions have $T \sim$ 8000 K, depending on abundances of heavy elements that provide the cooling radiation. Low-column-density regions with 10,000 K $< T <$ 400,000 K are seen directly, presumably the result of heating at the cloud edges from shocks, X rays, and thermal conduction. Isolated regions with $T > 10^6$ K are seen near sites of supernova explosions.

B. Densities

Densities, as determined from direct observation of excited states of atoms and molecules, are generally inversely proportional to temperature, implying the existence of a quasi-equilibrium state between the various phases of the medium. The effects of sources of disequilibrium in almost all cases last $\lesssim 10^7$ years, or less than one-tenth of a galactic rotation time, itself one-tenth of the age of the sun. The product nT (cm^{-3} K) is ~3000 to within a factor of 3 where good measurements exist. Thus, the molecular (dark) clouds have $n > 10^2$ cm^{-3}, while in diffuse clouds, $n < 10^2$ cm^{-3}. Higher densities (up to 10^5 cm^{-3}) occur in disequilibrium situations such as star-forming regions inside dense clouds and in HII regions.

C. Abundances: Gas and Solid Phases

By measuring column densities of various elements with respect to hydrogen, making ionization corrections as necessary, abundances of elements in interstellar diffuse clouds can be determined. Normally, the abundances are compared with those determined in the sun.

Different degrees of depletion are found for different elements. Oxygen, nitrogen, carbon, magnesium, sulfur, argon, and zinc show less than a factor of 2 depletion. Silicon, aluminum, calcium, iron, nickel, manganese, and titanium show varying degrees of depletion. Correlations of depletion with first ionization potential, or with the condensation temperature (the temperature of a gas in thermal equilibrium at which gas phase atoms condense into solid minerals), have been suggested, but none of these scenarios actually fits the data in detail.

The pattern of depletion suggests no connection with nucleosynthetic processes. Those elements that are depleted are presumed to be locked into solid material, called grains. Such particles are required by many other observations attributed to interstellar gas, as discussed earlier. In principle, the unknown makeup of the grains can be determined in detail by noting exactly what is missing in the gas phase. However, since there must be varying sizes and probably types of grains and since the most obviously depleted elements do not constitute enough mass to explain the total extinction per H atom, most of the grains by mass must be in carbon and/or oxygen. Establishing the exact mass of the grains amounts to measuring the depletions of C and O accurately, a task still beyond reach. High-resolution spectrographs on earth-orbiting UV telescopes should succeed in making the required measurements by 1990.

The grain structure (amorphous or crystalline) is not known. There are unidentified broad absorption features, called diffuse interstellar bands, that have been attributed to impurities in crystalline grains. However, these features may be caused by large molecules. It has been argued that even if grains are formed as crystalline structures, bombardment by cosmic rays would lead to amorphous structures over the life of the galaxy.

Theories of grain formation are uncertain. A general scenario is that they are produced in expanding atmospheres of cool supergiants, perhaps in very small "seed" form. They may then acquire a surface layer, called a mantle, probably in the form of water ice and solid CH_4, NH_3, etc. This growth must occur in cold dense clouds. The detailed process, and the distribution of atoms between minerals and molecules in solid phase, is unknown.

D. Evolution

Interstellar clouds can be large, up to 10^6 solar masses, and are often said to be the most massive entities in the galaxy. In this form, they may have a lifetime of more than 10^8 years. They are presumably dissipated as a result of pressure from stars formed within the clouds. Over the lifetime of the galaxy, interstellar clouds eventually turn into stars, the diffuse clouds being left over from the star formation process. Growth of new molecular clouds from diffuse material is poorly understood. Various processes to compress the clouds have been suggested, including a spiral density wave and supernovae blast waves. No one mechanism seems to dominate and several may be applicable. However, the existence of galaxies with up to 50% of their mass in gas and dust and of others with less than 1% of their mass in interstellar material leads to the inference that diffuse material and molecular clouds are eventually converted into stars.

VI. Properties of the Intercloud Medium

A. Temperatures

As already suggested, the medium between the clouds is at temperatures greater than 10^4 K. The detection of soft X rays from space indicates that temperatures of 10^6 K are common locally. Detection of ubiquitous OVI absorption suggests there are regions at $\sim 3 \times 10^5$ K. Various observations suggest widespread warm neutral and ionized hydrogen. Attempts to explain this 10^4-K gas as an apparent smooth distribution caused by large numbers of small clouds with halos have not been successful. Thus there is evidence for widespread intercloud material at a variety of temperatures, though large volumes of gas near 80,000 K are excluded. The more tenuous diffuse clouds, however formed, may be constantly converted to intercloud material through evaporation into a hotter medium.

B. Densities

In accordance with previous comments, all indications are that approximate pressure equilibrium applies in interstellar space. The above temperatures then imply intercloud densities of 10^{-1} H atoms/cm^3 to 10^{-3} H atoms/cm^3. While direct density measurements in such regions are possible at $T < 30{,}000$ K, through studies of collisionally excited C^+ and N^+, direct determinations in hotter gas are spectroscopically difficult. X-ray emission has not yet been resolved into atomic lines and so is of limited diagnostic value. Direct measurements of ions from 10^4 to 10^7 K in absorption over known path lengths must be combined with emission line data to fully derive the filling factor, hence the density, at different temperatures. Since emission lines arise over long path lengths, velocities must be used to guarantee the identity of the absorption and emission lines thus observed. Such data will not be available for several years.

C. Abundances

The depletion patterns already noted in the discussion of clouds appear qualitatively in all measures of gas at 10^4 K, ionized or neutral. In general, the intercloud gas is less depleted. Perhaps shocks impinging on this diffuse medium lead to spallation of grains and return of some atoms to the gas phase. Data on hotter gas come mainly from absorption lines of OVI, CIV, and NV. Since ionization corrections are not directly determinable and since the total H^+ column densities are not known at the corresponding temperatures of 5×10^4 to 5×10^5 K, abundances are not available. However, the ratios C/O and N/O are the same as in the Sun. It is not known whether elements such as iron, calcium, and aluminum are depleted in this hot gas. Optical parity-forbidden transitions of highly ionized iron or calcium may some day answer this important question.

D. Evolution

The evolution of the intercloud medium depends on the injection of ionization energy through supernova blast waves, UV photons, and stellar winds. A single supernovae may keep a region of 100-pc diameter ionized for 10^6 years because of the small cooling rate of such hot, low-density gas. Ionizing photons from O stars in a region free of dense clouds may ionize a region as large as 30–100 pc in diameter for 10^6 years before all the stellar nuclear fuel is exhausted. Thus in star-forming regions of galaxies with low ambient densities and with supernova rates of 1 per 10^6 years per $(100\ \text{pc})^3$ and/or comparable rates of massive star formation, a nearly continuous string of overlapping regions of 10^4 K to 10^6 K can be maintained. When lower rates of energy input prevail, intercloud regions will cool and coalesce, forming new clouds. In denser regions, comparable energy input may not be enough to ionize the clouds, except perhaps near the edges of the dense region, for periods as long as 10^8 years.

VII. The Interstellar Medium in Other Galaxies

While much is unknown about the actual balance of mechanisms that affect the distribution of gas temperatures and densities in our own galaxy, the facts that are known make interstellar medium observations in other galaxies an important way to determine properties of those galaxies as a whole. A few examples are mentioned here.

A. Supernova Rates

Supernova are difficult to find because the visible supernova occur only once per 30 to 300 years. Regions with higher rates are often shrouded in dust clouds or extinguished by nearby dust clouds. Thus, little is known about supernovae rates and their global effects on galaxies and on the orgin of elements. Nucleosynthesis in massive stars and in the supernovae explosions, with subsequent distribution to the diffuse interstellar medium, may have occurred at variable rates, perhaps much more frequently in the early stages of galaxy formation than now.

Studies of interstellar media in other galaxies can shed light on these subjects. X-ray emission and atomic line emission can reveal the presence of supernovae remnants, which, since they last up to 10^5 years or more, are easier to find than individual supernovae, which last only a few months. Absorption line measurements and emission line measurements can be used to determine abundances in other galaxies. Absorption line measurements reveal the velocity spread of interstellar gas, the stirring effect caused by supernovae integrated over 10^6 to 10^7 years. (Quasi-stellar objects, clumps of O stars, or the rare supernova can be used for background sources in such absorption line studies.)

By making the above-noted interstellar medium studies on samples of galaxies at different redshifts, the history of galaxy formation can be discerned over a time interval of roughly three-fourths the expansion age of the universe.

B. Cosmic-Ray Fluxes

The origin of cosmic rays is unknown. However, they account for a large amount of the total energy of the galaxy. In situ measurements are only possible near earth. However, cosmic rays provide the only explanation of the observed abundances of boron, beryllium, and lithium ($\sim 10^{-9}$–10^{-10} atoms/H atom). Thus the abundance of any of these elements is a function of the integrated cosmic-ray flux over the lifetime of the galaxy. Variations in the ratio [B/H] would imply different cosmic-ray fluxes. Comparison of [B/H] with other parameters related to galaxy history (mass, radius, total Hα flux, and interstellar cloud dispersions) may indicate the history of cosmic rays.

C. History of Element and Grain Formation

As is clear from previous sections, studies of various kinds of clouds in our own galaxy have not led to a clear empirical picture of how the interstellar medium changes with time. The trigger or triggers for star formation are poorly understood, and the history of the clouds themselves is unknown in an empirical sense. Numerous problems exist on the theoretical side as well.

Study of interstellar media in other galaxies should be very important in changing this situation. Absorption and emission measurements that provide data on individual clouds and on ensembles of clouds should allow classifications of the gas phase in galaxies that can be compared with other classifications of galaxies by shape and total luminosity. Because of the rarity of background sources for absorption studies, studies of optical emission lines offer the best chance of tracing several key parameters back through time. Key questions include these: Do elements form gradually over time, or are they created in bursts at the beginning of the life of the galaxy? Do earlier galaxies have the same extinction per hydrogen atom as is found in our own galaxy, or are differences seen perhaps because grains require long growth times to become large enough to produce extinction at optical wavelengths? Do the many unidentified interstellar features (optical absorption, IR emission and absorption) occur at all epochs, or are they more or less present at earlier times? Does the star formation rate depend only on the amount of hydrogen, or are other factors such as metallicity important?

D. Cosmological Implications

For various reasons the interstellar medium has proved to be fruitful ground for determining cosmological quantities. Without detailed comparison with other techniques, a few examples are given. [*See* COSMOLOGY.]

The light elements hydrogen and helium are thought mainly to be of nonstellar origin. They are currently thought to be formed in the Big Bang. Expansion of the early cosmic fireball leads to a small interval of time when the gas has the correct temperatures for fusion of hydrogen to deuterium and of deuterium to helium (^{3}He and ^{4}He). The helium reactions are so rapid that deuterium remains as a trace element, the abundance of which is dependent on the density of matter at the time of nucleosynthesis. By knowing the expansion rate of the universe, the derived density can be extrapolated to current densities. Comparison with other determinations of the current mean density of matter today shows that astronomers are detecting less than 10% of all the matter in protons and neutrons at the time of nucleosynthesis.

The amount of helium present is similarly important in deriving the properties of matter at the time of nucleosynthesis. In principle, the helium abundances today provide tests of fundamental particle physics because they depend on the number of neutrino types (currently thought to be three) and on the validity of general relativity.

Deuterium abundances are currently best determined in UV absorption line experiments in local interstellar matter. Helium abundances are best determined by measurements of optical recombination lines of He^{++} and He^{+} from HII regions in dwarf galaxies with low metal abundance.

The preceding comments suggest how interstellar medium studies allow a view of the very earliest stages of the formation of the universe through measurements of relic abundances of deuterium and hydrogen. Earlier comments related the importance of such studies to observing and understanding the formation and evolution of galaxies through studies of abundances and star formation rates. A third example is the study of clustering of galaxies at different redshifts. Since galaxies are very dim at cosmological distances and since they may not have central peaks in their light distributions, they are difficult to detect at $z > 2$. Even at $z = 1$, only the most luminous galaxies are detectable. However, interstellar medium observations of absorption lines depend not on the brightness of the galaxy, but on the brightness of an uncorrelated, more distant object, say a QSO. Thus, galaxies at very high redshift can be studied. Many QSOs side by side will pass through a number of galaxies in the foreground, and with adequate sampling, the clustering of absorption lines reflects the clustering of galaxies on the line of sight.

Depending on the total matter density of the universe, the galaxies at high redshift will be clustered to a comparable or lesser degree than they are today. Thus, changes in clustering between high-z galaxies (interstellar media) and low-z galaxies (direct photographs and redshifts) reflect the mean density of the universe. The material measured in this way includes any particles with mass, whereas the density measurement discussed earlier, using deuterium, counts only neutrons and protons. The difference between the mass density determined from changes in clustering and the density determined from deuterium gives a measure of the mass of the universe in particles that are weakly interacting with matter, such as axions and neutrinos. Current estimates are that 1%–2% of the total mass is in luminous stars, 10%–20% is in dark matter made of baryons and protons, (e.g., planets or black holes), and 80%–90% is in unseen, weakly interacting particles of unknown nature. Thus the clustering experiment described here can be regarded as fundamental to our understanding of the nature of the Universe. [*See* BLACK HOLES (ASTRONOMY).]

BIBLIOGRAPHY

Bally, J. (1986). Interstellar molecular clouds. *Science* **232,** 185.

Boesgaard, A. M., and Steigman, G. (1985). Big Bang necleosynthesis: Theories and observations. *Annu. Rev. Astron. Astrophys.* **23,** 319.

Cowie, L., and Songaila, A. (1986). High-resolution optical and ultraviolet absorption line studies of interstellar gas. *Annu. Rev. Astron. Astrophys.* **24,** 499.

McGray, R., and Snow, T. P. (1979). The violent interstellar medium. *Annu. Rev. Astron. Astrophys.* **17,** 213.

Savage, B. D., and Mathis, J. S. (1979). Observed properties of interstellar dust. *Annu. Rev. Astron. Astrophys.* **17,** 73.

ION BEAMS FOR MATERIALS ANALYSIS

Roger Bird *Lucas Heights Research Laboratories*

GLOSSARY

Blocking: Reduction of detector signal rate when aligned with a crystal axis or plane.

Channeling: Guided trajectory of incident ions between crystal axes or planes.

Collision cascade: Series of atom–atom collisions initiated by an ion–atom collision.

Cross section: Effective area presented by each atom or nucleus for a specific type of interaction with an incoming ion.

Implantation: Addition of controlled concentration of atoms to a near-surface layer by irradiation with a known dose of incident ions.

Shadowing: Reduction in probability of ion interactions with atoms that lie behind a surface atom in the direction of the incident ion beam.

Sputter profiling: Determination of variation in isotope concentrations with depth by analysis as a function of time during sputtering.

Sputtering: Emission of atoms or ions following a collision of an energetic ion with surface atoms.

Stopping power: Rate of energy loss of incident ion as it penetrates below the surface of a sample.

Ion beam analysis (IBA) involves the irradiation of a sample by a beam of ions and the detection of one or more types of emitted radiation that convey information on the sample composition and structure. At low energies (1–10 keV), O, Ne, or other heavy ion beams may be scattered from surface atoms or may cause removal of neutral, ionized, or excited atoms from the surface layer. At high energies (>100 keV), proton, alpha, or heavier ions scatter from the nuclei of sample atoms or cause X-ray, γ-ray, ion, or neutron emission from interactions at depths of up to many micrometers. These processes are used as the basis for four types of sample analysis:

1. composition analysis—determination of isotopic or elemental concentrations from the observed radiation yield;
2. depth profiling—from the time dependence of sputter induced signals or from the dependence of radiation yield on the energy of incident or emitted radiation;
3. structure analysis—from the angular dependence of radiation intensities; and
4. microprobe analysis—using a beam of 1 μm in diameter or less scanned across a sample to obtain a spatial distribution;

IBA is a suite of techniques that may either be used singly for specialized applications or in combinations to obtain more extensive and detailed information.

The principles of ion beam interactions have been known for many years, but there is still considerable work to do to extend data banks, optimize experimental conditions for each type of analysis, and improve the understanding of ion–atom and atom–atom interactions. However, IBA is already widely used, with a rapidly increasing number of facilities providing key information in many areas of science and technology.

I. Equipment Requirements

Except for external beam analysis, IBA is carried out in a vacuum. At low energies, a typical system uses an ion gun, a beam analyzer, a sample mount, a quadrupole mass analyzer or an electrostatic energy analyzer, and an ion detector mounted in a chamber at a pressure of 10^{-8} Torr or less. For neutral atom or photon spectrometry, special analysis and detection techniques are used. A complete system may be purchased, but it is often assembled from components selected to provide the performance required for specific applications. The secondary ion microscope uses a broad diameter incident beam and imaging optics to record the spatial distribution of secondary ions with a selected mass. The secondary ion microprobe (SIMP) uses sophisticated equipment for mass analysis, focusing and scanning the incident ion beam (1 μm in diameter or less). Detector signals are recorded as a function of sweep time to provide an isotope or element concentration as a function of position. Additional equipment may be included for electron beam and other surface analysis techniques that give information complementary to that from IBA. [*See* LASER AND PARTICLE BEAMS.]

At high energies, an ion source and MV accelerator are followed by a magnetic analyzer with feedback controls to maintain the accelerator voltage constant to within 0.1 to 1 kV. The ion beam can usually be deflected to one of a number of target chambers (operating at pressures from 10^{-5} to 10^{-7} Torr or lower) that have been set up for various types of IBA. Semiconductor or scintillation detectors record the energy of the radiation emitted; magnetic or electrostatic analyzers may also be used. A thin absorber foil can be placed in front of a detector to remove the lowest energy radiation. Such a facility may occupy a large laboratory and cost millions of dollars but many accelerators, installed originally for nuclear physics research, are now used partially or exclusively for IBA. A growing number of laboratories have purpose-designed accelerators operating full time for IBA.

Proton microprobes are also available commercially and include special beam focusing and scanning equipment plus multidimensional data recording. PIXE, PIGME, RBS, NRA, and channeling can all be used to obtain spatial distributions of one or more isotopes or elements. The minimum beam diameter and maximum beam current are dependent on the emittance of the ion source and energy stability of the accelerator. A spatial resolution of 1 μm or better can be obtained with a beam current of 100 pA. Even at this current, rapid scanning may be needed to minimize damage to some types of sample. The short working distance in a microprobe makes it difficult to position large detectors near the sample for high counting efficiency. Transmission ion microscopy requires much lower beam currents and utilizes forward ion scattering or ion-induced secondary electrons to study the structure of ~100-nm-thick samples with a spatial resolution of ~100 nm.

Depth profiling at low ion energies makes use of the sputter removal of surface atoms at rates up to ~5 nm min^{-1} depending on the incident ion current. The beam is scanned over an area larger than that to be analyzed and electronic gating of detector signals prevents acceptance of those generated while the beam is close to the walls of the sputter pit that is created. Recording of detector signals as a function of time or dose now gives a depth profile (usually for one isotope or element at a time). At high ion beam energies, nondestructive depth profiling, with a depth resolution of 1–100 nm, is an intrinsic capability of many ion beam techniques—the resolution depending on the technique. Resonance profiling with a resolution of ~1 nm is possible for some light isotopes and this is best done using an automatic beam-energy modulation system.

Structure studies exploit the effects of shadowing at low energies an channeling and blocking at high energies. These require a well-collimated beam with a divergence of <0.1° FWHM (for example, using 1-mm-diameter apertures spaced by several meters). A precision goniometer is also needed to position the sample to this accuracy in two, or preferably three, angular directions.

An external beam of >1 MeV protons can be produced by allowing them to pass through a thin foil (~10 μm of metal or plastic). Although there is a significant energy loss in the foil, the protons can still travel many centimeters in air or other gas (for example, He) and irradiate a sample for IBA. This is useful for the study of samples that are too large, fragile, or valuable to be mounted within a vacuum chamber.

II. Principles and Examples

In an ion–atom collision, the energy of the scattered or product ion is given by

$$E_p = X\, E_T\, [\cos\theta + Y/(X^2 - \sin^2\theta)^{1/2}]^2 \quad (1)$$

while the energy of the recoil atom is given by

$$E_r = W\, E_T\, [\cos\phi + (V/W - \sin^2\phi)^{1/2}]^2 \quad (2)$$

where $W = m_i\, m_r\, E_i/E_T\, m$; $V = m_p\, m_r\, (1 + m_i\, Q/m_a\, E_T)/m$; $X = m_i\, m_p\, E_i/E_T\, m$; $Y = m_a\, m_r\, (1 + m_i$

$Q/m_a E_T)/m$; $E_T = E_i + Q$; $m = (m_i + m_a)(m_p + m_r)$; θ is the product angle and ϕ is the recoil angle relative to the incident beam direction; E is energy and m is atomic mass with subscripts i = incident ion, p = product ion, a = target atom, and r = recoil atom; and Q is the energy balance that is zero for elastic scattering.

At low energies, collisions with atoms at the surface of the sample are most important, whereas at higher energies, an ion may penetrate to depths of many micrometers. Electrons associated with the incident ion and sample atoms may be excited or removed during ion–atom collisions, leading to gradual energy loss by the incident ion and neutralization, charge exchange, photon emission, etc. At high energies, scattering involves nucleus–nucleus collisions that also obey Eqs. (1) and (2).

The probability for each specific type of interaction is represented by the cross section ($d\sigma/d\Omega$) and the interaction yield is given by

$$Y_p = N_i \, e \, d\Omega \int_{E_i}^{0} [(d\sigma/d\Omega)/S] \, dE \qquad (3)$$

where $d\Omega$ is the detector solid angle and S is the rate of energy loss (eV per atom cm^{-2}), which is more important in ion–atom interactions than the physical distance traveled by an ion. The relative magnitudes of cross sections for some high-energy interactions are shown in Fig. 1 as a function of the atomic number of the target atoms.

A. Scattering

The energy spectrum of ions scattered from atoms consists of a peak for each isotope present (Fig. 2). It is thus a mass spectrum with a nonlinear mass scale [Eq. (1)] and peak heights

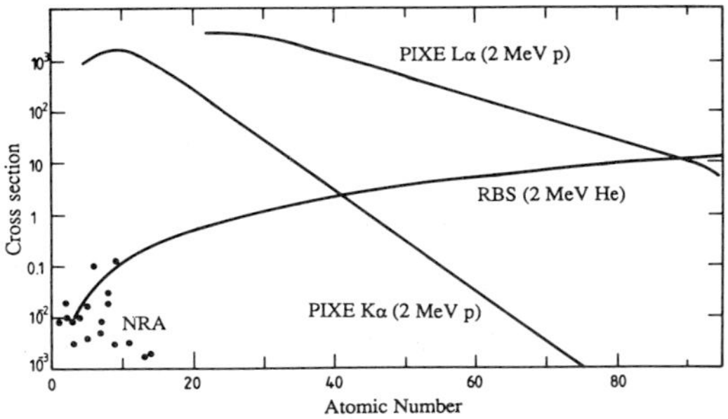

FIG. 1. Relative magnitudes of proton-induced X-ray emission (PIXE), Rutherford backscattering (RBS), and NRA cross sections as a function of the atomic number of the target atoms.

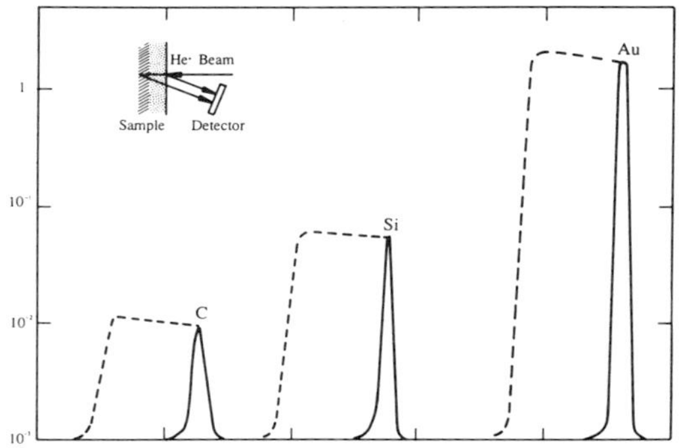

FIG. 2. Energy spectrum of ions scattered from surface atoms (full curve) and from atoms through a thin layer (dashed curve).

determined by Eq. (3). This type of spectrum is observed in low-energy ion scattering (LEIS) for which tabulated values or approximate expressions can be used for the cross section and neutralization probability. For example, rare gas ions have high neutralization probabilities and do not survive as ions beyond the first layer of atoms. They are, therefore, ideal probes for studying surface atom densities and surface structure (by exploiting shadowing and multiple collision effects) in materials such as catalysts, adsorbates, metallic glasses, and unusual alloys. Alkali and alkali metal ions have low neutralization probabilities and may produce scattering spectra with low-energy tails to each mass peak that arise from subsurface scattering. The tails increase as the incident energy is increased.

At high energies, the probability of scattering is given by the Rutherford backscattering (RBS) cross section, which has an analytical form that can be used for accurate calculation of atomic concentrations from observed scattering yields. Non-Rutherford cross sections are observed in cases such as proton scattering from light elements. It is therefore customary in RBS to use 2-MeV He ions to avoid non-Rutherford effects. Each RBS mass peak is extended toward low energies by an amount dependent on the sample thickness and the rate of ion energy loss (dashed curves in Fig. 2). The shape of each segment of the spectrum can be used to derive the depth dependence of concentration of one isotope by using Eqs. (2) and (3). The depth scale is given approximately by

$$d = -[(dE_p/dE_i)S_i/\sin\alpha + S_p/\sin\beta] \, \Delta E_p \qquad (4)$$

where ΔE_p is the difference in product energy at the surface and at depth d and α and β are the angles of beam and detector relative to the plane of the sample surface.

The mass resolution is best at an angle near 180°, but the count rate is then lowest. A detector angle near 90° is sometimes used for higher count rates and good depth resolution (low values of α or β). This is a nondestructive method for depth profiling that is used extensively in studying thin films, multilayer devices, the effects of ion implantation, diffusion, radiation damage, and other near-surface phenomena.

Elastic recoil analysis (ERA) exploits atomic recoil in the forward direction (for example, 10° to 40°) after a backscattering event. Atoms that are lighter than the incident ion recoil with higher energy than that of forward scattered ions and are easy to detect. ERA is thus a unique method for determining and depth profiling light isotopes in the presence of heavier elements. For example, H can be profiled using an incident He beam, and isotopes from H to O can be profiled using a Ne or heavier ion beam.

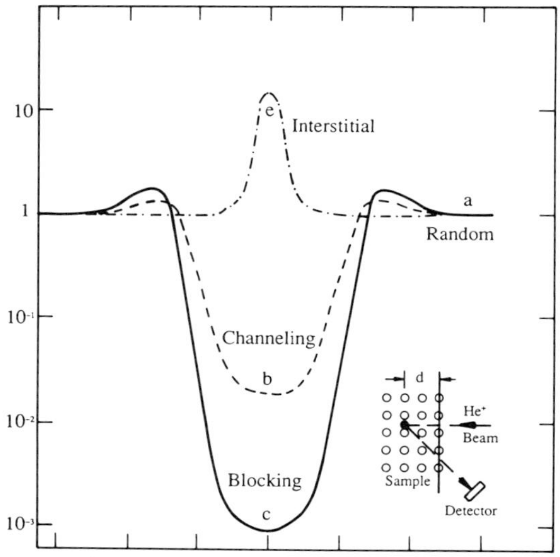

FIG. 3. The angle dependence of RBS yield from atoms in a crystal at a depth (d) below the sample surface (see text description).

B. Channeling

Channeling is most often used during RBS measurements on crystalline materials, although it is also used with other high-energy IBA measurements. The probability of scattering from subsurface atoms in a crystal is reduced by at least an order of magnitude for ions incident along the direction of a row or plane. Interactions with impurity atoms are also reduced if they occupy substitutional sites, but not if they are interstitial. A typical RBS channeling measurement, at a scattered energy corresponding to a depth (d) is shown in Fig. 3. The scattering rate is plotted as a function of the angle of orientation of the sample relative to the direction of the incident beam. The figure shows the count rate (a) for a nonchanneling (random) orientation, the reduced yield (b) for a channeled direction, the further reduction in yield (c) when the detector is placed in a blocking direction, and the increased yield (e) for scattering from interstitial atoms. Channeling is a powerful technique for studying the degree of crystallinity of a sample, atom vibrations, defect and impurity atom locations, epitaxial layers, strained superlattices, and many other topics requiring structural information.

C. Sputtering

A beam of O, Ne, Ar, or other heavy ions at 1–10 keV initiates collision cascades that result in the ejection of up to 20 surface atoms or ions per incident ion. Either positive or negative ion emission can be used in secondary ion mass spectrometry (SIMS), which is a very sensitive method for measuring atomic concentrations. Any element can be detected with detection limits as low as 10^{-9} g g^{-1} in favorable cases. However, the sensitivity varies by up to two orders of magnitude for different elements in the same substrate or one element in different substrates. A beam of reactive gas ions (for example, O) gives a high and relatively uniform yield of positive ions from many elements, whereas a Cs beam gives good negative ion yields from electronegative elements. SIMS is thus a powerful technique for studying traces of material, isotope ratios, etc., but quantitative analysis is only possible under carefully controlled conditions and when suitable calibration samples are available.

Neutral sputtered atoms can be ionized by laser or electron beams, plasma, or discharge cells to allow mass and energy analysis. Neutral yields are high and similar for most elements, so this is a valuable addition to other sputter techniques. Photon emission by excited atoms or ions is also useful, especially for the study of chemical bonding of surface atoms.

Sputter profiling uses the ion beam techniques described previously or independent electron or laser probes to analyze the freshly exposed surface. The depth resolution depends on the escape depth of the radiation detected (usually 0.1

to 1 nm) and the effects of ion beam induced atomic mixing and microroughness. Other processes, such as ion implantation, preferential sputtering, and redeposition of sputtered material, can also affect both the local composition and the sensitivity so that quantitative interpretation of results may be difficult. Nevertheless, very sensitive analysis can be carried out to depths of many micrometers and can provide valuable information for many topics.

D. X-Ray Emission

Proton-induced X-ray emission (PIXE) follows ionization and atomic excitation caused by passage of an energetic proton through matter. PIXE yields from a thin sample exposed to a proton beam can be calculated from Eq. (3) and used to derive absolute concentrations from observed X-ray intensities. For a thick sample, two integrations must be introduced to allow for the dependence of the cross section on ion energy (which decreases as the ion penetrates the sample) and the attenuation of the X-rays as they emerge from within the sample:

$$Y_x = N_i N_a e \, d\Omega \int_{E_i}^{0} [(d\sigma_x/d\Omega) T/S_i] \, dE \quad (5)$$

where the transmission is

$$T = \exp - \int_{E_i}^{E} (\mu \sin \alpha / S_i \sin \beta) \, dE \quad (6)$$

N_i is the number of incident ions and N_a is the number of target atoms per cm^2, and μ is the X-ray mass attenuation coefficient. Additional attenuation terms must be introduced to allow for any filters and other absorbers between the sample and the active volume of the detector. The effects of attenuation are most important for low X-ray energies and limit the precision that can be achieved for light elements ($Z < 20$). On the other hand, special absorbers can be used to preferentially attenuate high-intensity X-rays and allow higher ion currents to be used in the determination of trace elements. Other factors that must be considered during spectrum analysis include multiple X-ray lines, sum and escape peaks, non-Gaussian peak shapes, and various contributions to the background continuum. A number of computer packages are available for analysis of thick sample spectra, and verification of the results using standard samples is always desirable.

Protons at 2 to 3 MeV are most often used for PIXE measurements and detection limits < 10 μg g^{-1} are observed for $20 < z < 40$ (K X-rays) or $60 < Z < 90$ (L X-rays). However, the L X-rays are often difficult to resolve from K X-rays with similar energies from lighter elements. The main attractions of PIXE are the high sensitivity, including very high absolute sensitivity ($<10^{-12}$ g), and its versatility for nondestructive multielement analysis, and it is widely used for studies of minerals, air pollution, biomedicine, archaeology, etc.

E. Gamma-Ray Emission

Proton-induced γ-ray emission (PIGME) follows the excitation of nuclear levels. Gamma-ray energies and intensities are therefore isotope rather than element specific, although the same gamma ray may sometimes result from different reactions in different target isotopes. The intensities are highest for light ion (^{1}H, ^{2}D, ^{3}T, ^{3}He, ^{4}He) irradiation of light isotopes ($Z < 15$), especially for beam energies less than 3 MeV. At higher energies, inelastic scattering excites gamma-ray emission in most isotopes. Observed yields can be calculated from Eq. (5) but without the attenuation term, which is negligible for the gamma-ray energies usually used (>100 keV). Absolute isotopic concentrations can be calculated provided that the production cross sections are accurately determined for the experimental conditions used. Li, Be, F, Na, and Al can be determined in thick samples with a sensitivity of 10 μg g^{-1} or less using a 2–3 MeV proton or alpha beam. A major use of PIGME is to extend PIXE analysis to include a number of light elements.

Many gamma-ray producing reactions have narrow resonant cross-section peaks that can be exploited for high-sensitivity and selectivity studies of thin layers, including depth profiling. If the beam energy is that of the resonance maximum, a high yield of gamma rays is produced in a layer within ~1 nm from the sample surface. If the beam energy is increased in steps, the layer giving maximum yield is located at increasing depths. Proton-induced reactions at 872 keV in F and 992 keV in Al are two examples that have been used for depth profiling. An important application is the use of higher energy ^{7}Li, ^{15}N, or ^{19}F beams for measuring the depth profiles of H in near-surface layers.

F. Particle Emission

Many nuclear reactions result in the emission of high-energy ions or neutrons [high Q values in Eq. (1)]. For example, (d,p) reactions—an incident deuteron is absorbed and a proton emitted—in ^{12}C, ^{14}N, and ^{16}O give well-separated peaks in an energy spectrum from a thin layer containing these elements. A thin absorber is placed in front of the proton detector to remove low-energy scattered ions. For thicker layers, each peak is extended to lower energies and can be used to derive depth profiles in a similar manner to that described for RBS spectra (Fig. 2). Other examples are (p, α) reactions in ^{15}N, ^{18}O, and ^{19}F, which can be used for depth profiling these isotopes. Neutron emission can also be used, for example, to profile ^{2}D, ^{13}C, ^{15}N, and ^{18}O, but there have been only limited applications of this aspect of IBA.

G. Activation

The products of ion-induced activation can be used in a similar way to the better known neutron activation analysis (NAA). Ion energies of 3 to 10 MeV, or even higher, are needed to obtain good yields. Sensitivities down to 1 ng g^{-1} can be achieved for a different suite of isotopes to those for which NAA is most sensitive. A special feature of ion activation is that it is restricted to a surface layer, usually less than 1 mm thick, with the bulk of the sample remaining free of radioactivity. Thin-layer activation is valuable for studying processes such as surface wear.

III. Applications

The most extensive application of IBA has been in the research and development of advanced materials—particularly semiconductors involving special surface and near-surface properties. A second area of major importance has been the study of contamination, pollution, and other trace element problems. The potential of IBA for making valuable contributions to geoscience and minerals, bioscience and medicine, archeology, and art is well established, so that these and other analytical applications can be expected to expand rapidly.

Sequential measurements using different techniques can often be replaced by simultaneous measurements, for example, of RBS, PIXE, and PIGME or RBS, ERA, PIXE, and channeling. Depending on the nature of the sample, a selection of high-energy IBA techniques can give a total major element analysis as well as concentrations of a number of trace elements. Facilities have also been developed for carrying out both low-energy and high-energy IBA in the one-sample chamber, which may also be connected to an ion implanter to study implantation effects.

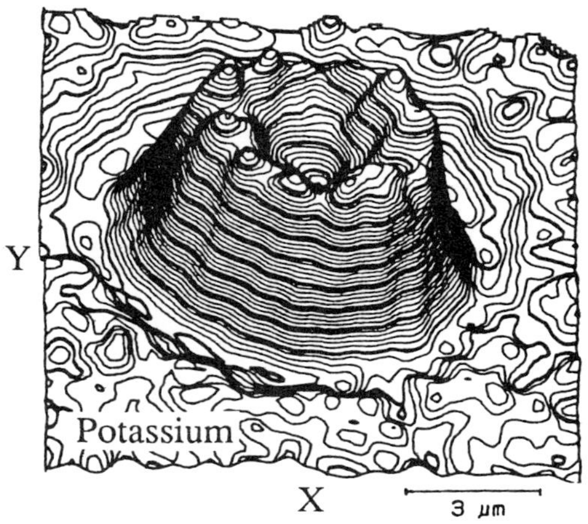

FIG. 4. The K distribution in a red blood cell measured with a scanning proton microprobe. (Courtesy of G. Legge, University of Melbourne.)

Low- and high-energy ion microprobes offer a versatility in analysis that is an important addition to the capabilities of other techniques, such as the electron microprobe. One example, shown in Fig. 4, is the K distribution in a red blood cell obtained from PIXE data recorded with a scanning proton microprobe (SPMP) resolution of < 1 μm. The complete set of recorded data (radiation intensity versus time) can be used to full advantage with computer graphics and spectrum processing to explore spatial or time distributions of a specific element or isotope, the element distribution at a specific location, or any time-dependent changes in element distributions. It is even possible to obtain three-dimensional distributions using detected radiation energy to provide depth information.

Bibliography

Benninghoven, A., Huber, A. M., and Werner, H. W., eds. (1988). "Secondary Ion Mass Spectrometry, SIMS VI." Wiley, New York.

Bethge, K., Rauch, F., and Misaelides, P., eds. (1990). Accelerators in applied research and technology. *Nucl. Instrum. Methods* **B50.**

Bird, J. R., and Williams, J. S., eds. (1989). "Ion Beams for Materials Analysis." Academic Press, Sydney, Australia.

Chu, W.-K., Mayer, J. W., and Nicolet, M.-A. (1978). "Backscattering Spectrometry." Academic Press, New York.

Deconninck, G. (1978). "Introduction to Radioanalytical Physics." Elsevier, Amsterdam.

Duggan, J. L., and Morgan, I. L., eds. (1991). Applications of accelerators in research and industry '90. *Nucl. Instrum. Methods* **B56/57.**

Feldman, L. C., and Mayer, J. W. (1986). "Fundamentals of Surface and Thin Film Analysis." North-Holland, Amsterdam.

Feldman, L. C., Mayer, J. W., and Picraux, S. T. (1982). "Materials Analysis by Ion Channeling." Academic Press, New York.

Legge, G. F. J., and Jamieson, D. N., eds. (1991). Nuclear microprobe technology and applications. *Nucl. Instrum. Methods* **B54.**

Vis, R. D., ed. (1990). Particle induced x-ray emission and its analytical applications. *Nucl. Instrum. Methods* **B49.**

Watt, F., and Grime, G. W., eds. (1987). "Principles and Applications of High-Energy Microbeams." Adam Hilger, Bristol.

Ziegler, J. F., Scanlon, P. J., Lanford, W. A., and Duggan, J. L., eds. (1990). Ion beam analysis 9. *Nucl. Instrum. Methods* **B45.**

ION KINETICS AND ENERGETICS

Sharon G. Lias *National Bureau of Standards*

GLOSSARY

Appearance potential: Minimum energy required to bring about the dissociation process $AB \rightarrow A^+ + B + e$ or $AB \rightarrow A^+ + B^-$.

Association ion: Long-lived ion–molecule collision complex for which, typically, no exothermic reaction channel is available to the complexed pair. The formation of association ions, which is the gas phase analog of solvation, typically follows third-order kinetics.

Breakdown graph: Plot of the relative abundances of a molecular (or parent) ion and its various fragment ions as a function of energy imparted to the initial ion in the ionization process.

Cluster theory: A now-outdated model describing the formation of products in systems under irradiation by ionizing radiation; cluster theory assumed that a positive ion would attract a "cluster" of neutral molecules, and neutralization of the positive entity would release energy in the cluster, promoting chemical reactions.

Collision-induced dissociation (CID): Technique for determining the structures of ions, in which the mass-selected ion of interest is energetically collided with a neutral species (such as helium atoms), undergoing dissociation to generate a mass spectrum of the ion.

Electron affinity: Maximum energy released in the electron attachment process $M + e \rightarrow M^-$, which is the same as the minimum energy required to remove the electron from M^-.

Enthalpy of ionization, ΔH(ionization): Enthalpy change associated with ionization at temperatures other than absolute zero; ionization potential at finite temperatures.

Franck–Condon principle: Statement that the most probable transition for ionization will be that in which the positions and momenta of nuclei are unchanged. Shapes of curves showing the onset of ionization as a function of energy are determined by this principle.

Gas phase acidity: Relative gas phase acidity is the Gibbs free energy change associated with proton transfer reactions $AH + B^- \rightarrow A^- + BH$. Absolute gas phase acidity is the enthalpy change of the reaction $AH \rightarrow A^- + H^+$.

Gas phase basicity: Negative of the Gibbs free energy change of the process $M + H^+ \rightarrow MH^+$.

Hydrogen affinity: Negative of the enthalpy change for the process $M^+ + H \rightarrow MH^+$.

Ionization potential: Adiabatic ionization potential is the minimum energy required to remove an electron from a molecule; it corresponds to the $0 \rightarrow 0$ transition from the lowest vibrational and rotational levels of the molecular ground state to the lowest vibrational and rotational levels of the ground state of the corresponding ion. Vertical ionization potential is the energy required to remove an electron to form an ion having the same geometry as the corresponding neutral molecule.

Langevin rate constant: Rate constant for collision of an ion with a nonpolar neutral molecule, based on a statistical mechanical derivation published in 1905 by Langevin.

Proton affinity: Negative of the enthalpy change of the process $M + H^+ \rightarrow MH^+$.

Quasi-equilibrium theory (QET): Statistical theory of unimolecular dissociations as applied to ionic fragmentation processes.

Ion kinetics and energetics is concerned with the physical chemistry of electrically charged species in the gas phase. The subject area can be divided into three major subdivisions: (1) ion kinetics, (2) ion energetics, and (3) ion spectroscopy. Ion kinetics is the study of the rates and mechanisms of elementary unimolecular and bimolecular chemical reactions in the gas phase involving species carrying an electrical charge. Ion energetics refers to the thermodynamics of charged species in the gas phase; information about the heats of formation of ions rests on determination of the energy required to remove an electron from a molecule (ionization potential) or to form a particular fragment ion (appearance potential). In this article the spectroscopy of ions will be mentioned only insofar as spectroscopic results provide information about ion energetics or ion kinetics.

I. History

The concept of the gas phase ion—an atom or molecule that gains or loses one or more electrons—can, like most of modern physics and chemistry, be traced to the dramatically productive period of modern science starting in the 1890s. After the discoveries of x rays by Roentgen in 1895, the radioactivity of uranium by Becquerel in 1896, and the electron by Thomson in 1897, and the fundamental insights of Planck, Einstein, Bohr, and others in the early 1900s, it was natural for researchers to measure conductivity in gases and liquids and to begin to examine the properties of the ions they detected.

Well before 1900, conductivity measurements on flames and gases exposed to high-energy radiation or subjected to electric discharges demonstrated that the molecules in such systems lose electrons to form positive ions. In 1902 organic chemists recognized the "saltlike character" of certain organic compounds and demonstrated the presence of ions through conductivity measurements, thus laying the groundwork for the concept of organic ions as reactive intermediates.

A. Ion Energetics

Perhaps an obvious starting point for research on the physicochemical properties of ions was the determination of the energy required to remove an electron from a molecule. In fact, work in this area began before the series of dramatic discoveries listed above. From the beginning of experimental optical spectroscopy, regularities in the distribution of spectral lines were observed, and attempts were made to interpret these regularities. The work in this area by Balmer, Rydberg, and Bohr between 1885 and 1913 led to the interpretation of so-called Rydberg series in optical spectra of atoms and molecules in terms of the energy required to remove an electron.

From around 1899, various workers experimented with the determination of ionization potentials by electron impact, generating electrons from a plate irradiated by ultraviolet light or from a heated filament; although the very early determinations of ionization potentials by such electron impact techniques were often in error by several electron volts, by 1917 the first "modern" ionization onset determinations were beginning to appear.

In the meantime, in 1912, Thomson generated ions in his cathode ray apparatus and separated them by molecular weight, laying the foundations for the development of the mass spectrometer, the versatile tool of modern chemistry and physics which, in various incarnations, has made possible most of the research described in this article.

Starting from the end of the 1920s, the development of good pumping systems and increasingly sophisticated mass spectrometric instrumentation gave impetus to research on ionic processes, mainly the development of mass spectrometry as an analytical technique and studies in which ionization potentials, appearance potentials, and bond dissociation energies were determined. This was the beginning of systematic investigations of the thermochemistry of gas phase ions, that is, determinations of ionization potentials and appearance potentials.

The usual mass spectrometric determination at this time involved exposing the gas of interest to electrons from a heated filament, varying the energy of the electron beam, and noting the energy (onset or threshold energy) at which a particular molecular ion or fragment ion could first be detected. The major problem with this approach was that the electron beams did not have well-defined energies; energy spreads of at least several tenths of an electron volt were usual. (The electron volt, eV, is the unit used most often for ionization potential data; 1 eV = 96.4845 kJ/mol or 23.06036 kcal/mol.) Starting in 1953, mass spectrometers were designed that used photons rather than electrons as the ionizing medium, thus obtaining better energy resolution for ionization potential measurements. In the early 1960s instrumentation was designed to permit high energy resolution of an electron beam, so that electron impact measurements of onset energies could be made nearly as reliable as photoionization onset determinations. Also starting in the mid-1960s, ionization energies were determined by effecting ionization with a photon of well-defined energy and measuring the energies of the ejected electrons; this technique, known as photoelectron spectroscopy, was actually developed to determine molecular orbital energy levels, but has also yielded a large body of accurate ionization potential information. [*See* DIELECTRIC GASES; PHOTOELECTRON SPECTROSCOPY.]

B. Ion Kinetics

In one experiment in his cathode ray apparatus, which was really a primitive mass spectrometer, Thomson examined the ions generated in hydrogen and observed species having a molecular weight of 3, which would correspond to H_3^+. We know today that an electron beam or high-energy radiation removes one electron from the hydrogen molecules:

$$H_2 + \text{energy} \rightarrow H_2^+ + e\ (+\ \text{energy}') \quad (1)$$

and that H_2^+ reacts at every collision with a hydrogen molecule to form H_3^+:

$$H_2^+ + H_2 \rightarrow H_3^+ + H \quad (2)$$

However, in 1912 the concept of an elementary chemical reaction involving a reactive intermediate species such as H_2^+ was not known to Thomson. Thomson, and later Dempster and other workers who examined the ions formed in hydrogen, believed either that some of the H_2^+ ions were collisionally dissociated to give H^+, which clustered with a neutral H_2 molecule to give H_3^+, or that hydrogen contained some H_3 molecules that underwent ionization.

Also in 1912 another researcher, S. C. Lind, correctly recognized that ions generated in systems under high-energy irradiation are responsible for chemical transformations. However, like Thomson, he failed to invoke what we would now call elementary chemical reactions. Instead, he suggested that an ion, once formed, collects about itself a cluster of neutral molecules, and when the positive entity recombines with an electron, the energy released in the cluster promotes chemical reactions among the clustered molecules:

$$A^+(M)_n + e \rightarrow \text{products} \quad (3)$$

It was not until 1925 that Hogness and Lunn correctly interpreted the occurrence of reaction (2). Other elementary reactions of ions with molecules were also observed in this period. For example, the reaction:

$$H_2O^+ + H_2O \rightarrow H_3O^+ + OH \quad (4)$$

was observed to occur in a mass spectrometer by Aston in 1924, Barton and Bartlett in 1928, and Mann, Hustrulid, and Tate in 1940. Furthermore, Hogness and Harkness in 1928 observed elementary reactions of ions with molecules in mass spectrometric examinations of I_2 and of CO; during the 1930s several workers reported observing ions in gaseous mixtures, which suggested the occurrence of chemical reactions involving ions (e.g., N_2H^+ in a mixture of N_2 and H_2).

In spite of this abundant evidence that ionic molecular species did react with neutral molecules, there was a lack of acceptance of the importance of elementary chemical reactions of ions with neutral molecules outside the ionization chamber of a mass spectrometer. In interpreting the chemistry of systems where ions were known to be formed, the so-called cluster theory [represented by reaction (3)] was universally accepted. It was believed that clustering and ion–electron neutralization would preclude the occurrence of elementary reactions of the ions in systems at pressures higher than those used in a mass spectrometer.

This situation lasted until 1936, when Eyring, Hirschfelder, and Taylor published a theoretical study of reaction (2) in which it was predicted that at atmospheric pressures, the probability that a hydrogen ion would collect a cluster of neutral hydrogen molecules about itself before undergoing neutralization was not large. However, even after the publication of this landmark paper, the interpretation of events occurring in systems in which ionization occurs at high pressures largely ignored the possibility of product formation through elementary reactions of ions. Although Eyring, Hirschfelder, and Taylor had correctly predicted that reaction (2) would occur on every collision between H_2^+ and H_2, the prevailing model used in interpretation assumed that ion–electron recombination would be rapid enough to prevent such reactions from occurring.

The first systematic studies of the elementary bimolecular reactions of ions with molecules were carried out in the Soviet Union by Tal'roze and collaborators starting in 1952. These investigators reported that following the ionization of methane by a beam of high-energy electrons:

$$CH_4 + e \rightarrow CH_4^+ + 2e \qquad (5)$$

and dissociation of a fraction of the CH_4^+ ions formed with excess energy:

$$CH_4^+ \rightarrow CH_3^+ + H \qquad (6)$$

the following bimolecular reactions occur:

$$CH_4^+ + CH_4 \rightarrow CH_5^+ + CH_3 \qquad (7)$$

$$CH_3^+ + CH_4 \rightarrow C_2H_5^+ + H_2 \qquad (8)$$

The same reaction sequence was reported independently in 1955 by Stevenson and Schissler, who had not had access to the literature from the Soviet Union.

By the mid-1950s, although the main focus of mass spectrometric research was on the determination of ionization potentials and bond dissociation energies, workers in several laboratories (Tal'roze starting in 1952, Stevenson starting in 1955, Hamill in 1956, Field, Franklin, and Lampe in 1957) began to take an active interest in research on the kinetics of ion–molecule reactions, using the ionization chambers of mass spectrometers as reaction vessels.

In a 1957 investigation of the chemical processes initiated in methane by gamma radiation, Meisels, Hamill, and Williams pointed out that occurrence of the unimolecular and bimolecular ionic processes observed in mass spectrometers along with certain assumed neutralization mechanisms could entirely explain the formation of all the observed products. However, the occurrence of ion–molecule reactions in this system was not yet firmly established and was, in fact, questioned by subsequent workers. After Field and Lampe, in 1958, observed hydride transfer reactions from alkanes to alkyl ions in a mass spectrometer:

$$C_nH_{2n+1}^+ + C_mH_{2m+2} \rightarrow C_nH_{2n+2} + C_mH_{2m+1}^+ \qquad (9)$$

it was suggested by Futrell that the occurrence of such reactions might explain the formation of products in irradiated alkanes. In 1962 Ausloos and collaborators conclusively proved that this was the case and began a systematic series of studies of the reactions of ions generated in gases by high-energy radiation or photoionization at atmospheric pressures. The kinetics of ion–molecule reactions had made the first step into the "real" world from the interior of the mass spectrometer. The studies of ion–molecule reactions carried on outside the ionization chamber of a mass spectrometer established that mass spectrometric observations could be generalized to other systems and experimental conditions. Within a decade, mass spectrometric studies of ionic processes were even accepted as a valid tool for explorations in the field of organic chemistry.

In a restudy of the ion chemistry in irradiated methane, Ausloos attempted to determine the fate of the CH_5^+ ion under high-pressure conditions. Adding traces of isotopically labeled hydrocarbons to the system and analyzing neutral products formed, he was able to demonstrate that the CH_5^+ ion readily transfers a proton to higher alkanes. In 1965 Munson and Field confirmed these observed proton transfer reactions in a high-capacity differentially pumped mass spectrometer. This led to the development of a practical application of ion–molecule reactions, namely the analytical chemistry technique now known as chemical ionization mass spectrometry; in this technique, products of ion–molecule reactions (such as proton transfer) are used to characterize the compound being analyzed.

Although most of the work carried out in that era was concerned with the chemistry of positive ions, as early as 1957 Muschlitz studied the anion reaction

$$H^- + H_2O \rightarrow OH^- + H_2 \qquad (10)$$

The study of ion kinetics and ion thermochemistry was gradually revolutionized during the 1960s and 1970s by the increasing sophistication of available technology. The early systematic mass spectrometric studies of ion–molecule reactions were primarily carried out with conventional analytical mass spectrometers in which the pressure was increased sufficiently that the ions generated by the electron beam would undergo collisions with neutral molecules before being collected. This approach had certain deficiencies; for instance, the reaction time of the ions was generally ill defined, so rate constant measurements were not very accurate. Pulsed ion sources to permit time-resolved observations of the kinetics in high-pressure sources were first used in 1960 by Tal'roze. This was followed by such innovations as the "flowing afterglow" technique, in which the reactant ions were generated in a flow tube in the presence of a large excess of a thermalizing carrier gas; instruments in which the ions were generated with well-defined energies by photoionization; tandem mass spectrometers in which the mass-selected ion of interest is extracted and sent into a second reaction chamber; and ion cyclotron resonance (ICR) spectroscopy, in which reacting ions are trapped for long times in cyclotron motion in a magnetic field. The concept of a tandem instrument, in which mass-selected ions are generated and injected into a reaction chamber, has been extended to flow tube studies (selected ion flow tube or SIFT) and to ion cyclotron resonance instruments.

In 1963 studies of gas phase equilibria involving ions were initiated. These investigations provided a vast body of thermochemical information about ions which supplemented that obtained from ionization potential and appearance potential determinations. The first systematic ion–molecule equilibrium studies, carried out by Kebarle and co-workers, examined the thermochemistry of ion solvation in the gas phase:

$$A^+ + M \rightleftarrows [A^+\cdot M] \qquad (11)$$

$$A^- + M \rightleftarrows [A^-\cdot M] \qquad (12)$$

Starting in 1971, studies began to appear concerning equilibria that are bimolecular in both directions:

$$A^+ + B \rightleftarrows C^+ + D \qquad (13)$$

$$A^- + B \rightleftarrows C^- + D \qquad (14)$$

Published ion–molecule equilibrium studies have provided quantitative information about energies of solvation and structures of cluster ions, relative heats of formation of alkyl carbonium ions, scales of relative ionization potentials and electron affinities, and relative proton affinities of molecules and anions.

II. Ion Kinetics

A. Bimolecular Reactions

In the pioneering studies of ion–molecule reactions it was realized that these reactions, in contrast to the reactions of free radicals, apparently occurred on every collision and appeared to show no temperature dependence. The assumption was made that if an exothermic reaction channel was available to a particular ion–molecule reactant pair, then reaction would occur on collision. Although we now know that not all ion–molecule reactions occur at every collision, one inheritance from those early days is the prevalence of the use of collision theory to describe ion–molecule reactions. It is a widespread practice to report reaction rates in terms of the "collision efficiency" or "reaction efficiency," which is defined as the rate constant of reaction divided by the rate constant for the ion–molecule collision, that is, the probability of a reactive collision. For this reason, much attention has been given to theoretical calculations of ion–molecule collision rate constants. [*See* CHEMICAL KINETICS, EXPERIMENTATION; KINETICS (CHEMISTRY).]

1. Ion–Molecule Collision Rates

The potential energy of interaction between a molecule and an ion includes interactions between the charge and any permanent dipole or other multipole moments that exist in the molecule plus additional interactions with such moments induced in the molecule by the charge. This potential may be represented as a series containing one term for each interaction. For example, for an axially symmetric molecule having just one nonzero component of the dipole and quadrupole and two polarizabilities, the complete potential of interaction between the molecule and a point charge q at a distance r may be represented by

$$\begin{aligned} V(r) = & -q\mu_D(\cos\theta)1/r^2 \\ & - \tfrac{1}{2}q\Theta(3\cos^2\beta - 1)1/r^3 \\ & - \tfrac{1}{6}q^2[3\alpha + (\alpha_\parallel - \alpha_\perp)] \\ & \times (3\cos^2\gamma - 1)1/r^4 + \cdots \end{aligned} \qquad (15)$$

where μ_D and Θ are the permanent dipole moment and quadrupole moment, α is the isotropic polarizability, $\alpha_\parallel$ and $\alpha_\perp$ are the components of α parallel and perpendicular to the principal molecular axis, respectively, and θ, β, and γ are the angles between the principal moment and the line joining the centers of the ion and the molecule. Additional terms would include the ion-induced quadrupole moment, which varies as $1/r^6$, and a repulsive term to account for the finite size of the molecule.

In the simplest possible case, a spherical molecule with isotropic polarizability and no permanent dipole or quadrupole moments, Eq. (15) reduces to

$$V(r) = q^2\alpha/2r^4 \qquad (16)$$

Langevin considered this case in 1905 (in attempting to explain the ion mobilities that had been determined by Thomson) and derived collision cross sections and trajectories for the collision of a point charge with such a structureless molecule. The trajectories predicted from the potential represented in Eq. (16) showed that the ion and the colliding molecule would attract one another at a distance and spiral toward one another. This treatment is called the Langevin theory or, because for certain trajectories the two species orbit one another, the Langevin orbiting theory.

From an analysis of Eq. (16), Gioumousis and Stevenson in 1958 derived the expression for the corresponding ion–molecule collision rate constant:

$$k_c = 2\pi q(\alpha/\mu)^{1/2} \qquad (17)$$

Equation (17), called the Langevin rate constant, Gioumousis–Stevenson rate constant, or orbiting rate constant, is almost universally used to predict collision rate constants of thermal energy ions with molecules having no permanent moments. The rate constant obtained in this way pertains to the formation of an ion–molecule complex. Considering the great simplifications made in deriving Eqs. (16) and (17), the agreement between the collision rates calculated in this way and experimentally derived values for ion–molecule collision rates involving nonpolar molecules is generally very good, as some results summarized in Table I demonstrate.

The most important case for which the Langevin–Gioumousis–Stevenson formulation is inadequate is that of the molecule with a permanent dipole moment, where the potential of interaction with the dipole must be included in the overall potential for the ion–molecule pair. Early attempts to arrive at an ion–polar molecule collision rate constant adopted the simplest possible model for such a system, assuming that the dipole of the molecule would assume the energetically most favorable orientation in approaching the ion. The resulting "locked dipole" collision rate constant represented the maximum possible rate constant for such a collision, but was much greater than ion–polar molecule collision rate constants derived from measurements of the mobilities of ions. Several other approaches have been taken in attempting to predict ion–polar molecule collision rates, of which the most notable will be summarized briefly. Ridge and collaborators suggested an approximation based on averaging the ion–dipole energy over a Boltzmann distribution to obtain a temperature-dependent central potential. Su and Bowers approached the problem by calculating the average dipole orientation (the so-called ADO theory), which led to a parameterized expression that, although superseded by more recent work, is still widely used for the empirical prediction of ion–polar molecule collision rates, apparently because of its great simplicity. Later, Chesnavich and Bowers developed so-called variational transition state theory, which gave results in good agreement with those from the earlier Ridge approach. Most recently, Su and Chesnavich have carried out extensive trajectory calculations for such ion–molecule pairs, arriving at an empirical parameterized expression that leads to values for ion–polar molecule collision rate constants in good agreement with the earlier predictions and with experimental results (Table I). This expression is

$$K_{\text{cap}} = \begin{cases} 0.4767x + 0.6200, & x \geq 2 \\ \dfrac{(x + 0.5090)^2}{10.529} + 0.9754, & x \leq 2 \end{cases} \qquad (18)$$

where $x = \mu_D/(2\alpha k_B T)^{1/2}$, k_B is the Boltzmann constant, and μ_D the dipole moment. The quantity calculated by Eq. (18) is the factor by which the Langevin rate constant [Eq. (16)] must be multiplied to obtain the correct collision rate constant.

TABLE I. Absolute Rate Coefficient Calculated for Collisions of Ions with Molecules: Comparison with Collision Rate Constants Derived from Experimental Results

	k (cm^3/molecule sec) $\times 10^{10}$		
Colliding pair	Langevin [Eq. (17)]	Su–Chesnavich [Eq. (18)] $T = 300$ K	Experimental
$H_2^+ + H_2$	21		21
$CH_5^+ + H_2$	15.7		15.8
$C_2H_5^+ + H_2$	15.3		14.6
$H_3O^+ + H_2$	15.6		16.0
$Na^+ + CH_4$	12.3		11.2
$CH_4^+ + CH_4$	13.3		12.5
$CH_5^+ + CH_3Cl$		28.9	26.0
$NH_3^+ + NH_3$		26.7	23
$H_2O^+ + H_2O$		29.6	26
$H_3^+ + m-C_6H_4F_2$		60.4	57.1
$(CH_3)_2O^+ + (CH_3)_2O$		16.6	15.8

2. Types of Ion–Molecule Reactions

Important classes of ion–molecule reactions include

charge transfer:

$$A^+ + B \rightarrow B^+ + A \tag{19}$$

$$A^- + B \rightarrow B^- + A \tag{20}$$

proton transfer:

$$AH^+ + B \rightarrow BH^+ + A \tag{21}$$

$$AH + B^- \rightarrow A^- + BH \tag{22}$$

hydride or halide transfer:

$$B^+ + AX \rightarrow BX + A^+ \tag{23}$$

(where X is H, F, Cl, Br, or I), and various other particle transfer reactions (i.e., H_2 transfer, H_2^- transfer), as well as so-called switching reactions

$$AB^+ + CD \rightarrow AC^+ + BD \tag{24}$$

Condensation reactions

$$A^+ + B \rightarrow AB^+ \tag{25}$$

may be followed by dissociation of the condensation ion to give other products such as

$$A^+ + B \rightarrow [AB^+]^* \rightarrow C^+ + D \tag{26}$$

Also important are association reactions:

$$A^+ + B \rightarrow A^+{\cdot}B \tag{27}$$

$$A^- + B \rightarrow A^-{\cdot}B \tag{28}$$

where the associating molecule is most often a polar species (such as H_2O or other solvent molecule).

3. Rates and Mechanisms of Ion–Molecule Reactions: Role of Ion–Molecule Complexes

In the pioneering studies of ion–molecule reaction kinetics, it was realized that the high probability for occurrence of exothermic reactions between an ion and a molecule could be explained in terms of the formation of a long-lived ion–molecule collision complex. Modern detailed systematic investigations of the kinetics of ion–molecule reactions have demonstrated several unusual features, all of which can be explained by the operation of a mechanism involving a long-lived ion–molecule complex. For example, at sufficiently high temperatures, rate constants of exothermic ion–molecule reactions often exhibit a negative temperature dependence. The onset of the regime in which negative temperature dependence is observed occurs at a higher temperature the more exothermic the reaction, and for very exothermic reactions it may not be seen at the temperatures reached in ordinary experiments (<800 K). As the temperature is increased, the lifetime of the complex is shortened, the probability of dissociation to regenerate the original reactants is increased, and the probability of chemical reaction is diminished. [*See* CHEMICAL KINETICS EXPERIMENTATION.]

Also, it has often been reported that the probability of a reactive ion–molecule collision is usually low (<~0.1–0.2) when the reaction occurring is thermoneutral or only marginally exothermic. Furthermore, in examinations of charge transfer, proton transfer, and hydride transfer reactions of a particular ion with a homologous series of molecules, the rate constants for the reaction increase with increasing reaction exothermicity until, with sufficient exothermicity, reaction occurs on every collision. The lowering of reaction efficiency for reactions that are not highly exothermic is understood as a lowering of the rate at which reaction occurs *in the complex* (a less efficient competition of step a with step b):

$$A^\pm + B \underset{b}{\overset{k_c}{\rightleftharpoons}} [A^\pm{\cdot}B] \overset{a}{\rightarrow} [C^\pm{\cdot}D] \overset{c}{\rightarrow} C^\pm + D \tag{29}$$

For most transfer reactions, such as proton transfer [reactions (21) and (22)], the potential surface will have two wells, one corresponding to $[A^\pm{\cdot}B]$ and one corresponding to $[C^\pm{\cdot}D]$. Theoretical and experimental results indicate that the complexed ion and molecule are not covalently bonded (i.e., the reaction does not involve formation of an intermediate condensation ion). Experiments in which one observes isotope exchange between reactant pairs for which there is no exothermic reaction channel (step c does not occur) show that the probability of exploring the second well of the double potential well surface is greater, the greater the energy gained in going to the second potential well. Although a quantitative understanding of the rates of ion–molecule reactions having lowered efficiencies is not well established at this writing, it is generally assumed that step a in reaction (29) may involve an energy barrier with height that is lower the more exothermic the overall reaction. [*See* POTENTIAL ENERGY SURFACES.]

Other experiments have shown that when the overall reaction is highly exothermic (>20–30 kcal/mol), formation of the final products is fast, and the lifetime of the complex is effectively shortened by the occurrence of reaction. Under these circumstances, the probability that the rate constant can be lowered by dissociation of the complex to regenerate the original reactants (step b) is negligible even when the temperature is increased. When two highly exothermic channels are available to a reacting pair, the short complex lifetime is manifested in an invariance of the relative probabilities of the two channels over a pressure range of many orders of magnitude.

Details of the mechanisms of many ion–molecule reactions can be rationalized in terms of the potential surfaces corresponding to formation of long-lived ion–molecule complexes. That is, reactions occur above the ion–molecule potential well predicted by Eq. (15), and the energy gained in the formation of the complex is available to the reacting pair. For example, for isolated molecular species there is an activation energy of about 18 kcal/mol for the isomerization reaction:

$$sec\text{-}C_4H_9^+ \rightarrow tert\text{-}C_4H_9^+ \qquad (30)$$

However, in systems where sec-$C_4H_9^+$ is allowed to collide with unreactive molecules, M, it is seen that such an isomerization occurs in some systems without any activation barrier:

$$sec\text{-}C_4H_9^+ + M \rightarrow M + tert\text{-}C_4H_9^+ \qquad (31)$$

The probability for the isomerization is greater the greater the dipole moment of M. The explanation of these results is that the energy gained in formation of the [sec-$C_4H_9^+ \cdot M$] complex is greater the greater the dipole moment of M, and this energy, which is more than 18 kcal/mole for many M, is available to bring about reaction.

B. Unimolecular Reactions

When a molecule is ionized and the parent ion originates with excess energy as

$$AB + \text{energy} \rightarrow AB^{+*} + e \qquad (32)$$

dissociation may occur as

$$AB^{+*} \rightarrow A^+ + B \qquad (33)$$

Two modes of description exist to deal with unimolecular dissociation processes of ions. The statistical description [corresponding to the well-known Rice–Ramsperger–Kassel–Marcus (RRKM) theory of chemical kinetics, usually called quasi-equilibrium theory when applied to ions] assumes that excess energy in the parent ion is statistically distributed through the various vibrational and electronic degrees of freedom of the ion and that the probabilities of various possible modes of dissociation will be governed by this energy distribution. So-called state-to-state chemistry describes a unimolecular dissociation in terms of a rate constant that is characterized by the entire set of electronic, vibrational, and rotational quantum numbers of the reacting species and of the products of the dissociation. Evidence from modern experimental techniques indicates that ionic dissociations are usually multistep processes (rather than concerted processes), that dissociation may be the last in a sequence of steps involving isomerization, and that the inherently multidimensional character of such processes in polyatomic species leads to behavior that often fits the statistical description.

Stated simply, for polyatomic ions it is generally observed that the relative probability of a given mode of dissociation depends on the amount of excess internal energy imparted to the ion in the ionization process, and the degree of fragmentation depends on the time available for decomposition to occur. A graph showing the relative abundances of the fragmenting parent ion and the various ions formed in the fragmentation processes as a function of energy is called the breakdown graph of the ion.

More detailed presentations include the time dependences of the various fragmentations. So-called metastable ions are ions that undergo fragmentation in the field-free regions of the mass spectrometer. Studies of such metastable decompositions and results from more sophisticated experiments (see discussion of photoelectron–photoion coincidence in Section III,A,2) can give a detailed understanding of the unimolecular dissociation kinetics of ions.

Evidence has been presented that mechanisms for some ionic dissociations may proceed through a pathway that can be described as (1) an initial bond cleavage to form an ion–molecule or ion–radical complex, followed by (2) a reaction or rearrangement within the complex and (3) dissociation leading to the final products. This mechanism explains why rearrangements in the ionic fragment that occur prior to dissociation are catalyzed by the presence of a permanent dipole in the neutral fragment species. For instance, in a study of the dissociation mechanisms of different isomers of $CH_3CH{=}O^+C_4H_9$, the results were interpreted in terms of an intermediate in which an incipient $C_4H_9^+$ carbonium ion is coordinated to neutral acetaldehyde, which has a permanent dipole moment.

III. Ion Energetics

A. Determination of Ionization Threshold Energies

We shall be considering the process

$$M \xrightarrow{IP_a} M^+ + e \quad (34)$$

where IP_a is the minimum energy required to remove an electron from a molecule M. Although IP_a is an energy, sometimes called the ionization energy, the term in general use for this quantity is the ionization potential or, more completely, the adiabatic ionization potential. The ion M^+ is called the molecular radical cation or simply the parent ion.

As discussed in Section II,B, when M^+ is formed with excess energy, fragmentation may occur. The minimum energy required to generate a particular fragment ion, starting from the neutral molecule:

$$AB \xrightarrow{AP} A^+ + B + e \quad (35)$$

is called the appearance potential or appearance energy.

The heterolytic cleavage of a molecule to give an ion pair:

$$AB + \text{energy} \rightarrow A^+ + B^- \quad (36)$$

is a ubiquitous process in chemistry and leads to the formation of anions. Anions are also generated in the gas phase by electron attachment to neutral molecules:

$$M + e \rightarrow M^- \quad (37)$$

This section will consider the experimental determination of ionization potentials, appearance potentials, dissociative pair production [reaction (36)] and electron detachment energies:

$$M^- + h\nu \rightarrow M + e \quad (38)$$

Since in general the same techniques are used for determinations of ionization potentials and appearance potentials, they will be discussed together; the inclusive term ''ionization threshold energies'' will be applied to both.

1. Franck–Condon Principle: Implications for Experimental Determination of Ionization Potentials

Ionization of a molecule by photoionization or by electron impact is governed by the Franck–Condon principle, which states that the most probable transition for ionization will be that in which the positions and momenta of the nuclei are unchanged. Thus, when the equilibrium geometries of an ion and its corresponding neutral species are closely similar, the onset of ionization will be a sharp step function leading to the ion vibrational ground state. However, when the equilibrium geometry of the ion is much different in one or more bond lengths or angles from that of the neutral species, the transition to the lowest vibrational level of the ion is no longer the most intense, and the maximum transition probability (the vertical ionization potential) will favor population of a higher vibrational level of the ion. If the geometry change is great, the transition to the lowest vibrational level of the ion may not even be observed.

2. Experimental Techniques

In the historical review presented above, the most important experimental approaches to determinations of ionization threshold energies were briefly described. These include (1) analysis of Rydberg series from optical spectra, (2) determination of the onset energy for formation of a molecular radical cation or fragment ion in experiments in which ionization is effected by photon absorption or a calibrated electron beam, and (3) photoelectron spectroscopy. For anions, the energies for photodetachment [process (38)] may be determined in ion beam studies of various design, by photoelectron spectroscopy, and through analyses of Rydberg series in the optical spectra of anions. Energies of dissociative pair production [reaction (36)] are determined by photoionization techniques analogous to those used to determine the photoionization onsets for cations.

Developments in these techniques now permit a high degree of sophistication in studies of ion energetics. For example, since the advent of lasers as common laboratory light sources, data have been obtained by using a tunable laser to raise a vibrationally and rotationally cool beam of molecules to a specific excited state and a second independently tunable laser to ionize the beam of excited molecules. The photon energy is tuned through the ionization onset for several different excited states. Since every intermediate state leads to an independent value of the ionization threshold, the experiment contains an internal consistency check.

In the powerful threshold technique known as photoelectron–photoion coincidence, the thermochemistry and detailed mechanism of an ionic fragmentation process can be mapped out very accurately. Ejected electrons that originated with "zero" kinetic energy are matched with their corresponding positive ions. At energies where parent ions M^+ are undergoing dissociation to form one or more fragment ions, one obtains the relative probabilities for the formation of the daughter ions from parent ions of known energy (i.e., the breakdown curve). The ions can be detected at different times after the ionization event to determine the time dependence of the dissociation process. Complete interpretation of such data requires a modeling of the dissociation by using statistical theories of unimolecular decomposition (i.e., quasi-equilibrium or RRKM theory). As pointed out by Dannacher, in spite of its great strengths, this technique has not been widely utilized, possibly because of the intricate instrumentation required, the complexity of the data analysis, and the fact that each determination requires the investment of a large amount of time on the part of the experimenter.

At this juncture it is worthwhile to discuss the important technique of photoelectron spectroscopy in somewhat more detail. In this technique, the energy change associated with an ionization process determined in experiments in which the molecule is ionized by a photon of well-defined energy and the energy of the ejected electrons is measured:

$$M + h\nu \rightarrow M^+ + e \tag{39}$$

If the species being studied is an anion, the experiment gives a direct measure of the electron affinity of molecule M. The photon sources most often used are the helium resonance lines at 58.4331 nm (21.218 eV) or 30.3781 nm (40.813 eV), although some work is done with neon resonance lines (73.589 and 74.370 nm, 16.848 and 16.671 eV) or other intense monochromatic sources. In such an experiment, the ejected electrons have different energies depending on the distribution of energy levels in the M^+ ions formed; this is called the photoelectron spectrum. The positions of the photoelectron bands show the energy levels of the different excited states of M^+, and the shapes of the bands give information about the $M \rightarrow M^+$ transition probabilities as governed by the Franck–Condon principle. In cases where the equilibrium geometries of the ion and the corresponding neutral are the same or similar, the observed onset of the first photoelectron band is usually a reliable indicator of the adiabatic ionization potential.

In addition to the techniques mentioned before, some information has been derived from determinations of the onset energies for the occurrence of endothermic ion–molecule reactions. Although one or two papers have presented straightforward kinetic treatments (Arrhenius plots) of the temperature dependences of the rate constants of endothermic ion–molecule reactions, quantitative studies have covered a much broader energy range by generating a beam of energy- and mass-selected ions, which is focused into a collision chamber containing the reactant gas; product ions are detected as a function of the energy of the ions in the beam. This technique has been employed particularly in determinations of electron affinities:

$$A^- + B \rightarrow B^- + A \tag{40}$$

where the production of B^- is observed as a function of the translational energy imparted to A^-.

3. Ion Heats of Formation Derived from Threshold Energies

The heat of formation of a positive ion in the gas phase is defined by a conventional analysis of the thermochemistry of reaction (34), assuming that the adiabatic ionization potential IP_a corresponds to the enthalpy change of the reaction:

$$\Delta H_f(M^+) = \Delta H_f(M) + IP_a - \Delta H_f(e) \tag{41}$$

This assumption is rigorously true at absolute zero. However, in obtaining a value for the heat of formation of an ion at temperatures other than 0 K, considerations unique to ion thermochemistry must be taken into account. The adiabatic ionization potential of a molecule is, in fact, a spectroscopic quantity—the $0 \rightarrow 0$ transition between the rotationless, vibrationless ground state of the molecule and the rotationless, vibrationless electronic ground state of the ion—and is not, strictly speaking, the same as the thermodynamic equilibrium property corresponding to the enthalpy change of reaction (34) at some temperature T. The relationship between IP_a and the enthalpy change of reaction (34) at temperature T, ΔH(ionization), is illustrated in the thermochemical cycle:

$$\begin{array}{ccccc} M_{(0\,K)} & \xrightarrow{IP_a} & M^+_{(0\,K)} & + & e_{(0\,K)} \\ \downarrow & & \downarrow & & \downarrow \\ M_{(298\,K)} & \xrightarrow{\Delta H(\text{ionization})} & M^+_{(298\,K)} & + & e_{(298\,K)} \end{array} \tag{42}$$

For IP_a and ΔH(ionization) to be equal, the integrated heat capacities of the products ($M^+ + e$) and reactant (M) must be equal over the temperature range $0 \rightarrow T$. It has been demonstrated that the integrated heat capacities of M and M^+ will be approximately equal; differences will arise if there are changes in vibrational frequencies on ionization or if either M or M^+ has a multiplet ground state with a split in energy, but at temperatures below 400 or 500 K these contributions will rarely cause differences greater than about 0.01 eV in the integrated heat capacities of M and M^+.

There are two conventions in use to account for the integrated heat capacity of the electron. In most mass spectrometric literature, the so-called stationary electron convention is adopted, in which the heat capacity of the electron is defined as zero at all temperatures, so that the electron can be ignored in all thermochemical considerations. Another equally arbitrary convention, also in widespread use, may be called the thermal electron convention; in this convention, one defines the ionization energy at temperature T as the energy required to form M^+ and e, both with thermal kinetic energies, and assumes that this ionization energy is equal to the adiabatic ionization potential. The electron is treated like an ideal gas with an integrated heat capacity at 298 K equal to 1.481 kcal/mol, 6.197 kJ/mol. The net result of the existence of two conventions is that heats of formation of ions at 298 K given in compilations of thermodynamic data are higher than those cited in the mass spectrometric literature by 1.481 kcal/mol (6.197 kJ/mol).

It can be concluded that for most species the simplifying assumption that the adiabatic ionization potential and the 298 enthalpy of ionization are approximately the same:

$$IP_a \sim \Delta H(\text{ionization}) \tag{43}$$

will not introduce significant errors in the 298 K heats of formation of molecular radical cations. In fact, experimental determinations of relative values of ΔH(ionization) have been made by measuring equilibrium constants in charge transfer reactions at temperatures in the range 300–400 K. Such experiments (described in more detail elsewhere in this article) give thermochemical ladders of relative ionization potentials, which closely reproduce equivalent scales of spectroscopic ionization potentials.

Thus, from Eqs. (41) and (43), it is seen that determination of the heats of formation of molecular ions is in principle straightforward, requiring only a value for the heat of formation of the corresponding neutral and a reliable determination of the adiabatic ionization energy. One must, however, also define the heats of formation of the many positive ions of interest that do not have long-lived neutral molecular counterparts, such as ions that originate by fragmentation of a molecular ion [reaction (33)]. Heats of formation of fragment ions, A^+, are generally based on a straightforward thermochemical treatment of reaction (35), using the stationary electron convention and making the assumption that the appearance potential (AP) corresponds to the enthalpy change of reaction. As with the analysis of the relationship between the ionization potential and the enthalpy change of reaction (34), it can be shown that the appearance potential is not strictly equivalent to the enthalpy change this reaction, except at absolute zero. A more complete treatment has shown that the heat of formation of a fragment ion at temperature T is more correctly given by

$$AP_T = \Delta H_f(A^+ + B + e)_T - \Delta H_f(AB)_T - \int_0^T C_p(A^+ + B + e)\,dT + \tfrac{5}{2}RT \tag{44}$$

Most heats of formation reported for fragment ions at temperatures other than absolute zero are derived by making the simplifying assumption that the last two terms of Eq. (44) will approximately cancel one another, that is, that one can combine an observed onset for a fragmentation process with 298 K heats of formation of relevant neutral species to obtain a 298 K heat of formation for A^+.

The interpretation of appearance potentials of fragment ions in terms of thermochemical quantities may also be complicated by the presence of energy barriers in the reaction coordinate and by a phenomenon known as the kinetic shift. Kinetic shift is the term applied to describe the experimental observation of ionization onsets that are higher than the thermodynamic onset energy because the apparatus samples the fragmenting ions at a certain time (usually around 10^{-5} sec) after ionization has occurred, when ions undergoing a slow fragmentation process have not yet had time to dissociate. In the past, these problems usually led to reported values for heats of formation of fragment ions that were too high. However, it is now possible to determine the appearance potential as a function of time, that is, to determine the unimolecular rate constant for dissociation of the fragmenting parent ion. Another approach is to determine the amount of kinetic energy carried away by the fragment ion (thus defining a barrier height), but the interpretation of such results is not well understood at present.

Entirely analogous arguments can be applied to an analysis of heats of formation of anions.

B. Thermochemical Information from Ion–Molecule Equilibrium Studies

At sufficiently high pressures or long reaction times that the ions generated in a system undergo hundreds or thousands of collisions with neutral molecules, an ion–molecule equilibrium:

$$A^{\pm} + B \rightleftarrows C^{\pm} + D \qquad (45)$$

may be established. The ion–molecule equilibrium constant can easily be determined in a high-pressure mass spectrometer, flow tube, or ion cyclotron resonance spectrometer by observing the relative abundances of the two ions, A^+ and C^+, or A^- and C^-, after a large number of collisions:

$$K_{eq} = \frac{[C^{\pm}][D]}{[A^{\pm}][B]} \qquad (46)$$

The neutral reactants, B and D, are present in great abundance compared to the ionic reactants (e.g., $1:10^{-6}$), and therefore the ratio [D]/[B] effectively does not change as equilibrium is established. A single measurement leads to a value for the Gibbs free energy change ΔG of reaction (45) at the temperature of the measurement, while a series of measurements at different temperatures permits an experimental evaluation of the entropy and enthalpy changes associated with the reaction:

$$-RT \ln K_{eq} = \Delta G^{\circ} = \Delta H^{\circ} - T\,\Delta S^{\circ} \qquad (47)$$

In practice, many studies have been published in which measurements are made at a single temperature, the (usually small) entropy change for the reaction is estimated from statistical mechanical considerations (e.g., symmetry numbers), and the corresponding enthalpy change is derived from these two pieces of information.

1. Relative Ionization Energies

Relative values of adiabatic ionization energies can be obtained by determining the equilibrium constant for charge transfer to another molecule of known ionization energy:

$$A^+ + B \rightleftarrows B^+ + A \qquad (48)$$

The enthalpy change for this reaction, which is obtained from the equilibrium constant determination, is just the difference between the ionization energies of species A and B. An extensive thermochemical ladder based on equilibrium constants for charge transfer reactions in alkylbenzenes and halobenzenes demonstrated that the enthalpy changes of reaction (48) were essentially identical to the differences in the spectroscopic adiabatic ionization potentials of the various molecules. An example of such a thermochemical ladder derived from charge transfer equilibrium constant measurements is given in Fig. 1.

When the equilibrium geometry of an ion is

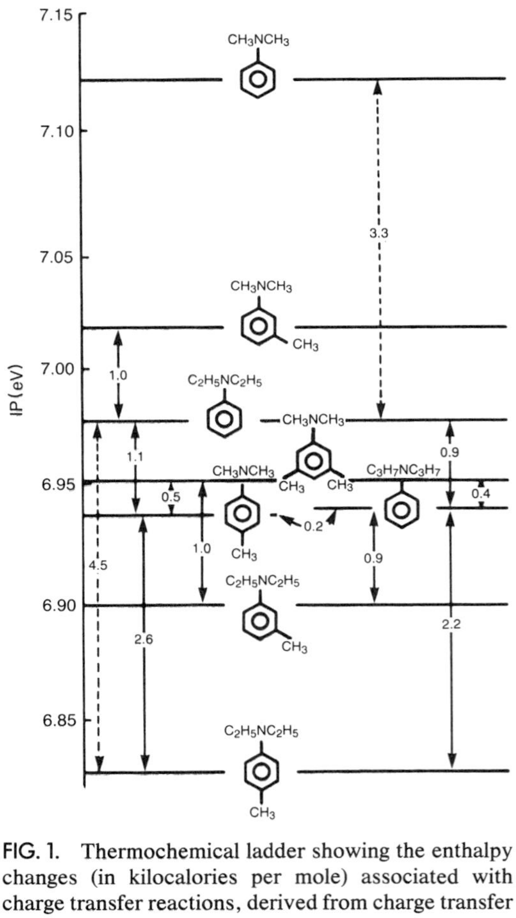

FIG. 1. Thermochemical ladder showing the enthalpy changes (in kilocalories per mole) associated with charge transfer reactions, derived from charge transfer equilibrium constants. The scale is effectively a scale of relative ionization energies. Based on a value for the ionization potential of *N*,*N*-dimethylaniline of 7.12 eV, the absolute ionization potential values shown on the scale at the left can be assigned. [From Lias, S. G., Jackson, J.-A. A., Argentar, H., and Liebman, J. F. (1985). *J. Org. Chem.* **50,** 333.]

very different from that of the corresponding neutral molecule, the lowest vibrational level may not be populated when ionization is effected by photon absorption or electron impact (Section III,A,1). Equilibrium constant determinations have proved very useful in obtaining adiabatic ionization potential data in this situation, since the technique determines thermochemical properties of the ions in their thermal equilibrium geometries. For example, hydrazines and *n*-alkanes (having seven or more carbon atoms) both undergo large geometry changes on ionization. For both these series of compounds, the only available reliable data on the adiabatic ionization potentials come from charge transfer equilibrium constant determinations; the experimental results led to values for the enthalpy changes for reaction (48) that could be translated into absolute values of the ionization potentials by including in the thermochemical ladders molecules having well-established adiabatic ionization potentials.

2. Proton Affinities of Molecules

Stable cations in the gas phase also include ions formed by protonating a neutral molecule:

$$BH^+ + M \rightarrow MH^+ + B \quad (49)$$

Formally, the relationship between the heats of formation of MH^+ and its neutral counterpart M is defined in terms of a quantity called the proton affinity, the negative of the enthalpy change of the hypothetical reaction

$$M + H^+ \xrightarrow{-PA} MH^+ \quad (50)$$

The Gibbs free energy change of reaction (50) is called the gas phase, basicity (GB) of molecule M.

Heats of formation of most MH^+ ions are derived from experiments in which the equilibrium constant of a proton transfer reaction such as (49) is determined (given that a heat of formation of a reference BH^+ ion is available from appearance potential determinations). Then

$$\Delta H_f(MH^+) = \Delta H_f(M) + \Delta H_f(H^+) - PA \quad (51)$$

A large body of ion–molecule equilibrium studies have been devoted to the determination of an extensive (>100 kcal/mol) scale of relative proton affinities of nearly 1000 organic and inorganic compounds. These results were derived mainly from interlocking ladders of enthalpy changes for reaction (49).

Absolute values for proton affinities of molecules quoted in the chemical literature have been assigned by taking as reference bases species for which a heat of formation of BH^+ is available from ionization potential or appearance potential determinations. For many years, chemists followed a tradition of citing values for proton affinities relative to an absolute proton affinity value for ammonia. Unfortunately, this was a singularly poor choice of primary standard, since neither the heat of formation of NH_4^+ nor the position of ammonia in the scale of relative proton affinities was well established. Internally consistent values have now been assigned to the scale of proton affinities of molecules based on well-established heats of formation of a number of different ions such as *tert*-$C_4H_9^+$ (protonated isobutene), *sec*-$C_3H_7^+$ (protonated propylene), $C_2H_5^+$ (protonated ethylene), CH_3CO^+ (protonated ketene), $HOCO^+$ (protonated carbon dioxide), and O_2H^+ (protonated molecular oxygen).

Analysis of the thermochemistry of proton transfer reactions has proved to be a fertile area for organic chemical research. Detailed analysis of the common structural effects known from liquid phase organic chemistry (inductive effects, resonance effects, hyperconjugation, aromaticity effects, polarization effects, steric effects, etc.) has given new insights into the influence of fundamental molecular properties on organic reaction mechanisms.

3. Gas Phase Acidity Scale

A determination of the equilibrium constant of the proton transfer reaction:

$$AH + B^- \rightleftarrows A^- + BH \quad (52)$$

leads to a value for the Gibbs free energy change of the reaction, called the relative acidity of molecules AH and BH. A series of such measurements leads to a scale of relative acidities of molecules. An absolute scale corresponding to the process

$$AH \rightarrow H^+ + A^- \quad (53)$$

can be obtained by incorporating standards in the scale for which both the enthalpy change and Gibbs free energy change of reaction (53) can be obtained. Heats of formation of anions A^- obtained in this way can also be combined with thermochemical data for relevant neutral compounds to obtain values for electron affinities.

Such scales, incorporating data on many hundreds of compounds, have been generated since the early 1970s, considerably expanding the number of anions for which thermochemical data are available. As with molecular proton affinities, discussed above, these data have been interpreted in terms of inductive effects, polar effects, resonance effects, and so on, allowing organic chemists to differentiate between intrinsic molecular properties and effects due to solvation.

4. Gas Phase Solvation of Ions

The earliest ion–molecule equilibrium studies were concerned with examinations of association reactions (27) and (28), as well as higher-order association (or clustering) reactions:

$$[A^{\pm}\cdot B_{n-1}] + B \rightleftarrows [A^{\pm}\cdot B_n] \quad (54)$$

The equilibrium constant is given by

$$K_{eq} = [A^{\pm}\cdot B_n]/[A^{\pm}\cdot B_{n-1}]P(B) \quad (55)$$

where $P(B)$ is the pressure of compound B. Such reactions may be thought of as the solvation of an ion by the neutral molecules of the medium in which it exists. As discussed in Section II,A,3, an ion–molecule complex will be formed whenever there is a collision between a thermal energy ion and molecule. Under conditions such that the collision is chemically unreactive, the "association ion" (i.e., the electrostatically bonded ion–molecule complex) may be sufficiently long-lived that equilibria such as (54) can be established in a high-pressure mass spectrometer or a flowing afterglow apparatus.

The nature of ion clustering reactions dictates that they will be increasingly important as the density is increased. Indeed, the real interest in studies of the thermodynamics of ion solvation in the gas phase lies in attempts to extrapolate the chemical and thermodynamic properties of isolated ions to understand the chemistry of reactive intermediate ions in the liquid phase.

Related equilibrium studies have given information about solvent switching reactions:

$$[A^{\pm}\cdot B] + C \rightleftarrows [A^{\pm}\cdot C] + B \quad (56)$$

Such reactions often result in the formation of products that could not result from a direct bimolecular interaction of the primary ion with the molecule. For example, hydrated oxygen ions react with water to form a water dimer ion:

$$O_2\cdot H_2O^+ \rightarrow (H_2O)_2^+ + O_2 \quad (57)$$

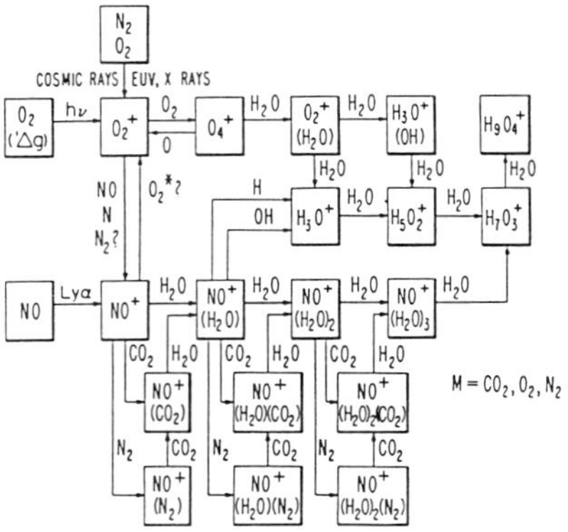

FIG. 2. Schematic diagram of positive ion reactions in the D region. [From Ferguson, E. E. (1975). In "Interactions between Ions and Molecules" (P. Ausloos, Ed.). Plenum, New York.]

although the water dimer ion can not be formed directly by reaction of H_2O^+ with water.

Such reactions can strongly influence the reaction mechanisms occurring in systems such as the earth's ionosphere. Much of the work in this area has been carried out in laboratories whose primary interests are atmospheric chemical processes. A schematic diagram of positive ion reactions predicted from such studies to occur in the earth's D region is shown in Fig. 2.

C. Ion Structures

In mass spectrometric studies of ions, the ion is detected by its charge and identified by its mass-to-charge ratio m/z. Obviously, in systems where more than one isomeric structure is possible, it is important to be able to determine the structure(s) of the ion(s) of interest. There are several reliable approaches for obtaining this information.

Early studies of ion chemistry relied on determinations of the heat of formation of a fragment ion to derive information about its structure. For example, in 1957 thermochemical and isotopic labeling information about the $C_7H_7^+$ ion generated in toluene led to the conclusion that this ion had the cyclic seven-membered ring tropylium structure, rather than the benzyl structure one might expect from a dissociating toluene ion. However, starting in 1971, a number of studies from different laboratories, using all the different techniques discussed here, demonstrated that only at the thermochemical onset are *all* the $C_7H_7^+$ ions in the tropylium ion structure; the fraction of such ions in the benzyl ion structure increases with increasing energy up to the threshold for dissociation of $C_7H_7^+$. This example shows that it is not always valid to assume that the isomeric structure of an ion which predominates at a fragmentation threshold is necessarily the same, or the only, structure that would be present when more energy is imparted to the dissociating species.

Some of the early ion–molecule reaction studies in which ionization was effected outside a mass spectrometer by use of a vacuum-ultraviolet light source or gamma rays as the ionizing agent yielded detailed information about ionic structures and isomerization processes based on analyses of neutral products. For example, the structures of the $C_4H_8^+$ ions formed in irradiated ethylene:

$$C_2H_4^+ + C_2H_4 \rightarrow C_4H_8^+ \qquad (58)$$

were obtained by analyzing the neutral C_4H_8 products formed in the presence of an added molecule of sufficiently low ionization potential that charge transfer from all the $C_4H_8^+$ isomers would occur:

$$C_4H_8^+ + M \rightarrow C_4H_8 + M^+ \qquad (59)$$

In recent years, a technique known as collision-induced dissociation or collisional activation has come into vogue for determinations of ion structures. In this approach, mass-selected ions that do not have enough internal energy to dissociate are passed through a chamber where they undergo collisions with a nonreactive activating gas, picking up sufficient energy from the collisions to undergo fragmentation. One thus obtains a mass spectrum of the ion of interest, which is analyzed like an ordinary mass spectrum of a stable molecule. One limitation of the technique is that one must have a spectrum of an "authentic" sample of a particular isomer, or must make certain assumptions about probable modes of decomposition, in order to establish its mass spectrum.

A number of ion structures have been characterized in experiments in which the ions of interest, generated in mass spectrometers of various possible designs, are irradiated by monochromatic light (from a monochromator or laser), and the decrease in the ion signal due to ionic dissociation is followed as a function of photon energy. The so-called photodissociation spectrum thus generated is analogous to the optical spectrum of the ion and is structure-specific.

In many systems, isomeric ions with differing structures will exhibit different reactivities. Such differences in kinetic behavior have also been exploited to determine structures of ions. In the example discussed above concerning the structures of $C_7H_7^+$ ions, several studies obtained information about the relative abundances of $C_7H_7^+$ ions in the tropylium (c-$C_7H_7^+$) or benzyl (c-$C_6H_5CH_2^+$) structure by following the time dependence of the $C_7H_7^+$ ions formed in various precursor compounds such as toluene or ethylbenzene. A fraction of the initially generated ions (the benzyl ions) would react with the precursor molecules or other added compounds, while the balance of the $C_7H_7^+$ species (the tropylium ions) did not react at all.

D. Trends in the Data

1. Correlations of Different Thermochemical Quantities

The proton affinity of molecule M, defined by Eq. (50), is equal to the M—H$^+$ bond energy of the MH$^+$ ion. The M$^+$—H bond energy is defined by the hydrogen affinity (HA) of M$^+$:

$$M^+ + H \xrightarrow{-HA} MH^+ \qquad (60)$$

Consider the thermodynamic cycle constructed from reactions (50) and (60):

$$\begin{array}{ccccc} M & + & H^+ & \xrightarrow{-PA} & MH^+ \\ \downarrow{\scriptstyle IP(M)} & & \downarrow{\scriptstyle -IP(H)} & & \\ M^+ & + & H & \xrightarrow{-HA} & MH^+ \end{array} \qquad (61)$$

From cycle (61) we write

$$\begin{aligned} PA(M) &= HA(M^+) + IP(H) - IP(M) \\ &= HA(M^+) + 13.6\ \text{eV} - IP(M) \end{aligned} \qquad (62)$$

A detailed statistical analysis of the relationships between proton affinities and ionization potentials for many different compound types (alcohols, ethers, primary, secondary, and tertiary amines, nitriles, mercaptans, sulfides, aldehydes, ketones, carboxylic acids, esters, amides, and atoms) demonstrates that the hydrogen affinity is constant for the radical cations of sulfides and mercaptans and approximately constant for the parent ions of aliphatic ethers, thioethers, and secondary and tertiary amines. For other compound types (alcohols, aldehydes, ketones, primary amines, cyclic ethers, and esters), the hydrogen affinity itself varies linearly

TABLE II. Relationship between Proton Affinity and Ionization Potential—Hydrogen Affinities of Homologous Series: $PA(M_x) = C + K\,IP(M_x)$

	IP[a]	PA[b]	HA[c]
Alcohols			
$K = -0.54$, $C = 319$			
CH_3OH	10.85	181.9	118
C_2H_5OH	10.47	188.3	116
n-C_3H_7OH	10.22	190.8	113
n-C_4H_9OH	10.06	191.1	109
i-C_3H_7OH	10.12	191.2	111
s-C_4H_9OH	9.88	191.1	105
i-C_4H_9OH	10.09	192.4	111
t-C_4H_9OH	9.97	193.7	110
Ethers			
$K = -0.77$, $C = 370$			
CH_3OCH_3	10.025	192.1	110
$C_2H_5OCH_3$	9.72	196.4	107
$C_2H_5OC_2H_5$	9.51	200.2	106
n-C_3H_7O(n-C_3H_7)	9.27	202.3	102
n-C_4H_9O(n-C_4H_9)	<9.43	203.7	107
s-C_4H_9O(s-C_4H_9)	9.11	209.0	105
Cyclic ethers			
$K = -0.40$, $C = 285$			
c-C_2H_4O	10.566	187.9	118
c-C_3H_6O	9.668	196.9	107
c-C_4H_8O	9.41	198.8	102
c-$C_5H_{10}O$	9.25	199.7	99
Aldehydes			
$K = -0.50$, $C = 305$			
CH_3CHO	10.229	186.6	109
C_2H_5CHO	9.953	189.6	106
n-C_3H_7CHO	9.84	191.5	105
i-C_3H_7CHO	9.705	192.6	103
i-C_4H_9CHO	9.70	192.6	103
Ketones			
$K = -0.39$, $C = 284$			
CH_3COCH_3	9.705	196.7	107
$C_2H_5COCH_3$	9.51	199.8	106
$C_2H_5COC_2H_5$	9.31	201.4	102
i-$C_3H_7COCH_3$	9.30	203.5	104
(i-$C_3H_7)_2CO$	8.95	204.9	98
t-$C_4H_9COCH_3$	9.11	202.3	99
(t-$C_4H_9)_2CO$	8.67	206.5	93
Primary amines			
$K = -0.59$, $C = 336$			
CH_3NH_2	8.97	214.1	107
$C_2H_5NH_2$	8.86	217.0	108
n-$C_3H_7NH_2$	8.78	217.9	107
i-$C_3H_7NH_2$	8.72	218.6	106
n-$C_4H_9NH_2$	8.71	218.4	106
s-$C_4H_9NH_2$	8.70	220.5	107
i-$C_4H_9NH_2$	8.70	218.8	106
t-$C_4H_9NH_2$	8.64	220.8	106
n-$C_5H_{11}NH_2$	8.67	218.9	105
t-$C_5H_{11}NH_2$	8.46	222.3	104
n-$C_6H_{13}NH_2$	8.63	218.9	104
Secondary amines			
$K = -0.72$, $C = 359$; HA = 95 ± 2			
$(CH_3)_2NH$	8.23	220.6	97
$(CH_3)(C_2H_5)NH$	8.15	222.8	97
$(C_2H_5)_2NH$	8.01	225.9	97
(n-$C_3H_7)_2NH$	7.84	227.5	95
(i-$C_3H_7)_2NH$	7.73	230.2	95
(n-$C_4H_9)_2NH$	7.69	228.4	92
(s-$C_4H_9)_2NH$	7.63	230.9	93
(i-$C_4H_9)_2NH$	7.81	228.6	95
Tertiary amines			
$K = -0.83$, $C = 376$; HA = 92			
$(CH_3)_3N$	7.82	225.1	92
$(CH_3)_2(C_2H_5)N$	7.74	227.5	92
$(CH_3)(C_2H_5)_2N$	7.50	230.0	89
$(C_2H_5)_3N$	7.50	232.3	92
Aromatic amines			
$K = -1.0$, $C = 391$; HA = 73			
$C_6H_5NH_2$	7.68	209.5	73
$C_6H_5N(CH_3)_2$	7.12	223.4	74
3-$(CH_3)C_6H_4N(CH_3)_2$	7.02	224.5	73
4-$(CH_3)C_6H_4N(CH_3)_2$	6.93	225.6	72
3,5-$(CH_3)_2C_6H_3N(CH_3)_2$	6.95	227.0	72
$C_6H_5N(C_2H_5)_2$	6.98	227.6	75
3-$(CH_3)C_6H_4N(CH_3)_2$	6.90	228.9	74
4-$(CH_3)C_6H_4N(CH_3)_2$	6.83	228.6	73
$C_6H_5N(C_3H_7)_2$	6.93	228.6	75
Mercaptans			
$K = -0.98$, $C = 401$; HA = 91			
CH_3SH	9.44	187.4	91
C_2H_5SH	9.285	190.8	91
n-C_3H_7SH	9.195	191.6	90
i-C_3H_7SH	9.14	194.1	91
t-C_4H_9SH	9.03	196.9	91
Thioethers			
$K = -0.83$, $C = 366$; HA = 86			
CH_3SCH_3	8.69	200.6	87
$C_2H_5SCH_3$	8.54	203.5	87
$(C_2H_5)_2S$	8.43	205.0	86
(n-$C_3H_7)_2S$	8.30	206.5	84
(i-$C_3H_7)_2S$	8.25	209.6	86
(n-$C_4H_9)_2S$	8.22	208.7	85
(t-$C_4H_9)_2S$	8.07	212.8	85
Esters			
$K = -0.58$, $C = 335$			
$HCOOCH_3$	10.815	188.9	125
$HCOOC_2H_5$	10.61	193.1	124
HCOO(n-C_3H_7)	10.52	194.2	123
HCOO(i-C_3H_7)	10.44	196.0	123
HCOO(n-C_4H_9)	10.50	194.8	123
CH_3COOCH_3	10.27	197.8	121
$CH_3COOC_2H_5$	10.01	200.7	118
$CH_3COOC_3H_7$	10.04	200.6	118
$C_2H_5COOCH_3$	10.15	200.2	121
n-$C_3H_7COOCH_3$	10.07	200.1	119

[a] Ionization potential in electron volts; 1 eV = 96.4845 kJ/mol = 23.06036 kcal/mol.
[b] Proton affinity in kilocalories per mole; see Eq. (50).
[c] Hydrogen affinity in kilocalories per mole; see Eq. (60).

with the ionization potential, leading to the expression

$$PA_x = C + KIP_x \qquad (63)$$

relating the proton affinity and ionization potential of a molecule. Some illustrative data and values for C and K derived from a statistical analysis of the data are given in Table II for several compound types.

Attention has also been given to relating ionization potentials and proton affinities of various series of compounds to the appropriate Taft substituent constants. Such thermochemical parameters of ions as the adiabatic ionization potentials or the proton affinities can be linearly correlated with appropriate substituent constants derived from solution phase reactivity data. For example, the adiabatic ionization potentials of compounds RX (where R is an alkyl group) correlate linearly with $\sigma^*(R)$ and $\sigma_I(R)$ (measures of the polarizability and electron-releasing ability of R) for a constant electron withdrawing group X. This is easily understood in terms of a lowering of the energy required to remove an electron with increasing electron-donating ability of the groups R.

Linear correlations between ion–molecule well depths [or the enthalpy changes of association reaction (54)] and the differences in the proton affinities of molecules A and B have been reported for many series of compounds. That is, it is generally observed that for a series of reacting pairs

$$AH^+ + B \rightarrow [AH^+ \cdot B] \qquad (64)$$

where proton transfer from AH^+ to B is endothermic, the exothermicity of the association reaction (64) will be greater the smaller the difference in the proton affinities of A and B. This has usually been explained in terms of a probability for "partial proton transfer" in the complex. Although useful empirical relationships can be written, which allow one to predict approximate proton affinities from well depths and vice versa, results on the probabilities of isotope exchange in such association ions give evidence that such "linear" correlations are probably accidental by-products of the double-welled potential surfaces discussed in Section II,A,3.

2. Estimation Schemes for Heats of Formation of Cations

A sufficient amount of reliable information on ionization potentials and heats of formation of many classes of positive ions has become available that the regular trends observed as a function of molecular size and structure can be used to develop empirical schemes for estimating ionization energies and/or heats of formation of cations. Since ionization energies for a homologous series do not have a linear dependence on molecular size, values for heats of formation of ions cannot be reproduced satisfactorily by simple additivity systems like those used for the prediction of heats of formation of neutral molecules. The predictive schemes put forward to date use equations that are completely empirical.

One scheme is designed to predict values for the heat of formation of positive ions at 298 K from equations of the form

$$\Delta H_f(M^+) = A - Bn + C/n \qquad (65)$$

where A, B, and C are constants derived from the data for any particular series and n is the total number of atoms in the molecule. Another scheme is geared to the estimation of ionization potentials of alkenes, alkynes, aldehydes, ketones, alcohols, ethers, mercaptans, and thioethers. This empirical equation takes the form

$$\log_{10} \frac{IP(R_1XR_2) - IP_\infty}{IP_0 - IP_\infty} = 0.106[I(R_1) + I(R_2)] \qquad (66)$$

where X is a functional group (i.e., —CH=CH— or —C=CH$_2$ for alkenes, —O— for alcohols and ethers, —(C=O)— for aldehydes and ketones, etc.), R_1 and R_2 are the attached alkyl groups, IP_0 is the ionization potential of the reference compound for which $R_1 = R_2 = H$, and IP_∞ is a constant for each compound type, determined empirically from the asymptotic leveling off of plots of ionization potentials of compounds in the series. Each alkyl group (i.e., ethyl, *tert*-butyl, etc.) has a characteristic constant $I(R_x)$ that remains the same for every compound type.

For both predictive schemes, the agreement between estimated values and experiment is generally quite good—good enough to inspire confidence in the use of such schemes for filling in blanks in the data series.

Bibliography

Ausloos, P. (ed.). (1975). "Interactions between Ions and Molecules." Plenum, New York.

Ausloos, P. (ed.). (1979). "Kinetics of Ion–Molecule Reactions." Plenum, New York.

Bowers, M. T. (ed.). (1979). "Gas Phase Ion Chemistry," Vol. 1. Academic Press, New York.

Bowers, M. T. (ed.). (1979). "Gas Phase Ion Chemistry." Vol. 2. Academic Press, New York.

Brundle, C. R., and Baker, A. D. (1977). "Electron Spectroscopy: Theory, Techniques and Applications." Academic Press, New York.

Dannacher, J. (1984). The study of ionic fragmentation by photoelectron–photoion coincidence spectroscopy. *Org. Mass Spectrom.* **19,** 253.

Ferreira, M. A. A. (ed.). (1984). "Ionic Processes in the Gas Phase." Reidel, Dordrecht, Netherlands.

Holmes, J. L., Fingas, M., and Lossing, F. P. (1981). Towards a general scheme for estimating the heats of formation of organic ions in the gas phase, Part I: Odd-electron cations. *Can. J. Chem.* **59,** 80.

Journal of Physics D, Applied Physics, Special Issue on Plasmas with Negative Ions. **23**(8), Aug. 14, 1991.

Lias, S. G., Liebman, J. F., and Levin, R. D. (1984). Evaluated gas phase basicities and proton affinities of molecules; heats of formation of protonated molecules. *J. Phys. Chem. Ref. Data* **13,** 695.

Taft, R. W. (1983). Protonic acidities and basicities in the gas phase and in solution: Substituent and solvent effects. *Prog. Phys. Org. Chem.* **14,** 248.

IONOSPHERE

A. F. Nagy *The University of Michigan*
R. W. Schunk *Utah State University*

GLOSSARY

Auroral oval: Oval-shaped region in the high-latitude atmosphere into which energetic particles from deep space penetrate.

Conjugate ionospheres: Ionospheric regions on both sides of the hemispheres connected by a magnetic field line.

Diffusion: Net plasma transport due to forces such as pressure gradient and gravity.

D-region: Region of the ionosphere extending from about 70 to 90 km above the earth, where there are significant positive and negative ion populations.

Dynamo electric field: Electric field created in the E region by plasma that is dragged along with the neutral wind across magnetic field lines.

E region: Region of the ionosphere extending from about 90 to 145 km above the earth, where molecular positive ions dominate.

F region: Region of the ionosphere extending from about 145 to 1000 km above the earth, where atomic ions play an important role.

Ionopause: Boundary separating the ionospheric plasma from the shocked and decelerated solar wind plasma; this transition region has also been called the contact discontinuity in cometary environments.

Mid-latitude trough: Region of low electron densities located just equatorward of the nocturnal auroral oval.

Photochemistry: Chemical processes influenced by sunlight.

Photoelectrons: Electrons created in the ionosphere by photoionization.

Plasma: Gas containing a significant fraction of free electrons and ions.

Plasma convection: Large-scale motion of charged particles in the ionosphere, driven by electric fields created at high latitudes by the interaction of the solar wind with the geomagnetic field.

Polar cap: High-latitude region of the atmosphere, poleward of the auroral oval, from which magnetic field lines extend deep into space.

Polar wind: High-speed plasma outflow from the high-latitude ionospheres.

Solar wind: Supersonic plasma flow from the sun.

The ionosphere is understood to be that region of the upper atmosphere where significant numbers of free electrons and ions are present. In general, the ionosphere of the earth is the region from about 70 to over 1000 km above the earth, where the electron and ion densities vary from below 10^3 to over 10^6 cm^{-3}.

I. Background

The first suggestions for the presence of charged particles in the upper atmosphere were made more than 150 years ago. Gauss, Lord Kelvin, and Balfour Stewart hypothesized the existence of electric currents in the atmosphere to explain the observed variations of the magnetic field at the surface of the earth. In 1901, Marconi succeeded in sending radio signals across the Atlantic, which implied that the radio waves were deflected around the earth in a manner not immediately understood. The following year, working independently, Heaviside in England and Kennelly in the United States proposed that a layer of free electrons and ions in the upper atmosphere is responsible for the reflection of these radio waves. The first experimental proof of this reflecting layer did not come until 1925 when Appleton and Barnett demonstrated the existence of downcoming waves. The following year Breit and Tuve devised a technique, known today as the ionosonde method, in which pulses of radio waves are vertically transmitted and the reflected signals analyzed; the electron densities present in the reflection region can be deduced from the characteristics of the received signal. The name *ionosphere* for the region of the upper atmosphere containing a significant population of free electrons and ions was coined by R. A. Watson–Watt in 1926. Experimental observations of the ionosphere were limited to remote sensing by radio waves until the end of World War II, when sounding rockets first became available to allow in-situ measurements. The International Geophysical Year in 1959 provided the next large impetus to ionospheric research. During the following decades the introduction of satellites and powerful ground-based radar systems capable of measuring a variety of the important parameters resulted in tremendous advances in our understanding of the physical and chemical processes that control the behavior of our terrestrial ionosphere. Beginning with the flyby of Venus by Mariner 5 in 1965, the ionospheres of other bodies in the solar system also began to receive a great deal of attention. [*See* RADIO PROPAGATION.]

II. Basic Theory

Ionosphere research during the last two decades has shown that the earth's ionosphere exhibits significant variations with altitude, latitude, longitude, universal time, solar cycle, season, and geomagnetic activity. These variations are a consequence of the competition among the forces acting within and on the ionosphere. Of particular importance are the forces that result from the coupling to the denser neutral atmosphere. At high latitudes, the ionosphere also strongly couples to the overlying hot, tenuous plasma that extends deep into space. Consequently, before presenting the basic theory of ionospheric behavior, it is useful to describe the ionospheric environment and the average plasma conditions in the ionosphere.

A. Ionospheric Environment

The earth's magnetic field and the different flow regimes in the ionosphere are shown schematically in Fig. 1. The earth possesses a relatively strong intrinsic magnetic field that has a dipole character in the ionosphere. However, far from the earth the magnetic field configuration is distorted by the interaction of the earth's intrinsic field with the hot plasma that is continually emitted from the sun (solar wind). At high latitudes, the magnetic field lines extend deep into space in the antisunward direction. Along the so-called open field lines, ions and electrons are capable of escaping from the ionosphere in a process termed the polar wind, in analogy to the solar wind. This loss of plasma can have an appreciable effect on the temperature and density structure in the high-latitude ionosphere. Also, the hot plasma that exists in deep space is capable of penetrating to ionospheric altitudes at high latitudes, and this affects ambient densities and temperatures. In addition, the interaction of the solar wind with the earth's magnetic field sets up an electrical potential difference across the polar region, and the resulting electric field causes the high-latitude ionospheric plasma to flow in an antisunward direction over the polar region. [*See* GEOMAGNETISM.]

At mid-latitudes, the ionospheric plasma is not appreciably affected by external electric fields, and consequently the plasma tends to corotate with the earth. However, the plasma can readily flow along magnetic field lines like beads on a string. As a consequence, the plasma can escape from the topside ionosphere in one hemi-

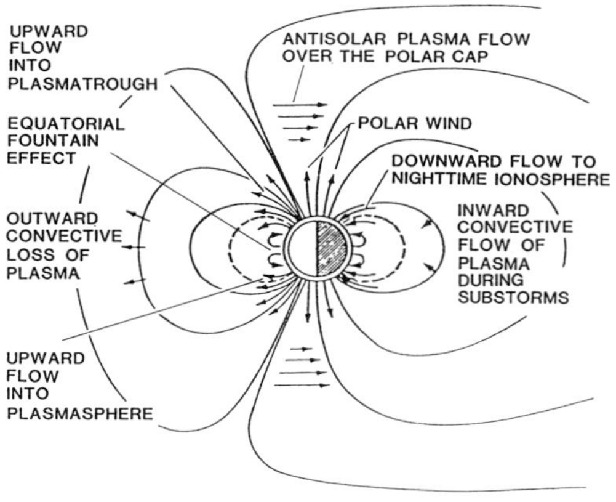

FIG. 1. Schematic diagram showing the earth's magnetic field and the flow regimes in the ionosphere. (Adapted from a figure by C. R. Chappell.)

sphere, flow along geomagnetic field lines, and then enter the conjugate ionosphere. This interhemispheric flow of plasma is a source of ionization for one hemisphere and a sink for the other hemisphere.

At mid-latitudes, the ionospheric plasma is strongly affected by the motion of the earth's upper atmosphere (neutral wind). In general, this neutral wind blows away from the subsolar point on the dayside and around to the nightside. The ionospheric plasma at mid-latitudes is confined to move along magnetic field lines; therefore the meridional wind exerts a major influence on the ionosphere. On the dayside, this wind blows toward the poles, and the ionization is driven downward. On the nightside, the meridional wind blows toward the equator, and the ionization is driven up field lines.

At low latitudes, the geomagnetic field lines are nearly horizontal, which introduces some unique transport effects. First, the meridional neutral wind can very effectively induce an interhemispheric flow of plasma along geomagnetic field lines. At solstice, the dayside wind blows across the equator from the summer to the winter hemisphere. As the ionospheric plasma rises on the summer side of the equator, it expands and cools, while on the winter side it is compressed and heated as it descends.

Another interesting transport effect at low latitudes is the so-called equatorial fountain. In the daytime equatorial ionosphere, eastward electric fields associated with neutral wind-induced ionospheric currents drive a plasma motion that is upward. The plasma lifted in this way then diffuses down the magnetic field lines and away from the equator due to the action of gravity. This combination of electromagnetic drift and diffusion produces a fountainlike pattern of plasma motion.

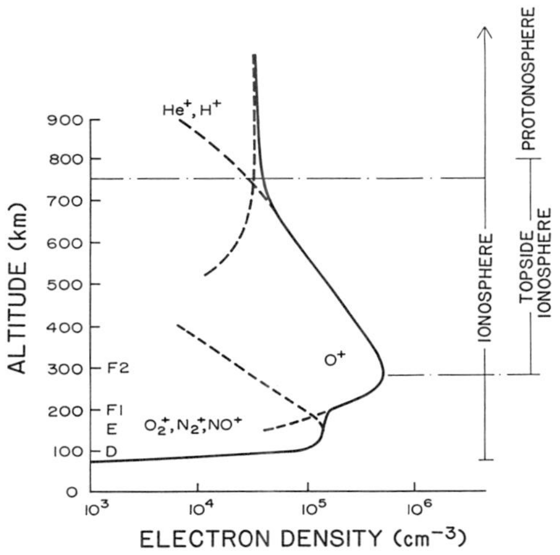

FIG. 2. Schematic diagram of the mid-latitude ionosphere showing the various regions: D, E, F1, and F2. [From Banks, P. M., Schunk, R. W., and Raitt, W. J. (1976). *Annl. Rev. Earth and Planet Sci.* **4**, 381–440.]

B. Plasma Conditions

One of the early (1925–1930) discoveries in ionospheric research was that the ionosphere is stratified into regions (D, E, F_1, and F_2). This layered structure is shown schematically in Fig. 2 for typical daytime, mid-latitude conditions. The corresponding neutral gas density profiles are shown in Fig. 3. The E region ($\approx$120 km alt.) is dominated by molecular species, with NO^+, O_2^+, and N_2^+ being the major ions and N_2 and O_2 being the dominant neutrals. The total ion density is of the order of 10^5 cm^{-3}, while the neutral density is greater than 10^{11} cm^{-3}. Therefore the E region plasma is weakly ionized, and collisions between charged particles are not important. In the F region ($\approx$200–700 km alt.), the atomic species dominate, with O^+ and O being the major ion and neutral species, respectively. The peak ion density in the F region is roughly a factor of ten greater than that in the E region, while the neutral density is about two orders of magnitude higher. The plasma in this region is partially ionized, and collisions between the different charged particles and between the charged particles and neutrals must be considered. The topside ionosphere is generally defined to be the region above the F region peak, while the protonosphere is the region where the

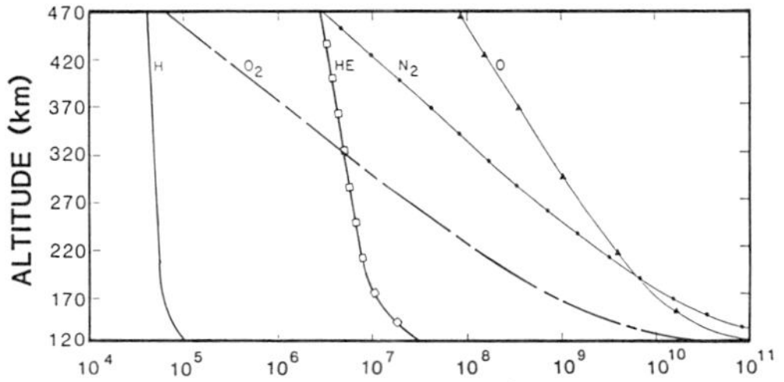

FIG. 3. Altitude profiles of the earth's daytime neutral gas densities at mid-latitudes. (From Schunk and Nagy, 1980; based on the empirical model of Hedin *et al.*, 1977.)

lighter atomic ions (H^+, He^+) dominate. Although the neutrals still outnumber the ions in the protonosphere, the plasma is effectively fully ionized owing to the long-range nature of charged particle collisions. The D region (~70–90 km alt.) differs from the E region in that both negative and positive molecular ions exist and three-body collisions are important.

The bulk of the following discussion will be devoted to the F region, where the main ionization peak occurs.

C. PHOTOCHEMISTRY

Solar extreme ultraviolet (EUV) radiation photoionizes the neutral constituents of the upper atmosphere, producing free electrons and ions. The photoionization process occurs predominantly at the lower levels of the ionosphere, where the neutrals are abundant. Typically, the peak in the ionization rate occurs at about 150 km owing mainly to the absorption of radiation with wavelengths λ less than 796 Å (the ionization threshold of N_2). The ionization thresholds of the more common atmospheric species are given in Table I. Photons (denoted as $h\nu$ in all equations appearing in this chapter) with wavelengths in the range of 796 to 1027 Å penetrate down into the E region. For the E and F regions of the ionosphere, the most important photoionization processes are

TABLE I. Ionization Threshold Potentials[a]

Neutral constituent	Ionization potential (eV)	Ionization potential (nm)
C	11.260	110.100
CH_4	12.550	98.790
CO	14.010	88.490
CO_2	13.770	90.040
H	13.600	91.160
H_2	15.430	80.350
H_2O	12.620	98.240
He	24.590	50.420
Mg	7.460	162.200
N	14.530	85.330
N_2	15.580	79.580
NH_3	10.170	121.900
NO	9.264	133.800
Na	5.139	241.300
O	13.620	91.030
O_2	12.060	102.800
OH	13.180	94.070
S	10.360	119.700

[a] Information obtained from Rosenstock, N. H., *et al.*, *Ion Energetic Measurements,* Washington DC: U.S. Department of Commerce, National Bureau of Standards, 1980.

$$N_2 + h\nu \rightarrow N_2^+ + e \quad (1a)$$

$$\rightarrow N^+ + N + e \quad (1b)$$

$$O_2 + h\nu \rightarrow O_2^+ + e \quad (2)$$

$$O + h\nu \rightarrow O^+ + e \quad (3)$$

where Eq. (1b) is produced with an efficiency of about 21%. [*See* PLANETARY ATMOSPHERES; SOLAR PHYSICS.]

The calculation of ion production rates due to photoionization requires knowledge of the solar radiation flux incident upon the top of the atmosphere, the neutral gas densities as a function of altitude, and the absorption and ionization cross sections of the neutral species as a function of wavelength. Generally, these quantities can be obtained from satellite, ground-based, and laboratory measurements.

Although the calculation of photoionization rates usually requires a computer, a simplified expression can be obtained for the F region, where the neutral atmosphere is optically transparent and atomic oxygen is the dominant neutral. For overhead sun, the O^+ production rate $P(O^+)$ is simply proportional to the atomic oxygen number density $N(O)$,

$$P(O^+) = \beta N(O) \quad (4)$$

where β is a constant. However, in the F region, the atomic oxygen density decreases exponentially with altitude (see Fig. 3),

$$N(O) = N_0(O) \exp\left[-\frac{z - z_0}{H}\right] \quad (5)$$

where z is altitude and $N_0(O)$ the density at some reference altitude z_0. H, the neutral-gas scale height, is given by the following expression:

$$H = \frac{kT}{mg} \quad (6)$$

where k is the Boltzmann constant, T the neutral-gas temperature, m the mass of the neutral gas, and g the acceleration due to gravity. Substituting Eq. (5) into Eq. (4) yields

$$P(O^+) = P_0(O^+) \exp\left[-\frac{z - z_0}{H}\right] \quad (7)$$

where $P_0(O^+) = \beta N_0(O)$, a constant. If the sun is not overhead but at an angle with respect to the zenith, then Eq. (7) becomes a function of the solar zenith angle χ.

After the ions are produced by photoionization, they can undergo chemical reactions with the neutral constituents in the upper atmosphere. These chemical reactions act to create and destroy ions. Some of the important chemical reactions in the E and F regions are

$$O^+ + N_2 \rightarrow NO^+ + N, \quad k_8 = 5.1 \times 10^{-13} \tag{8}$$

$$O^+ + O_2 \rightarrow O_2^+ + O, \quad k_9 = 1.3 \times 10^{-11} \tag{9}$$

$$N_2^+ + O_2 \rightarrow O_2^+ + N_2, \quad k_{10} = 1.5 \times 10^{-11} \tag{10}$$

$$N_2^+ + O \rightarrow O^+ + N_2, \quad k_{11} = 7.6 \times 10^{-12} \tag{11}$$

$$N_2^+ + O \rightarrow NO^+ + N, \quad k_{12} = 8.2 \times 10^{-11} \tag{12}$$

where k_s is the rate constant for reactions in cm^3 sec^{-1}. The chemical reaction rates are usually measured in the laboratory and are typically functions of temperature (cf. Schunk and Nagy, 1980). The values given above are for a representative temperature of 1000 K.

The molecular ions can also recombine with electrons,

$$N_2^+ + e \rightarrow N + N, \quad \alpha_{13} = 1.1 \times 10^{-7} \tag{13}$$

$$O_2^+ + e \rightarrow O + O, \quad \alpha_{14} = 8.3 \times 10^{-8} \tag{14}$$

$$NO^+ + e \rightarrow N + O, \quad \alpha_{15} = 1.5 \times 10^{-7} \tag{15}$$

where the recombination rates α_s are for 1000 K, and the units are cm^3 sec^{-1}. These recombination reactions are fairly rapid, and they account for the main loss of ionization in the E region.

In the E and the lower F regions of the ionosphere, photochemical processes dominate, and the electron density can be calculated simply by equating local production and loss rates,

$$P_e = L_e N_e \tag{16}$$

where N_e is the electron density and L_e is the loss frequency. For example, if NO^+ is the dominant ion in the E region, then

$$L_e = \alpha_{15} N_e \tag{17}$$

and therefore:

$$P_e = \alpha_{15} N_e^2 \tag{18}$$

D. Plasma Diffusion

In most of the F region (above about 300 km), both wind-induced plasma drifts and magnetic field aligned plasma diffusion are important in addition to photochemical reactions, and consequently, it is not possible to calculate the electron density simply by equating local production and loss processes. In this case, a more general conservation equation governs the spatial and temporal variation of the electron density:

$$\frac{\partial N_e}{\partial t} + \frac{\partial (N_e U_e)}{\partial s} = P_e - L_e N_e \tag{19}$$

where $\partial/\partial t$ is the time derivative, $\partial/\partial s$ the spatial derivative in the magnetic field direction, and U_e the bulk flow velocity of the electron gas along the magnetic field direction. Equation (19) indicates that in a given region of space, a temporal variation of the electron density occurs in response to electron production P_e, electron loss $L_e N_e$, and a nonuniform flow of electrons into or out of that region of space. [*See* SOLAR SYSTEM, MAGNETIC AND ELECTRIC FIELDS.]

The field-aligned flow of electrons is influenced by gravity, the neutral wind, and density and temperature gradients. Owing to the small electron mass, the effect of gravity is to cause a charge separation, with light electrons trying to settle on top of the heavy ions. However, a charge-separation electric field develops that acts to prevent a large charge separation. Once this electric field develops, the ions and electrons move together as a single gas under the influence of gravity, the neutral wind, and the density and temperature gradients. Such a motion is called ambipolar diffusion. For motion along the magnetic field, the diffusion equation takes the following form:

$$U_e = U_n - D_a \left(\frac{1}{N_e} \frac{\partial N_e}{\partial s} + \frac{1}{T_p} \frac{\partial T_p}{\partial s} + \frac{1}{H_p} \right) \tag{20}$$

where the ambipolar diffusion coefficient D_a, the plasma scale height H_p, and the plasma temperature T_p are given by

$$D_a = \frac{k(T_e + T_i)}{M_i \nu_{in}} \tag{21}$$

$$H_p = \frac{2kT_p}{M_i g_s} \tag{22}$$

$$T_p = \frac{T_e + T_i}{2} \tag{23}$$

where U_n is the component of the neutral wind along the magnetic field, g_s the component of gravity along the magnetic field, k Boltzmann's constant, T_e the electron temperature, T_i the ion temperature, M_i the ion mass, and ν_{in} the momentum transfer collision frequency between ions and neutrals. Note that in the F region the most abundant ion is O^+, and the neutral is O. The collision frequency is given in Schunk and Nagy (1978). Here we merely note that $\nu_{in} \propto N(O)$: the more O atoms there are, the greater is the frequency of collisions between O^+ and O.

To obtain the variation of the electron density and bulk-flow velocity along the magnetic field, Eqs. (19) and (20) must be solved simultaneously, which generally requires a computer. However, at altitudes above the F region peak density, a simplified expression for N_e can be obtained. First, it is useful to express Eq. (20) in the form

$$\frac{1}{N_e}\frac{\partial N_e}{\partial s} = -\frac{1}{H_p} - \frac{1}{T_p}\frac{\partial T_p}{\partial s} + \frac{U_n - U_e}{D_a} \quad (24)$$

Note that $D_a \propto (1/\nu) \propto [1/N(O)]$. Since $N(O)$ decreases rapidly with altitude (see Fig. 3), D increases rapidly with altitude. Consequently, above the F region peak, the last term in Eq. (24) is negligible. Also, above the F region peak, the plasma temperature is nearly constant. Therefore Eq. (24) reduces to

$$\frac{1}{N_e}\frac{\partial N_e}{\partial s} = -\frac{1}{H_p} \quad (25)$$

If the small variation of gravity with altitude is ignored, Eq. (25) can be easily integrated to yield

$$N_e = [N_e]_r \exp\left[-\frac{s - s_r}{H_p}\right] \quad (26)$$

where the subscript r corresponds to some reference altitude. Equation (26) indicates that above the F region peak the electron density decreases exponentially with altitude, as shown in Fig. 2. The electron density variation given by Eq. (26) is called a diffusive equilibrium distribution.

E. THERMAL STRUCTURE

The flow of energy in the earth's upper atmosphere is shown schematically in Fig. 4. The main source of energy for the ionosphere is extreme ultraviolet radiation from the sun. The absorption of EUV radiation by the neutral atmosphere results in both photoionization and excitation of the neutral gas. The resulting excited atoms and molecules lose their energy either by radiation or in quenching collisions with

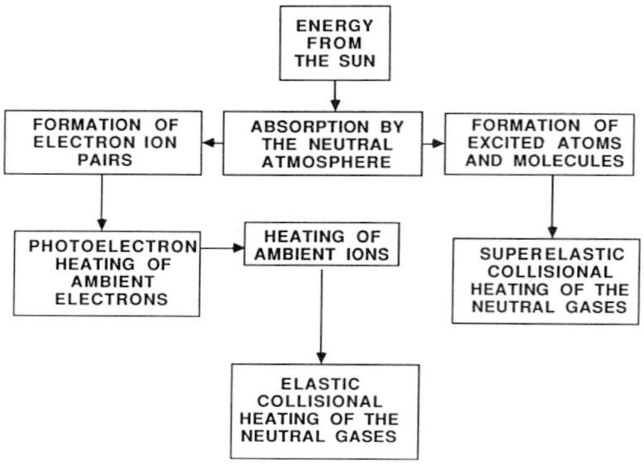

FIG. 4. Block diagram showing the flow of energy in the earth's upper atmosphere.

electrons and neutral particles. Photoionization produces energetic photoelectrons, since the energy carried by the ionizing photons, in general, exceeds the energy required for ionization. Typically, photoionization produces photoelectrons with initial energies of some tens of electron volts.

Only a relatively modest amount of the initial photoelectron energy is deposited directly in the ambient electron gas. Most of the excess kinetic energy is lost in elastic and inelastic collisions with neutral particles and in Coulomb collisions with the ambient ions. If the photoelectrons lose their energy near the altitude at which they were produced, the heating is said to be local, while if the photoelectrons lose their energy over a distance greater than about a neutral scale height, the heating is termed nonlocal. Nonlocal heating effects occur mainly at high altitudes where ambient densities are low and at high photoelectron energies. Photoelectrons with sufficient energy can even escape from the ionosphere, travel along geomagnetic field lines, and deposit their energy in the conjugate ionosphere. Typically, photoelectron energy deposition above about 300 km constitutes nonlocal heating.

Shortly after creation a photoelectron undergoes a number of inelastic and elastic collisions. Briefly, for photoelectron energies greater than about 50 eV, ionization and optically allowed excitation of the neutral constituents are the dominant energy loss processes. At energies of about 20 eV, the energy loss via excitation of metastable levels of the major constituents is comparable to the energy loss through allowed transitions, becoming increasingly important as the energy decreases. At photoelectron energies below about 5 eV, energy loss through excitation of the vibrational levels of N_2 becomes important. Finally, below about 2 eV, energy loss to the ambient thermal electrons through elastic collisions is the dominant photoelectron energy loss process, although loss due to excitation of the rotational levels of N_2 is not entirely negligible.

Although photoelectrons are the primary source of heat for the ambient electron gas, other heat sources exist. At high latitudes, the hot electrons that exist in deep space can penetrate to ionospheric altitudes, and these hot electrons can heat the ambient electrons in a manner similar to that of the photoelectrons. However, these hot electrons reach ionospheric altitudes only in a narrow latitudinal band known as the auroral oval. (This region will be discussed in more detail later.) Another important heat source for the ambient electrons arises as a result of thermal conduction. As noted earlier, some of the photoelectrons can escape the ionosphere and hence can lose energy at high altitudes. This energy can then be conducted down along geomagnetic field lines to the ionosphere, thereby providing an additional heating mechanism.

A number of processes are effective in cooling the ambient electron gas. In the lower F region where the molecular species are abundant, rotational excitation of N_2 and O_2 and excitation of the fine structure levels of atomic oxygen are the most important cooling processes. However, at electron temperatures greater than about 1500 K, vibrational excitation of N_2 and O_2 and electronic excitation of O and O_2 have to be considered. At high altitudes, Coulomb collisions with the ambient ions are an important energy loss mechanism for thermal electrons.

At low altitudes, below about 250 km, the electron temperature can be obtained simply by equating local heating and cooling rates. However, above this altitude, electron thermal conduction is important, and the equation governing the electron temperature becomes more complicated (see Schunk and Nagy, 1978).

The primary heat source for the ion gas in the ionosphere is the ambient electron gas. Although additional ion heat sources exist, such as electric field heating, heating by exothermic chemical reactions, and frictional heating by means of neutral winds, these sources are usually characteristic of certain regions of the ionosphere and are seldom the primary heat source for the ions. The heat gained by the ions is sufficient to raise the ion temperature above the neutral gas temperature. The heated ions then lose energy through collisions with the colder neutrals. To a good approximation, the ion temperature in the E and F regions can be calculated simply by equating the heat gained from the ambient electrons to the heat lost to the neutrals.

III. The Low- and Mid-Latitude Ionosphere

The mid-latitude ionosphere has been extensively studied during the last two decades using rockets, satellites, and ground-based radar and optical facilities. These studies have shown that the ionosphere at mid-latitudes displays a marked variation with altitude, local time, season, and solar cycle. Figure 5 shows altitude profiles of the ion densities in the daytime ionosphere, as measured by the Atmosphere Explorer C satellite. The density profiles were obtained by averaging three years of data gathered by a variety of instruments on the satellite. These data indicated that NO^+ and O_2^+ are the dominant ions below 175 km and that O^+ dominates above this altitude. Note, however, that the O^+ profile in the F region does not have a sharp peak as shown in the schematic diagram presented earlier (Fig. 2). The height of the density peak moves up and down depending on the strength of the neutral wind, and the effect of averaging data over several years is to broaden the peak. Altitude profiles obtained at a given instant of time by the incoherent scatter radar technique and by rockets are very similar to that shown in Fig. 2.

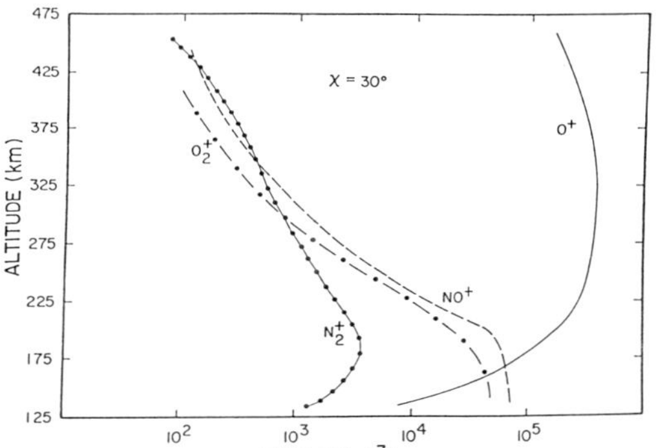

FIG. 5. Ion density for the mid-latitude ionosphere at a solar zenith angle of 30 deg. (Courtesy D. G. Torr, private communication.)

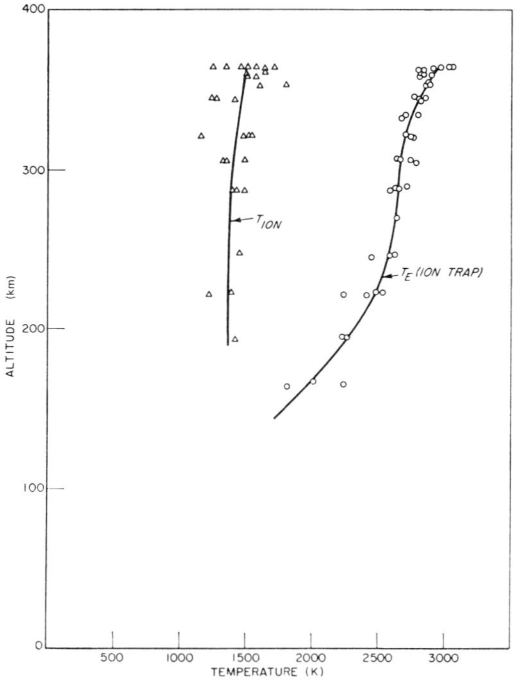

FIG. 6. Electron (○) and ion (△) temperature profiles from the downleg portion of a daytime rocket flight at mid-latitudes. [From Nagy, A. F., Brace, L. H., Carignan, G. R., and Kanal, M. (1963). *J. Geophys. Res.* **68,** 6401.]

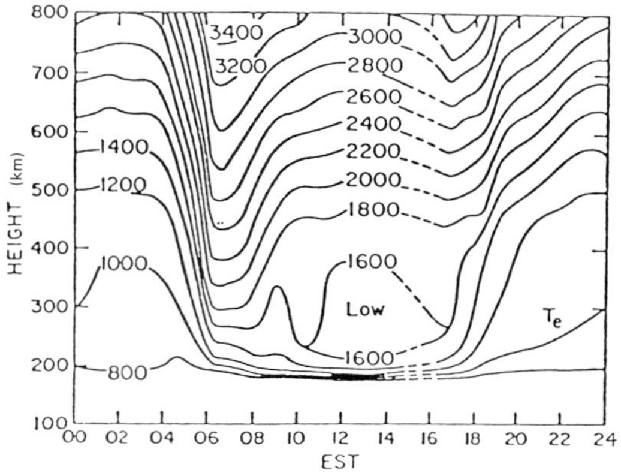

FIG. 8. Contours of the electron temperature (K) measured by the Millstone Hill incoherent scatter radar on March 23–24, 1970. [From Roble, R. G. (1975). *Planet. Space Sci.* **23,** 1017.]

Altitude profiles of the electron and ion temperatures in the daytime mid-latitude ionosphere are shown in Fig. 6. These profiles were obtained from a rocket flight in 1962 and were the earliest measurements that clearly showed that the electron temperature is greater than the ion temperature in the daytime ionosphere. As noted in Section II, the energy lost by photoelectrons to the thermal electrons is the main heat source responsible for raising T_e above T_i.

Figures 7, 8, and 9 show the diurnal variations of the electron density, electron temperature, and ion temperature measured by the Millstone Hill incoherent scatter radar on March 23–24, 1970. Also shown in Fig. 7 is the height of the F region peak. The physical processes that control the diurnal variation of the electron density change with altitude and local time. After sunrise, the ionization increases rapidly from its nighttime minimum, due to photoionization. The

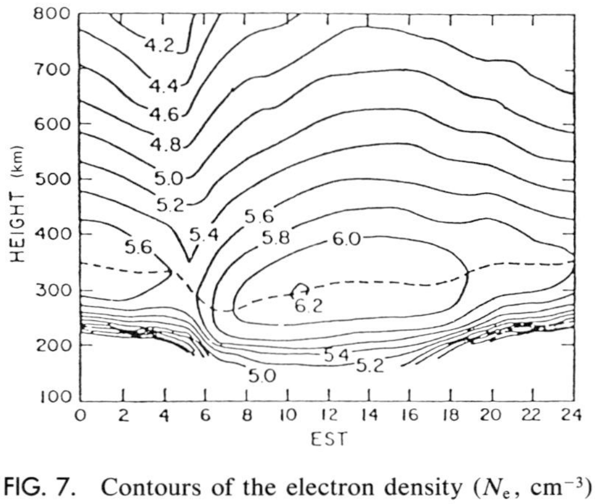

FIG. 7. Contours of the electron density (N_e, cm^{-3}) measured by the Millstone Hill incoherent scatter radar on March 23–24, 1970. Dashed line is the height of the F region peak. [From Roble, R. G. (1975). *Planet. Space Sci.* **23,** 1017.]

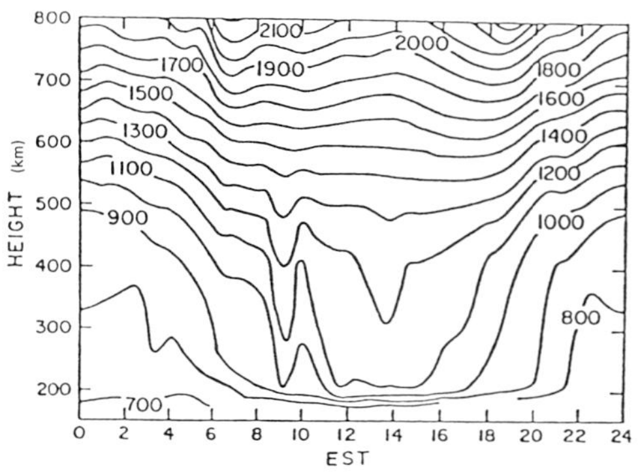

FIG. 9. Contours of the ion temperature (K) measured by the Millstone Hill incoherent scatter radar on March 23–24, 1970. [From Roble, R. G. (1975). *Planet. Space Sci.* **23,** 1017.]

ionization in the F region below about 300 km is under strong solar control, peaking at noon when the solar zenith angle is smallest and then decreasing symmetrically as the sun decreases. Ionization above 300 km, however, is influenced by other effects such as neutral winds, electron and ion temperatures, neutral composition, and plasma flow into and out of the ionosphere. Therefore the electron density contours in this region do not show a strong solar zenith angle dependence, and the maximum ionization occurs late in the afternoon near the time when the neutral temperature peaks. At night, the electron density at the F region peak is controlled by several processes, including a downward-directed ionization flux, neutral winds, and ambipolar diffusion in the lower F region (below 300 km). However, the height of the F region peak is controlled primarily by the neutral winds forcing ionization up and down the inclined geomagnetic field lines. During the day, the wind is toward the poles, and the F region is driven downwards; at night the wind is toward the equator, and the F region is driven upwards. Consequently the F region peak is higher at night than during the day.

The ambient electrons are heated by photoelectrons that are created in the photoionization process and by a downward flow of heat from high altitudes. During the day, photoelectron heating dominates, and the electron temperature is greatest at noon when the solar zenith angle is the smallest. When the sun sets (18:00 to 19:00 local time), the electron temperature decreases rapidly due to the decrease in photoelectron production. At night, photoelectron heating is absent, and the electron temperature is maintained by a downward heat flow from high altitudes, which produces the positive gradient in the nocturnal electron temperature above 200 km.

The ions gain energy from the warmer electrons and lose energy to the colder neutrals. Below about 400 km, the ions strongly couple to the neutrals, and the ion temperature variation merely reflects the variation in the neutral temperature, which is not as dramatic as the electron temperature variation. Above 400 km, the ion temperature increases with altitude due primarily to the increased thermal coupling to the warm electrons; there is also a small downward ion heat flow from high altitudes. Note that above 400 km the ion temperature displays a very small variation from day to night.

The dominant ionospheric features seen at low latitudes are the equatorial fountain and the Appleton density peaks. Near the equator, atmospheric winds in the E region generate electric fields by a dynamo action. These electric fields are transmitted along the curved geomagnetic field lines to the equatorial F region. During the daytime, these dynamo electric fields cause the equatorial F region to drift upward across magnetic field lines. The plasma lifted in this way then diffuses down the magnetic field lines and away from the equator because of the action of gravity. This combination of electromagnetic drift and diffusion produces a fountainlike pattern of plasma motion, as shown in Fig. 10.

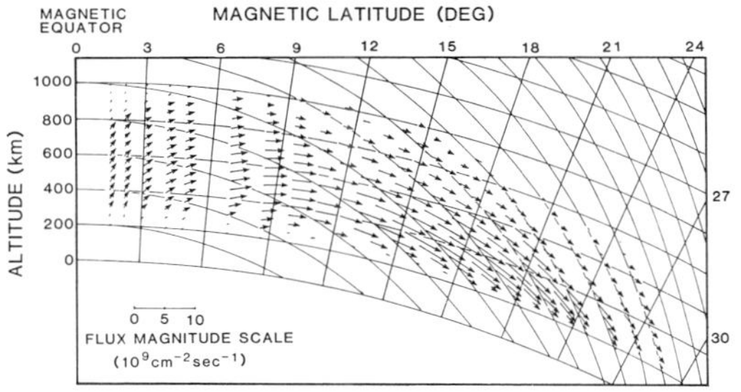

FIG. 10. The pattern of plasma drift at low latitudes due to the combined action of an electromagnetic drift across magnetic field lines and plasma diffusion along field lines. The magnetic field lines are shown every 200 km above the equator. [From Hanson, W. B., and Moffett, R. J. (1966). *J. Geophys. Res.* **71,** 5559.]

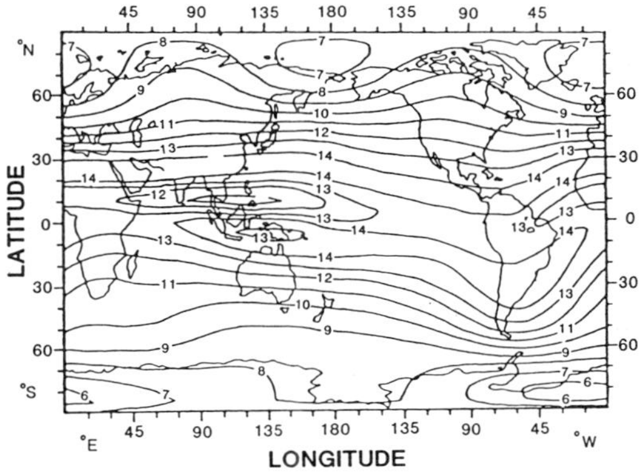

FIG. 11. Contours of the ionospheric critical frequency foF2 (in megahertz) as measured by the topside sounding satellite ISS-B. The F region peak electron density is proportional to $(foF_2)^2$. [From Matuura, N. (1979). "Atlas of ionospheric critical frequency (foF2) obtained from ionosphere sounding satellite-b observation." Part 1, August to December 1978. Radio Research Lab., Ministry of Posts and Telecommunications, Japan.]

A result of the equatorial fountain is that ionization peaks are formed in the subtropics on each side of the magnetic equator. These so-called Appleton peaks are shown in Fig. 11 for 14:00 local time (the usual time for maximum peak development). At this time, the Appleton peaks are the most developed over the east Asia region. Typically, the Appleton peaks lie between 10° and 20° from the magnetic equator. With regard to diurnal variations, the peaks form around noon and disappear during the night.

IV. The High-Latitude Ionosphere

The ionosphere at high latitudes exhibits a more complex behavior than at low and mid-latitudes owing to a variety of physical processes that are unique to this region. Foremost among these are the electric fields generated by the solar wind–geomagnetic field interaction, the presence of intense particle precipitation within the auroral oval, the polar wind escape of thermal plasma, and other features resulting from the auroral disturbance of the neutral atmosphere.

As noted earlier, the interaction of the solar wind with the earth's magnetic field generates electric fields that are mapped down along geomagnetic field lines to the high-latitude ionosphere. These electric fields cause the high-latitude ionosphere to drift (or convect) horizontally across the polar region. In the F region, the electric field induced convection pattern is a two-cell pattern with antisunward flow over the polar cap and sunward flow at slightly lower latitudes. However, the ionospheric plasma at high latitudes also has a tendency to co-rotate with the earth. When this co-rotation velocity is added to the two-cell convection pattern, the resulting drift pattern for the F region plasma is as shown schematically in Fig. 12; this figure is a polar diagram with the magnetic pole at the center and magnetic local time displayed on the outer circle. The plasma flow is basically antisunward over the polar cap (white area poleward of the auroral oval) and sunward outside of this region. At dusk (18 magnetic local time, MLT) and near 65° invariant latitude, the sunward convection of plasma driven by the solar wind–geomagnetic field interaction opposes the co-rotation velocity, and a near stagnation of plasma occurs. This stagnation region plays an important role in the formation of the main electron density trough, which will be discussed below.

An important region shown in Fig. 12 is the auroral oval. In this region, energetic electrons from deep space can penetrate to ionospheric altitudes, and these energetic electrons can ionize the neutral atmosphere and heat the ambient electrons and ions. The exact effect that these energetic electrons have on the ionosphere depends not only on the intensity of these electrons but also on the length of time the ambient plasma spends in the auroral oval since the plasma is continually circulating through this region. [*See* AURORA.]

The effect of the plasma motion (Fig. 12) on the electron density depends on both the speed of the flow and the seasonal conditions. For summer, most of the polar region is sunlit; consequently, the electron densities are elevated due to photoionization. In winter, on the other hand, most of the polar region is in darkness, and the electron densities tend to be low.

In Fig. 12, two electron density features are shown: a polar hole and the main trough. Both of these features occur in winter when the plasma flow speeds are low. The polar hole is a low-density, low-temperature region that is situated in the polar cap just poleward of the nocturnal auroral oval. This polar hole results from the

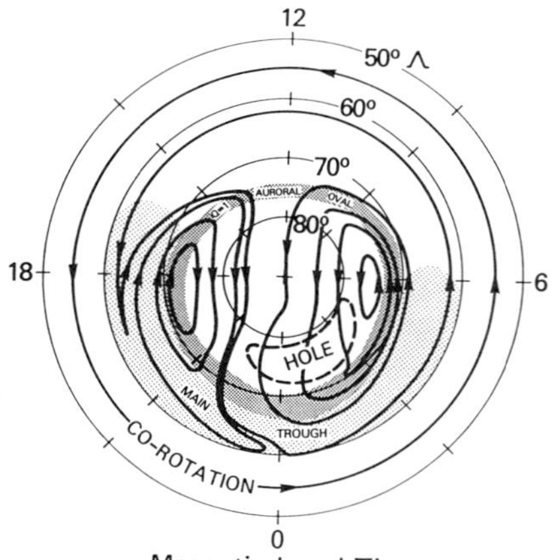

FIG. 12. Schematic illustration of the polar ionosphere showing the plasma convection trajectories in the F region (solid lines) in a magnetic local time (MLT), magnetic latitude reference frame. Also shown are the locations of the high-latitude ionization hole, the main plasma trough, and the quiet time auroral oval. [From Brinton, H. C., Grebowsky, M. M., and Brace, L. H. (1978). *J. Geophys. Res.* **83,** 4767.]

slow antisunward drift of the plasma in the dark polar cap, during which time the ionosphere decays. The lowest densities are obtained just before the plasma enters the nocturnal auroral oval; the F region peak density in the polar hole can be as low as 5×10^2 cm^{-3}. Upon entering the nocturnal auroral oval, the densities begin to build up owing to electron–ion production from precipitating energetic electrons. For a slow traversal through the oval, the F region peak density can increase to 10^5 cm^{-3}. The main electron density trough is situated just equatorward of the nocturnal auroral oval. This region has a limited latitudinal extent but is extended in local time (16–6 MLT). The trough is composed of plasma that has stagnated near dusk, decayed in the darkness, and then either co-rotated around the nightside or moved slowly back toward the dayside. The F region peak density in the trough can get as low as 10^3 cm^{-3}.

The electron density features shown in Fig. 12 occur only if the plasma flow speed is low. When the solar wind–geomagnetic field interaction is strong, large plasma flows can occur (~1 km/sec). In this case, the polar hole does not form, and instead a tongue of ionization extends over the polar cap, as shown in Fig. 13. In this figure, contours of the F region peak electron density N_mF_2 are plotted for the winter southern hemisphere. The contours numbered 31, 45, and 61 on the dayside show the increase in ionization

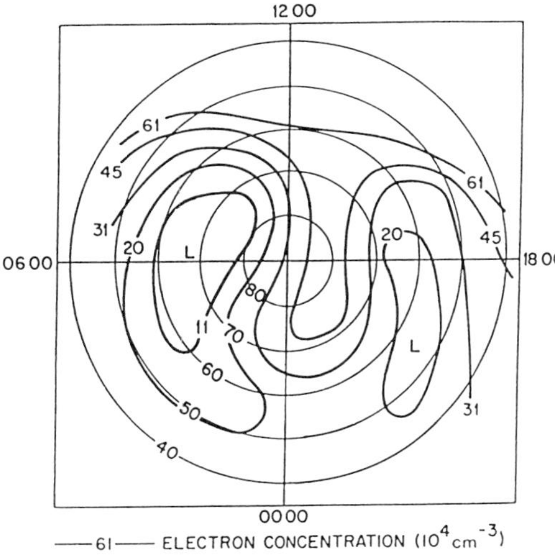

FIG. 13. Synoptic NmF2 contours for the Antarctic polar region in geographic coordinates. [From Knudsen, W. C., Banks, P. M., Winningham, J. D., and Klumpar, D. M. (1977). *J. Geophys. Res.* **82,** 4784.]

for a decreasing solar zenith angle. Near noon, the rapid antisunward flow of plasma carries the high dayside densities into the dark polar cap. Since the plasma flow speed is high, the ionosphere does not have sufficient time to decay, and a tongue of ionization extends across the polar region.

V. Planetary Ionospheres

All bodies in our solar system that have a surrounding neutral-gas envelope, due either to gravitational attraction (e.g., planets) or some other process such as sublimation (e.g., comets), also have an ionosphere. The very basic processes of ionization, chemical transformation, and diffusive as well as convective transport are analogous in all ionospheres; the major differences are the result of the background neutral gas compositions and the differing importance of some of the controlling mechanisms (e.g, photoionization versus particle impact ionization). The remainder of this section describes the characteristics of the Venus ionosphere as a representative example of the so-called inner or terrestrial planets, the ionosphere of Jupiter as representative of the outer or major planets, and finally the ionosphere of comets as the representative case of situations in which the neutral envelope is not gravitationally bound.

A. Venus

The ionosphere of Venus is the most explored and best understood besides that of the Earth. The atmosphere at the surface of Venus consists of approximately 96% CO_2 and 4% N_2; because of the photodissociation of CO_2, atomic oxygen, O becomes the major constituent of the atmosphere above about 150 km. Chemical processes control the behavior of the Venus ionosphere below about 180 km. This region of the Venus ionosphere is analogous to the E and F1 regions of the terrestrial ionosphere from the point of view of the controlling processes; however, there is a very important difference between the two ionospheres because on Venus the maximum plasma densities are found within this region, near 145 km (Fig. 14). Venus is an excellent example of the importance of chemical processes in establishing the nature of some important aspects of an ionosphere. The most abundant ion on Venus is O_2^+, and yet there is practically no neutral O_2 in the upper atmosphere of Venus. As mentioned earlier, the ma-

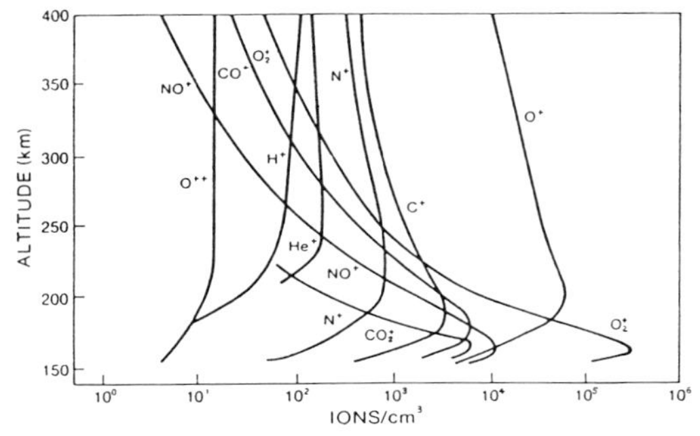

FIG. 14. Ion densities measured by the ion mass spectrometer during one orbit of the Pioneer Venus orbiter spacecraft. [Bauer, S. J., Donahue, T. M., Hartle, R. E., and Taylor, H. A. (1979). *Science* **205,** 109.]

jor upper atmospheric neutral gas constituents are CO_2 and O. The photoionization of these neutral gas species is very rapidly followed by the following reactions, which very effectively turn these initial ions into O_2^+:

$$CO_2^+ + O \rightarrow O_2^+ + CO, \qquad k_{27} = 1.64 \times 10^{-10} \quad (27)$$

$$\rightarrow O^+ + CO_2, \qquad k_{28} = 9.6 \times 10^{-11} \quad (28)$$

$$O^+ + CO_2 \rightarrow O_2^+ + CO, \qquad k_{29} = 9.5 \times 10^{-10} \quad (29)$$

where the rate constants k_s are for a temperature of 300 K, and the units are $cm^3\ sec^{-1}$.

At altitudes above about 200 km, transport processes control the distribution of the electron and ion densities in a way very similar to the terrestrial topside ionosphere. Venus does not have an intrinsic magnetic field, therefore, unlike the earth, processes associated with transport between magnetically conjugate ionospheres do not take place. The lack of an intrinsic magnetic field also means that the solar wind is not deflected around the planet but interacts directly with the atmosphere and ionosphere. As the result of this interaction, the ionosphere has a sharp upper boundary, called the ionopause, which varies with the changing pressure exerted by the solar wind; the dayside ionopause is usually between 300 and 1000 km.

The effective night on Venus lasts about 58 earth days, during which time an ionosphere would be expected to disappear because of the lack of new photoionization and the recombination of the ions and electrons. Therefore it was a surprise when Mariner 5 established in 1967 the presence of an ionosphere on the nightside of Venus. Since that time other measurements confirmed the presence of a significant but highly variable nightside ionosphere with a peak electron density of about $2 \times 10^4\ cm^{-3}$. It is now understood that most of the plasma on the nightside is the result of very rapid (few km/sec) plasma transport from the dayside to the nightside and impact ionization by precipitating electrons.

Summary of the observed altitude and solar zenith angle variations of electron densities and temperatures is shown in Fig. 15. The observed dayside electron temperatures imply not only that the ionospheric plasma is heated by photoelectrons but also that very likely heat is deposited at the top of the ionosphere by some mechanism associated with the solar wind–ionosphere

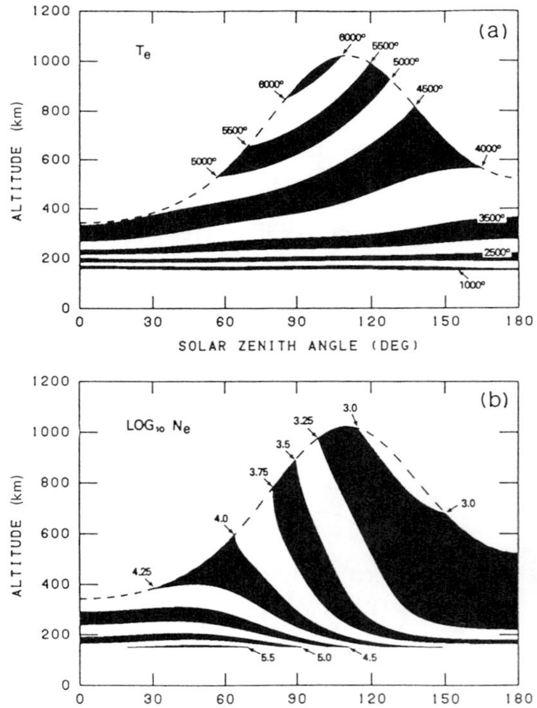

FIG. 15. Empirical model values of electron densities and temperatures of Venus based on data obtained by the Electron Temperature Probe on the Pioneer Venus Orbiter Spacecraft. [Brace, L. H., Gombosi, T. I., Kliore, A. J., Knudsen, W. C., Nagy, A. F., and Taylor, H. A. (1983). In "Venus" (D. M. Hunten, L. Colin, and T. M. Donahue, eds.), pp. 779–840. University of Arizona Press, Tuscon.]

interaction in the ionopause region; this heat is then conducted down deep into the ionosphere. On the dayside, most of the energy for the ions comes from Coulomb collisions with the electrons. The ion temperatures in most of the nightside region are maintained by a combination of horizontal advection from the dayside followed by heating due to adiabatic compression resulting from downward plasma motion. Good summaries of our present day knowledge of the Venus ionosphere can be found in Brace *et al.* (1983), Nagy *et al.* (1983), and Brace and Kliore (1990) and that of Mars in Schunk and Nagy (1980) and Cravens and Nagy (1983).

B. JUPITER

The upper atmosphere of Jupiter consists mainly of molecular hydrogen H_2 and some lesser amounts of helium and atomic hydrogen; in the lower atmosphere, methane, CH_4, is also an important neutral gas constituent. Jupiter has no easily identifiable surface, therefore the altitude scales are referred to a given atmospheric pressure level; in ionospheric use this level is usually that at 1 mb (millibar; bar = 10^5 N/m^2). The only direct information we have available on the ionosphere of Jupiter at this time comes from altitude profiles of the total electron density obtained, using radio occultation techniques, by the Pioneers 10 and 11 and the Voyagers 1 and 2 spacecrafts during their flyby of the planet. The Voyager results are shown in Fig. 16.

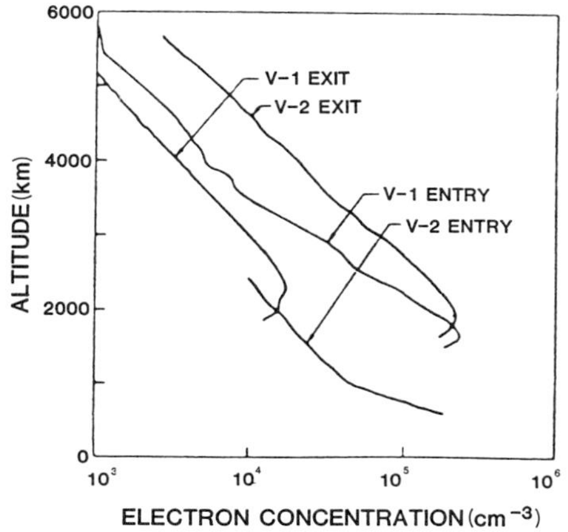

FIG. 16. Voyagers 1 and 2 measurements of the electron number density profiles. The zero of the altitude scale corresponds to the 1 mb pressure level. (Courtesy V. A. Eshelman, private communication.)

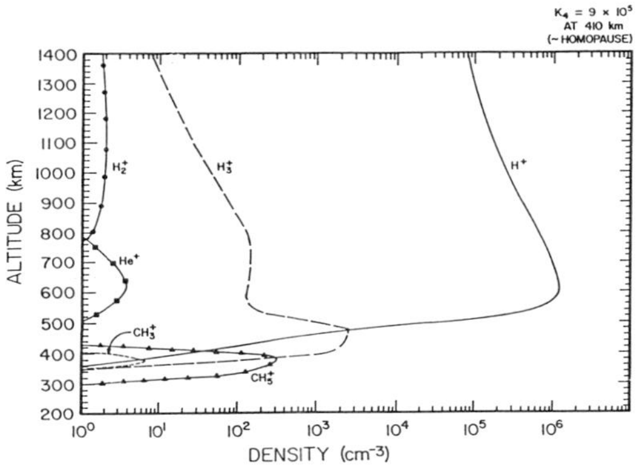

FIG. 17. Ion density profiles obtained from theoretical model calculations for the dayside ionosphere of Jupiter. (Courtesy H. Waite, private communication.)

Direct photoionization of H_2, resulting in H_2^+, is probably the major ionization source in the mid- and low-latitude regions; at high latitudes, impact ionization by energetic particles becomes dominant. There is insufficient information to establish uniquely the nature of these energetic particles (e.g., are they electrons, ions, or neutral gas particles?). The principal initial ion H_2^+ very rapidly reacts with H_2 to form H_3^+. The rate at which the following dissociative recombination process takes place in the Jovian ionosphere is also very fast:

$$H_3^+ + e \rightarrow H_2 + H, \qquad k_{30} = 1.0 \times 10^{-7}\ \text{cm}^3\ \text{sec}^{-1} \tag{30}$$

Therefore the equilibrium densities of H_2^+ and H_3^+ are relatively small, and H^+ is the dominant ion throughout most of Jupiter's ionosphere, as indicated by the results of model calculations shown in Fig. 17. H^+ is created either by direct photoionization of H or dissociative ionization of H_2:

$$H_2 + h\nu(\lambda < 723\ \text{Å}) \rightarrow H^+ + H + e \tag{31}$$

where λ is the wavelength of the ionizing radiation, and $h\nu$ denotes a photon. The atomic H^+ ions recombine radiatively at a rather slow rate ($\sim 3.5 \times 10^{-12}$ cm^3 sec^{-1}), and therefore their lifetime is so long that they are transported via diffusion to low altitudes, where they recombine rapidly. Recombination with vibrationally excited H_2 is another possible removal mechanism for H^+.

There is no direct information available on the electron and ion temperatures in the ionosphere. Theoretical calculations indicate that these temperatures are close to the neutral gas temperatures (~1050 K) at altitudes below the electron density peak. More detailed summaries of the Jupiter ionosphere can be found in Atreya (1986) and Waite and Cravens (1987); for the Saturn ionosphere refer to Atreya *et al.*, (1984), given in the bibliography.

C. COMETS

Atmospheres of comets differ from those of planets in two important aspects: (1) as comets approach the sun in highly elliptical orbits, their atmospheres grow as a result of the increasing sublimation–evaporation of the condensed gases from the surface of the nucleus; and (2) because of the negligibly small gravitational attraction of the cometary nucleus, the atmosphere flows radially outward, with speeds of the order of a km sec^{-1}, and extends to great distances.

Until very recently, the only information on cometary atmospheres and ionospheres came from optical remote sensing, which gave indirect indications of highly variable chemical compositions. However, a number of spacecraft have now made direct measurements in the neighborhood of comets, starting with the International Cometary Explorer (ICE) mission, which flew past comet Giacobini-Zinner in September 1985, followed by the two VEGA, the Sakigake and Suisei, and Giotto missions which explored the environment of comet Halley during March 1986.

The Giotto spacecraft flew within about 600 km of comet Halley's nucleus and obtained excellent data on its inner atmosphere and ionosphere. The neutral mass spectrometer instrument carried by Giotto [*Nature* **321** (6067) contains all the preliminary results from the Vega and Giotto missions] established that water was the main gaseous atmospheric constituent throughout the encounter. More specifically, it established that water vapor accounts for more than 80% of the gases escaping the comet. It also found that the upper limits on the relative abundance of CO_2, NH_3 and CH_4 are 3.5, 10, and 7%, respectively. This experiment also obtained an estimate of 900 ± 200 m sec^{-1} for the neutral gas expansion velocity, which agrees well with earlier theoretical predictions.

The predominance of water vapor in the atmosphere of comet Halley means that preencounter "water" models of the ionosphere are applicable (see Mendis *et al.*, 1985). The main photochemical processes involved in such a model are:

$$H_2O + h\nu \rightarrow H_2O^+ + e \quad (32)$$

$$H_2O^+ + H_2O \rightarrow H_3O^+ + OH, \quad k_{33} = 2 \times 10^{-9} \quad (33)$$

$$H_3O^+ + e \rightarrow OH + H_2, \quad \alpha_{34} = 2.33 \times 10^{-7} \quad (34)$$

$$\rightarrow OH + H + H, \quad \alpha_{35} = 2.33 \times 10^{-7} \quad (35)$$

$$\rightarrow H_2O + H, \quad \alpha_{36} = 2.33 \times 10^{-7} \quad (36)$$

where the recombination rates α's are given for 300 K and the units are $cm^3\ sec^{-1}$ for all rates given. The large rate coefficient for reaction (33) means that even though H_2O^+ is the primary initial ion, the major ion in water-dominated cometary atmospheres, such as Halley, is H_3O^+. The Giotto spacecraft carried an ion mass spectrometer that measured the detailed variation of the ion composition along its trajectory; these results are shown in Fig. 18. These observations indicate that H_3O^+ is truly the major ion in Halley's ionosphere; minor ions of importance include H_2O^+, OH^+, O^+, and S^+. Photoionization of H_2O ($\lambda > 984$ Å) and other atmospheric species is certainly a major source of ionization; the unresolved question at this time is whether other ionization mechanisms play an important role or not. Impact ionization by electrons of a few keV

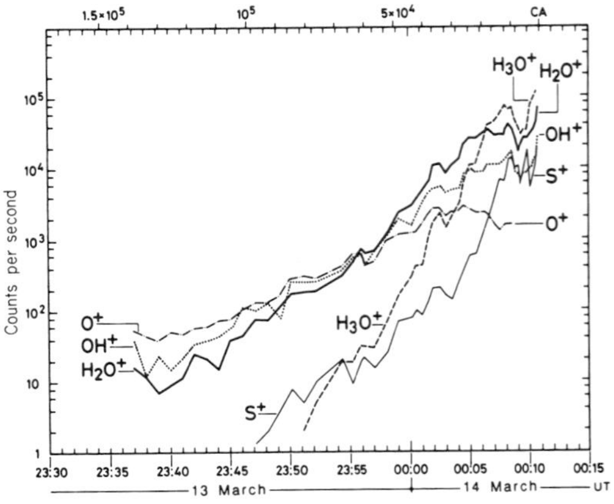

FIG. 18. Measured ion composition variation along the Giotto spacecraft trajectory. (Balsiger *et al.* (1986). *Nature* **321**, 330.)

has been suggested as a possible mechanism, based on measurements obtained by instruments on the VEGA spacecraft.

Theoretical calculations of electron and ion temperatures have to be carried out self-consistently with calculations of the plasma velocities, which makes such calculations very difficult. As in the case of the neutral atmosphere, the lack of an effective gravitational force leads to large radial plasma velocities, which are believed to approach supersonic values only a few hundred meters from the comet. These plasma velocities will eventually decrease rapidly, mainly due to their interaction with the decelerated solar wind. A number of such models (see Cravens, 1987; Nagy, 1987) have been completed recently and they predict that the ion temperatures increase from about 100 K near the nucleus to about 1000 K at cometocentric distances of a few thousand kilometers. The ion temperatures measured by the Giotto ion mass spectrometer are similar but slightly higher than these model values. The region of transition from solar wind plasma to ionospheric plasma is called the contact discontinuity or ionopause and in some respects is analogous to that at Venus. The location of the ionopause is estimated to be a few thousand kilometers from the nucleus on the dayside for typical active comets. The Giotto measurements found that for comet Halley, at a heliocentric distance of 1.35×10^8 (0.9 astronomical unit), this ionopause, or confact discontinuity, is at about 4500 km from the nucleus.

A good summary of our pre-1986 understanding of cometary ionospheres can be found in Mendis *et al.* (1986), while very brief summaries of the post-comet-Halley encounter status are given by Cravens (1987) and Nagy (1987).

Bibliography

Atreya, S. K., Waite, J. H., Donahue, T. M., Nagy, A. F., and McConnell, J. C. (1984). *In* "Saturn" (T. Gehrels and M. S. Mathews, eds.). University of Arizona Press, Tuscon.

Atreya, S. K. (1986). "Atmospheres and Ionospheres of the Outer Planets," Springer-Verlag, New York.

Brace, L. H., Gombosi, T. I., Kliore, A. J., Knudsen, W. C., Nagy, A. F., and Taylor, H. A. (1983). *In* "Venus" (D. M. Hunten, L. Colin, and T. M. Donahue, eds.), pp. 779–840. University of Arizona Press, Tuscon.

Brace, L. H., and Kliore, A. J. (1990). *Space Sci. Rev.* (in press).

Cravens, T. E. (1987). *Adv. Space Res.* **7**(12), 147.

Cravens, T. E., and Nagy, A. F. (1983). *Rev. Geophys. and Space Phys.* **21,** 263.

Mendis, D. A., Houpis, H. L. F. and Marconi, M. L. (1985). *Cosmic Phys.* **10,** 1–380.

Nagy, A. F. (1987). *Adv. Space Res.* **7**(12), 89.

Nagy, A. F., Cravens, T. E., and Gombosi, T. I. *In* "Venus" (D. M. Hunten, L. Colin, and T. M. Donahue, eds.), pp. 841–872. University of Arizona Press, Tuscon.

Schunk, R. W., and Nagy, A. F. (1978). *Rev. Geophys. and Space Phys.* **16,** 355–399.

Schunk, R. W., and Nagy, A. F. (1980). *Rev. Geophys. and Space Phys.* **18,** 813–852.

Strobel, D. F., and Atreya, S. K. (1983). "Physics of the Jovian Magnetosphere" (A. J. Dessler, ed.). Cambridge University Press, Cambridge.

Waite, J. H., and Cravens, T. E. (1987). *Adv. Space Res.* **7**(12), 119.

J

JET PROPULSION

A. R. Karagozian *University of California, Los Angeles*

GLOSSARY

Adiabatic efficiency: Relationship between the actual work and the ideal (isentropic) work done in an engine component; the ratio is defined differently based on the particular rotating component.

Drag: Total force acting to oppose the motion of a body in a fluid.

Expansion wave: Isentropic process acting in a two-dimensional, steady flow to turn the flow while increasing Mach number and decreasing static pressure.

Heating value *h*: Amount of heat released per unit mass in a given chemical reaction.

Isentropic: Process occurring adiabatically (i.e., without heat transfer) and without dissipation (i.e., without viscous losses).

Mach number *M*: Ratio of the local fluid velocity to the local speed of sound.

Propulsive efficiency: Ratio of the useful power delivered by the engine to the net mechanical power in the engine exhaust.

Shock wave: Nonisentropic process through which there is a sharp drop in velocity, Mach number, and stagnation pressure, with a sharp increase in static pressure and temperature.

Stagnation pressure: Pressure of a fluid brought isentropically to rest.

Stagnation temperature: Temperature of a fluid brought isentropically to rest.

Static pressure: Pressure of a fluid that is in motion.

Static temperature: Temperature of a fluid that is in motion.

Thrust: Total force acting to propel a body in a fluid.

The field of jet propulsion deals with locomotion in which the momentum of matter ejected from a given body imparts motion to the body. The most common types of jet propulsion devices are rockets, in which the ejection of stored matter called the propellant produces a thrust acting on the rocket, and air-breathing engines, in which the surrounding medium passes through the device and is utilized as the working fluid. The following section outlines the general characteristics of these engines, while later sections deal with specific aspects of the design and analysis of jet propulsion devices.

I. Overview and Description of Propulsive Devices

Rocket engines are most commonly classified according to the type of energy source used, whether the propellant is chemical (e.g., liquid or solid propellant rockets) or nonchemical (e.g., nuclear or electrical) in nature. The major advantage of the rocket is that since it requires no atmospheric oxygen, the operating altitude is virtually unlimited, and the speed possibilities are much greater than for engines requiring ambient air.

In chemical rocket engines, energy is released in a high pressure combustion reaction which occurs in the portion of the engine called the combustion chamber. The gaseous combustion products are formed at very high temperatures, and are then expanded through an exhaust nozzle at very high velocities. Liquid propellant rockets utilize liquid fuel and oxidizer as propellants which are fed under high pressure into the combustion chamber. A typical liquid rocket system is shown schematically in Fig. 1. Solid propellant rockets carry the propellant in the combustion chamber in solid form. Once ignited, the propellant "grain" burns smoothly on

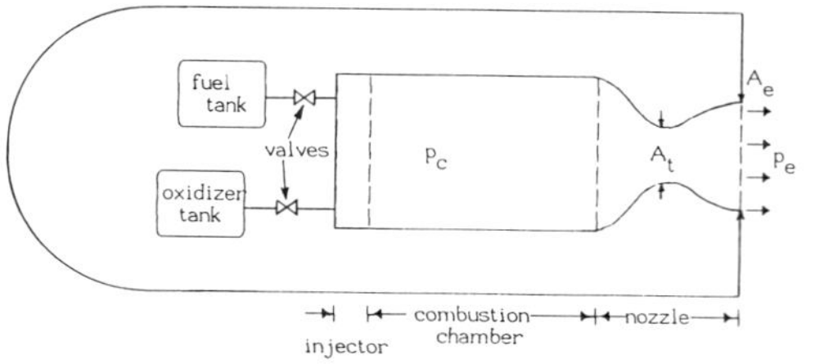

FIG. 1. Schematic diagram of liquid propellant rocket system.

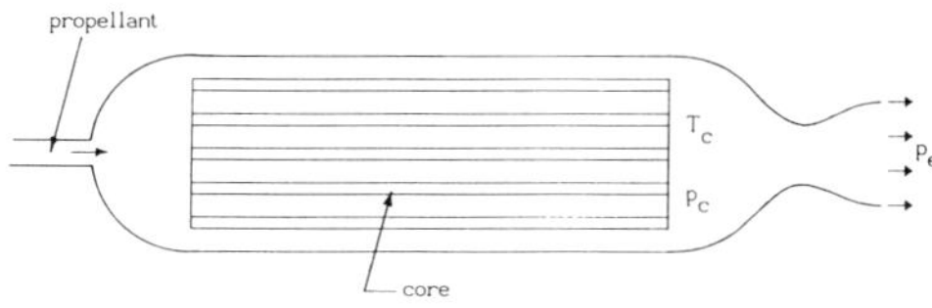

FIG. 3. Schematic diagram of nuclear-powered rocket system. [After Oates (1984).]

its exposed surface, forming high pressure, high temperature gaseous combustion products. As with the liquid propellant rocket, these hot gases are exhausted through a nozzle. A general configuration for the solid propellant rocket is shown in Fig. 2. [*See* LIQUID ROCKET PROPELLANTS; SOLID PROPELLANTS; SOLID ROCKET MOTORS.]

Among the types of nonchemical rockets, nuclear rocket engines deliver heat to a working fluid (usually liquid hydrogen) by means of a nuclear energy source. This source could be a fission reactor, a radioactive isotope decay source, or a fusion reactor. A typical configuration for a nuclear rocket engine is shown in Fig. 3. Electrical rockets consist of three basic types: electrothermal rockets, in which electrical energy is transformed into heat in an arc jet; electrostatic rockets, in which the working fluid is ionized and accelerated by electrostatic fields that are set up; and electromagnetic rockets, in which a plasma is accelerated by interaction of the electric currents and magnetic fields present. [*See* ELECTRIC PROPULSION.]

Among air-breathing engines, the ramjet and scramjet are conceptually the simplest, followed by the turbojet and its numerous modified cycles. In air-breathing engines, it is primarily the increase in the momentum of the working fluid (air) that produces thrust. In the ramjet, shown schematically in Fig. 4, air enters the engine through the diffuser. It is mixed with fuel and burned in the combustion chamber, and hot gaseous combustion products are then expanded in the nozzle and ejected with a speed exceeding that of the entering air. The *s*upersonic *c*ombustion ramjet, or scramjet, engine is conceptually similar to the ramjet except that the combustion process is to take place supersonically, so that a much greater flight Mach number may be accommodated. The ramjet's performance is optimal at supersonic flight speeds to Mach 6 (although combustion takes place subsonically), while the scramjet potentially could accommodate flight Mach numbers as high as 15–20.

The simple turbojet, shown in Fig. 5, has a compressor and turbine that contribute to the thrust capabilities of the overall engine. Turbojets have good performance at low Mach numbers. The compressor works on the air that has entered the diffuser, increasing its stagnation pressure and temperature in order for the combustion process to take place downstream. The turbine acts to expand the hot air and combus-

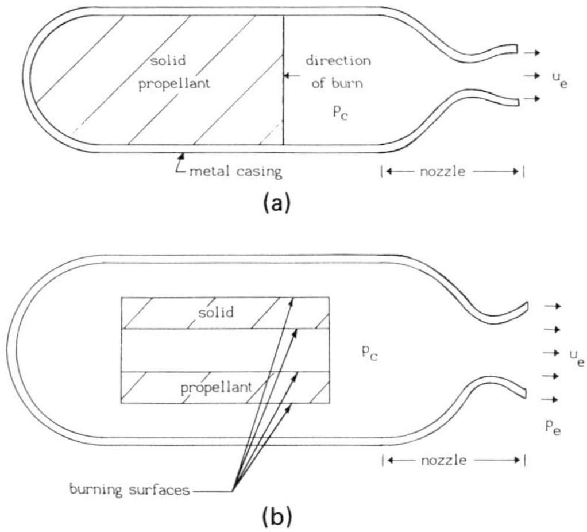

FIG. 2. Schematic diagram of alternative solid propellant rocket systems. (a) Cigarette burning, (b) unrestricted burning.

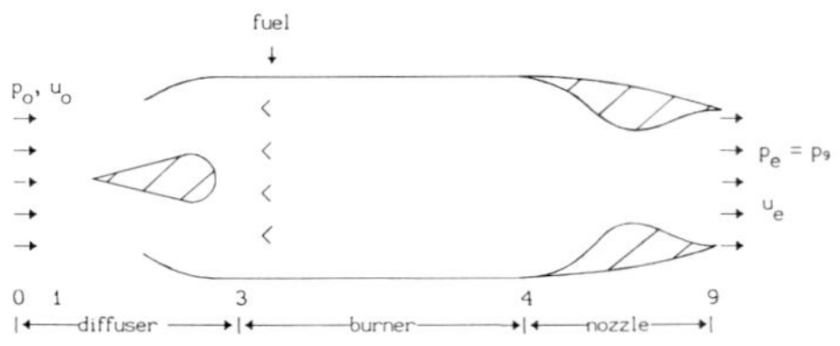

FIG. 4. Schematic diagram of ramjet engine.

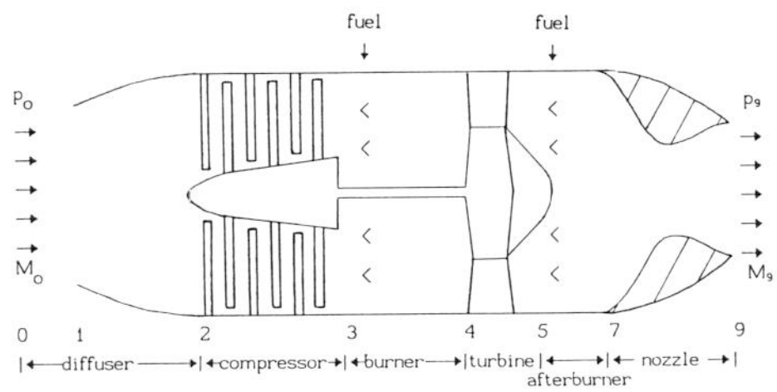

FIG. 5. Schematic diagram of turbojet engine with afterburner.

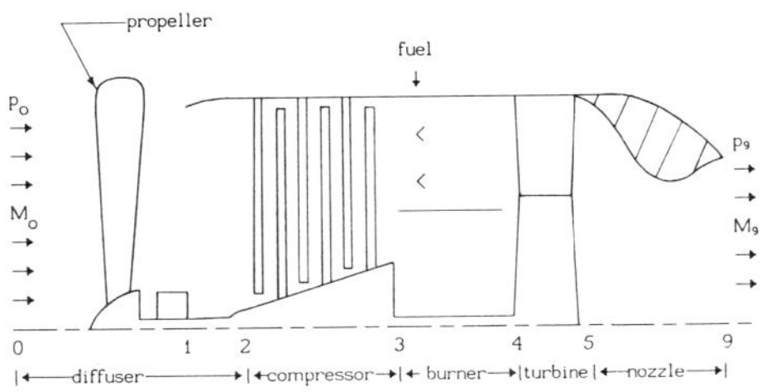

FIG. 7. Schematic diagram (center-line cut) of turboprop engine.

tion products before they are exhausted through the nozzle; the work done on the turbine by the hot gases is used to drive the compressor. If an afterburner is placed between the turbine and nozzle, the injection of additional fuel allows excess air and fuel to continue to be burned and exhaust gases brought to high temperatures once again. The effect of this additional component is the achievement of greater thrust for the engine.

Modifications to the basic turbojet cycle can be made that will improve engine performance under certain flight conditions. The turbo-bypass, shown in Fig. 6, improves the propulsive capabilities of the basic turbojet by having a portion of the primary compressor pump air through a secondary burner and nozzle. This air then bypasses the main engine flow as shown, so that the effective thrust is increased but the fuel consumption is lowered. Turboprop engines are also similar to the turbojet, except that they utilize a propeller to provide most of the propulsive thrust. The propeller and compressor are both driven by the turbine, as indicated in Fig. 7. The turboprop is frequently used in high take-off thrust or low-speed cruise applications. Other variations on the basic turbojet cycle are possible with the addition of different combinations of

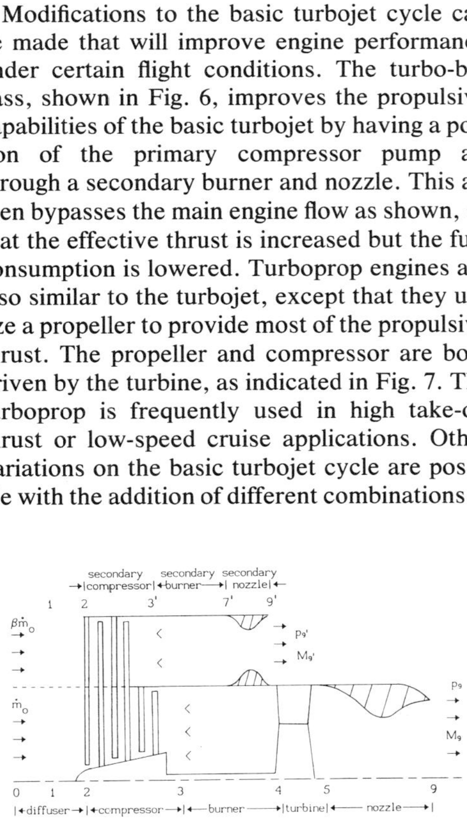

FIG. 6. Schematic diagram (center-line cut) of turbo-bypass engine.

the components mentioned above, such as the turbofan with afterburning.

II. Rocket Propulsion

A. General Features

A variety of parameters are used characteristically to describe the performance of the rocket. The thrust of the engine is a force resulting from changes in the momentum or pressure of the working fluid passing through the engine. Since by definition the working fluids of the rocket are stored (or formed) in the engine and then ejected, only the momentum of the ejected gases and the pressure difference between the exhaust and the surrounding medium contribute to thrust. In the notation of Figs. 1 and 2, with the assumption of unidirectional flow, an approximate equation for the thrust of a rocket engine takes the form

$$T = A_e(p_e - p_0) + \dot{m}_e u_e \qquad (1)$$

where $\dot{m}_e$, u_e, p_e, and A_e refer to the mass flux, velocity, static pressure, and cross-sectional area at the nozzle exit, respectively, and p_0 is the static pressure of the surrounding fluid. The total drag on an engine results from changes in the momentum of fluid passing over the exterior of the vehicle and from pressure changes across the external surface. The propellant specific impulse I_{sp} is defined as the ratio of the thrust to the weight flow rate of gases ejected by the rocket; the specific propellant consumption is defined as the reciprocal of this impulse. The effective exhaust velocity C can also be used as a performance parameter in rockets. C is defined as the ratio of the thrust to the mass flow rate of propellant, hence the specific impulse $I_{sp} \equiv C/g$ is typically given in units of seconds, where g is the acceleration due to gravity.

B. Chemical Rockets

Chemical rockets are typically categorized according to the type of propellant used. In the liquid propellant combustion chamber, the propellants are first isolated in pressurized form from the chamber. After injection, the propellants atomize and vaporize so that burning of a gaseous mixture will take place in the combustion chamber. There are a variety of different injection modes possible in the design of the combustion chamber to achieve different modes of liquid droplet breakup. Among these injection modes are the introduction of jets of fuel and oxidizer by opposing impingement, by coflowing injection, or by coaxial injection. Given an injection mode, the design of the combustion chamber in terms of size will depend on the "residence time" of the reactants in the chamber and its relation to the time required in the reaction for attaining a near-equilibrium product composition.

The selection of a propellant feed system for a given liquid rocket will depend on the particular application of the rocket, including its flight and thrust requirements, as well as propellant properties. One of the simplest methods for pressurizing propellants is to force them out of their respective tanks by displacing them with high-pressure gas; as gas is discharged from an external tank, the propellants are discharged in a controlled manner. Another type of feed system is the turbopump rocket feed system, in which propellants are pressurized by pumps that are driven by turbines within the rocket itself. These turbines derive energy from the expansion of hot gases emanating from a gas generator utilizing the fuel and oxidizer in its operation. In an open-cycle turbopump system, the working fluid exhausting from the turbine is simply discharged from the rocket, whereas in a closed cycle, the working fluid is actually injected back into the rocket combustion chamber, thus utilizing the propellants more efficiently.

The solid propellant combustion chamber contains the entire mass of propellant at the beginning of the rocket's operation. As the solid burns, its exposed surface recedes at a rate r, so that high pressure, high temperature gaseous products are formed, which flow through the exhaust nozzle at a mass flow rate $\dot{m}_e = \rho_p A_b r$. Here ρ_p is the density of the solid propellant and A_b is the exposed surface area for burning. The rate of recession r is determined empirically to depend on chamber pressure p_c according to the relation $r = ap_c^n$, where the coefficient a depends on the freestream velocity tangential to the burning surface and the exponent n depends on the type of propellant used. Based on stability requirements, n must be less than unity, and in most commonly used solid propellants lies in the range 0.4–0.9.

The solid propellant grain inside the rocket motor can take on a variety of shapes and cross-sectional areas. Since the propellant will burn on all its exposed surfaces to form hot gases, the geometrical configuration of the grain actually determines many of the performance characteristics of the engine. While most rockets have only a single grain, some have grains consisting of segments of different propellant composition. Typical grain configurations for the solid propellant rocket are shown in Fig. 2. The end-burning or "cigarette-burning" grain burns solely in the axial direction; this configuration was used in earlier rocket designs during the 1940s. Since then, increases in burning rate have been achieved by incorporating alternative geometries, such as the star-shaped solid grain, into the combustion chamber.

In both liquid and solid propellant rockets, the crucial phenomenon that creates engine thrust is the expansion of the gaseous products of combustion through the nozzle. Depending on the relationship between the pressure in the combustion chamber and the pressure of the atmosphere surrounding the rocket, either subsonic ($M < 1$) or supersonic ($M > 1$) flow will be exhausted from the nozzle. An optimum expansion process would involve the acceleration of subsonic flow in the converging section of the nozzle (see Fig. 8), sonic flow ($M = 1$) at the throat, and continued acceleration to supersonic flow through the diverging section, with a supersonic exhaust at a pressure $p_e|_{opt}$ equal to the surrounding pressure. If the atmospheric and exit pressures are greater than $p_e|_{opt}$, then the formation of a normal shock wave in the divergent portion of the nozzle takes place. Across a shock wave there is a very sharp reduction in the velocity of the flow, so that the flow undergoes a transition from supersonic to subsonic, with a sharp increase in the pressure of the fluid. The presence of the shock wave is necessary to achieve the required exit conditions in terms of pressure, although it causes a reduction in the engine thrust due to the subsonic exit flow.

The other flow situations depicted in Fig. 8 represent the underexpanded nozzle, in which the nozzle exit pressure is greater than the sur-

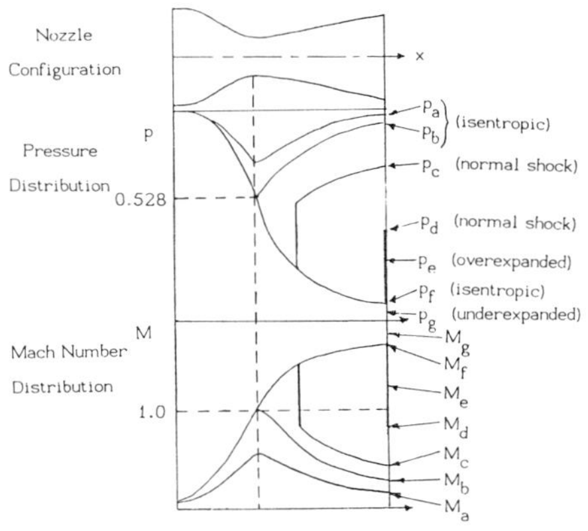

FIG. 8. Exhaust nozzle pressure and Mach number distributions. The pressure $p_e|_{opt}$ corresponds to p_f.

rounding atmospheric pressure, and the overexpanded nozzle, in which the exit pressure is actually lower than atmospheric. If the nozzle is underexpanded, expansion waves necessarily form at the nozzle exit in order to reduce the exhaust pressure beyond the exit, so that it is equivalent to the atmospheric pressure. If the nozzle is overexpanded, oblique or conical shock waves form at the nozzle exit, so that the pressure of the exit flow is increased (after it is exhausted) to be compatible with atmospheric.

C. Nonchemical Rockets

For rocket applications involving large velocity changes, such as in space missions, chemical rockets are limited as an energy source due to the limitation in the degree of heat release associated with the propellant chemical bonds. These rockets are able to attain specific impulses as high as 400–500 sec. Alternative modes of energy generation are possible using a nuclear reactor or an electrical energy input to achieve a higher specific impulse for the engine. In either case, as in the chemical rocket, the acceleration of propellants through an exhaust nozzle creates the high exit velocities needed to maintain high thrust.

In the nuclear-powered rocket, shown schematically in Fig. 3, a gaseous propellant typically passes through a high temperature reactor core, with the propellant temperature raised through heat transfer from the walls of the passages. Nuclear (fission) reactions occurring within the core material typically supply heat to maintain high solid core temperatures. A major limitation in the attainable impulse of this type of rocket, however, is the structural integrity of the rocket casing and cores; temperatures within the core must then be restricted to values that do not cause structural weakening of the rocket. In addition, chemical compatibility of the propellant and the core surfaces is required, lest further structural weakening occur. Nuclear rockets can attain specific impulses as high as 900 sec.

While the nuclear-powered rocket does increase the amount of thrust available to the engine, if the application of manned planetary missions were anticipated, an even greater rocket specific impulse would be required. In this situation, the electrical rocket emerges as the most viable candidate. Electrical rockets can be classified in terms of three major categories: according to thrust generation by electrothermal, electromagnetic, or electrostatic means.

In an electrothermal thrustor within the rocket, electrical energy provided to the thrustor is converted to thermal energy of the propellant; the high temperature propellant is then exhausted from the rocket nozzle. A typical electrothermal thrustor is the arc jet, in which the presence of a cathode and anode in the engine passes an electric current directly through the flow of propellant, thus heating the propellant directly. Arc jets presently can achieve values of I_{sp} up to 1500 sec. A limitation in the design of this type of thrustor is the degree of dissociation or ionization of H_2 that occurs at high temperatures. In the electromagnetic thrustor, an attempt is made to circumvent this limitation by using the interaction of an electrical current and a magnetic field to increase the kinetic energy of the propellant. Current work in this area, however, has determined that most of the electrical energy goes into accelerating the ions, with a much lesser degree of acceleration of the propellant. Finally, the electrostatic thrustor provides a source of ions that is attracted to a highly negatively charged cathode; the beam of ions is then immediately neutralized by electrons supplied by electron emitters, and the neutralized ions are accelerated through the nozzle. Simple calculations here indicate a fundamental limitation here, that even for the very high specific impulses obtained in the engine ($I_{sp} \sim$ 10,000 sec), the thrust per area of the rocket actually becomes quite low. The colloid rocket represents an attempt to alleviate this problem, whereby charged liquid droplets are accelerated in the thrustor, resulting in boiling and the ultimate release of colloid particles that are further charged and accelerated through the nozzle by attachment to the ions present.

III. Air-Breathing Engine Propulsion

A. General Features

As the name implies, air-breathing engines utilize air passing through the device as the working fluid. It is thus the change in the momentum of the fluid (occurring between the entrance and the exit to the engine), in addition to pressure differences, that contribute to the engine's thrust. A modification to the thrust equation [Eq. (1)] appropriate to air-breathing engines takes the form

$$T = A_e(p_e - p_0) + \dot{m}_e u_e - \dot{m}_0 u_0, \quad (2)$$

where now $\dot{m}_0$, p_0, and u_0 refer to flight conditions far upstream of the inlet to the engine. Characteristic parameters commonly used to describe air-breathing engine performance are the air specific impulse $I_{sp}|_a$, the thrust per unit weight flow rate of air, and the specific fuel consumption, the weight flow rate of fuel injected into the engine per unit thrust delivered by the engine.

B. Ideal Cycle Analysis

This type of examination of the performance of an air-breathing engine neglects losses that actually occur in various engine components, with the objective of estimating performance parameters (e.g., thrust, specific fuel consumption) as a function of flight conditions (e.g., Mach number), design limitations (e.g., the maximum turbine inlet temperature), and design choices (e.g., the stagnation temperature ratio across the compressor). Based on the ideal cycle analysis, important relationships may be derived that will assist later in the incorporation of loss factors. Fundamental correlations here will be evolved in terms of stagnation pressure and stagnation temperature ratios across components. For example, with reference to Fig. 5 for the turbojet, the term $\pi_c \equiv p_{t3}/p_{t2}$ represents the stagnation pressure ratio across the compressor, and the term $\tau_t \equiv T_{t5}/T_{t4}$ represents the stagnation temperature ratio across the turbine. Hence, the numbering scheme for stagnation temperatures, pressures, etc., will refer to the stations in a particular engine, while the letter designations (d, c, b, t, etc.) will refer to specific components of a given engine. [*See* FLIGHT (AERODYNAMICS); INTERNAL COMBUSTION ENGINES.]

In the ideal ramjet cycle (Fig. 4), viscous losses occurring in the diffuser, the burner, and the nozzle are neglected. This means that in the diffuser and in the nozzle, isentropic flow is assumed. Accordingly, stagnation temperature and pressure ratios across each of these components are related by the equation $\pi = (\tau)^{\gamma/(\gamma-1)}$, where the value for γ, the ratio of specific heats, is 1.4 for air. The effect of the presence of combustion products and other gases in the exhaust nozzle in terms of altering γ is ignored here. Since in the diffuser and the nozzle there is no shaft work being performed on the working fluid, an isentropic assumption means that $\tau_d = 1 = \pi_d$ and $\tau_n = 1 = \pi_n$. In the burner, an idealization typically made is that heat is added at a constant stagnation pressure, so that $\pi_b = 1$. In addition, the rise in the stagnation temperature of air across the burner is considered to be due only to the heat release from the combustion reaction, which can be written in terms of h, the heating value of the fuel. Finally, an idealized assumption typically made in the analysis of air-breathing engines is that the static pressures at the entrance and the exit to the engine are equal (i.e., $p_0 = p_e$). Hence the thrust developed in the ideal analysis here will result only from an increase in the momentum of the air passing through the engine. As will be seen in the discussion on components, all of these assumptions can break down under certain flight conditions.

Substitution of these idealized assumptions into the fundamental equation for thrust, Eq. (2), allows expressions for the air specific impulse, $I_{sp}|_a$, and the specific fuel consumption (SFC) of the ramjet to be evolved. These are summarized in Table I, where τ_r refers to the recovery temperature ratio, the ratio of the stagnation to the static temperature of the free stream (T_{t0}/T_0), which can be expressed in terms of the flight Mach number M_0. Clearly, in order to maximize $I_{sp}|_a$ (and hence thrust), a large value of τ_b, the stagnation temperature ratio across the burner, is desired. In this ideal analysis, τ_b is a strong function of M_0, so that the air specific impulse for the ramjet is actually a maximum in the Mach number range $2 \leq M_0 \leq 3$. Based on the expression for SFC given in Table I, and the dependence of τ_b on M_0, SFC is minimized in the range $2 \leq M_0 \leq 5$. This ideal cycle analysis then indicates that the operation of the ramjet is optimized for supersonic flight, so that

TABLE I. Performance Parameters for Ideal Air-Breathing Engines

Engine type		
Ramjet	$I_{sp}\vert_a$	$\frac{M_0 a_0}{g}(\tau_b^{1/2} - 1)$
	SFC	$\frac{c_p T_0}{h}\left(\frac{\tau_r(\tau_b - 1)}{I_{sp}\vert_a}\right)$
Turbojet	$I_{sp}\vert_a$	$\frac{M_0 a_0}{g}\left\{\left(\frac{1}{(\tau_r - 1)}\left[\tau_\lambda\left(1 - \frac{1}{\tau_r\tau_c}\right) - \tau_r(\tau_c - 1)\right]\right)^{1/2} - 1\right\}$
	SFC	$\frac{c_p T_0}{h}\left(\frac{\tau_\lambda - \tau_r\tau_c}{I_{sp}\vert_a}\right)$
	τ_t	$1 - \frac{(\tau_c - 1)\tau_r}{\tau_\lambda}$
Turbojet with afterburner	$I_{sp}\vert_a$	$\frac{M_0 a_0}{g}\left\{\left(\frac{\tau_{ab}}{(\tau_r - 1)}\left[\tau_\lambda\left(1 - \frac{1}{\tau_r\tau_c}\right) - \tau_r(\tau_c - 1)\right]\right)^{1/2} - 1\right\}$
	SFC	$\frac{c_p T_0}{h}\left(\frac{(\tau_\lambda - \tau_r\tau_c)\tau_{ab} + \tau_r(\tau_{ab} - 1)}{I_{sp}\vert_a}\right)$
	τ_t	$1 - \frac{(\tau_c - 1)\tau_r}{\tau_\lambda}$
Turbo-bypass	$I_{sp}\vert_a$	$\left(\frac{1}{1+\beta}\right)\frac{M_0 a_0}{g}\left\{\left[\frac{\tau_\lambda}{(\tau_r - 1)}\left(\tau_t - \frac{1}{\tau_r\tau_c}\right)\right]^{1/2} - 1\right\}$ $+ \left(\frac{\beta}{1+\beta}\right)\frac{M_0 a_0}{g}\left\{\left[\frac{(\tau_r\tau_c' - 1)}{(\tau_r - 1)}\tau_b'\right]^{1/2} - 1\right\}$
	SFC	$\frac{1}{(1+\beta)I_{sp}\vert_a}\left(\frac{c_p T_0}{h}\right)\left[(\tau_\lambda - \tau_r\tau_c) + \beta\tau_r\tau_c'(\tau_b' - 1)\right]$
	τ_t	$1 - \frac{\tau_r}{\tau_\lambda}\left[(\tau_c - 1) + \beta(\tau_c' - 1)\right]$
Turbofan	$I_{sp}\vert_a$	$\frac{M_0 a_0}{g}\left\{\left[\frac{\tau_\lambda}{(\tau_r - 1)}\left(\tau_t - \frac{1}{\tau_r\tau_c}\right)\right]^{1/2} - 1\right\}$
	SFC	$\frac{c_p T_0}{h}\left(\frac{\tau_\lambda - \tau_r\tau_c}{I_{sp}\vert_a}\right)$
	τ_t	$\left[1 - \frac{(\tau_c - 1)}{\tau_r\tau_c}\right] - \frac{W_{prop}}{\tau_\lambda c_p T_0}$

this engine would be an appropriate selection for use in supersonic aircraft.

It should be noted here that the ramjet generally operates with the incoming air slowed to subsonic conditions across the diffuser, so that combustion takes place subsonically. With the current interest in the development of very high-speed, high performance air-breathing engines, focus has been placed on the development of a ramjet in which supersonic combustion occurs, known as the scramjet. Scramjets potentially will be able to accommodate much higher flight Mach numbers than for other air-breathing engines. Although diffuser losses can be reduced since the flow does not have to be slowed to subsonic before entering the combustor, excessive thermal loads on solid components such as struts pose serious problems. For this reason, liquid hydrogen fuel is likely to be used as a coolant passing through the struts, so that its latent heat may relieve thermal stresses. The hydrogen finally enters the combustion chamber in the gaseous phase. The combustion process under supersonic conditions is considerably altered from that in ramjets, due to the possibilities of shock formation and dissociation effects. A number of alternative fuel injection schemes are currently under evaluation for use in the scramjet combustor, among them, fuel injection parallel to the direction of (supersonic) air entering the engine, parallel injection of a swirled fuel jet, fuel injection perpendicular to the air stream, and jet injection behind a rearward facing step, which assists in flame stabilization. Optimization of the injection scheme based on stability of the combustion process and minimization of shock losses continues to be sought. Thus supersonic combustion constitutes an important area of the current national research effort.

Cycle analysis for the ideal turbojet engine follows along lines similar to those for the ramjet. In this situation, where rotating components are present, it is assumed that the compressor and turbine each operate isentropically. A fundamental constraint here is that the turbine is used to drive the compressor (without any additional shaft work generated), so that the rise in stagnation temperature across the compressor is proportional to the drop in stagnation temperature across the turbine. This implies that τ_t, the stagnation temperature ratio across the turbine, is actually a dependent variable, shown in Table I for the ideal turbojet. By incorporating the same assumptions for the diffuser, burner, and nozzle as were made in the ideal ramjet analysis, complete expressions for the air specific impulse and specific fuel consumption can be derived (indicated in Table I).

It should be noted that a new variable has been introduced here, τ_λ, the ratio of the stagnation temperature at the turbine entrance to the freestream static temperature, T_{t4}/T_0. τ_λ is actually an important input parameter to the analysis of the turbojet engine, since it represents a limitation in the stagnation temperature that can be present at the turbine inlet, T_{t4}. While a large temperature increase across the burner generally increases the specific impulse for air-breathing engines, the presence of a turbine downstream of the burner limits this temperature rise due to the possibility of degradation of the blades from thermal stresses.

Hence, in determining the performance of a turbojet engine operating ideally, flight conditions are given (u_0 and T_0, yielding M_0 and τ_r), in addition to fuel properties (h) and the constraint on the turbine inlet temperature (τ_λ). The stagnation temperature ratio across the compressor τ_c then becomes an independent variable. In this ideal situation, the value of τ_c that maximizes air specific impulse is given by $\tau_c|_{max} = (\tau_\lambda)^{1/2}/\tau_r$. It becomes clear that this value of τ_c does not produce a minimum in the specific fuel consumption, however, so that in the selected operation of the turbojet, there exists a trade-off between maximizing thrust attained while minimizing fuel utilized. In fact, the value of τ_c here which actually minimizes SFC is one that causes the $I_{sp}|_a$ to become zero; hence in the ideal cycle analysis for the turbojet, it is not possible to obtain an actual minimum in fuel consumption in the useful impulse range.

When an afterburner is added downstream of the turbine in the ideal turbojet cycle (Fig. 5), a capacity for higher specific impulse is achieved. This straightforward analysis is identical to that for the turbojet without the afterburner, with the exception that the total amount of fuel added contributes to heat release and stagnation temperature rise in both the primary burner and the afterburner. Resulting expressions for characteristic performance parameters are indicated in Table I; it should be noted that when the stagnation temperature across the afterburner τ_{ab} exceeds unity, both the air specific impulse and the specific fuel consumption are increased in comparison with values for the simple ideal turbojet. It would thus appear to be profitable to use the afterburner as an auxiliary device only for short periods of high thrust during an aircraft's operation in order to minimize excessive fuel consumption.

In the turbo-bypass engine (Fig. 6) the secondary airstream can be analyzed in the same manner as for the simple turbojet, except for the absence of the turbine. Analysis of the primary air stream is identical to that for the ideal turbojet up until the point at which the turbine and compressor are coupled. In the turbo-bypass engine, the turbine drives the primary as well as the secondary portion of the compressor, so that the stagnation temperature drop across the turbine is balanced by the stagnation temperature rise between stations 2 and 3 and between stations 2′ and 3′. The total impulse for the entire cycle is then a result of the overall change in the momentum of the primary and the secondary air streams, accounting for the fact that a fraction β of the air entering the primary engine actually passes through the secondary portion.

The equations for air-specific impulse and specific fuel consumption in the turbo-bypass engine are given in Table I. It should be noted that these expressions are appropriate to the case where there is no mixing of the exhaust streams (at stations 9 and 9′). The degree of fuel consumption in this bypass engine is significantly reduced in comparison with that for the simple turbojet; for typical operating conditions, SFC is actually minimized when the bypass ratio $\beta \simeq 4$. The specific impulse of the engine, however, is reduced in the turbo-bypass engine when compared with the turbojet.

The turboprop represents an effort to make more efficient use of the power generating capability of the gas turbine engine. In this modified cycle, the shaft power generated by the turbine drives a propeller in addition to running the compressor (see Fig. 7). In general, for air-breathing engines, the propulsive efficiency is increased when the impulse is reduced for a given mass flow of air through the engine. In the turboprop, the propeller upstream of the diffuser is responsible for up to 90% of the total engine thrust, so that the propulsive efficiency is much larger here than in the conventional turbojet. The fuel needed in the rest of the engine is only that required for the turbine to provide sufficient shaft power to the propeller, hence the specific fuel consumption is significantly reduced.

As indicated in Table I, the air specific impulse and specific fuel consumption for the ideal turboprop are the same as those of the ideal turbojet, with the exception that the expression for τ_t is additionally dependent on the work extracted to drive the propeller. A more common performance parameter for the turboprop engine is actually the total work per mass flow available for propulsion (due to the propeller and the turbojet portion of the engine), written as

$$W_t = c_p T_0 \left\{ \tau_\lambda \left(1 - \frac{\chi}{\tau_r \tau_c}\right) - (\tau_c - 1)\tau_r + 2(\tau_r - 1)\left[\left(\frac{\tau_\lambda(\chi - 1)}{\tau_r \tau_c(\tau_r - 1)}\right)^{1/2} - 1\right]\right\}$$

Now $\chi \equiv \tau_r \tau_c \tau_t$ is a variable that can be chosen by the designer to optimize the division of power generation between the propeller and the jet engine. Based on simple differentiation, it becomes clear that the value of χ that maximizes W_t produces a situation in which $u_0 = u_e = u_9$, so that the impulse from the jet engine itself goes to zero. Hence, a consequence of maximizing the propulsive power of the ideal turboprop is that all of the thrust work is produced by the propeller and none by the jet engine. Of course, in order to drive the propeller, the jet engine actually is in operation; when losses in various components are taken into account, performance can be optimized in a more realistic operating regime. Nevertheless, the ideal cycle analysis for the turboprop gives an indication of its power producing capabilities at relatively small fuel consumption rates.

C. Real Cycle Analysis

Thus far, our description of the analysis of the performance of air-breathing engines has assumed ideal behavior in specific components, namely, isentropic flow in all components except for the burner and afterburner, and heat addition at constant stagnation pressure in the combustion process. While this ideal cycle analysis has provided important information concerning the effects of varying certain parameters, in order to represent more closely the real behavior of such engines, losses in each component must be considered.

In the diffuser and the nozzle portions of the air-breathing engine, stagnation pressure losses are the most important real effect requiring description. Since no heat transfer of any significance takes place in either component, the assumption that $\tau_d \simeq \tau_n \simeq 1$ is still reasonable. This is appropriate even in supersonic inlets where oblique or normal shock waves may be present. Thus, in both the diffuser and the nozzle, to represent actual fluid mechanical processes present, a given input of the stagnation pressure ratios π_d and π_n are required, or, alternatively, enough information provided such that these values may be computed.

In the compressor, the actual amount of work done to compress the entering gas is greater than the work that would be done in an ideal, isentropic process. One means of representing losses that occur in the compressor due to viscous effects in the compressor's adiabatic efficiency, η_c, defined as

$$\eta_c = \frac{\text{work required to compress gas through } \pi_c \text{ by an isentropic process}}{\text{work required to compress gas through } \pi_c \text{ by a real process}} = \frac{(\pi_c^{(\gamma-1)/\gamma} - 1)}{\tau_c - 1}$$

In general, data that characterize the real behavior of a compressor are the adiabatic efficiency η_c and the stagnation pressure ratio π_c; the stagnation temperature ratio τ_c then can be determined from the preceding relation.

Similarly, the operation of the turbine is characterized by the stagnation pressure ratio π_t and an adiabatic turbine efficiency η_t. Since the actual amount of work extracted by the turbine is lower than the work extracted in an ideal, isentropic process, the turbine adiabatic efficiency is defined as

$$\eta_t = \frac{\text{actual work extracted by turbine}}{\text{ideal work extracted by turbine}} = \frac{(1 - \tau_t)}{1 - (\pi_t)^{(\gamma-1)/\gamma}}$$

In the burner or afterburner of an air-breathing engine, the combustion process does not actually take place at a constant stagnation pressure. Hence, the parameter π_b (or π_{ab}) is typically specified or calculable in evaluating primary or afterburner performance. In addition, not all of the fuel injected into the combustion system is completely burned in an engine in general. Thus, a burner efficiency η_b can be defined as the ratio of the actual stagnation enthalpy change in the burner to the total heat release possible in the complete combustion reaction. The expression for η_b then reduces to

$$\eta_b = \frac{c_p T_0}{\text{hf}} \tau_r \tau_c (\tau_b - 1)$$

with a similar definition for η_{ab}, the efficiency of the afterburner.

Based on the introduction of efficiencies and other parameters representing the nonideal behavior of individual air-breathing engine components, complete cycle analyses for the actual performance of engines may be evolved as done previously. In the analysis of the cycle with losses, relationships between efficiency, stagnation pressure ratio, and stagnation temperature ratio are utilized now instead of the isentropic relationships used in the ideal analysis. Modifications to the expressions in Table I, accounting for these losses, can be obtained. Clearly, a general trend among these air-breathing engines is that with a less than ideal behavior, the air specific impulse is reduced and the required specific fuel consumption is increased. It should be noted, however, that incorporation of real effects causes the optimal performance for the turbojet and turbofan engines to lie in the useful operating regime, contrary to the ideal formulation.

D. Air-Breathing Engine Components and Performance

In general, air-breathing engines consist of a series of rotating and nonrotating component which act together in a consistent way to achieve an efficient thermodynamic cycle of the working fluid. In order to understand more fully the complex relationships that exist between these components, it is important to describe in detail the operation and behavior of each component in certain operating regimes; the overall matching of components then becomes more tractable.

Among nonrotating components, the inlet acts to retard the incoming airstream to achieve conditions downstream that are more favorable for efficient combustion. This could mean that the inlet slows already subsonic free-stream flow ($M_0 < 1$), as in commercial aircraft engines such as the turbo-bypass, or that the inlet slows supersonic free-stream flow to subsonic ($M_0 > 1$, $M_2 < 1$), as in most applications of the ramjet, or that the inlet slows supersonic free-stream flow to somewhat less supersonic flow ($M_0 > M_2 > 1$), as in the supersonic combustion ramjet (or scramjet). Typical inlet configurations for these alternative modes are shown in Fig. 9.

When the inlet is designed to slow a supersonic free-stream flow to subsonic, two different design methodologies are frequently employed. One, known as the internal compression inlet, compresses the incoming air through a converging–diverging channel (similar to the nozzle configuration), by which air decelerates isentropically to sonic flow at the throat, then decelerates further to subsonic flow at the diffuser exit. The sequence of events necessary to attain this ideal flow situation from engine startup involves a number of complex phenomena and significant losses; hence, the internal compression inlet is typically configured with a variable diffuser geometry. A more common design in supersonic inlets is that in which a central body is present at

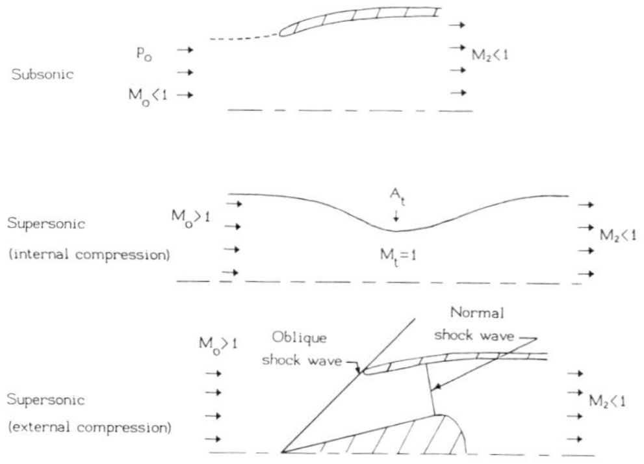

FIG. 9. Typical subsonic and supersonic inlet (diffuser) configurations.

the inlet to form an oblique or conical shock wave as the flow enters the engine. A series of ramps in the central body can actually slow the flow to subsonic with relatively minimal stagnation pressure losses arising from the presence of the shocks.

The principles governing the internal compression inlet or diffuser are similar to those for the exhaust nozzle, in that a converging–diverging channel can ideally be used to decelerate or, in the case of the nozzle, accelerate entering flow. Just as described for the operation of the rocket nozzle, the air-breathing engine nozzle is such that subsonic flow exiting the turbine or afterburner is accelerated to sonic flow at the throat and then accelerated further to supersonic flow as it is exhausted. This is actually the ideal operation of the nozzle. Again, in reality the relationship between the exit pressure of the exhaust gases and the surrounding pressure (or back pressure) plays an important role in determining the presence of nonisentropic phenomena such as shocks.

The last nonrotating component to be considered, the combustion chamber, is the least susceptible of all components to an ideal analysis; this is owed to the inherent complexity of the combustion process. Most of the features of the afterburner follow along similar lines to the present discussion concerning the primary burner. In both combustion situations, heat is added in the chamber to the main flow of the operating fluid (air), which in general results in an increase in the temperature of the flow. Only when the Mach number of the flow entering the combustion chamber is in the range $\gamma^{-1/2} < M < 1$ does the paradoxical situation occur (in theory) in which heat addition leads to a decrease in the temperature of the gas.

The geometry of the combustion chamber, specifically the presence and orientation of bluff bodies or flame holders, has a considerable effect on the burning efficiency. In general, whether the resulting flame structures are laminar or turbulent in nature, it is desired that the flame sheet be oriented at an angle with respect to the main flow through the combustor (see Fig. 10). In this way, higher axial flow speeds entering the burner can be accommodated. It should be noted, however, that if velocity of the entering gas is too high, the flame could blow out or blow off, this occurrence being a function of the fuel type and flame holder type as well. The "bluff body" flame holder also acts to stabilize the (usually turbulent) flame and augment the mixing processes that contribute to flame spread, the consumption of fuel, and the important rise in the stagnation temperature.

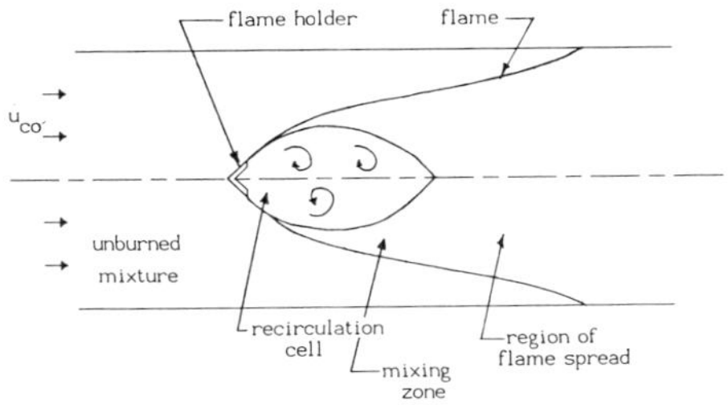

FIG. 10. Schematic diagram of V-gutter bluff body acting as flameholder in air-breathing engine combustor.

Compressors are classified according to their principal direction of flow: axial compressors are such that the main flow is along the axis of rotation, and centrifugal compressors have the flow guided tangentially but with a net radial flow variation. As indicated in previous schematic diagrams, the axial compressor consists of a rotating hub, to which are attached a large number of blades, the rotors, in rows. A similar set of blades, the stators, are attached to the stationary casing of the compressor. The operation of this type of compressor provides an axial pressure gradient. In the centrifugal compressor described in Fig. 11, the rotating member is known as the impeller; the attached curved flow passages induce a tangential flow that sets up a primarily radial pressure gradient and flow variation. The two compressor types are also distinguished by their general performance characteristics: in the axial compressor, a high mass flow per unit frontal area may be accommodated, with a relatively low compression ratio per stage (rotor plus stator); in the centrifugal compressor, a low mass flow per unit frontal area is re-

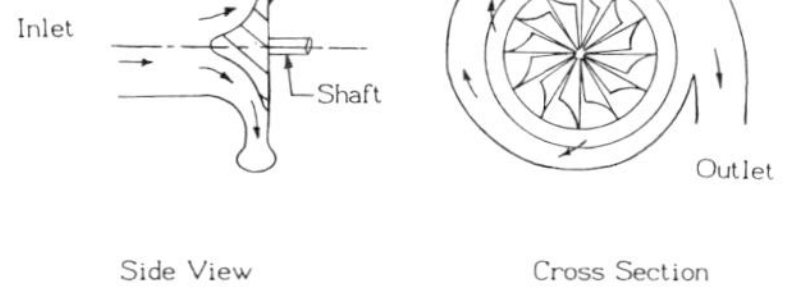

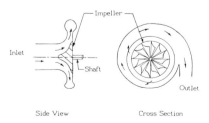

FIG. 11. Schematic diagram of centrifugal compressor. [After Hill and Peterson (1970).]

quired, with a relatively high compression ratio per unit stage. These characteristics make the axial compressor more appropriate for high performance air-breathing engines, whereas the centrifugal compressor is more commonly used in small engines and in automotive applications.

While by definition the flow in the axial compressor is in the direction of the main engine flow, the fact that the flow is turned (tangentially) through the series of rotating and stationary blades actually causes the rise in the stagnation pressure across the compressor to take place. Consider the schematic diagram in Fig. 12, describing in two dimensions the flow through a series of blade rows in the compressor. The first blade row, known as the inlet guide vanes, act to turn the incoming axial flow of velocity V through the angle β_1. When the next blade row, the rotor, rotates with angular velocity ωr as shown, it acts to turn the flow again, in a reference frame relative to the rotor, by the angle θ_r. It is across the rotor that the local rise in the stagnation pressure takes place. After passing through the rotor blade row, the flow continues through another stationary blade row, the stator. The stator acts to turn the flow again, so that it is prepared to enter the next rotor blade row, across which an additional stagnation pressure rise will occur, and so on. The actual compressor configuration may consist of a large number of rotor–stator pairs until the flow exits to the burner. When losses are taken into account, the complete performance of the compressor is described by a compressor map, a graphical representation of the overall stagnation pressure rise as a function of the flow rate of air entering the component, of the rate of rotation of the rotor blades, and of the adiabatic efficiency of the compressor.

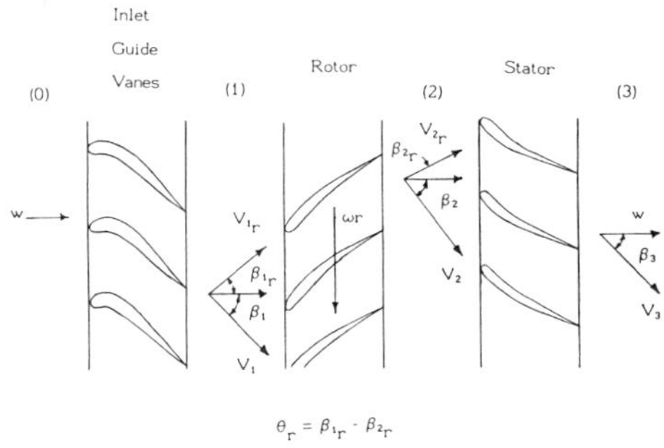

FIG. 12. Typical blade diagram for flow through axial compressor.

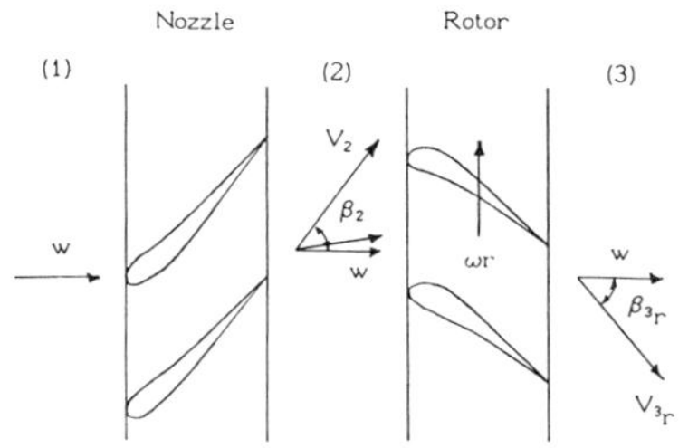

FIG. 13. Typical blade diagram for flow through axial turbine.

The operation of the axial turbine is similar in terms of blading characteristics to the axial compressor. The turbine typically consists of a stationary blade row known as the nozzle, which acts to turn the incoming hot gases, and a rotating blade row, also called the rotor. The orientation of the blades, as sketched in Fig. 13, is such that the rotation causes a net decrease in the stagnation pressure across the turbine, appropriate in an expansion process. A turbine map is the representation of the overall performance of the turbine, relating stagnation pressure ratio, flow rate, rotational speed, and adiabatic efficiency.

Once the configuration and performance characteristics of individual engine components are specified, it becomes necessary to match the overall operation of the engine components in a consistent manner. For example, conditions typically used to match engine components are that (1) the rotational speed of the axial compressor must equal the rotational speed of the turbine, since the turbine drives the compressor; (2) the mass flow of air is conserved through the engine (unless additional air is bled in); and (3) the rate of work delivered by the turbine is equal to the rate of work absorbed by the compressor. An iterative type of solution for the design and off-design performance of the entire engine is then required, resulting in the dependence of certain pumping characteristics (e.g., an overall generator stagnation pressure ratio $\pi_e \equiv \pi_c \pi_b \pi_t$) on input characteristics such as rotational speed and fuel type. These pumping characteristics allow for a more complete method of determining the air-specific impulse, thrust, and specific fuel consumption for a given air-breathing engine.

E. Engine Noise

Among the fundamental problems associated with air-breathing engines is jet noise. Since the engine cycles described here are open (air enters the engine and exits to the atmosphere), there is low frequency noise associated with the acoustic energy from gas emissions, as well as noise associated with instabilities in the rotating machinery. In either instance, noise generation is due to the inherent unsteadiness and compressibility effects of the fluid motion.

A major advance in noise reduction in aircraft engines has been achieved through the development of the high bypass turbofan (or turbo-bypass) engine. Not only is this cycle more fuel-efficient than most, but the engine is inherently less noisy due to the following factors:

1. Rotor–stator interactions in the compressor are reduced by limiting the number of blade rows present.
2. Spacing between blade rows is increased (although there exits a trade-off here with ultimate engine weight).
3. The interior wall of the engine is porous in order to absorb acoustic energy.
4. With a high degree of bypass, the exit velocity from the main part of the engine is reduced, thus reducing the degree of turbulence generation, which is the major source of jet noise.
5. The exhaust nozzle is designed to increase the degree of mixing inside the engine in order to reduce the amount of external mixing needed, thus decreasing the accompanying noise generation. This enhanced mixing is typically achieved by alternative nozzle cross-sections, such as in the so-called daisy suppressor design.

Bibliography

Hill, P. G., and Peterson, C. R. (1970). "Mechanics and Thermodynamics of Propulsion." Addison-Wesley, Reading, Massachusetts.

Kerrebrock, J. L. (1977). "Aircraft Engines and Gas Turbines." MIT Press, Cambridge, Massachusetts.

Loh, W. H. T. (1968). "Jet, Rocket, Nuclear and Electric Propulsion: Theory and Design." Springer-Verlag, New York.

Oates, G. C. (1984). "Aerothermodynamics of Gas Turbine and Rocket Propulsion." American Institute of Aeronautics and Astronautics Education Series, New York.

Oates, G. C. (ed.) (1985). "Aerothermodynamics of Aircraft Engine Components." American Institute of Aeronautics and Astronautics Education Series, New York.

Sutton, G. P. (1986). "Rocket Propulsion Elements," 5th ed. Wiley (Interscience), New York.

K

KALMAN FILTERS AND NONLINEAR FILTERS

Vytas B. Gylys *Texas Instruments Inc.*

GLOSSARY

Brownian motion process: Process $\{x_t\}$, $t \geq 0$ is a (scalar) *constant-diffusion Brownian motion process* if (a) $\{x_t\}$ is a process with independent increments and (b) for any nonnegative t_1 and t_2, the increments $(x_{t_1} - x_{t_2})$ are Gaussian random variables with $E[(x_{t_1} - x_{t_2})] = 0$ and $E[(x_{t_1} - x_{t_2})^2] = q|t_1 - t_2|$, where $q > 0$.

Covariance function of a stochastic process: If $\{x_t\}$ is a second-order, scalar- or vector-valued process (that is, if $E[x_t x_t^{\mathrm{T}}] < \infty$ for every t in the parameter space T_0), its covariance function is defined as

$$R(t, s) = E[(x_t - Ex_t)(x_s - Ex_s)^{\mathrm{T}}]$$

for all t, s in the parameter set T_0. This function is also known as the autocovariance function of the process.

Estimation: Process of observing the values taken on by random measurements and using these measurements to compute (with the assistance of an estimator) the values of some unknown parameters expressible as functions of measurements. In this article, the term *estimation* is used synonymously with *filtering*. See also Estimator.

Estimator: An estimator $\hat{\theta}$ of some θ from a parameter space Θ is a function of random measurements $M_k \equiv \{m_0, m_1, \ldots, m_k\}$ (and hence itself is a random variable) constructed for inferring the unknown value of θ. The value taken on by the estimator of θ *after* the observation of a particular set of measurements is called an *estimate* of θ. To be consistent with the notational conventions set up for this article, we do not distinguish notationally between an estimator (a random variable) and a resulting estimate (a value taken on by this random variable as a function of actually observed measurements). The term *estimator* in this article also refers to a computational procedure (algorithm) for computing estimates. In general, it is used synonymously with the term *filter*.

Extended Kalman filter (EKF): Nonlinear filter (for a system with nonlinearities in the dynamics equation or in the measurement equation of its model) that relinearizes at each measurement update time t_k the nonlinear parts of the system model, while using a vector-valued Taylor expansion around some reference trajectory $\{s_{0k}; k = 0, 1, \ldots\}$, and then applies Kalman filter equations. The reference trajectory used is obtained at each t_k from $\hat{s}_{k-1\,|\,k-1}$ (for the computation of $\hat{s}_{k\,|\,k-1}$ and $P_{k\,|\,k-1}$) and then from $\hat{s}_{k\,|\,k-1}$ (for the computation of $\hat{s}_{k\,|\,k}$ and $P_{k\,|\,k}$). Here, $\hat{s}_{k\,|\,j}$ and $P_{k\,|\,j}$, with $k \geq j$, denote the minimum-mean-square-error estimates of the state and the state error covariance matrix based on measurements $\{m_0, m_1, \ldots, m_j\}$. The discrete-time EKF algorithm is defined in terms of Eqs. (36)–(44) in the text. A slightly different version of the linearized extension of the Kalman filter is obtained by linearizing the model around some known trajectory. This version is often called a linearized Kalman filter (LKF).

Gaussian process: A scalar- or vector-valued stochastic process $\{x_t\}$ is said to be Gaussian if for every finite subset $(t_1, t_2, \ldots, t_n)$ of points from the parameter set T_0, random variables $(x_{t_1}, x_{t_2}, \ldots, x_{t_n})$ are jointly Gaussian; that is, jointly they are distributed as a

Gaussian random variable. It follows from the properties of Gaussian distribution that all finite-dimensional distributions of a Gaussian process $\{x_t\}$ are completely specified by its means $\bar{x}_t \equiv E[x_t]$ and its covariance functions $R(t, s) = E[(x_t - \bar{x}_t)(x_s - \bar{x}_s)^{\mathrm{T}}]$.

Linear system model: Model in which both the stochastic differential (or difference) equations of system dynamics and the measurement equations relating the system state to the noisy measurements of the system are linear equations with respect to the state, measurement, and noise vectors. The discrete-time linear system model, considered in this article for the Kalman filter and other related estimation schemes, is defined in the text in terms of Eqs. (2) and (3) and Assumptions 1D and 4D.

Markov process: A process $\{x_t\}$ is a kth-order Markov process if for all $t_1 < t_2 < \cdots < t_n$ in the parameter set T_0 and some fixed integer k $(1 \leq k < n)$, the conditional probability $p[x_{t_n} < b_n \mid x_{t_1} = b_1, \ldots, x_{t_{n-1}} = b_{n-1}] = p[x_{t_n} < b_n \mid x_{t_{n-k}} = b_{n-k}, \ldots, x_{t_{n-1}} = b_{n-1}]$ holds for all n-tuples of real numbers $(b_1, b_2, \ldots, b_n)$. The forgetting-of-the-remote-past property of process $\{x_t\}$, defined by the above probability statement, is called the Markov property.

Minimum-mean-square-error (MMSE) estimator: An estimator $\hat{\theta}$ of some parameter θ (fixed or random) from a parameter space is said to be a minimum-mean-square-error estimator of θ based (conditioned) on measurements $M_k \equiv \{m_0, m_1, \ldots, m_k\}$, if

$$E[(\hat{\theta} - \theta)(\hat{\theta} - \theta)^{\mathrm{T}} \mid M_k] \leq E[(\hat{\theta}_0 - \theta)(\hat{\theta}_0 - \theta)^{\mathrm{T}} \mid M_k]$$

where $\hat{\theta}_0$ is any other estimator of θ. If θ and M_k are two jointly distributed random variables, it can be shown that the MMSE estimator $\hat{\theta}$ must be of the form $E[\theta \mid M_k]$; that is, $\hat{\theta}$ is a conditional mean estimator.

Noise process: Zero-mean stochastic process.

Positive definite and positive semidefinite matrices: Matrix B is *positive definite* if and only if $x^{\mathrm{T}}Bx > 0$ for all nonzero vectors x of compatible length; B is *positive semidefinite* if and only if $x^{\mathrm{T}}Bx \geq 0$ for all nonzero vectors x of compatible size.

Process with independent increments: Process $\{x_t\}$ such that, for every ordered set

$$t_0 < t_1 < t_2 < \cdots < t_n$$

of parameter values from the parameter set T_0, the random variables $(x_{t_k} - x_{t_{k-1}})$ are mutually independent for $k = 1, 2, \ldots, n$.

Recursive estimation of system state: Estimation scheme that does not require that all past measurements of the system and the past system state data be saved for estimation of the current state. To estimate the current system state, a typical recursive estimator uses only the current measurements and the most recent estimate of the system state. In a more general case, a recursive estimator may use a finite, fixed-size set of most recent measurements and system state estimates. This property greatly facilitates the implementation of a recursive estimator for real-time operation on a digital computer. Nearly all filters considered in this article, including the Kalman filter, are recursive estimators.

Second-order process: Scalar- or vector-valued stochastic process $\{x_t\}$ such that $E[x_t x_t^{\mathrm{T}}] < \infty$ for every t in the parameter set T_0.

Square root filtering: Collection of related computational algorithms for (measurement) updating, in a numerically stable manner, of estimates P of the state error covariance matrix in a Kalman filter and for computing the filter gain matrix. These algorithms utilize a result from matrix theory, according to which any nonnegative definite symmetric P can be factored as $P = SS^{\mathrm{T}}$, where S is usually a square matrix that is not necessarily nonnegative definite symmetric.

Stationary process: A process $\{x_t\}$ is said to be stationary if for any set of values $t_1, t_2, \ldots, t_n$ from the parameter set T_0 and for any t_0 such that $t_j + t_0$ is in T_0 *for all* $j = 1, \ldots, n$, the joint distribution of $(x_{t_j}, j = 1, 2, \ldots, n)$ is identical to that of $(x_{t_j + t_0}, j = 1, 2, \ldots, n)$.

System measurements: Sets of noisy measurements of the system. Each measurement set is associated with some instant or interval of time and contains the measured values, corrupted by random noise, of all (or of a selected subset of) observable system outputs. For example, if the sensor tracking an aircraft is a radar, the set of measurements obtained at the sampling epoch t_k may consist of the range and range-rate measurements at t_k.

System measurement *m*: A vector that contains the values of system measurements, which are assumed to be noisy and associated with some instant of time. In this article, the letter m is reserved for the measurement vector. In particular, m_t or $m(t)$ refers to the measurement vector m at time t; m_k refers to m at a discrete sampling epoch t_k. The measurement vector has two interpretations: Either it represents a scalar or vector-valued random variable (RV), or it represents actually observed values taken on by this RV. Notationally we do not distinguish between these two meanings of m.

System model (in recursive filtering): Mathematical specification of those characteristics of a system that pertain to the construction of a recursive filtering scheme for the system. Suppose that at any instant of time the state of a system is specified by a vector-valued quantity, known as the state vector. Then the model of such a system typically consists of (a) vector-valued stochastic differential (or difference) equations that specify the dynamics (evolution) of system state with respect to time, (b) vector-valued measurement equations that relate the system state to the noisy measurements of the system, and (c) probabilistic assumptions that specify the distributions of three stochastic components in the system model (the process noise term in system dynamics equations, the measurement noise term in measurement equations, and the initial distribution of state) and the probabilistic interdependence among these components. Often the process noise and the measurement noise terms additively enter the system dynamics and the measurement equations, respectively.

System state: Complete, quantitative, typically time-dependent description of the system at some instant of time. What constitutes a complete description depends on the purpose for which the information about the system state is to be used. For example, if one is interested in predicting into the near future the position and the velocity of a particle moving in a known gravitational field, it may suffice only to specify for the particle the current values of its position coordinates and its velocity and acceleration vectors relative to some suitable coordinate frame.

(System) state vector s: Data array, usually structured as a vector, that contains the quantitative description of the system state at some time point. In this article, the letter s denotes the system state vector. In particular, s_t or $s(t)$ refers to the state vectors at time t; s_k refers to s at a discrete sampling epoch t_k. Note that the state vector has two interpretations: Either it represents a random vector [then it is a vector-valued random variable (RV)] or it represents a vector of specific values taken on by this RV. Notationally we do not distinguish between these two meanings of s.

Unbiased estimator: An estimator $\hat{\theta}$ of some θ from a parameter space is said to be unbiased if $E[\hat{\theta}] = \theta$.

White noise process: White process $\{x_t\}$ such that $E[x_t] = 0$ for all t.

White process: Scalar- or vector-valued, wide-sense stationary stochastic process $\{x_t\}$ with $E[x_t] = \bar{x}$ for all t and the covariance function defined by

$$E[(x_t - \bar{x})(x_s - \bar{x})^{\mathrm{T}}] = C\delta(t - s)$$

where constant C is a positive scalar or a positive definite matrix and $\delta(\cdot)$ denotes the Dirac delta function defined by the property

$$\delta(t) = 0 \text{ for } t \neq 0 \text{ and}$$

$$\int_{-\infty}^{\infty} \delta(t)\, f(t)\, dt = f(0)$$

for all functions f continuous at 0. Thus, the above definition requires $\{x_t\}$ to be an uncorrelated process with respect to t, while each x_t may be a vector-valued random variable with a nonzero covariance matrix $E[(x_t - \bar{x})(x_t - \bar{x})^{\mathrm{T}}] = C$. This definition of white process is not unique. For example, some authors replace the wide-sense stationarity assumption with the less restrictive "second-order process" property. In such a case, the time-invariant fixed (scalar or matrix) C, appearing above in the definition of covariance structure, is replaced by C_t, that is, with a fixed (i.e., nonrandom) scalar or matrix that may vary with time. In this article, we define (for operational convenience) a discrete-time white process $\{x_t\}$ by requiring only that x_t and x_s be independent random variables for any $t \neq s$.

Wide-sense stationary process: Scalar- or vector-valued, second-order stochastic process $\{x_t\}$ such that (a) its mean $\bar{x} \equiv E[x_t]$ is independent of t and (b) its covariance function

$$R(t, s) \equiv E[(x_t - \bar{x})(x_s - \bar{x})^{\mathrm{T}}]$$

is a function of only the difference $t - s$, that is, $R(t, s) \equiv R_0(t - s)$.

Filtering of a stochastic dynamic system (i.e., a system the dynamics of which can be adequately described by means of a mathematical model containing stochastic components and possessing certain well-defined properties) is a process of estimating the current state of the system while utilizing the recent estimates as well as the past and current measurements (observations) of the system. The system model used in the filtering process describes the system dynamics by means of stochastic differential or stochastic difference equations and contains a transformation relating the system state to the measurements. These measurements are assumed to be noisy. The system dynamics part of the model may also be noisy.

A Kalman filter is a recursive, unbiased, minimum-mean-square-error (MMSE) estimator that uses linear models for system dynamics and state-to-measurement transformation. Both the dynamics part of the model and the state-to-measurement transformation incorporate the noise through additive stochastic components (terms). *Recursive* here means that new estimates are produced iteratively throughout the period of observation and that only the current and recent knowledge about the system is used to estimate its current state.

Nonlinear filters considered in this article are estimators of systems that can be adequately described only by means of nonlinear models. Such filters are often constructed by linearizing locally the system model and then applying a Kalman filter to this model.

I. Introduction

A. Filtering

Originally the term *filtering* was adopted in electrical engineering to refer to that aspect of signal processing which is concerned with the removal from signal of unwanted components such as noise. Until the advent of digital technology, especially of digital computers, filtering was performed exclusively by means of electrical circuits or devices called filters. A filter was tagged as linear or nonlinear depending on the type of circuits or devices (linear or nonlinear) from which it was built.

Presently the term *filtering* also refers to one of the three basic modes of information processing: filtering or estimation, smoothing, and prediction. Consider, for example, the description of the state of a time-varying system expressed in terms of a scalar or a vector quantity s. We shall call s the system state. Suppose that this system is observed (measured) by means of noisy measurements m, which like s may also be scalar- or vector-valued. (The letter t in this article always represents the time viewed as a variable. Specific values of t will be indicated by means of a superscript or a subscript appended to t; in particular, t_0 will always denote the initial time.) We assume that s and m are related for all $t \geq t_0$ through the expression

$$m(t) = h[s(t)] + v(t)$$

where h is a function mapping $s(t)$ into $[m(t) - v(t)]$ and v represents the unobservable measurement noise (zero mean random error). For example, consider a particle moving in the xy plane. Assume that the state of the particle at time t is adequately described by means of its position coordinates (x, y) and the corresponding velocity components $(\dot{x}, \dot{y})$. Then the state vector $s \equiv s(t)$ can be written as $s^{\mathrm{T}} = (x, y, \dot{x}, \dot{y})$. Suppose that the system is observed at discrete time epochs $t_0, t_1, t_2, \ldots$ and that at each t_j one measures the polar coordinates (r, θ) of the particle. Thus, the measurement equation can be written

$$r = (x^2 + y^2)^{1/2} + v_1 \quad \text{and} \quad \theta = \arctan(y/x) + v_2$$

where v_1 and v_2 represent the noise associated with the measurements of r and θ, respectively.

We shall use the terms *filtering* and *estimation* synonymously to describe inference about the value $s(t')$ of s at epoch t', which utilizes all information contained in measurements $m(t)$ accumulated over the period $t_0 \leq t \leq t'$. The term *smoothing* will refer to recovery of the value $s(t')$ of s at time $t'(<t_e)$ from measurements $m(t)$ accumulated over the period $t_0 \leq t \leq t_e$. Finally, the term *prediction* will refer to inference about the value $s(t')$ of s at time $t'(>t_e)$ made on the basis of measurements $m(t)$ accumulated over the period $t_0 \leq t \leq t_e$. This terminology is not completely universal; some authors use the term *estimation* to refer collectively to all three above-defined activities—filtering, smoothing, and prediction.

In general we shall write $\hat{s}_{t'|t_e}$ to denote the value of $s(t')$ inferred from the measurements $m(t)$ accumulated over the time period $t_0 \leq t \leq t_e$. Thus, $\hat{s}_{t'|t_e}$ will represent an estimate (or a filtered value) of $s(t')$ if $t_e = t'$; a smoothened value of $s(t')$ if $t_e > t'$; and a predicted value of $s(t')$ if $t_e < t'$. In the case of measurements sampled at discrete epochs $t_k (k = 0, 1, 2, \ldots)$, if $t' =$

t_j and $t_e = t_h$, we shall simplify this notation by writing $\hat{s}_{j|h}$.

B. Historical Connections

The origins of the Kalman filter can be traced back to the ideas on least squares estimation formulated by K. F. Gauss. (Gauss first applied the estimation method around 1795, but his first published account of it appeared only around 1810.) He considered the problem of estimating essentially constant parameters of planetary orbits from noisy observations and derived a recursive estimation procedure for updating past estimates, without having to discard them, on the basis of newly available measurements. However, his recursive least squares estimation method did not apply to a situation in which the estimated parameters would dynamically evolve over time. The extension of recursive estimation to dynamic system models is relatively recent.

Between the 1930s and 1960s three major developments made a strong impact on the state of signal processing: (a) the advent of digital technology (digital circuits, devices, and stored-program computers); (b) advances in mathematics and in its application to the theory of linear systems, in particular to communication and control systems; and (c) the infusion of statistical and probabilistic ideas into the theory of these systems. These advances were further stimulated by the demands of World War II and the geopolitical situation after the war. The Wiener filter is a well-known example from that era.

With the emergence of digital technology after World War II, it became possible for the first time and economically attractive to process complex signals digitally in real-time. These advances in hardware had a revolutionary effect on both the theory and the implementation of filters. Software started to replace hardware as the medium of implementation; research shifted toward construction of algorithms for digital computing. The fast Fourier transform and the Kalman filter are examples of algorithms that were specifically designed for or naturally lend themselves to implementation on a digital computer. (To be precise, one should conceptually distinguish between an algorithm, the function it computes or approximates, and the applications for which it is used. Viewed as a mathematical function, the filters considered in this article are stochastic estimators of the system state. However, we shall often refer to them as algorithms and use expressions such as "the Kalman filter algorithm," especially when the function itself clearly indicates a computational procedure.)

The period between the turn of the century and the beginning of World War II witnessed important advances in the evolution of mathematics, especially in the generalization and abstraction of mathematical concepts, which later had an impact on the development of estimation theory and digital technology. Algebra, topology, functional analysis, and mathematical logic are a few examples of these developments. Two noteworthy developments from that era that were later used in filtering theory were (a) the formulation by A. N. Kolmogorov of the axiomatic theory of probability, based on the new theories of measure and (Lebesque) integration; and (b) the emergence of a generalized theory of linear spaces and operators. Mathematical measure and integration theories unified the conceptual setup of discrete and continuous probability spaces; they also furnished powerful tools, in the form of convergence theorems, for dealing with sequences of random variables. Axiomatic probability theory very soon led to a flurry of results in the theory of stochastic processes and in the application of this theory to practical areas such as time series analysis.

C. Wiener Filter

The injection of probabilistic and statistical ideas into the filtering and control theories not only changed the view of how a system driven by randomly perturbed signals and observed by means of noisy measurements should be modeled, but also provided the tools for estimating the behavior of such systems. Wiener filtering stands as a major milestone in this process of adoption of the statistical approach to filtering and control. The basic problem considered in the 1940s by N. Wiener was as follows. Suppose that $\{x_t\}$ and $\{y_t\}$, where $-\infty < t < \infty$, represent two zero-mean, jointly wide-sense stationary stochastic processes with *known* joint autocovariances and cross-covariances. More precisely stated,

$$y_t = x_t + v_t, \qquad -\infty < t < t_f$$

where

$$\begin{aligned} E[v_t v_s^{\mathrm{T}}] &= I_p \delta(t - s) \\ E[x_t v_s^{\mathrm{T}}] &= \text{arbitrary}, \qquad t \geq s \\ &= 0, \qquad t < s \end{aligned}$$

and $\delta(\cdot)$ represents the Dirac delta function defined by the property

$$\delta(t) = 0 \text{ for } t \neq 0 \text{ and}$$
$$\int_{-\infty}^{\infty} \delta(t)\, f(t)\, dt = f(0) \qquad (1)$$

for all functions f continuous at 0.

Here y_t, x_t, v_t represent p-valued vectors (Wiener originally considered only the scalar-valued case with $p = 1$) and I_p is $p \times p$ identity matrix. Given sample observations $\{y_t(\omega), t_0 < t < t_f\}$ of process $\{y_t\}$, the problem is to find the MMSE estimate $\hat{x}(t_f + \Delta t \mid t_f)$ of x at time $t_f + \Delta t$ for some fixed Δt (≥ 0). It turns out that the task is to find a function $h(t)$ so that, for $t_0 < t_f < \infty$,

$$\hat{x}(t_f + \Delta t) = \int_{t_0}^{t_f} h(t_f - t')y(t')\, dt'$$

and the expectation $E[(\hat{x}(t_f + \Delta t) - x(t_f + \Delta t))^2]$ is minimized.

Wiener explicitly solved the above-stated estimation problem under the assumptions of a scalar observation process ($p = 1$) and a semiinfinite observation time interval ($t_0 = -\infty$). He handled this problem in the frequency domain by showing how to find a closed-form solution to a causal transfer function, say H, of h.

Actually, the optimal filtering theory, now known as the Wiener filter (WF), was independently and at about the same time developed both by N. Wiener and A. N. Kolmogorov. Whereas the continuous-time theory is mainly Wiener's work, Kolmogorov is credited with the development of its discrete-time version. He introduced the notion of innovation sequence (a discrete-time white stochastic process associated with the measurement process, which we shall elaborate in our discussion of the Kalman filter) as a technique for orthogonalizing the data and then exploited the idea of orthogonal projections to simplify the estimation problem. These ideas were utilized years later to attain another view and deepen the understanding of the Kalman filter.

The publication of Wiener's work after World War II triggered a flurry of research in the 1950s and early 1960s. Attempts were made with some success to weaken (generalize) the underlying mathematical assumptions and to derive filtering schemes that would satisfy the requirements of the practical applications of that time period. Consequently, results were obtained extending the WF to nonstationary processes, to vector-valued processes, and to finite time intervals of observation. Despite these theoretical successes certain difficulties with the WF remained. More precisely, (a) the results were mathematically complicated and thus were difficult to implement while using the signal-processing hardware of that period; (b) the WF did not lend itself easily to recursive estimation in which the estimates would be updated (improved) with each new batch of data—for example, with each pass of an earth satellite over the view of a tracking station; (c) implementational difficulties with the estimation of vector-valued processes persisted. Furthermore, for some applications, certain theoretical assumptions made in the formulation of the WF (such as the wide-sense stationarity of stochastic processes, the existence of spectral densities, or the knowledge of second-order moments) fail to hold. For example, the stochastic components of dynamic systems typically are nonstationary. Most important, the WF, being a product of the era of analog hardware, did not lend itself easily to the newly emerging mode of processing on a stored-program digital computer with finite memory and limited throughput capacity. The aerospace signal-processing problems in the 1950s started to point to the need for a robust algorithm for recursive estimation of vector-valued processes in dynamic systems, with the observations made and estimates updated at discrete time epochs. Furthermore, such an algorithm was to be implemented for real-time processing on a still primitive digital computer. The Kalman filter (KF) turned out to be an answer to these needs.

D. Transition to State-Variable-Based Filtering

Although the use of state variables rather than impulse response is now largely credited to R. Kalman, P. Swerling actually was the first person (in a 1959 journal article) to describe an estimation scheme that essentially was identical to that presented the next year by Kalman. One reason for crediting Kalman with what today is known as the Kalman filter was that subsequently Kalman extended his results considerably beyond those obtained by Swerling.

In addition to practical applications of linear filtering theory developed in the 1960s, foundations for nonlinear estimation were laid during the same period. At the time when Kalman's (and also R. C. Bucy's) work was becoming known in the West, R. L. Stratonovich in the Soviet Union published results on his pioneering work in nonlinear estimation, that is, recursive estimation of the states of a nonlinear system driven by white noise. He also looked into the linearized system model and, while doing this, obtained in 1960 the KF equations. Though Stratonovich's work in nonlinear estimation remained unknown for a while in the West, some of his results were independently replicated in early 1960s by H. J. Kushner and W. M. Wonham.

II. Linear Estimation Problem and Kalman Filters

The KF is a recursive, unbiased, MMSE estimator of the state s of a dynamic system observed (i.e., measured) by means of noisy measurements m. In general, both s and m are vector-valued. This system is assumed to be linear in the sense that (a) the dynamics of state s is described in terms of linear differential or difference equations that may be additively perturbed by a random process, called process noise; and (b) noisy measurements m are related to the state s by means of a linear transformation.

A. Discrete-Time Linear System Model

The system model used by Kalman is roughly of the following form. For $t_{k+1} = t_k + \Delta t_k$ ($\Delta t_k > 0$ and $k = 0, 1, 2, \ldots$),

$$s_k = \Phi_{k-1} s_{k-1} + B_{k-1} u_{k-1} + G_{k-1} w_{k-1}, \quad k = 1, 2, 3, \ldots \tag{2}$$

and

$$m_k = H_k s_k + v_k, \qquad k = 0, 1, 2, \ldots \tag{3}$$

Equation (2) is called the system dynamics equation, and Eq. (3) the measurement equation. Subscript k refers to the kth sampling epoch t_k. Then s_k denotes the value of state at time t_k. $\{w_k, k = 0, 1, 2, \ldots\}$, or simply written $\{w_k\}$, is a random sequence (a discrete-time stochastic process) that represents the process noise, also known as the input, driving, or plant noise of process $\{s_k\}$. The $\{m_k\}$ represents the measurements, also known as the ouput process, which at time t_k are perturbed by random noise v_k. Matrix (operator) Φ_{k-1}, which propagates the state from time t_{k-1} to t_k, is called the system state transition matrix. The optional term $B_{k-1}u_{k-1}$ represents deterministic control inputs with $\{u_k\}$ being a known sequence. Matrix H_k defines the state-to-measurement transformation at t_k. The subscripts attached to Φ, B, G, and H indicate that these matrices may vary over time. It is assumed that these matrices are a priori known; that is, they do not depend on estimates of s or on measurements m.

As already noted the random processes $\{w_k\}$, $\{v_k\}$, $\{s_k\}$, and $\{m_k\}$ usually are vector-valued. We use n_s to denote the length of vector s_k and n_m to denote the lengths of v_k and m_k. As a special case we may have $n_s = 1$ or $n_m = 1$.

Notationally, we will *not* distinguish between scalar-valued and vector-valued quantities. Upper-case letters, English or Greek, will be reserved mainly for matrices (operators). We will also notationally not distinguish between the random variables (RVs), or random functions, and the specific values taken on by these RVs. For example, depending on the context, w_k will denote either the RV representing the process noise at t_k or a specific value taken by this RV.

The system model given by Eqs. (2) and (3) is incomplete unless we specify the underlying probabilistic assumptions, which are as follows:

ASSUMPTION 1D. The process noise $\{w_k\}$ is a zero-mean, Gaussian (normal), white process with the covariance matrix

$$E[w_k w_j^{\mathrm{T}}] = Q_k \, \delta_{kj} \tag{4}$$

where Q_k is a *known* $n_s \times n_s$ nonnegative definite matrix and δ_{kj} denotes the Kronecker delta, that is, $\delta_{kj} = 1$ if $k = j$, else $\delta_{kj} = 0$. (If $\{w_k\}$ is absent from the system model for some or all k, then for each such k, Q_k may be thought of as being a zero matrix.)

ASSUMPTION 2D. The measurement noise $\{v_k\}$ is a zero-mean, Gaussian, white process with the covariance matrix

$$E[v_k v_j^{\mathrm{T}}] = R_k \, \delta_{kj} \tag{5}$$

where R_k denotes a *known* $n_m \times n_m$ positive definite matrix, and δ_{kj} is the Kronecker delta.

ASSUMPTION 3D. For all k and j, v_k and w_j are statistically independent RVs.

ASSUMPTION 4D. The value s_0 of system state s at the starting time t_0 is a Gaussian RV whose mean $\bar{s}_0$ and covariance matrix Σ_0, that is,

$$\bar{s}_0 \equiv E[s_0] \text{ and } \Sigma_0 \equiv E[(s_0 - \bar{s}_0)(s_0 - \bar{s}_0)^{\mathrm{T}}] \tag{6}$$

are known. Furthermore, the RV s_0 is statistically independent of RVs w_k and v_k for all $k \geq 0$.

In Assumptions 1D–4D, the letter "D" indicates discrete-time. In this article, a discrete-time white process is defined to be a discrete-time stochastic process, say $\{x_i\}$, for which x_k and x_j are statistically independent RVs whenever $k \neq j$. Collectively, all a priori distributional assumptions concerning the random components (s_0, $\{w_k\}$, and $\{v_k\}$) of the model will be referred to as the a priori probability assumptions, or simply as the a priori probabilities. All above-stated assumptions of Gaussian distribution, taken together, will be referred to as the Gaussianity assumption. As a relaxation of the original assumptions in Wiener filtering, Assumptions 1D–4D do not require $\{w_k\}$ or $\{v_k\}$ to be a stationary process in the sense that matrices Q_k and R_k may be time dependent.

B. Properties

The system model defined in terms of Eqs. (2) and (3), restricted by the distributional assumptions (1D–4D), has the following easily verifiable properties:

a. System state s_k (for $k = 1, 2, \ldots$) can be expressed as

$$s_k = \Phi_{k,0} s_0 + \sum_{i=0}^{k-1} \Phi_{k,i+1}(B_i u_i + G_i w_i)$$

where the multistep state transition matrix $\Phi_{k,j}$, defined in terms of the single-step state transition matrix Φ_i as $\Phi_{i+1,i} \equiv \Phi_i$, possesses the following properties:

(i) $\Phi_{k,k} \equiv I_s (= n_s \times n_s \text{ identity matrix})$

(ii) $\Phi_{k,j} = \Phi_{k-1}\Phi_{k-2} \cdots \Phi_j \quad \text{for} \quad k > j \geq 0$

(iii) $\Phi_{k,i} = \Phi_{k,j}\Phi_{j,i} \quad \text{for all} \quad k \geq j \geq i \geq 0$

b. Each s_k is a multivariate Gaussian RV of length n_s; actually, we can say more: The process $\{s_k\}$ is a Gaussian random process.

c. $\{s_k\}$ is a Markov process, which implies that for any $0 \leq k_1 < k_2 < \cdots < k_n < k$ the conditional probability (density) function of s_k given $s_{k_1}, s_{k_2}, \cdots, s_{k_n}$ has the Markov property

$$p(s_k \mid s_{k_1}, s_{k_2}, \ldots, s_{k_n}) = p(s_k \mid s_{k_n})$$

d. The measurement process $\{m_k\}$ is a Gaussian process, but it is *not* a Markov process.

e. Processes $\{s_k\}$ and $\{m_k\}$ jointly form a Gaussian process $\{(s_k^{\mathrm{T}}, m_k^{\mathrm{T}})^{\mathrm{T}}\}$.

The preceding properties of the system model are used in the derivation of the KF algorithm and in proving its optimality properties. Recursiveness of the KF algorithm essentially is a consequence of (Markov) property c.

The first two moments of $\{s_k\}$ and $\{m_k\}$ follow directly from properties a–e. First consider the process $\{s_k\}$, and for $k \geq j \geq 0$ define

$$\bar{s}_k \equiv E[s_k]$$
$$\Sigma_{k,j} \equiv E[(s_k - \bar{s}_k)(s_j - \bar{s}_j)^{\mathrm{T}}]$$
$$\Sigma_k \equiv \Sigma_{k,k}$$

It follows from properties a and b that

$$\bar{s}_k = E[s_k] = \Phi_{k,0}\bar{s}_0 + \sum_{i=0}^{k-1} \Phi_{k,i+1} B_i u_i \quad \text{for} \quad k \geq 0$$

$$\bar{s}_{k+1} = \Phi_k \bar{s}_k + B_k u_k \qquad \text{for} \quad k \geq 0$$

$$\Sigma_k = \Phi_{k,0}\Sigma_0(\Phi_{k,0})^{\mathrm{T}} + \sum_{i=0}^{k-1} (\Phi_{k,i+1}G_i)Q_i(\Phi_{k,i+1}G_i)^{\mathrm{T}}$$

$$\Sigma_{k+1} = \Phi_k \Sigma_k \Phi_k^{\mathrm{T}} + G_k Q_k G_k^{\mathrm{T}}$$

$$\Sigma_{k,i} = \Phi_{k,i}\Sigma_i \qquad \text{if} \quad k \geq i$$

The first two moments of measurement process $\{m_k\}$ turn out to be

$$\bar{m}_k \equiv E[m_k] = H_k \bar{s}_k$$

and

$$E[(m_k - \bar{m}_k)(m_i - \bar{m}_i)^{\mathrm{T}}] = H_k \Phi_{k,i} \Sigma_i H_i^{\mathrm{T}} + R_k\, \delta_{kj} \quad \text{for} \quad k \geq i \geq 0$$

where δ_{kj} is the Kronecker delta defined following Eq. (4). The above-listed expressions for the first two moments of s_k and m_k remain valid even if the initial state s_0 or at least one of the noise processes, $\{w_k\}$ or $\{v_k\}$, is non-Gaussian.

C. Discrete-Time Filtering Problem

In this subsection as well as in the next, it is important to view the mesurements m_k, the state s_k, and the state estimator as RVs but not as the values taken on by these RVs. Let the RV $M_k \equiv \{m_0, m_1, \ldots, m_k\}$ represent the set of all measurements obtained over the time period $t_0 \leq t \leq t_k$. Use $\hat{s}_{k|j}$ to denote an estimator of s_k that is a function of (is conditioned on) M_j. As noted earlier, we have an estimation problem if $k = j$; a prediction problem if $k > j$ (in such a case, $\hat{s}_{k|j}$ more appropriately is called the predictor of s_k); and a smoothing problem if $k < j$. The KF is concerned only with the first two problems.

The optimality criterion used in the derivation of the KF algorithm is minimization of mean square error. Thus, the KF is an estimator $\hat{s}_{k|j}$ conditioned on M_j, which minimizes

$$E[(s_k - \hat{s}_{k|j})^{\mathrm{T}}(s_k - \hat{s}_{k|j}) \mid M_j] \quad \text{for} \quad k = 0, 1, 2, \ldots \tag{7}$$

It can be shown that such $\hat{s}_{k|j}$ is of the form

$$\hat{s}_{k|j} = E[s_k \mid M_j] \tag{8}$$

In the literature, the MMSE estimator is also alternatively known as the minimum variance (MV) or the least squares (LS) estimator. The latter name is technically imprecise. Furthermore, these names are somewhat misleading because they fail to indicate that the resulting estimates depend on a priori probability assumptions and that these estimates are conditional in nature. Also note that the MMSE criterion can be applied to a more general system model than one defined by Eqs. (2) and (3) and Assumptions 1D–4D. Even then the minimization of Eq. (7) implies the conditional mean estimator of Eq. (8). However, the resulting estimator may not be mathematically or implementationally tractable.

Given the starting conditions $\bar{s}_0$, Σ_0, and the initial measurements M_0 ($=\{m_0\}$), the KF provides a procedure for computing recursively at each t_k the values of

$$\hat{s}_{k|k-1} = E[s_k \mid M_{k-1}] \quad \text{and} \quad \hat{s}_{k|k} = E[s_k \mid M_k] \tag{9}$$

and the associated error covariance matrices

$$P_{k|k-1} \equiv E[(s_k - \hat{s}_{k|k-1})(s_k - \hat{s}_{k|k-1})^{\mathrm{T}} \mid M_{k-1}] \tag{10a}$$

and

$$P_{k|k} \equiv E[(s_k - \hat{s}_{k|k})(s_k - \hat{s}_{k|k})^{\mathrm{T}} \mid M_k] \tag{10b}$$

One noteworthy property of the resulting KF estimator is that it is *unbiased*. This follows from Eq. (8):

$$\begin{aligned} E[s_k - \hat{s}_{k|j}] &= E[s_k] - E[E[s_k \mid M_j]] \\ &= E[s_k] - E[s_k] = 0 \end{aligned}$$

The MMSE and unbiasedness properties of the KF imply that it also is an MV estimator. Another important property of the KF estimator is that it is *linear* in the sense that the estimators $\hat{s}_{k|k-1}$ and $\hat{s}_{k|k}$ are of the form

$$\hat{s}_{k|k-1} = \Phi_{k-1}\hat{s}_{k-1|k-1} + B_{k-1}u_{k-1}$$

and

$$\hat{s}_{k|k} = K_k(m_k - H_k\hat{s}_{k|k-1}) + \hat{s}_{k|k-1}$$

where K_k is the so-called Kalman gain matrix.

What happens if the Gaussianity assumptions for $\{w_k\}$, $\{v_k\}$, or s_0 are dropped? Then the KF algorithm still provides the best and unbiased estimator among all linear estimators of the state. It is best in the sense that it produces the smallest mean square error among all linear estimators of the state. However, in such a situation there may exist a nonlinear filter which in the MMSE sense is better than the KF.

D. Alternative Approaches to Discrete-Time Linear Filtering

The MMSE optimality criterion [Eq. (7)] is not the only one used in recursive estimation. The LS principle of residual minimization, the maximum likelihood (ML) principle, or various optimality principles used in conjunction with the Bayes method are examples of other possibilities. In the case of a linear estimation problem [i.e., for a system model of the form of Eqs. (2) and (3)], if the initial conditions and the noise processes have Gaussian distributions, as is implied by Assumptions 1D–4D, the methods of LS (with appropriate weights), ML, and Bayes (with a quadratic performance criterion) yield estimators of the same (KF) type.

The weighted LS method, which can be expressed in recursive form for sampled measurements [Eq. (3)], is the simplest of the three above-mentioned methods because it does not require making any explicit assumptions, with one exception, about the distribution of RVs involved in the estimation process. The exception concerns the assumption of a priori knowledge of the process and measurement noise covariance matrices, the inverses of which are used as weights in the LS estimation procedure. The optimality criterion at time t_k is the minimization of the sum of squares of the weighted residuals (i.e., the weighted differences between the measurements and their values predicted by the model) accumulated over the epochs t_0, t_1, ..., t_k. As already noted, this approach under the Gaussianity assumptions for noise processes leads to an estimator of KF type.

The LS method (recursively or nonrecursively formulated, weighted or unweighted) has been widely used since Gauss to estimate the parameters of static systems. A static system may be thought of as a special case of the system model [Eqs. (2) and (3)] in which Φ_k is an $n_s \times n_s$ identity matrix, and B_k and G_k are zero matrices, that is, the system is time invariant and so Eq. (2) is not needed to describe the system dynamics. The weighted or unweighted LS method, usually expressed in nonrecursive form, constitutes the backbone of regression analysis and currently is one of the principal methods in statistical inference.

The ML method has also been used for years in statistical inference as a point estimation technique. It is based on viewing the probability (density) function $p_s(M_k)$ of measurements $M_k = \{m_0, m_1, \ldots, m_k\}$ as a function $\lambda_s \equiv p_s(M_k)$ of the unknown parameters s (in our case, s represents the unknown system state) on which the form of this function depends. Then, given measurements M_k, the ML estimate of s is that value, say s^*, of s that maximizes λ_s. This principle has been extended to the construction of recursive estimators for linear dynamic systems of the type defined by Eqs. (2) and (3). As already noted, under the Assumptions 1D–4D, the resulting recursive estimator is identical to the KF.

In engineering literature, an estimator derived from the Bayes conditional probability inversion formula

$$p(x \mid y) = p(x, y)/p(y)$$

$$= p(y \mid x)p(x)/\int p(y \mid x)p(x)\, dx \quad (11)$$

by applying some optimality criterion is often, although somewhat imprecisely, called the Bayes estimator of x. More precisely, the resulting estimator is a Bayes estimator only if, in addition, the $p(x)$ appearing on the right-hand side of Eq. (11) is a Bayes prior (also known as Bayes a priori) probability of x. The term *prior* here means that $p(x)$ is postulated prior to observing the value of y. In estimation, y and x would represent the measurements and the unknown parameters (state), respectively. Hence, in the problems considered here, y and x would be replaced by variously subscripted M (or m) and s, respectively. The left-hand side of the Bayes inversion formula would then give the posterior (also known as Bayes a posteriori) probability of unknown parameters (state) s conditioned on measurements M (or m).

Using Eq. (11) and the RV independence conditions implied by Assumptions 1D–4D, and also noting that

$$M_k \equiv \{m_0, m_1, \ldots, m_{k-1}, m_k\} = \{M_{k-1}, m_k\}$$

one can derive the so-called Bayes probability recursion formulas

$$p(s_k \mid M_k) = p(s_k \mid M_{k-1})p(m_k \mid s_k)/p(m_k \mid M_{k-1}) \quad (12a)$$

and

$$p(s_k \mid M_{k-1}) = \int p(s_k \mid s_{k-1})p(s_{k-1} \mid M_{k-1})\, ds_{k-1} \quad (12b)$$

with the denominator in Eq. (12a) expressible as

$$p(m_k \mid M_{k-1}) = \int p(m_k \mid s_k)p(s_k \mid M_{k-1})\, ds_k \quad (12c)$$

Equations (12a) and (12b) recursively define the measurement updating and the time propagation (also called time updating) of probability densities for $k = 0, 1, \ldots$. To get the recursive process started at t_0, one must interpret correctly the meaning of $p(s_0 \mid M_{-1})$. Since M_{-1} constitutes an empty set (i.e., no measurements), $p(s_0 \mid M_{-1})$ represents the Bayes prior $p(s_0)$. As an example, this prior for a KF is specified in terms of the first two moments, $\bar{s}_0$ and Σ_0, of the Gaussian distribution of state s at the initial time t_0. It is worth noting that, in Eqs. (12a)–(12c), $p(s_k \mid s_{k-1})$ is obtained from the state time-propagation equations (2) with the assistance of the a priori known probability (density) $p(w_{k-1})$ of process noise w_{k-1} at t_{k-1}. Similarly, $p(m_k \mid s_k)$ is determined from the measurement equations (3) and with the assistance of the a priori known probability (density) $p(v_k)$ of measurement noise v_k at t_k. Knowledge of all these probability densities and $p(s_0)$ recursively determines $p(s_k \mid M_k)$ for all $k = 0, 1, \ldots$.

Using the recursive probability equations (12a)–(12c) in conjunction with various optimality criteria produces a variety of recursive estimation schemes. However, due mainly to mathematical and implementational considerations, the MMSE criterion, equivalent to Eq. (7) and yielding an estimator of the type in Eq. (8), is the most widely used criterion at present. As already noted, this criterion is applied to derive the KF equations.

E. Discrete-Time Kalman Filter

Given the discrete-time linear system model (including the distributional Assumptions 1D–4D) and the defining relation of Eq. (8) there are several ways in which the discrete-time KF algorithm can be derived. One technique, which is mathematically straightforward although tedious in detail, is based on the use of recursive probability equations (12a)–(12c) and the repeated application of conditional multivariate Gaussian distribution to express the probability densities $p(s_k \mid M_{k-1})$ and $p(s_k \mid M_k)$ for all $k = 0,$

1, ... in terms of m_k, $\hat{s}_{k-1|k-1}$, $P_{k-1|k-1}$, the matrices appearing in the system model, and the covariances of noise processes $\{w_k\}$ and $\{v_k\}$. Due to the regenerative properties of Gaussian distribution, densities $p(s_k \mid M_{k-1})$ and $p(s_k \mid M_k)$ remain Gaussian for all $k \geq 0$. By Eqs. (9), (10a), and (10b), the first two moments of $p(s_k \mid M_{k-1})$ and $p(s_k \mid M_k)$ are $\hat{s}_{k|k-1}$ with $P_{k|k-1}$ and $\hat{s}_{k|k}$ with $P_{k|k}$, respectively. Hence, the mathematical expressions for these quantities, giving the recursive estimation equations (13)–(18), are explicitly obtainable from the mathematical expressions for $p(s_k \mid M_{k-1})$ and $p(s_k \mid M_k)$.

Another technique for deriving the KF algorithm uses the notion of innovations, defined as

$$r_k = m_k - E[m_k \mid m_{k-1}] = m_k - H_k\hat{s}_{k|k-1}$$

In the innovation process $\{r_k\}$, each r_k constitutes that part of the measurement at t_k that contains new information not provided by m_0, m_1, ..., m_{k-1}. Innovations $\{r_k\}$ constitute a zero-mean white process. It follows that r_k represents the error in the orthogonal projection of s_k on the subspace generated by $M_k = \{m_0, m_1, \ldots, m_k\}$. This projection, being a linear combination of the vectors in M_k, defines a linear MMSE estimator of s. Using this notion of orthogonality, the whiteness of $\{r_k\}$, and the system model [Eqs. (2) and (3)], especially the Markov property of state propagation, it is then rather simple to derive the KF recursion expressions.

Using the preceding system model and probabilistic assumptions, one can state the KF algorithm for a discrete-time linear system as follows:

Discrete-Time Kalman Filter Algorithm. At each $t_k = t_{k-1} + \Delta t_{k-1}$ ($k = 0, 1, 2, \ldots$) proceed as follows:

a. If $k = 0$ (i.e., at the initial time t_0), initialize the estimation process by setting

$$\hat{s}_{0|-1} = \bar{s}_0 \quad \text{and} \quad P_{0|-1} = \Sigma_0 \tag{13}$$

where $\bar{s}_0$ and Σ_0 are defined by Eq. (6).

b. If $k \geq 1$, propagate the estimates of system state vector s and state error covariance matrix P from t_{k-1} to t_k by computing

$$\hat{s}_{k|k-1} = \Phi_{k-1}\hat{s}_{k-1|k-1} + B_{k-1}u_{k-1} \tag{14}$$

and

$$P_{k|k-1} = \Phi_{k-1}P_{k-1|k-1}\Phi_{k-1}^{\mathrm{T}} + G_{k-1}Q_{k-1}G_{k-1}^{\mathrm{T}} \tag{15}$$

respectively.

c. Use measurements $m_k = H_k s_k + v_k$ to update the propagated estimate of s by computing the Kalman gain matrix

$$K_k = P_{k|k-1}H_k^{\mathrm{T}}[H_k P_{k|k-1}H_k^{\mathrm{T}} + R_k]^{-1} \tag{16}$$

and the update of state estimate

$$\hat{s}_{k|k} = \hat{s}_{k|k-1} + K_k[m_k - H_k\hat{s}_{k|k-1}] \tag{17}$$

Next, update the estimate P of state error covariance matrix by computing

$$P_{k|k} = [I - K_k H_k]P_{k|k-1} \tag{18}$$

The preceding algorithm assumes that one knows the values of $\bar{s}_0$ and Σ_0 and also knows how to compute for all k the matrices Φ_k, B_k, R_k, Q_k, and H_k. In the literature, $\hat{s}_{k|k}$ is often called the measurement update of $\hat{s}_{k|k-1}$ and $\hat{s}_{k+1|k}$ the time update of $\hat{s}_{k|k}$.

If the state estimate update equation (17) is rewritten as

$$\hat{s}_{k|k} = K_k m_k + [I - K_k H_k]\hat{s}_{k|k-1} \tag{17$'$}$$

an equivalent expression for $P_{k|k}$ is

$$P_{k|k} = K_k R_k K_k^{\mathrm{T}} + [I - K_k H_k]P_{k|k-1}[I - K_k H_k]^{\mathrm{T}} \tag{18$'$}$$

which is known as the Joseph form (named after P. D. Joseph) of error covariance update. Since the right-hand side of Eq. (18′) is the sum of two symmetric matrices (the first a nonnegative definite, the second a positive definite matrix), the state error covariance update in this form numerically is more stable, although computationally more expensive, than the same operation in the short form [Eq. (18)].

EXAMPLE 1. FILTERING OF AN AUTOREGRESSIVE PROCESS. This example illustrates the application of the discrete-time KF to a simple linear system in which both the state s and the measurement m are scalars. The system model is of the form

$$s_k = \phi s_{k-1} + w_k \quad \text{and} \quad m_k = h s_k + v_k$$

where ϕ and h are scalar multipliers, that is, $n_s = n_m = 1$. Both noise processes, $\{w_k\}$ and $\{v_k\}$, and the initial conditions are assumed to satisfy Assumptions 1D–4D. In the present case, the process noise covariance matrices Q and R are 1×1; that is, Q and R represent the time-invariant variances of w_k and v_k, respectively, and are scalar quantities.

The KF equations now reduce to the following procedure:

a. If $k = 0$, initialize the estimation process by specifying s_0 and $P_{0|-1}$.

b. If $k \geq 1$, propagate the estimates by computing

$$\hat{s}_{k|k-1} = \phi \hat{s}_{k-1|k-1}$$
$$P_{k|k-1} = \phi^2 P_{k-1|k-1} + Q$$

c. For all $k \geq 0$, update the estimates by computing

$$K_k = hP_{k|k-1}/[h^2 P_{k|k-1} + R]$$
$$\hat{s}_{k|k} = \hat{s}_{k|k-1} + K_k[m_k - h\hat{s}_{k|k-1}]$$
$$P_{k|k} = K_k^2 R + [1 - hK_k]^2 P_{k|k-1}$$

Figure 1 summarizes the results of a sample simulation of this KF. Graph (a) shows the generated time history of the true system state s. Graph (b) summarizes the time history of estimation error, which at t_k is defined as $e_k = \hat{s}_{k|k} - s_k$. The values of parameters of the true system model are

$$\phi = 1.02; \qquad h = 100.0; \qquad Q = 4.0;$$
$$\text{and} \qquad R = 1.0$$

The values of the corresponding parameters in the system model assumed by the KF are equal in value to those of the true model. The true initial value of state is $s_0 = 5.0$. The initialization values used by the KF are $\bar{s}_0 = 4.0$ and $P_{0|-1} = 25.0$.

Since, according to the true system model, the measurements are very precise compared with

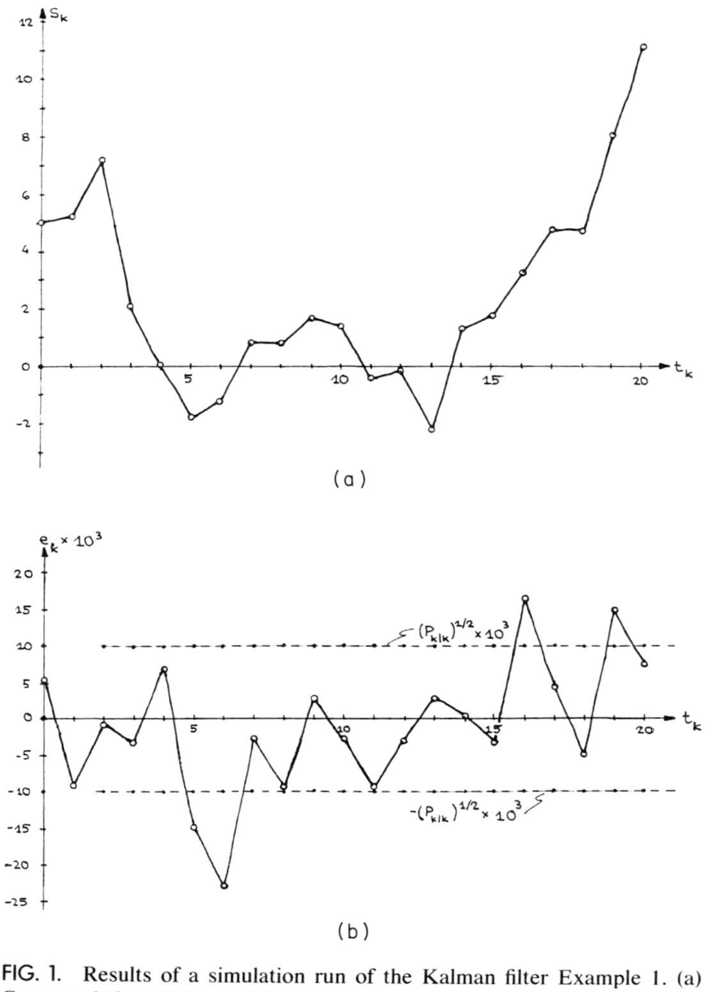

FIG. 1. Results of a simulation run of the Kalman filter Example 1. (a) Generated time history of the true system state and (b) time history of estimation error e (multiplied by 10^3).

the level of process noise (i.e., the variance of m/h is $R/h^2 = 0.0001 \ll Q$) and the system model assumed in the KF agrees with the true model, the filter practically converges at t_0 after the first measurement update. One can easily see this by observing in graph (b) of Fig. 1 that (for all $k \geq 0$) the points $\pm(P_{k|k})^{1/2}$ lie on two horizontal lines that are symmetrically located with respect to the time axis.

In many respects, the above-described filtering problem for a random walk is trivial. Its only purpose was to illustrate the KF computations for a very simple (scalar) case. The following "reversion" of this problem has practical applications in time series analysis and is known as a system identification problem. Suppose that the value of scalar multiplier ϕ is continuously undergoing random perturbations and so is not completely known. Assume that the dynamics of ϕ is adequately described by means of an equation of the form

$$\phi_k = \phi_{k-1} + w'_{k-1}$$

and that we are now directly observing the state s via measurement equation of the form

$$s_k = s_{k-1}\phi_k + v'_k$$

which essentially is the state transition equation of the original problem with a modified noise term. Making the usual probabilistic assumptions for the noise processes $\{w'_k\}$ and $\{v'_k\}$ and the initial distribution of ϕ completes a system model for the KF of the system identification problem (estimation of the unknown and possibly time-varying values of parameters in the system model).

F. Continuous-Time Kalman Filter

A year after the publication of Kalman's seminal work on discrete-time filtering, R. Bucy and R. Kalman laid the foundation for continuous-time KFs. Although presently the KFs, probably without exception, are implemented as computer programs for processing on a digital computer, strong interest in the continuous-time KFs persists. Often the estimation problem for a stochastic dynamic system can be precisely formulated only in terms of stochastic differential equations. Thus, the continuous-time KF is an important modeling tool to a designer.

The system model for a continuous-time KF is summarized next. (As much as possible, the same notation as in the discrete-time model is used here. Also, to simplify the discussion of the continuous-time KF, the term representing the control inputs has been deleted from the system dynamics model; the presence of such a term would affect in an *a priori* known way only the mean value of the state, not its covariances.) The dynamics of the system state, at least *formally*, is described in the continuous-time case by a stochastic differential equation of the form

$$ds_t/dt = F_t s_t + G_{(c)t} w_t, \qquad t \geq t_0 \tag{19}$$

The measurement equation is written

$$m_t = H_t s_t + v_t, \qquad t \geq t_0 \tag{20}$$

The time argument t presently ranges over a continuum (an interval) of real numbers and is, as indicated, finitely bounded from below. Thus, $\{w_t\}$, $\{s_t\}$, $\{v_t\}$, and $\{m_t\}$ are now continuous-time stochastic processes with $t \geq t_0$. With regard to vector and matrix sizes, the assumptions made and the notation used earlier continue to hold. The subscript "c" distinguishes a continuous-time entity from its discrete-time counterpart. The probabilistic assumptions about the model specified by Eqs. (19) and (20) are similar to those stated for the discrete-time version of the KF.

ASSUMPTION 1C. The process noise $\{w_t\}$ is a continuous-time, zero-mean, Gaussian white process with the covariance structure of the form

$$E[w_t w_{t'}^{\mathrm{T}}] = Q_{(c)t}\, \delta(t - t') \tag{21}$$

where $Q_{(c)t}$ is a known $n_s \times n_s$ nonnegative definite matrix (which may optionally be a zero matrix) and $\delta(\cdot)$ denotes the Dirac delta function defined by Eq. (1).

ASSUMPTION 2C. The measurement noise $\{v_t\}$ is a continuous-time, zero-mean, Gaussian white process with

$$E[v_t v_{t'}^{\mathrm{T}}] = R_{(c)t}\, \delta(t - t') \tag{22}$$

where $R_{(c)t}$ is a known $n_m \times n_m$ positive definite matrix and $\delta(\cdot)$ represents the Dirac delta function defined by Eq. (1).

ASSUMPTION 3C. For all t and $t' \geq t_0$, RVs w_t and $v_{t'}$ are independently distributed RVs.

ASSUMPTION 4C. The value s_0 of s at t_0 is distributed as a Gaussian RV whose mean and covariance matrix, that is,

$$\bar{s}_0 \equiv E[s_0]$$

and

$$\Sigma_0 \equiv E[(s_0 - \bar{s}_0)(s_0 - \bar{s}_0)^{\mathrm{T}}], \tag{23}$$

are known. Furthermore, the RV s_0 is statistically independent of the RVs w_t and $v_{t'}$ for all t and $t' \geq t_0$.

Mathematically the stochastic differential equation (19) is not meaningful because of the white noise assumption (Assumption 1C) for the continuous-time process $\{w_t\}$. It is well known, however, that white Gaussian noise is the formal derivative of a Brownian motion process $\{\beta_t\}$, with $t \geq t_0$, which has the property that the increments

$$\{\beta_{t_j} - \beta_{t_{j-1}}\}, \qquad j \geq 1$$

are independent Gaussian RVs for any ordered set $t_0 < t_1 < t_2 < \cdots < t_n$ of epochs. Thus, the differential equation (19) can be viewed as being equivalent to

$$ds_t = (F_t s_t)\,dt + (G_{(c)t})\,d\beta_t, \qquad t \geq t_0 \quad (24)$$

and so to

$$s_t - s_{t_0} = \int_{t_0}^{t} F s_\tau \,d\tau + \int_{t_0}^{t} G_{(c)\tau}\,d\beta_\tau \quad (25)$$

On the right-hand side of Eq. (25), the first integral is ordinary (Riemann or Lebesque), but the second is an Itô stochastic integral. (Integrals of this type were defined in the 1940s by the Japanese mathematician K. Itô.)

Replacement of Eq. (19) by Eq. (24) requires the corresponding modification of Assumptions 1C–4C. In these assumptions, $\{w_t\}$ must be replaced by $\{d\beta_t\}$, where $\{\beta_t, t \geq t_0\}$ is a Brownian motion process and

$$E[d\beta_t\, d\beta_{t'}^{\mathrm{T}}] = Q_{(c)}\,\delta(t - t') \quad (21')$$

The modified assumptions will be referred to as Assumptions 1C′–4C′.

Rigorous treatment of continuous-time stochastic processes and, in particular, of stochastic differential equations requires considerably more mathematical sophistication than that of discrete-time stochastic processes (sequences of RVs). Consequently, derivation of a continuous-time KF is technically more difficult than derivation of its discrete-time counterpart. Except for noting that mathematically it is more rigorous to use Eq. (24) in place of Eq. (19), we will not dwell any longer on these theoretical issues and proceed to an intuitive definition of a continuous-time KF.

According to whether the measurements are incorporated continuously over the time or are just sampled at discrete time points, one could distinguish two variations of continuous-time KF: a continuous-dynamics, continuous-measurement KF and a continuous-dynamics, discrete-measurement KF. Since the first is of little interest in practice, we will not consider it at all in this article. Hence, from now on the term *continuous-time KF* will imply a continuous-dynamics, discrete-measurement KF.

Continuous-Time (Discrete-Measurement) Kalman Filter Algorithm. For the system model given by Eqs. (24) and (20) and the modified Assumptions 1C′–4C′, the evolution of the conditional mean $\hat{s}_{t|t}$ and the state error covariance matrix $P_{t|t}$, *during* an interval $t_k \geq t > t_{k+1}$ *between* two consecutive measurement sampling epochs t_k and t_{k+1}, satisfies the differential equations

$$d\hat{s}_{t|t}/dt = F_t \hat{s}_{t|t}$$

and

$$dP_{t|t}/dt = F_t P_{t|t} + P_{t|t} F_t^{\mathrm{T}} + G_{(c)t} Q_t G_{(c)t}^{\mathrm{T}}$$

At a measurement epoch t_k (say $= t$), the estimates of state vector and state error covariance matrix are

$$\hat{s}_{t|t} = \hat{s}_{t|t-} + K_t[m_t - H_t \hat{s}_{t|t-}] \quad (26)$$

and

$$P_{t|t} = P_{t|t-} - K_t H_t P_{t|t-} \quad (27)$$

respectively, where

$$K_t = P_{t|t-} H_t^{\mathrm{T}} [H_t P_{t|t-} H_t^{\mathrm{T}} + R_{(c)t}]^{-1} \quad (28)$$

Above, $\hat{s}_{t|t-}$ (or $P_{t|t-}$) denotes the value of $\hat{s}$ (or of P) measurement-updated at t_{k-1} and then time-propagated up to $t = t_k$. At the initial time $t = t_0$ the solution process is started while using

$$\bar{s}_0 = E[s_0]$$

and

$$P_{0|0-} = \Sigma_0 = E[(s_0 - \bar{s}_0)(s_0 - \bar{s}_0)^{\mathrm{T}}]$$

as the initial conditions, which are assumed to be known.

As in the discrete-time KF, the matrices F_t, $Q_{(c)t}$, and $R_{(c)t}$ are also assumed to be known, but they differ from the corresponding matrices of a discrete-time model even for the same dynamic system.

To handle (on a computer) the integration of differential equations implied by the propagation forward in time of estimates, a common approach is (a) to construct a discrete-time system model corresponding to the continuous-time system model defined by Eqs. (24) and (20) and (b) then to apply the discrete-time KF algorithm to this discrete-time system model. Heuristically this can be done by considering a time interval

$t_{k-1} \leq t \leq t_{k-1} + \Delta t_{k-1} = t_k$ and replacing ds_t, dt, and $d\beta_t$ in Eq. (24) with $s_k - s_{k-1}$, Δt_{k-1}, and $\beta_k - \beta_{k-1}$ respectively, which yields

$$s_k \simeq \Phi_{k-1} s_{k-1} + G_{k-1} w_k$$

if for all $k = 0, 1, 2, \ldots$ one defines $\Phi_k \equiv \mathrm{I} + \Delta t_k F_k$, $G_k \equiv \Delta t_k G_{(c)k}$, $Q_k \equiv \Delta t_k Q_{(c)k}$, and $w_k \equiv \beta_k - \beta_{k-1}$.

III. Modifications of Kalman Filters and Nonlinear Filtering

A. Filter Divergence

Discrepancies between the actual performance (the actual quality of estimates) of a filter and its apparent performance as indicated by the estimated state error covariance matrices $P_{k|k-1}$ and $P_{k|k}$ are called filter divergence. One variation of this phenomenon, known as apparent divergence, occurs when the actual estimation errors of state, although they remain bounded, become by at least an order of magnitude larger than indicated by P matrices. In such a case, performance of the KF can often be adequately improved by means of small parametric or structural adjustments in the linear system model, by changing the characterization of noise (R and Q matrices) or the initialization values s_0 and P_0 of estimates, or by switching to more accurate numerical procedures. Collectively such improvements are referred to as filter tuning. What is important to note is that apparent divergence usually does not require changing from the linear system model or the basic KF algorithm.

A more serious situation, called true divergence, arises when the state error covariance estimates $P_{k|k-1}$ and $P_{k|k}$ remain bounded while the actual errors in the state estimates start growing without bounds. True divergence may be caused by the numerical instability of filter algorithms or by modeling flaws. For example, certain critical factors or state components have not been included in the model, the system dynamics equation or the measurement-to-state transformation is incorrectly defined, or the noise model is structurally or distributionally incorrect. Numerical instability can usually be removed by resorting to better numerical algorithms. (This problem is briefly discussed in Section IV). Modeling flaws can be detected by means of simulation in which the filter constructed on the basis of the assumed (say, linear) model is tested against a scenario generated while using a true (say, nonlinear) model. Model inadequacies arising from inherent nonlinearities in the modeled system, if they are not too strong, can often be compensated for by the techniques that do not require complete abandonment of the KF algorithm. One may be able to linearize locally the system model and then use an extended form of the KF algorithm. Otherwise, if they cannot be removed by such techniques, one must resort to nonlinear filtering, which is characterized by the use of nonlinear models for system dynamics and (or) measurements. By comparison with the KF, nonlinear filtering is considerably more difficult to attain both theoretically and practically.

B. Filter Tuning and Modifications

Certain deviations of the assumed linear system model or noise from the actual behavior of the modeled system (from its true model), leading to apparent divergence, can often be compensated for by means of a combination of the following techniques: (a) modifying, typically raising, the assumed levels of process or measurement noise through appropriate changes in noise covariance matrices Q and R; (b) bounding from below the main-diagonal elements of state error covariance matrix P and then appropriately adjusting the off-diagonal elements; (c) introducing the so-called fading (finite) memory filtering or overweighting the most recent measurements; (d) whitening (decorrelating) the process or measurement noise, also removing singularity or near-singularity from matrix R; (e) adding more states, that is, increasing the length of the state vector. The foregoing list of possibly useful measures is by no means complete.

Raising the level of process noise by an appropriate modification of matrix Q often compensates for small nonlinearities and factors, such as states, unaccounted for in the assumed model. Raising or lowering the assumed level of measurement noise by modifying matrix R forces the filter to decrease or increase, respectively, the dependence on measurements.

Bounding from below the estimates of state error variances (the main-diagonal elements of matrix $P_{k|k}$) and then correspondingly adjusting the estimated covariances (the remaining elements of $P_{k|k}$) usually increases the numerical stability of the estimation process and protects the filter from blowing up. For example, the estimation process can easily be destabilized by the cumulative effect of rounding errors that destroys the positive definiteness or symmetry of matrix P. Also, as the estimation process progresses, the elements of matrix P tend to become smaller; consequently, the filter starts to depend too much on the assumed model and to little on the incoming measurements.

Fading memory techniques and the overweighting of the most recent measurements (discussed in Maybeck's Vol. 2) help in situations where, for example, the true system model changes over time, perhaps in a manner dependent on the system state. In such a case we may want to suppress the effects of more remotely past estimates on the current estimates.

Next we will briefly examine how to handle several situations that arise when some of the distributional assumptions 1D–4D (or 1C–4C) are violated. To compensate for nonwhiteness (autocorrelation over time) in the measurement noise $\{v_k\}$ or in the process noise $\{w_k\}$ one can resort, at the cost of increased computing load, to one of several known "whitening" techniques. For example, if the measurement noise $\{v_k\}$ is nonwhite so that the covariance matrix $E[v_j v_k^{\mathrm{T}}]$ is not zero for some $j \neq k$, one can conceptually model the process $\{v_k\}$ as a finite-dimensional system driven by white noise. This can be done only by adding new states to the overall system model and, thereby, increasing the processing cost. On the other hand, it saves the optimality properties of the filter.

A different situation arises when both noise processes $\{w_k\}$ and $\{v_k\}$ are white but the measurement noise covariance matrix R_k is nonnegative definite with nullity q (has q zero eigenvalues) for all k. Then (as shown in Anderson and Moore) q functionals of the state are exactly known and the length of the state vector can be shortened by q. If the covariance matrices are nonsingular, one can construct a suboptimal filter of reduced dimenson.

Another pathological situation, violating the distributional Assumption 3D or 3C, comes up in feedback control applications when the process and measurement noise processes $\{w_k\}$ and $\{v_k\}$ are correlated or even identical. This problem can be solved by modifying the KF covariance processing equations (15), (16), and (18).

Filter tuning and stabilization techniques mentioned in the preceding paragraphs are critically important in applications work, that is, in designing filters for real-life situations and then making them work properly. Actually, every such development requires at least some tuning.

C. Nonlinear System Model

We generalize now the discrete-time system model defined in terms of Eqs. (2) and (3) to

$$s_k = f_{k-1}(s_{k-1}, u_{k-1}) + G_{k-1}(s_{k-1})w_{k-1} \quad (29)$$

and

$$m_k = h_k(s_k) + v_k \quad (30)$$

We do it by replacing the linear terms $\Phi_{k-1}s_{k-1}$ and $B_{k-1}u_{k-1}$ of the linear dynamics model by a function $f_k(\cdot, \cdot)$, allowing the process-noise-to-state transformation matrix G_{k-1} to depend on system state, and generalizing the state-to-measurement transformation matrix H_k to a function $h_k(\cdot)$. The subscripts attached to f, G, and h emphasize that these functions may be of time-dependent form. Furthermore, f may be nonlinear in s and possibly in u; h may be nonlinear in s. The same distributional assumptions as those made earlier for the linear discrete-time model (Assumptions 1D–4D) will be used for the nonlinear model defined by Eqs. (29) and (30). Now as before, the noise is included in the model through additive terms; also, functions f and h in general are vector-valued so that their dimensions, respectively, agree with the lengths of vectors s and m. More general nonlinear system models are possible.

One could similarly define a continuous-time nonlinear system model, but we will not do it in this article.

D. General Approach to Nonlinear Filtering

Nearly all presently known approaches to nonlinear filtering are based, in one way or another, on the application of Bayes recursive probability equations (12a)–(12c) to a nonlinear system model, say to one of the form defined by Eqs. (29) and (30). The underlying problem is then to estimate from measurements $M_k = \{m_0, m_1, \ldots, m_k\}$ the evolution of the posterior probability densities $p(s_k \mid M_k)$ over t_k for $k = 0, 1, \ldots$. Knowing $p(s_k \mid M_k)$ at each sampling epoch t_k enables one to apply the optimization criterion of a desired type (such as the MMSE, the maximum *a posteriori*, or one of some other type) in order to obtain the corresponding estimates of state.

When the low-order moments or some other statistics are sufficient in the sense that they define or adequately approximate $p(s_k \mid M_k)$, optimal or nearly optimal filtering schemes can be derived for certain limited classes of problems. Typically, this can be done when a combination of the following conditions exists: (a) the nonlinearities in Eqs. (29) and (30) locally can be well approximated at each t_k by a linearized model (e.g., by a Taylor series approximation to the original model); (b) an adequate approximation to the state trajectory (known as a nominal state trajectory) is *a priori* available; (c) the actual noise levels are low and both noise processes are Gaussian. Several versions of the linearized extensions of Kalman filter, discussed below, are the most commonly used representatives of such nonlinear estimators. In general, although the manner in which $p(s_k \mid M_k)$ evolves can be described by means of difference (in discrete-time case) or differential (in continuous-time case) equations, these equations usually are too complex to be solved for practical implementation analytically in closed form, or even numerically. This is especially true for real-time filter implementations. Because of these difficulties, much of the research thrust has been in the direction of developing tractable approximations to $p(s_k \mid M_k)$.

E. Linearized Extensions of Kalman Filters

If the functions f and h are sufficiently smooth and can be locally expanded in Taylor series with respect to the estimates or with respect to an *a priori* generated nominal time history of system states, then one can apply the KF algorithm to the linearized system model

$$s_k = F_{k-1}s_{k-1} + G_{k-1}w_{k-1} \tag{31}$$

and

$$m_k = H_k s_k + v_k \tag{32}$$

with the matrices F, G, and H defined in terms of their (i, j)th elements as

$$\begin{aligned} F_k &\equiv F_k[s_{0k}, u_k] \equiv ((F_{i,j)t}))_{t=t_k} \\ &\equiv ((\delta f_{(i)t}(s, u)/\delta s_{(j)t}))_{s=s_{0k},\, u=u_k,\, t=t_k} \end{aligned} \tag{33}$$

$$G_k \equiv G_k(s_{0k}) \equiv ((G_{(i,j)t}(s)))_{s=s_{0k},\, t=t_k} \tag{34}$$

and

$$H_k \equiv H_k[s_{0k}] \equiv ((\delta h_{(i)t}(s)/\delta s_{(j)}))_{s=s_{0k},\, t=t_k} \tag{35}$$

Here we introduce the notational convention $X = ((X_{(i,j)t}))$ to denote matrix X at time t in terms of its (i, j)th element $X_{(i,j)t}$. For example, the right-hand side of Eq. (33) indicates that the (i, j)th element of matrix F_k is the partial derivative at $t = t_k$ of the ith component of f_k with respect to the jth component of s; the subscript expression to the right of double parentheses specifies at what point these partial derivatives are to be evaluated. In (33), this point is

$$s = s_{0k}, \quad u = u_k, \quad t = t_k$$

where: $s = s_{0k}$ indicates the value of the nominal state vector s_0 at $t = t_k$; $u = u_k$ is the value of control u at $t = t_k$.

The two most common choices for the nominal state trajectory $\{s_{0k}\}$ are as follows: (a) $s_{ok} \equiv \hat{s}_{k|k}$ or $\hat{s}_{k|k-1}$, which yields the extended Kalman filter (EKF), or (b) $\{s_{0k}\}$ is *a priori* set to be a nominal state trajectory, which gives the so-called linearized Kalman filter (LKF). As an example, we state next in detail the algorithm for the discrete-time EKF, which is similar in form to the discrete-time KF algorithm defined in terms of Eqs. (13)–(18).

Discrete-Time Extended Kalman Filter Algorithm. At each $t_k = t_{k-1} + \Delta t_{k-1}$ $(k = 0, 1, 2, \ldots)$ proceed as follows:

a. If $k = 0$ (i.e., at the initial time t_0), initialize the estimation process by setting

$$\hat{s}_{0|-1} = \bar{s}_0 \qquad \text{and} \qquad P_{0|-1} = \Sigma_0 \tag{36}$$

where $\bar{s}_0$ and Σ_0 are as defined by Eq. (6).

b. If $k \geq 1$, propagate the estimates of system state vector s and the state error covariance matrix P from t_{k-1} to t_k by computing

$$\hat{s}_{k|k-1} = f_{k-1}(\hat{s}_{k-1|k-1}, u_{k-1}) \tag{37}$$

and

$$P_{k|k-1} = F_{k-1}P_{k-1|k-1}F_{k-1}^{\mathrm{T}} + G_{k-1}Q_{k-1}G_{k-1}^{\mathrm{T}} \tag{38}$$

respectively.

c. To update the estimates, first compute

$$H_k = H_k[\hat{s}_{k|k-1}] \tag{39}$$

according to Eq. (35) and evaluate the Kalman gain matrix

$$K_k = P_{k|k-1}H_k^{\mathrm{T}}[H_k P_{k|k-1} H_k^{\mathrm{T}} + R_k]^{-1} \tag{40}$$

Next use the current measurements m_k to update the estimate of s by means of

$$\hat{s}_{k|k} = \hat{s}_{k|k-1} + K_k[m_k - h_k(\hat{s}_{k|k-1})] \tag{41}$$

Then update the estimate of state error covariance matrix P by computing

$$P_{k|k} = [I - K_k H_k]P_{k|k-1} \tag{42}$$

d. Finally, compute the matrix

$$F_k \equiv F_k[\hat{s}_{k|k}, u_k] \tag{43}$$

according to Eq. (33) and evaluate the process-noise-to-state transformation matrix

$$G_k \equiv G_k[\hat{s}_{k|k}] \tag{44}$$

The above-stated discrete-time EKF reduces to the standard discrete-time KF with its all-optimality properties if the *true* system model is linear, that is, if the true model is defined by Eqs. (2) and (3). When the EKF algorithm is applied to a nonlinear system whose true model is of the form given by Eqs. (29) and (30), the resulting estimator is no longer linear or optimal, which makes it more prone to various problems. For example, if the time step Δt used is too large to accommodate nonlinearities in system dynamics or in measurements, the estimates may be biased or even the entire estimation process may be destabilized by filter divergence. Thus, the tuning and the performance validation of an EKF or an LKF typically require considerably more work (simulation and analysis) than performing the same tasks for a KF applied to a truly linear model.

In addition to the LKF and the EKF several other types of linearized extensions of KF are known. One class of variations can be derived by including more than the first-order term in the Taylor series expansions of functions $f_k(s_k, u_k)$ or $h_k(s_k)$. For example, the estimation algorithm obtained by including the first- and second-order terms is known as the second-order extended (or linearized) Kalman filter. Another variation can be constructed by using several, say I, iterations to perform the measurement update of state with each set of measurements m_k. In such a scheme, step c of discrete-time EKF algorithm is repeated I times. One enters the ith pass of this step with $\hat{s}_{k|k}(i-1)$, then computes $\hat{s}_{k|k}(i)$ and all other quantities dependent on $\hat{s}_{k|k}(i)$. The first iteration is entered by defining $\hat{s}_{k|k}(0) \equiv \hat{s}_{k|k-1}$. At the end of the Ith iteration, one defines $\hat{s}_{k|k} \equiv \hat{s}_{k|k}(I)$.

Although the measures described in the foregoing two paragraphs often stabilize the EKF and produce satisfactory results, they fail for some nonlinear or non-Gaussian systems. The cause of such failures is usually ascribed to two kinds of approximations used in the construction of EKF: (a) the linearization of system equations relative to some reference values and (b) the assumption of Gaussianity for all a priori distributions in the system model. Approximations of the second kind enforce the retention of a false illusion that the probability densities $p(s_k \mid M_k)$ continue to be Gaussian for all k. For example, if the true conditional distribution of state is multimodal [i.e., densities $p(s_k \mid M_k)$ have multiple peaks], the EKF functions more as a maximum likelihood than as an MMSE estimator and the estimated mean may end up following one (if any) of the peaks.

EXAMPLE 2. ESTIMATING THE MOTION AND THE DRAG CHARACTERISTICS OF A BALLISTIC PROJECTILE ENTERING THE ATMOSPHERE. Consider the problem of estimating the motion and the drag (air resistance) characteristics of a *ballistic projectile* (BP). To simplify the problem without robbing from it its illustrative value, assume that the BP is aimed at the North Pole and is approaching the earth along the polar axis. We will denote this axis as the Y axis of the one-dimensional coordinate system whose origin is assumed to coincide with the North Pole and whose positive direction points "upward" from that pole.

Notation. In this example, the individual components of a vector will be referred to by means of parenthesized subscripts. For example, if z is a column vector of length 2, we shall write $z = [z_{(1)}, z_{(2)}]^T$. In particular, to refer to the values of these components at time t, we shall write either $[z_{(1)t}, z_{(2)t}]$ or $[z_{(1)}, z_{(2)}]_t$. If t represents a sampling epoch, say t_k, we shall write either $[z_{(1)k}, z_{(2)k}]$ or $[z_{(1)}, z_{(2)}]_k$. Another notational convention to be adopted here is the use of dots above a symbol to denote the derivatives with respect to time of the quantity represented by the symbol. For example, $\dot{y}_k$ and $\ddot{y}_k$ respectively denote the values of dy/dt and d^2y/dt^2 at time t_k. In addition, we will use "hats" over lower case letters to denote unit vectors. For example, $\hat{v}$ will denote the unit vector in the direction of velocity vector v.

Physical Model. We will model the earth as a perfect sphere of radius

$$R_E = 6{,}378{,}135 \text{ (m)}$$

For the present problem, the gravitational field at any point P on the polar (Y) axis, y meters above the sea level, will be approximated by

$$-g(y)\hat{y} = -(g_0)(C)(1.0 + y/R_E)^{-2}\hat{y} \text{ (m/sec}^2\text{)}$$

where

$$g_0 = 9.7803327 \text{ (m/sec}^2\text{)}$$

and

$$C = 1.00530246$$

The air density at P (y meters above the sea level) will be approximated by

$$\rho \equiv \rho(y) = \rho_0 \exp(-\gamma_y) \text{ (kg/m}^3)$$

where

$$\rho_0 = 1.22 \text{ (kg/m}^3)$$

$$\gamma = 1.6404 \times 10^{-4} \text{ (m}^{-1})$$

The drag force on the BP, divided by its unknown mass and moving with velocity $\dot{y}$, will be approximated by

$$d \equiv d(-\hat{v}) = (\dot{y})^2[\rho(y)](D_F) \text{ (m/sec}^2)$$

where $\hat{v}$ = unit vector in the direction of velocity; D_F = unknown drag factor (m/kg). In the present case, $\hat{v} = -\hat{y}$. Hence, the drag can be written as

$$d(y, \dot{y})\hat{y} = (\dot{y})^2[\rho(y)](D_F)\hat{y}$$

It follows that the differential equation of motion for the BP is of the form

$$\ddot{y} = -g(y) + d(y, \dot{y}) + \text{process noise.}$$

System Model. Analysis of the physical model suggests the use of a four-dimensional ($n_s = 4$) state vector (SV) defined by letting

$$s_{(1)} \leftrightarrow y,\ s_{(2)} \leftrightarrow \dot{y},\ s_{(3)} \leftrightarrow \ddot{y},\ s_{(4)} \leftrightarrow D_F$$

The state transition equations for this SV can be directly written from the time-propagation equations

$$y_{k+1} = y_k + h\dot{y}_k + (0.5)h^2\ddot{y}_k + w_{(1)k}$$

$$\dot{y}_{k+1} = \dot{y}_k + h\ddot{y}_k + w_{(2)k}$$

$$\ddot{y}_{k+1} = \ddot{y}_k + h\dddot{y}_k + w_{(3)k}$$

$$(D_F)_{k+1} = (D_F)_k + w_{(4)k}$$

where:

$$h \equiv \Delta t_k = t_{k+1} - t_k;$$

$$\dddot{y}_k = \{(d/dy)[-g(y)]\dot{y} + (d/dy)[d(y, \dot{y})]\dot{y} + (d/d\dot{y})[d(y, \dot{y})]\ddot{y}\}_k$$

is a function of y, $\dot{y}$, $\ddot{y}$, and D_F (all evaluated at $t = t_k$); $w_{(j)k}$ are components of process noise vector w_k. Hence writing

$$s_{(j)k+1} = f_{(j)}(s_k) + w_{(j)k} \qquad \text{for } j = 1, \ldots, n_s$$

we get

$$f_{(1)}(s_k) = (s_{(1)} + hs_{(2)} + (0.5)h^2 s_{(3)})_k$$

$$f_{(2)}(s_k) = (s_{(2)} + hs_{(3)})_k$$

$$f_{(3)}(s_k) = (s_{(3)} + h\dot{s}_{(3)})_k$$

$$f_{(4)}(s_k) = (s_{(4)})_k$$

where, as it follows from a previous expression for $\dddot{y}_k$, the time-derivative $\dot{s}_{(3)k}$ can be expressed in terms of $s_{(1)}$, $s_{(2)}$, $s_{(3)}$, and $s_{(4)}$ (all evaluated at t_k).

We assume that at each observation epoch t_k a ground based sensor measures both the position (y) and the velocity ($\dot{y}$) of the incoming ballistic missile. Hence the measurement equations are of the form

$$m_{(1)k} = y_k + v_{(1)k}$$

$$m_{(2)k} = \dot{y}_k + v_{(2)k}$$

or (in vector/matrix form),

$$m_k = Hs_k + v_k.$$

Here: v_k represents the measurement noise and

$$H = \begin{pmatrix} 1 & 0 & 0 & 0 \\ 0 & 1 & 0 & 0 \end{pmatrix}$$

Filter implementation requires a procedure for evaluating the F matrix. As noted in the description of *EKF* algorithm, the (i, j)th element of F_k is obtained by differentiating $f_{(i)}$ with respect to $s_{(j)}$ and then evaluating this derivative at t_k. For example, in the present case, we get

$$F_{(1,2)k} = (\delta f_{(1)}/\delta s_{(2)})_k = h = \Delta t.$$

In our implementation of the filter for the present problem, we included an algorithm for bounding the state error covariance matrix P. (This algorithm is described in Maybeck's vol 2.) We found it to be effective in stabilization of the filtering process.

Results of a Simulation Run. Figures 2(A–E) illustrate the results of a computer simulation run performed for the parameter values and the initial conditions summarized below in Fig. 2(A). The filter was tuned up to respond rapidly to relatively accurate measurements. Note that the drag factor D_F (expressed in square meters per kilogram) is treated as an unknown constant parameter that is estimated along with the dynamic variables of system state.

F. Other Approaches to Nonlinear Filtering and the Gaussian Sum Approximation Filter

Since it is generally impossible to construct for a nonlinear or non-Gaussian system an exact representation of *a posteriori* probability density functions (PDFs) $p(s_k \mid M_k)$, various types of finite approximations to $p(s_k \mid M_k)$ have been investigated. As an illustration of this approach we outline next one specific technique, known as the Gaussian sum approximation (GSA).

Let R^n denote the n-dimensional Euclidean space. The GSA method is based on a theoretical result, according to which any probability function p of a vector- (or scalar-) valued RV x, say of length n, can be approximated as closely as desired in the $L_1(R^n)$ space (i.e., the integral $\int_{R^n} | p(x) - p_A(x) | \, dx$ can be made arbitrarily small) by a function of the form

$$p_A(x) = \sum_{i=1}^{L} \alpha_i N[x - a_i, B_i] \tag{45}$$

for some positive integer L, positive scalars α_i such that $\alpha_1 + \alpha_2 + \cdots + \alpha_L = 1$, suitably selected n-dimensional vectors a_i, and $n \times n$ positive definite matrices B_i. In Eq. (45), $N[x - a_i, B_i]$ represents the n-variate Gaussian PDF

$$(2\pi)^{-n/2} | B_i |^{-1/2} \exp\{-\tfrac{1}{2}(x - a_i)^{\mathrm{T}} B_i^{-1}(x - a_i)\} \tag{46}$$

with $| B_i |$ denoting the determinant of B_i. Furthermore, it can be shown that $p_A(x)$ converges uniformly in x to any PDF of practical interest as the covariance matrices B_i tend to a zero matrix and L increases. There are many ways of selecting the parameters a_i, B_i, and α_i. For construction of a filtering scheme, it is convenient (a) to choose the values of a_i so as to build up in the state space a grid covering at least a substantial part of the mass of the PDF to be approximated and (b) to set $B_i = bI$ (with I representing an identity matrix) for some small positive scalar b. Then each term in the Gaussian sum on the right-hand side of Eq. (45) converges to an impulse function centered at a_i as b (>0) converges down to zero. Hence, for a small $b > 0$, each term in the Gaussian sum is practically zero outside a small open neighborhood (hypersphere) in R^n containing a_i. Since $p_A(x) \geq 0$ and $\int p_A(x)\, dx = 1$, p_A is a PDF.

Next suppose that $p(s_k | M_k)$ is approximated by

$$p_A(s_k | M_k) = \sum_{i=1}^{L} \alpha_{ik} N[s_k - \bar{s}_{ik}, B_{ik}] \tag{47}$$

Then, $p_A(s_k | M_k)$ also is a PDF and, while using appropriately selected values of $\bar{s}_{ik}$, one can show that

$$\hat{s}_{k|k} \equiv E[s_k | M_k] = \sum_{i=1}^{L} \alpha_{ik} \bar{s}_{ik} \tag{48}$$

and

$$P_{k|k} \equiv E[(s_k - \hat{s}_{k|k})(s_k - \hat{s}_{k|k})^{\mathrm{T}} | M_k]$$

$$= \sum_{i=1}^{L} \alpha_{ik}[B_{ik} + (\hat{s}_{k|k} - \bar{s}_{ik})(\hat{s}_{k|k} - \bar{s}_{ik})^{\mathrm{T}}] \tag{49}$$

This suggests that perhaps the conditional MMSE estimator $\hat{s}_{k|k}$ can be approximated as a weighted sum of conditional mean estimators, each representing an EKF. It can be proved that this indeed is the case. Combining the foregoing ideas with the nonlinear system model given by Eqs. (29) and (30) and Assumptions 1D–4D, the latter ones now possibly relaxed by dropping some or all Gaussianity assumptions, leads to a filtering scheme, which we outline next.

Discrete-Time Gaussian Sum Approximation (GSA) Filter Algorithm

This algorithm applies to the system model defined by Eqs. (29) and (30), and by the probabilistic assumptions 1D through 4D. Let n_s be the dimension of state vectors.

a. Let $k = 0$ (i.e., initialize the sampling time t_k to t_0) and select appropriate values of the parameters $\bar{s}_{ik}$ and $\alpha_{i,k-1}$ (all $\alpha_{i,k-1} \geq 0$ and $\sum_{i=1}^{L} \alpha_{i,k-1} = 1$) for $i = 1, \ldots, L$.

b. In order to complete a GSA

$$\sum_{i=1}^{L} \alpha_{i,k-1} N[s - \bar{s}_{ik}, \bar{B}_{ik}]$$

to $p(s_k | M_{k-1})$, where $M_k = \{m_k, M_{k-1}\}$ and M_{k-1} is an empty measurement set when $k = 0$, initialize (reinitialize) all L covariance matrices $\bar{B}_{ik}$ to bI, with b representing a small positive constant and I the $n_s \times n_s$ identity matrix.

c. Approximate $p(s_k | M_k)$ by means of the following measurement-update procedure. For $i = 1, \ldots L$ compute

$$H_{ik} = ((\delta h_k(s)/\delta s))_{s=\bar{s}_{ik}}$$

$$D_{ik} = (H_{ik}\bar{B}_{ik}H_{ik}^{\mathrm{T}} + R_k)^{-1}$$

$$K_{ik} = \bar{B}_{ik}H_{ik}^{\mathrm{T}}D_{ik}$$

$$B_{ik} = \bar{B}_{ik} - \bar{B}_{ik}H_{ik}^{\mathrm{T}}D_{ik}H_{ik}\bar{B}_{ik}^{\mathrm{T}}$$

$$s_{ik} = \bar{s}_{ik} + K_{ik}[m_k - h_k(\bar{s}_{ik})]$$

with the new weights determined by

$$S_k = \sum_{j=1}^{L} \alpha_{j,k-1} N[m_k - h_k(\bar{s}_{jk}), D_{ik}^{-1}]$$

and

$$\alpha_{ik} = \alpha_{i,k-1} N[m_k - h_k(\bar{s}_{ik}), D_{ik}^{-1}]/S_k$$

Finally, compute $\hat{s}_{k|k}$ and $P_{k|k}$ by means of Eqs. (48) and (49), respectively.

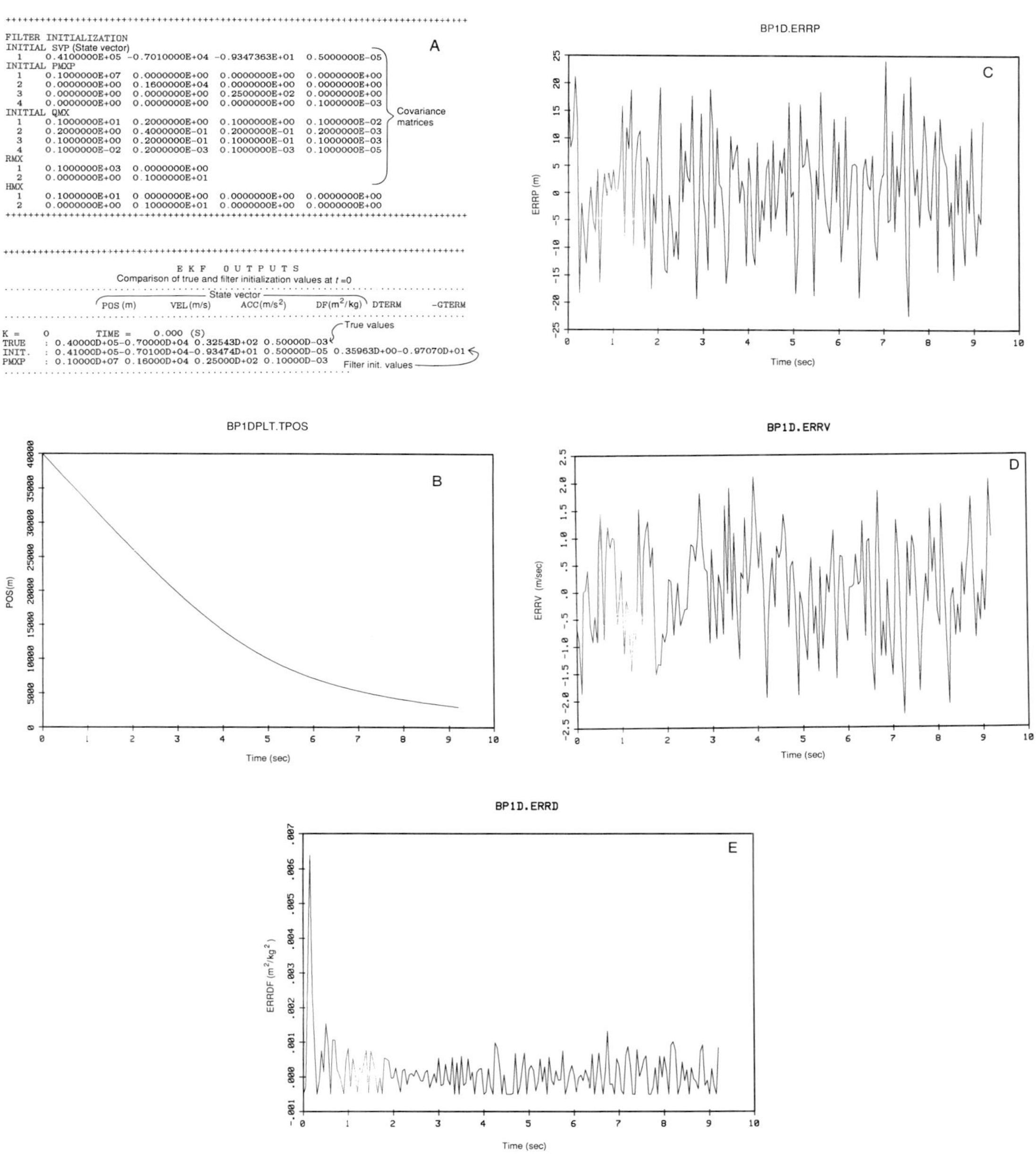

FIG. 2. (A) The upper part shows the state vector and filter matrices at the initialization time t_0. The lower part compares the true and initialized state vectors at t_0. (B) True position (the Y coordinate) of the ballistic projectile vs. time. (C) Error in position estimates vs. time. Because of the compression of time scale, the initialization error of 1 km is invisible on the graph. (D) Error in velocity estimates vs. time. Because of the compression of time scale, the initialization error of 10 m/sec is not visible on the graph. (E) Error in D_F estimates vs. time.

d. Approximate $p(s_{k+1} \mid M_k)$ by means of the following time-update procedure:

$$\sum_{i=1}^{L} \alpha_{ik} N[s_{k+1} - \bar{s}_{i,k+1}, \bar{B}_{i,k+1}]$$

where

$$F_{ik} = ((\delta f_k(s)/\delta s))_{s=s_{ik}}$$

$$\bar{s}_{i,k+1} = f_k(s_{ik})$$

$$\bar{B}_{i,k+1} = F_{ik} B_{ik} F_{ik}^{\mathrm{T}} + G_k(s_{ik}) Q_k G_k(s_{ik})^{\mathrm{T}}$$

e. Let $k \leftarrow k + 1$ (i.e., increment the sampling time by setting $t_k \leftarrow t_{k+1}$). If the new $t_k > t_{\max}$ (= estimation end time), then *quit*; else proceed to step f.

f. Test whether $\bar{B}_{ik} < bI$ (i.e., whether $[bI - \bar{B}_{ik}]$ is a positive definite matrix) for all i. If yes, go to step c; else go to step *b*.

In the preceding algorithm, use the same rule for computing matrices H_{ik} and F_{ik} as that given for matrices H_k and F_k (see the text following Eqs. (33)–(35)). As the above algorithm indicates, both the measurement-update and time-propagation equations for each constituent filter in the Gaussian sum are essentially those of an EKF; besides, when any covariance matrix $\bar{B}_{ik}$ becomes too "big" (in the sense explained in step f), all L covariance matrices $\bar{B}_{ik}$ must be reinitialized. If $L = 1$, the GSA filter reduces to an EKF.

The following two important advantages of the GSA come from the choice of the Gaussian weighting PDFs and the positive weighting coefficients that add to 1: (a) any finite Gaussian sum is a PDF; (b) the presence of Gaussian weighting PDFs allows the utilization of certain Gaussian properties in the computation of approximations to $p(s_k \mid M_k)$, though the resulting approximation function p_A is not Gaussian. However, the GSA approach has one disadvantage: The series obtained from the Gaussian sum expansion cannot be orthogonalized. Consequently, it is difficult to obtain useful error bounds. Thus, as an alternative to GSA, the use of approximations based on orthogonal series expansions (e.g., the Edgeworth and Gram–Charlier series) has been investigated. Despite the attractiveness of orthogonality, such approaches have one distinct disadvantage. The resulting truncated sum approximations are not PDFs.

Finally, we should mention the nonlinear filtering methods based on the assumption that $p(s_k \mid M_k)$ is Gaussian for all k. The EKF was one example of this approach. As we already noted, this assumption often leads to discarding a great deal of information present in the actually true PDF, especially in the multimodal case.

IV. Filter Implementation

Filters of the type considered in this article are usually implemented in software form. Besides a filter is typically designed for ultimate implementation as part of a real-time system, which means that it will be subject to timing constraints of that system. Thus, in addition to tasks already discussed (e.g., definition of the system model, selection of a filter algorithm, and making a trial filter work), one must (a) select appropriate numerical procedures to be used with the filter algorithm and (b) adapt the program implementing the filter to the real-time processing environment in case the filter is to become part of a real-time system. In the latter case, one must also time and size the algorithms for a particular real-time computer.

A. Numerical Procedures

The accuracy, stability, and computing efficiency of a filter critically depend on the adopted numerical procedures. For example, the unnecessary use of multiple precision arithmetic may be prohibitively expensive in some real-time applications; on the other hand, careless computation of dot products while using operands of insufficient length may quickly lead to an unbounded accumulation of roundoff error and destabilization of the estimation process. As another example, consider a continuous-time nonlinear filter. It often uses numerical integration to propagate the estimates of the state to the next time point, and thus one faces the problem of selecting an appropriate method for propagating numerically the solution of underlying differential equations.

There are several simple rules of thumb with regard to matrix operations in Kalman filtering of linear systems: (a) Dot products should in general be computed while using higher precision arithmetic than the precision used in remaining matrix operations; (b) matrices that theoretically are symmetric should be periodically resymmetrized [this simply requires replacing each member of every pair of elements a_{ij} and a_{ji}, where $i \neq j$, of a theoretically symmetric matrix A with $(a_{ij} + a_{ji})/2$]; (c) positive definiteness of theoretically positive definite matrices should be preserved. Furthermore, in many applications, such as in precision navigation, the state must be known to many more significant digits than the gain and the state error covariances. Hence, nearly all gain–covariance processing can be performed in lower precision than the processing of the state vector, but this approach is safe only if the gain–covariance processing is computationally stable. Square root filtering, discussed next, provides a numerically stable method for preserving the positive definiteness in state error covariance matrices.

B. Square Root Filtering

By far the greatest trouble spot in computer mechanization of the KF is the updating of state error covariance matrix P, that is, the computation of $P_{k|k}$ according to Eq. (18). As the estimation process progresses, the elements of $P_{k|k}$ typically continue to decrease in magnitude and so matrix $P_{k|k}$ keeps approaching the zero matrix, although theoretically it should forever remain positive definite, no matter how small in magnitude its elements become. Hence, unless special measures are taken, accumulation of roundoff error in the repetitive use of Eq. (18) may cause the computed $P_{k|k}$ to loose its positive definiteness. As suggested by the matrix inversion operation appearing on the right-hand side of Eq. (16) for computing the Kalman gain, this situation is aggravated if several components of the measurement vector are very accurate and consequently the positive definite measurement error covariance matrix R is ill-conditioned, that is, if R has eigenvalues of both relatively very large and small magnitudes.

Let A be a nonnegative definite symmetric matrix; then there exists a matrix S such that $A = SS^{\mathrm{T}}$. Matrix S is often called the square root of A. The Cholesky decomposition algorithm provides a method of constructing from A the matrix S so that S is lower triangular; that is, all elements of S above the main diagonal are zero. Square root filtering is motivated by the observations that, if the state error covariance matrix $P = SS^{\mathrm{T}}$, then (a) since SS^{T} is always nonnegative definite, matrix P expressed as SS^{T} cannot become negative definite, and (b) matrix S is generally less ill conditioned than matrix P.

Several versions of the square root filtering algorithm are known. The earliest form was developed by J. E. Potter in 1964 for applications in which the process noise is absent (i.e., covariance matrix Q is zero) and the measurements are sequentially processed as scalars. In 1967 J. F. Bellantoni and K. W. Dodge extended Potter's results to vector-valued measurements. A. Andrews in 1968 and then S. F. Schmidt in 1970 published two alternative procedures for handling the process noise. N. A. Carlson in 1973 described a procedure that considerably improved the speed and decreased the memory requirements of square root filtering and in which, as in Potter's algorithm, vector valued measurements are processed sequentially as scalars. Finally, the so-called UDU^{T} covariance factorization method is the most recent major milestone in numerical handling of Kalman filters. This method, developed by G. J. Bierman and C. L. Thornton, represents the state error covariances before and after the measurement update step as

$$P_{k|k-1} = (U_{k|k-1})D_{k|k-1}(U_{k|k-1})^{\mathrm{T}}$$

and

$$P_{k|k} = (U_{k|k})D_{k|k}(U_{k|k})^{\mathrm{T}}$$

with D being a diagonal matrix and U an upper triangular matrix with 1s on its main diagonal. In this method, the square root of covariance matrix, which now would correspond to $UD^{1/2}$, is never computed explicitly, which avoids numerical computation of square roots. Like Carlson's algorithm, the UDU^{T} factorization method maintains the covariance matrix in factored form and so (like Carlson's algorithm) is considerably more efficient in processor time and storage than the original Potter algorithm.

As a quick comparison of computational efficiency, the conventional Kalman method, the less efficient form of Carlson's algorithm, and the UDU^{T} factorization method are roughly equal: The processing of each time step (consisting of one time propagation and one measurement update) requires on the order of $\frac{1}{6}[9n_s^3 + 9n_s^2n_m + 3n_s^2n_w]$ adds and about the same number of multiplies, plus a relatively modest number of divides and square roots (square roots are required only in some, as in Potter's or Carlson's square root algorithms). Here, as before, n_s is the length of the state vector, n_m the length of measurement vector, and n_w the length of process noise vector w. The faster version of Carlson's algorithm is more efficient and requires only on the order of $\frac{1}{6}[5n_s^3 + 9n_s^2n_m + 3n_s^2n_w]$ adds and $\frac{1}{6}[5n_s^3 + 12n_s^2n_m + 3n_s^2n_w]$ multiplies, plus $2n_sn_m$ divides and n_sn_m square roots, at each time point. The stable (Joseph) form of the KF [as given by Eq. (18′)] fares more poorly: At each time step, it requires of the order of $\frac{1}{6}[18n_s^3 + 15n_s^2n_m + 3n_s^2n_w]$ adds and about the same number of multiples.

As a summary, (a) a square root filter is a numerically stable form for performing the KF covariance–gain processing defined by Eqs. (15), (16), and (18); (b) the efficiency of its more recent versions roughly compares with that of these three equations; (c) the increased stability allows one to use relatively low precision arithmetic in the KF gain–covariance processing, with a possible exception of some dot products.

Real-time implementation of a filter involves additional issues that are unimportant in the nonreal-time environment. Besides the adequacy of functional performance, the most important of these issues is the requirement to produce timely responses to external stimuli. Thus, resorting to a parallel or concurrent processing may be the only way out. This usually implies the use of special hardware architectures such as parallel, vector pipelined, or systolic processors.

As one example, consider the use of a filter in the tracking of multiple objects in a hard real-time environment characterized by strict deadlines. In such a case one may want to maintain simultaneously many estimation processes, each handling a single object. Parallel processors may seem to be a suitable hardware architecture for this problem, but if separate estimation processes in such an application progress at different rates and at any time some of them require a great amount of special handling, then parallel architecture, such as a single-instruction multiple-data-stream computer, may not be the best choice. As another example, consider a KF to be implemented as part of a navigation system on a small airborne computer (uniprocessor). Suppose that the navigation measurements come at a certain fixed rate. If the filtering process cannot keep up with the arrival rate of measurements and so not all of them can be utilized, the estimation performance may deteriorate. In this problem, if there is an upper bound on hardware resources, the only solution may be to decompose the estimation algorithm into concurrently executable processes. For instance, the time-propagation step (which, say, is to be executed at a relatively high rate) may constitute one process and the measurement-update step (which needs to be executed only at some lower rate, say, at the rate of measurement arrivals) may constitute another. Such a decomposition of an estimation algorithm into concurrent procedures often creates a surrogate algorithm that performs more poorly than the original algorithm.

The effects of the finite-length word computing is another issue that must be considered in filter implementation for real-time applications. The computer on which a filter is developed and validated through successive off-line simulations is often more powerful and uses higher-precision arithmetic and number representations than the ultimate real-time processor. Hence, one must in advance determine in advance what effect a shorter word length will have on performance.

V. Applications

A good part of present-day technology would be unthinkable without recursive estimators, especially modern computer-based control and communication systems. Kalman and other types of recursive filters have been widely adopted by the defense and aerospace communities for such applications as navigation, aircraft flight control, satellite tracking, and orbit determination.

Early applications of recursive filtering were mainly in the estimation and identification of uncertain dynamic or control systems. Many of these applications, although in general successful, were hastily executed in the sense that insufficient thought was given to various theoretical, numerical, and purely implementational issues. The first two decades were also marred by a flood of papers describing specific applications, published in the technical literature or presented at various engineering conferences. However, during that period many important theoretical issues, especially gaps in theoretical knowledge, were identified and resolved.

In contrast to the quick, widespread adoption of recursive estimators to control and of dynamic systems during the 1960s and 1970s, their penetration of signal processing was considerably less decisive. One reason for that was the inadequacy of computer hardware and software with respect to the stringent timing constraints of on-line signal processing, although there are several application areas of signal processing, such as the analysis of economic time series, in which real-time constraints are virtually nonexistent. Another factor was the technological culture of that period, which was also reinforced by the nature of the problem. In communication problems, one is usually interested in steady-state behavior. Alternative signal processing techniques, notably those based on frequency domain analysis, such as the fast Fourier transform, were developed and then adapted to digital signal processing. However, developments in computer hardware and software technologies (e.g., the introduction of gallium arsenide devices, very large scale integration, and data-flow architectures such as systolic processors) promise to change this situation.

Several interesting types of functional extensions of filtering are known. We briefly mention only one of them, which is known as adaptive filtering. Adaptive filtering is concerned with the generalization of estimation algorithms, especially of KFs, to state estimation situations in which the system model is not completely known. For example, one may want to estimate the state of a stochastic dynamic system for which some parameters, such as the covariance matrices of noise processes or a few coefficients in the system dynamics equation, are unknown or are changing in an unknown way in time. A filter that estimates the state while concurrently estimating the values of the unknown components of the system model is called an adaptive filter. Example 2 illustrates a relatively simple case of adaptive filtering: estimation of the parameters that define the drag force while estimating the trajectory. In that example, the adaptive filtering problem is solved by introducing an additional component into the state vector.

BIBLIOGRAPHY

Anderson, B. D. O., and Moore, J. B. (1979). "Optimal Filtering." Prentice-Hall, Englewood Cliffs, New Jersey.

Davis, M. H. A., and Vinter, R. B. (1985). "Stochastic Modelling and Control." Chapman and Hall, New York.

Jazwinski, A. H. (1970). "Stochastic Processes and Filtering Theory." Academic Press, New York.

Kailath, T. (1974). *IEEE Trans. Inf. Theory* **IT-20**(2), 146–179.

Kalman, R. E. (1960). *Trans. ASME J. Basic Eng. Ser. D* **82,** 34–35.

Kalman, R. E., and Bucy, R. S. (1961). *Trans. ASME Ser. D. J. Basic Eng.* **83,** 95–107.

Maybeck, P. S. (1979, 1982). "Stochastic Models, Estimation, and Control," vol. 1 and vols. 2 and 3, respectively. Academic Press, New York.

Schmidt, G. T. (1976). "Linear and Nonlinear Filtering Techniques," Control and Dynamic Systems, Vol. 12, pp. 63–98. Academic Press, New York.

Thornton, C. L., and Bierman, G. J. (1980). "UDU^T Covariance Factorization for Kalman Filtering," Control and Dynamic Systems, Vol. 16, p. 177–248. Academic Press, New York.

KINETICS (CHEMISTRY)

Keith J. Laidler *University of Ottawa*

GLOSSARY

Activated complex: Configuration of atoms corresponding to an arbitrarily small region near to the col in a potential energy surface.

Activation energy: Energy defined by the equation

$$E \equiv -R \frac{d \ln k}{d(1/T)}$$

where k is the rate constant, T the absolute temperature, and R the gas constant. This energy is related to the heights of energy barriers to reaction.

Catalysis: Substance that increases the rate of a chemical reaction without itself being consumed, and without affecting the energetics of the overall reaction, is called a catalyst. The process is called catalysis.

Composite (complex or stepwise) reaction: A reaction that involves more than one elementary reaction.

Elementary reaction: Reaction in which no reaction intermediates (other than transition species) have been detected or need to be postulated in order to explain the behavior.

Half-life: Time required for a reactant concentration to reach a value that is the arithmetic mean of its initial and final values.

Inhibition: Process by which a substance (called an inhibitor) reduces the rate of a chemical reaction.

Molecularity: Number of reactant particles (atoms, molecules, free radicals, or ions) that are involved in the microscopic event occurring in an elementary reaction.

Order of reaction: For some reactions the rate of reaction is expressible as

$$v = k[\mathrm{A}]^{\alpha}[\mathrm{B}]^{\beta}$$

where k, α, and β are independent of concentration and time. The exponent α is the order with respect to A, and β is the order with respect to B. These are partial orders; the sum of the partial orders, often written as n, is the overall order.

Photochemical reaction: Chemical reaction brought about by electromagnetic radiation having insufficient energy to bring about ionization.

Potential energy surface: Surface resulting from a plot of potential energy against two parameters, such as two interatomic distances. If more than two parameters are used the term hypersurface is employed.

Pre-exponential factor: The factor A when the rate constant is expressed as

$$k = Ae^{-E/RT}$$

where E is the activation energy.

Rate of reaction: Rate of formation of a product, $d[Z]/dt$, or the rate of consumption of a reactant, $-d[A]/dt$, divided by the corresponding coefficient in the stoichiometric equation.

Rate constant: For a reaction having an order, the rate constant k is the constant appearing in the rate equation.

Radiation-chemical reaction: Chemical reaction brought about by electromagnetic or particle radiation having sufficient energy to bring about ionization.

Reaction cross section: Quantity that is used in collision theory to give a measure of the rate of a bimolecular reaction; it is the probability of reaction multiplied by πd^2, where d is the collision diameter, i.e., the distance between the centers of two colliding reactant molecules.

Reaction (or molecular) dynamics: A field that deals with the intermolecular and intramolecular motion that occurs during the course of a chemical reaction and the quantum states of the reactant and product molecules.

State-to-state kinetics: Study of the transformation of reacting molecules in specified quantum states into product molecules in specified quantum states.

Steady-state treatment: Application of the hypothesis that for an intermediate X present at very low concentrations, $d[X]/dt = 0$.

Transition-state theory: Theory of rates that focuses attention on activated complexes and assumes them to have a concentration corresponding to equilibrium with the reactant molecules.

Transition species: Species having a state intermediate between reactants and products.

Chemical kinetics deals with the rates of chemical processes and how the rates depend on factors such as concentrations, temperature, and pressure. The ultimate objective of a chemical-kinetic investigation is to gain information about the mechanisms of chemical reactions. Such information is also provided by certain nonkinetic studies, but little can be known about the mechanism of a reaction until its kinetics have been investigated. Even then, some doubt must remain about a reaction mechanism; an investigation, kinetic or otherwise, can disprove a proposed mechanism but cannot establish a mechanism with absolute certainty. Chemical kinetics has very far-reaching implications in that it relates to many branches of biology, geology, engineering, and even psychology. Theories of chemical kinetics are also applicable to purely physical processes, such as flow processes.

I. Basic Kinetic Principles

Several rates can be defined with reference to a chemical reaction. Substances whose concentrations decrease with time are known as reactants, and the rate of decrease of a reactant concentration is known as the rate of consumption (removal or disappearance) of that reactant. Concentration is amount of substance (S.I. unit: mol) divided by volume (S.I. unit: m^3), and the concentration of a substance A is conveniently written as c_A or [A]. The rate of consumption of A is thus defined as

$$v_A = -d[A]/dt \tag{1}$$

Its S.I. unit is mol m^{-3} s^{-1}, but mol dm^{-3} s^{-1} (also written as mol L^{-1} s^{-1} or as M s^{-1}) is more commonly used.

Rates of consumption of two reactants A and B are only the same if 1 mol of A reacts with 1 mol of B. If, for example, the stoichiometric equation is of the type

$$A + 2B \rightarrow Y + Z$$

the rate of consumption of B is twice the rate of consumption of A.

The rate of formation of a product of reaction is defined as the rate of increase in its concentration: thus for a product Z

$$v_Z = d[Z]/dt \tag{2}$$

Again, the rates of formation of different products are not always the same, nor are they necessarily equal to the rates of consumption of reactants. Thus if the stoichiometry of the reaction is

$$3A + B \rightarrow 2Y + Z$$

and this stoichiometry is preserved throughout the course of reaction,

$$\frac{v_A}{3} = v_B = \frac{v_Y}{2} = v_Z \tag{3}$$

The S.I. unit is the same for all of these rate expressions, and mol dm^{-3} s^{-1} is most commonly used.

Sometimes, but not always, it is possible to define a quantity, known as the rate of reaction, which is independent of the reactants and products. This can only be done if the reaction is of known stoichiometry; for some reactions there are numerous minor products and the stoichiometry is uncertain. Another condition for defining a rate of reaction is that the stoichiometric equation must remain the same throughout the course of reaction: for some reactions intermediates are formed in significant amounts, and the stoichiometry varies as the reaction proceeds. If these two conditions are satisfied, i.e., if the stoichiometry is known and is time independent, the rate of reaction is given by any of the expressions that appear in Eq. (3). In other words, the rate of reaction is the rate of consumption or formation divided by the appropriate coefficient that appears in the stoichiometric equation. In the case of products these coefficients are called the stoichiometric coefficients; in the case of reactants the stoichiometric coefficients are the *negatives* of the coefficients in the rate equation. As seen in Eq. (3), this division has made the four rates equal to one another, so that the rate of reaction is unique for the reaction under the particular conditions of the experiment.

It is important to note that rate of reaction, unlike rates of consumption and formation, only has meaning with reference to a specified stoichiometric equation for the reaction. Thus, if the stoichiometric equation had been written as

$$\tfrac{3}{2}\mathrm{A} + \tfrac{1}{2}\mathrm{B} \rightarrow \mathrm{Y} + \tfrac{1}{2}\mathrm{Z}$$

the rate of reaction would be

$$v = \tfrac{2}{3}v_{\mathrm{A}} = 2v_{\mathrm{B}} = v_{\mathrm{Y}} = 2v_{\mathrm{Z}} \qquad (4)$$

and would therefore be *twice* the rate specified with reference to the first form of the equation.

Note also that some kineticists define rates with reference to the rates of change of amounts of substances rather than their concentrations; the S.I. unit is then mol s^{-1}, there being no division by volume.

In general, rates depend on concentrations of reactants and sometimes on concentrations of products and other substances. For some reactions the rate of reaction v can be expressed by an equation of the form

$$v = k[\mathrm{A}]^{\alpha}[\mathrm{B}]^{\beta} \qquad (5)$$

where k, α, and β, are independent of concentration and time. Similar equations apply to rates of consumption and formation. The exponent α is known as the order of reaction with respect to A. The term *order* was introduced in 1887 by F. W. Ostwald (1853–1932), but the concept of order had been used in 1884 by J. H. van't Hoff (1852–1911). Similarly the exponent β is the order with respect to B. When there is more than one such order, as in this example, each one is called a partial order, and their sum, $\alpha + \beta + \cdots$, is known as the overall order and is often given the symbol n.

A simple case is when the rate equation is given by

$$v = k[\mathrm{A}] \qquad (6)$$

An example of such a first-order reaction is the conversion of cyclopropane into propylene

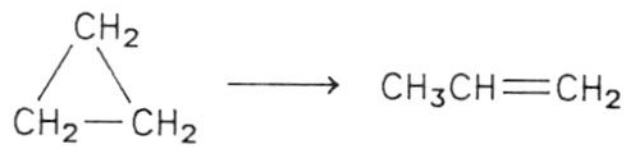

A second-order reaction can involve a single reactant

$$v = k[\mathrm{A}]^2 \qquad (7)$$

or two reactants

$$v = k[\mathrm{A}][\mathrm{B}] \qquad (8)$$

In the latter case the partial orders are unity, and the overall order is two. The process

$$\mathrm{H_2 + I_2 \rightleftharpoons 2HI}$$

is an example, being second order in both directions. Reaction orders are not necessarily integral; in the case of the acetaldehyde decomposition, for example,

$$\mathrm{CH_3CHO \rightarrow CH_4 + CO}$$

the order is $\tfrac{3}{2}$:

$$v = k[\mathrm{CH_3CHO}]^{3/2} \qquad (9)$$

This failure of the kinetics to correspond to the stoichiometry indicates that the reaction occurs by a composite mechanism, the nature of which is considered in Section IX.

The constant k that appears in the preceding equations is known as the rate constant. Its units depend on the order of reaction. Thus, if a reaction is first order [Eq. (6)] and v is expressed as mol dm^{-3} s^{-1} and [A] as mol dm^{-3}, the unit of k is s^{-1}. Similarly, for a second-order reaction the unit of k is usually dm^3 mol^{-1} s^{-1}. Just as rates of consumption and formation depend, in general, on the reactant or product under consideration, so do the corresponding rate constants. The rate constant that derives from the rate of reaction, for a specified stoichiometric equation, is unique.

By no means do all equations have rate equations of the type shown in Eq. (5). Sometimes reactant concentrations appear in the denominator of the rate equation, and this is indicative of a composite mechanism.

If a chemical reaction is sufficiently slow it is possible to mix reactants together or to raise the temperature of the reaction system very rapidly so as to start the reaction, and then to measure concentrations of reactants or products at various times. Such concentrations may be measured by chemical methods or by physical methods such as spectrophotometry. Two procedures are then available for determining orders of reactions and rate constants. One method is the method of integration, which involves integrating the differential equation for the rate and obtaining expressions for concentrations of reactants and products as a function of time. This integrated equation, which describes the time course of the reaction, is then fitted to the experimental results.

A second method, the differential method, involves determining rates from the slopes of concentration–time curves. An analysis is made of the way in which the rates depend on the concentrations of reactants, and the order and rate constant can then be deduced.

For rapid chemical reactions special methods must be used. For reactions that are not extremely rapid, flow methods are useful. Reactants may be mixed together in specially designed vessels and then passed along a tube, concentrations being measured at various positions by physical techniques such as spectrophotometry which allow instantaneous determinations to be made. A commonly used technique is the stopped-flow method, in which reactants are mixed and the flow suddenly stopped, so that the mixture is trapped in a vessel in which, by physical methods, concentrations can be studied as a function of time. The results can be analyzed by suitable adaptations of either the method of integration or the differential method. [*See* CHEMICAL KINETICS, EXPERIMENTATION.]

Some reactions, however, are so rapid that mixing cannot be achieved sufficiently rapidly. For such reactions the relaxation methods, such as the temperature-jump (T-jump) method may be used. They were developed in 1954 by M. Eigen (b. 1927). In this technique a reaction system at equilibrium is subjected to a very rapid rise in temperature which causes the equilibrium to shift (relax) to a new position of equilibrium. Physical methods are available for following the concentration changes during this relaxation, and the results can be analyzed to give the rate constants and the order of reaction.

A quantity that has proved useful for comparing rates of different reactions is the half-life, or half-period. The half-life of a given reactant is the time that it takes for half of it to be consumed during the reaction. The way in which the half-life depends on reactant concentrations varies with the order of the reaction; for the special case of a first-order reaction there is no dependence of half-life on reactant concentration. For a reaction of any order the half-life is inversely proportional to the rate constant; half-lives are therefore useful in giving an inverse measure of the rate of a reaction and can be used for comparing reactions of different orders.

Sometimes the rate of a chemical reaction is affected by the addition of a substance that is not consumed in the process and does not affect the equilibrium constant for the reaction. When the rate is increased in this way the added substance is known as a catalyst, and the effect is called catalysis, this name having been coined in 1836 by J. J. Berzelius (1779–1848). Catalysis can be classified as homogeneous catalysis (Section XI) in which only one phase is involved, and as heterogeneous or surface catalysis (Section VIII) in which the reaction occurs at an interface between phases. In biological systems catalysis is brought about by enzymes, which are proteins: the action is sometimes homogeneous and sometimes heterogeneous. A special type of catalysis, brought about by the product of a reaction, is known as autocatalysis. For example, ester hydrolysis is catalyzed by acids, which are products of the reaction; the process may therefore first accelerate. The term *catalyst* is sometimes applied to a substance that is consumed but which in other ways acts like a catalyst: such substances, however, are better called pseudocatalysts or activators. Mechanisms of catalysis are considered in Sections VIII and XI.

An inhibitor is a substance that reduces the rate of a chemical reaction. Such substances were formerly called negative catalysts, but this terminology is not recommended since their action is quite different from that of a true catalyst. Inhibitors, in fact, act either by interacting with a catalyst and rendering it less effective or by removing active intermediates such as free radicals. The term *inhibitor* is often applied to substances that are consumed during the course of reaction. If a reaction in the absence of an inhibitor proceeds with a rate v_0, and in the presence of inhibitor with rate v, the degree of inhibition is defined as

$$\varepsilon_i = \frac{v_0 - v}{v_0} = 1 - \frac{v}{v_0} \tag{10}$$

II. Molecularity

Chemical reactions can be classified as either elementary or composite. An elementary reaction is one which, as far as can be determined, goes in a single stage; the reactants pass smoothly through an intermediate state and then become products. If a reaction is elementary no specific intermediates can be detected or need to be postulated in order to explain the kinetic behavior. Composite reactions, also known as complex or stepwise reactions, occur in more than one stage, and therefore involve two or more elementary reactions: they are considered in more detail in Section IX.

For an elementary reaction, but not for a composite reaction, the term *molecularity* can be employed. The molecularity of an elementary reaction is the number of reactant particles (atoms, molecules, free radicals, or ions) that are involved in each individual chemical event. For example, the cyclopropane isomerization appears to be elementary, in that each chemical act involves a single cyclopropane molecule: the molecularity is unity, and the reaction is said to be unimolecular. For the elementary reaction

$$Br + H_2 \rightarrow HBr + H$$

the molecularity is two, and the reaction is said to be bimolecular. A reaction having molecularity of three, such as

$$2NO + Cl_2 \rightarrow 2NOCl$$

is said to be trimolecular. Reactions of higher molecularities are unknown: it is unlikely for more than three molecules to come together in a single chemical event, and instead the mechanism is composite.

It is important to distinguish clearly between the molecularity and the order. The latter is a purely experimental quantity, which is concerned with how the rate depends on reactant concentrations; the concept of order applies to some composite reactions. The molecularity of an elementary reaction, on the other hand, is arrived at by inference from all of the evidence available about the reaction. One such piece of evidence is the order. If a reaction in the gas phase appears to be elementary and has an order of one, it is reasonable to conclude that it is unimolecular. However, as will be seen in Section VI, unimolecular gas reactions become second order at low pressures, and it is therefore unsafe to conclude that a second-order gas reaction is bimolecular: it may be a unimolecular reaction in its second-order region.

With reactions in solution the question arises as to whether the solvent should be included in the molecularity. It is usually considered that it counts in the molecularity if it enters into the overall reaction but not if it exerts only an environmental effect. Thus, a process in aqueous solution in which a compound was being hydrolyzed, with the reaction of a water molecule with each solute molecule, would be regarded as bimolecular. The isomerization of cyclopropane in solution, however, is unimolecular.

Similar conventions are applied to reactions on surfaces. If individual molecules undergo decomposition or isomerization on a surface the reaction is usually described as unimolecular, even though the surface atoms are also involved. This, however, would not be done if the material of the surface entered into the final products.

III. Temperature and Reaction Rates

A considerable number of empirical equations have been proposed to express the dependence of reaction rates on temperature, and for over 60 years—from about 1850 to about 1910—there was much uncertainty and confusion. The difficulty was that several of the proposed equations fitted the data equally well, and the problem was finally resolved in favor of equations for which there was a useful physical interpretation.

One of the earliest equations relating the rate constant k to the absolute temperature T was

$$k = Ae^{DT} \quad \text{or} \quad \ln k = \ln A + DT \qquad (11)$$

This equation was proposed in 1862 by M. Berthelot (1827–1907). The parameters A and D are empirical quantities, and this equation requires that a plot of ln k against the absolute temperature T will be linear, as is approximately true in many cases. It is of interest that recently (1982–1985) C. M. Hurd and co-workers have shown that this equation is obeyed when a process occurs by quantum-mechanical tunneling (see Section IV), and they have provided an interpretation in terms of atomic vibrations.

In 1884 J. H. van't Hoff presented the equation, derived from thermodynamics, for the temperature dependence of an equilibrium constant K:

$$\frac{d \ln K}{dT} = \frac{\Delta H^\circ}{RT^2} \qquad (12)$$

where R is the gas constant and ΔH° the standard change in heat constant (enthalpy) during the overall process. He then noted that an equilibrium constant is the ratio of rate constants for the reaction in forward and reverse directions, his argument being as follows: If a reaction

$$A + B \rightleftharpoons Y + Z$$

is elementary in both directions, the rate from left to right is $k_1[A][B]$ and that from right to left is $k_{-1}[Y][Z]$. At equilibrium the two rates are equal so that

$$\left(\frac{[Y][Z]}{[A][B]}\right)_{eq} = \frac{k_1}{k_{-1}} = K \quad (13)$$

This being so, van't Hoff argued, k_1 and k_{-1} must show the same kind of temperature dependence as K, and therefore for a rate constant k

$$\frac{d \ln k}{dT} = \frac{E}{RT^2} \quad (14)$$

where E is some energy term. van't Hoff did not assume that E itself is temperature independent but considered several possibilities. If E is temperature independent Eq. (14) integrates to

$$\ln k = \ln A - \frac{E}{RT}$$

or

$$k = Ae^{-E/RT} \quad (15)$$

where A is a constant. Another possibility considered by van't Hoff is that E is linear in temperature; in that case the equation reduces to the form

$$k = AT^m e^{-E/RT} \quad (16)$$

where m is a constant. Most kinetic data fit this equation very satisfactorily, and it is often used in modern compilations of kinetic data. The reason that equations of such different forms fit data reasonably well is that in kinetic work the temperature range is usually quite limited.

In 1889 S. A. Arrhenius (1859–1927) showed that van't Hoff's simplest equation [Eq. (15)] applied satisfactorily to a number of results, and he also suggested a very simple interpretation for the equation; consequently this equation, although first given by van't Hoff, is now always called the Arrhenius equation. Arrhenius pointed out that increasing the temperature by 10°C often approximately doubles the rate of reaction, but that the average molecular energies do not increase to anything like that extent. He concluded that reaction rates cannot depend on the average molecular energies, and he postulated that a pre-equilibrium is first established between reactant molecules and some highly energized intermediate. Thus, for a bimolecular reaction between A and B the process would be represented as

$$A + B \rightleftharpoons AB^* \rightarrow Y + Z$$

The intermediate complex AB^*, being of high energy, is formed only in very small amounts, and its concentration increases strongly with increase in temperature. The rate is proportional to the concentration of AB^*, and the large temperature coefficients are therefore explained.

Arrhenius's interpretation is essentially correct, and it was later made more precise by the application of statistical procedures to reaction systems. Figure 1 shows the distribution of energy in a system, as given by the treatments of J. Clark Maxwell (1831–1879) and L. E. Boltzmann (1844–1906). The fraction of molecules having energy in excess of a specified value E (per mole) is $e^{-E/RT}$, which is the fraction that appears in the Arrhenius equation [Eq. (15)]. The interpretation of the equation is that only those colliding molecules having joint energy in excess of E are able to undergo reaction; other collisions are ineffective, the reactant molecules merely separating unchanged. [*See* STATISTICAL MECHANICS.]

The energy E that appears in Eq. (15) is known as the activation energy or the energy of activation. The parameter A, which has the same units as the rate constant, is called the preexponential factor (formerly the frequency factor). The activation energy is obtained experimentally by plotting ln k against $1/T$ and measuring the slope, as shown schematically in Fig. 2; the slope is equal to $-E/R$. On the basis of a statistical argument it was shown in 1939 by R. H. Fowler and E. A. Guggenheim that the activation energy obtained in this way is the average energy of the molecules actually undergoing reaction minus the average energy of all of the reactant molecules.

The activation energy is conveniently considered with reference to a potential energy sur-

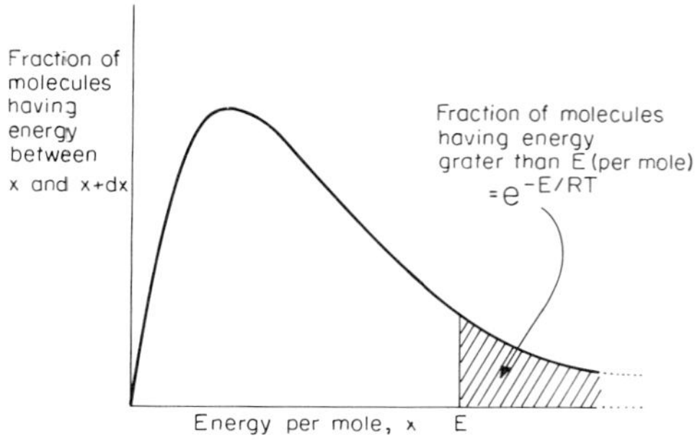

FIG. 1. Distribution of energy in a gas, according to the treatments of Maxwell and Boltzmann.

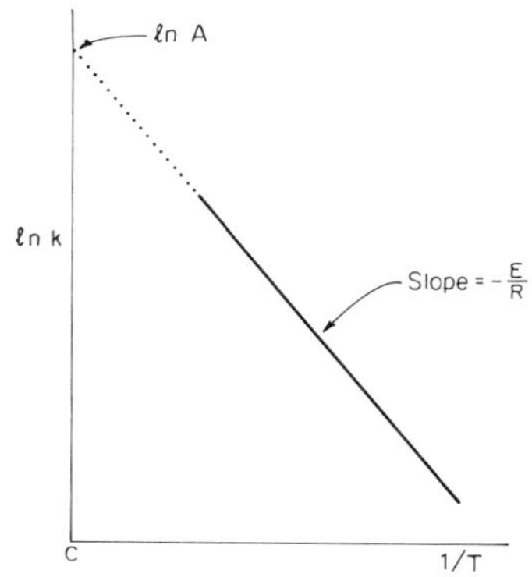

FIG. 2. Schematic Arrhenius plot of ln k against $1/T$. The slope is $-E/R$, and the activation energy E is thus defined by $E \equiv -R[d \ln k/d(1/T)]$.

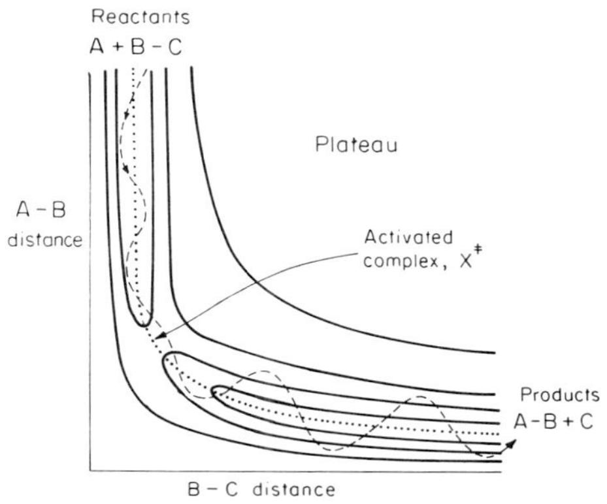

FIG. 3. Schematic potential energy surface for a reaction showing the minimal reaction path (dotted line) and a typical trajectory (dashed line).

face, in which potential energy is plotted against bond distances and angles. A simple type of surface is obtained for a reaction

$$A + B—C \rightarrow A—B + C$$

in which A, B, and C are atoms. The system A ... B ... C requires three parameters to describe it; these might be the A–B, B–C, and A–C distances, or two of the distances and an angle. The potential energy would therefore have to be plotted against three parameters, which would require a four-dimensional diagram. Since such a diagram cannot be constructed or visualized it is necessary to use a series of three-dimensional diagrams in which one parameter has been fixed at a particular value. For example, the A–B–C angle might be fixed at 180°, and for some systems this is the most probable configuration. [*See* POTENTIAL ENERGY SURFACES.]

This type of three-dimensional diagram is conveniently represented on a two-dimensional surface as a contour diagram, and an example of such a diagram is shown in Fig. 3. The course of the reaction is then represented by motion of the system from the top left-hand region to the bottom right-hand region. In the top left-hand region the A–B distance is large, and the configuration therefore corresponds to A + B—C; in the bottom right-hand region the B–C distance is large and the system is A—B + C. Many calculations have been made to determine the general shapes of potential energy surfaces, some of them involving pure quantum-mechanical theory and others introducing a certain amount of empiricism. All of the calculations have shown that the surfaces for A ... B ... C systems are of the general form shown in Fig. 3. The course of an individual reaction involves the motion of the system along the lower part of a rising valley until it reaches a col or saddle-point; then the system descends into another valley and finally reaches the state A—B + C. The dotted line in the diagram shows what is called the minimal reaction path, which corresponds to the path of steepest descent from the col into the two valleys. If it were to follow this minimal reaction path the system would make the least expenditure of energy. In reality, however, systems will follow a variety of reaction paths, or trajectories, depending on the initial conditions of the reactants A and B–C. A typical trajectory is illustrated by the dashed line in Fig. 3. This particular trajectory leads to considerable vibrational energy in the product molecule B–C, a matter that is referred to further in Section V.

Those configurations of atoms that correspond to an arbitrary small region near the col of a potential energy surface are known as activated complexes, and are often represented as $X^{\ddagger}$. The state of an activated complex is known as the transition state. Activated complexes play a very important role in theories of reaction rates, as will be seen in Sections IV and V.

The preceding discussion has been confined to a system of three atoms, with the angle A–B–C held constant. If more atoms are involved, it is necessary to consider potential energy hypersurfaces for which there are more than three dimensions. These can be dealt with by extensions of the methods outlined; the data for the hypersurfaces can be stored in a computer, and activated complexes can again be identified.

Sometimes much more complicated reaction systems are treated in an approximate way in terms of three-dimensional surfaces such as that shown in Fig. 3, and such treatments, although not precise, are very helpful in considering the course of reactions.

IV. Statistical Theories of Rates

Most measurements of rates of chemical reactions are made on bulk systems in which the reacting molecules are distributed over a range of energy states (cf. Fig. 1). Some theories of reaction rates therefore focus on the bulk, or macroscopic, systems. This requires them to be statistical treatments.

It is useful to consider theories of reaction rates in terms of the Arrhenius equation [Eq. (15)] which has two parameters, the pre-exponential factor A and the activation energy E. If each one of these can be calculated from first principles a complete theory of rates has been attained. If a potential energy surface has been calculated the height of the barrier to reaction is known, and the activation energy can be deduced from this height (although it is somewhat difficult to do this precisely). Progress is being made towards the reliable calculation of potential energy surfaces by quantum-mechanical methods, but success has so far only been achieved for systems involving few nuclei and electrons; no doubt the problems for more complicated systems will be overcome in the future.

For the treatment of the pre-exponential factor A there have been several useful treatments, and there has been much more success in calculating values that agree with experiment.

The first of these was simple collision theory, in which reacting molecules were treated as if they were hard spheres, and the frequencies of their collisions were calculated on the basis of kinetic theory. This treatment leads to a collision frequency factor z, and the rate constant is then obtained by multiplying z by $e^{-E/RT}$, which is the fraction of collisions in which there is sufficient energy for reaction to occur:

$$k = ze^{-E/RT} \tag{17}$$

A particularly clear formulation of this kind was presented in 1918 by W. C. McC. Lewis (1885–1956), and on its basis he calculated a value of the pre-exponential factor for the reaction $2HI \rightarrow H_2 + I_2$ that was in excellent agreement with experiment.

However, later work showed that rather large deviations from experiment are obtained for reactions in which the reacting molecules are more complicated. This collision theory is evidently too simple and unlikely to be generally reliable. One weakness is the assumption that molecules are hard spheres, which implies that any collision with sufficient energy will lead to reaction; if the molecules are more complicated, this is not the case. A more fundamental objection to the treatment is that when applied to forward and reverse reactions it cannot lead to an expression for the equilibrium constant that involves the correct thermodynamic parameters. More recent work has involved a similar approach but has treated molecular collisions in a more realistic and detailed way.

The most successful of the later statistical treatments has been transition-state theory, first formulated simultaneously and independently in 1935 by H. Eyring (1901–1981) and by M. G. Evans (1904–1952) and M. Polanyi (1891–1976). Transition-state theory treats the rates of elementary reactions as if there were a special type of equilibrium, having an equilibrium constant $K\ddagger$, between reactants and activated complexes. The rate constant is then given by

$$k = (\mathbf{k}T/h)K^{\ddagger} \tag{18}$$

where $\mathbf{k}$ is the Boltzmann constant (the gas constant per molecule) and h is the Planck constant. This assumption of equilibrium can be justified in most cases, but it breaks down for certain types of potential energy surfaces, and particularly when the barrier is low so that the reaction is rapid. An important and simplifying feature of transition-state theory is that it focuses attention on the activated complex. How the system reaches the transition state and how it behaves after reaching the transition state, is not considered to affect the rate of reaction.

The equilibrium constant $K^{\ddagger}$ can be treated in two different but equivalent ways. In the first procedure, the methods of statistical mechanics are used. Equilibrium constants can be calculated reliably in terms of partition functions for the molecules involved, and the same can be done for the particular equilibrium constant $K^{\ddagger}$. What are required are the masses of the reactant molecules and the activated complex, their moments of inertia, and their vibrational frequencies. For the reactant molecules this is usually straightforward. These parameters are also known for an activated complex if a reliable potential energy surface has been calculated. If it has not, the parameters can usually be estimated sufficiently well to lead to useful approximate rate constants.

The second procedure is to employ a thermodynamic formulation. The equilibrium constant $K^{\ddagger}$ can be expressed as $e^{-\Delta^{\ddagger}G/RT}$, where $\Delta^{\ddagger}G$, known as the Gibbs energy of activation, is the change in Gibbs energy when the reactants become activated complexes. The Gibbs energy of activation can, in turn, be expressed as $\Delta^{\ddagger}H - T\Delta^{\ddagger}S$, where $\Delta^{\ddagger}H$ is the enthalpy of activation and $\Delta^{\ddagger}S$ the entropy of activation. The rate constant k can thus be formulated as

$$k = \frac{\mathbf{k}T}{h} e^{-\Delta^{\ddagger}G/RT} = \frac{\mathbf{K}T}{h} e^{\Delta^{\ddagger}S/R} e^{-\Delta^{\ddagger}H/RT} \quad (19)$$

This equation is of the same form as Eq. (16); the factors $e^{-\Delta^{\ddagger}H/RT}$ corresponds to $e^{-E/RT}$, while the pre-exponential factor $(\mathbf{k}T/h)e^{\Delta^{\ddagger}S/R}$ shows dependence on temperature. However, $\Delta^{\ddagger}H$ is not quite the same as the activation energy E, but adjustments can easily be made for different types of reactions.

Much effort has gone into testing the validity of the original formulation of transition-state theory (now often referred to as conventional transition-state theory) and to improving it or proposing alternative theories. Useful extensions of the theory have been suggested, some of them involving locating the activated complex at a position other than at the col in the potential energy surface. Improvement has been achieved, but only at the cost of making very extensive calculations and making assumptions the justification for which is not always entirely clear. In addition to these extensions of conventional transition-state theory there have been some entirely different approaches, such as the dynamical treatments to be considered in Section V.

Imperfect as it is—as are all scientific theories—conventional transition-state theory is of importance in providing a conceptual framework with the aid of which much insight is gained into how chemical reactions occur. It is possible without even making any numerical calculations to make qualitative predictions of many important kinetic effects. So far no alternative treatment has provided any such insight.

Sometimes chemical reactions occur to some extent by quantum-mechanical tunneling. Usually systems must surmount the col in the potential energy surface (Fig. 3), but quantum-mechanical theory allows the possibility of going from the initial state A + BC to the final state AB + C without passage over the col. This arises when very light species, such as electrons and hydrogen atoms, are involved in the reaction. For example, in a reaction such as

$$Tl^{2+} + Fe^{2+} \rightarrow Fe^{3+} + Tl^{+}$$

there is simply the transfer of an electron, which tunnels through the potential energy barrier without going over it. Tunneling is also important in a reaction such as

$$D + H_2 \rightarrow DH + H$$

where D is a deuterium atom. Here there is a transfer of a hydrogen atom H, and the reaction involves some passage over the energy barrier but also some tunneling. Since the rate of tunneling increases much less with temperature than the passage over the barrier, quantum-mechanical tunneling is relatively more important at low temperatures, and it is at such temperatures that much of the evidence for tunneling has been obtained.

Quantum-mechanical tunneling is an important factor that must be considered in connection with kinetic-isotope effects. Suppose, for example, that the reactions

$$D + H_2 \rightarrow DH + H$$

and

$$D + D_2 \rightarrow D_2 + D$$

are compared. The ratio of rate constants depends on certain factors that enter into the partition functions for the reactants and activated complexes but also on the fact that quantum-mechanical tunneling is important for the first reaction but not for the second. The deuterium atom D is twice as heavy as the H atom, and tunneling is quite unimportant when D, or any heavier atom, is transferred in a chemical process.

V. Reaction Dynamics

It is important to have knowledge, on the molecular or microscopic level, of the elementary act that occurs during the course of chemical change. Work in this field, referred to as reaction dynamics or molecular dynamics, deals with the intermolecular and intramolecular motions that occur in a chemical reaction and the quantum states of the reactant and product molecules. There are two main reasons for studying chemical dynamics. One is to test the validity of the statistical theories that were outlined in the preceding section. The other is that there are important applications (e.g., lasers) in which it is necessary to have information about the energy states of products of reaction, information that is not provided by the statistical theories. [*See* ATOMIC AND MOLECULAR COLLISIONS.]

The results of dynamical calculations and experiments are frequently expressed in terms of reaction cross sections rather than rate constants. The reaction cross section for a bimolecular reaction is defined as $P_r \pi d^2$, where P_r is the probability of reaction and d, the collision diameter, is the distance between the centers of the reactant molecules when they collide. In practice the reaction cross section, given the symbol σ, is the quantity that has to be postulated in using collision theory to interpret calculated or experimental rates.

Much of the theoretical work in molecular dynamics has been based on potential energy surfaces that have been calculated for individual reactions. Dynamical calculations are then carried out for various initial states of the reacting molecules. For a reaction A + B—C, for example, one chooses a particular vibrational and rotational state for the molecule B–C, and particular translational states for A and B–C. Other details of the collision between the two are also selected. One then calculates, on the basis of dynamics, the path that the system takes on the potential energy surface. A diagram or mathematical description that describes the motion of a reaction system over a potential energy surface is known as a trajectory. Ideally the dynamical calculations are based on quantum mechanics, but this presents difficulty and more often classical calculations are made; there is good reason to conclude that not much error is then introduced. Even when the trajectories are obtained classically, the initial states of the reactants are usually selected on the basis of quantum theory.

A large number of trajectories have been calculated, and the results have provided considerable insight into how reactions proceed. Calculations by Karplus and co-workers on the reaction

$$H + H_2 \rightarrow H_2 + H$$

have revealed a number of interesting features. One is that not all of the vibrational energy of H_2 can contribute to allowing the system to surmount the potential energy barrier. Another is that, as assumed in transition-state theory, the system passes directly through the col and does not remain there and perform a number of vibrations. On the basis of calculations made for a variety of initial conditions it was possible to compare calculated rates with those obtained from transition-state theory, and the agreement was very good. For the reaction

$$Br + H_2 \rightarrow HBr + H$$

the agreement is not as good. Other trajectory calculations have been made for potential energy surfaces that do not have the shape shown in Fig. 3 but instead have a basin at the col. It is then found that the activated complexes are trapped for a short period in the basin, and perform several vibrations before they become products.

A number of trajectory calculations have been made, particularly by J. C. Polanyi (b. 1929) and co-workers, with the object of exploring how the slopes of potential energy surfaces affect the transfer of energy during the course of a chemical reaction. Three questions of particular importance are:

1. If energy is released in a chemical reaction, i.e., if the reaction is exothermic, what is the distribution of the energy among the translational, vibrational, and rotational states of the product molecules?
2. What type of energy is particularly effective in leading to a successful chemical reaction?
3. If a collision occurs with substantially more than enough energy to surmount the barrier, in what form is the excess energy released?

The answers to all three questions depend on the form of the potential energy surface. In the schematic potential energy surface shown in Fig. 3 the energy level of the products, A—B + C, is lower than that of the reactants; i.e., the reaction is exothermic. Also, the surface was drawn in such a way that at the activated state there is not much change in the B–C distance, but that the A–B distance is considerably greater than it becomes in the product A–B. This type of surface is called an attractive or an early downhill surface. In the trajectory shown in Fig. 3 there is not much vibrational energy in the reactant B–C, but much more in the product A–B, and this is typical of this type of surface. If, on the other hand, an exothermic reaction has a late downhill surface, or a repulsive surface, the calculations showed that not so much of the energy released passed into vibrational energy of A–B, most of it becoming translational energy of A–B and C.

The answer to the second question can be appreciated by considering the reverse processes. Suppose that the surface is as shown in Fig. 3 but that the reaction is

$$\text{A—B} + \text{C} \rightarrow \text{A} + \text{B—C}$$

The reverse of the trajectory shown in Fig. 3 therefore applies, and the reaction absorbs energy (i.e., it is endothermic). Vibrational energy is now much more important than translational energy in surmounting the barrier. If there is only translational energy the system is likely to bounce against the inner wall of the surface and return to the entrance valley.

With regard to the third question, the disposition of excess energy, there is a tendency for excess translational energy to appear as translational energy in the products and for excess vibrational energy to appear as vibrational energy. This effect has been referred to as adiabaticity, and theoretical reasons for it have been proposed.

These conclusions have been amply confirmed by many experimental results. Broadly speaking the experimental investigations fall into two main classes:

1. Experiments in which narrow beams of reactant molecules, in preselected states, are brought into contact with each other. The primary purpose of these molecular-beam studies is to determine the fate of the reactants and products after the beams have come together.
2. Experiments carried out in bulk systems in which the energy states of the reaction products are determined by spectroscopic techniques. The reaction itself may occur in a static or flow system, and often the reactant molecules have been put into particular energy states. The term chemiluminescence is applied to such studies, since they are concerned with radiation emitted by the products.

Ideally, in both types of investigation, the reactant molecules are put into selected translational, vibrational, and rotational states, and the corresponding states of the reaction products are determined. When this objective is more or less achieved the expression state-to-state kinetics is applied.

Molecular-beam studies have only been carried out to any extent since the 1950s, and the techniques have developed considerably since that time. A particular advance has been the use of mass spectrometers for determining the nature, speeds, and direction of the molecules after the collision has occurred. Analysis of the results yields detailed information about the distribution of angular momentum among the reaction products, the reaction cross sections, the quantum states of the product molecules, and the lifetime of the collision complex. Many reactions fall into one of two main classes:

1. Reactions having high reaction cross sections (i.e., occurring at relatively high rates) and in which the reaction products are scattered forward with respect to the center of mass of the system. This type of process is said to occur by a stripping mechanism.
2. Reactions having small cross sections, in which there is backward scattering of the reaction products. The mechanism is then said to be a rebound mechanism.

It has been found that reactions for which the potential energy surface is attractive (Fig. 3) tend to occur by a stripping mechanism, while when it is repulsive there is a rebound mechanism. The reasons for this have been worked out.

When a reaction occurs either by a stripping or a rebound mechanism the lifetime of the activated complex must be short; if it were long enough for rotation to occur the products would separate in random directions and the reaction is then said to occur by an indirect or complex-mode mechanism. When the lifetime of the complex is short, as in the stripping and rebound mechanisms, the expression direct or impulsive is used. The occurrence of a reaction by a complex-mode mechanism appears to be associated with the existence of a basin in the potential energy surface.

The chemiluminescence investigations of chemical reactions have as their origin some pioneering investigations carried out in the 1920s and 1930s by M. Polanyi. In the course of these studies it was found, for example, that in the reaction

$$\text{Cl} + \text{Na}_2 \rightarrow \text{NaCl}' + \text{Na}$$

a good deal of the energy liberated resides in the product NaCl molecule in the form of vibrational energy, as indicated by the prime. These investigations have been extended, particularly by J. C. Polanyi and co-workers, who have introduced new experimental techniques and have studied reactions of a variety of types. It was these investigations, together with parallel theoretical studies, that led to the classification of different types of potential energy surfaces.

Both the molecular-beam and chemiluminescence techniques have been applied to the investigation of state-to-state kinetics. In a molecular-beam experiment the translational energies of the reactant molecules can be well controlled, and by laser excitation the molecules can be put into particular vibrational and rotational states. In the chemiluminescence experiments the reactant molecules are sometimes put into particular vibrational and rotational states by forming them in prereactions.

State-to-state studies have been carried out only since the early 1970s, but they have already revealed much important information. By and large they have confirmed and amplified the previous theoretical and experimental studies in reaction dynamics. One general result that has been obtained is that when reactions are substantially endothermic, their barriers are usually late ones, so that they are enhanced more by vibrational than by translational energy. On the other hand, when reactions are only slightly endothermic or are exothermic, the barriers are generally earlier, and translational energy then plays a more important role in leading to reaction. State-to-state studies have also led to some clarification of the influence of rotational energy on reactivity, although the matter is still not entirely clear. When the translational and vibrational energies are held constant and the rotational quantum state of a reactant molecule is steadily increased, the rates sometimes first decrease and then increase. As rotational speeds increase, the time that a molecule spends in a favorable orientation decreases, and this factor leads to a decrease in reaction probability. At higher rotational speeds, however, the preferred orientations are obtained again at short intervals during the approach of the reactants, and this can give rise to higher rates as the rotational energies increase. Also, at the higher rotational speeds there is a greater proportion of energy in the form of rotational energy, and this again can contribute to the effects observed.

An important development has been the spectroscopic detection of transition species, which are defined as molecular entities having configurations between those of the reactants and products of a chemical reaction. The term *transition species* covers a much broader range of configurations than does the term *activated complex*, which is defined as existing in an arbitrarily small region of space. It has long been known that spectral lines are broadened when a gas is at higher pressures, and this was interpreted in 1915 by H. A. Lorentz (1853–1928) as being due to collisions between the molecules. It was only in 1980, however, that J. C. Polanyi and coworkers were successful in detecting similar effects from molecules that were undergoing reactive collisions. For example, they studied the reaction

$$F + Na_2 \rightarrow F \ldots Na \ldots Na \rightarrow NaF + Na^*$$

The product Na^* is in an electronically excited state and emits the familiar yellow D-line. On both sides of this line there was "wing" emission, and the evidence indicated that this was due to the transition species F ... Na ... Na.

VI. Reactions in the Gas Phase

Reactions in the gas phase are in some respects easier to understand than those in solution or on surfaces, and what is learned about gas reactions is valuable in leading to an understanding of the other types of processes. The most straightforward of gas reactions are those that are elementary and bimolecular. There are few bimolecular reactions involving molecules, as opposed to atoms and free radicals, since most second-order reactions involving molecules occur in more than one stage, i.e., they are composite. Such composite reactions are dealt with in Section IX.

The prototype of all bimolecular reactions is the process

$$H + H_2 \rightarrow H_2 + H$$

The measurement of the rate of this reaction is made possible by the fact that H_2 exists in two forms, designated ortho (o) and para (p). To explain the kinetics of this reaction a large number of theoretical studies have been made. It is now possible to calculate, by pure quantum mechanics, an accurate potential energy surface for this reaction. For this particular reaction, which has a symmetrical potential energy surface, conventional transition-state theory is in good agreement with the best of the dynamical treatments.

One matter of considerable interest is the kinetic isotope effect observed when H atoms are replaced by deuterium (D) or tritium (T) atoms in this system. These kinetic isotope effects still cannot be treated completely satisfactorily, largely because the theory of quantum-mechanical tunneling is by no means satisfactory. The effects are, however, broadly understood in a semiquantitative way.

Among other bimolecular gas reactions that have been extensively investigated are so-called abstraction or metathetical reactions involving atoms and free radicals. An example is

$$CH_3 + C_2H_6 \rightarrow CH_4 + C_2H_5$$

In this process the free methyl radical CH_3 abstracts a hydrogen atom from the ethane molecule. There has also been much study, by mass spectrometric techniques, of bimolecular reactions involving ions, such as the reaction

$$O^+ + N_2 \rightarrow NO^+ + N$$

For most such reactions conventional transition-state theory provides a useful, but not always precise, interpretation of the results.

A few trimolecular reactions in the gas phase have also been investigated; examples are

$$2NO + Cl_2 \rightarrow 2NOCl$$

and

$$2NO + O_2 \rightarrow 2NO_2$$

The interpretation of these reactions was a considerable triumph for conventional transition-state theory. Simple collision theory proved unsatisfactory for trimolecular reactions, owing to the difficulty of defining a collision between three molecules, and usually led to very serious overestimations (by several powers of ten) of the rate constants. Similar difficulties are encountered with dynamical treatments, and these have still not been satisfactorily resolved. Conventional transition-state theory, by regarding the activated complex as being in equilibrium with the reactants, leads to a very simple formulation of the rate constant and to values in good agreement with experiment. It also very neatly explains the rather marked negative temperature dependence of the pre-exponential factors for these reactions.

The elucidation of unimolecular gas reactions proved to be much more difficult than that of bimolecular and trimolecular reactions. Whereas the rates of the latter reactions can be interpreted in terms of collisions between two and three molecules respectively, no such treatment appears at first sight to be possible for unimolecular reactions. At one time it was widely held that collisions are not at all involved in unimolecular reactions, and that instead the reactions occur as a result of the absorption of radiation emitted by the vessel walls. However, this proved to be incorrect, and the problem was resolved as a result of a suggestion made in 1921 by F. A. Lindemann, later Lord Cherwell (1886–1957).

Lindemann's hypothesis, as later interpreted and developed by C. N. Hinshelwood (1897–1967) and others, is as follows. In a unimolecular process an energized molecule A* is first formed by a collision between two molecules of the reactant A:

$$A + A \rightleftharpoons A^* + A$$

The energization process is second order, the rate being $k_1[A]^2$, and the rate of the reverse de-energization process is $k_{-1}[A^*][A]$. The energized molecule A* may undergo de-energization, but it may also undergo a process in which the reaction products are formed:

$$A^* \rightarrow \text{products}$$

The rate of this first-order process is $k_2[A^*]$.

If the pressure is high enough the de-energization process will be more rapid than the reaction to form products. This being so, the energized molecule A* is essentially in equilibrium with normal molecules, and its concentration [A*] is proportional to the *first* power of the concentration [A]. Since the rate is proportional to [A*] it is also proportional to [A]; i.e., the kinetics are first order.

At sufficiently low pressures, on the other hand, the time between successive collisions between A* and A becomes longer than the time that elapses before A* can become products. The removal of A* molecules by chemical change then seriously diminishes the concentration of activated molecules. At extremely low pressures the energized molecules A* almost inevitably become products, as there are few collisions to inactivate them. The rate of reaction is then equal to the rate of energization and is thus proportional to the *square* of the concentration.

If this Lindemann–Hinshelwood hypothesis is correct, unimolecular gas reactions should be first order at high pressures and should become second order at low pressures. This behavior has now been confirmed for a large number of reactions. In its original form the hypothesis had some difficulty in interpreting results quantitatively, but a number of extensions of the original hypothesis have been made, notably by R. A. Marcus whose treatment is consistent with transition-state theory.

VII. Reactions in Solution

Reactions in solution or in the liquid phase are intrinsically more difficult to understand than reactions in the gas phase because of the complications arising from the effect of the liquid. When a solvent is present there are two possibilities: the solvent may exert purely an environmental effect on the reaction, or it may also enter into the reaction. The latter case is exemplified by the hydrolysis of an organic compound in aqueous solution; water molecules are chemically involved in the reaction.

Some understanding of solvent effects has been provided by comparisons of the same reaction in the gas phase and in solution. Some reactions, however, do not occur at all in the gas phase, and one must then be content with comparing their rates in different solvents. When such comparisons are made it is sometimes found that the solvent does not have much effect on the rate. When, on the other hand, ions are involved as reactants or products, solvents usually have a much greater effect on rates, because of the rather strong electrostatic interactions between ions and solvent molecules.

Theoretical studies have also contributed to an understanding of reactions in solution. For reactions between neutral species the frequencies of collisions are of the same order of magnitude in solution and in the gas phase. However, there are important differences between the *distribution* of collisions. When two molecules collide in solution they are "caged" in by surrounding molecules and within a very short period of time they are likely to undergo one or more additional collisions before they separate. Such a set of collisions, occurring in rapid succession, is known as an encounter. This tendency for collisions in solution to occur in sets has no effect on reactions involving an activation energy, because reaction may occur on any collision within the set. However, atomic and free-radical combinations do not involve an activation energy and occur on every collision. They therefore occur at the first collision in the set, so that the remaining collisions in the encounter do not contribute to the rate. The pre-exponential factor is therefore not related to the frequency of collisions but rather to the frequency of encounters.

This cage effect, also known as the Franck–Rabinowitch effect, has other important consequences. In a photochemical reaction in solution, for example, a pair of free radicals produced initially may, owing to their being caged in by the surrounding molecules, recombine before they can separate from each other. This effect is known as primary recombination.

When reaction occurs between ions in solution some rather special effects become important. These can be understood in an approximate but very useful way by focusing attention on the dielectric constant of the solvent. The forces between charges, whether they are attractive or repulsive, are inversely proportional to the dielectric constant of the medium. The dielectric constant of water, for example, is about 78 at room temperature, and the force of repulsion between two ions A^+ and B^+ in water is only $\frac{1}{78}$ of that in the gas phase. Even in aqueous solution the forces are still strong enough to have a substantial effect on the collision frequencies and therefore on the pre-exponential factors of such reactions. In water at 25°C, for example, the pre-exponential factor of a reaction of the type $A^+ + B^+$ is apt to be about two orders of magnitude lower than for the corresponding reaction between neutral molecules. By contrast, for a reaction in aqueous solution between singly charged ions of opposite signs, $A^+ + B^-$, the pre-exponential factor at 25°C is usually about 10^2 greater than that between neutral molecules.

Similar considerations allow useful predictions to be made about the effects or different solvents on reaction rates. If a reaction is of the type $A^+ + B^+$ the forces are repulsive and will be smaller the higher the dielectric constant of the solvent. The reaction therefore proceeds more rapidly in aqueous solution than in alcohol, since water has a higher dielectric constant than alcohol and reduces the repulsions to a greater extent. When on the other hand the reaction is of the type $A^+ + B^-$, the rate will be greater in alcohol than in water, since water greatly reduces the attractions between the reactants. Quantitative formulations of these effects have been worked out.

Another matter of considerable importance in connection with ionic reactions in solution is the effect on rates of the ionic strength. This property, introduced in 1921 by G. N. Lewis (1875–1946), is defined as

$$I = \frac{1}{2} \sum_i z_i^2 c_i \tag{20}$$

where c_i is the concentration of each ion in solution and z_i is its charge number (e.g., +1 for

Na^+, -2 for SO_4^{-2}): the summation is made over all of the ions present in the solution. Qualitatively the ionic strength has the same kind of effect as the dielectric constant; increasing I reduces the forces between ions. Thus for a reaction of the type $A^+ + B^+$, increasing the ionic strength increases the rate by reducing the repulsion. For a reaction $A^+ + B^-$, increasing the ionic strength decreases the rate by reducing the attraction. These ideas were put into quantitative form in 1922–1924 by J. N. Brønsted (1879–1947), N. J. Bierrum (1879–1958), and J. A. Christiansen (1888–1969).

Special effects arise for a solution reaction that is extremely rapid, in which case the rate may depend on the rate with which the reactant molecules diffuse through the solvent. Two effects are to be distinguished, macroscopic diffusion control and microscopic diffusion control. If a rapid bimolecular reaction in solution is initiated by mixing solutions of the two reactants, the observed rate may depend on the rate with which the solutions mix, and one then speaks of mixing control or macroscopic diffusion control.

Even if this effect has been eliminated the rate of a reaction may be influenced by the rate with which the reactant molecules diffuse towards each other. This effect is known as microscopic diffusion control or encounter control. If the measured rate is almost exactly equal to the rate of diffusion one speaks of full diffusion control. An example of this is provided by the combination of H^+ and OH^- ions in solution, a reaction that is so fast that the rate is almost entirely controlled by the diffusion of the ions towards each other. For some reactions the rates of chemical reaction and diffusion are similar to each other, and one then speaks of partial diffusion control.

Quantitative formulations have been worked out for the rate constants for both full and partial diffusion control. Diffusion rates do not vary greatly from one system to another and for uncharged reactants in aqueous solution at 25°C diffusional rate constants are approximately 7×10^9 dm^3 mol^{-1} s^{-1}. If the chemical rate constant is substantially greater than this there is therefore appreciable diffusion control. Most reactions, however, have much smaller rate constants because of an energy barrier to reaction, and are therefore not affected by diffusion. For reactions between ions the diffusion rates and chemical rates are increased if the ions are of opposite signs, and they are decreased if they are of the same sign.

VIII. Reactions on Surfaces

Many reactions are affected by the surface of the vessel in which they occur, with an increase in rate. The effect is often a catalytic one, the surface remaining unchanged, and substances are often deliberately introduced into reaction systems with the object of increasing the rates. Surface catalysis is of very great importance in technical work. [*See* CATALYSIS, INDUSTRIAL.]

The fact that the enhanced rates are due to adsorption at the surface has long been known. An important advance was made in 1916 by I. Langmuir (1881–1957) who showed that in many cases of adsorption the gas molecules are held to the surface by bonds of the same character as covalent chemical bonds, and the term chemisorption has been applied to this type of adsorption. Langmuir also developed adsorption isotherms that relate the fraction of surface covered to the pressure or concentration of a gas. [*See* SURFACE CHEMISTRY.]

Later H. S. Taylor (1890–1974) emphasized the fact that surfaces are never smooth on the atomic scale, and that surface sites are therefore of variable activity. Certain sites, which he called active centers, are particularly active and it is on these that catalysis occurs for the most part. Taylor also showed that the process of chemisorption itself is accompanied by an activation energy, and he referred to this type of adsorption as activated adsorption.

The kinetic equations that apply to reactions on surfaces are given to a good approximation on the basis of the Langmuir isotherm, which can be derived as follows. Let θ be the fraction of a surface that is covered by adsorbed molecules, so that $1 - \theta$ is the fraction that is not covered. If [A] is the concentration of gas molecules, then the rate of adsorption, which can only occur on bare surface, is $k_a[A](1 - \theta)$, where k_a is a constant. The reverse desorption process is a unimolecular process and its rate is $k_d\theta$. At equilibrium the two rates are the same so that

$$k_a[A](1 - \theta) = k_d\theta \quad (21)$$

from which it follows that

$$\theta = \frac{K[A]}{1 + K[A]} \quad (22)$$

where K is equal to k_a/k_d.

Equation (22) leads at once to kinetic equations that apply to unimolecular processes on surfaces. The rate is proportional to θ and is therefore given by

$$v = \frac{kK[A]}{1 + K[A]} \tag{23}$$

If [A] is sufficiently small that $k[A] \ll 1$, this reduces to

$$v = kK[A] \tag{24}$$

and the reaction is first order. If [A] is sufficiently large that $K[A] \gg 1$ the rate is

$$v = k \tag{25}$$

and is now independent of concentration; the order of the reaction is thus zero. One example of a reaction that changes from zero-order kinetics at high concentrations to first-order kinetics at low concentrations is the decomposition of ammonia on the surface of a metal such as tungsten or iron.

When two substances are undergoing reaction at a surface there are two possibilities. The reaction may be an interaction between two molecules that are adsorbed side-by-side on a surface, or it may be an interaction between an adsorbed molecule of one kind and a gas molecule of the other. The kinetics are satisfactorily interpreted by an extension of Langmuir's isotherm [Eq. (22)], which for two gases A and B gives the following expressions for the fractions of surface covered by A and B respectively:

$$\theta_A = \frac{K_A[A]}{1 + K_A[A] + K_B[B]} \tag{26}$$

$$\theta_B = \frac{K_B[B]}{1 + K_A[A] + K_B[B]} \tag{27}$$

Reactions involving interaction between two adsorbed molecules are said to occur by Langmuir–Hinshelwood mechanisms, and their rates are proportional to the product $\theta_A\theta_B$:

$$v = k\theta_A\theta_B = \frac{kK_AK_B[A][B]}{(1 + K_A[A] + K_B[B])^2} \tag{28}$$

If either concentration is held constant and the other one increased, the rate passes through a maximum. The most favorable situation is for equal numbers of A and B molecules to be on the surface, since then the number of A–B pairs is a maximum. If the concentration of either is then increased, the other is displaced from the surface, and the number of A–B pairs diminishes.

Mechanisms in which a gas molecule reacts with an adsorbed molecule of the other kind are known as Langmuir–Rideal mechanisms. If, for example, the interaction is between gaseous A and adsorbed B the rate is proportional to $[A]\theta_B$ and is therefore

$$v = \frac{kK_B[A][B]}{1 + K_A[A] + K_B[B]} \tag{29}$$

There is therefore no longer a maximum in the rate, which now approaches a limiting value if the concentration of one reactant is increased with the other held constant. This difference in kinetic behavior allows a discrimination between the two mechanisms, both of which sometimes occur simultaneously.

Since about 1970 there have been many important advances in experimental techniques for the study of surfaces and adsorbed layers of molecules on surfaces. Techniques that have been particularly valuable in the investigation of solid surfaces are field-ion microscopy (FIM) and low-energy electron diffraction (LEED). These techniques have shown that surfaces have different types of surface sites, such as atoms at terraces, atoms at steps, atoms at kinks, and adatoms which project out of the surfaces. [*See* CATALYST CHARACTERIZATION.]

A technique that has provided valuable information about adsorbed films is infrared spectroscopy. As an example of its use we mention some work on the adsorption of ethylene (C_2H_4) on various surfaces. It has been found that the manner in which ethylene is adsorbed depends on the availability of hydrogen. If no hydrogen is available the adsorption tends to be of the dissociative type; the ethylene splits into C_2H_2 and 2H, all of which are adsorbed separately. With hydrogen present, however, adsorbed H atoms add on to C_2H_4 and ethyl radicals (C_2H_5) become attached to the surface. Evidence of this kind is of great importance in understanding the kinetics and mechanisms of the hydrogenation of ethylene and many other processes.

Reactions on surfaces frequently undergo inhibition by added substances, which themselves become adsorbed on the surface and reduce its catalytic activity. This effect is commonly referred to as poisoning of the surface.

IX. Composite Reaction Mechanisms

Many of the reactions familiar to the chemist occur in more than one stage, and their mechanisms are therefore described as composite, complex, or stepwise. One indication that a reaction is composite is that the kinetic equation does not correspond to the stoichiometric equation. A simple example is the gas-phase reaction between nitric oxide and hydrogen, the stoichiometric equation for which is

$$2NO + 2H_2 \rightarrow N_2 + 2H_2O$$

If the process were elementary it would be second order in NO and second order in H_2, with an overall order of four. In fact, the rate is proportional to $[NO]^2[H_2]$. The reason is that the reaction occurs in two steps,

$$2NO + H_2 \rightarrow N_2 + H_2O_2$$

$$H_2O_2 + H_2 \rightarrow 2H_2O$$

The second reaction is rapid compared with the first, so that the overall rate is that of the first reaction and is proportional to $[NO]^2[H_2]$.

Because reactions can occur in steps, the order of a reaction is often less than corresponds to the stoichiometry. A reactive collision between three molecules is much less likely than one between two, and one between four molecules is exceedingly unlikely; indeed it is doubtful whether elementary reactions between four molecules ever occur. A reaction whose stoichiometric equation involves more than three molecules always proceeds more rapidly by two or more processes of lower molecularity.

Even if the kinetics of a reaction does correspond to the stoichiometry it may still be the case that the mechanism is composite. For example, the reaction

$$H_2 + I_2 \rightarrow 2HI$$

and the reverse decomposition are both second order, and the processes were formerly thought to occur in a single stage. Later work, however, has shown that reactions involving I atoms are also involved. The decomposition of ethane,

$$C_2H_6 \rightarrow C_2H_4 + H_2$$

is first order and was long thought to be elementary; however it occurs entirely by a free-radical mechanism, to be considered later.

Composite mechanisms can be classified in a number of different ways. First, there is the usual classification according to whether the process occurs in the gas phase, the liquid phase, or on a surface. Another classification is according to whether the process is thermal, photochemical, or radiation chemical. A thermal reaction occurs simply by virtue of the heat energy present in the system; molecules can pick up more energy on colliding with other molecules, and eventually an energetic collision will lead to reaction. Photochemical and radiation-chemical reactions are brought about as a result of radiation absorbed in the system.

Another characterization of composite mechanisms is in terms of the types of elementary reactions occurring. Sometimes reactions occur in parallel, such as

$$A \rightarrow Y$$

$$A \rightarrow Z$$

and are called simultaneous reactions. When there are simultaneous reactions, there is sometimes competition, as in the scheme

$$A + B \rightarrow Y$$

$$A + C \rightarrow Z$$

where B and C compete with one another for A.

Reactions occurring in forward and reverse directions are called opposing:

$$A + B \rightleftharpoons Z$$

Reactions occurring in sequence, such as

$$A \rightarrow X \rightarrow Y \rightarrow Z$$

are called consecutive reactions. Reactions are said to exhibit feedback if a substance formed in one step affects the rate of a previous step. For example, in the scheme

$$A \rightarrow X \rightarrow Y \rightarrow Z$$

the intermediate Y may catalyze the first reaction (positive feedback) or inhibit it (negative feedback). More than one of the above features may of course occur in a composite mechanism.

Sometimes a composite reaction mechanism involves a cycle of reactions such that certain reaction intermediates consumed in one step are regenerated in another. The intermediates may be atoms, free radicals, or ions. For example, the reaction between hydrogen and bromine, to be considered later, includes the steps

$$Br + H_2 \rightarrow HBr + H$$

$$H + Br_2 \rightarrow HBr + Br$$

When this feature exists, and the cycle is on the average repeated more than once (as it is in this reaction under usual conditions), the reaction is called a chain reaction, and the active intermediates (here H and Br) are referred to as chain carriers. The preceding two reactions are referred to as chain-propagating steps.

Substances that are formed during the course of a reaction but do not remain to any extent as final products are known as transient intermediates, or transients. A simple reaction scheme is

$$A \rightarrow X \rightarrow Z$$

and if the reaction goes to completion the way in which the concentrations of A, X, and Z vary with time is illustrated in Fig. 4. The rate of formation of Z is proportional to [X], and since [X] starts at zero and passes through a maximum, the initial rate of formation of Z is zero. This rate, however, increases, and passes through a maximum when [X] is at its maximum.

In a composite mechanism it is sometimes possible to identify a rate-determining or rate-controlling step. An example is provided by the mechanism previously given for the $2NO + 2H_2$ reaction. Since the first step is slow and the second rapid, the first step determines the rate. The rate may also be controlled by a step that is not the first; in that case the overall rate is not equal to the rate of the slow step but is proportional to it.

Only in the case of very simple reaction mechanisms is it possible to obtain explicit expressions for concentration changes as a function of time. In some situations a reliable solution to the problem may be obtained by application of the steady-state treatment. The condition for this to be valid is that the intermediates are present only at concentrations that are very low compared to those of the reactants. If this condition is satisfied by an intermediate X, the rate of change of its concentration is always much less than those of the reactants, and to a good approximation can be set equal to zero:

$$d[X]/dt = 0 \qquad (30)$$

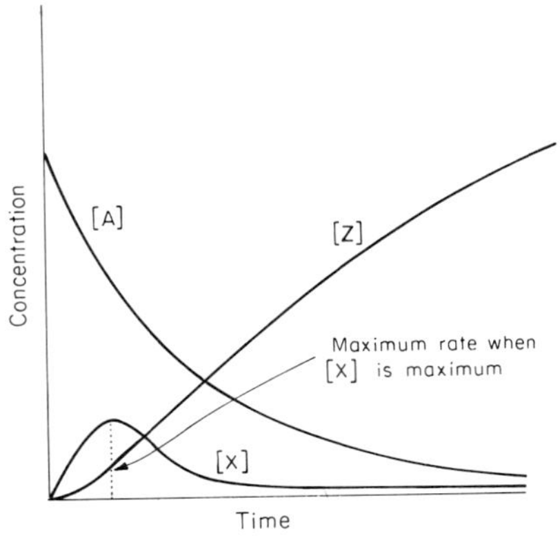

FIG. 4. Variations with time of the concentrations of A, X, and Z for the mechanism A → X → Z.

This approximation can be safely applied to intermediates such as atoms and free radicals.

The reaction between hydrogen and bromine provides a good example of a composite mechanism to which the steady-state treatment can be applied, since the intermediates are the atoms Br and H. If the back reaction is prevented from occurring (by removal of the product HBr as it is formed) the mechanism is

$$(1) \qquad Br_2 \rightarrow 2Br$$

$$(2) \qquad Br + H_2 \rightarrow HBr + H$$

$$(3) \qquad H + Br_2 \rightarrow HBr + Br$$

$$(-1) \qquad 2Br \rightarrow Br_2$$

Reactions (2) and (3) constitute chain-propagating reactions. Reaction (1) is referred to as chain-initiation process and reaction (−1) as a chain-ending step. Application of the steady-state treatment to the Br atoms gives

$$k_1[Br_2] - k_2[BF][H_2] + k_3[H][Br_2] - k_{-1}[Br]^2 = 0 \qquad (31)$$

For H atoms the steady-state equation is

$$k_2[Br][H_2] - k_3[H][Br_2] = 0 \qquad (32)$$

There are thus two equations in the two unknowns [Br] and [H], and the solution for [Br] is

$$[Br] = \left(\frac{k_1}{k_{-1}}\right)^{1/2} [Br_2]^{1/2} \qquad (33)$$

The rate of consumption of H_2 is $k_2[Br][H_2]$, and therefore

$$v_{H_2} = k_2 \left(\frac{k_1}{k_{-1}}\right)^{1/2} [H_2][Br_2]^{1/2} \qquad (34)$$

This is also the rate of consumption of Br_2. Experimentally the reaction is, in fact, first order in H_2 and one-half order in Br_2. Much work has shown this mechanism to be almost certainly close to the truth.

Many organic decompositions in the gas phase occur by composite mechanisms involving the participation of atoms and free radicals, and in 1934 F. O. Rice (b. 1890) and K. F. Herzfeld (1892–1978) proposed several types of chain mechanisms to explain the kinetic behavior observed. The acetaldehyde decomposition appears to occur largely by a mechanism that can be simplified to

$$(1) \qquad CH_3CHO \rightarrow CH_3 + CHO$$

$$(2) \qquad CH_3 + CH_3CHO \rightarrow CH_4 + CH_3CO$$

(3) $$CH_3CO \rightarrow CH_3 + CO$$

(4) $$2CH_3 \rightarrow C_2H_6$$

The radical CHO produced in reaction (1), the initiation reaction, breaks down into CO + H, and H atoms combine to form H_2 which is found as a minor product. The C_2H_6 formed in the termination reaction is also a minor product. Reactions (2) and (3) are chain-propagating steps. The steady-state equations are now, for CH_3:

$$k_1[CH_3CHO] - k_2[CH_3][CH_3CHO] + k_3[CH_3CO] - k_4[CH_3]^2 = 0 \quad (35)$$

and for CH_3CO:

$$k_2[CH_3][CH_3CHO] - k_3[CH_3CO] = 0 \quad (36)$$

The solution for $[CH_3]$ is

$$[CH_3] = \left(\frac{k_1}{k_4}\right)^{1/2}[CH_3CHO]^{1/2} \quad (37)$$

The rate of formation of the product CH_4 is $k_2[CH_3][CH_3CHO]$ and is therefore

$$v_{CH_4} = k_2\left(\frac{k_1}{k_4}\right)^{1/2}[CH_3CHO]^{3/2} \quad (38)$$

The three-halves-order kinetics actually observed for this reaction is thus explained.

Ethane decomposition is also a chain reaction, and the main features have now been elucidated. The initiation process is the dissociation of the ethane molecule into two methyl radicals:

$$C_2H_6 \rightarrow 2CH_3$$

These, however are not chain carriers; they abstract a hydrogen atom from a C_2H_6 molecule

$$CH_3 + C_2H_6 \rightarrow CH_4 + C_2H_5$$

Methane (CH_4) is, in fact, found as a minor product of the reaction. The C_2H_5 radical is a chain carrier, since it decomposes into C_2H_4 and H, which then abstracts a hydrogen atom from an ethane molecule:

$$C_2H_5 \rightarrow C_2H_4 + H$$

$$H + C_2H_6 \rightarrow H_2 + C_2H_5$$

In this pair of chain-propagating steps the major products of the reaction, ethylene (C_2H_4) and hydrogen, are formed without any loss of chain carriers.

There is a special class of reactions in which there is chain branching, a concept suggested in 1927–1928 by N. N. Semenov (1896–1846) and by C. N. Hinshelwood. When a pair of ordinary chain-propagating steps occurs there is no change in the number of chain carriers. When there is chain branching, however, there is an increase in the number of carriers. An example is the pair of reactions

$$H + O_2 \rightarrow OH + O$$

$$O + H_2 \rightarrow OH + H$$

In each of these reactions two carriers have been formed from one; if the two reactions are added together the result is

$$H + O_2 + H_2 \rightarrow 2OH + H$$

so that the H atom is regenerated but has produced two OH radicals which can undergo further reactions. When such chain branching occurs the number of chain carriers in the reaction can increase extremely rapidly. The rate of reaction thus increases, and the result may be an explosion. Mixtures of oxygen with substances such as hydrogen, carbon monoxide, and various organic substances do in fact explode under certain conditions, and the reason is that chain branching is involved. [*See* COMBUSTION.]

Reactions in which substances react together with the formation of much larger molecules known as polymers are frequently chain reactions. Thus, a substance containing a carbon–carbon double bond may be caused to polymerize by introduction of a free radical R which adds on to the double-bonded compound to form another free radical:

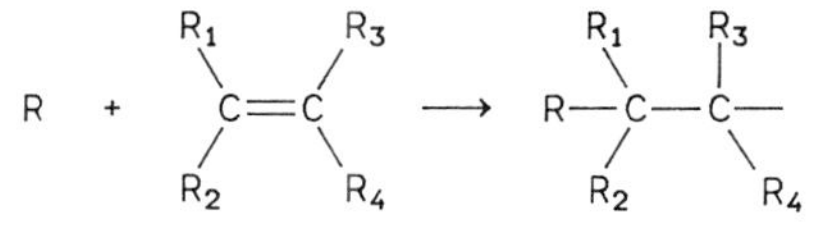

The resulting free radical adds on to another monomer molecule and the process continues with the eventual formation of a much larger molecule.

X. Photochemical and Radiation-Chemical Reactions

There are two kinds of radiation, electromagnetic and particle. The former behaves in some experiments as if it were a beam of photons, but these have no mass and can be regarded as packets of energy. Particle radiation, on the other hand, consists of beams of particles having mass. Cathode rays and β radiation, for example, consist of beams of electrons, and α radiation consists of a beam of helium nuclei. Particle-generating machines such as cyclotrons produce beams of protons, deuterons, and other particles. [*See* RADIATION PHYSICS; LASER AND PARTICLE BEAMS.]

All of these types of radiation are capable of bringing about chemical reaction provided that the energies are sufficiently high. Reactions induced in this way are referred to as either photochemical or radiation-chemical reactions. The distinction between the two types is not sharp and is sometimes made on the basis of whether ions are produced in the reaction. With radiation of lower energies, such as electromagnetic radiation in the visible and near-ultraviolet regions of the spectrum, there is no ion formation, and the resulting reaction is referred to as photochemical. With ultraviolet radiation of higher frequencies, with X rays and γ rays, and with high-energy particle radiation, ions are usually formed, and the process is then described as radiation-chemical.[1] Sometimes a distinction is based on specificity. With radiation of lower energy the resulting reaction is often of simple stoichiometry and can then be called photochemical. Higher-energy radiation, however, breaks up molecules into a number of fragments which lead to a variety of products; the term *radiation-chemical* can then be applied.

In order for a photochemical reaction to occur the radiation must be absorbed, and with the advent of the quantum theory it became possible to understand the relationship between the amount of radiation absorbed and the extent of the chemical change that occurs. It was first realized by A. Einstein (1879–1955) that electromagnetic radiation can be regarded as a beam of particles, which G. N. Lewis (1875–1940) later called photons; each of these particles has an energy equal to $h\nu$, where ν is the frequency of the radiation and h is the Planck constant. In 1911 J. Stark (1874–1957) and independently in 1912 Einstein proposed that one photon of radiation is absorbed by one molecule. This relationship, usually referred to as Einstein's Law of Photochemical Equivalence, applies satisfactorily to electromagnetic radiation of ordinary intensities but fails for lasers of very high intensity. The lifetime of a molecule that has absorbed a photon is usually less than about 10^{-8} sec, and with ordinary radiation it is unlikely for a molecule that has absorbed one photon to absorb another before it has become deactivated. In these circumstances there is therefore a one-to-one relationship between the number of photons absorbed and the number of excited molecules produced. Because of the high intensity of lasers, however, a molecule sometimes absorbs two or more photons, and one then speaks of multiphoton excitation. [*See* LASERS; MULTIPHOTON SPECTROSCOPY.

Even with ordinary radiation it may appear that the law of photochemical equivalence is not obeyed, and this arises because of two factors. One is that a molecule that has absorbed a photon may become inactivated before it has had time to enter into reaction. When this alone is the case the ratio of the number of molecules undergoing reaction to the number of photons absorbed (a quantity known as quantum yield or photon yield) is less than unity. The second factor is that the reaction may occur by a composite mechanism. For example, in the photochemical decomposition of hydrogen iodide (HI) into hydrogen and iodine, the quantum yield is 2; that is, one photon brings about the decomposition of two molecules of hydrogen iodide. The reason is that the mechanism is

(1) $HI + h\nu \rightarrow H + I$

(2) $H + HI \rightarrow H_2 + I$

(3) $I + I \rightarrow I_2$

In the first step one photon, designated by its energy $h\nu$, breaks apart an HI molecule, and the H atom produced interacts with a second HI molecule [reaction (2)]. The sum of reactions (1), (2), and (3) is

$$2HI + h\nu \rightarrow H_2 + I_2$$

which explains the quantum yield of 2.

This mechanism is not a chain reaction, since no cycle of reactions is repeated. When chain processes are involved the quantum yields may be very large. In the photochemical reaction between hydrogen and chlorine, quantum yields of over 10^6 have been reported, and it was this fact that led W. Nernst (1864–1941) to propose, in 1918, the following chain mechanism for the reaction:

(1) $Cl_2 + h\nu \rightarrow 2Cl$

(2) $Cl + H_2 \rightarrow HCl + H$

(3) $H + Cl_2 \rightarrow HCl + Cl$

(4) $2Cl \rightarrow Cl_2$

Reactions (2) and (3) are chain-propagating steps, and since they occur rapidly they are re-

[1] They should not be called "radiochemical," which would cause confusion with radiochemistry, which is concerned with radioactive substances.

peated many times, leading to high quantum yields.

One important photochemical technique is flash photolysis, in which an intense flash of radiation of very short duration initiates a reaction by producing excited molecules, atoms, and free radicals. The method, first used in 1950 by G. Porter and R. G. W. Norrish (1887–1978), has been applied extensively to the study of fast reactions, both in the gas phase and in solution. Extremely rapid processes can be studied by the use of pulsed lasers, which can have a duration of less than 1 psec (10^{-12} sec). This is sufficiently short to allow the study of the fastest of chemical reactions, and even molecular relaxation process in which molecules are changing their vibrational and rotational states.

Some molecules do not absorb radiation at convenient wavelengths, and the technique of photosensitization is then useful. This term applies to the absorption of radiation by a substance known as a photosensitizer, which then transfers energy to a colliding molecule, causing it to undergo chemical change. For example, hydrogen does not absorb in the near ultraviolet, but mercury vapor does so at a wavelength of 253.7 nm which corresponds to an energy of 469.4 kJ mol^{-1}. If hydrogen saturated with mercury vapor is irradiated at this wavelength, the mercury atoms, normally in a 6^1S_0 state, are excited to the 6^3P_1 state:

$$\mathrm{Hg}(6^1S_0) + h\nu \rightarrow \mathrm{Hg}(6^3P_1)$$

On collision with a hydrogen molecule an excited Hg atom can bring about dissociation into atoms:

$$\mathrm{Hg}(6^3P_1) + \mathrm{H_2} \rightarrow \mathrm{Hg}(6^1S_0) + 2\mathrm{H}$$

The dissociation of a mole of H_2 atoms requires 432 kJ of energy, so that the excited Hg atoms have more than enough energy for this process to occur. Other molecules, such as hydrocarbons, can be decomposed by similar photosensitization processes.

Radiation-chemical reactions have mechanisms similar to photochemical reactions, the difference being in the nature of the radiation-chemical primary process. Unlike photochemical primary processes, these processes are usually composite, leading in a series of steps to atoms, ions, and free radicals which undergo further reactions. For example, if hydrogen is irradiated with α particles the overall primary process is largely the production of hydrogen atoms, and the process is usually written as

$$H_2 \overset{\alpha}{\rightsquigarrow} 2H$$

Several elementary processes lead to this dissociation. One is the ejection of an electron by the α particle, the hydrogen molecule becoming an H_2^+ ion which dissociates into $H + H^+$:

$$\alpha + \mathrm{H_2} \rightarrow \mathrm{H_2^+} + \alpha + e^-$$

$$\mathrm{H_2^+} \rightarrow \mathrm{H^+} + \mathrm{H}$$

The H^+ ion produced is then likely to pick up an electron with the formation of a hydrogen atom.

In radiation chemistry the analog of flash photolysis is pulse radiolysis. For example, linear electron accelerators have been used to give pulses of very high energy with durations of a few microseconds, and with special techniques much shorter pulses, of the order of a nanosecond (10^{-9} sec), have been achieved.

The term chemiluminescence is used to describe the radiation emitted as a result of a chemical reaction. Some of the radiation emitted by flames is produced in this way, although some of it is blackbody radiation resulting from the high temperature of the burnt gases. The radiation emitted by fireflies and by certain tropical fish is chemiluminescence.

XI. Homogeneous Catalysis

Catalysis at surfaces, or heterogeneous catalysis, has been outlined in Section VIII, and the present section deals with homogeneous catalysis, where only one phase is involved. [*See* CATALYSIS, HOMOGENEOUS.]

Substances whose reactions undergo homogeneous catalysis are commonly known as substrates. There are several different types of homogeneous catalysis. Examples in the gas phase sometimes involve chain mechanisms. Reactions in solution are commonly catalyzed by acids and bases, and many reactions in biological systems are catalyzed by enzymes, which are proteins. Reactions in aqueous solution are often catalyzed by ions of variable valency.

No single mechanistic pattern applies to all cases of catalysis, but several different types of catalysis occur according to the following scheme:

$$\mathrm{C} + \mathrm{S} \rightleftharpoons \mathrm{X} + \mathrm{Y}$$

$$\mathrm{X} + \mathrm{W} \rightarrow \mathrm{P} + \mathrm{Z}$$

Here C is the catalyst and S the substrate, while X is a reaction intermediate which forms the product P in the second step. The species Y, W, and Z undergo further processes that do not affect the kinetics. In the case of a unimolecular surface-catalyzed reaction the scheme is simplified to:

$$C + S \rightleftharpoons X$$
$$X \rightarrow P$$

The intermediate X is now an addition compound formed from C and S, and in the second step it forms products. This scheme also applies to many reactions catalyzed by enzymes. For reactions catalyzed by acids and bases, however, it is necessary to include the additional species Y, W, and Z.

Suppose, for example, that the reaction of a substrate S is being catalyzed by an acid HA. A typical mechanism is

$$HA + S \rightleftharpoons SH^+ + A^-$$
$$SH^+ + B \rightarrow P + BH^+$$

In the first step a proton H^+ is transferred to the substrate, with the formation of the intermediate SH^+. In the second step this intermediate SH^+ transfers a proton to a basic species B (which may be identical with A^- or may be a water molecule), and in this step the product P is formed.

For example, the reaction between acetone and iodine,

$$CH_3COCH_3 + I_2 \rightarrow CH_3COCH_2I + HI$$

is catalyzed by acids, and the rate is proportional to the acetone concentration and also to the concentration of acid. The rate is, however, independent of the concentration of iodine, and indeed the rate remains the same if iodine is replaced by bromine. This suggests that the slow and rate-determining step does not involve iodine at all, but is the conversion of the ordinary form of acetone (known as the *keto* form) into another form (the *enol* form) which can react with iodine or bromine very rapidly:

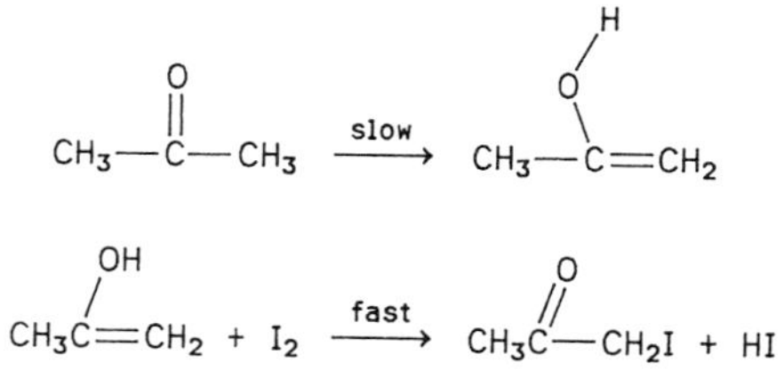

The way in which an acid HA catalyzes the formation of the enol form is believed to be as follows. First the acid transfers a proton to the oxygen atom on the acetone molecule:

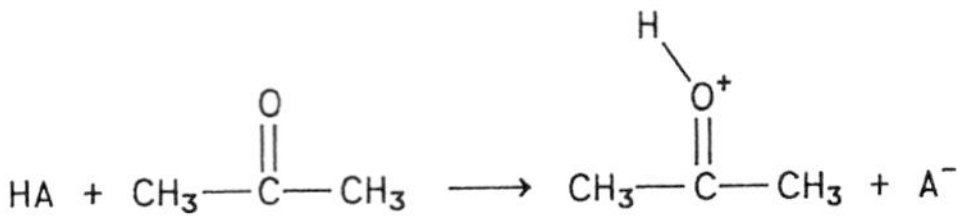

The protonated acetone then gives up a different proton to a basic species B present in solution:

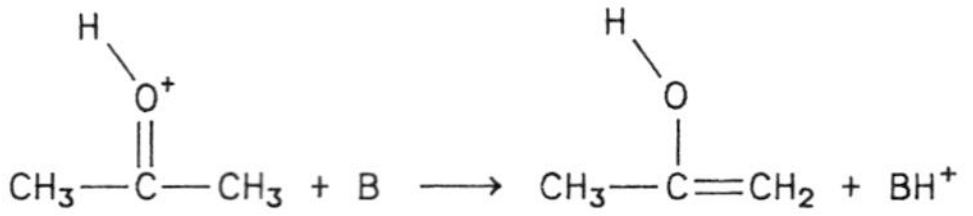

This is a very common pattern in acid catalysis. In the first step the acid transfers a proton to the substrate, which in the second step transfers another proton, the product being formed either simultaneously or in a subsequent step. In basic catalysis (which also occurs with the iodination of acetone), the substrate molecule first transfers a proton *to* the basic catalyst, and in a second step accepts a proton at another position.

Sometimes when reactions are catalyzed by acids and bases there is little sign of any effect other than catalysis by hydrated hydrogen ions (usually written as H_3O^+) or by hydroxide ions. One then speaks of specific acid–base catalysis, and the rate of reaction might be of the form

$$v = k_0[S] + k_{H^+}[S][H_3O^+] + k_{OH^-}[S][OH^-] \quad (39)$$

The coefficient k_0 relates to any uncatalyzed reaction, and k_{H^+} and k_{OH^-} are catalytic coefficients.

It is sometimes found that acidic species other than hydrogen ions and basic species other than hydroxide ions are capable of catalyzing reactions. One then speaks of general acid–base catalysis. For example, in an aqueous solution containing acetic acid and sodium acetate the rate coefficient $k(=v/[S])$ can be expressed as

$$k = k_0 + k_{H^+}[H_3O^+] + k_{OH^-}[OH^-] + k_{HA}[HA] + k_{A^-}[A^-] \quad (40)$$

where HA is acetic acid and k_{HA} the corresponding catalytic coefficient; A^- is the acetate ion and k_{A^-} its catalytic coefficient.

If an acid has a large dissociation constant, for its dissociation into ions, it tends to have a large catalytic coefficient; similarly the catalytic strength of a base is greater the larger the base dissociation constant. In 1924 J. N. Brønsted proposed the following relationship between k_a, the catalytic coefficient of an acid, and K_a, its acid dissociation constant:

$$k_a = G_a K_a^{\alpha} \tag{41}$$

where G_a and α are constants. A similar relationship applies to a base catalyst.

Catalysis by enzymes, the biological catalysts, is much more specific than that by acids and bases. Some enzymes show absolute specificity, in that they are only known to be able to catalyze a single chemical reaction. Others show a lower specificity, in that they are able to catalyze only a certain type of reaction, such as ester hydrolysis. Enzymes commonly show stereochemical specificity, being capable of catalyzing a reaction of one stereochemical form of a substance and not the other.

All enzymes are proteins, and they are often associated with nonprotein substances, known as co-enzymes or prosthetic groups. Some enzymes require the presence of certain metal ions. The catalytic action of an enzyme appears to involve only a small region of the enzyme surface, known as the active center.

The mechanism of action of enzymes is similar in some respects to that of acids and bases but shows some important differences. One difference relates to the influence of the pH of the solution. If there is catalysis by acid and base the rate passes through a minimum as the pH is varied, because there is acid catalysis at low pH and base catalysis at high pH. With enzymes the rate passes through a *maximum* as the pH is varied. This is explained as due to the presence of at least two ionizing groups at the active center. For catalysis to be possible one of these groups must be in its acidic form and the other in its basic form, and this combination can only occur at intermediate pH values.

The rates of enzyme-catalyzed reactions also pass through a maximum as the temperature is varied. The increase at lower temperatures is the normal effect, due to there being an activation energy for the enzyme-catalyzed reaction. Enzymes, however, like all proteins, become denatured at higher temperatures and lose their catalytic activity.

Many patterns of behavior are found for the effect of substrate concentration on the rate of an enzyme-catalyzed reaction. For a reaction involving a single substrate the simplest behavior, described as Michaelis–Menten kinetics, is when there is a hyperbolic relationship between the rate v and the substrate concentration [S]:

$$v = \frac{V[\mathrm{S}]}{K_\mathrm{m} + [\mathrm{S}]} \tag{42}$$

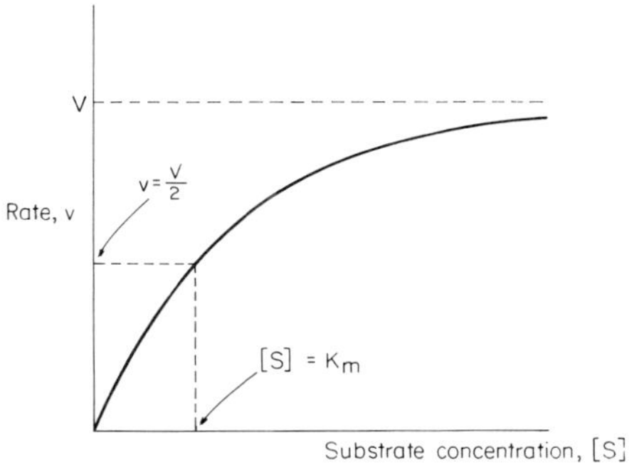

FIG. 5. Variation of rate v with substrate concentration [S] for a reaction obeying Michaelis–Menten kinetics [Eq. (42)].

Here K_m is called the Michaelis constant and V is the limiting rate at high substrate concentrations. Figure 5 illustrates this behavior and notes that K_m is equal to the concentration at which v is equal to $V/2$.

This type of kinetics was explained by L. Michaelis (1875–1949) and M. L. Menten (1878–1960) in terms of the formation of an addition complex between the enzyme and the substrate, the complex breaking down in a second step into products with release of the enzyme:

$$\mathrm{E} + \mathrm{S} \rightleftharpoons \mathrm{ES}$$

$$\mathrm{ES} \rightarrow \mathrm{E} + \mathrm{P}$$

Under usual conditions the substrate is greatly in excess of the enzyme, so that the concentration of free enzyme [E] may be less than the total concentration $[\mathrm{E}]_0$, since some enzyme has been converted into the enzyme–substrate complex ES; thus

$$[\mathrm{E}]_0 = [\mathrm{E}] + [\mathrm{ES}] \tag{43}$$

Application of the steady-state treatment to the reaction scheme gives

$$k_1[\mathrm{E}][\mathrm{S}] - k_{-1}[\mathrm{ES}] - k_2[\mathrm{ES}] = 0 \tag{44}$$

and elimination of [E] through Eq. (43) gives

$$[\mathrm{E}]_0 = [\mathrm{ES}]\left(\frac{k_{-1} + k_2}{k_1[\mathrm{S}]} + 1\right) \tag{45}$$

The rate is $k_2[\mathrm{ES}]$, and thus

$$v = \frac{k_2[\mathrm{E}]_0}{\dfrac{k_{-1} + k_2}{k_1[\mathrm{S}]} + 1} \tag{46}$$

or

$$v = \frac{k_2[\mathrm{E}]_0[\mathrm{S}]}{\dfrac{k_{-1} + k_2}{k_1} + [\mathrm{S}]} \tag{47}$$

This is equivalent to Eq. (42) with $V = k_2[E]_0$ and $K_m = (k_{-1} + k_2)/k_1$.

This is the simplest mechanism leading to Michaelis–Menten kinetics, but many other mechanisms also do so. To investigate mechanisms in more detail it is necessary to use special techniques for studying very rapid reactions, such as the stopped-flow and temperature-jump methods (Section I). Various factors give deviations from Michaelis–Menten kinetics. For example, sometimes the complex ES adds on an additional substrate molecule to give ES_2; if this does not react as rapidly as ES there is a falling off of the rate at higher substrate concentrations.

Many enzyme-catalyzed reactions involve two substrates, one of which for example may oxidize the other. In such cases several mechanisms have been identified. Sometimes one substrate A first forms a complex EA with the enzyme, and EA then reacts with the other substrate B to form a ternary complex EAB which then gives products; this is the ordered ternary complex mechanism. Alternatively, in the random ternary complex mechanism the ternary complex EAB may be formed either via EA or EB. In another mechanism the reaction of enzyme with one substrate A leads to one product of reaction, together with an intermediate which reacts with B to give another product. All of these mechanisms lead to similar types of kinetic behavior, and discrimination between them requires careful investigation.

In recent years there has been much interest in immobilized enzymes, where the enzyme has been attached to a solid support. This has the advantage in technical work of allowing an enzyme preparation to be used many times. The study of the kinetics of immobilized enzymes is also valuable in leading to an understanding of how enzymes behave in living systems, where they are often immobilized. Kinetic studies have shown that in such systems the rate is sometimes diffusion controlled (Section VII).

Other types of homogeneous catalysis do not follow a general pattern. Sometimes, for example, substances bring about catalysis in gas reactions by bringing about chain-initiation processes, or by becoming involved in chain-propagating processes. Ions of variable valency are good catalysts for certain solution reactions. For example, singly charged silver ions (Ag^+) can bring about a reduction with the formation of Ag^{2+}, which then can bring about an oxidation; the Ag^+–Ag^{2+} system can therefore act as a mediator in oxidation–reduction systems.

It is almost always the case that a catalyst exerts its action by reducing the activation energy, which means that it introduces the possibility of an alternative reaction path involving less energy and therefore a higher rate of reaction.

BIBLIOGRAPHY

Bamford, C. H., and Tipper, C. F. H. (eds.) (1969). "Comprehensive Chemical Kinetics," Elsevier Publishing Co., Amsterdam. [This series of many volumes, begun in 1969, is a valuable source of reference to all aspects of chemical kinetics].

"Compendium of Chemical Terminology" (1987). (I.U.P.A.C. recommendations compiled by V. Gold, K. L. Loening, A. D. McNaught, and P. Sehmi). Blackwell Scientific Publications, Oxford.

Jordan, P. C. (1979). "Chemical Kinetics and Transport." Plenum Press, New York.

Laidler, K. J. (1987). "Chemical Kinetics," 3rd ed. Harper & Row, New York.

L

LASER COOLING AND TRAPPING OF ATOMS

John E. Bjorkholm *AT&T Bell Laboratories*

GLOSSARY

Dipole force: Force exerted on an atom due to the stimulated scattering of light by the atom. Also called the stimulated force or the gradient force.

Laser cooling: Using laser radiation pressure forces to extract kinetic energy from atomic motion.

Laser radiation pressure: Radiation pressure exerted by a laser beam. Because laser beams are very bright, laser radiation pressure forces are generally much larger than the radiation pressure forces exerted by beams of incoherent light.

Optical molasses: Three-dimensional configuration of laser beams used to cool atoms to very low temperatures (on the order of 10^{-4} K).

Optical trapping: Using laser radiation pressure forces to confine an atom, or a group of atoms, within a small region of space.

Quantum heating: Heating of atomic motion caused by the fluctuations of the radiation pressure forces around their average values.

Radiation pressure: Forces exerted on a body due to the generalized scattering of light by that body.

Resonance-radiation pressure: Radiation pressure exerted on an atom by light tuned close to the frequency of one of the atom's resonance transitions.

Spontaneous force: Force exerted on an atom due to the spontaneous scattering of light by the atom. Also called the scattering force.

Laser light can exert significant forces on a free atom when the light frequency is tuned to be close to, or equal to, the frequency of one of the atom's resonance-absorption lines. These resonance-radiation pressure forces have found unique application with atomic beams. Most noteworthy, gaseous collections of atoms in vacuum have been cooled to ultralow temperatures (as low as 10^{-4} K); also, such untracold atoms have been optically trapped within a small volume of space for appreciable periods of time (many seconds). When viewed in hindsight, 1987 may well be seen as the year when the study of laser radiation pressure on atoms came of age. In previous years efforts were mainly devoted to understanding the forces in detail and to learning how to use them. In the years ahead most of the effort will be focused on using these techniques to help in carrying out measurements of a more fundamental nature. The purpose of this article is to discuss the basic forces exerted on atoms by resonance-radiation pressure and to describe some of the new optical techniques that can be used to manipulate atoms in ways not heretofore possible.

I. Introduction

It is well known that a beam of light carries momentum and that it will exert forces on objects that it illuminates. These forces arise out of the generalized scattering of the light by the object. Before the invention of the laser, however, applications of radiation pressure were virtually nonexistent. This was because the light emitted by conventional incoherent light sources is neither intense enough nor spectrally narrow enough to cause large effects. Nonetheless, in 1933 O. Frisch was able to demonstrate the transverse deflection of some of the atoms in an atomic beam of sodium caused by the light from a resonance lamp. The deflection observed was very small, about 3×10^{-5} rad, and was caused by the absorption and re-emission of a single photon by each deflected atom! The invention of the laser, with its intense and highly directional light beams, dramatically changed the situation. Now it was possible for an atom or other body to interact with a large number of photons in a short period of time. This was made clear in 1970 when A. Ashkin used a laser beam to accelerate, trap, and manipulate micrometer-sized, transparent dielectric spheres suspended in water. He further pointed out that significant radiation pressure forces similarly could be exerted on an atom if the frequency of the light was tuned near the frequency of one of the atomic resonance transitions. This was an attractive idea since neutral atoms are not easily manipulated using conventional techniques. Ashkin's seminal paper started worldwide thinking about laser radiation pressure on atoms. Experiments demonstrating these forces followed less rapidly. As laser radiation pressure became better understood throughout the 1970s, new applications became apparent. In 1975 it was realized that light pressure could be used to cool atoms to very low temperatures and in 1978 Ashkin proposed a particularly simple optical trap for atoms. It was not until the mid-1980s that some of these interesting possibilities were actually demonstrated experimentally. The delay between initial conception and eventual realization was caused by the need to develop the complex techniques and equipment required for the experiments. The first demonstrations of the basic forces and of the optical cooling and trapping of atoms utilized sodium atoms and precisely tuneable, cw dye lasers operating near the 589-nm resonance line of sodium. The lasers and the associated apparatus were quite complex and expensive. Recent advances have led to great simplification. In particular, since 1986 relatively simple and inexpensive cw GaAs diode lasers have been used to cool and trap cesium atoms, using the cesium resonance line at 852 nm.

II. Radiation Pressure Forces

The forces of laser radiation pressure are of two types. The first is usually referred to as the spontaneous force, but is sometimes called the scattering force. The second is variously referred to as the dipole force, the stimulated force, or the gradient force. A complete-description of these forces is complex since it must account for the quantized nature of light. That is, an atom scatters only one photon at a time and this fact leads to statistical fluctuations of the forces in direction and in time. These quantum fluctuations tend to heat the atomic motion and are a limiting factor in many applications of radiation pressure. A complete description of these fluctuations is beyond the scope of this article, but some of the consequences of these fluctuations will be discussed.

A. Spontaneous Force

The spontaneous force of radiation pressure arises because of the spontaneous scattering of nearly resonant light by the atom. It is most easily understood using the photon picture of light. Consider Fig. 1 which shows an atom illuminated by a traveling-wave light beam of frequency $\nu = c/\lambda$, where c is the speed of light and λ is the light wavelength. Because the light is tuned to be nearly resonant with the atom, the atom occasionally absorbs a photon from the beam and makes the transition to its excited state. In absorbing the photon the atom picks up the photon momentum h/λ. After a short time the atom decays back to its ground state and, in the process, re-emits a photon of frequency ν in some random direction, as shown by the outgoing wavey lines in the figure. When averaged over many scattering events, the outgoing pho-

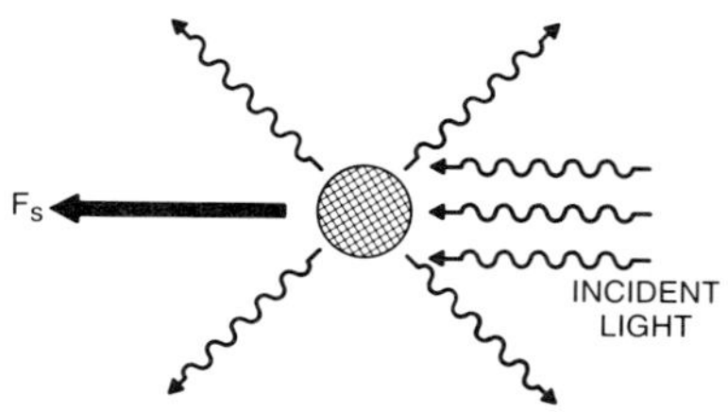

FIG. 1. Schematic diagram showing an atom being illuminated by a beam of nearly resonant light. The outgoing wavey lines indicate photons spontaneously scattered by the atom and the vector F_S denotes the resulting average spontaneous force exerted on the atom.

tons carry away no momentum since the scattering distribution is symmetric. Thus F_s, the average force exerted on the atom due to spontaneous scattering, is in the direction of the light propagation. Its magnitude is the rate at which momentum is absorbed from the incoming photons and is given by

$$F_s = (h/\lambda)(f/\tau)$$

where f is the probability that the atom is in its excited state and τ is the excited-state lifetime. To proceed further, we make the simplifying assumption that the atom can be described by the two-level model. This model assumes that the atom has only two energy levels, those of the ground and excited states. While this model is usually overly simplistic, its use makes a discussion of the basic physics much easier. The model is widely used, but rarely can it be applied to actual situations without at least some modification. For the two-level atom,

$$f = p/2(1 + p)$$

where p is the saturation parameter and is given by

$$p = (I/I_s)/(1 + q^2)$$

In this equation, I is the light intensity, I_s the saturation intensity for the transition, and q the normalized detuning given by $q = 2(\nu - \nu_0)/\Delta\nu_n$ where ν_0 is the resonant frequency of the transition and $\Delta\nu_N = 1/2\pi\tau$ its natural linewidth (FWHM). Figure 2 shows the dependence of F_S on detuning of the light from resonance for several values of I/I_s. The frequency dependence of the force reflects the atomic absorption line shape. For $p << 1$ the line shape is Lorentzian.

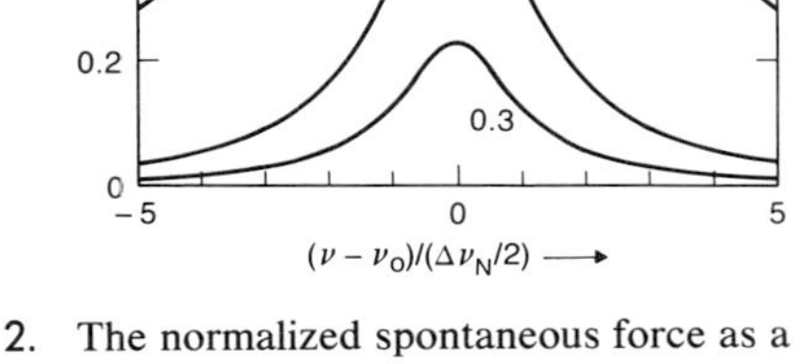

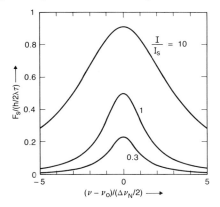

FIG. 2. The normalized spontaneous force as a function of the normalized light frequency for three values of I/I_S.

The natural linewidth is usually quite narrow, $\Delta\nu_N = 10$ MHz for the sodium atom and 5.2 MHz for cesium; this is why precisely tuneable lasers are required to exert significant spontaneous forces on atoms. When $p >> 1$ the line exhibits broadening and the maximum force saturates. The maximum force is small but nonetheless significant; for sodium and cesium, the corresponding accelerations amount to roughly 10^5 and 6×10^4 times the acceleration of gravity, respectively. [*See* LASERS.]

A number of experiments have demonstrated or have used the spontaneous force on neutral atoms of sodium and cesium, which are alkali metals. Alkali atoms are particularly useful since they have a single electron in their outermost shell and a correspondingly simple atomic energy level structure. Atoms with more than one outermost electron have more complicated level structure and this leads to experimental difficulties. Nonetheless, spontaneous forces have been exerted on excited neon atoms in which a metastable excited level functioned as an effective ground state. Spontaneous forces have also been utilized on singly ionized atoms of magnesium and barium contained in ion traps. These atoms have two electrons in their outermost shell, so the singly ionized species have a reasonably simple "alkali-metal-like" level structure.

B. Fluctuations of the Spontaneous Force

The force F_s is the net force averaged over many spontaneous scattering events. Because an atom scatters only one photon at a time, and because each photon is scattered into a random direction, there are fluctuations of the instantaneous force around the average. These fluctuations cause the atomic motion to contain a significant random component, which grows with time. This heating of the atomic motion is described by a so-called momentum diffusion coefficient, D_p. The rate at which W, the kinetic energy associated with the random motion, grows is given by $dW/dt = D_p/m$, where m is the atomic mass. For a uniform, traveling, plane wave and in the limit $p << 1$, this expression becomes

$$dW/dt = (m/2)(h/m\lambda)^2(p/\tau)$$

The quantity $h/m\lambda$ is the speed of atomic recoil due to the absorption of a single photon; for the sodium atom it is abut 3 cm/sec and for cesium it is 0.35 cm/sec. For situations in which p is large or when the light field contains intensity gradients the expression for D_p becomes much more complex. Counteracting quantum heating is crucial for the cooling and trapping of atoms.

C. Dipole Force

The dipole force of resonance-radiation pressure is most easily understood using the wave picture of light. In this picture it is simply the force exerted on an induced dipole situated in an electric field gradient. It can also be viewed as arising from the stimulated scattering of light by the atom. The average dipole force can be written as

$$\overline{F}_d = (4\pi/c)\alpha\, \overline{\nabla} I$$

where α is the atomic polarizability and I is the light intensity. For the idealized two-level atom,

$$\alpha = -\frac{1}{2}\frac{(\lambda/2\pi)^3 q}{(1 + q^2)(1 + p)}$$

Several characteristics of this force should be stressed. First, it exists only when there is a gradient of the light intensity. Second, the dipole force has no upper limit; importantly, it can be much larger than the spontaneous force. Finally, the frequency dependence of this force is dispersive in character, as shown in Fig. 3. The force is zero for $\nu = \nu_0$; for $\nu < \nu_0$, the direction of the force is such as to pull the atom into the high-intensity regions of the light beam; for $\nu > \nu_0$, the atom is pushed away from the intense regions. Notice also that the force can be large even for $q >> 1$.

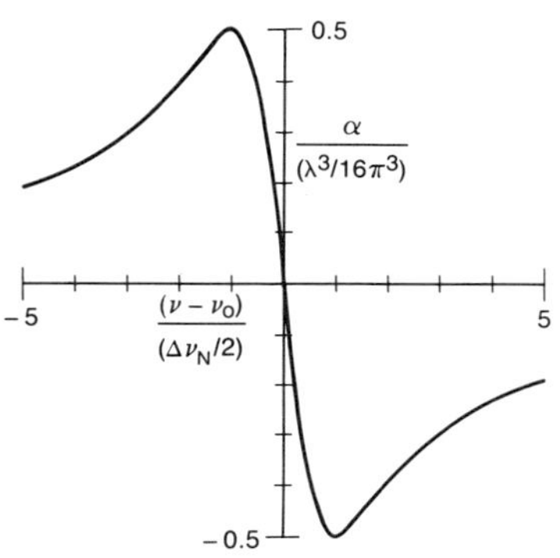

FIG. 3. The normalized atomic polarizability as a function of the normalized light frequency for $I/I_S << 1$.

It is often convenient to think of the dipole force as being derivable from a conservative optical potential $U(\overline{r})$, which is given by

$$U(\overline{r}) = (h\, \Delta\nu_N/4)q \ln[1 + p(\overline{r})]$$

This potential energy is the same as the shift in energy of the atomic ground state caused by the optical Stark effect. Thus, whenever dipole forces are exerted on an atom, there will also be optical Stark shifts of the atomic energy levels. Because these level shifts can often be large compared with $\Delta\nu_N$, it is usually difficult to effectively apply the spontaneous force to an atom that is simultaneously subjected to a dipole force.

D. Fluctuations of the Dipole Force

Due to the quantum nature of light there are also random fluctuations of the dipole force about its average. These fluctuations are much more difficult to describe and understand than are those of the spontaneous force. We will not consider them here, but it must be realized that the quantum heating caused by these fluctuations can be very large, often very much greater than that due to spontaneous fluctuations. The dipole force and its fluctuations are proportional to the gradient of the light intensity. This dipole force quantum heating can be exceptionally large in light fields that have large intensity gradients, as in a standing-wave field.

E. Early Demonstrations of the Forces

Early demonstrations of the spontaneous force were made by illuminating a sodium atomic beam at normal incidence with the light from a cw dye laser tuned onto the atomic resonance. The spontaneous force caused substantial deflection of the atoms. Deflection angles as large as 5×10^{-3} rad were observed, corresponding to the scattering of about 200 photons and an acquired transverse velocity of 600 cm/sec. The maximum deflections obtained were limited by the Doppler shifts associated with the transverse speed. That is, as the atoms acquired transverse speed, they were Doppler shifted out of resonance with the light and the force was greatly diminished. The transverse speed of 600 cm/sec corresponds to a Doppler shift of 10 MHz, the full natural linewidth of sodium.

The first demonstration of the dipole force was made around 1980 by superimposing a copropagating cw dye laser beam on top of an atomic beam of sodium atoms. The laser beam

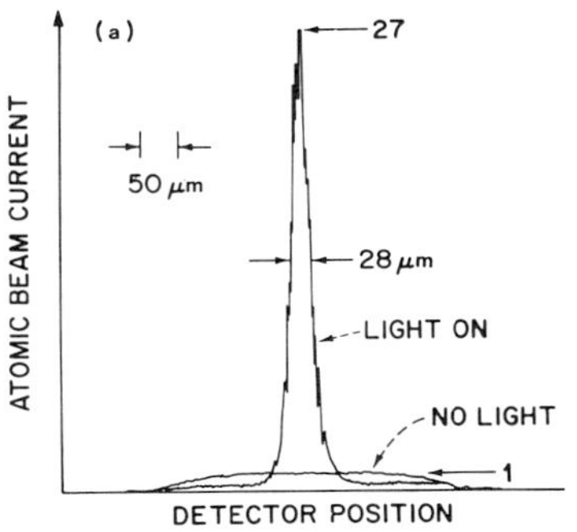

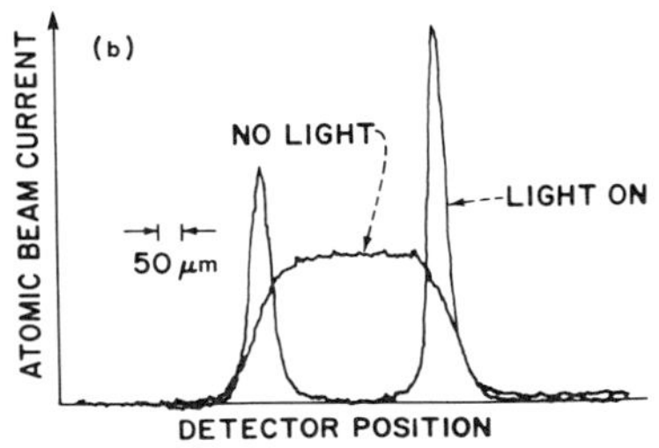

FIG. 4. Focusing and defocusing of an atomic beam by a superimposed, Gaussian laser beam. The figures show the atomic beam current density as a function of position, with the light on and off. In (a) the light frequency is less than the atomic resonance frequency and the atomic beam is focused by the light. In (b) the light is tuned above the atomic resonance and defocusing takes place.

had a Gaussian intensity profile (TEM_{00} mode) and was tuned several gigahertz away from the atomic resonance. Because of the intensity gradients and the cylindrical symmetry of the illumination, transverse dipole forces were exerted on the atoms. For tunings below resonance the forces were such as to pull the atoms to the axis of the laser beam; in other words, the light exerted focusing, confining forces on the atoms. For tunings above resonance the light forces were opposite and brought about defocusing effects on the atoms. The dramatic changes in the atomic beam profile caused by these forces are shown in Fig. 4. Because the light was tuned far from resonance, the effects caused by the average spontaneous force were small. Significantly, however, it was demonstrated that the size of the spot to which the atomic beam could be focused was determined by the transverse heating of the atomic motion caused by the fluctuations of the spontaneous force. While not yet demonstrated, it should be possible to focus atomic beams to very small spot sizes by using a TEM_{01}, or donut-mode, laser beam tuned above the atomic resonance. In this case the atoms would tend to be concentrated on the laser beam axis where the light intensity is lowest and where the spontaneous heating is minimized.

In a generalized sense these experiments demonstrated that laser beams can be used to manipulate atomic motion in useful ways. It is expected that the use of lasers to modify and control atomic motion will become a useful technique in atomic beams work.

III. The Single-Beam, Dipole-Force Optical Trap

The first optical trap to be demonstrated is deceptively simple to describe. As shown in Fig. 5, this trap is formed by a sharply focused Gaussian-mode laser beam tuned far below the atomic resonance ($q << -1$). The intensity of a Gaussian (or TEM_{00}-mode) laser beam propagating along the z axis (the longitudinal direction) and focused at $z = 0$ is given by

$$I(r, z) = (2P/\pi w^2)\exp(-2r^2/w^2)$$

where $w(z) = w_0[1 + (\lambda z/\pi w_0^2)^2]^{1/2}$, w_0 is the focal spot size at $z = 0$, and P is the power in the laser beam. As shown in Fig. 5, there is a point of stable equilibrium for the atom just beyond the focus. Transverse confinement of the atom is provided by the transverse dipole forces. Longitudinal confinement is brought about by balancing the longitudinal spontaneous force with the longitudinal dipole force that exists because of the strong longitudinal gradients of the intensity (strong focusing). It is useful to consider the depth of the trap for parameters comparable to those used in the first demonstration of optical trapping. In those experiments, which trapped

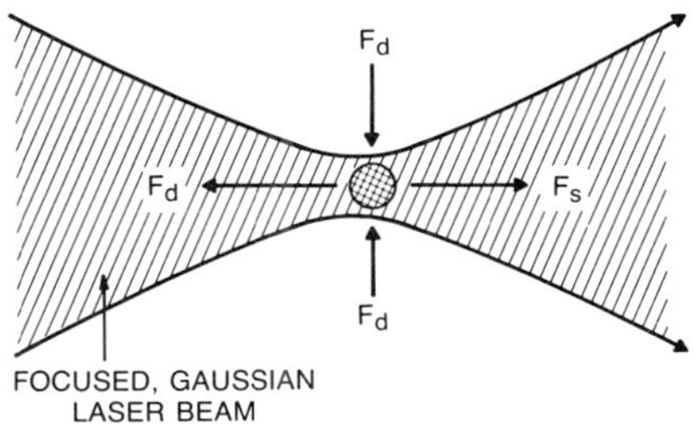

FIG. 5. Schematic diagram of the single-beam, dipole-force optical trap. There is a point of stable equilibrium for the atom just beyond the focus of the light beam. The dipole and spontaneous forces exerted on the atom are shown.

the sodium atom, the laser power P was 200 mW, the focal spot size w_0 was 10 μm, and the longitudinal trap depth was maximized by detuning the laser −150 GHz from the resonance (corresponding to $q = -3 \times 10^4$). For these parameters, and approximating the sodium atom with the two-level model, the transverse well depth is found to be equivalent to an atomic temperature of 25 mK and the longitudinal trap depth equivalent to 15 mK. For reasons to be explained later, the trap depths for the actual experiment were only about 40% of the above values.

From this example it now can be readily understood why it took a number of years to develop the techniques required to demonstrate an optical trap. The problems that needed to be confronted and solved were as follows. First, since the trap is very shallow, a collection of ultracold atoms ($T << 1$ mK) is needed to load it. No source of such cold atoms existed prior to 1985. Second, the trap volume is very small, on the order of 10^{-7} cm^3. Thus, to efficiently load the trap, the collection of cold atoms must also be dense. Finally, even if cold atoms could be loaded into the trap, the quantum fluctuations of the forces would rapidly heat them. Without an effective means for counteracting this heating, the initially cold atoms would "boil" out of the trap about 10 msec after being loaded. Thus, before an optical trap could be demonstrated it was necessary to develop techniques for cooling atoms to ultralow temperatures and for keeping them cold in the presence of quantum heating. As will shortly be described, the solution to these problems is a technique called "optical molasses," which was first demonstrated in 1985.

IV. Laser Cooling of Atoms

In this section we will discuss the techniques that have been used to cool atoms to temperatures low enough for placing them in optical traps.

A. Atomic Beam Slowing

The seemingly most straightforward way to slow, or cool, the atoms in an atomic beam is to let them propagate against a light beam tuned to the atomic resonance. The deceleration corresponding to the maximum spontaneous force is $h/2m\lambda\tau$; for sodium and cesium, this amounts to -9.15×10^7 cm/sec^2 and -5.7×10^6 cm/sec^2, respectively. Consider a typical thermal atomic beam of sodium atoms, for which the longitudinal velocity distribution peaks at roughly 10^5 cm/sec. In principle, atoms moving at this speed could be brought to rest in about 1 msec, during which time the atoms would travel over a distance of about 46 cm while scattering about 3×10^4 photons. Unfortunately, such efficient deceleration is not straightforward to achieve because of the Doppler shifts of the light frequency that occur as the atom slows down. For instance, a velocity change of only 10^3 cm/sec causes a Doppler shift of about 17 MHz, which is larger than the 10-MHz linewidth of the sodium absorption line. In other words, unless something is done, the atoms quickly shift out of resonance with the light and the deceleration is greatly reduced.

Several experimental techniques have been devised to counteract these Doppler shifts and to keep the atoms in resonance with the light as they slow down. The first technique uses spatially dependent Zeeman shifts of the atomic energy levels to compensate for the changing Doppler shifts. In this method, the atomic beam is directed down the bore of a solenoid having a tapered longitudinal magnetic field. The field varies in such a way that the Zeeman shifts of the atomic energy levels compensate for the changing Doppler shifts as the atoms slow down. In the second technique the frequency of the laser is directly "chirped," or swept in frequency, at a rate appropriate for keeping the atoms in resonance with the light. Both techniques work well and both have been used to bring the mean longitudinal velocity of some of the atoms in an atomic beam to zero.

These "stopped" atoms, however, are not cold enough for use in optical trap experiments because of the quantum heating that occurs as they are slowed down. Considering sodium once again, an atom starting with a longitudinal velocity of 10^5 cm/sec scatters 3×10^4 photons in being stopped. Because of the random scattering of the emitted photons, there is a spread in the velocity distribution along each axis given approximately by $(h/m\lambda)\sqrt{N/3}$, where N is the number of photons scattered in bringing the atom to rest. For sodium this amounts to roughly 300 cm/sec; the corresponding atomic temperature is roughly 75 mK. In order to achieve optical trapping, even colder atoms are required.

Atoms having temperatures of this magnitude have found other applications. For example, the first trapping of neutral atoms was demonstrated in 1985 using a magnetic trap that had a potential well depth on the order of 5 K. This trap was filled using cold atoms obtained using the Zeeman slowing technique. Techniques similar to the chirping technique have also been used to cool hot atoms confined in ion traps that have well depths on the order of 10 eV (corresponding to a temperature of about 2×10^5 K). Ions in traps have been cooled to temperatures of about 10 mK.

B. Optical Molasses

"Optical molasses" is a technique that uses the spontaneous force to rapidly cool already cold atoms to much lower temperatures.

The basic idea behind optical molasses is easily described for one dimension. Consider an atom illuminated from opposite directions by two laser beams of equal intensity traveling along the x axis. The light frequency is tuned to be slightly below the atomic resonance. When the light intensity is low, the net force acting on the atom is simply the sum of the forces of each beam acting alone. When the atom is at rest it sees no net spontaneous force since the forces exerted by the two light beams are equal and opposite. Now let the atom have a velocity component along the x axis. In this situation the frequency of the beam propagating against the atomic motion is Doppler shifted closer to resonance and the force it exerts on the atom increases. The opposite holds for the copropagating light beam. As a result, there is a net average force that opposes the atomic velocity and that is proportional to it. For small velocities it is given by

$$F_x = (8\pi h/\lambda^2)(I/I_s)(q/1 + q^2)v_x = -\beta v_x$$

where I is the intensity of each beam. This expression is valid as long as the Doppler shifts are small compared with $\Delta\nu_n$; for sodium this corresponds to velocities less than 150 cm/sec. This force appears as a viscous damping force to the atom. Damping is maximized for $q = -1$, which corresponds to a detuning a $\Delta\nu_N/2$ below the atomic resonance. An initial velocity exponentially damps to zero with a decay time of m/β. For the sodium atom, $q = -1$, and $I/I_s = 0.1$, this decay time is 16 μsec; thus the damping is seen to be quite strong.

Optical molasses is the extension of the above ideas to three dimensions, using three pairs of oppositely propagating laser beams along the three orthogonal axes. A slowly moving atom situated in the mutual intersection of the six laser beams experiences strong three-dimensional viscous damping and its average velocity is rapidly reduced to zero. Because of the quantum fluctuations of the optical forces, the atoms do not actually come to rest. As will be discussed, the atoms execute a random walk motion. Consequently, atoms find it difficult to escape from the optical molasses and they are confined within it for a long time. In spite of containment times approaching 1 sec that have been achieved with sodium, optical molasses is not an optical trap since there are no restoring forces exerted on the atoms.

The long time required for an atom to escape from optical molasses is easily understood in terms of the quantum fluctuations. An atom in optical molasses with an average velocity of zero experiences a velocity "kick" of $h/m\lambda$ in a random direction each time it scatters a photon. Each velocity kick is damped out and the net result is that the atom executes a random walk motion in three dimensions with a step size of $(\lambda/2\pi)(I/I_s)^{-1}$. After a time t, the mean-square deviation of the atom from its starting point is

$$\langle r^2 \rangle = (\lambda/2\pi)^2(I/I_s)^{-2}N$$

where N is the number of scattered photons and is roughly given by $(6I/I_s)(t/\tau)$, for $I/I_s << 1$. Confinement times of about 0.5 sec are obtained using optical molasses with a diameter of 1 cm. More careful analysis yields somewhat shorter confinement times.

While the average atomic velocity in optical molasses is zero, the mean-square atomic velocity is determined by the interplay of the heating caused by the fluctuations of the optical forces and the cooling caused by the average spontaneous force. Equilibrium is established when the rate of heating equals the average cooling rate. A careful analysis, which includes the dipole heating rate due to the standing-wave nature of the light beams, yields an equilibrium temperature for the collection of atoms given by

$$kT_{eq} = m\langle v^2 \rangle = h\Delta\nu_N/2$$

For the sodium atom $T_{eq} = 240$ μK and for cesium it is 100 μK.

Optical molasses was first demonstrated in 1985 using the sodium atom and cw dye lasers. The experiments were carried out using a pulsed atomic beam. Atoms initially traveling with a speed of 2×10^4 cm/sec were decelerated to 2×10^3 cm/sec using a chirped slowing laser beam.

These slow atoms were then allowed to drift into the optical molasses region, which was roughly spherical in shape and about 0.5 cm^3 in volume, where final cooling and retention took place. Atomic densities of 10^6 cm^{-3} and retention times of several tenths of a second were obtained. A direct measurement of the temperature of the atoms in optical molasses was made using a time-of-flight technique. It was found that T_{eq} was 240 μK, in agreement with the quantum heating prediction. During 1987 similar, but experimentally simpler, optical molasses experiments were carried out using cw laser diodes and the cesium atom; the atomic temperature achieved was the predicted limit of 100 μK.

The ideas discussed in this section apply only in the low intensity limit, $I < I_s$. In the high intensity limit, $I >> I_s$, the behavior of the optical forces becomes much more complicated and, in some situations, can confound our physical understanding. As an example, for low intensities optical molasses provides damping of the atomic motion for tunings below the atomic resonance and heating for tunings above resonance. In the high intensity limit, the situation is reversed! In this case it is the dipole forces, which exist because of the standing waves in the optical molasses configuration, that do the cooling. This situation is usually referred to as "stimulated molasses." The damping rate can far exceed that for the usual optical molasses, but so does the heating. The equilibrium temperature achieved with stimulated molasses is not as low as that achieved with spontaneous molasses.

V. Optical Trapping of Atoms

A. Single-Beam, Dipole-Force Trap

The successful demonstration of optical molasses in 1985 provided experimentalists with the remaining tools needed to accomplish optical trapping. Optical trapping of atoms was first carried out in 1986 using sodium atoms, cw dye lasers, and the single-beam, dipole-force optical trap described in Section III.

The experiment was carried out by first injecting sodium atoms into optical molasses. After a delay of several milliseconds to allow the atoms to reach equilibrium, the optical trap beam was introduced into the interior of the optical molasses, as shown schematically in Fig. 6. Trapping was observed as the buildup of a small, but intense, spot of fluorescence situated within the much larger and much weaker cloud of fluorescence from the atoms in the optical molasses (see Fig. 7). The brightness of the small spot indicated that the density of trapped atoms was much higher than the density of atoms in optical

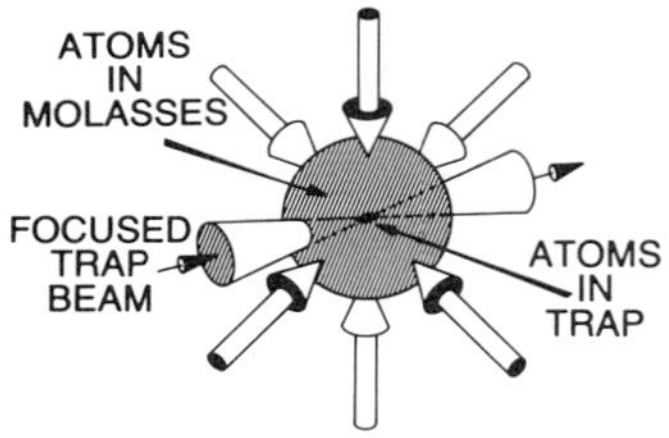

FIG. 6. Schematic diagram of the interaction region used for trapping atoms. The broad arrows represent the collimated laser beams that intersect to form "optical molasses." The shaded sphere represents the fluorescence emitted by the collection of ultracold atoms contained and executing random-walk motion within the optical molasses. The optical trap is formed just beyond the focus of the trap laser beam, which is also shown. The black spot represents the intense fluorescence emitted by the dense collection of atoms confined within the optical trap.

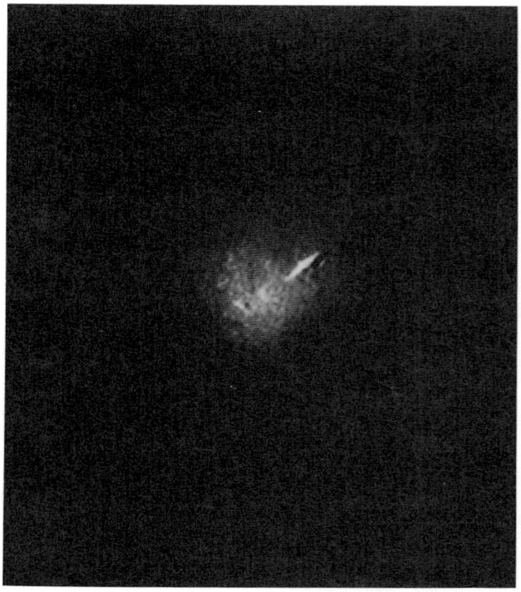

FIG. 7. Photograph of trapped atoms. The large, diffuse cloud is fluorescence emitted by atoms contained within optical molasses. The small, bright spot is the fluorescence from the much higher density of atoms confined within the optical trap.

molasses. Recall that optical molasses is needed to keep the trapped atoms cool. However, optical molasses is not effective when the trapping light is present because of the large optical Stark shifts associated with the potential well of the trap. Thus, in this experiment it was necessary to alternatively chop on and off the trap and optical molasses beams. Furthermore, it was important that the chopping be done rapidly enough; if too slow, the oscillation of the atoms within the optical potential well becomes unstable and trapping does not occur.

The optical trap was observed to behave as expected from calculations in all respects but one. The one discrepancy was the observed trap lifetime; it was found only to be about 1 sec, about four orders if magnitude less than expected from simple calculations. It was surmised, and later confirmed, that the short lifetime was determined by the imperfect vacuum in the vacuum chamber (about 10^{-9} Torr). Trapped atoms were ejected from the trap by even very weak collisions with the residual gas atoms, which were at a temperature of about 300 K.

A summary of the operating parameters for the original optical trap and the results obtained with it are as follows. The trap beam was focused within optical molasses to a spot size of 10 μm, its power was 200 mW, and it was tuned approximately 150 GHz below the sodium D1 resonance line. Good results were obtained for chopping periods ranging from about 0.4 to 10 μsec. Under best conditions about 10^3 atoms were trapped within a volume of 10^{-9} cm^3 at a density of 10^{12} cm^{-3}. The atomic temperature was inferred to be about 400 μK.

B. Spontaneous Force Optical Traps

In the early 1980s there was a good deal of speculation about the various forms that optical traps might take. This speculation led to what has come to be called the optical Earnshaw's theorem. Simply put, the theorem states that it is impossible to form a dc optical trap using only forces that are directly proportional to the light intensity. Since the spontaneous force is proportional to I in the low intensity limit, this theorem initially was interpreted as stating that optical traps could not be constructed using only the spontaneous force. However, it is now realized that there are at least two ways to avoid this conclusion. The first is to allow for time dependence of the forces. Thus spontaneous force traps can be constructed in which at least some of the optical beams exhibit time dependence. These traps are sometimes referred to as "optodynamic" traps. Another way around the theorem is to break the assumption that the forces are linearly related to the optical intensity. Thus saturation of the forces due to high intensities, the optical pumping of real multilevel atoms, and the application of other force fields can all be used to allow dc, spontaneous force traps to be constructed. Similar techniques have been used in ion traps to avoid the consequences of the electrical Earnshaw's theorem.

The first spontaneous force optical trap was demonstrated during 1987 and is referred to as the "magnetic molasses" trap. This trap is constituted by superimposing a simple spherical quadrupole magnetic field on an optical molasses formed using circularly polarized light beams. The magnetic field causes spatially dependent Zeeman shifts of the atomic energy levels. For sodium these Zeeman shifts result in restoring forces that are proportional to the displacement of an atom from the origin (defined by the magnetic field). This trap is much larger (several millimeters diameter) and much deeper (about 500 mK) than the single-beam, dipole-force trap. As a result, it is easier to fill and many more atoms could be trapped. Trap lifetimes were increased by reducing the chamber background pressure. Figure 8 shows an example of the exponential decay of the trap population exhibiting a 1/e-lifetime of 65 sec. Trap lifetimes as long as 100 sec were obtained at a background pressure of 2×10^{-10} Torr. As many as 10^7 sodium atoms were confined in the mag-

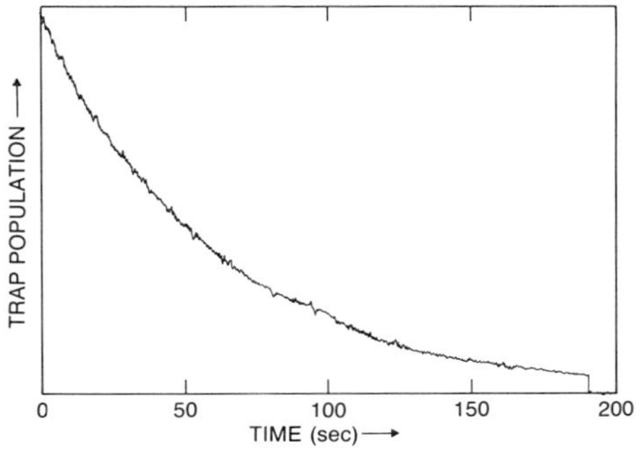

FIG. 8. Time dependence of the atomic population in a "magnetic molasses" optical trap as a function of time. The decay is well described by an exponential curve having a 1/e-lifetime of 65 sec.

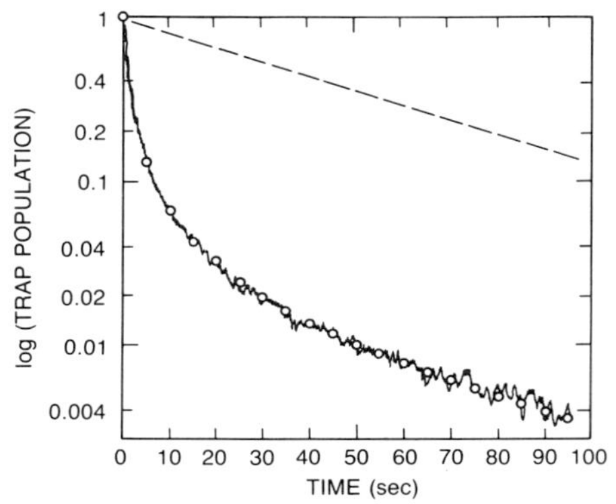

FIG. 9. A logarithmic plot of the nonexponential decay of the atomic population in a magnetic molasses trap observed for a high initial atomic density (about 10^{11} cm^{-3}). The initial decay is 150 times faster than the decay that would be obtained in the absence of density-dependent losses, as shown by the dashed straight line.

netic molasses trap at densities as high as 10^{11} cm^{-3}.

When the magnetic molasses trap was loaded with a high initial atomic density, the decay with time of the number of trapped atoms was observed to be nonexponential and faster than the exponential decay observed with low initial fills. An example of such an observation is shown in Fig. 9. It was found that the departure from exponential decay was proportional to the square of the density of trapped atoms, indicating that the additional losses were caused by collisions between the ultracold trapped atoms. This finding is of interest for several reasons. First, density-dependent losses such as these as detrimental since they limit the maximum atomic densities that can be achieved in an optical atom trap. This will make it difficult to push a great deal further into a new regime of gas physics in which high atomic densities and ultralow temperatures are simultaneously achieved. On the other hand, it is now possible to observe the effects of the relatively infrequent collisions between slow atoms. In work with thermal atomic beams or gas cells such collisions are swamped out by the much more frequent collisions between fast atoms. Collisions between slow atoms are not well understood and are only beginning to be studied. Recent observations of associative ionization between slow atoms in an optical trap have indicated that the cross section for the process is several orders of magnitude larger than for atoms traveling at typical thermal velocities.

VI. Conclusion

The year 1987 is somewhat of a "watershed" year in that the nature of work on laser radiation pressure on atoms is undergoing a subtle change. In the past, efforts were directed towards demonstrating and understanding the basic forces and the ways in which they can be utilized to affect atomic trajectories and to cool and trap atoms. In the future, the emphasis will be placed on using these forces and techniques as experimental tools that will make it possible to carry out measurements of a fundamental nature that had not heretofore been possible. Areas of interest include the study of atomic collisions at slow speeds, collisions between slow atoms and surfaces, the possible observation of collective quantum effects between cold atoms, possible extension of laser radiation pressure to molecules, and precision spectroscopic measurements. Because of these tantalizing prospects, the number of scientists interested in applying laser radiation pressure on atoms is undergoing rapid growth.

Bibliography

Theoretical discussions:

Cook, R. J. (1979). *Phys. Rev. A* **20,** 224.

Dalibard, J., and Cohen-Tannoudji, C. (1985). *J. Opt. Soc. Am. B* **2,** 1707.

Gordon, J. P., and Ashkin, A. (1980). *Phys. Rev. A* **21,** 1606.

Experimental demonstrations:

Bjorkholm, J. E., Freeman, R. R. Ashkin, A., and Pearson, D. B. (1980). *Opt. Lett.* **5,** 111.

Bjorkholm, J. E., Chu, S., Ashkin, A., and Cable, A. (1987). *In* "Advances in Laser Science—II" (Lapp, M., Stwalley, W. C., and Kenney-Wallace, G. A., eds.), *Am. Inst. Phys. Conf. Proc.* **160,** 319. Am. Inst. Phys. New York.

Chus, S., Hollberg, L. W., Bjorkholm, J. E., Cable, A., and Ashkin, A. (1985) *Phys. Rev. Lett.* **55,** 48.

Chu, S., Bjorkholm, J. E., Ashkin, A., and Cable, A. (1986). *Phys. Rev. Lett.* **57,** 314.

Ertmer, W., Blatt, R., Hall, J. L., and Zhu, M. (1985). *Phys. Rev. Lett.* **54,** 996.

Migdall, A., Prodan, J., Phillips, W. D., Bergeman, T., and Metcalf, H. (1985). *Phys. Rev. Lett.* **54,** 2596.

Phillips, W. D., and Metcalf, H. J. (1982). *Phys. Rev. Lett.* **48,** 596.

Phillips, W. D., and Metcalf, H. J. (1987). *Sci. Am.,* March, p. 50.

Prodan, J., Migdall, A., Phillips, W. D., So, I., Metcalf, H., and Dalibard, J. (1985). *Phys. Rev. Lett.* **54,** 992.

Raab, E. L., Prentiss, M. G., Cable, A., Chu, S., and Pritchard, D. E. (1987). *Phys. Rev. Lett.* **59,** 2631.

Watts, R. N., and Wieman, C. E. (1986). *Opt. Lett.* **11,** 291.

Wineland, D. J., and Itano, W. M. (1987). *Phys. Today,* June, p. 34.

LASER–MATERIALS INTERACTIONS

Michael Bass *University of Southern California*

Glossary

Complex propagation constant: Quantity γ ($= \alpha + j\beta$) used to describe the propagation of light in a general medium; α gives the attenuation and β the wave vector magnitude, both in reciprocal centimeters.

Laser-driven plasma: Optically thick plasma found near a surface heated to the point of vaporization by an intense laser beam; the beam ionizes some of the vapor and through the process of avalanche breakdown creates the plasma.

Nonlinear absorption: Process in which the attenuation coefficient itself is a function of the light intensity.

Photoablation: Process by which short-wavelength laser light breaks molecular bonds in matter and causes material to be ejected from the surface with very little heating of the sample.

Surface electromagnetic wave: Wave formed on an irradiated surface when an irregularity on the surface scatters the light energy; the amount of energy coupled can be significant.

The interaction of laser light with matter is in many ways like the interaction of ordinary light with matter. The difference between them and the interest in laser light arises from the fact that laser light can be much more intense than light from other sources. This property of laser light has opened new research areas in nonlinear optics, laser plasma generation, and new types of materials processing. It has also led to applications such as laser cutting, drilling, welding, and heat treating. The high fluxes possible allow consideration of such futuristic applications as power generation through inertial confinement fusion, X-ray generation for microelectronics, and laser weaponry.

I. Deposition of Light Energy in Matter

A. Absorption

The interaction between light, a form of electromagnetic energy, and materials takes place between the optical electric field and the most nearly free electrons in the medium. In quantum mechanical terms, one speaks of interactions between photons and electrons in the presence of the lattice of nuclei. The lattice must be present to ensure momentum conservation. For the purposes of this article, the classical viewpoint of an electric field causing electrons to move in the presence of damping or frictional forces is sufficient to describe the process of optical absorption.

Conduction band electrons in metals are able to interact with an optical electric field. Their motion is damped by collisions with the vibrating lattice and so some of the light energy is transferred to the lattice. In this manner the material is heated. In semiconductors the motions of both electrons in the conduction band and holes in the valence band must be considered. In dielectrics the electrons are effectively bound to the atoms or molecules that compose the material. The applied optical field induces a polarization in the material. Upon relaxation some of the energy in the polarization is coupled to the lattice and the material is heated. These processes of absorption of energy from an optical field can be treated by classical electromagnetics. That is, Maxwell's equations, the constitutive equations

ENCYCLOPEDIA OF PHYSICAL SCIENCE
AND TECHNOLOGY, VOL. 8

of matter, and the boundary conditions for each material can be solved in each case. [*See* ELECTROMAGNETICS.]

1. Absorption from an Electromagnetic Point of View

a. Propagation in a General Dielectric Material. Let the propagation of the optical electromagnetic wave in a medium be given by the complex propagation constant γ where

$$\gamma = \alpha + j\beta \tag{1}$$

so that a plane wave electric field is described by

$$E(z, t) = \text{Re}\{E(0) \exp(-\gamma z) \exp[j(\omega t - \beta z)]\} \tag{2}$$

Here ω is the radian frequency of the field, α the attenuation coefficient, and β the propagation coefficient.

A dielectric is described by the complex dielectric constant

$$\varepsilon = \varepsilon_1 + j\varepsilon_2 \tag{3}$$

and a magnetic susceptibility μ. This enables us to define a complex index of refraction

$$\eta = n + jk \tag{4}$$

in which n determines the propagation vector and k determines the attenuation of the wave in the medium. It is easy to show that

$$n = \{[(\varepsilon_1^2 + \varepsilon_2^2)^{1/2} + \varepsilon_1]/2\}^{1/2} \tag{5}$$

and

$$k = \{[(\varepsilon_1^2 + \varepsilon_2^2)^{1/2} - \varepsilon_1]/2\}^{1/2} \tag{6}$$

By applying Maxwell's equations and the dielectric boundary conditions as to the case of a lossy dielectric we find that

$$\gamma = j\omega\{(\mu\varepsilon_1)[1 - j(\varepsilon_2/\varepsilon_1)]\}^{1/2} \tag{7}$$

Note that if we had treated the lossy dielectric as a medium having a finite conductivity σ, we would have obtained

$$\gamma = j\omega\{(\mu\varepsilon)[1 - j(\sigma/\omega\varepsilon)]\}^{1/2} \tag{8}$$

where ε is the dielectric permittivity. It is clear that Eqs. (7) and (8) are identical with ε replaced by ε_1 and σ/ω by $-\varepsilon_2$.

Lossless dielectrics are media having σ identically zero. The complex propagation constant is then purely imaginary and there is no absorption in the medium.

b. Perfect Metals. A perfect metal is a material having an infinite conductivity or a material in which

$$\alpha/\omega\varepsilon \gg 1$$

In this case we find

$$\alpha = \beta = (\omega\mu\sigma/2)^{1/2} \tag{9}$$

which means that a field propagating in a metal will be attenuated by a factor of $1/e$ when it has traveled a distance

$$\delta = (2/\omega\mu\sigma)^{1/2} \tag{10}$$

The quantity δ is called the skin depth and at optical frequencies for most metals it is ~50 nm or about one-tenth of the wavelength of green light. After a light beam has propagated one skin depth into a metal, its intensity is reduced to $1/e^2$ or 0.135 of its value on the surface.

The energy that is no longer in the electromagnetic wave when light is attenuated in a metal drives conduction currents in the so-called skin layer. These in turn produce heating through ohmic losses and the light energy thereby appears in the metal as heat. Heating of the metal at depths below the skin layer takes place by means of thermal conduction.

c. Lossy, Nonconductive Dielectrics. As mentioned above, the results derived for a general dielectric are equivalent to those for a metal when the proper substitutions are made for ε_1 and ε_2. This allows us to consider the case where

$$\varepsilon_2/\varepsilon_1 \gg 1$$

and write the attenuation coefficient for the lossy dielectric as

$$\begin{aligned} \alpha &= \omega(\mu\varepsilon_2/2)^{1/2} \\ &= (2\pi/\lambda_0)(\mu_R\varepsilon_{2R}/2)^{1/2} \end{aligned} \tag{11}$$

where $(\mu_0\varepsilon_0)^{1/2}$ is recognized as the speed of light in free space, $\omega = 2\pi c/\lambda_0$, and the subscript "R" indicates the relative permittivity and susceptibility. For electromagnetic radiation with a free space wavelength of 1000 nm propagating in such a dielectric we see that

$$\alpha > 10^4 \text{ cm}^{-1}$$

This means that the electromagnetic energy will be reduced to $1/e^2$ of its value within 10^{-4} cm.

The nonconductive dielectric is a medium with very few free or conduction band electrons at room temperature and so we cannot consider ohmic losses as the mechanism for heating. Its interactions with electromagnetic radiation involve valence band electrons. When such electrons in this type of material absorb light energy they can be raised either to the conduction band or to some impurity state lying within the band gap. They then relax back to the valence band. The process of relaxation can be radiative (fluorescence and phosphorescence) or nonradiative. In either case phonons (lattice vibrations) are generated and the material is heated. The heat generation is localized to the region in which the absorption occurs and, as in metals, heating beyond this region takes place by thermal heat conduction.

2. Lorentz and Drude Models

The classical theory of absorption in dielectric materials is due to H. A. Lorentz and in metals it is the result of the work of P. K. L. Drude. Both models treat the optically active electrons in a material as classical oscillators. In the Lorentz model the electron is considered to be bound to the nucleus by a harmonic restoring force. In this manner, Lorentz's picture is that of the nonconductive dielectric. Drude considered the electrons to be free and set the restoring force in the Lorentz model equal to zero. Both models include a damping term in the electron's equation of motion which in more modern terms is recognized as a result of electron–phonon collisions [*See* ELECTRICAL RESISTIVITY OF METALS.]

These models solve for the electron's motion in the presence of the electromagnetic field as a driving force. From this, it is possible to write an expression for the polarization induced in the medium and from that to derive the dielectric constant. The Lorentz model for dielectrics gives the relative real and imaginary parts of the dielectric constant as

$$\varepsilon_{1R} = 1 + (Ne^2/\varepsilon_0 m)\frac{\omega_0^2 - \omega^2}{(\omega_0^2 - \omega^2)^2 + \Gamma^2\omega^2} \tag{12}$$

and

$$\varepsilon_{2R} = (Ne^2/\varepsilon_0 m)\frac{\Gamma\omega}{(\omega_0^2 - \omega^2)^2 + \Gamma^2\omega^2} \tag{13}$$

In these expressions N is the number of dipoles per unit volume, e the electron charge, m the electron mass, Γ the damping constant, ω_0 the resonance radian frequency of the harmonically bound electron, ω the radian frequency of the field, and ε_0 the permittivity of free space. Equations (12) and (13) are sketched in Fig. 1. The range of frequencies where ε_1 increases with frequency is referred to as the range of normal dispersion, and the region near $\omega = \omega_0$ where it decreases with frequency is called the range of anomalous dispersion.

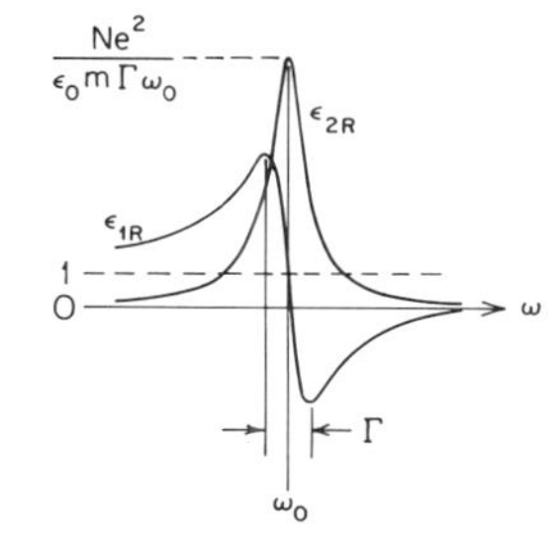

FIG. 1. Frequency dependences of ϵ_{1R} and ϵ_{2R}.

In the preceding discussion the contributions of the electronic polarizability to the dielectric constant were considered. Other contributions occur such as stimulation of vibrations of ions in ionic crystals. This type of contribution is very small at optical frequencies because of the large mass of the ions compared to that of the electrons. In other words, the ionic polarizability is much smaller than the electronic polarizability at optical frequencies. We can therefore consider only the electronic terms when evaluating optical absorption. By inserting Eq. (13) into Eq. (11) we obtain the absorption coefficient of the lossy, nonconductive dielectric in terms of the properties of the electron's kinematics assumed by Lorentz. That is,

$$\alpha = (2\pi/\lambda)(\mu_R/2)(Ne^2/\varepsilon_0 m) \times \left(\frac{\Gamma\omega}{(\omega_0^2 - \omega^2)^2 + \Gamma^2\omega^2}\right)^{1/2} \tag{14}$$

The Drude model for metals assumes that the electrons are free to move. This means that it is identical to the Lorentz model except that ω_0 is set equal to zero. The real and imaginary parts of the metal's dielectric constant are then given by

$$\varepsilon_{1R} = 1 - (Ne^2\varepsilon_0 m)\frac{1}{\omega^2 + \Gamma^2} \tag{15}$$

$$\varepsilon_{2R} = (Ne^2\varepsilon_0 m)\frac{\Gamma}{\omega(\omega^2 + \Gamma^2)} \tag{16}$$

The quantity Γ is related to the mean time between electron collisions with lattice vibrations. T (i.e., to the problem of electron–phonon scattering). By considering the motion of electrons able to make collisions with lattice vibrations in an electric field E having radian frequency ω, it is straightforward to show that the average velocity is

$$\nu = -\frac{eE}{m}\frac{\mathrm{T}}{1 - j\omega\mathrm{T}} \tag{17}$$

The conductivity at this frequency is then

$$\sigma = \frac{Ne^2\mathrm{T}}{m}\,\frac{1}{1 - j\omega\mathrm{T}} \tag{18}$$

where the dc conductivity is given by

$$\sigma_{\mathrm{dc}} = Ne^2\mathrm{T}/m \tag{19}$$

From Eqs. (15) and (16) we see that if we allow $\Gamma = 1/\mathrm{T}$, then

$$\varepsilon_1 = 1 - \left(\frac{\sigma_{\mathrm{dc}}}{\varepsilon_0}\right)\mathrm{T}\,\frac{1}{\omega^2\mathrm{T}^2 + 1} \tag{20a}$$

and

$$\varepsilon_2 = \left(\frac{\sigma_{\mathrm{dc}}}{\varepsilon_0}\right)\left(\frac{1}{\omega}\right)\frac{1}{\omega^2\mathrm{T}^2 + 1} \tag{20b}$$

At electromagnetic field frequencies that are low, that is, when $\omega\mathrm{T} \ll 1$, we have

$$\varepsilon_1 = 1 - \sigma_{\mathrm{dc}}\mathrm{T}/\varepsilon_0 \tag{21}$$

and

$$\varepsilon_2 = \sigma_{\mathrm{dc}}/\varepsilon_0\omega \tag{22}$$

At such frequencies $\varepsilon_2 \gg \varepsilon_1$, and since $\Gamma = 1/\mathrm{T}$ Eq. (14) gives

$$\alpha = (\omega\mu\sigma/2)^{1/2} \tag{23}$$

which is exactly the result we obtained earlier when treating absorption from an electromagnetic point of view. In other words, the optical properties and the dc conductivity of a perfect metal are related through the fact that each is determined by the motion of free electrons. At high frequencies transitions involving bound or valence band electrons are possible and there will be a noticeable deviation from this simple result of the Drude model. However, the experimental data reported for most metals are in good agreement with the Drude prediction at wavelengths as short as 1 μm.

3. Temperature Dependence

Another aspect of the absorption of light energy by metals that should be noted is the fact that it increases with temperature. This is important because during laser irradiation the temperature of a metal will increase and so will the absorption. The coupling of energy into the metal is therefore dependent on the temperature dependence of the absorption. This property is easy to understand if we remember that all the light that gets into a metal is absorbed in it. The question that must be addressed is how the amount of incident optical energy that is not reflected from the metal's surface depends on temperature. Recalling the Fresnel expression for electric field reflectance and applying to it the real and imaginary parts of the complex index of refraction for a metal–air interface, we can write the field reflectivity. Multiplying this by its complex conjugate, we find the intensity reflection coefficient for a metal

$$R_{\mathrm{I}} = 1 - 2\mu\varepsilon_0\omega/\sigma \tag{24}$$

Since the conductivity σ decreases with increasing temperature, R_{I} decreases with increasing temperature. As a result, more incident energy actually gets into the metal and is absorbed when the temperature is raised. This is true even though the absorption at high temperatures takes place in a deeper skin depth.

B. Nonlinear Absorption

Since the advent of lasers made possible high-intensity optical fields it has been possible to explore interactions of light with matter in which the response of the material is not linear with the optical electric field. This subject, known as nonlinear optics, has become a major field of research and has led to such useful optical devices as frequency converters, tunable parametric devices, and optically bistable elements. This section presents a semiclassical discussion of nonlinear optics and how it gives rise to nonlinear absorptions, in particular two-photon absorption (TPA).

The polarization of a medium and the optical electric field applied to it are linked by the material's susceptibility X, a tensor quantity. In the previous section we considered the limit of small optical fields, where the susceptibility is a function of the dielectric constants only and is independent of the field. In this case the polarization vector **P** is related to the optical electric field **E** by the expression

$$\mathbf{P} = \mathrm{X} * \mathbf{E} \tag{25}$$

Equation (25) is the relationship on which optics was built prior to 1961. As a result of lasers and the high fields they produce it is now necessary to allow that X can be a function of the optical field. This is accomplished by writing the field-dependent susceptibility as a Taylor series expansion in powers of the optical field and thus expressing the polarization as

$$\mathbf{P} = \mathrm{X}_1 * \mathbf{E} + \mathrm{X}_2 * \mathbf{E} * \mathbf{E} + \mathrm{X}_3 * \mathbf{E} * \mathbf{E} * \mathbf{E} + \cdots \tag{26}$$

Maxwell considered this form of relation in his classical treatise on electricity and magnetism but, for simplicity, retained only the first-order term.

The first term on the right of Eq. (26) gives rise to the "linear" optics discussed previously. The second term gives rise to optical second-harmonic generation or frequency doubling and optical rectification. The third term results in third-harmonic generation and self-focusing.

Absorption processes involving one or more photons are also described by the susceptibilities X_n employed in Eq. (26). By considering the continuity equation for the flow of energy and the fact that the susceptibilities are complex quantities,

$$X_n = X_n' + jX_n''$$

the imaginary part of the third-order term can be shown to give rise to an altered form of Beer's law. That is,

$$I(z) = \frac{I(0)\exp(-\alpha_0 z)}{1 + (\alpha_{\mathrm{TPA}}/\alpha_0)I(0)[1 - \exp(-\alpha_0 z)]} \tag{27}$$

where $\alpha_0 = 4\pi k X_1$ is the conventional linear attenuation coefficient, k the propagation vector in the medium, and α_{TPA} the nonlinear attenuation coefficient, given by

$$\alpha_{\mathrm{TPA}} = \frac{32\pi^2}{c^2}\,\omega X_3'' I \tag{28}$$

This is the part of the absorption that is linearly dependent on the intensity. From a quantum mechanical point of view, such a property is the result of processes in which two photons are absorbed simultaneously. In other words, a material with energy levels separated by U must be considered able to absorb simultaneously two photons, each having energy $U/2$. As a result, when studying the absorption of light in materials it is no longer sufficient to measure it at one low intensity. Contributions from such higher-order processes as TPA can occur and must be measured. For example, TPA is sufficient in some semiconductors to enable their excitation to lasing inversions. It is also a powerful tool for studying the presence of deep-level dopants in semiconductors, since they contribute energy levels that enhance TPA.

Higher-order multiphoton absorption processes are possible. There is some evidence that three-photon processes have been detected. However, nonlinear processes higher than TPA require optical fields that are very high. These fields may result in TPA, and the electrons that are thereby freed may be accelerated by the optical field to form a catastrophic electron avalanche breakdown. When this happens the material's effective absorptivity becomes 100%, too much energy is deposited in the irradiated volume, and severe mechanical damage known as intrinsic laser-induced damage follows. This sequence of events is responsible for setting intensity limits for materials and, consequently, for fixing the minimum size of optical components used in high-power lasing systems.

C. Laser-Driven Plasma Coupling and Decoupling

One of the most spectacular features of laser–materials interactions is the formation of a laser-driven plasma in the irradiated region (see Fig. 2). This phenomenon occurs in almost all types of intense laser irradiation, continuous wave (cw) or pulsed, on surfaces, and in the bulk of solids, liquids, and gases. It can prevent the laser light from further coupling to the sample or it can enhance the coupling. Its most important applications are in driving the target compression used to produce fusion energy by inertial confinement and in creating point sources of soft X-rays for X-ray lithography in microelectronics.

When an intense laser beam is focused inside a transparent medium a laser-induced break-

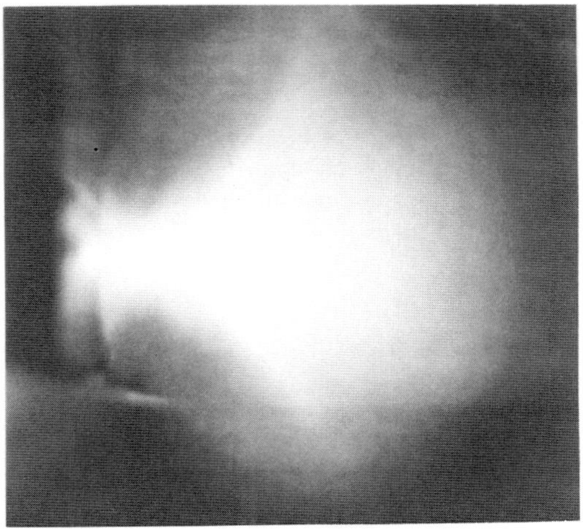

FIG. 2. Plasma generated by a pulsed CO_2 transverse electrical discharge at atmospheric pressure (TEA) laser incident from the right on a copper target in vacuum. The outer region contains hot copper atoms. The central region is a very bright blue-white color, indicating highly ionized, very hot copper vapor.

down and plasma can be formed in as short a time as 6 psec. This very fast formation is the result of the very highly nonlinear process of plasma formation. The process is so complex that it remains a major subject of current research. As a result, only a qualitative discussion is presented in this article.

If the target reaches a high enough temperature to induce mass loss, it is essential to account for the energy carried away by the removed material in order to determine the energy absorbed. Mass can be removed by such processes as vaporization, melt removal, and pyrolysis or burning. When vaporization occurs some of the ejected material can be ionized. Then, through the process of inverse bremsstrahlung, the vapor can be broken down by the optical field to produce an optically thick plasma. This plasma is a very hot blackbody radiator and emits an intense blue-white light called a laser-induced spark.

As most irradiations take place in air, we consider that case. At laser intensities slightly greater than the plasma formation threshold intensity, a laser-supported combustion (LSC) wave can be ignited. These waves occur at intensities from 2×10^4 to 10^7 W/cm^2 with both pulsed and cw lasers. The ignition of an LSC wave takes place in the ejected target vapor and the heated vapor transfers energy to the surrounding air. The LSC wave thus generated propagates away from the target surface along the beam path and drives a shock wave ahead of itself in the air (see Fig. 3).

The nature of the coupling of the light to the material when a plasma is formed depends on the beam parameters of energy, spot size, and pulse duration as well as air pressure and target material. For long pulse times and low laser intensities the formation of an LSC wave usually results in decreased coupling as the wave propagates away from the surface. This is the case in most laser materials processing applications requiring melting or material removal (i.e., welding, drilling, and cutting).

At high intensities a laser-supported detonation (LSD) wave is ignited. In this case absorption takes place in a thin zone of hot, high-pressure air behind the detonation wave (see Fig. 4). Since this wave takes air away from the surface, expansion fans form to satisfy the boundary conditions at the target surface. The plasma remains nearly one-dimensional until the expansion fans from the edge reach the center. This time is given approximately by the beam radius divided by the speed of sound in the plasma. In the vicinity of the surface there is no laser absorption and the plasma properties are determined by its isentropic expansion. The LSD wave plasma expansion away from the surface is very rapid. As a result, though it intercepts and absorbs incoming laser energy, the LSD wave plasma does not reradiate this energy as strongly absorbed ultraviolet light into the area originally irradiated.

Computations for two-dimensional LSD wave plasmas show that for short laser pulses (i.e., shorter than 1 μsec) the overall coupling of light to metal targets can be as large as 25%. Since most metals have absorptions near 1–2% in the infrared, this represents a substantial enhancement of the coupling. However, the coupling remains the same for increasing intensities but is spread out over increasing areas compared to that of the irradiated spot. Therefore, for short pulses, while the total coupling coefficient may be large, the energy deposited in the irradiated area may be smaller than if the LSD wave plasma had never been formed.

When an LSC wave plasma is formed, it is possible to find enhanced coupling in the irradi-

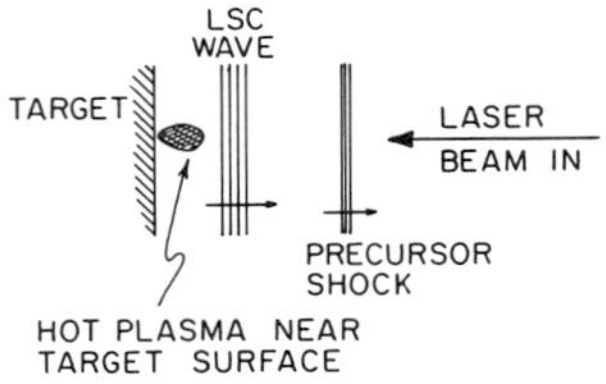

FIG. 3. Sketch of a one-dimensional laser-supported combustion (LSC) wave. The hot plasma near the target can radiate ultraviolet light, which is strongly absorbed by the target material. The LSC wave is of low enough density to allow the laser light to reach and heat the plasma.

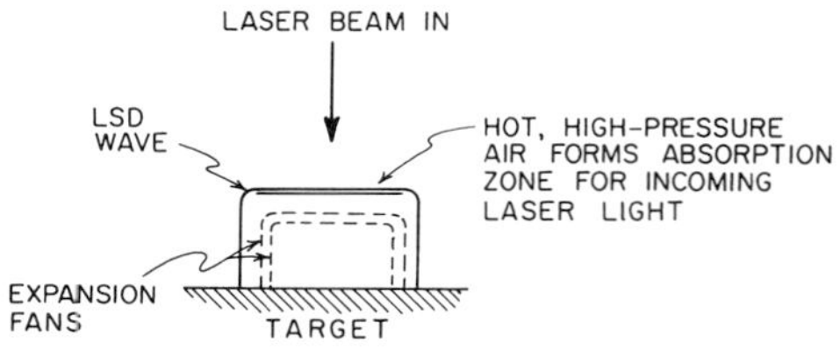

FIG. 4. Sketch of a laser-supported detonation (LSD) wave. The incoming laser light is absorbed in the LSD wave front as it propagates away from the target. This spreads any reradiated energy in the ultraviolet over a large area and reduces the local energy deposition.

ated region. This results from energy transfer by radiation from the hot, high-pressure plasma adjacent to the surface. The LSC wave propagates into the air at a low speed, and a large fraction of the incoming laser energy is used to heat the plasma to a temperature in excess of 20,000 K. This plasma radiates very efficiently in the ultraviolet part of the spectrum, where most materials, in particular, metals, absorb more strongly than in the visible and infrared. As long as the LSC wave expansion remains nearly one-dimensional the plasma-radiated ultraviolet light remains localized in the originally irradiated area and the local heating is enhanced.

Efficient local coupling of incident energy to the sample requires that the plasma be ignited near the surface, an LSC wave be generated, and the plasma expansion remain one-dimensional during the irradiation. These requirements define a range of intensities over which enhanced coupling will be observed. The minimum intensity is clearly that which ignites a plasma at the surface in the vaporous ejecta. The maximum intensity is that which generates an LSD wave instead of an LSC wave. Pulse durations or dwell times of cw sources must be less than that required for radial expansion of the plasma to set in over the dimension of the irradiated spot. Thus, enhanced coupling will occur for pulses shorter than the spot radius divided by the speed of sound in the plasma ($\sim 5 \times 10^5$ cm/sec). Once radial expansion begins, the pressure and the plasma temperature drop rapidly. Concomitantly, so does the efficiency of the plasma as an ultraviolet light radiator.

As mentioned above, the irradiation conditions used in many laser materials processing applications correspond to the two-dimensional LSC wave plasma case. Therefore, plasma formation reduces the coupling of laser energy into the irradiated region, and further increases in the laser intensity, either by increasing the laser power or decreasing the spot size, are futile. To deal with this problem, He cover gas is often used to suppress plasma formation. In some cases strong gas jets are used to blow the plasma away and allow the laser light to enter the irradiated material.

Another aspect of laser-driven vaporization and plasma formation that should be considered is the momentum transferred to the surface. In leaving the surface at high speed the ejected material carries away a substantial amount of momentum. This appears as a recoil momentum of the surface and, since it occurs during the short duration of the laser irradiation, it results in a substantial impulse to the surface. This process has been used to shock-harden certain materials. An ablative coating is placed on the area to be shock-hardened and it is struck by a pulsed laser beam. The impulse due to the removal of the ablative coating produces the desired hardening. The transfer of an impulse by laser irradiation is another subject of major research interest, in part due to its potential value as a laser weapons effect.

D. Surface Electromagnetic Waves

Researchers studying such diverse topics as laser processing of semiconductors, laser-induced damage, laser materials processing, and laser-driven deposition processes have observed the formation of "ripples" in the irradiated region (see Fig 5). All of these observations had in common the facts that linearly polarized lasers were used and that the material in the irradiated region had reached its melting point. The ripples were spaced by the light wavelength when the light was at normal incidence. These facts and

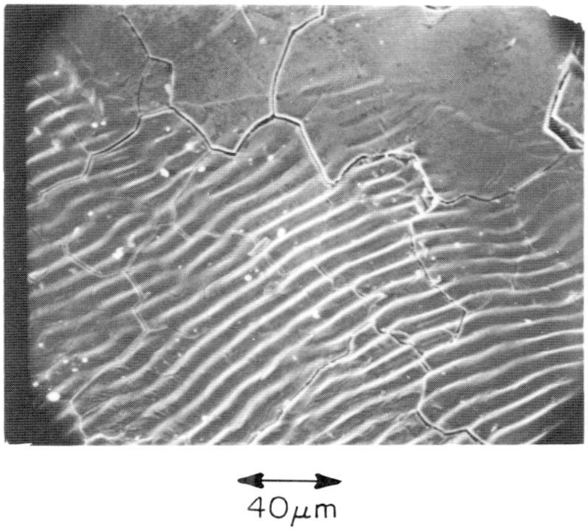

FIG. 5. Scanning electron micrograph of ripples spaced by ~ 10 μm produced in 304 stainless steel exposed to a cw CO_2 laser able to melt metal. The sample was stationary under a normally incident 10.6-μm beam polarized perpendicular to the ripples. The residual ripples are found near the edges of the melt pool, where freezing is sufficiently rapid to preserve the ripples. In the central part of the melt pool convective motion in the melt obscures the ripples. The ripples are the result of surface electromagnetic waves (SEW) launched by scattering the incident light and subsequent interference between two electromagnetic waves.

additional data demonstrated that the ripples were the result of the following sequence of events:

1. The incident light was scattered by some surface irregularity and a surface electromagnetic wave was launched.
2. In the region irradiated this wave was able to interfere with the incident light.
3. The interference pattern produced localized differences in the surface temperature, and when the material became molten it flowed due to surface tension effects or differential vapor pressures to conform with the varying light intensity.
4. The molten material froze quickly enough following irradiation that the ripples were detectable afterward.

The key element in the formation of these ripples is the fact that surface electromagnetic waves (SEW) were generated. This is another means by which light energy can be coupled into a material and one that was not obvious from prelaser knowledge. The fact that a gratinglike interference pattern is set up allows one to apply the electromagnetic theory of gratings to understand the process. From this theory, it is clear that for a particular line spacing, there is a particular grating height that can dramatically enhance the absorption of a material over that of a smooth surface. The generation of SEW can therefore result in greatly enhanced coupling of laser light to materials.

On the other hand, if the surface waves propagate, they may carry energy away from the irradiated area. If the dimension of the irradiated area is small compared to the SEW attenuation length, this may be a major factor in redistributing the absorbed energy. The irradiated region will not become as hot as it might if no SEW were generated. It should be noted that this effect would give rise to a beam spot size dependence of laser heating when the beam diameters used are in the range of one SEW attenuation length.

E. Photoablation

A new and exciting light–matter interaction called photoablation has been demonstrated with the advent of high peak intensity ultraviolet lasers. This occurs with the excimer lasers (i.e., ArF, KrF, XeF, or XeCl) operating at wavelengths from ~250 to 350 nm. The lasers provide high energies (~1 J or more per pulse) in pulses

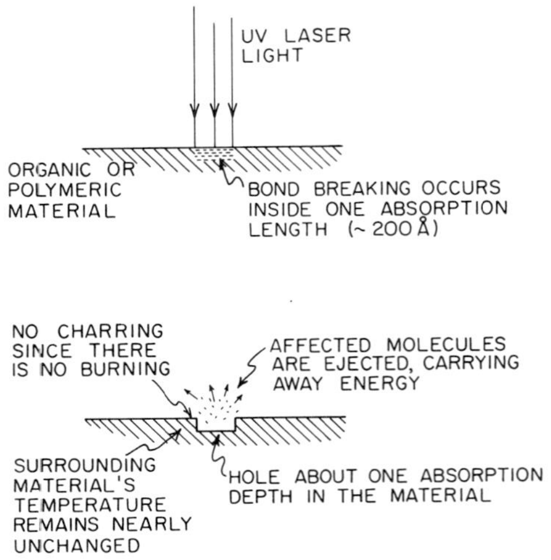

FIG. 6. Sketch of the process of ultraviolet laser irradiation-induced photoablation.

of ~30 nsec duration. Most organic materials absorb very strongly at these wavelengths. The energies of photons in the ultraviolet are sufficient to efficiently break bonds in such materials. When this happens the fragments are subjected to very high pressures and are ejected from the surface (see Fig. 6). The process takes place entirely within one absorption depth (~20 nm) and so provides a very controllable means of material removal. In addition, the energy deposited in the material is removed as kinetic energy of the ejecta. As a result, there is very little thermal heating of the sample and the process is confined to the area irradiated. With lasers operating at reasonably high repetition rates, this process can be used to remove significant amounts of material.

The use of excimer lasers and photoablation is still under consideration in research and development laboratories. However, it is clearly suitable for removing protective coatings or insulation and for certain medical applications where great delicacy is required.

II. Laser Heating of Materials

A. Thermal Diffusion Problem and Thermal Diffusivity

We are concerned with the heating of materials that results from several of the laser light absorption processes discussed in the previous sections. This can be approached in a number of nearly equivalent ways, all of which require a knowledge of (1) the target's optical and thermal properties during the irradiation, (2) the laser beam distribution, (3) the dynamics of the irradiation process, and (4) the processes of phase change in the target material. As would be expected, it is extremely difficult to solve the heat flow problem exactly in the general case and so reasonable approximations are used. In addition, only problems that are easy to solve are attempted. These are then useful as guides to the solution of other problems.

Consider the equation of heat conduction in a solid with the laser energy absorbed on the irradiated surface as a heat source. By judiciously selecting the beam geometry, dwell time, and sample configuration, the problem may be reduced to solvable one- and two-dimensional heat flow analyses. Phase transitions can be included and the temperature distributions that are produced can be calculated. Examples will be selected to provide specific guidance in the choice of lasers and materials. The result of all this will be an idea of the effects that one may produce by laser heating of solids.

The equation for heat flow in a three-dimensional solid is

$$\rho C \frac{\partial T}{\partial t} = \frac{\partial}{\partial x}\left(K \frac{\partial T}{\partial x}\right) + \frac{\partial}{\partial y}\left(K \frac{\partial T}{\partial y}\right) + \frac{\partial}{\partial z}\left(K \frac{\partial T}{\partial z}\right) + A(x, y, z, t) \quad (29)$$

where ρ is the material density in grams per cubic centimeter, K the thermal conductivity in watts per centimeter per degree Celsius, and C the heat capacity in joules per centimeter per degree Celsius; these are material properties that will depend on temperature and position. The quantity $A(x, y, z, t)$ is the rate at which heat is supplied to the solid per unit time per unit volume in joules per second per cubic centimeter and $T = T(x, y, z, t)$ is the resulting temperature distribution in the material. Figure 7 defines the coordinate system used.

The temperature dependence of the properties results in a nonlinear equation that is very difficult to solve exactly. Where the functional dependence of these quantities on temperature is known, it is sometimes possible to use numerical integration techniques to obtain a solution. A further complication arises from the temperature dependence of $A(x, y, z, t)$ through that of the material's absorptivity. When phase transitions occur one can attempt a solution of the problem by solving for each phase separately

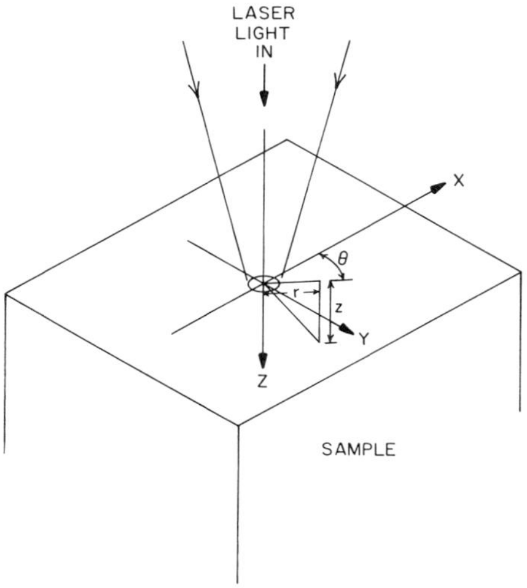

FIG. 7. Sketch of coordinate system used in evaluating responses of materials to laser irradiation.

and including the heat required for the transition where appropriate.

For most materials the thermal properties do not vary greatly with temperature and can be assigned an average value for the temperature range to be studied. In this case it is possible to solve the heat flow problem. A further simplification is obtained by assuming that the material is homogeneous and isotropic. Under these conditions Eq. (29) reduces to

$$\nabla^2 T - \frac{1}{\kappa}\frac{\partial T}{\partial t} = -\frac{A(x, y, z, t)}{K} \quad (30)$$

where $\kappa = K/\rho C$ is the thermal diffusivity. In the steady state $\partial T/\partial t = 0$, resulting in

$$\nabla^2 T = -\frac{A(x, y, z, t)}{K} \quad (31)$$

If there is no heat source, as in the case of cooling of heated material, the temperature distribution will be given by

$$\nabla^2 T = \frac{1}{\kappa}\frac{\partial T}{\partial t} \quad (32)$$

in the time-dependent case and

$$\nabla^2 T = 0 \quad (33)$$

in the steady state.

A physical insight into the meaning of the quantity κ is useful. A simple analysis of the units show that

$$(\kappa t)^{1/2} = \text{distance}$$

This distance or a multiple thereof is generally known as the thermal diffusion distance for the particular problem and is a handy quantity to use when scaling the effects of laser heating. It is often useful to know how the optical absorption depth compares with the thermal diffusion distance during a laser irradiation. To see the meaning of the thermal diffusion depth more clearly, consider the following particular solutions of Eq. (32):

$$T = T_0 e^{t/\mathrm{T} \pm z/z_\mathrm{D}}$$

and so

$$\frac{\partial T}{\partial t} = \frac{1}{\mathrm{T}} T$$

and

$$\frac{\partial^2 T}{\partial z^2} = \left(\frac{1}{z_\mathrm{D}}\right)^2 T$$

Thus

$$\left[\left(\frac{1}{z_\mathrm{D}}\right)^2 - \frac{1}{\kappa \mathrm{T}}\right] T = 0$$

and we have a solution if

$$z_\mathrm{D} = (\kappa \mathrm{T})^{1/2}$$

Therefore a characteristic distance is related to a characteristic time by $(\kappa \mathrm{T})^{1/2}$.

For a more realistic case consider

$$T = G T_0 t^{-1/2} e^{-z^2/4\kappa t} \qquad \text{for } t > 0$$

where G is a constant having units of $(\mathrm{sec})^{1/2}$. Then we have

$$\frac{\partial T}{\partial t} = G T_0 \left(-\frac{1}{2t^{3/2}} + \frac{z^2}{4\kappa t^{5/2}}\right) e^{-z^2/4\kappa t}$$

and

$$\frac{\partial^2 T}{\partial z^2} = G T_0 \left(-\frac{1}{2\kappa t^{3/2}} + \frac{z^2}{4\kappa t^{5/2}}\right) e^{-z^2/4\kappa t}$$

which satisfy

$$\frac{\partial^2 T}{\partial z^2} - \frac{1}{\kappa}\frac{\partial T}{\partial z} = 0$$

At $t = 0$ we will set $T = T_0$ for $z = 0$ and $T = 0$ for $z > 0$. Now consider that at any time $t_\mathrm{p} > 0$ the temperature at

$$z_\mathrm{D} = 2(\kappa t_\mathrm{p})^{1/2}$$

is $1/e$ times that at $z = 0$.

The second case corresponds to the release of the quantity of heat $2\rho C T_0 (\pi\kappa)^{1/2}$ per unit area over the plane $z = 0$ at time $t = 0$. This could be a decent approximation to the case of laser heating of a semi-infinite metal irradiated by a short pulse [defined in terms of the relative values of beam radius and $(\kappa t_\mathrm{p})^{1/2}$] in a uniform beam where we wish to know a temperature on the beam axis. The quantity of heat per unit area would be the laser intensity I times the pulse duration $\mathrm{T_p}$ times the fraction absorbed or

$$I \mathrm{T_p} \alpha = 2\rho C T_0 (\pi\kappa)^{1/2}$$

where α is the absorptance of the metal. Then

$$T_0 = \frac{\alpha I \mathrm{T_p}}{2\rho C (\pi\kappa)^{1/2}}$$

and

$$T(z, t) = \frac{\alpha I \mathrm{T_p}}{2\rho C (\pi\kappa)^{1/2}} t^{-1/2} e^{-z^2/4\kappa t}$$

or

$$T(z, t) = \frac{\alpha I \mathrm{T_p}}{\rho C \pi^{1/2}} \frac{e^{-z^2/4\kappa t}}{(4\kappa t)^{1/2}} \qquad \text{for } t > 0$$

The important role of the quantity $z_\mathrm{D} = 2(\kappa t)^{1/2}$ in describing the process of laser heating is clear; z_D defined above is the thermal diffusion distance.

B. Absorption in a Very Thin Surface Layer

These are cases where

$$\alpha^{-1} \ll (\kappa \mathrm{T_{laser}})^{1/2}$$

where $\mathrm{T_{laser}}$ is the duration of the irradiation.

1. Uniformly Illuminated Surface

The incident intensity is given by

$$I_0(t) = \begin{cases} 0, & t < 0 \\ I_0, & t \geq 0 \end{cases}$$

and is assumed to be uniformly distributed. The temperature distribution on-axis is sought by assuming no heat diffusion in the x and y directions, even though this may be important in certain applications. The results of this special case are very useful since most often the on-axis temperature is the desired quantity.

The thermal diffusion equation with this heat source and the boundary condition

$$T(z, t) = 0 \qquad \text{for } t < 0 \text{ and all } z$$

has the solution

$$T(z, t) = \left(\frac{2\alpha I_0}{K}\right) (\kappa t)^{1/2} \operatorname{ierfc}\left[\frac{z}{2(\kappa t)^{1/2}}\right] \tag{34}$$

where

$$\operatorname{ierfc}(X) = \int_X^\infty \operatorname{erfc}(X')\, dX'$$

and

$$\mathrm{erfc}(X) = 1 - \mathrm{erf}(X) = \frac{2}{\pi}\int_X^\infty e^{-(X')^2}\,dX'$$

and

$$\mathrm{erf}(X) = \frac{2}{\pi}\int_0^X e^{-(X')^2}\,dX'$$

The error function $\mathrm{erf}(X)$ has the following properties:

$$\mathrm{erf}(0) = 0 \qquad \mathrm{erf}(\infty) = 1 \qquad \mathrm{erf}(-X) = -\mathrm{erf}(X)$$

$$\mathrm{erfc}(0) = 1 \qquad \mathrm{erfc}(\infty) = 0$$

and

$$\mathrm{ierfc}(0) = 1/\sqrt{\pi}$$

Thus the surface temperature is given by

$$T(0, t) = \frac{2\alpha I_0}{K}(\kappa t)^{1/2}\left(\frac{1}{\pi}\right)^{1/2} \tag{35}$$

It is proportional to $t^{1/2}$, and if there were no phase changes (i.e., melting and vaporization) the temperature would continue to increase. Note that the energy flux absorbed by the surface is

$$E = \int_0^t \alpha I\,dt = I_0 t\alpha_0$$

but because of conduction the surface temperature increases more slowly, that is, as $t^{1/2}$. This means that a greater surface temperature can be achieved for a given laser pulse energy by shortening the pulse and increasing I_0.

Since we have mentioned pulses, let us model a simple pulse as one where

$$I = \begin{cases} 0, & t < 0 \\ I_0, & 0 \le t \le \mathrm{T} \\ 0, & \mathrm{T} < t \end{cases}$$

During the interval 0 to T the temperature is as given above with the maximum temperature obtained at $t = \mathrm{T}$. For $t > \mathrm{T}$

$$T(z, t) = \frac{2\alpha I_0}{K}\left\{(\kappa t)^{1/2}\,\mathrm{ierfc}\left[\frac{z}{2(\kappa t)^{1/2}}\right] - [\kappa(t - \mathrm{T})]^{1/2}\,\mathrm{ierfc}\left[\frac{z}{2\kappa(t - \mathrm{T})}\right]^{1/2}\right\} \tag{36}$$

Remembering that this problem is only a one-dimensional approximation to the actual case and that the assumption of an infinitely thick medium requires that the slab thickness L be

$$L > 2(\kappa \mathrm{T})^{1/2}$$

allows one to use these results to calculate the temperature distribution achieved. As pointed out above, the result will only be correct near the beam axis. The cooling rate following the irradiation in this example is obtained by taking the time derivative of $T(z, t)$ in Eq. (36).

2. Uniformly Illuminated Circle of Radius *A*

The power is

$$P = \begin{cases} 0, & t < 0 \\ P_0, & t \ge 0 \end{cases}$$

Using cylindrical coordinates as shown in Fig. 7, one finds

$$T(r, z, t) = \frac{\alpha P_0}{2\pi A K}\int_0^\infty \frac{d\lambda}{\lambda} J_0(\lambda r) J_1(\lambda A) \times \left\{e^{-\lambda z}\,\mathrm{erfc}\left[\frac{z}{2(\kappa t)^{1/2}} - \lambda(\kappa t)^{1/2}\right] - e^{\lambda z}\,\mathrm{erfc}\left[\frac{z}{2(\kappa t)^{1/2}} + \lambda(\kappa t)^{1/2}\right]\right\} \tag{37}$$

where J_0 and J_1 are Bessell functions of the first kind. This expression may be evaluated numerically. It is far more useful in planning experiments to evaluate the result directly under the beam since this will be the hottest place. In other words, set $r = 0$ and $z = 0$, to find

$$T(0, 0, t) = \frac{2\alpha P_0(\kappa t)^{1/2}}{\pi A^2 K} \times \left\{\frac{1}{\pi^{1/2}} - \mathrm{ierfc}\left[\frac{A}{2(\kappa t)^{1/2}}\right]\right\} \tag{38}$$

Note that if $A \gg 2(\kappa t)^{1/2}$, then at those values of t one can treat the problem as the simple one in Section II,B,1. In other words, while the beam radius is greater than the thermal diffusion distance, the problem can be reduced to the simple case for the on-axis temperature. However, as time marches on this will break down and there will be differences. Most obviously, T does not become infinite but instead as $t \to \infty$

$$T(0, 0, \infty) = \alpha P_0/\pi A K = T_{\max} \tag{39}$$

This reveals a curious point—the quantity P_0/A determines the maximum achievable temperature. If, for example, we wish to heat the material without melting the surface, then we must choose P_0/A such that $T_{\max} < T_{\text{melt}}$.

3. Uniformly Illuminated Rectangle

It is often the case that the focused laser beam is not circular. In fact, most excimer laser beams are rectangular. Assuming that the light distribution is uniform, we can examine the rectangular distribution. The solution on-axis and on the surface is

$$T(0, 0, \infty) = [\alpha P/2K\pi la] \\ [a \sinh^{-1}(l/a) + \sinh^{-1}(a/l))] \quad (40)$$

at late times. Here a is the width and l the length of the irradiated rectangle.

For example, if the width of the rectangle a and the radius in the circular case A were set equal and we asked what power would be needed to reach a specific temperature in each case we would have

$$\frac{P_{\text{circ}}}{P_{\text{rect}}} = \frac{1}{2l}\left[a \sinh^{-1}\left(\frac{l}{a}\right) + l \sinh^{-1}\left(\frac{a}{l}\right)\right] \quad (41)$$

Even a square beam (l = a) requires more power to produce a specific temperature than a circular beam. This is obvious since a larger area is irradiated and the absorbed energy must heat up more material. To achieve the same maximum temperature, more input must be provided. If $l/a = 3$, then we see from Eq. (41) that the power must be increased by a factor of ~ 2. This simple example demonstrates the importance of good beam quality and focusing optics in order to obtain maximum heating from laser irradiation.

4. Gaussian Beam Illumination

The Gaussian beam intensity distribution is

$$I = I_0 e^{-r^2/w^2} \quad (42)$$

[Note: It is common to describe a Gaussian mode of a laser by the electric field distribution

$$E = E_0 e^{-r^2/w_0^2}$$

and then give

$$I = I_0 e^{-2r^2/w_0^2} = I_0 e^{-r^2/(w_0/\sqrt{2})^2}$$

The beam parameter w used in this treatment is the radius at which the *intensity* has fallen to $1/e$ of its on-axis value. It is the radius at which the electric field has fallen to $e^{-1/2}$ of *its* on-axis value. If we used w_0 to describe the Gaussian, then it corresponds to the radius at which the intensity has fallen to e^{-2} of its on-axis value.]

The following expression can be obtained for the temperature distribution in a semi-infinite solid due to irradiation at the surface by an instantaneous ring source of radius r' and total deposited energy Q:

$$T_{\substack{\text{inst.}\\ \text{ring}}}(r, z, t) = \frac{Q}{4\rho C(\pi\kappa t)^{3/2}} \times \exp\left(\frac{-r^2 - r'^2 - z^2}{4\kappa t}\right) \mathcal{I}_0\left(\frac{rr'}{2\kappa t}\right) \quad (43)$$

In this expression $\mathcal{I}_0$ is the modified Bessel function of order zero.

For a Gaussian source we have

$$Q = q_0 e^{-r'^2/w^2} 2\pi r' \, dr'$$

where q_0 is the energy per unit area at the origin. Inserting this into Eq. (43), we integrate to obtain

$$T_{\substack{\text{inst.}\\ \text{Gaussian}}}(r, z, t) = \frac{q_0 w^2}{\rho C(\pi\kappa t)^{1/2}(4\kappa t + w^2)} \times \exp\left(-\frac{z^2}{4\kappa t} - \frac{r^2}{4\kappa t + w^2}\right) \quad (44)$$

If q_0 is replaced by $\alpha I_0 T_p$, where T_p is the duration of a pulse, and

$$w \gg (4\kappa T_p)^{1/2}$$

we can use Eq. (44) for the temperature distribution following irradiation by a short pulse. (*Note: Short pulse is defined in terms of whether heat diffuses significantly with respect to the beam dimension during the pulse. If it does not, then the pulse is "short."*)

Rewriting Eq. (44) gives

$$T_{\substack{\text{inst.}\\ \text{Gaussian}}}(r, z, t) = \frac{\alpha I_0 T_p}{\rho C(\pi\kappa t)^{1/2}}\left(\frac{1}{4\kappa t/w^2 + 1}\right) \times \exp\left[-\frac{(z/w)^2}{4\kappa t/w^2} - \frac{(r/w)^2}{4\kappa t/w^2 + 1}\right] \quad (45)$$

Defining the unitless quantities

$$T' = w\rho C\pi^{1/2}T/2\alpha I_0 T_p \qquad t' = 4\kappa t/w^2$$

$$z' = z/w \qquad r' = r/w$$

enables writing

$$T' = \left(\frac{1}{t'}\right)^{1/2} \frac{1}{t' + 1} \exp[-z'^2/t' - r'^2/(t' + 1)] \quad (46)$$

For any z' and t', we see that T' decreases with r' as $e^{-r'/t'+1}$. Similarly for any t' and r', T' decreases as $e^{-z'^2/t'}$. Thus, having found the on-axis surface temperature, one can easily find the temperature at any point in the material!

For copper $\kappa \sim 1$ cm²/sec and when $w = 0.5$ mm we would require

$$T \ll 6 \times 10^{-4} \text{ sec}$$

For steel $\kappa \sim 0.15$ cm²/sec and for $w = 0.5$ mm we would require

$$T_p \ll 4 \times 10^{-3} \text{ sec}$$

In the case of pulsed Nd:YAG lasers where $T_p \sim 10^{-5}$ sec, Eq. (44) is quite adequate. For CO_2 TEA laser pulses with $T_p \sim 10^{-6}$ sec, Eq. (44) is again acceptable. However, for discharge pulsed CO_2 lasers with $T_p \sim 10^{-3}$ sec or for cw lasers (or for smaller w) the noninstantaneous form must be used.

The case of cw Gaussian illumination can be treated by setting $q_0 = \alpha I_0(\mu)\, d\mu$ (where μ is a dummy variable for time) and integrating $T_{\substack{\text{inst.}\\ \text{Gaussian}}}$ from 0 to t. This gives

$$T_{\substack{\text{noninst.}\\ \text{Gaussian}}}(r, z, t) = \frac{\alpha I_0^{\max} w^2}{K} \frac{\kappa^{1/2}}{\pi} \times \int_0^t \frac{p(t-\mu)\, d\mu}{(\mu)^{1/2}(4\kappa\mu + w^2)} \times \exp\left(-\frac{z^2}{4\kappa\mu} - \frac{r^2}{4\kappa\mu + w^2}\right)$$

where $I_0(\mu) = I_0^{\max} p(\mu)$. Setting

$$\mu' = 4\kappa\mu/w^2, \qquad z' = z/w, \qquad r' = r/w$$

gives

$$T_{\substack{\text{noninst.}\\ \text{Gaussian}}}(r', z', t') = \frac{\alpha I^{\max} w}{K 2\pi^{1/2}} \times \int_0^{t'} \frac{p(t'-\mu')\, d\mu'}{(\mu')^{1/2}(\mu'+1)} \times \exp\left(-\frac{z'^2}{\mu} - \frac{r'^2}{\mu+1}\right)$$

and so for a dimensionless $T' = 2\pi^{1/2} KT/\alpha I_0^{\max} w$ we have

$$T' = \int_0^{t'} \frac{p(t'-\mu')\, d\mu'}{(\mu')^{1/2}(\mu'+1)} \times \exp\left(\frac{z'^2}{\mu} - \frac{r'^2}{\mu+1}\right) \tag{47}$$

At the surface $z' = 0$ and at the center $r' = 0$ and so

$$T' = \int_0^{t'} \frac{p(t'-\mu')\, d\mu'}{(\mu')^{1/2}(\mu'+1)}$$

For a cw laser or one where $T_p \gg w^2/4\kappa$

$$P(t' - \mu') = 1$$

and

$$T' = 2 \tan^{-1}(t')^{1/2}$$

or

$$T(0, 0, t) = \frac{\alpha I_0^{\max} w}{K\pi^{1/2}} \tan^{-1}\left(\frac{4\kappa t}{w^2}\right)^{1/2} \tag{48}$$

5. Comparison of Results

The several expressions for the induced surface temperature are summarized below.

For the uniformly irradiated surface of a semi-infinite sample (Section II,B,1)

$$T_A(0, 0, t) = \frac{2\alpha I_0}{K}\left(\frac{\kappa t}{\pi}\right)^{1/2}$$

For the uniformly irradiated beam of radius A (Section II,B,2)

$$T_B(0, 0, t) = \frac{2\alpha P_0}{\pi A^2 K}(\kappa t)^{1/2} \times \left[\frac{1}{\pi_{1/2}} - \operatorname{ierfc} \frac{A}{2(\kappa t)^{1/2}}\right]$$

and

$$T_B(0, 0, \infty) = \frac{\alpha P_0}{\pi A K}$$

For the noncircular uniform beam (Section II,B,3)

$$T_C(0, 0, \infty) = \frac{\alpha P_0}{2K\pi l a}\left[a \sinh^{-1}\left(\frac{l}{a}\right) + l \sinh^{-1}\left(\frac{a}{l}\right)\right]$$

For the Gaussian beam (Section II,B,4) with $I = I_0 e^{-r^2/w^2}$

$$T_D(0, 0, t) = \frac{\alpha I_0 w}{K\pi^{1/2}} \tan^{-1}\left(\frac{4\kappa t}{w^2}\right)^{1/2}$$

and

$$T_D(0, 0, \infty) = \frac{\alpha I_0 w \pi^{1/2}}{2K}$$

It is appropriate to ask how much difference there is between these results. For example, if a Gaussian beam were used but treated as if it were a circular beam of radius w with $I = I_0$, what would happen?

By comparing cases II,B,4 and II,B,2 at equilibrium it is clear that

$$\frac{T_D(0, 0, \infty)}{T_B(0, 0, \infty)} = \frac{\alpha I_0 w \pi^{1/2}/2K}{\alpha P_0/\pi w K} = \frac{\pi^{1/2}}{2} = 0.886$$

The error in approximating the Gaussian by a uniform circle with average intensity equal to the peak on-axis intensity of the Gaussian is only 11%. Considering the approximations involved in setting the thermal and optical properties equal to some average value, this is acceptable. A similar conclusion could be reached when comparing the other on-axis surface temperatures at other times. Thus, an acceptable estimate of the on-axis surface temperature produced by a beam with $I(r = 0) = 0$ is obtained from the simplest case with a finite beam radius, that is, case II,B,1.

6. Some Numerical Examples

Now consider some numbers to get a feeling for the scale of things and for when to include phase changes. The properties of three interesting materials are listed in Table I.

The other property needed to estimate the temperatures that can be obtained is the material's absorptivity for the laser in question. The carbon phenolic can be assumed with reasonable accuracy to absorb 100% of incident 1.06- and 10.6-μm laser light. The Al and 204 stainless steel absorptivities can be questioned as they will depend on surface finish and the presence of any molten material. Also, the absorptivity of a metal is expected to increase with temperature. Recent measurements for Al and 1016 steel show that at 10.5 μm the Drude model gives accurate values for both the absorptivity and its temperature coefficient. At 1.06 μm the experimental results do not agree with the Drude model. The absorptivity is higher than predicted. Furthermore, whenever even a small amount of any metal is melted ~20% of the incident laser light seems to be absorbed. This may be due to an unexpected increase in absorptivity at the melting temperature or to geometric considerations on melting. However, a fair estimate of the absorptivity of almost any metal exposed to 1.06- and 10.6-μm laser beams is ~10%. (You cannot go too far wrong with this estimate, particularly if a little melting occurs.)

For a Gaussian beam at the surface and on-axis

$$T(0, 0, t) = \frac{\alpha I_0 w}{K\pi^{1/2}} \tan^{-1}\left(\frac{4\kappa t}{w^2}\right)^{1/2}$$

$$= \frac{\alpha I_0}{K\pi^{1/2}} 2(\kappa t)^{1/2}$$

for small t or for $w \gg 2(\kappa t)^{1/2}$

$$= \frac{\alpha P_0}{K\pi w^2} 2\left(\frac{\kappa t}{\pi}\right)^{1/2}$$

and

$$T(0, 0, \infty) = \frac{\alpha I_0 w \pi^{1/2}}{2K}$$

$$= \frac{\alpha P_0}{2K\pi^{1/2} w}$$

TABLE I. Material Thermal Properties

Material	K (W/cm °C) Solid	K (W/cm °C) Liquid	C (J/g °C)	ρ (g/cm³)	κ (cm²/sec)
Al	2.0	1.0	1.0	2.7	0.74
304 S.S.	0.26	0.26	0.6	8.0	0.054
Carbon phenolic	0.01	—	1.7	1.45	0.004
Material	L_m (kJ/g)	L_v (kJ/g)	T_m[a] (°C)	T_v[a] (°C)	
Al	0.4	11	640	2430	
304 S.S.	0.27	4.65	1430	2980	
Carbon phenolic		14.6		4000	

[a] T_m and T_v are measured as the increase from 20°C need to melt or vaporize, respectively.

Let us assume a 500-W beam focused to a spot with $w = 0.02$ cm (200 μm). Then we have $T(0, 0, \infty) = 353$°C for Al, 2712°C for 304 S.S., and 705,237°C for carbon phenolic. Obviously, Al gets warm, 304 stainless steel melts, and carbon phenolic vaporizes. We can see from this the role of K and α. Note that more power or smaller w enters the answer linearly.

Now

$$\frac{T(0, 0, t)}{T(0, 0, \infty)} = \frac{4(\kappa t)^{1/2}}{w\pi}$$

Let us assume that the approximation $w \gg 2(\kappa T)^{1/2}$ holds if

$$w/2(\kappa t)^{1/2} = 5$$

For times such that this inequality holds we have

$$\frac{T(0, 0, t)}{T(0, 0, \infty)} \sim 0.3$$

In other words, we reached one-third of the final temperature in the following times: Al, 5.4×10^{-6} sec; 304 S.S., 7.4×10^{-5} sec; and carbon phenolic, 1×10^{-3} sec.

C. Time Required to Achieve Melting or Vaporization

It is interesting to consider the time required to achieve melting or vaporization for a given intensity. Assuming that this can be accomplished while we are in the "short time" or diffusion-free range, we have

$$T(0, 0, t) = \frac{2\alpha P_0}{K\pi^{3/2}w^2}\,(\kappa t)^{1/2}]$$

and so

$$t_m = \pi^3 w^4 K^2 T_m^2 / 4\alpha^2 P_0^2 \kappa$$

or

$$t_v = \pi^3 w^4 K^2 v / 4\alpha^2 P_0^2 \kappa \qquad (49)$$

This expression is quite useful in designing a process for a given laser. For example, if the laser is fixed in output capability and a certain material is to be treated, the only variable that can be adjusted to obtain melting is w. Thus it is crucial to prepare proper beam-handling optics. (Of course, it helps to have t_m or $t_v \propto w^4$.)

1. Rates of Heating and Cooling

Some elementary considerations are presented concerning pulsed heating and cooling. (These matter a great deal when considering studies of rapid resolidification, special alloying, annealing, and metastable phases.) We are concerned with order-of-magnitude estimates of the heating and cooling rates and for this purpose will assume no latent heat due to phase transitions. There are two limiting cases.

1. When α is very large or the optical absorption depth α^{-1} is very small compared to the thermal diffusion depth $(\kappa t_p)^{1/2}$. Here t_p is the duration of the irradiation.

In this case the energy absorbed per unit area (assuming a uniform beam) is $I_0 t_p$ and it is used to heat a layer $(\kappa t_p)^{1/2}$ thick. Thus

$$\Delta T = \alpha I_0 t_p / C\rho(\kappa t_p)^{1/2}$$

and the heating rate is

$$\Delta T/t_p = \alpha I_0 / C\rho(\kappa t_p)^{1/2}$$

After the laser pulse it takes about the same time, t_p, for the heat from the layer to diffuse a distance $(\kappa t_p)^{1/2}$ into the material. During this time the temperature at the surface drops by an amount that is of order of magnitude equal to ΔT. Thus the cooling rate is also

$$\Delta T/t_p = \alpha I_0 / C\rho(\kappa t_p)^{1/2}$$

2. If α^{-1} is greater than $(\kappa t)^{1/2}$, the light is absorbed in the medium according to

$$I = I_0 e^{-\alpha z}$$

and a temperature distribution is created that is roughly given as

$$T(z) = (1 - R)I_0(e^{-\alpha z})t_p/C$$

where R is the reflectivity at the surface. After the pulse, cooling will occur if heat diffuses a distance of $\sim 1/\alpha$, and so the cooling time is given approximately as

$$t_c = (\alpha^{-1})^2/\kappa$$

Thus the cooling rate at the surface is

$$\Delta T(z)/t_c = (1 - R)\alpha^3 I_0 \kappa t_p/\rho C$$

In many applications it is necessary to obtain $T = T_m$. By comparison it is clear that the cooling rate for case 1 will always be very high. In fact,

$$dT/dt = T_m/t_p$$

and if one has sufficient energy to obtain T_m in, say, a 10^{-9} sec pulse, one will have

$$dT/dt \approx 10^{12}\ \text{°C/sec}$$

III. Responses of Materials

When laser light is absorbed by a material it results in localized heating and sometimes in a physical change in the heated matter. The change may be desired, as in the many materials processing applications that have been demonstrated, or undesired, as in the formation of laser-induced damage in optical components.

The variety of materials responses to laser heating is so great that not all can be covered here. The key to understanding this phenomenon is to recognize that laser heating is often very localized and very rapid. As estimated in Section II,C, the cooling rate for very localized surface heating can be very large. The result is an ability to rapidly heat and cool materials to produce desired changes. Such desired changes as hardening, annealing, melting, and vaporization are obtained routinely in laser materials processing.

Hardening steels and cast irons requires heating above the martensitic transition point and quenching the material. The laser does this by heating a surface layer (the material in which either the absorption occurred or the heat diffused during the irradiation) and then allowing it to quench by cooling conductively into the bulk. This process has a significant advantage over bulk heating and more conventional quenching methods in that there is very little workpiece distortion. That is, a laser-hardened sample is ready for use with little or no remachining.

In hardening large areas the laser beam can be spread out by defocusing or by scanning a focused beam across the surface. This is possible because in the hardening process one wishes to heat the metal and not to melt it. The overlapped trails of hardened material that are produced contain annealed metal in the regions where they intersect. However, it is often possible to design the beam and scan parameters to minimize this effect.

Sometimes it is necessary to create alloys on the surface by local rapid heating and cooling. Again, the laser is an ideal tool for this type of controlled melting process. Use of this type of alloying can reduce the amount of expensive hard alloy required for a given purpose. One step beyond alloying is forming metastable forms of alloyed metals by very rapid melt resolidification. This technique, which owes its existence to the very high cooling rates discussed in Section II,C, is used to create and study certain glassy forms of metals. It is hoped that these corrosion- and wear-resistant forms can be reliably created by laser heating and cooling techniques.

The process of melting and vaporizing materials is the way in which lasers weld and drill or cut. These require more tightly focused light to achieve the necessary temperatures. When matter becomes molten, the vapor pressure above it can depress the surface and form a hole. The hole can be supported by the vapor pressure and, because light is more strongly absorbed in the hole, a deep hole is generated. This is the process of forming a "keyhole" to obtain deep-penetration drilling, cutting, or welding. In the welding process the atmosphere and irradiation conditions are chosen to encourage proper mixing of the materials to be welded. In drilling or cutting the conditions are chosen to enhance material removal from the irradiated zone; thus, auxiliary gas jets are used to blow away the molten material and sometimes to react with the heated matter to speed the reaction.

While laser treatment of metals was the first area of laser materials processing to receive major attention, it is by no means the only activity in which lasers are used to process materials. A great deal of work has gone into developing laser techniques for processing organic materials, composites, and ceramics. One type of processing, readily visible in many homes, is the use of lasers in carving very detailed images in wood. This type of artwork is made possible by the selective nature of laser heating and the ease with which optical imaging techniques and computer-controlled workpiece handling can be integrated.

Laser processing of semiconductors, in particular silicon, has generated very wide interest in the electronics industry. The application arose from the need to find efficient and effective ways to anneal ion-implanted silicon. The process of ion implantation creates structural damage in semiconductor material. Annealing an ion-implanted silicon wafer by conventional means requires heating in a convection furnace at temperatures over 1000°C for times of the order of $\frac{1}{2}$ hr. As a result, wafers are often warped and undergo some degree of chemical decomposition. With microelectronic devices dependent on precise electronic and physical properties these present serious problems. In the mid-1970s researchers in the Soviet Union, and later in the United States and Europe, began to study the use of lasers to anneal the implanted surfaces of silicon wafers. While the work began as a way to treat damage due to ion implantation, it has been applied to such other problems as the removal of dislocation networks introduced by high-temperature diffusion and the reduction of misfit defects in epitaxial silicon on sapphire. Lasers have also been used to provide localized, controllable heat sources for epitaxial growth of evaporated silicon on crystalline silicon, for the growth of large-grain polysilicon from small-grain polysilicon, and for the formation of metallic silicides and metal overlayers on silicon.

The interaction that makes this type of processing possible is again that of localized rapid heating and cooling. When sufficient heating has taken place there can be a solid phase rearrangement of atoms in the silicon that was damaged by the implantation or, if melting has been achieved, recrystallization can occur with the undamaged material serving as the seed. There is no debate that the processes of interaction that allow these effects to take place are thermal when cw lasers or lasers with pulse durations greater than 100 nsec are used. If pulses less than 100 nsec in duration are employed, solid phase rearrangements cannot take place quickly enough and the material must be melted by the irradiation. The process is similar to that of laser glazing of metals by very rapid melting and resolidification.

Initially there was some concern over the process of semiconductor annealing using pulses with durations in the subpicosecond range. This centered on the issue of whether there was time for thermal processes to operate or whether some other interaction had to be invoked to explain the observed phenomenon. Elegant experiments were performed to which the process of melting and resolidification with ultrashort pulse irradiation was monitored by Raman scattering. The interaction process was confirmed to be thermal in nature. This is a very important scientific result in laser–materials interactions research in that it confirms the fact that thermalization takes place in times as short as several femtoseconds.

Other laser–materials interactions applied in the electronics industry involve the unique ability of laser light to be focused to very small areas and to heat only the areas irradiated. This allows lasers to serve a wide range of resistor and capacitor trimming applications. Also, when properly focused, lasers are able to remove unwanted bridges in microcircuits. If the atmosphere above the substrate is selected to form desired deposits when the substrate or the gas is heated, then lasers can be used to personalize microcircuit masks and to repair damaged circuits. Work with ultraviolet lasers may make it possible to process microcircuit components with submicrometer dimensions.

Lasers of sufficient intensity can cause very highly reflective or transparent materials to be damaged as a result of very high order processes that come into play when very high optical intensities are employed. In Section I,B, the process of nonlinear absorption and breakdown was described. These processes result in very rapid conversion of the nonabsorbing matter into matter that absorbs nearly 100% of the incident light. The absorption takes place locally in the irradiated region and the heated material melts and may vaporize. When melting or vaporization occurs in in the bulk of a transparent substance severe cracking also takes place. In addition, some materials display slip banding after intense laser irradiation, indicating that they were heated to the point where plastic deformation could occur.

While breakdown due to nonlinear processes represents the intrinsic failure mechanism of nonansorbing materials, laser-induced damage is most often determined by the presence of some discrete inclusion or irregularity in the irradiated volume. Damage due to absorption at such defects can be detected as arrays of discrete, randomly located damage sites within the irradiated region. In thin films and on most bare surfaces this type of defect-determined damage dominates the interaction and response of the matter with laser light.

Bibliography

Bass, M. (1983). *In* "Physical Processes in Laser Materials Interactions," pp. 77–116. Plenum, New York.

Bertolotti, M., ed. (1983). "Physical Processes in Laser Materials Interactions," pp. 175–220. Plenum, New York.

Brown, W. L. (1983). *In* "Laser Materials Processing" (M. Bass, ed.), pp. 337–406. North-Holland Publ., Amsterdam.

Duley, W. W. (1976). "CO_2 Lasers: Effects and Applications." Academic Press, New York.

Ready, J. F. (1971). "Effects of High Power Laser Radiation." Academic Press, New York.

Wooten, F. (1972). "Optical Properties of Solids." Academic Press, New York.

Yardley, J. T. (1985). *In* "Laser Handbook" (M. Bass and M. L. Stitch, eds.), Vol. 5, pp. 405–454. North-Holland Publ., Amsterdam.

LASER AND PARTICLE BEAMS

Heinrich Hora *CERN, Geneva, and University of New South Wales*

GLOSSARY

Ablation: Blowoff of highly ionized material from a target irradiated by an incident laser or particle beam.

Beam instabilities: Temporally growing oscillations, waves, ripples, or kinetic effects in plasmas by laser or particle beam irradiation of plasma.

Bremsstrahlung: X-ray emission from electrons colliding with ions, for instance, produced by slowing down of electrons in an X-ray tube or from thermal motion in a plasma (which produces a continuous spectrum).

Debye sheath: Length within a plasma where strong electric fields may occur, given by $6.9(T/n_e)^{1/2}$ (centimeters) where T (kelvins) is temperature and n_e (per cubic centimeter) is electron density.

Indirect drive: Compression and heating of a spherical pellet or a capsule with deuterium tritium fusion fuel for inertial confinement fusion (ICF) by laser or particle beams whose energy is first converted into X-radiation in the plasma corona of interaction, with subsequent compression and heating of the interior of the fusion fuel by the X rays for an exothermic reaction.

Inertial confinement fusion (ICF): Exothermic reaction of light nuclei resulting in larger ones (e.g., deuterium and tritium forming helium(4) and a neutron plus 17.5 MeV energy) by heating an amount of this fuel of highest possible density to reaction temperatures of 1 to 17 keV (about 10 to 170 million degrees Kelvin) and letting this freely expand, producing a gain G of fusion energy divided by the energy put into the fuel for heating and compression.

Mode-locked laser: Laser oscillator having a nonlinearly absorbing and saturable dye within the optical cavity, for instance, to produce a 50 nsec long train of 20 psec pulses 500 psec apart.

Nonlinear force: Force in a plasma produced by the high-frequency field of an intense electromagnetic wave due to nonthermal direct dielectric interaction; generalization of the ponderomotive or Lorentz force.

Plasma frequency: Electrostatic or Langmuir oscillation frequency of plasma electrons between ions; its value is $\omega_p = (4\pi e^2 n_e/m)^{1/2}$ with charge e, density n_e, and mass m of the electrons.

***Q*-switching:** Switching of the quality of the optical cavity of a laser oscillator, for instance, switching reflectivity from 1 to 100% with a dye or a rotating mirror (passively) or an electro-optic Pockels cell (actively) to produce one very powerful short-time laser pulse.

Relativistic threshold: Laser intensity at which the oscillation energy of the electrons moving coherently in the field reaches mc^2, where m is the electron mass, and c the speed of light.

Stopping power: Measure of reduction of the energy E per length (or per time) of an energetic ion (e.g., an alpha particle or other product of a nuclear reaction) by collisions in a high-temperature plasma.

ENCYCLOPEDIA OF PHYSICAL SCIENCE
AND TECHNOLOGY, VOL. 8

Laser and particle beams are defined, for purposes of this article, as directed energy beams of photons, electrons, ions, or neutral atoms, with power densities currently in ranges of up to 10^{22} W/cm^2 for laser sources, 10^6 A/cm^2 for electron beams, 10^{14} W/cm^2 for ion beams, and 10^4 W/cm^2 for neutral particle beams.

These power densities are generally many orders of magnitude greater than electromagnetic radiation or high energy particle fluxes produced in nuclear explosions. Beams of these intensities have expanded the horizons of physics. New plasma physics phenomena have been discovered, including observation of nonlinear forces, nonlinear optical response, and relativistic quantum effects in interaction with nuclei and elementary particles.

Exploitation of these new phenomena can result in numerous practical applications, including novel welding and material processing methods, medical techniques, and potentially economic large scale, clean, and safe power generation from a virtually inexhaustible fuel source. Fusion power has the potential to overcome the catastrophic effects on the earth's atmosphere of burning fossil fuels. Thus, one solution to the problems of acid rain and global warming is to increase nuclear fission power production in the near term and then transition to laser fusion power in the future. In fact, some cost forecasts indicate that laser fusion might produce energy at a cost as low as that of typical light water reactors and possibly at a much lower cost after full commercialization is achieved—and without resulting in radioactive waste.

Approaches to laser fusion which show promise include (1) the simple scheme of the General Atomic CASCADE reactor, which has the potential to avoid the ubiquitous wall erosion problems associated with fusion energy, and (2) improvements in driving inertial confinement by light-ion beams or by heavy-ion beams based on advanced accelerator technology.

I. Generation of Intensive Laser Beams

Since the first realization of a laser, the ruby laser by T. Maiman in 1960, based on Einstein's discovery of stimulated (induced) emission of radiation in 1916, and the combination of optical cavities and levels of electrons with slow (forbidden) spontaneous transitions evaluated by C. H. Townes, N. G. Bosov, M. A. Prokhorov, N. Bloembergen, and A. L. Schawlow, it has been evident that the spatial concentration in the focus of laser beams and the temporal concentration in the form of very short pulses will provide electromagnetic energy of intensities beyond those of any earlier scheme. Today it is possible to produce neodymium glass laser beams of 100-terawatt (TW) power focused by relativistic self-focusing to an intensity of 10^{22} W/cm^2, which is 10^{23} times brighter than spectrally integrated sunlight. When the narrow spectrum of the neodymium glass laser radiation, due to its high coherence and high directivity, is compared with that part of the spectrum of sunlight, the ratio is a number of magnitudes larger. [*See* LASERS.]

A. High-Power Lasers of Different Wavelengths

Lasers with high output power can have a large range of different wavelengths. For the longest wavelengths in the microwave range, a free electron laser of wavelength 1 to 8 mm with an output power exceeding 200 MW was achieved by D. Prosnitz and A. M. Sessler in 1985. These types of free electron lasers (FEL) produced 10^{10} W for 0.1 mm wavelength. The next interesting range of powerful lasers is in the middle infrared at the 10 μm wavelength of the well-developed carbon dioxide laser. In addition, with the hydrogen–fluorine laser at wavelength 2.6 μm it is possible to merge jets of hydrogen gas and fluorine gas, as used in rocket propulsion, to convert a considerable amount of chemical reaction energy into optical energy by an optical cavity around the reaction zone. Another powerful laser is the photochemical iodine laser. Irradiating the gas CF_3I (or higher aliphatic analogs) with ultraviolet (UV) radiation of at least 4.5 eV photon energy causes dissociation of the iodine atom, which is in an electronically excited state after splitting off from the molecule. This electronic state spontaneously decays as a forbidden (quadrupole) transition in a long time (0.1 sec) to the ground state. These excited iodine states are ideal for the laser medium emitting at 1.3 μm. [*See* LASERS, CHEMICAL.]

Going to the next shorter wavelength, 1.06 μm, of neodymium ions in glass or in YAG crystals, one of the best developed high-power lasers is realized by optical pumping of the neodymium ions by wavelengths only 15% shorter than the laser wavelength into an electronically excited state of about 0.1-msec lifetime for spontaneous transition. This long time, compared to the nanosecond transition time of usual levels, is again ideal for a laser. As this is a four-level laser, it is an improvement over the three-level ruby laser of wavelength 694.4 nm (visible red light), which is also a powerful laser.

Of the more than 1000 different lasers of low or moderate output power, high-power continuous wave (cw) or constant emission can be achieved with gas discharge pumped lasers such as the helium-neon laser, the argon laser, and the krypton laser. Powers of 100 W or more can be achieved in the visible range of red, green, or blue light. [*See* GAS, LASERS.]

In the UV region the excimer lasers are very powerful, working with pulses in the range of nanoseconds or less. The lasers are based on gas discharge in mixtures of krypton and iodine, xenon, and so forth or excitation by electron beams. Wavelengths extend down to 150 nm. A big krypton fluoride laser system of wavelength 250 nm is being built at Los Alamos National Laboratory to produce energy pulses of 1 MJ for nuclear fusion studies in the future.

Interesting lasers for the weak X-ray range and for the entire X-ray range have been realized by producing a cylindrical plasma from a solid material (strontium, carbon, aluminum, etc.) by irradiation with a very powerful neodymium glass laser, which results in the helium–neon-like or Hα-like transitions of highly stripped heavier atoms. Laser action X-ray lasers for wavelengths down to 4.315 nm for tungsten and 4.48 nm for tantalum with a gain of 2 cm^{-1} have been realized. At the shorter wavelength of 1.4 nm, emission of more than 100 TW was reported for pumping of the cylindrical laser medium by the intense X-ray irradiation from a nuclear explosion.

Very high power laser pulses are expected from the new development of extremely short laser pulses. It is possible to produce neodymium glass laser pulses of 6 femtoseconds (fsec) duration, corresponding to three wavelength pulses which, even for a rather low energy per pulse, produce very high powers. The carbon dioxide laser with pulses of 100 fsec has similar properties. The most unexpected result is that the intensity of the laser wave front traveling through the electron beam-pumped gas can be so high that the gas is transformed into a plasma without disturbing the laser emission.

For high power, very short laser pulses, the excimer laser, for example, KrF, has advantages since its broad band properties are ideal for amplifying femtosecond laser pulses. Such pulses are produced in dye laser oscillators and have their frequency upshifted. Pulses of 45 fsec duration and 45 mJ energy have been produced. Amplification to 100 J is being planned for KrF. The concept of producing X-ray lasers by depleting K-electrons by X rays or with megaelectron-volt ions may provide pulses in the 100 attosecond range and energies equal to or greater than 1 kJ.

The very large KrF excimer laser AURORA at the Los Alamos National Laboratory produces 10 kJ pulses of 5 nsec duration. A more compact system, SPRITE, was developed at the Rutherford Appleton Laboratory in England. A very compact system with special condensors for the electron beam injection for the laser excitation was developed at the Troitzk Atomice Energy and Efremov Institute in Leningrad, with laser pulses of 13 kJ and 5 nsec duration, with 1 Hz output and 2% efficiency, which may be a serious successor the glass lasers for 10 MJ laser pulses for fusion energy.

For very high power, high energy laser pulses of 1–1000 nsec duration, pumping of the laser medium by the intense and very uniform neutron emission of nuclear reactors (especially of microsecond pulsed systems) is designed to provide excitation of media of large volume and large diameter and may result in 50-MJ pulses of the desired short duration with wavelengths in the visible and near infrared and the UV. [*See* LASERS, NUCLEAR PUMPED.]

B. Carbon Dioxide Lasers

Continuous wave carbon dioxide lasers have been used for materials treatment since the mid-1960s. The first type was the longitudinal discharge laser. In a tube filled with carbon dioxide and possibly other gases such as nitrogen and helium at nearly 1 atm pressure or less, an electric discharge was produced by voltage in the 10 kV range. In equilibrating the translational, vibrational, and rotational states of the molecules, the vibrations have an exceptionally long lifetime, and their energy can be used for stimulated optical emission in combination with an optical cavity along the tube axis. In this way, emission of 100 W to some kilowatts is possible.

Another cw carbon dioxide laser is based on gas dynamics. If a mixture of carbon dioxide with nitrogen and other gases is being pumped in a closed circle with high speed up to the speed of

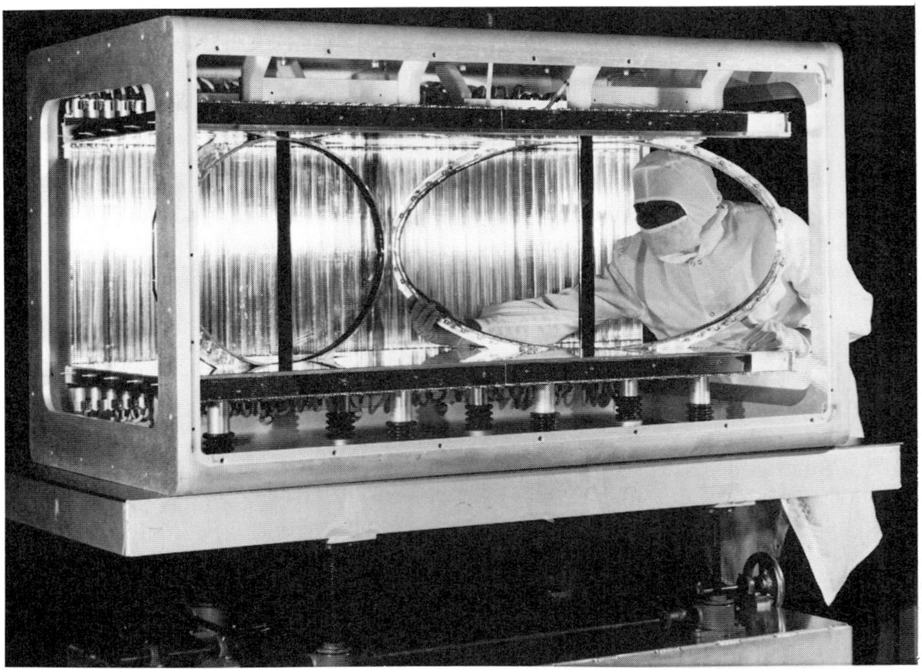

FIG. 1. Two-plate 46-cm-diameter neodymium glass disk laser amplifier of NOVA at Lawrence Livermore National Laboratory. (Courtesy of J. L. Emmett, Livermore.)

FIG. 2. Inner gallery of the Nova laser at Livermore. The 10 lines of neodymium glass amplified chains are finally extended to 78-cm-diameter beams, which each pass large-scale KDP crystal arrays for higher harmonic upconversion of the frequency. (Courtesy J. L. Emmett, Livermore.)

sound or not much below, and if a strong gas discharge for heating is produced across the tube before the gas streams into a supersonic Laval nozzle, the resulting supersonic speed occurs at the cost of fast cooling. The vibrational states again have a long lifetime before equilibrating. Use of an optical cavity across the tube at the beginning of the nozzle results in optical stimulated emission of the vibrational energy. It has been possible to produce lasers with an output power of 100 kW cw or more.

The largest carbon dioxide laser with short-pulse operation was ANTARES at Los Alamos National Laboratory. The beam was generated in an oscillator by an electron beam preexcited discharge in the CO_2 gas with single mode selection and pulse shaping. After several amplification stages, the beam went through an amplifier 12 m long and 2 m in diameter made of stainless steel with preexcitation and discharges. Such a beam provided 20-TW pulses of 800 psec duration or even 80-TW pulses of 150 psec duration with a rather steep profile of the pulse front. Apart from fusion studies, this laser, which was later dismantled, was ideal for developing new schemes for laser acceleration of ions and electrons to energies far beyond the range of giga-electron-volts with pulses of accelerated particles above 10 A. Another remarkable carbon dioxide laser system is the LEKKO 4 at ILE, Osaka, with economic multipath operation of the main amplifiers. These developments also include the use of high-pressure (up to 100 atm) compact amplifiers for production of intense short pulses. Another economic type of intense carbon dioxide laser is the transverse excited–atmospheric pressure (TEA) laser developed by A. J. Beaulieu in 1969, which produced pulses of 100 nsec duration or less and kilojoule energies in rather compact systems.

C. Neodymium Glass Lasers

The most widely used systems for high-power operation are the neodymium glass lasers. An oscillator is used under very stable thermally controlled conditions to generate pulses of 10 psec to 10 nsec duration by *Q*-switched or mode-locked operation of the laser. The undesired axial and transverse laser modes are suppressed and the single mode pulse can then be shaped temporally in the predetermined form. A nearly rectangular pulse front with a suppression of prepulse intensities up to a ratio of 10^{-8} of the peak value can be achieved. The pulse diameter is increased by telescopic optics, and the pulse is then sent through a cascade of amplifiers consisting mostly of flash tube-pumped glass laser rods. From a certain diameter on, the rods are replaced by disk amplifiers. Rods have been used up to a diameter of 12 cm, although uniform distribution of the excitation and thermal effects are then quite critical due to the decaying intensity of the pumping flash light in the rods. There are different conceptual views. The Institute of Laser Engineering at the University of Rochester had negative experiences with disks and built its large systems with 24 parallel rod amplifier chains, similar to the developments in Limeil, France, or the large number of parallel rod amplifiers (up to 216) by the Delfin, Lebedev Institute, Moscow. However, disks are necessary for larger diameters to achieve uniform pumping and to avoid thermal insufficiency. Disk amplifiers have been developed by an extraordinarily clean and reproducible technique to diameters of 46 cm (NOVA, at Livermore) (see Figs. 1 and 2) or 35 cm (Gekko 12, Osaka).

Currently, glass lasers provide the most advanced technology for producing pulses in the megajoule range, despite problems of nonlinear glass birefringence and Raman scattering that could be avoided by gas lasers. The ATHENA project at Livermore condenses the NOVA laser into an amplifier of 1.5×1.5 m^2 cross section (Fig. 3), releasing 400 kJ of 10 nsec pulses. Thus, 63 beams at this energy and wavelength may provide 10 MJ pulses, even after frequency tripling at 40% energy conversion.

D. Powerful Iodine Lasers

The ISKRA-5 iodine laser, a remarkably powerful unit, is located in a laboratory near Gorki, Russia, and has operated since November 1989. It produces pulses of 120 TW power with 250 psec duration. This is thus about twice the ca-

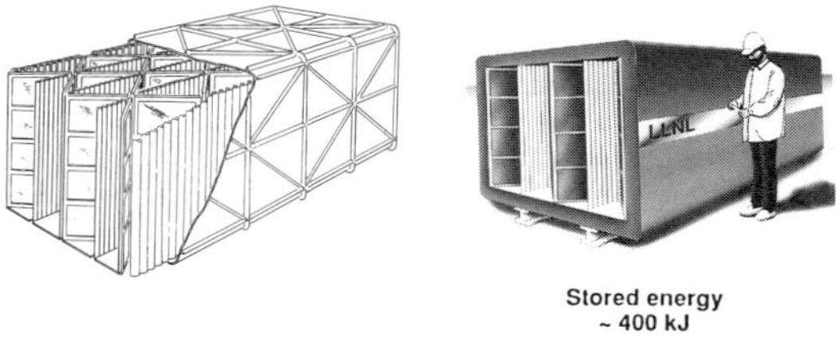

FIG. 3. Final glass amplifiers of the ATHENA laser developed at Lawrence Livermore National Laboratory to produce laser pulses of 400 kJ energy and 10 nsec duration. (Courtesy of E. M. Campbell, Livermore.)

pacity of the NOVA glass laser at Livermore, which has produced beams of 125 TW power and 100 psec duration up to January of 1990. The excitation source is UV pumping of photodissociation of iodine atoms from iodofluoro propane in a 1 atm gas mixture containing other gases for Doppler broadening of the narrow laser lines. This scheme and the use of very fast UV-irradiation of gas was pioneered by K. Hohla, who hypothesized 100 kJ iodine laser systems, of which one with 2 kJ pulses (Asterix) is scheduled for operation. The ISKRA-5 laser is pumped by a sliding wall discharge inside the amplifier. The laser amplifiers are 8 m long and 70 cm in diameter. Twelve beams of this kind produce 120 TW at 1.3 μm wavelength, which is frequency tripled to arrive at power and wavelength similar to that of the NOVA system.

E. Efficiencies

An important question for the economy of laser operation is the efficiency given by the ratio of the laser energy to the input energy (electrical, mechanical, chemical, etc.) for operation. The ideal of nearly 100% efficiency is achieved by only a few laser systems, for instance, the *p*–*n* junction semiconductor lasers. The efficiency of the carbon dioxide laser in longitudinal discharge operation can be up to 39%. For pulsed operation in the TEA laser or in the electron beam (or UV) preexcited transverse discharge system, the efficiency is between 5 and 10%.

The efficiency of the iodine laser with dissociation by flash tube light is 1% or less. For the neodymium glass laser, the efficiency related to the electrical energy input into the condensers for the discharges of the flash tubes is usually much less than 1%. With illumination by hot tungsten filaments, cw-like pulsed output with 3% efficiency is possible. With pumping by infrared radiation near 900 nm, e.g., by semiconductor laser diodes, a maximum efficiency of about 20% should be possible as an absolute limit, while 8% has been verified experimentally.

II. Generation of Intense Particle Beams

The generation of beams of electrons or ions of low currents and intensities goes back to the past century and was highly developed up to the very large scale accelerators that now produce electrons with energies up to 30 GeV and protons or heavy nuclei with energies up to tera-electron-volts. These types of beams are not considered in this article, which treats only the developments of the past 30 years in which exceptionally high energy densities have been attained.

After generation of the intense beams, which is discussed in detail in the following subsections, the transport of the beams, their directivity for bending, control, focusing, and so forth follow principles that are well known from the cases mentioned above. For charged particles (electrons or ions), the particle optics, as known from the electron microscope, is the first-order approximation. However, because of the high current densities, additional effects come into play, such as space charge effects and self-interaction of the beam particles. Furthermore, for very high beam currents, pinching (squeezing of the beam diameter) by the beam's self-magnetic field or effects known from collective accelerators can be important.

A special mechanism for guiding electron beams a few millimeters in diameter with 2 MV voltage and megaampere currents in straight lines along a distance of 5 m was discovered by using evacuated metal tubes. In spite of the numerous known instabilities, the beams penetrate in a very stable way; some interaction with the walls was observed by G. Yonas, but with negligible loss of energy. This mechanism is of special importance in relation to guiding the intense electron beams from a pulsating source to a target at a distance.

A. Generation of High-Current Electron Beams

In order to increase the electron emission current from the tungsten filament (cathode) of electron microscopes, a special shape of the surrounding metal was provided by the far-focus cathode discovered by K. H. Steigerwald. While the emission currents were well within the space charge limitations of the Child-Langmuir law, the currents were so high that the beams have been used since 1958 for material treatment and welding.

In order to provide higher electron emission, other types of cathodes were developed; an example is a pencil-type bundle of sharp metal peaks from which high field emission (by E. W. Müller) is possible, called a febetron. Another way to generate electron emission with high current densities was to use lasers. A special effect appeared on irradiation of metal targets with laser pulses of power near 1 MW. Below this threshold, emission of ions in the range of a few electron volts was observed, corresponding to target temperatures of some 10,000 K. The electron emission corresponded to a space charge limitation of at most 100 mA/cm^2.

Above a laser power of 1 MW, however, ion energies of kiloelectron-volts and much more were observed (Linlor effect), and the electron emission current densities were larger by a factor of 100 or more, in disagreement with all space charge laws. The current densities were finally measured as 1 kA/cm^2, 10,000 times larger than classical. This anomaly could be explained in terms of a threshold of self-focusing, above which the filaments permit the action of the nonlinear force of electrodynamic acceleration of the ions in the plasma and the generation of high electric fields. While this type of electron emission (cathode) is most promising, its general use is difficult as each laser irradiation produced a crater in the cathode and only a fast change of the cathode spots may lead to the miraculous electron source.

The production of dense electron beam currents was drastically extended beyond the classical limitations and the technologies of the past when the laser was introduced for switching the plasma conduction of air gaps connecting megavolt capacities. A. H. Guenther found that the jitter of the switching could be controlled within 100 psec or less, the charges of several megavolt condensers could be merged together at the right time. It was then possible to produce a discharge of 2 MV along 2 cm either through a wire or through low-density gas, where currents of 0.5 to 1 MA of 50 nsec duration were produced, pinching to few millimeters in diameter.

With other techniques using the high-voltage capacity of a Marx generator connected by a Blümlein line (water condenser) with a diode, similar electron beam currents have been produced. The resulting 1 to 10 MeV electron beams had current densities up to 10 MA/cm^2. Famous installations for these purposes are those of Physics International Co. (Fig. 4), of Sandia National Laboratory's PBFA-II (with compatibility to ion beams) (Figs. 5a and 5b), and of project Angara 5 at the Kurchatov Institute, Troitzk. A new, highly repetitive, semiconductor operated generator for 5 MJ electron pulses of 5 MV and 5 MA was developed in 1986 by Ian Smith. This generator can also be used for light ion-beam pulses.

B. Generation of High-Current Ion Beams

The classical way to produce currents of potassium (or similar) ions is to use the Langmuir effect. If a hot plate of tungsten is in a gas of potassium, the gaseous atoms hitting the surface lose electrons to the metal and are reflected back to the gas as positively charged ions. These can then be removed or guided by electric fields to produce ion beams. Other classical sources of ions are the plasmatron, the electron cyclotron resonance (ECR) source, and similar kinds of discharges. In all cases the current density is low and of the classical values. The alternative method of irradiating targets by laser pulses and using the ions (sometimes preaccelerated to energies of kiloelectron-volts or even megaelectron-volts) as sources for accelerators is now used in large scale accelerators. As in the case of the laser-produced electron emission, conditions much better than those in the classical cases have been confirmed. Pulses of 10^9 C^{4+} ions or 10^8 Mg^{12+} ions were achieved after pre-acceleration by a LINAC in the Dubna synchrotron reaching 2 GeV/μm (K. A. Monchinski) and 10^6 pulses of 1 Hz (B. Y. Sharkov).

The era of high-intensity ion beam sources began with the similar operation of a Marx generator with a Blümlein line to discharge some megavolts along a small diode. One possibility is to use a magnetic field insulation diode as developed at Cornell University and Sandia National Laboratory or to use the pinch discharge diode GAMBLE at Naval Research Laboratory. In both cases, ion currents in the mega-ampere range of megaelectron-volt particle energy have been produced. Similar diodes were used in the large installation Aurora at Henry Diamond Laboratories and on Python at Physics International.

The GAMBLE diode (G. Cooperstein) (Fig. 6) is an especially simple structure. One electrode is a disk of aluminum 15 cm in diameter. The other electrode is a thin foil of metal bent concavely toward the other electrode. Between the electrodes is a deuterium gas. When the foil is used as the cathode of a Marx generator, Blümlein line 2-MV discharge, the deuterons traverse (and destroy) the foil in a current of up to megaamperes. The applied-B and hybrid diodes are most used today and have demonstrated a beam divergence of 0.13 mrad for intensities of more than 10^{13} W/cm^2 megavolt light ion beams. PBFA-II produced 6 MV proton pulses of 3 MA and 20 nsec duration. Target irradiation at 5.4 TW/cm^2 was achieved.

FIG. 4. Aurora electron beam experiment producing 1-MV beams of a combined current of 2 MA and a total energy of 2 MJ. (Courtesy of J. Benford, Physics International Co.)

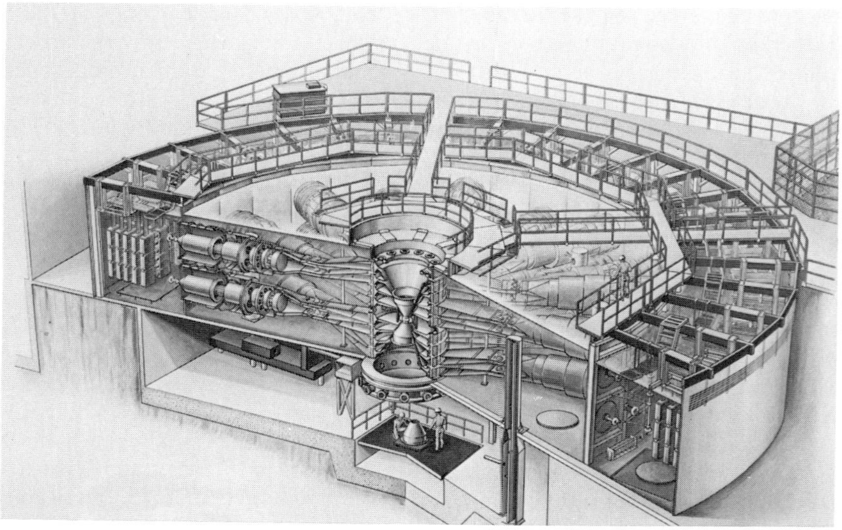

FIG. 5a. The 1-MJ particle beam fusion installation PBFA-II at Sandia National Laboratory. (Courtesy of P. VanDevender, Sandia.)

FIG. 5b. Loading a target into the focus of the PBFA two light ion beam fusion installation at Sandia National Laboratory. (Courtesy of P. VanDevender, Sandia.)

C. Generation of High-Current Neutral Beams

Apart from the classical generation of neutral beams, for instance, by the sodium beam oven, high-intensity neutral beam technology has been developed since the 1970s for the neutral beam injection of fusion fuel into magnetic confinement apparatuses such as the tokamak or the stellarator. Intense deuterium currents are produced in the classical way from plasmatrons and then accelerated electrostatically and guided and focused toward their final application in magnetically confined plasmas. Before reaching the magnetic fields, however, the ions traverse a low-density xenon gas trap (confined by strong vacuum pumps at both ends), which provides electrons to the ions to produce neutral atoms by charge exchange. This happens to a considerable fraction of all ions, which then move into the center of the toroidal plasma, where they are ionized and incorporated in the plasma by interaction with the plasma ions. It is also possible to "Lorentz" the atoms, that is, ionize them by their fast motion through the magnetic field due to the Lorentz forces. The experimental Joint European Torus facility (JET) at Culham, England, produces deuterium atom pulses of 25 MJ energy on the order of 1 sec duration and 30 cm beam diameter with an energy of 80 keV per atom. [*See* FUSION DEVICES, EXPLOSIVE; PLASMA CONFINEMENT.]

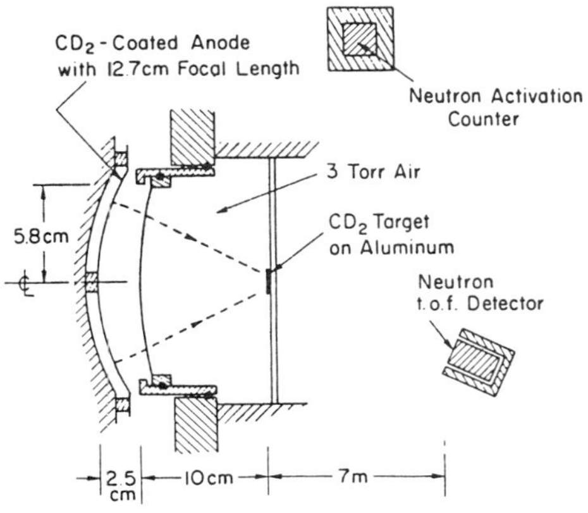

FIG. 6. Cross section of the pinch reflex diode of the GAMBLE light ion beam fusion experiment at Naval Research Laboratory. (Courtesy of G. Cooperstein, NRL.)

Another way to produce high-density neutral particles is by the generation of *clusters*. A technique has been developed by E. W. Becker in which a stream of hydrogen gas through a nozzle automatically produces small speckles of solid hydrogen containing 1000 to 1 million atoms depending on the conditions of production. The solid clusters develop some electric charge spontaneously, as in the Millikan experiment, so that electrostatic postacceleration of the clusters is possible. It has been shown that energies per atom of 1 keV can be achieved in clusters and current densities corresponding to kiloamperes in deuteron ions.

For pulsed neural beam generation, the rail gun should be mentioned. Small, nearly macroscopic pellets of solid material, much larger than the clusters mentioned above, can be accelerated by the electric discharge field between the rails touching and guiding the particles up to velocities of some kilometers per second.

III. Physics of Laser Beam Interaction with Targets

When a laser beam of high power density (identical with intensity or irradiance) hits a material, the response or interaction will be that of classical optics with reflection, scattering, and absorption (corresponding to energy dissipation with subsequent heating and possible reemission) as long as the intensity of the beam is low, as happens in all initial stages of the pulse. At increasing intensities, nonlinear deviations from the classical values will occur—for example, via the intensity-dependent complex optical refractive index $n = \varepsilon^{1/2}$ (ε is the complex dielectric constant). The mechanisms of interest in this article begin at the next higher intensities, when the material is melting, evaporating, and ionized. This change can take place in such a short time (picoseconds or some femtoseconds) that the treatment of the ionized state, the fourth state of matter called the plasma, is then important. [*See* LASER-MATERIALS INTERACTIONS; PLASMA SCIENCE AND ENGINEERING.]

We shall discuss here mostly the plasma state and the dynamic development of the gaseous plasma, which expands like a gas but with emission of radiation (bremsstrahlung with a continuous spectrum or line radiation from electronic transitions in ions that are not fully ionized), with interaction with electric and magnetic fields, and with numerous anomalies. The processes of melting of the target surface and laser welding are special cases of the intermediate physical conditions to be studied individually.

A. Optical Gas Breakdown

Apart from the generation of plasma by laser beam irradiation of a solid target in a vacuum, another method of generation of plasma by lasers is possible: focusing the laser beam in air or another gas produces such high electric field strengths E of the electromagnetic fast oscillation that an electrical breakdown or optical breakdown will occur. This was first observed in 1963 by R. W. Terhune *et al.* at the Ford Research Laboratory using a Q-switched ruby laser pulse of about 20 nsec duration. The electric field amplitude was around 10^6 V/cm, which is remarkably higher than the static field for electrical breakdown in air. Using carbon dioxide lasers with more than 10 times longer wavelengths, the first air breakdown was reported by A. M. Prokhorov *et al.* with a field strength threshold of about 10^5 V/cm. It should be noted that ruby or similar neodymium glass laser pulses of 1000 times shorter duration require a threshold of 10^8 V/cm. The laser-produced breakdown in air is accompanied by a loud bang.

The mechanism of optical gas breakdown has some similarities to the microwave breakdown in gases. One can distinguish cases where an avalanche breakdown occurs due to spontaneously present electrons whose strong oscillation in the laser field causes rapidly multiplying ionization by collisions, and cases where the laser field produces a nonresonant multiphoton ionization of a molecule, as the energy of the laser photons is generally much smaller than the energy of excitation or ionization of gaseous atoms. A third mechanism is Keldysh tunneling, which was experimentally clarified in 1980 by B. Boreham *et al.* A great deal of the physics of optical breakdowns is unexplored, and several anomalies of prebreakdown, unexplainably low thresholds, and so forth, found by R. Papoular in 1971 are still not understood.

B. Interaction with Solid Targets

The hydrodynamics involved in the interaction of a laser beam irradiating a target and producing and driving an expansion of the plasma toward the vacuum (ablation) has been studied numerically since 1969. One result is shown in Fig. 7, where one observes a positive velocity of the ablated plasma (toward the right-hand side, from which the laser is incident on a block of solid hydrogen) until which depth limit the laser light is permitted to penetrate the target. The depth is given at electron densities in the plasma where the laser frequency does not exceed the plasma frequency. The corresponding cutoff electron density is 10^{21} cm^{-3} from neodymium glass lasers. The indirect action of the laser, however, goes much deeper into the target: thermal conduction heats up the target below the area of irradiation, called the corona, and the mechanical momentum of the ablated plasma causes a recoil that can be seen immediately from the numerical output in Fig. 7 from parts with negative velocities below the corona. This causes compression and heating of the target material, even at depths to which no laser radiation can penetrate.

This classical gas dynamic ablation and compression of the target by laser irradiation is correct only if the laser intensities are not too high. At higher intensities, the plasma dynamics are dominated by nonlinear effects, anomalies, parametric instabilities, and resonances that usually have a threshold near laser intensities of 10^{14} W/cm^2 for neodymium glass lasers and 10^{12} W/cm^2 for carbon dioxide lasers. The dominating mechanism then is the working force of direct (nonthermal) electromagnetic interaction of the laser radiation and the plasma. The nonlinear force density acting in addition to the thermokinetic force (gradient of the gas dynamic pressure P) given (in Gausian cgs units) by

$$\mathbf{f}_{\mathrm{NL}} = \frac{1}{c}\,\mathbf{v} \times \mathbf{H} + \frac{1}{4\pi}\,\mathbf{E}\,\nabla\cdot\mathbf{E} + \frac{1}{4\pi}\,\nabla\cdot(n^2 - 1)\mathbf{E}\mathbf{E} \qquad (1)$$

where **E** and **H** are the high-frequency electric and magnetic fields in the plasma and the complex optical refractive index n is given by

$$n^2 = 1 - \omega_p^2/[\omega^2(1 - i\nu/\omega)] \qquad (2)$$

with the radian frequency ω of the laser radiation, the plasma frequency ω_p, and the electron–ion collision frequency ν. If this is not modified by anomalies, the collision frequency is given by Coulomb interaction, which must be modified over its classical value ν_{cl} by quantum interaction

$$\nu = \begin{cases} \nu_{cl} & \text{if } T < T^* \\ \nu_{cl}\, T/T^* & \text{if } T < T^* \end{cases} \qquad (3)$$
$$T^* = \tfrac{4}{3}mc^2\alpha^2Z^2$$

known also from the anomalous electric resistivity of plasmas at high temperatures, where the fine structure constant α and the ionic charge Z are used.

The first term in Eq. (1), the Lorentz term, for monochromatic plane electromagnetic waves perpendicularly incident on a stratified collisionless plasma, is identical with the Helmholtz and Kelvin formulation of the ponderomotive force $(n^2 - 1)\, \nabla \mathbf{E}^2/8\pi$. Therefore, it was called the electrostriction, or $\mathbf{v} \times \mathbf{H}$ force, or field gradient force, but it is always the ponderomotive force (identical with the Lorentz force in this case) frequently used in laser-plasma interaction theory. With collisions in the plasma, the first term in Eq. (1) contains nonponderomotive parts. The other terms in Eq. (1) mostly are effective only at oblique irradiation of the plasma by the laser. Some of these nonlinear terms were known earlier; however, the proof that the complex Eq. (1) contains all of the terms required for an exact description, and not more, was given for the dispersive and dissipative plasma from the momentum balance of the radiation pressure by H. Hora in 1969 and by direct derivation of the complete two-fluid equation of motion in 1981.

The nonlinear force [Eq. (1)] is valid only for the time-averaged monochromatic (time-independent) electromagnetic radiation of the laser field. In the beginning of the 1980s, several additional terms were introduced in Eq. (1) for the transient process. After a series of disputes in the literature, the most general—and the final complete formulation—emerging from these discussions with some additions is the following force density in a plasma:

$$\begin{aligned}\mathbf{f} &= \mathbf{f}_{th} + \mathbf{f}_{NL} \\ &= -\nabla P + \frac{1}{c}\mathbf{v} \times \mathbf{H} + \frac{1}{4\pi}\mathbf{E}\,\nabla\cdot\mathbf{E} \\ &\quad + \left(1 + \frac{1}{\omega}\frac{\partial}{\partial t}\right)\frac{1}{4\pi}\,\nabla\cdot(n^2 - 1)\mathbf{E}\mathbf{E} \end{aligned} \qquad (4)$$

where P is the gas dynamic pressure based on the best possible equation of state in the plasma determining the thermokinetic force $\mathbf{f}_{th}$.

Using the nonlinear force in the hydrodynamic computation and using the intensity-dependent nonlinear deviation of the optical constant in the correct form, by substituting the temperature in the plasma by an effective value given by the sum of the chaotic temperature and the average coherent quiver motion of the electrons in the laser field, the one-dimensional result, extending the purely thermokinetic case (Fig. 7), is shown in Fig. 8 by the distribution of plasma velocities. The initial density profiles of the irradiated plasma with collisions were nearly

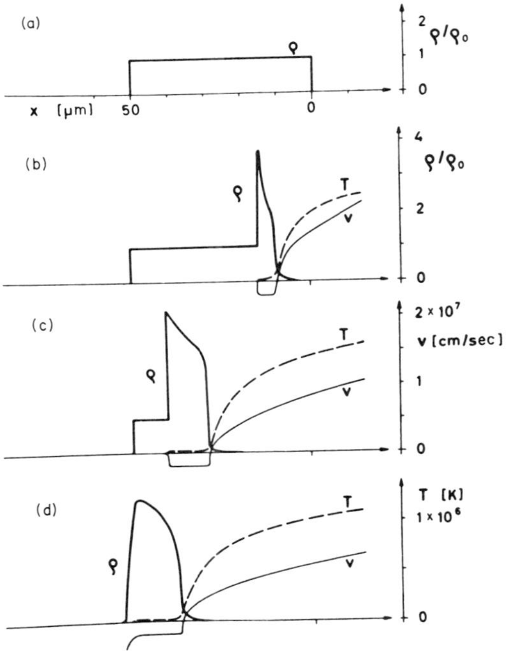

FIG. 7. One-dimensional computation of the hydrodynamic equations of conservation for laser light with a steplike intensity I of 10^{12} W/cm² incident on a 50-μm-thick slab of solid hydrogen (density ρ_0). The resulting density $\rho = n_i m_i$, velocity v, and temperature T are shown for times t = (a) 0, (b) 0.5, (c) 1.5, and (d) 2.0 nsec. (Courtesy of P. Mulser, TH Darmstadt.)

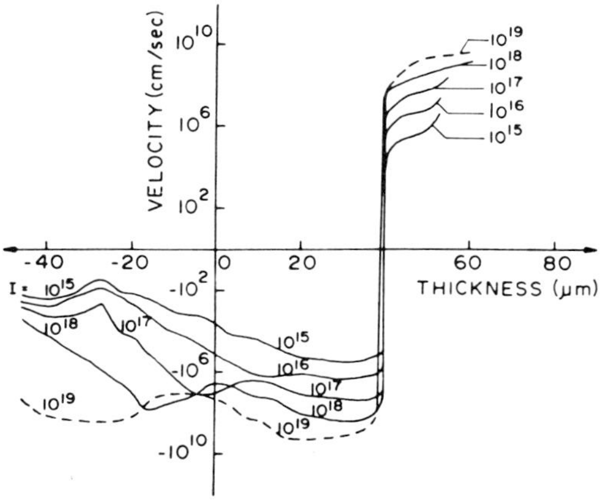

FIG. 8. Velocity profiles of nonlinear force-driven blocks of plasma at the time 1.5-psec after the beginning of the irradiation of 100-μm-thick dense hydrogen plasma by the indicated neodymium glass laser pulses with intensities between 10^{15} and 10^{19} W/cm^2. The full collisional gasdynamic calculation includes the correct nonlinear expression of the intensity-dependent optical constants for refraction and absorption. (Hora *et al.*, 1978.)

rectangular, nearly cut-off dense slabs with a thickness of 100 wavelengths of the incident neodymium glass laser radiation. The initially rectangular shape was slightly modified parabolically to reduce the initial reflection of the laser radiation, which became stronger and approached total reflection at later states. The result was that most of the laser energy was transferred directly almost without further heating into kinetic energy of thick plasma blocks of compression and ablation. The nonlinear force caused a kind of dielectric explosion of the plasma. The main reason is that the electric field $E = E_v/n^{1/2}$, with the vacuum value E_v, increases in the plasma to high values as the refractive index n decreases strongly, and the forces are determined by the negative gradients of the square of the electric field driving the outer plasma corona as a block against the laser light (ablation) and moving a thick block of the inner plasma to compression (Fig. 8).

The mechanical recoil to the plasma can be calculated (H. Hora, 1969; R. Klima and V. A. Petrzilka; 1972), and it turns out that the momentum of the electromagnetic energy in the plasma is identical with half the value of the Minkowski momentum plus half the value of Abraham. This was the starting point of the Abraham-Minkowski controversy, which has existed since 1910. Solutions have been obtained for the high-frequency limit in the plasma, where the asymmetric Minkowski tensor is an approximation of the symmetric Abraham tensor, which also explains why measurements at low frequency agree with the Abraham value and those at high frequency with the Minkowski value. It is possible to infer a consequence of symmetry breaking with a reasonable result of an effective photon mass linearly increasing to the rest mass of the electrons at intensities of 10^{27} W/cm^2. The completeness of the transient nonlinear force [Eq. (4)] has been derived from Lorentz and gauge invariance.

The predominance of the nonlinear force over the thermokinetic force is given by the threshold of 10^{14} W/cm^2 for neodymium glass laser radiation. The first detailed numerical study, by J. W. Shearer, R. E. Kidder, and J. W. Zink in 1970, led to the discovery that the nonlinear force causes a density minimum near the critical density when ablating the whole block of the corona away from the plasma interior, where the edge of the compressed interior block experiences a strong steepening of the density profile. The density minimum was later called a caviton and is characteristic for the action of the nonlinear force. Sophisticated measurements of the caviton and profile steepening by numerous laboratories confirmed the predominance of the nonlinear force.

C. Double Layers and Energetic Electrons

Another intriguing phenomenon was discovered in basic macroscopic plasma theory from the study of the nonlinear force. The results mentioned above were derived at the beginning of the 1950s only within the assumptions of the two-fluid model, where the use of space charge quasi-neutrality was essential. This was the reason why this model could not derive the plasma oscillations and their coupling and generation by electromagnetic irradiation macroscopically. For these purposes kinetic (microscopic) theory had always been used; however, this provides so many terms and phenomena that it was always difficult to find out with certainty which process is dominating. However, the knowledge that the action of the laser field via the nonlinear force within the bulk plasma is on the electrons only, and that the pushed or pulled electron clouds are followed by the ions with strong electrostatic fields to produce the nearly neutral block motion described by Eq. (1), motivated the study of a genuine two-fluid model in which the restriction of quasi-neutrality was dropped (P. Lalousis and H. Hora, 1983). It was then shown that all the details of dynamically driven and laser-driven plasma oscillations appeared damped by the collision frequency. Further, it turned out that under "quiet" conditions, nearly constant electric fields were produced that were given by the gradient of the thermokinetic pressure, the electrodynamic pressure of the laser field at high intensities.

It was found that the cavitons produced by the nonlinear force on irradiation with moderate laser intensities could generate longitudinal electric fields of 10^9 V/cm. It was further shown in 1984 by Eliezer and Ludmirski that in the case of these cavitons, the electric double layer generated is inverted and has oscillations in full agreement with simultaneously and independently measured electric fields, potentials, and double layers in laser-produced plasmas.

The analysis of the longitudinal electric oscillations also demonstrated that there are strong second-harmonic plasma oscillations at perpendicular incidence which result in a new resonance. This resonance is basically different from the Denisov resonance absorption, which occurs at oblique incidence of the radiation only at *p*-polarization. In Denisov's case it is the laser field that has the resonance maximum, while in the new case it is the internal plasma field that has the resonance maximum. The new second-harmonic resonance occurs at high profile steepening at four times the critical density and can be remarkably high. Another second-harmonic effect is that the longitudinal electric oscillations can be driven even in a low-density plasma at the same field strength as in a high-density plasma. Measurements of this unexpected phenomenon were of widespread uniform second harmonics emission from the corona of a laser-produced plasma and were in full agreement with the theory. The theory also reproduced the spatial periodicity.

The electric fields inside plasmas are also of importance for the physics of the magnetically confined plasmas. The radial inhomogeneity of these plasmas with respect to density and temperature generates electric fields **E** which, together with the confining magnetic fields **B**, result in a rotation by the $\mathbf{E} \times \mathbf{B}$ force of the plasma, in full agreement with the marginal measurements that earlier disregarded these rotations and assumed suprathermal ions to rotate only due to banana and neoclassical regimes. The first measurements of the internal fields in tokamaks were published, by K. A. Razumova, B. B. Kadomtsev, *et al.* in 1983, at the same time as the discovery of the inhomogeneity fields from the laser-produced plasmas, valid for all plasmas. The generalized hydrodynamic theory without space charge quasi-neutrality made it possible to understand the generation of electrostatic waves and their propagation and coupling with the electromagnetic field directly without the necessary inclusion of kinetic theory.

The study of double layers—known earlier from the properties of the Debye sheath in expanding laser-produced plasmas similar to the expanding plasmas in space given by Alfvén in 1981—led to the conclusion that these double layers prevent electrons from penetrating through the Debye sheath. Since Debye sheaths can be spread to larger areas and since the double layers were also confirmed to be inside plasmas—for instance, between the hot laser-heated corona and the cold interior of a target—the inhibition of electron transport and the stopping of electronic thermal conduction became evident. Thermal conduction can then be at the much lower level of ionic conduction only, for which the double-layer mechanism provided quantitative formulas.

Since there are so many strange phenomena related to new aspects of the fundamentals of relativity theory, quantum collisions [Eq. (3)], and the generalization of the concepts of macroscopic plasma theory, and since we may expect further surprising phenomena in the future, it is not unexpected that many of the observations in laser-produced plasmas are not understood satisfactorily. One such phenomenon is that of energetic electrons. Confusing results were obtained for temperatures measured from the spectra of X-ray emission, which were sometimes very high and at other times not so high. These observations were clarified in 1971 by K. Eidmann, who realized that there was a spectrum corresponding to a usual temperature of the plasma of some 100 or 1000 keV, while there was a distinct difference due to energetic electrons, which are sometimes called "hot" electrons. When these electrons were related to Denisov resonances, or to parametric instabilities, profile steepening, and self-generated magnetic fields, the real reason for the measured energetic electrons was not clear. The simple explanation that they may be related to the quiver motion of the electrons in the laser field was not accepted. Indeed, this explanation would have required some increase of the quiver motion due to the dielectric swelling (increasing the vacuum oscillation energy to higher values because of division of this value by a dielectric constant of much less than unity in the plasma), which would imply special assumptions on the plasma dynamics that were rather unconvincing too, if such an alternative explanation had been evident.

In 1983, results of G. McCall *et al.* and S. Nakai *et al.* from measurements of carbon dioxide-irradiated plasmas showed that the spectrum of the energetic electrons had a clear high-energy edge. This can be explained only by quiver motion in the (swelled) laser field or in resonance maxima, as the interaction with other particles during successive thermalization leads only to lower energies than the maximum energy, which is determined sharply by the externally driven laser interactions. The discovery of double layers and internal dynamic electric fields in plasmas supports a first derivation of surface tension in plasmas. While surface tension in dielectrics is due to unsaturated dipoles and while high temperature plasmas do not contain molecules with dipoles, it was surprising to find that the electrostatic field energy in the double layers of the plasma surface (or at any other internal plasma inhomogeneity or interface) produces an energy density approximating surface tension values. This stabilizes surface waves working against the Rayleigh Taylor instability as in water droplets observed in laser-produced plasmas.

The plasma model could be extended to the degenerate electrons in metals leaving the ion lattice as in a plasma and produce a swimming electron layer at the surface of about an Angstrom thickness. The resulting surface tension correlates with the measured values for metals. Even for the measured charge distribution in nuclei, the plasma model results in peripheral decay (a kind of Debye length). This results in surface energies in full agreement with the experimental values where, however, the nuclear forces substitute the action of the positive charges in plasmas or metals.

D. The Problem of Laser–Plasma Interaction with Solution by Smoothing

While the properties described in Sections III, B and C concerning plasma dynamics, nonlinear force effects, double layers and internal electric fields, and the facts about energetic electrons are now fully accepted, there has been uncertainty about other observed phenomena. For example, spontaneous magnetic fields are generated in laser-produced plasmas at levels exceeding megagauss. Further, the laser beams can be self-focused in the produced plasma, either in toto or due to the hot spots of local intensity maxima within the beam cross section. Two basically different mechanisms have been identified. The first is ponderomotive (or nonlinear force) self-focusing, due to H. Hora in 1969, where the forces radial to the laser beam expel plasma until the thermokinetic counterforce is compensated. Adding the condition of the optics of total reflection due to the radial gradient of the electron density and the condition of diffraction, a laser power threshold for the stationary filament can be calculated depending on the plasma temperature and density. The threshold is always near 1 MW. In the filament, the electromagnetic energy density equals the gaskinetic value, which is defined by the threshold near 10^{14} W/cm^2 intensities for neodymium glass lasers at which the nonlinear forces dominate the thermokinetic force. Using this, the calculated diameter of the laser filament for a 10-MW ruby laser pulse is about 3 μm, exactly as measured. Even the depletion of the plasma density has been measured interferometrically (by M. C. Richardson and A. J. Alcock in 1971). This self-focusing mechanism takes on the order of 100 psec or more as the plasma must be removed mechanically from the center of the filament.

The other type is relativistic self-focusing, due to H. Hora in 1975. When the quiver energy of the electrons in the high-intensity laser field reaches mc^2 (m is the rest mass of the electron), the optical constant n changes in the values of the plasma frequency and the collision frequency. The relativistic threshold intensity is at 3×10^{18} W/cm^2 for neodymium glass lasers and depends inversely on the square of the wavelength. As a result, the effective wavelength, as the distance between wave fronts in the plasma, is shorter for higher than for lower laser intensities. The plane wave front of a beam with Gaussian radial intensity decay in a homogeneous plasma is bent and shrinks down to filaments of half-wavelength diameter within a propagation length comparable to the initial beam diameter. This fast relativistic shrinking of the beam occurs instantaneously in the homogeneous plasma, which dynamically will not remain homogeneous as the radial nonlinear forces will expel the plasma. It was shown numerically that for neodymium glass laser powers of 10 TW a rise time of the pulses of less than a few picoseconds is necessary to realize the shrinking to half-wavelength diameter. Otherwise the beam simply drills holes through the plasma (Yamanaka effect). Relativistic self-focusing could be related to the generation of the measured ions of megaelectron-volt energy emitted from the laser-irradiated plasma. In 1982, D. A. Jones *et al.* found agreement with measurements up to 300-MeV ion energies, and detailed computations for higher beam powers reach ion energies of 6 GeV.

Furthermore, the Foersterling–Denisov resonance absorption, as known from p-polarized microwaves obliquely incident on a stratified plasma, is acting in laser-produced plasmas; however, it is being superimposed by the aforementioned new internal field resonance processes appearing at perpedicular incidence.

A great deal of attention has been given to parametric instabilities. Such instabilities emerged from Landau's instability solutions of Mathieu's differential equation of an oscillating system subjected to another oscillation frequency. For the interaction of electromagnetic waves with plasmas, Sagdeev and Oraevski derived in 1961 what was rediscovered by numerous scientists later and summarized by F. F. Chen (1973) by using the consequent nonlinear force description. Electromagnetic energy is converted into electron (Langmuir) oscillations, called stimulated Raman scattering (SRS), or into acoustic plasma waves, called stimulated Brillouin scattering (SBS), or into two stream instabilities and similar and mixed mechanisms. These processes were considered the reason for the dilemma of the confusing observations of laser–plasma interaction and studied extensively.

It was established experimentally, however, by R. P. Drake (1987) and by Christine Laboune (1985), that—apart from artificially chosen plasma profiles—the amount of SRS and SBS contributing to the energy transfer at laser plasma interaction is small. The instability mechanisms nevertheless exist as seen from higher or broken harmonics backscatter and are quite useful for diagnostics purposes.

The question remained then: What—if not the instabilities—are the reasons for the most complex and confusing properties of laser–plasma interaction? A first indication appeared from the computations (1974) of laser irradiation of an initially linear density profile with complete nonlinear force hydrodynamics of a collisional plasma, nonlinear optical constants, and a complete Maxwellain solution of the laser field for each dynamically varying temperature and density profiles, including the partially reflected light. While the laser light was reflected initially at the critical density as expected, after a few picoseconds, the light was reflected strongly at the outermost low density part of the plasma corona. The reason was evident: the partially standing laser wave field moved plasma to the nodes which ripple resulted in a Bragg reflection of the laser light at very low plasma densities.

This process was observed by M. Lubin, J. Soures *et al.* in 1974, who measured the reflectivity of laser light from a plasma which was pulsating irregularity between a few percentage points and nearly 100% within 10 to 15 psec up and down. The same was observed in 1988 by A. Maddever and B. Luther-Davies, with the further result from time resolved spectra that the plasma is accelerated to a few 10^7 cm/sec velocity within the first few picoseconds, after which the interaction stops. Then, 15 psec later another acceleration occurs to add up a similar velocity, and so on. The spectra of the backscattered light receive then a periodicity of about 4 Å independent of the mass of the ions of the plasma, an observation which had been unresolved for years.

Exactly this mechanism was reproduced from a hydrodynamic calculation (including most general properties of real plasmas) as shown in Fig. 9. Light is incident from the left-hand side into a plasma with an initially linearly increasing density up to the critical value. Light is reflected there and partial standing wave ripples the density until after a few picoseconds the light is reflected at the low density. The then untouched plasma corona relaxes from its ripples hydrodynamically until 6 psec later the light can penetrate to the critical density again, again producing ripple, etc. The reflectivity is then pulsating from low to high values within 7 to 10 psec periods. The net velocity of the ions is lifted up to 10^7 cm/sec during the first few picoseconds, then moves with constant velocity, gets another upshift at about 7 psec, and so on.

It is evident that such a complicated laser plasma interaction is most undesirable for applications as laser fusion. Proposals to overcome this have been discussed since 1974 by M. Lubin *et al.* A first step to reach a smooth interaction (i.e., without the mentioned pulsation) was veri-

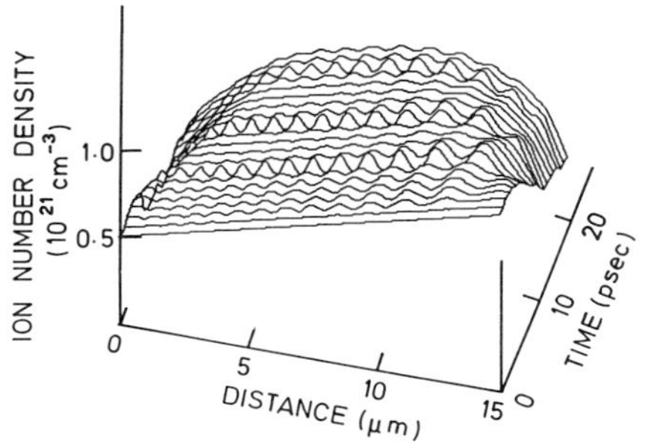

FIG. 9. Genuine two fluid computation of the density of an initially 30 eV plasma of a linear density ramp from half to 1.1 critical density irradiated from the left-hand side by a neodymium glass laser of 1015 W/cm^2 intensity and its temporal development. This shows the generation and relaxation of density ripple due to the nonlinear force action of the partially standing wave when it is propagating each 6 psec to the critical density while relaxing hydrodynamically during the times of Bragg reflection at low density.

fied by Y. Kato and K. Mima by the random phase plate (RPP), splitting the laser beam into 100 or more beamlets whose phases are shifted randomly. The interaction of such a beam laterally washes out the density ripple from the standing waves such that the interaction is smooth; no pulsation of reflectivity and no stuttering acceleration appears. The smoothness of interaction can be seen immediately from the pictures of the irradiated targets.

Another smoothing method is the induced spatial incoherence (ISI) introduced by S.P. Obenschain, where it is taken care that the laser field has no coherence longer than 1 to 3 psec. It is evident then that no standing wave field with the spatially fixed production of density ripple is possible; therefore, a smooth laser plasma interaction will occur as confirmed from the ideal pictures of the light reflected from the targets. This again can be explained by the mechanism described by Fig. 9, although an interrelation with suppression of self-focussing and other mechanisms may be possible. A further result is that the smoothing by ISI suppresses SRS and SBS to less than 0.1% of the transferred energy.

It seems that the just mentioned smoothing methods solved the problem of the otherwise complicated laser–plasma interaction. Furthermore, an understanding of the mechanism by the density ripple generation and relaxation apart from processes of self-focusing and filamentation, from double layer effects with a new type of resonance and the widespread second harmonics generation in the plasma corona, including the correct nonlinear devations of the optical response (dielectric constant and absorption), up to relativistic effects may have been achieved. The conclusion is that other mechanisms as SRS and SBS are of secondary importance only and that the mission for research to understand these instabilities has been solved by using the techniques of RPP, ISI, or broad band laser irradiation.

IV. Applications of Laser Beams

A. Annealing, Welding, Cutting

Medium laser intensities are used for numerous treatments of materials in industrial processing. The surfaces of steel components are heated to achieve a special hardening due to recrystallization, and laser pulses are used for highly programmed heating to evaporate other metals and melt and alloy special surfaces. [*See* LASER-MATERIALS INTERACTIONS.]

Special attention has been given to the annealing of silicon crystals in producing microelectronic chips, as the laser pulses can be focused to diameters of a few micrometers and guided in highly sophisticated ways. The need for such treatment came from the ion implantation of doping atoms into silicon single crystals—for instance, using implantation of As to produce *n*-conducting and of Al to produce *p*-conducting areas for rectifying *p–n* junctions or combinations for polar transistors or field effect transistors. Doping by thermal diffusion took hours and resulted in undesired inhomogeneities due to preferential diffusion along lines of areas of crystal defects.

Around 1969 an alternative process was proposed involving homogeneous implantation by firing the doped atoms into the crystal as ions after acceleration by several hundred thousand volts. However, not only did this result in an inhomogeneous distribution with depth (Bragg maximum), but also implantation at a rate of about 10^{15} ions/cm^2 caused so many crystal defects and voids in the silicon crystal that the density increased by 10% or more. The structure was indeed amorphous silicon but not of the usual kind, as the voids resulted in 20 times lower thermal conductivity (H. J. Goldsmid, 1984). As the implanted atoms were on interstitial sites (and electrically not immediately active), they had to be brought into the crystal by heat treatment, by which the crystal defects could be reduced. The best treatment took long times in diffusion stoves at 800°C and was expensive. To reduce the expense, heat treatment with short laser and electron beam pulses was introduced. The recrystallization of the buried amorphous layers, however, was not of the same quality as that achieved by the stove treatment. It could be seen electron microscopically that more voids remained after the short-time treatment (H. Krimmel, K. Bethge, *et al.*, 1980).

Nevertheless, the laser-produced recrystallization process received extensive attention and careful physical analysis. When the crystal was irradiated with picosecond laser pulses, it was not immediately clear whether the energy deposition really caused melting and ordered recrystallization (N. Bloembergen *et al.*) of the material or a submelting process (van Vechten). For both cases, thermionic emission and other measurements were performed.

Another important laser treatment is the welding of metals of the same or different kinds. For this purpose the cw carbon dioxide laser is preferred. It has been shown that a 60 kW beam of a gasdynamic laser can weld steel 3 cm thick with especially high quality.

Using another type of focusing, cutting of materials can be done by cw laser beams, and again the carbon dioxide laser is preferred. Computer-controlled motion of the beam gives advantages for cutting textile fabrics, brass, exotic metals, carbon, or timber, and high-quality cuts result that do not require further treatment.

B. Medical Treatment

Medium- or higher-intensity laser treatment in medicine was introduced early in the history of lasers. Attachment of the retina in eyes had already been done with noncoherent optical pulses, and the use of lasers provided a much more reproducible, more precise, and safer treatment of this kind. In the early 1980s more powerful focused laser pulses were used to produce higher temperatures locally, for instance, to drill holes for openings in treating glaucoma.

With the use of higher laser powers and the generation of microscopic high-temperature plasmas, the shock waves and global heating were still tolerable, and the remaining defocused light could not damage the function of the eye. Plasmas generated in the opaque areas of the (natural or artificial) lens or in their neighborhood could be used to heal cataracts, as the laser-destroyed tissue was finally filled by water. Picosecond (mode-locked) Nd:YAG laser pulses, as pioneered by Danielle Aaron-Rosa, were used successfully to remove opaque areas of up to 2 mm even in the vitrea. The physics of the processes involved the mechanisms of plasma generation and the limitations by self-focusing, in which case the picosecond pulses or the more frequently used nanosecond pulses from *Q*-switched neodymium glass lasers followed the basically different regimes of relativistic self-focusing and ponderomotive self-focusing, respectively (see Section III,C). The result was safer and much more flexible use (C. J. Walter, 1983) of the mode-locked laser.

Laser beams have been used for cutting or removing living tissues in operations since the 1970s. Carbon dioxide lasers provide ideal cuts with a minimum of blood loss, as the mechanical squeezing by the knife is completely avoided. The simultaneous coagulation of the surface of the tissue is rather weak with the carbon dioxide laser. When cw green argon laser light is used instead, the selective high absorption in blood causes, apart from the cutting mechanism, a strong coagulation. Argon laser pulses are used to stop bleeding in the eye and to treat cancerous tissues at the surface of the bladder, of the stomach, and other surfaces to which a light pipe for the transport of the laser pulse can be moved with pipes for diagnostics and adjustment. Even undesired crusts inside blood vessels of inactive areas in the heart tissue are being removed by such laser treatment.

C. Fusion Energy

Huge amounts of energy can be produced by the reaction of fusing light nuclei to heavier ones. The most important fusion reaction is that of the heavy hydrogen isotope deuterium (D), which is available from all natural water, or the superheavy hydrogen isotope tritium (T), which was discovered by Oliphant, Harteck, and Lord Rutherford in 1933 from the first measured reaction.

$$D + D \rightarrow \begin{cases} n + {}^3He + 3.27 \quad \text{MeV (50\%)} \\ H + T + 4.03 \quad \text{MeV (50\%)} \end{cases} \tag{5}$$

$$D + T \rightarrow {}^4He + n + 17.6 \text{ MeV}$$

where the energy is given per reaction. As chemical reactions provide energies in the range of electron volts, the megaelectron-volt range indicates the million times higher energy production by the exothermal nuclear reactions of Eq. (5). Because of the classical error of applying linear theory only (see the last six paragraphs of Section V), it was concluded around 1950 that an exothermal fusion reaction of Eq. (5) cannot be produced by firing a deuterium or a tritium particle beam with optimized energy at a solid deuterium or tritium target. Instead, one had to provide the reacting nuclear fuel at thermal equilibrium at about 100 million K (about 10 keV on the scale of average energy per particle) up to 100 keV. The problem then was that such a high-temperature thermonuclear plasma had to be confined long enough for more fusion reaction energy to be produced than was put in to ignite it. One way to achieve this is to produce confinement by magnetic fields (stellarator, tokamak, magnetic bottle, mirror machine, etc.). The fusion energy source is inexhaustive in view of the heavy water as fuel and clean and safe with respect to the resulting helium, i.e. without radioactive waste. Radioactivity within the reactor can be solved by appropriate containment. It has to be underlined, however, that the just mentioned magnetic confinement schemes may not be competitive economically (Pfirsch and Schmitter, 1989). The most advanced scheme, the tokamak, may produce—if the yet unsolved physical problems could be solved and the very damaging wall erosion (0.1 to 1 cm per day of operation) could be overcome—energy more expansive only then 10 times that of light water reactors. [*See* NUCLEAR FUSION POWER.]

The advent of the laser, with its strong spatial and temporal concentration of energy, suggested the possibility of heating and igniting a solid fuel pellet by laser irradiation. The first serious calculations were published by Basov and Krokhin (1963) and by Dawson (1964). The parameters then reached for fusion gains were very bad, and an improvement by orders of magnitude could be achieved by optimizing the gains G (fusion energy/input energy), which very sensibly depend on the parameters used expressed by the following Hora–Pfirsch formula (contrary to the Lawson criterion):

$$G = \left(\frac{E_0}{E_{BE}}\right)^{1/3} \left(\frac{n_0}{n_s}\right)^{2/3} \quad \text{at} \quad T = T_{opt} \qquad (6)$$

where n_0 is the density of the fuel atoms in the initial pellet, n_s the solid-state density of the fuel (hydrogen or its isotopes of 6×10^{22} cm^{-3}), E_0 the laser energy put into the spherical pellet of radius R_0, and E_{BE} the breakeven energy, which is the value of the input energy for which a gain of 1 results when working with the uncompressed or diluted pellet at solid-state density. These values were achieved for the optimum condition of heating the pellet before its self-similarity expansion against vacuum and adiabatic cooling, where an optimum temperature at the beginning of 17 keV for the DT reaction or 52 keV for the DD reaction was necessary.

The breakeven energy was nevertheless very high, 7.6 MJ for the DT reaction and 10 GJ or more for DD and similar reactions. However, it should be noted that the initial nanosecond laser pulses had an energy on the order of only 1 J in 1964, which increased to the range of megajoules in the 1980s. An advantage was given by the fact that there was a quadratic relation between input energy and initial density in Eq. (6): compression to 100 times solid state requires 10,000 times less input energy to achieve the same gain of fusion energy. Equation (6) is algebraically identical to the gain formula published much later, G = const n_0R_0, at the same optimum initial temperature (R. E. Kidder, 1974).

It was then obvious not only to use the laser to heat the plasma but also to use the ablation and compression process to improve the fusion conditions. This fact was well known in the unpublished literature at Los Alamos in 1943 before publication of the independently derived results of Eq. (6), with its absolute value based on better measured fusion cross sections and detailed computations. The compression by ablation was evident from the hydrodynamic calculations (Fig. 7), and detailed computations on the ignition of spherical pellets using smooth time profiles of laser pulses with 100 psec main width arrived at fusion gains of 50 with pulses of 100-kJ laser energy first disclosed by J. H. Nuckolls, E. Teller, *et al.*, in 1972.

The first experiments on producing fusion neutrons by laser irradiation of lithium deuteride were reported in 1968, and a convincing number of fusion neutrons were measured by F. Floux *et al.* (1969), where it was ensured that the laser pulse fired on a solid deuterium target had a sharp initial profile by suppressing any prepulse by a factor of 1 to 1 million.

Since then, numerous large scale experiments have been established with big laser systems (Table I; Figs. 10a and 10b), and most sophisticated techniques have been developed to pro-

TABLE I. Large Operational Laser Systems (1990)

Name	Location	Laser (wave length in μm)	Number of beams	Pulse Energy	Pulse Duration	Power
NOVA	Livermore	Nd (1.06)	10	125kJ	2 nsec	62 TW
		Nd (0.35)	10	50kJ	2 nsec	20 TW
		Nd (1.06)	10	12.5kJ	0.1 nsec	125 TW
		Nd (1.06)	10	1.5kJ	0.01 nsec	150 TW
GEKKO 12	Osaka	Nd (1.06)	12	4.3kJ	0.1 nsec	43 TW
		Nd (0.35)	12	2kJ	0.1 nsec	20 TW
AURORA	Los Alamos	KrF (0.25)	2	10kJ	5 nsec	2 TW
ISKRA-5	Arzamas-16 (Gorki)	I (1.3)	12	30kJ	0.25 nsec	120 TW

duce spherical pellets, or capsules, with deuterium–tritium fuel and to measure the interaction processes. Time resolved measurements with picosecond resolution of plasma temperatures, densities, and velocities with a local resolution down to micrometers resolution have been developed. The detection of the X rays from the plasmas was first done with pinhole cameras, then with penumbral diagnostics (B. Luther-Davies) and with bent crystals (E. Förster) magnifying a high aperture narrowband X-ray line picture up to 30 times. Time resolution of neutron emission was developed with a resolution down to 10 psec, and penumbral high quality imaging of the neutron emission from a pellet was developed at Livermore, where the largest known experiment is being performed (Fig. 11), receiving the special U.S. award IR100.

The initial difficulties of the laser–plasma interaction for driving the pellet directly by the laser light were avoided by the ingenious concept of J. H. Nuckolls (1982), covering the pellets with a layer of heavy atoms which convert the laser radiation into 70% of X-radiation and let then these X rays compress and ignite the fusion fuel pellet. This is called indirect drive.

A further unfortunate result was that fusion gains of Eq. (6) arrived at the low value of only 41—much too low, taking into account the low efficiency of lasers, if a burn of only 25% of the DT fuel is assumed, independent of what compression is used and despite the fact that the mechanism on which Eq. (6) is based excludes hydrodynamic losses since it follows the adiabatically ideal compression. In order to reach higher gains, K. Brueckner and J. H. Nuckolls developed the scheme that there should not be a volume-like adiabatic compression, but a different ablation of the peripheric plasma by the radiation due to a temporarily programmed recoil. This should produce shock waves which compress the small central part of the plasma to densities of 1000 to 10,000 times the solid state and to temperatures of 10 keV which ignites a self-sustained fusion combustion wave through the outer less dense cold plasma. By this spark ignition, very high fusion gains should be expected.

Since the recent development of smooth laser–plasma interaction techniques, the indirect drive concept may not be necessary, and direct drive could be used, saving at least a factor of three in efficiency by avoiding the conversion into X rays.

The hitherto most successful experiment for producing fusion neutrons was performed at the Osaka Institute of Laser Engineering with the Gekko 12 neodymium glass laser (Figs. 10a and 10b). Direct drive laser irradiation on glass microspheres filled with high pressure DT gas initially were aimed to produce central shock compression according to the spark ignition. For good shocks, however, very low neutron gains were measured and the bremsstrahlung emission was extremely nonuniform. Against this intention, if a stagnation-free compression (Yamanaka–Nakai compression) with adiabatic hydrodynamics as in the volume compression of Eq. (6) was used, the neutron gain was maximum (10^{13} neutrons from 12 kJ 530 nm neo-

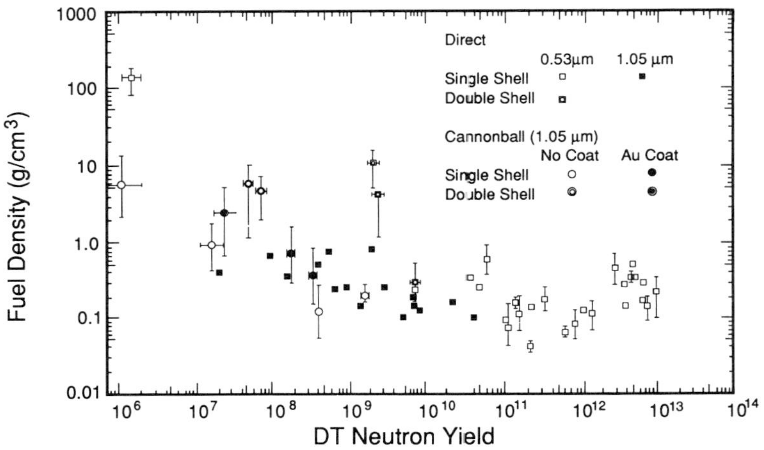

FIG. 10a. Fusion neutron yields and deuterium–tritium compression density of laser fusion experiments for Gekko 12 measurements at Osaka University. (Courtesy of C. Yamanaka.)

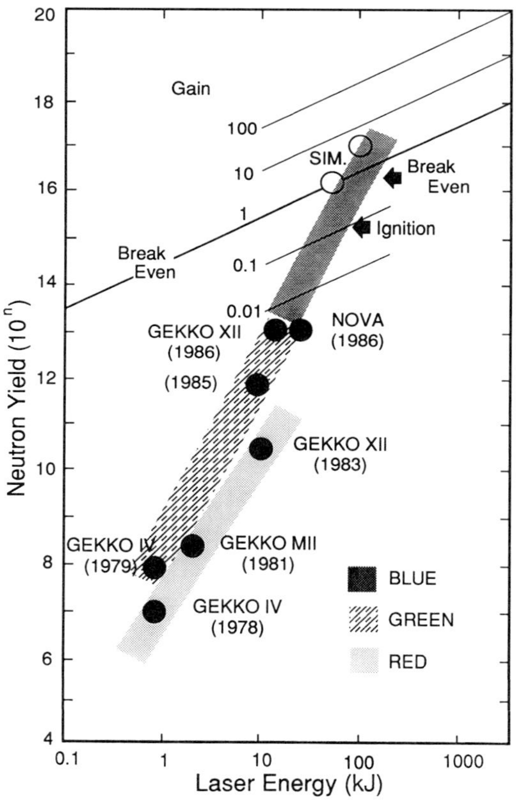

FIG. 10b. Measured direct drive fusion neutron yields from the GEKKO and NOVA irradiation of given laser pulse energy for neodymium glass wavelength (red), frequency doubling (green), and frequency tripling (blue), including simulation calculations (SIM). (Courtesy of S. Nakai).

dymium glass laser irradiation) and the bremsstrahlung was very uniform.

The advantage of this ideal adiabatic volume compression could be understood immediately from the result (H. Hora and P. S. Ray, 1978) that much higher gains than the afore mentioned disappointing value of 41 could be reached if the self-heat of the plasma by the generated alpha particles was taken into account. This ignition dropped the optimum initial temperature from 17 keV of simple burn [see Eq. (6)] to 4.5 keV, and the reaction temperature intermediary reached high temperatures of 50 keV and more by the alpha self-heat. Gains of 400 and more were possible with compression to 100 times the solid state only. If reabsorption of the bremsstrahlung took place in cases of very high compression (1000 times the solid state) and very high energy input (above 10 MJ), the initial temperatures dropped close to 1 keV only and gains exceeding 1200 were reached with 80% fuel consumption.

This volume ignition, together with the result of direct drive, may be an example of how laser fusion may result in an energy generation remarkably less expensive than light water reactors.

Laser fusion is still based on indirect drive and spark ignition. The densities reached there are very high, but the temperatures are in the 1 to 2 keV range only; therefore the neutron gains are not yet more than 10^{11}. For these aims densities of 1000 times the solid state have been reached in Osaka using carbon polymers. Densities of 1000 g/cm^3 were produced in a laboratory for the first time.

The confirmation of laser fusion came from the Centurion–Halite underground nuclear test experiment. The generated X-radiation is similar to that for the indirect drive, where 100 MJ radiation input on DT capsules convincingly demonstrated the solution of inertial confinement fusion. Though only a limited amount of information was disclosed, S. Kahalas (US Department of Energy) stated, "Laser fusion is no longer a question of "if" but of "when." Based on all the detailed knowledge, the ATHENA laser project (see Fig. 3) predicted a glass laser power station of $700 million which will generate 10 MJ laser pulses for indirect driving and spark ignition in a DT capsule producing 1000 MJ energy. Taking that into account, an economic pellet fusion reactor of the type CASCASE (General Atomics, San Diego) can be built with lithium granules as absorber to avoid the otherwise devastating wall problems of magnetic confinement. Any radiation damage in the lithium ceramics granulate will be regenerated when the pebbles, after some time of operation, have to be melted again when the generated tritium has to be harvested. One can conclude that *the physics for a laser fusion reactor for energy production at cost of light water reactors (the most economic case at all) has been solved.* [*See* NUCLEAR FUSION.]

Various predictions and estimations conclude that economically competitive laser fusion power stations can be developed within 10 to 15 years with a crash program of $20 to 30 billion. This takes into account the mentioned $700 million for the ATHENA 10 MJ glass laser fusion installation and a simultaneous development of high efficiency, high repetition laser and reactor technology.

A further reduction of the cost of electricity by a factor 3 to 5 below the current cheapest power generation is possible by further development at least within the next 10 years since the present concepts permit a lot of further improvements. This all is based on a DT fusion technology including a cycle of radioactive tritium and some neutron damage in the reactor vessel though this is strongly reduced by the lithium bubble blanket technology. The better reaction [instead of Eq. (5)] is the burning of light hydrogen (protons) with boron(11) where three alphas of equal energy result for an 80% efficiency conversion of this nuclear energy into electricity. No neutrons appear, and any radioactivity generated is less than from burning coal. This dream reaction, however, is more difficult than the DT reaction.

Since the estimations for the establishment of a magnetic confinement (tokamak) power station is projected to be a further 50 years and need $150 billion, it may be interesting to note that after a 15-year DT laser fusion power station program, a further 25-year improvement may lead to the laser fusion of the dream fuel proton-boron(11). What is needed are lasers of more than 40% efficiency, compression 100 times higher than the currently achieved 1000 times solid state, and 20 times larger reaction chambers than in the ATHENA project. This is based on the fact that volume ignition of HB(11) has a decrease of the optimum reaction temperature to 23 KeV because of alpha self-heat.

D. Laser Acceleration of Particles and Other Applications

A relatively new field of application of high and very high intensity laser beams is for the acceleration of charged particles in the next generation of accelerators of electrons, protons, deuterons, or heavy nuclei for research in high energy, elementary particle, and nuclear physics. Conventional production of proton beams with up to teraelectron-volt energies for collision experiments has been achieved. Hadron colliders may still be important up to 100 TeV; for energies beyond they may not be of interest (B. Richter, 1985) as the protons are highly composite entities (soups) and direct results for elementary particles may not be expected. There is interest in producing teraelectron-volt electrons to study basic interaction phenomena. Present-day accelerators provide 100-GeV electrons in electron-positron colliders, and further extensions are under way. One project that will involve a multiyear program is the superconducting super collider (SSC) accelerator, for which an expenditure of $10 billion is projected.

For such large-scale projects, the question arose of whether laser techniques may not provide less expensive systems. One alternative is to develop the free electron laser with a wavelength of 1 mm to powers of gigawatts for driving linear accelerator (LINAC) cavities of the usual type. The shorter wavelengths would reduce the size of such LINACs drastically and reduce the costs. The result of Prosnitz and Sessler (1985) in achieving such a free electron laser output is encouraging in this respect.

FIG. 11. Target chamber of the NOVA laser experiment, where the 10 laser beams of 76 cm diameter are focused to the fusion pellet of less than 0.5 mm diameter at Lawrence Livermore National Laboratory. (Courtesy of J. L. Emmett, Livermore.)

For use as alternative particle accelerators, consideration has been given to combinations of intense carbon dioxide laser beams guided closely along gratings, combinations of inverse Čerenkov radiation mechanisms, or inversions of the free electron laser. For some of these concepts the first experimental confirmations exist. In these cases, however, the particle energies achieved are at least 10^6 below the goals for alternative accelerators.

One very extensively studied scheme is the beat wave accelerator (T. Tajima, J. M. Dawson, 1979). By firing the interference field of two CO_2 laser beams of slightly different frequencies through a plasma so that their difference (beat wave) frequency fits the plasma frequency, a nonlinear force-type acceleration of electrons is induced. With present-day parameters, a simple linear computation showed the production of gigaelectron-volt electron energies along 1 m only. These calculations were based on a multiparticle simulation including all dimensions for the velocities and the fields but only one spatial dimension. The result is thus valid only for infinite plane waves. For the more realistic case of a beam with radial divergences, space charge effects, instabilities, and relativistic self-focusing mechanisms, less optimistic results were obtained. For instance, when only some of these effects were included, it was found that the accelerated electron beam will oscillate and split and will reach only 40 MeV (J. M. Kindel, 1984). Nevertheless, the mechanism deserves study and some of the difficulties may be overcome.

The upshift of 10 MeV electrons to 20 MeV was demonstrated by the beat wave acceleration scheme (Y. Kitagawa *et al.*, 1990) using carbon dioxide laser beat waves. It has to be taken into account that under these conditions the acceleration mechanism can work for 80 psec only; then conditions of chaos are produced, preventing a further acceleration (H. Takabe, K. Mima, and T. Oosuga, 1985).

Another acceleration scheme is to use the high electric fields in the cavitons of the laser-produced plasma. These are typical nonconservative fields similar to those in the high-frequency cavities of accelerators and permit energy transfer from the fields to electrons passing the fields. The pumping mechanism of the caviton fields is much more complicated than the HF fields; it involves external manipulation of the hydromechanical development of the plasma at the high-intensity laser irradiation. Assuming a carbon dioxide laser of the size of the ANTARES system with 100 TW output and a broad area of cavitons moving with the clouds of electrons to be accelerated, accelerations up to 30 GeV or more per interaction with one caviton should be possible.

The ideal solution would be the acceleration of electrons by the laser fields where amplitudes of electric field strengths of 10^{12} V/cm or of magnetic fields of 3 Gigagauss have been achieved. The general result, however, is that the energy of an electron—if damping losses by scattering are neglected—is the same after an electromagnetic pulse has passed as before.

Other ways that electrons can be accelerated by laser fields in vacuum are known from the experiments by B. W. Boreham (1979), where electrons are emitted from the focus of a laser beam in radial direction to kiloelectron-volt energy which corresponds to half of the quiver energy of the electrons in the neodymium glass laser field of about 10^{16} W/cm^2. A further mechanism (Hora, 1988) is to consider the electrons trapped in the intensity minima of a standing wave or interference field by the nonlinear force and to accelerate them by accelerating the minima in space. This is possible, for example, by bending the mirror of a Fresnel double prism for an interference field or by moving the mirror of a "standing" wave field. All details of this acceleration have been demonstrated numerically (L. Cicchitelli *et al.*, 1990).

Another solution for electron acceleration of electrons in vacuum is to use linearly polarized half waves (e.g., after rectification) of plane laser waves. There is indeed first a strong motion to the side due to the transversal E-field, but a Lorentzian forward motion is strongly pronounced relativistically. A pulse of a KrF laser of 900 kJ energy *accelerates an electron up to teraelectron-volt energy* along a length of 9 cm which is just the time the optical half wave needs to overtake the electron moving very close to the speed of light. The necessary lateral motion by about 500 wavelengths requires a large focus of the laser beam in agreement also with a long 9 cm focus length, thereby causing the great energy. The same can be achieved instead, using rectified laser beams, by using a short wave train of five or so wavelengths of a beam of the just mentioned dimensions where a lateral injection of the electrons is performed with the necessary energy with respect to the nonlinear force, where the parameters are selected in such a way that the electron leaves the beam at the other side after the acceleration by half of a wavelength has been performed. These conclusions are based on exact relativistic solutions of the Maxwellian equations. Acceleration of electrons due to these lateral asymmetries of a beam results in a gain up to 90 MeV in a 20 TW laser pulse, 0.9 GeV in a 2 PW pulse, while TeV electrons need 2.5×10^{21} W.

The disadvantages of the beat-wave acceleration could be overcome basically by another plasma scheme, the wake field accelerator, where a very short laser pulse generates a longitudinal (Langmuir) half wave in a plasma which then acts similarly to the aforementioned half wave of the laser field in vacuum. This is indeed a most transparent and straightforward mechanism and should succeed in a simple way. Compared to the very similar—and mutually supporting—earlier mentioned mechanism of half waves (or lateral injection with longer beams), the efficiency is always less than the vacuum case. The results of the genuine two fluid model indicate that the amplitude of the longitudinal waves driven in a plasma by a laser field are always less than one-tenth the electrical laser field amplitude and the length of the wake is at least 10 times larger than the optical wavelengths. This results in at least 10,000 times less acceleration energy of the electrons by a wake field than by a laser field in vacuum.

Although the acceleration schemes mentioned above may still seem quite far from realization, one experimentally well developed scheme for ions and heavy ions is based on the usual laser irradiation of targets. With megawatt laser powers, kiloelectron-volt ions have been measured. Higher laser powers produced megaelectron-volt energies, indeed, 500 MeV has been measured. There is agreement on the mechanism of relativistic self-focusing and the result of linear separation of ions according to their degree of ionization Z. This is a reasonable basis for accepting the two-dimensional detailed computation for the next higher laser powers for production of heavy ions with energies of 10 GeV or more (Fig. 12). The advantage of these ion pulses is that they are of high current (kiloam-

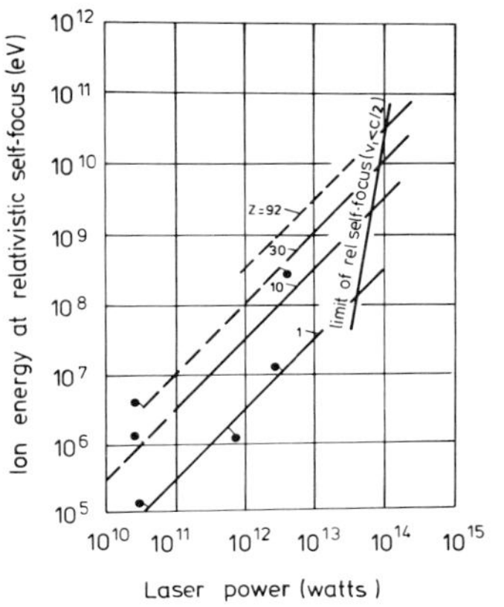

FIG. 12. Energy of ions from a target with relativistic self-focusing (calculated lines) as a function of laser power. There is no dependence on wavelength. The dependence on the ion charge number Z is restricted by the expected degree of ionization. The measured ion energies are shown by filled circles.

peres) and limited to very short times (picoseconds). This short time scale may be useful for measuring the properties of nuclear reactions and daughter products.

Another application of very intense laser beams is in laser beam weapons. The idea that laser beams could be used to destroy enemy targets originated in science fiction. The only difficulty was that the energy per laser pulse was very low, although the intensity was sufficient for plasma production and generation of electrical discharge phenomena. To appreciate the quantities involved, one should remember that the chemical combustion energy of 100 g of petrol is nearly 4 MJ.

Considering the next generation of lasers with pulses of microsecond duration in the 100-MJ range and of larger specifications, for instance, from pulsed nuclear reactor-pumped lasers (G. H. Miley, 1981) or from nuclear explosion-pumped X-ray lasers, there is indeed a possibility of reaching the technical aims if defense concepts required it. The use of advanced nonlinear optics for guiding and focusing of the beams is quite feasible with the most advanced developments in physics.

Laser-produced plasmas with electron quiver energies exceeding many megaelectron-volts are available now and may result in laser-induced nuclear reactions or in changes of beta decay (M. Scully), a method which is of interest for cleaning radioactive waste from nuclear fission reactors. The first change of nuclear states by lasers was produced by C. Yamanaka *et al.* (1979), where uranium-235 nuclei were excited to isomeric levels as detected by the subsequent gamma emission. Focusing PW-psec neodymium glass laser pulses into the interaction volume of 100 GeV electrons and positrons in the LEP accelerator will change the energy of the bottom mesons thanks to their lifetime of picoseconds. The non-Liouvillian energy gain as in the Boreliam experiment (Section VII) will provide further diagnostics between the B- and the decay mode particles.

Another potential new application of lasers is the concept for efficient production of antihydrogen. The production of antiprotons with present-day accelerators is quite inefficient. The Serpukhov accelerator produces 100 ng of antiprotons per year. Based on the energy input on the order of gigawatts, this means an efficiency of conversion of electrical energy into antimatter of 10^{-12}. Even if techniques for storing these antiprotons and combining them with positrons to form antihydrogen atoms and for their cooling and levitation in extreme vacuum are developed, the efficiency is so small that no application would justify the effort, thought it has been discussed for propulsion of spacecraft on very long distance missions (R. L. Forward, 1985).

In laser-produced plasmas at intensities five times the relativistic threshold, production of electron-positron pairs by the trident process is expected and may even have been achieved (J. W. Shearer *et al.*, 1974). The threshold for the production of antiprotons by the same trident mechanism for carbon dioxide laser radiation is near 10^{23} W/cm^2. These values may be achieved with present laser technology; for example, by relativistic self-focusing of 100 fsec pulses of 100 kJ. The advantage of this laser mechanism over the classical accelerator process is the density. The efficiency increases linearly with the density of the interacting gigaelectron-volt particles. The quivering of the protons in the case of the laser can be of the solid-state density; therefore, the efficiency can be 10 or more orders of magnitude larger than in present-day accelerator beams. These missing 10 orders of magnitude would raise the efficiency to 10% despite some losses by annihilation—a value where the production of antihydrogen, e.g., for propulsion of spacecraft, will be interesting. The highly relativistic koino and antielectrons and protons in the laser focus cannot be distinguished by their masses. As their "temperature" exceeds for *Greiner–Stöcker limit* of the Hagedorn theory of 10^{12} K, the laser then produces a state of protomatter.

V. Physics of Particle Beam Interaction with Targets

Although the physics of particle beams and their interaction with matter (solids, atoms, nuclei, elementary particles) goes back to the past century, beam interaction with essential destruction of the irradiated target dates back to the 1950s. Particle beam treatment is therefore older than the laser treatment. Nevertheless, the stream of development of these phenomena in physics was not so broad and turbulent as that of lasers.

A. Interaction of Electron Beams

The anomalous phenomenon in the treatment of materials with electron beams (after the purely classical processes of melting, recrystallization, and evaporation at low intensities, was a surprising deep penetration effect, while at conditions of even higher irradiance, an unexpected reduction of the penetration length was discovered too.

The classical penetration of electrons with energies of 100–150 keV in solids was determined by the Whiddington law and later quantum mechanically by the *Bethe-Bloch formula*. The penetration in usual materials was then on the order of 10 μm. However, on increasing the intensity of the electrons, say to 0.1 A, focusing to 10 μm diameter, and producing about 10^{10} W/cm^2 power densities (intensities), a deep penetration of the beam was observed which could be used for drilling holes and cutting microscopic profiles in materials. From 1 A on, the beam penetrated steel more than 2 cm and was used for welding.

This deep penetration effect is not yet understood. It can be analyzed only from the initial dynamics of melting the surface and generating a liquid funnel. The electron beam expels evaporated atoms out of its path, and the electrons move like a gas in the channel that is generated, with the counterpressure of the surrounding metal gas compensated dynamically by the electron gas of a density for nondegenerate states and possibly by a pressure given by the electrostatic field.

Another anomaly was observed when electron beams with a few orders of magnitude less current density than in the deep penetration effect and of 75 keV energy were used to irradiate silicon. In the evaporated silicon layers such a strong disturbance of the subcrystalline structure occurred that the optical absorption was changed strongly, not only in the defect range but also in the fundamental band absorption. The spectrum was shifted by 0.2 eV, indicating a basic change of the solid structure. It was remarkable that at a little higher irradiation intensity the evaporated layers were broken or cracked.

Another phenomenon observed with similar electron beam irradiation was the change of *n*-type to *p*-type silicon. For much lower irradiation intensities with an electron energy of 0.5 MeV, workers at Purdue University produced Frenkel defects in silicon, which correspond to the change from *n*- to *p*-type. Based on the epitaxial crystal energy, the generation of these defects by the light electrons knocking a silicon atom to an interstitial site required an electron energy of 200 keV, which was confirmed in the classical experiments at Purdue University in 1958.

It was surprising that the same effect could be achieved with highly intense irradiation with 75-keV electrons. From the specification of diode characteristics it was possible to see that from a threshold irradiation rate at a certain pulse duration onward, the rectification appeared, grew to a maximum, and disappeared at high rates. At longer electron beam pulses the characteristic curve was shifted to higher rates. This indicates that at least the decay may be a thermal effect of annealing of the defects.

These experiments of 1961 were repeated by several groups, with some proving the nonexistence of the effect and some reproducing the subthreshold defect generation (V. S. Vavilov *et al.*, 1975). Finally, subthreshold defect generation was confirmed and observed in other materials such as CdS, and a theory was developed by B. Ya. Yurkov (1966) that the intense electron beam excites a high density of plasmons. Their energy is greater than the energy for defect generation and may be exchanged in this way. It is remarkable that electron beam irradiation at doses similar to those required for subthreshold defect generation in crystals can be used for selective removal of photoresist films (R. M. Hardy, 1965). Subthreshold defect generation can also be used to produce low-cost solar cells made of polymers.

The other strangeness of the phenomena of high-intensity electron beam interactions is illustrated by experiments by Kern *et al.* (1973). Electron beams of 2 MeV, 0.5 MA, and 2 mm in diameter were fired onto solid targets, and the penetration depth was measured in the following way. With deuterated polyethylene as the target, the electrons produce nuclear fusion reactions as measured by the emission of fusion neutrons. When the thickness of the target was varied, the saturation value of the neutron emission corresponded to the penetration depth. This value was reduced to only 3 mm, whereas the Bethe-Bloch theory, in agreement with the measured transmissivity of electrons with very low current density, would permit a penetration of 13.5 cm or more, depending on additional channeling or weavon effects (J. C. Kelly and H. Nibb).

The remarkable reduction of the penetration of the intense electron beam was initially explained by numerical studies showing a turning around of the electrons and so forth. A straightforward explanation was possible by modifying the Bethe-Boch formula according to Bagge, using the electrostatic energy in the Debye sphere instead of the usual energy of solids (Hora *et al.*, 1974). The effect was then a collision process with the collective plasma electrons. Similar results showing reduced penetration of high-current electrons in agreement with the collective interaction theory were observed with 0.5-MeV electrons by S. Nakai (1978).

B. Interaction of Ion Beams

In ion beam interaction physics, one problem in material treatment was encountered (R. Hodgson *et al.*, 1980) when ion implantation into silicon was attempted at such a high beam irradiation intensity that, instead of producing the usual buried amorphous layers with internal stress and voids for subsequent annealing, the local heating in the silicon was so high (about 800°C) that the implantation, annealing, and recrystallization process took place in one step. This had the advantage that the stress and void problems could be overcome implicitly. However, experiments have not yet been performed with the necessary high ion beam intensities, and experiments with the available high-intensity ion beam sources from fusion experiments should be a next step.

In view of the problems mentioned before, it cannot be predicted with certainty whether the aim of producing high-quality *p-n* structures will be achieved. The difficulties of laser annealing should be a warning that unsolvable problems may be involved. For high-intensity ion beam implantation, however, the parameters are basically different and success may be possible. It has been estimated that the costs for producing multicrystalline silicon solar cells can be reduced by a factor of 10 or more, which might well lead to a change in the outlook for the economy of solar energy. The mechanism is of importance for microelectronics as well, as the ion beam can be concentrated precisely to submicroscopic dimensions.

The physics of ion beam interactions with targets such that high-energy plasmas are produced may imply difficulties and anomalous phenomena similar to those observed with laser interactions; these beams have not yet been explored to the same extent as laser beams. One long-standing problem, which goes back to the study of the self-sustained fusion combustion wave, concerns the stopping power (penetration depth) of energetic ions in high-temperature plasmas. The problem is that when the stopping power is treated in terms of individual collisions on the basis of the Fokker–Planck equation, the interaction with electrons is strongly reduced when the velocity of the fast particle, such as an alpha particle with an initial energy of 4 MeV, interacts with the faster electrons of a plasma at a temperature of 20 keV. The stopping lengths are then very long. The interaction with the ions is still important and leads to a reduction of the stopping length to about 70% or less. Another mechanism is the radiation transport in Marshack waves (J. Meyer-ter-Vehn and T. Yabe, 1985), which may dominate the propagation and dissipation of the energy. However, when the interaction of the energetic ions with the electrons is described by the collective mechanism of hitting the whole assembly of electrons in the Debye sphere—as in Bagge's modification of the Bethe–Bloch formula to understand the strong reduction of the penetration of intense MeV electrons—the stopping length of ions is reduced further to about 10% of the values in the Fokker–Planck case (Long and Tahir, 1986).

These open questions concerning the interaction of intense ion beams with plasmas were alluded to by J. H. Nuckolls (1978) when he was asked what stopping powers he used in his laser–fusion pellet codes. The answer given was that none of the then existing theories could be used and that only empirical values derived from large-scale fusion reactions were used. Direct experimental studies of the penetration of intense megaelectron-volt ion beams with dense high-temperature plasmas—produced by additional laser irradiation—were performed on a small scale only. It was remarkable that even for a plasma temperature of 30 eV (not the controversial 10 keV), the stopping length of the ions was reduced by about a factor of 2 (F. C. Young *et al.*, 1983).

Another basic problem that is not yet fully solved is the new type of nonlinear dynamics of the plasma irradiated by intense ion beams. Some first numerical steps have been taken but without solving or completely including the problems of the stopping power, reduced thermal conduction, electric double layers, and interpenetration of the energetic ions with those of the cold target. This type of nonlinear dynamics was the missing point when one of the classical errors in the history of fusion energy was made around 1950 [see remark after Eq. (5)].

To achieve controlled fusion energy, it was proposed that solid deuterium–tritium targets be irradiated with ~100-keV ion beams, as done when the first fusion reaction [Eq. (5)] was discovered and as used today as a commercial intense neutron source. This direction was favored by physicists including E. O. Lawrence, M. Oliphant, and W. Salibury. The counterargument made by theoreticians was that the cross section of a 100-keV deuterium ion with an electron (in the cold target) is 300 times larger than the cross section with a tritium nucleus for the desired fusion reaction. The ratio for the D–D reaction is even worse. The beam would then mostly lose energy to electrons and only a little for fusion reactions such that exothermal power generation would never be possible.

It was concluded that the deuterium and tritium nuclei as well as the electrons would have to have nearly the same temperature of some 10 million degrees so that the collision of ions would not cause undesired loss of the ion energy and only fusion reactions would remain. This led to the belief that controlled fusion in such thermonuclear plasmas would require confinement by magnetic fields (before the pellet concept was rediscovered in connection with the laser).

This conclusion is fully correct in physics, mathematics, and logics, but it is not the truth. What is wrong is the linear thinking, while nonlinearity arrives at the contrary.

While nothing needs to be changed in terms of the cross sections and hard numbers, the point has been missed that nonlinear physics will appear when the irradiated ion beams are of extreme intensity at the initially solid fusion target. There will be highly turbulent hydrodynamics with inhomogeneous heating of the target material, including the electrons, to conditions of the exothermal fusion reaction, including ablation and compressing, realizing the vision of E. O. Lawrence for beam fusion.

Experience with the laser and nonlinear physics has shown the error in too much linear thinking. The involvement of nonlinear physics may be the key to further understanding of the interaction of very intensive beams with matter.

VI. Applications of Particle Beams

A. Material Ttreatment

The use of electron or ion beams in materials technology has been touched on in the preceding discussions of the physics. Some of the significant successes will be mentioned here. Welding of 3-cm-thick steel with electron beams has been possible since 1959 (Steigerwald), and steel plates more than 25-cm thick can now be penetrated by electron beams and those 20-cm thick can be welded. There is interest in the possibility of welding without additional material and without oblique edges for filling inhomogeneous material between the steel plates as in the classical techniques. Electron beams (as well as laser beams) can simply weld "end on." Because of the quick solidification, the crystal structure in the welding zone is of high quality, almost the same as that in the original material (Fig. 13). High-quality welding of parts such as the blades in the turbines of jet engines or other kinds of turbines is possible.

Welding of materials such as tungsten and tantalum and of different materials such as metals and ceramics is possible. Only if the metals to be connected are chemically so different that a Hume–Rothery phase is produced is it not possible to produce a homogeneous connection between the parts to be joined.

The welding must usually be performed under vacuum. Electron beams engines have been developed where the beams go into air and vacuum steps are introduced between the entire beam generator and the outlet of the beam. Because of

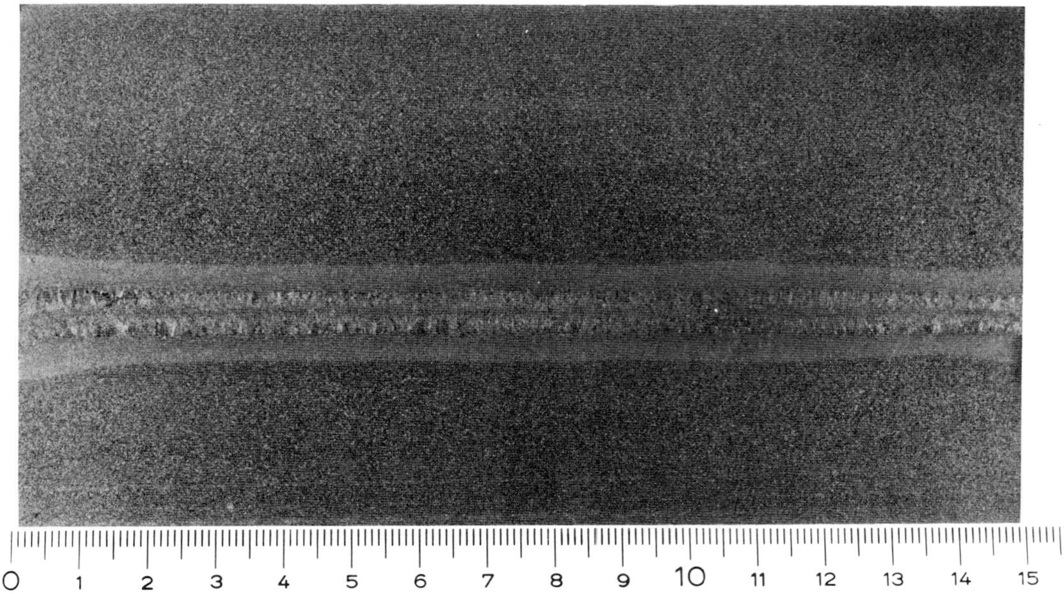

FIG. 13. Photomicrograph of the cut of an electron beam-welded part 15 cm thick. (Courtesy of F. Schwarz, Messer-Griessheim, Munich.)

the interaction with the air, the accuracy of the beam's interaction with the target in welding is not as precise as in a vacuum, but it is sufficient for many purposes, especially where a vacuum cannot be used. It was even possible to lead the electron beam into water for underwater welding (B. Schumacher, Ford Research Laboratory).

The general problem with all these electron beam machines is the generation of intense X rays. The persons involved must be protected by thick plates of lead or the whole operation must be done under remote control.

Particle beam–target interactions are also studied in connection with beam weapons. Transport of the beams through self-produced (or laser-produced) channels in the air is possible. For transport in the vacuum of upper space, the problems of beam bending by the earth's magnetic field must be taken into account. However, for direct shots this can be overcome if the particle beam energy is high enough. For example, present-day technology produces teraelectron-volt proton beams with pulses of less than 100 nsec duration and an energy of 10 MJ or more. By using relativistic focusing effects and pinching of such beams, their application for these strategic purposes seems possible. However, the interaction of such a focused beam of protons of such high individual energy with a target should lead to very unusual phenomena of destruction.

B. Fusion Energy

Since intense laser beams were used to ignite nuclear fusion fuel in irradiated pellets, the concept of using particle beams instead of lasers (F. Winterberg, 1971) has been considered. Particle beams provide nearly the same energy densities, but they have the advantage that there is a relatively well-developed technology for particle beam generation with highly efficient energy conversion (which is not the case for most lasers). In particular, the use of heavy ions could apply the very well developed technology of classical accelerators, adding techniques for non-Liouvillian phase space conditions by use of laser ionization of accelerated ions.

This heavy ion beam fusion concept uses the indirect drive of fusion fuel pellets, where the heavy ion beam is absorbed in a high-Z wire and its energy is converted into Planck radiation of a temperature of 200 to 500 eV in a hohlraum between a confining high-Z mantle and the pellet. This radiation of 10^{16} W/cm^2 intensity and 10^8 bars pressure is sufficient to compress, heat, and ignite the pellet (C. Rubbia). The physics of the conversion of the heavy ion beam energy in the wire is still in the stage of research since, for example, collective effects at very high beam intensities have to be clarified.

Electron or light ion beam fusion developments were undertaken on a large scale in the early 1970s at the Sandia Laboratory in Albuquerque, New Mexico (G. Yonas) and the Kurchatov Institute in Moscow (L. I. Rudakov), with related activities at numerous other places (e.g., Cornell University: R. N. Sudan, H. H. Fleischmann; Novosibirsk: D. D. Ryutov). Although progress was made in the development of new technology and such unexpected effects as the long-range tube transport of electron beams were discovered, the final aim of fusion by electron beams is being followed up today only at the Kurchatov facility. The Sandia project was changed to the use of ion beams.

While the electron beam interactions with targets of fusion material produced considerable numbers of fusion neutrons, the use of light ion beams instead yielded the most successful result to date on fusion gains achieved from controlled fusion reactions. The experiment was done by G. Cooperstein and co-workers at Naval Research Laboratory, and a large-scale extension of their approach is one of the alternatives now studied at Sandia Laboratories. The experiment consisted in the use of the GAMBLE diode (Fig. 6) with a 2 MW discharge between the electrodes filled with deuterium gas. The concave bending of the thin cathode caused a ballistic (free-falling) focusing of the 0.5 MA deuterium ion beam through a tube containing a low pressure of nitrogen for space charge neutralization such that the beam was focused to a 4-mm diameter. The irradiation of a deuterated polyethylene target resulted in the generation of 10^{13} fusion neutrons for an input energy of 30 kJ to the whole electric installation of the generated beam.

The "neutral beam fusion experiment" is the result of the Joint European Torus (JET) facility, where a toroidal, magnetically confined deuterium plasma is produced by an input of 5 MJ. This plasma of some kiloelectron-volt temperature is the target to which a neutral deuterium beam of 80 keV energy and about 1 sec duration is injected with an energy of 25 MJ. The resulting 4×10^{16} D–D fusion neutrons (B. Green, 1989) correspond to a record gain of 50% (converted to D–T). With this gain as well as with the gain from the afore-mentioned low-cost GAMBLE experiment, an energy producing fusion–fission hybrid reactor could be built, which just may be economic compared to light water reactors (Pfirsch and Schmitter, 1989).

The development should, however, be extended to arrive at the pure fusion reactor without fission as in the aforementioned laser fusion with pellets or in the particle beam fusion. These developments are obviously less mature than the laser fusion concept based on the ATHENA laser and a CASCADE reactor with a physics of high gain ignition proved by the Centruion-Halite underground tests. This provided an economic fusion power station.

VII. Mutual Interaction of Particle Beams with Laser Beams

Now that we have reviewed the interactions of laser and particle beams with targets, we discuss some physical aspects of the mutual interaction of intense laser beams with particle beams.

At this point an important technological crossing point of the fields should be mentioned, even though there is no immediate beam interaction. In microelectronics, in the surface of silicon crystals or in covering films of photoresist or similar material, submicroscopic patterns of rectangular or other forms are produced by irradiation with X-rays. The first problem in producing the masks is solved by electron beam drilling of slits in thin metal foils such that parallel slits with edge-to-edge distances down to 10 nm have been achieved. For the irradiation through these masks by intense and nearly pointlike X rays, the sources of laser-produced plasmas are used.

A. Intense Microwave Sources

Although there may be more examples of the kind mentioned here, it should be considered typical for laser beams to interact with intense electron beams to produce microwaves. In the search for a very powerful microwave source in the gigawatt range for the next generation of accelerators, the powerful electron emission from a Görlich photocathode (a Cs_3Sb cathode, as used in 70% of the multipliers of vacuum photocells) has been induced by irradiation with a train of picosecond pulses from a mode-locked neodymium glass laser after frequency doubling to green light. This had the advantage that the pulses had a very precise distance in the gigahertz range given by the optical cavity of the emitting laser. The emission of the photoelectrons was within a temporal broadening of less than 10 psec as clarified in the Forrester–Gudmundsen effect (1958). By using a grating as an anode through which most of the electrons could pass, an intense electronic current in a vacuum with gigahertz modulation was produced. This beam moved in a closed high-vacuum tube, called a Lasertron (Y. Fukushima, H. Kuroda, *et al.*, 1986), through a microwave cavity of a frequency identical to the modulation given by the frequency of the mode-locked laser pulses. As expected from an earlier prediction, there was an intense emission of microwaves. Their power up to 30 kW from a rather compact apparatus of a few centimeters cylindrical diameter increased as the 2.7th power of the anode voltage between the grid and the Görlich cathode.

The operation was limited only by discharges between the grid and the cathode. The high power law is expected to be extendable to the microwave emissions in the interesting high power range after suppression of the discharges.

B. Kapitza-Dirac and Schwarz-Hora Effect

A further example of the interaction of intense laser beams with intense electron beams is the Kapitza–Dirac effect (1932). It was predicted theoretically and consists of the generation of a high-intensity standing optical wave, as produced by the total reflection of a laser beam in vacuum. If an electron beam is transmitted perpendicular to the optical beam, the electrons are diffracted by the nodes and antinodes of the standing electromagnetic wave field. The essential mechanism is a coherent interaction of the Thomson scattering type.

Studies in the 1960s revealed the theoretical limitations and saturation and resulted in an oscillation-type modification of the Kapitza–Dirac effect for high laser intensities. Experimental confirmation must overcome the difficulty that the diffraction angle of the electrons is very small, given by the ratio of the de Broglie wavelength and the laser wavelength. To obtain reasonable results, the electron velocity must then be rather small. Of several attempts to measure the effect, none came to a positive or convincing result. Even Schwarz's most sophisticated use of grids in 1967, with slowing down and reacceleration of the electrons in the interaction area of the standing laser wave field, did not give unequivocal results, as can be seen from the kinks in the oscilloscope traces, which cannot be understood in terms of the natural properties of the near-Gaussian radial decay of the intensities of the optical and electron beams. Nevertheless, the effect may attract renewed attention from experimentalists with more advanced techniques in the future.

As a continuation of these attempts, combined with an idea of D. Gabor's, the following experiment was done. A 50-keV electron beam was crossed with a laser beam whose **E** vector oscillation was parallel to the electron beam, and a 100-nm-thick crystal of silicon dioxide in the crossing area caused an interaction of the electrons with the laser light in which the crystal provided the necessary balance of momentum transfer. The result was quantum modulation (in contrast to classical beating based on a new formulation of the correspondence principle for electromagnetic interaction) of the electron beam in such a way that the electron beam was modulated by the optical frequency (Schwarz–Hora effect, 1969).

The quantum modulation state then causes reemission of the optical frequency from a nonluminescent screen on which the modulated electron beam is incident. This was demonstrated in the color of the green argon laser that was used, and the electron diffraction pattern from the interaction with the quartz crystal was reproduced in the same spot locations as on a luminescent screen. The modulation process implies a coherent upshift and downshift of the energy of the electrons by multiples of the photon energy. Depending on the energy spread of the electron beam, the degree of modulation decays along the electron beam behind the quartz crystal. There was a further long-wavelength modulation with a length of about 1.7 cm which is a basic property of the second-order difference between optical and electron waves.

As there were some unusual arrangements in reproducing the initial experiment, it was of importance to reproduce the quantum modulation by another experiment in which, instead of the quartz crystal, nitrogen molecules were used for the momentum transfer. The quantum modulation could be seen immediately from the upshift and downshift of the electron energy by the energy of the laser photons first observed by D. Andrick and L. Langhans in 1976. Further studies by A. Weingartshofer showed higher multiples of the up- and down-shifts. It was even more interesting that in both experiments this modulation process did not change the scattering angle of the electrons; modulation by molecules was in the same beam direction as without modulation, and modulation by crystals produced Laue patterns at the same spot locations as those observed without the modulation. In the case of the molecules, the quantum modulation decays exponentially when the angle of polarization is changed from its maximum value. This has been explained theoretically in terms of a Bessel function expression. The same exponential decay was one of the curious unexplained earlier results when the quartz was used. The measurements with molecules were within the quantum range of the electromagnetic correspondence principle (Hora, 1986), and experiments by Weingartshofer *et al.* (1985) directly indicate the threshold of the correspondence principle where the lower intensity I than the threshold

$$I^* = \alpha\pi^2 c^3/2\lambda^3 = 1.66/\lambda^3 \tag{7}$$

is the quantum range where I^* is in watts per square centimeter and the wavelength of the electromagnetic radiation is in centimeters.

It should be noted that the long beating wavelength detected was longer than the classical value, whereas the relativistic correction should have resulted in a shorter than classical value. The longer value can be explained in a straightforward way from the dispersion model of Varshalowich and Diakonov, using the Dirac equation and selecting the Peierls dispersion (rather than the Landau–Lifshitz dispersion or other controversial formulations). The values reported by Schwarz could not have been influenced by this sophisticated knowledge as well as his exponential polarization dependence to justify his results apart from the full agreement with the later and fully independent molecule scattering results. The problem of coherence in the modulation process has been studied by P. W. Hawkes in 1983.

The emission of the optical frequency at demodulation has not yet been reproduced directly. It also is difficult to understand the mechanism of this transfer of a quantum state by the electrons, which seems to be a further new property of the wave picture of particles. However, indirect proof of this demodulation or transfer has been given by the observation of a strong microwave amplification in a nonequilibrium plasma; this can be described not by stimulated effects but by a transfer of energy as a modulated state between collisions of the electrons in the microwave-irradiated plasma. Another transfer mechanism by quantum modulated states in large series is the result of the $1/f$ noise, which can be derived from basic principles and formulated by an expression determined by the fine structure constant (Handel effect).

A special interaction of electron beams of very high energies with lasers of very high intensity results in stimulated Compton scattering, which can be understood as a high energy extension of the Kapitza–Dirac effect. It has been shown by B. G. Danly, R. C. Davidson, J. S. Wurtele, and others (1988) that the energy of the scattered photons (index s) is given by the energy of the laser photons (index L) given by the relativistic factor $\gamma = (1 - v^2/c^2)^{-1/2}$ of the electrons

$$\hbar\omega_s = 2\gamma^2\hbar\omega_L \tag{8}$$

where ω is the radian frequency and $\hbar$ is Planck's constant divided by 2π. Using a photon energy of 5 eV (of the excimer lasers) and teraelectron-volt electrons results in 37 TeV photons. Although the cross sections for these scattering mechanisms are extremely small (as known from the simpler case of Thomson scattering), the nonlinear deviations at very high laser intensities and very high electron currents and energies may reach interesting gains for applications in high energy physics.

C. Free Electron Lasers

Although this article is not intended to discuss laser mechanisms in detail, the free electron lasers represent basic aspects of high-intensity electron beam and laser beam interaction. A related interaction experiment with intense carbon dioxide laser beams and intense relativistic 40-MeV electron beams was done in connection with the Schwarz–Hora effect (R. H. Pantell, M. A. Piestrup, *et al.*, 1975). With the same high-quality 40-MeV electron beam at Standford, J. M. J. Meady *et al.* (1976) carried out an interaction experiment between a nearly parallel CO_2 laser beam and the relativistic electron beam moving through a wiggler field of counter-polarized magnetic fields as a laser amplifier. The recoil for the interaction of the electrons with the laser is given by the magnetic field, and the basic mechanism involved is the nonlinear force [Eq. (1)], used in the most simplified from as the ponderomotive force, as first elaborated by P. Sprangle (Naval Research Laboratory) and Maria Zales-Caponi (TRW). By adding an optical cavity for the laser radiation, the initial amplification of the laser beam at the cost of electron energy was discovered by J. M. J. Meady *et al.* (1976). Without the initial optical beam, it was possible through the action of the optical cavity along the electron beam in the magnetic wiggler field to produce a free electron laser generator (oscillator) for a 10-μm wavelength—though any continuously selectable wavelength should be possible (J. M. J. Meady *et al.*, 1977).

It should be noted that one model of the laser action can also be based on a coherent second-order correlation, similar to the Hanbury–Brown–Twiss effect, as shown by S. Pellegrini (1978). The free electron laser oscillator was difficult to reproduce. It took 3 years for the same team at Stanford just to reproduce the effect of laser emission at the 10-μm wavelength. As the operation of free electron lasers goes as the square of the wavelength (more precisely, the 3/2 power of the laser wavelength and the 1/2 power of the wiggler field wavelength), operation in the desired shorter-wavelength visible spectrum is much more difficult. It took great effort at Saclay with intense highly relativistic electron beams to produce for the first time free electron laser radiation in the visible range (green and further on) in 1984.

In addition to the wiggler field free electron laser with nearly parallel laser and electron beams, another type of free electron laser amplifier without a wiggler field is possible with nearly perpendicularly interacting optical and electron beams. The inverse experiment was performed by B. W. Boreham *et al.* (1979), where a laser beam was focused into a low-density helium gas. The maximum intensity of the neodymium glass laser was first 10^{15} W/cm^2 and 10^{16} W/cm^2 in a later experiment. The generated electrons were expelled radially from the center of the laser beam by the nonlinear force, where, according to the theory, half of the energy of oscillation was transformed into kinetic energy, with the maximum values of 100 or (in the later case) 1000 eV corresponding to the maximum kinetic energy of quivering at the maximum focus intensity.

Closer analysis of the phenomenon disclosed difficulties in the exact description in terms of the nonlinear force and the quiver drift of the electron within the radially decaying fields. The mistake in the usual analysis was to take the electric and magnetic field of the laser beam as that of plane linear polarized waves with a radial Gaussian or other decay. This field does not exactly follow Maxwellian equations. For the treatment it was necessary to derive the longitudinal components of the laser field starting from the initially truncated plane wave field in order to obtain nonlinear forces in agreement with the measurements. The appearance of longitudinal components of electromagnetic radiation in vacuum seems anomalous as the transversality of electromagnetic waves is a special triumph of Maxwell's theory; this is valid only for infinitely plane waves. For beams the longitudinal components are phase shifted by 90°, preventing Poynting vector components in radial directions and resulting in a concave profile corresponding to the angle of internal diffraction.

It is remarkable how such a small longitudinal component changed the theoretical result from negative to positive. This shows that to derive correct predictions the nonlinear theory requires completeness and correctness of the linear theory even more than does the linear theory itself.

Reviewing the experiment of Boreham *et al.* and being aware of the complex theoretical implications, it was evident that the radially emitted electrons had taken optical energy from the beam through a complicated nonlinear absorption process. The inverse experiment, firing electrons into a laser beam and converting its translational energy into (coherent) optical energy, was of interest. For this purpose it was necessary to work with laser pulses and to use the switching-on and -off mechanisms of the pulses and the conversion of the translational energy of the electrons into oscillation energy including the necessary forward shift of the electrons. This shift turned out to describe the balance of the momentum for the increased optical energy in the laser pulse, and simultaneously proved the correctness of the Klima–Petrzilka model of the switching process.

The amplification of this "lateral injection free electron laser" (LIFEL) is again dependent on the square of the wavelength and is of interest for present-day high-intensity electron beam densities in the far-infrared optical range. Another problem is the space charge effect of the electrons. One solution is to inject small solid-state particles, e.g., cluster beams, instead of electrons. In this case this very efficient (80%) laser amplifier has excellent amplification values in the visible and UV range and even acceptable values in the X-ray range, where the injection of large numbers of clusters is needed.

VIII. Concluding Remarks

I have tried to show how the developments of high-intensity laser and particle beams in the past 30 years have provided many new tools in technology and led to the discovery of numerous interesting new phenomena in physics. A general aspect of the whole direction in physics is the basic experience of nonlinear physics. This not only describes processes which are not dealt with in linear physics, but also requires a more precise knowledge of linear physics and a more critical revision of the basic laws than the treatment of linear physics permits.

This was demonstrated by the example that the Maxwellian exact formulation of optical beams with the then necessary (sic!) longitudinal optical fields was the only basis for arriving at correct predictions of the nonlinear force action of radial emission of electrons from laser beams. Another example is the historical approach to fusion energy by driving the reaction in solid pellets by irradiation with high-intensity particle beams; linear considerations forbid this concept and lead to the simplified but technically complex concept of magnetic confinement, whereas considerations of the nonlinearity at very high beam intensity with all kinds of plasma dynamics and turbulence lead to a straightforward solution with beams. This type of conceptual consideration may be extended from the field of nonlinear beam physics to all fields of physics as a new horizon in physical discovery.

Bibliography

Ahlstrom, H. G. (1982). "Physics of Laser Fusion." Nat. Tech. Service, Springfield, Virginia.

Campbell, E. M. (1991). Recent results from the NOVA program at LLNL. *Laser and Particle Beams* **9**(1), 209.

Cicchitelli, L., *et al.* (1990). Acceleration of electrons by moving of laser fields with dynamic superposition. *IEEE J. Quantum Electronics* **26,** 1833.

Cicchitelli, L., *et al.* (1990). Longitudinal field components of laser beams in vacuum. *Phys. Rev.* **A43,** 3727.

Eliezer, S., *et al.* (1989). Double layers in laser produced plasmas. *Physics Reports* **172,** 339.

Eliezer, S., Ghatak, A. K., and Hora, H. (1986). "Introduction to the Equations of State." Cambridge Univ. Press, London and New York.

Hora, H., and Miley, G. H. (eds) (1988, 1992). "Laser Interaction and Related Plasma Phenomena," Vols. 7, 8, 9, and 10. Plenum, New York.

Hora, H., Min, G. Eliezer, S. Lalousis, P., Pease, R. S., and Szichman, H. (1989). On surface tension in plasma. *IEEE Trans. Plasma Sci.* **PS-17,** 284.

Hora, H., Min, G. Cicchitelli, L., Kasotakis, G., Miley, G. H., and Stening, R. J. (1990). Leading role of laser fusion and its advances by volume ignition and by pulsation free direct drive. "Laser Interaction and Related Plasma Phenomena," Vol 9, p. 95–123. Plenum, New York.

Hora, H. (1991). "Plasmas at High Temperature and Density." Springer, Heidelberg.

Manes, K. R., *et al.* (1985). Novette facility: activation and experimental results. *Laser and Particle Beams* **3,** 173–188.

Miller, R. B. (1983). "Particle Beam Physics." Plenum, New York.

Nakai, S. (1989). Pellet and implosion scaling. *Laser and Particle Beams* **7,** 711.

Nuckolls, J. H. (1982). The feasibility of inertial confinement fusion. *Physics Today* **35**(9), 23.

Pfirsch, D. and Schmitter, K.-H. (1989). On the economic prospects of nuclear fusion with tokamaks. *Fushion Technology* **15,** 1471.

Rubbia, C. (1991). On heavy ion accelerators for inertial confinement fusion. IAEA Tech. Cttee., Osaka, April 1991; CERN Rept. PPE/91-117.

VanDevender, J. P., *et al.* (1985). Proof-of-principle experiment for the light ion beam fusion facility BPFA II, *Laser and Particle Beams,* **3,** 92–106.

Yamanaka, C., and Nakai, S. (1986). High gain laser fusion. *Nature* **319,** 757.

Yonas, G. (1979). Fusion power with particle beams, *Scientific American* **239** (5), 40.

LASER PULSATIONS, DYNAMICAL

Neal Abraham *Bryn Mawr College*

GLOSSARY

Beat frequency: Modulation frequency of the laser intensity, which is the difference between two optical frequencies found for the optical field.

Chaos: Irregular fluctuations resulting from deterministic nonlinear interactions.

Dynamics: Deterministic evolution.

Laser: Combination of an optical resonator and a medium that can store energy and amplify light over some range of wavelengths.

Mode: Particular solution for a resonant wave pattern in the laser resonator that corresponds to a particular optical frequency.

Mode locked: Operating condition for which modes have fixed amplitudes, equal spacings in frequency, and fixed phase differences.

Nonlinear: Proportional to some power of the variable or to the product of two variables. Nonlinear laser medium—the amplification by the medium is not simply a constant times the intensity of the light. Nonlinear equations: each variable depends on powers or products of variables.

Period doubling: Change of a periodic pulsing pattern to one that takes twice as long (twice as many pulses) to repeat.

Population inversion: Stored energy in a laser medium by having more atoms (molecules) in the relevant high-energy state than in the relevant low-energy state. This ratio of the two populations is inverted with respect to the usual thermodynamic equilibrium conditions.

Q switching: Modulation of the amount of light energy lost on transiting the laser cavity. A common way to excite mode locking or giant pulses.

Quasiperiodic pulsing: Pulsing governed by two independent frequencies.

Rabi oscillation: Oscillating extraction and storage of energy in the laser medium by a constant intensity light field.

Relaxation oscillation: Oscillatory exchange of energy between the laser medium and the light field in the laser cavity.

Slowly varying amplitude approximation: It is assumed the light can be described as a wave of nearly fixed frequency and wavelength, which has an amplitude that changes slowly with respect to the period of the optical frequency of the wave.

Spontaneous emission: Random incoherent light emitted by the laser medium.

Stimulated emission: Light emitted by the laser medium in the presence of another field. The stimulated emission matches the present field in wavelength, phase, and direction.

Stochastic: Random fluctuations such as resulting from a large number of independent effects.

Lasers may emit their intense, highly directional and coherent beams either at a constant rate [sometimes called continuous wave (cw)] or in a pulsed fashion. Pulsations are often of greater use than constant intensity, so the history of lasers is replete with efforts to both understand spontaneous pulsations and regulate them. In the last few years, it has become clear that many laser pulsations originate in internal dynamical processes and cannot be attributed to internal or external noise or simply to the con-

ENCYCLOPEDIA OF PHYSICAL SCIENCE
AND TECHNOLOGY, VOL. 8

structive interference of emissions at the resonant frequencies of the laser cavity. In this respect, the recent discoveries and studies of laser pulsations draw on the language of the relatively new field of nonlinear dynamics and descriptions of behavior in terms of dynamical chaos or turbulence. This provides an alternative perspective to the more conventional engineering view of lasers as devices and gives new insight into how laser pulsations can be generated or controlled. [*See* LASERS; ULTRAFAST LASER TECHNOLOGY.]

The key features of a laser are a nonlinear medium (in which energy can be stored and from which it can be extracted in the form of light) and a resonant cavity formed by mirrors that recirculate a portion of the emitted light for further interaction with the medium. As the recirculated light is an electromagnetic wave, it will build up only if it constructively interferes with the field from previous round trips in the cavity and only if the medium can be stimulated to emit at the wavelength of the circulating field. Usually, the range of possible emission wavelengths of the medium is only a small fraction of the most resonant wavelength. Typical values range from 10^{-5} for gas lasers and 10^{-3} for solid-state lasers to as much as 10^{-2} for dye lasers. Nevertheless, because optical wavelengths are small (of order 10^{-6} m), there is the possibility that more than one wavelength within the resonance bandwidth of the medium is also resonant with the laser cavity. The simplest cavity resonance condition is given by the requirement that the length of the laser cavity equal a multiple of the wavelength. If the laser cavity is about 1 m in length then the cavity resonance frequencies are spaced by only 10^{-6} of their absolute value. The number of cavity resonance frequencies interacting with the medium provides the basis for a fundamental classification of laser operation as being either single mode or multimode.

I. Characteristic Times for Laser Processes

A laser cannot be imagined as involving an instantaneous process of turning a control signal into light. Instead, because emission involves energy transfer from a source to an atomic or molecular medium and then to light and because the light energy can be reabsorbed by the emitting medium, there is a dynamical response with associated delays that can reshape or distort any control signal or lead to spontaneous pulsations.

Four characteristic times exist for laser pulsations. The first is the round-trip time in the laser cavity (the inverse of the "mode-beating" frequency between adjacent cavity modes), which is most important if the light energy is compressed in time to a pulse that is much shorter than the time for it to travel once around the path defined by the laser mirrors. Such pulsations are characteristic of multimode operation. The second time is the period of oscillatory energy exchange, called relaxation oscillations, between the energy of the light field in the laser cavity and the energy stored in the medium. The third is the period of coherent modulation of the emission of light by the medium that occurs in the presence of a strong and constant intensity light field. These oscillations are known as *Rabi oscillations*. The fourth is the characteristic time of external perturbations of the laser resulting from modulation of the rate of excitation of the medium, the length of the laser cavity, the energy loss from the laser, or some other parameter of the system. The possibility of having sustained pulsations is enhanced whenever two or more of the characteristic processes have nearly equal frequencies.

The general focus here will be on dynamical processes in the laser or on its response to the time dependence of the external control of the laser. The first sections deal with single-mode pulsations, the phenomena under which a single resonant mode of the laser field displays slow modulation of its amplitude. The later sections consider how the intermode beat frequencies lead to complex modulation of the laser or how they can be created by external controls. A few simple examples are discussed first.

A. Mode Beating

When the laser operation includes modes of different wavelengths, the total intensity is modulated in time as illustrated by the following example. Suppose frequencies f_1 and f_2 correspond to two modes given by

$$f_1 = c/\lambda_1, \qquad f_2 = c/\lambda_2$$

where λ_1 and λ_2 are the wavelengths and c is the speed of light. Then, the total electric field at a fixed point in space in the output of the laser can be written

$$E(t) = E_1 \cos(2\pi f_1 t + \phi_1) + E_2 \cos(2\pi f_2 t + \phi_2)$$

where E_1 and E_2 are the amplitudes of the two modes. The total intensity at this point is given by the square of the electric field and can be written as

$$\begin{aligned} I(t) = {} & E_1^2 \left[\tfrac{1}{2} + \tfrac{1}{2}\cos(4\pi f_1 t + 2\phi_1)\right] \\ & + E_2^2 \left[\tfrac{1}{2} + \tfrac{1}{2}\cos(4\pi f_2 t + 2\phi_2)\right] \\ & + E_1E_2 \cos[2\pi(f_1 - f_2)t + \phi_1 - \phi_2] \\ & + E_1E_2 \cos[2\pi(f_1 - f_2)t + \phi_1 - \phi_2] \end{aligned}$$

Since the optical frequencies are very high (of order 10^{14} Hz), no detector can provide an electronic output at these frequencies. Instead, it must average over oscillations at $2f_1$, $2f_2$, and $f_1 + f_2$. The possible detected signal denoted by I is then

$$\begin{aligned} I(t) = {} & \tfrac{1}{2}E_1^2 + \tfrac{1}{2}E_2^2 \\ & + E_1E_2 \cos[2\pi(f_1 - f_2)t + \phi_1 - \phi_2] \end{aligned}$$

The result shows intensity oscillations at the frequency that is the difference between the frequencies of the two modes. If the modes have the same transverse spatial pattern, then the period of these pulsations corresponds to the time for the light in the laser cavity to make one round trip. Much of the multimode pulsation phenomena can be understood from simple generalizations of this example, as will be discussed in Section III.

B. Relaxation Oscillations

The relaxation oscillation of energy exchange between the optical field and the laser material is damped in most laser systems and thus can typically be observed only if the laser is switched in some way. Then the laser restores itself to a steady, time-independent operation after an oscillatory transient. An example for a NdP_5O_{14} laser is shown in Fig. 1. These pulsations occur only if the average rate of decay of the field in the empty laser cavity is greater than the decay rate for the energy stored in the medium. Many lasers exhibit this property, including other solid-state lasers (ruby, Nd: glass, Nd: YAG); many low-pressure molecular lasers, such as (CO_2, N_2O, CO, and NO); and semiconductor lasers.

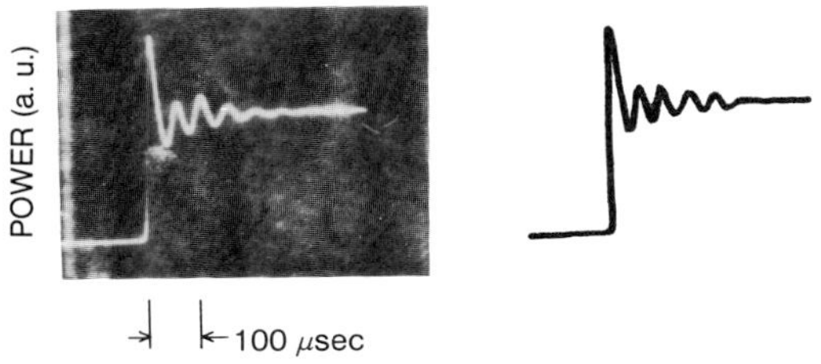

FIG. 1. Damped oscillatory transient in the output of a NdP_5O_{14} laser at 1.3 μm after an abrupt switch in the otherwise constant excitation of the laser. [Reprinted with permission from W. Klische, H. R. Telle, and C. O. Weiss (1984). *Opt. Lett.* **9**, 561.]

II. Single-Mode Pulsations

A. Homogeneously Broadened Lasers

The classic model studied by laser theorists for spontaneous pulsations in a single-mode laser is that for a simple medium made of a collection of identical two-level atoms. First introduced by Uspenskiy and Oraevsky in 1963 and popularized in the Western literature by Haken, it has been extensively studied and has been shown to be practically equivalent to a model developed by Lorenz to describe convective turbulence in fluids. Hence, the Haken–Lorenz model is of special interest because it is one of the simplest models rooted in physical reality that has irregular pulsation solutions of the type known as dynamical chaos. In this model, the laser operates with a constant intensity output for a range of excitation levels reaching from the threshold value needed for laser operation to a value 10 or 20 times higher. Above this second threshold, the laser output spontaneously changes to chaotic pulsations. If the laser cavity is slightly detuned from resonance with the medium, the pulsations become more periodic, showing an inverse period-doubling cascade before becoming periodic and then disappearing in favor of stable laser intensity for large enough detunings. The origin of this spontaneous modulation can be thought of as a matching between the relaxation oscillations and the coherent Rabi oscillations. Despite (or because of) the simplicity of this model, the minimum conditions for reaching the second laser threshold have been difficult to achieve experimentally. The decay rate of the laser field in the cavity must be larger than the sum of the decay rates of the population inversion and the atomic polarization—called "the bad cavity condition." This typically requires a relatively lossy cavity because the material polarization usually relaxes very quickly, and then one must have sufficient excitation of the medium to have optical amplification to offset these losses. The stringency of these conditions made it seem for more than 20 yr after the model was developed that it could not be achieved for any laser material. Quite recently, however, Weiss and co-workers at the PTB in the Federal Republic of Germany have demonstrated that optically pumped FIR lasers (discussed further below) can closely approximate the predicted behavior of the Lorenz–Haken model as shown in Fig. 2.

B. Inhomogeneously Broadened Lasers

Perhaps the easiest spontaneous single-mode pulsations to observe experimentally are those in inhomogeneously broadened lasers as first reported by Casperson and Yariv in 1974. In 1978, Casperson outlined a clever intuitive picture for the origin of these pulsations. The single mode of the laser interacts with only those atoms whose resonant frequencies are close to the laser frequency while other atoms are largely unaffected. The number of these atoms is depleted by the strong field. The missing atoms in a narrow frequency range near the laser frequency cause the index of refraction (and hence the speed of light and the wavelength of light in the medium) to vary rapidly with frequency. The result is that weak fields at nearby frequencies can have the same wavelength as the laser mode and hence they are also resonant, and, having gain from undepleted atoms, they grow. The resulting beat frequencies between the sidebands and the original frequency cause intensity pulsations. Complex patterns of periodic and chaotic intensity patterns are observed for excitations only a few times above the lasing threshold. Samples of experimental results and numerical solutions of a theoretical model are shown in Fig. 3. More recently more formal numerical and analytical solutions of models and detailed experiments have expanded the understanding of spontaneous pulsations in these lasers in both ring and standing wave geometries.

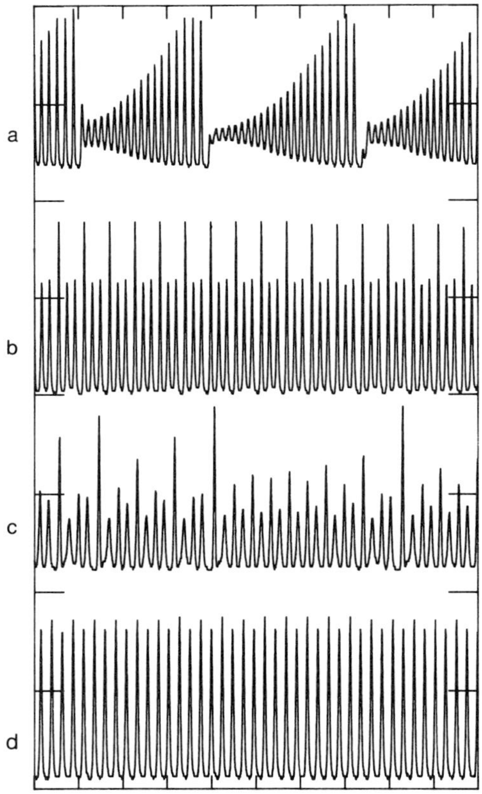

FIG. 2. Intensity pulsations from an optically pumped NH_3 laser at 81 μm showing behavior emulating that predicted for the single-mode homogeneously broadened laser. (a) Irregular Lorenz-like spiral chaotic pulsations for a resonant cavity; (b) period-three pulsations for a small detuning; (c) period-doubling chaos; and (d) period-two pulsations with increasing detuning. (Courtesy of C. O. Weiss.)

C. Optically Pumped Users

The dynamics of optically pumped lasers have been intensively studied since 1984 when Weiss and Klische proposed that they might be used to achieve the Haken–Lorenz model of a laser with a homogeneously broadened two-level material. Theoretical work shows that it is hard to justify a two-level model when the upper lasing level is not incoherently excited but rather is pumped by a constant laser intensity from a lower (nonlasing) level. Three-level models are inherently more complex than two-level ones and the various types of dynamical pulsations that are predicted include many more periodic pulsations

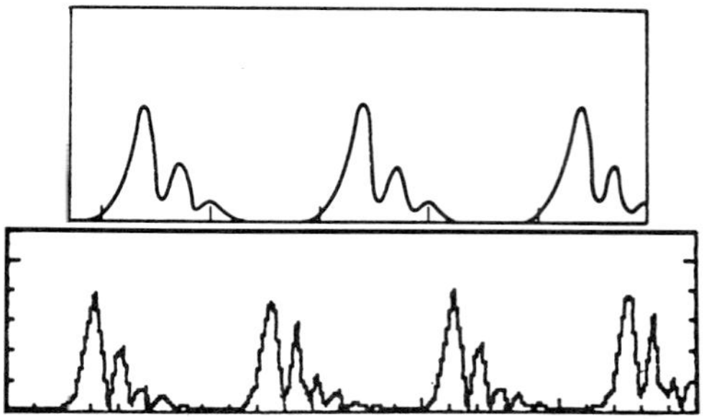

FIG. 3. Intensity pulsation patterns from experiments and numerical modeling for a Xenon laser at 3.51 μm. [Reprinted with permission from L. W. Casperson (1978). *IEEE J. Quantum Electron.* **QE-8,** 756. Copyright © 1978 IEEE.]

and types of pulsations not found in the Haken–Lorenz model. Many of these features have been found in work with far infrared and mid-infrared lasers in the range of 12 to 400 μm for which the upper level is pumped by such molecular lasers as CO_2. Periodic pulsing is frequently observed, and the transition with increasing excitation from stable laser operation is noted for the appearance of periodic pulsations (at about the Rabi and relaxation oscillation frequencies) followed by period doubling to chaos. Surprisingly, despite the difficulty of theoretical justification, it does appear that experimental behavior remarkably similar to the predictions of the simpler two-level model can be achieved in some of these lasers (see Section II, A).

D. Lasers with Saturable Absorbers

For the wide class of lasers that do not spontaneously generate single-mode pulsations, it is possible to induce such behavior by adding an optically absorbing medium inside the laser cavity. The key feature of the absorber is that it must be bleachable, that is, it must become more transparent upon illumination with sufficient light. In this case, it is easy to show that lasers which would otherwise exhibit only transient damped relaxation oscillations will, instead, provide sustained trains of pulses. The pulsing frequency can be approximately that of the relaxation oscillations (if the absorber has a fast recovery time) or at some mean between the relaxation oscillation rates of the laser medium and absorbing medium separately (if the absorber relaxes more slowly). Pulsing of this type has been found in ruby lasers, molecular gas lasers with other absorbing gases, and semiconductor lasers with impurities, damaged regions or separate subsections of the material acting as the absorber. Samples of this behavior are shown in Fig. 4. This method of inducing pulsations is sometimes called *passive Q switching:* passive because the dynamics occur within the laser itself and are not driven from the outside, and Q switching as the overall quality of the laser cavity, as governed by its losses, is changed by the saturable opacity of the absorber.

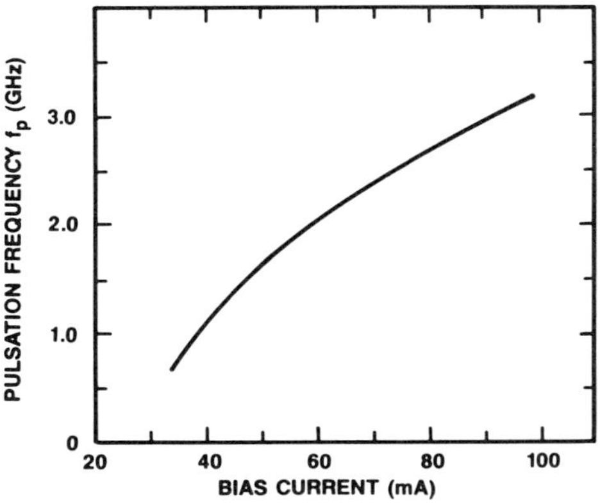

FIG. 4. Frequency of sustained pulsations at the relaxation oscillation frequency, induced in a semiconductor laser by the presence of saturable absorbers from proton-bombardment damage. [Reprinted from M. Kuznetsov, D. Z. Tsang, J. N. Walpole, Z. L. Lau, and E. P. Ippen (1987). *Appl. Phys. Lett.* **51,** 895.]

E. Modulation

Modulation of the excitation or loss of a laser at a frequency close to the relaxation oscillation

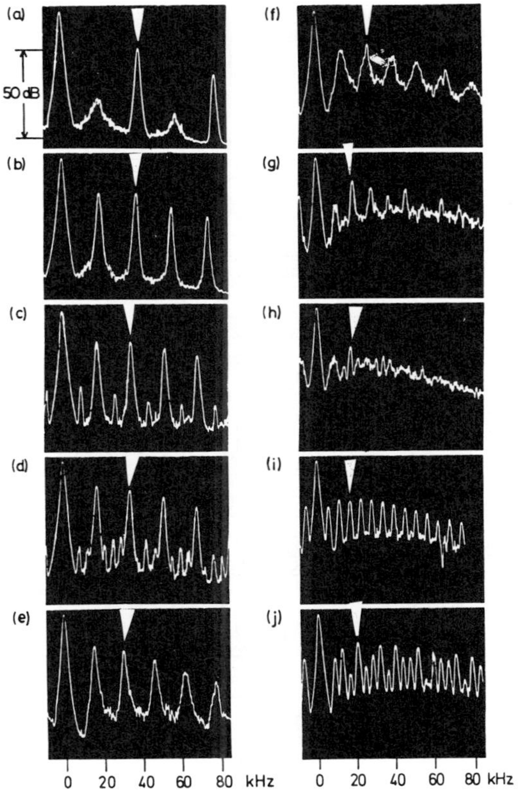

FIG. 5. Spectra of intensity of pulsations for modulation of the excitation of the solid-state laser in Fig. 1 showing period doubling (subharmonics) to chaos (h) and period-3 and period-5 windows. The modulation frequency is marked by an arrow. [Reprinted with permission from W. Klische, H. R. Telle, and C. O. Weiss (1984). *Opt. Lett.* **9,** 561.]

frequency is an *active* way to induce sustained pulsations. Long used since the work of Helleman in the early 1960s as a way to generate regular Q-switched pulses, it has more recently been shown by Arecchi and others that it is a convenient way to achieve period doublings in the pulsations or chaos. The specific response of the laser is quite sensitive to detuning of the modulation frequency from the relaxation frequency or to changes in the degree of modulation. Sample results are shown in Figs. 5 and 6 for modulation of CO_2 and solid-state lasers. Generally, it is found that modulation of the loss of the laser (with an electro-optic modulator, for example) is much more effective in generating complicated pulsation patterns than is modulation of the laser excitation.

Because the response of the laser and the interactions of the field and the lasing material are nonlinear, the laser will also resonantly respond when the modulation frequency is a harmonic or subharmonic of the relaxation oscillation frequency. This is obvious from some of the results of Fig. 5. The optimum frequency for resonant response also shifts somewhat depending on the amplitude of the modulation, another common effect in nonlinear systems. Winful and Chen in 1984 combined the intracavity absorber (making a free-running laser that pulsed) and modulation to find a variety of quasiperiodic and locked phenomena in a semiconductor laser with locking occurring for many different rational ratios of the two frequencies.

F. Injection Locking

An important way to stabilize the amplitude, frequency, and phase of a laser is to *seed* it by injecting a portion of light from another laser. When successful in slaving the injected oscillator to the master oscillator, this method is useful for achieving stronger signals or high spatial and temporal coherence in arrays of lasers. However, if the injected signal is not large enough compared to that of the free-running slave laser, locking will not occur. Instead the free-running slave laser field and the injected signal combine to form a modulated intensity which then drives the nonlinear dynamics of the slave laser. Some-

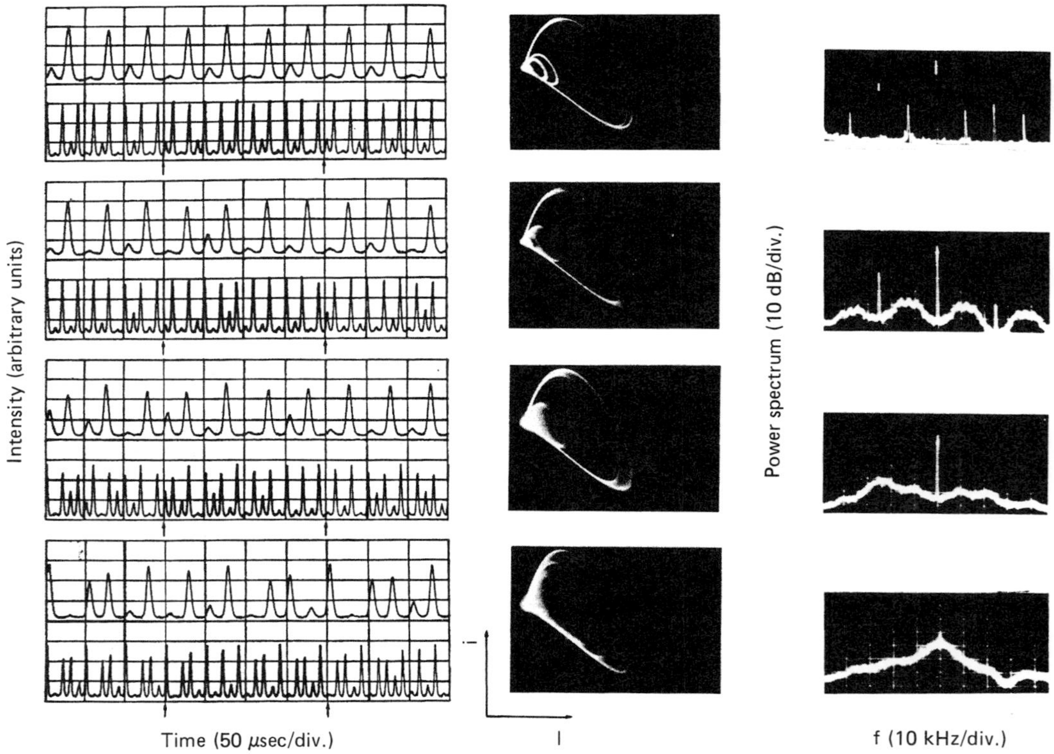

FIG. 6. Periodic and chaotic pulsations from the modulation of the loss of a CO_2 laser (time traces, phase portraits, spectra). [Reprinted with permission from R. Meucci, A. Poggi, F. T. Arecchi, and J. R. Tredicce (1988). *Opt. Commun.* **65**, 151.]

times this results in no more than the simple beat frequency (effectively no interaction). However, especially if the beat frequency is close to the relaxation oscillation frequency, the pulsations that result are much like the Q switching induced spiking in the intensity. On closer examination, one can observe that the frequency and phase of the slave laser nearly lock to the master oscillator, and then rather suddenly the phase of the slave laser slips by 2π and nearly locked conditions resume. While not yet of great technological interest, the case of not-quite-locked interaction of two laser oscillators has provided rich patterns of periodic and chaotic pulsations.

III. Multimode Pulsation

A. Bidirectional Ring Laser

In a standing wave laser, the forward and backward going waves are not independent because they are connected by reflection at the mirrors. In contrast, the forward and backward waves in a ring laser are less strongly coupled, interacting only through their mutual drawing of energy from the single lasing medium. If the laser is rotated about an axis perpendicular to the plane of the ring cavity, the forward and backward waves have different resonant frequencies for the same mode number (same number of wavelengths). This frequency difference can be detected by combining the outputs of two waves. The beat frequency provides the basis of laser gyroscopes now used in advanced guidance systems. In practical devices, it is found that if the frequency difference is too small the modes couple strongly enough to lead either to frequency locking or to irregular dynamical pulsations. Usually this is attributed to scattered light from one mode that acts as an injected signal for the other mode.

Even in the absence of backscattering, the two beams are coupled strongly through interaction in the medium. Not only do the modes compete for the available energy stored in the medium, but the standing wave interference pattern of the two waves saturates the medium more strongly at points of constructive interference and less strongly where there is destructive interference. The resulting corrugated pattern in the medium acts like a coherent scatterer and reflects each wave into the other.

In some cases, the grating is not important because the population either diffuses quickly or naturally relaxes rapidly. In these cases, usually one mode dominates the other, although the relative dominance can be inverted, and switches can be induced by noise or other disturbances. When the grating lasts a relatively long time, the modes can dynamically interact leading to regular and chaotically irregular pulsations. Samples of pulsations predicted and observed for such lasers are shown in Fig. 7. The fast modulation is typically the residual of relaxation oscillations, and the slower switching depends on the population inversion recovery rate and on the cavity detuning.

B. Mode Locking

Short pulses are most easily generated by the constructive interference of many equally spaced modes of the same spatial pattern. Then, the height of each pulse depends on the square of the number of modes, and its time duration is approximately the time for light to make one round trip in the laser cavity divided by the number of modes. The interval between output pulses is the time for the pulse formed in the laser to circulate once in the cavity. However, because the modes interact with the same medium, they compete with each other to some degree and one cannot directly obtain simultaneous free-running operations on many modes. In addition, the dispersive effects of the medium cause the mode frequencies to be unequally spaced to some degree, making mode-locked operations more difficult. A mechanism for spontaneous mode locking was proposed in 1964 by Lamb, who noted that any two modes at different frequencies interacting with the medium can combine to generate a third optical frequency. If the modes are nearly equally spaced, the third frequency lies near a third mode and the *combination frequency* may act as an injected signal to pull the third mode into a locked condition. By this mutual interaction, some many-mode lasers spontaneously enter the phase-locked and equal frequency spacing conditions necessary for short pulse generation.

Mode locking can also be accomplished if the laser is modulated at the intermode spacing frequency (active mode locking) or if a saturable absorber is placed within the laser (passive mode locking) to strengthen mode interactions and to stimulate the circulation of spatially localized pulses in the laser cavity.

The relaxation oscillation frequency and the Rabi frequency can also play strong roles in

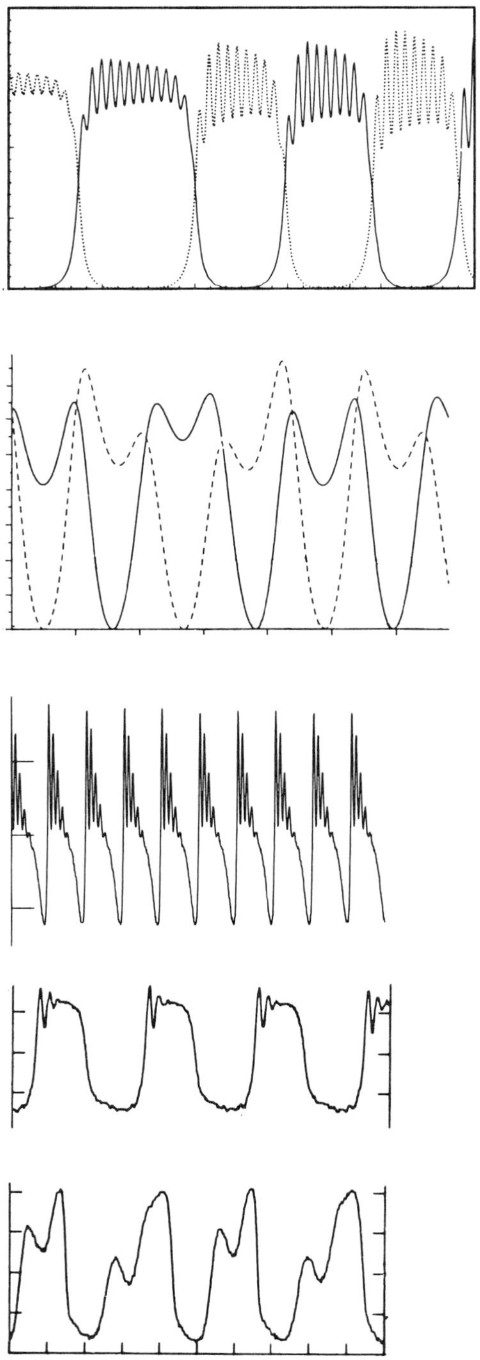

FIG. 7. (a) and (b) Predictions for the intensity pulsations in the two modes of a bidirectional CO_2 laser. (Courtesy of L. M. Hoffer, G. L. Lippi, and N. B. Abraham.) Also, observations of the pulsations of one mode of a bidirectional NH_3 FIR laser at 81.5 (c) and 153 μm (d) and (e). (Courtesy of C. O. Weiss and N. B. Abraham.)

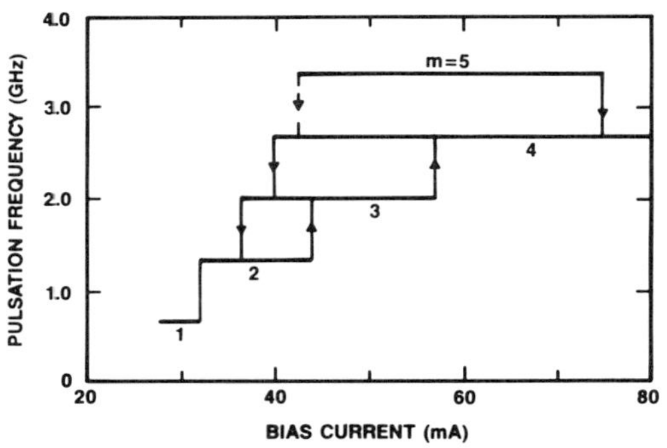

FIG. 8. Mode-locked operation involving modes spaced by different numbers of quiescent modes as indicated for a semiconductor laser for which the relaxation oscillation frequency is adjusted by changing the laser excitation. The laser mode spacings were reduced by using antireflection coating of the laser diode and a 22-cm-long external cavity. Proton bombardment of the laser also provided fast internal saturable absorbers. [Reprinted with permission from M. Kuznetsov, D. Z. Tsang, J. N. Walpole, Z. L. Lau and E. P. Ippen (1987). *Appl. Phys. Lett.* **51,** 895.]

mode locking. Coupling between modes is enhanced if their frequency spacing matches either of these two dynamical oscillation frequencies of the field-matter interactions. Examples of these results for semiconductor and dye lasers are shown in Figs. 8 and 9, respectively.

The foregoing discussion has been limited to the interaction of longitudinal modes, those having the same transverse field pattern and differing only in the number of wavelengths in the

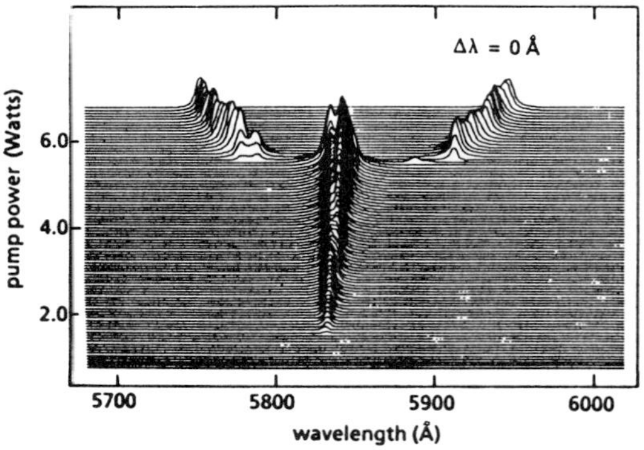

FIG. 9. Optical spectrum of dye laser operation showing splitting of single-mode operation into two-mode operation where the mode spacing grows with laser excitation according to the growth in the Rabi oscillation frequency. [Reprinted with permission from C. R. Stroud, Jr., K. Koch, S. Chakmajian, and L. W. Hillman (1986). *In* "Optical Chaos" (J. Chrostowski and N. B. Abraham, eds.), *Proc. SPIE* **667,** 47.]

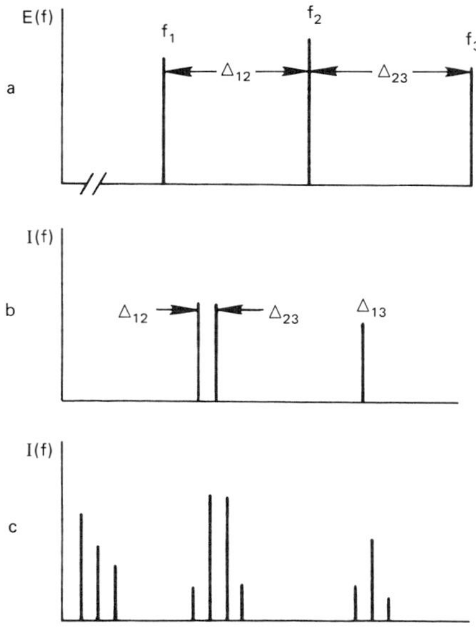

FIG. 10. Schematic origin of combination tone pulsing. (a) Optical spectrum of a three-mode laser, (b) intensity pulsation spectrum of uncoupled three-mode operation, and (c) intensity pulsation spectrum from combination tone pulsing with low-frequency pulsing generated by the second-order differences in the mode frequencies.

longitudinal direction needed to complete a round trip in the cavity. Modes of different transverse field patterns have different intermode frequency spacings, and in some circumstances, they too can be locked together. The resulting pulsation rate is not directly related to the round-trip time in the cavity but rather to the frequency spacing. The laser output pulsations in this case also appear in a spatially varying transverse pattern as the modes of different field profiles interfere constructively at different places at different times.

C. Combination Tones

If three or more modes coexist in a laser without locking, they can generate overall modulations that are at frequencies much lower than the mode spacing frequencies. These arise from a beating between the combination frequencies and the adjacent modes. The resulting beat frequency is given by the difference between the adjacent intermode spacings and is often in the range of tens of kilohertz to a few megahertz. This low frequency noise is typical of unlocked multimode operation and vanishes completely when mode locking is accomplished. Systematic studies of this phenomena by Weiss and coworkers and by Halas and co-workers in 1983 revealed that period doubling and quasiperiodic routes to chaotic low-frequency modulation are possible in these systems. In both cases, multiple transverse mode operation in inhomogeneously broadened lasers was studied. Inhomogeneous broadening of the laser medium reduces the mode interaction and provides intensity dependent dispersive effects that tend to favor the combination tone pulsing over mode locking. A sequence of optical and intensity spectra illustrating this effect is shown in Figs. 10 and 11.

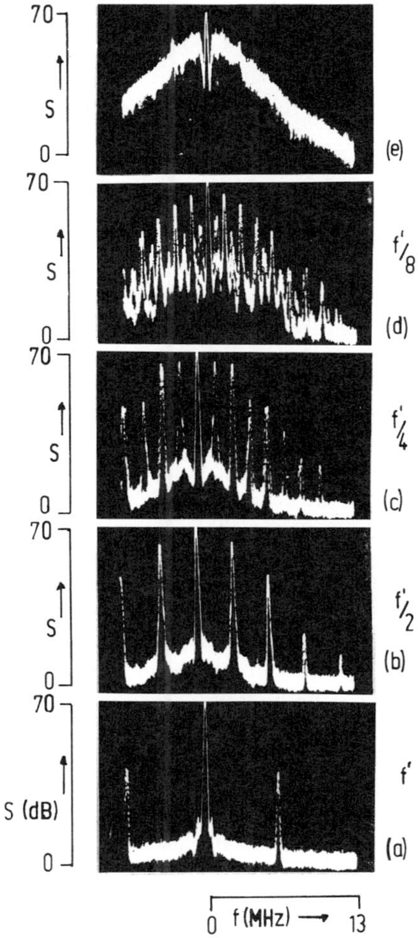

FIG. 11. Period-doubling route to chaotic low-frequency combination tone pulsing in the HeNe 6328-μm laser. [Reprinted with permission from C. O. Weiss, A. Godone, and A. Olafsson (1983). *Phys. Rev. A* **28**, 892.]

When the combining modes are transverse modes, then one can also study the spatial patterns of the laser output. When there is simple mode-beating, the pattern blinks on and off rapidly at different points in the pattern in a kind of "machine-gun" pattern. However, if the modes are very close together in frequency, they may lock to a common frequency with the result being a time-independent though spatially distorted pattern. When the modes are far apart and when many modes are involved, the spatiotemporal dynamics has complexity similar to that of two-dimensional fluid turbulence.

D. External Cavities

In some lasers, particularly semiconductor lasers used for coherent applications, one wishes to suppress multimode operation in favor of stable single-mode behavior. A design to accomplish this in long laser cavities (which have modes closely spaced in frequency) is to insert an extra pair of reflecting surfaces (called an etalon) within the round-trip path in the laser cavity. The resonant frequencies can be widely spaced because of a short distance between the surfaces. Oscillation on a mode of the laser cavity, which also is resonant with the etalon, is selected while other modes of the cavity are suppressed by their lack of resonance with the etalon.

For lasers that use the reflection from the end surfaces of the laser material as the laser mirrors, as is done in most semiconductor lasers, it is not possible to insert another etalon in the cavity. Tsang at AT&T Bell Laboratories overcame this by splitting the semiconductor in two pieces (called "c^3" for *cleaved coupled cavity*), creating an etalon between the pieces and also providing two regions for differing excitation.

Another approach for semiconductor lasers has been the addition of an external third mirror with the idea that optical feedback might suppress noise and provide selective enhancement of one of the laser modes. Often this has been found to lead to spontaneous pulsations. This occurs when the external path length provides delay of the optical feedback roughly corresponding to the period of the relaxation oscillations in the laser. As such frequencies are of order 109 Hz, the corresponding external cavity round-trip length is 30 cm. Muller and Glas in 1984 and Otsuka have demonstrated that a wide range of periodic and chaotic oscillations can be excited by even very weak feedback from such external reflectors.

IV. Noise

Lasers carry with them their own intrinsic noise, that of spontaneously emitted incoherent light from the laser medium. In addition, thermal, mechanical, acoustical, electrical, and excitation fluctuations can all be present in practical laser devices. Noise disrupts the coherent dynamical interaction of the optical field and the laser medium. This can provide modulation of otherwise stable, constant intensity lasers, and it can also disrupt periodic or chaotic oscillations making them either more or less regular depending on the particular operating conditions. For example, when systems that respond to abrupt disturbances with damped relaxation oscillations are continuously disrupted by noise, they tend to retain a relatively large amplitude of noisy modulation at the relaxation oscillation frequency. Noise-driven irregular pulsations can be distinguished from irregular chaotic pulsations because of the higher degree of coherence and correlation inherent in the dynamical processes that generate the chaos.

Bibliography

Abraham, N. B. (1983). A new focus on laser instabilities and chaos, *Laser Focus* **19,** 73 (May).

Abraham, N. B., and Firth, W. E. (1990). Transverse effects in nonlinear optics, *J. Optical Society of America* B **7,** June and July.

Abraham, N. B., Lugiato, L. A., and Narducci, L. M., eds. (1985). Special issue on instabilities in active media, *J. Optical Society of America* B **2,** 5–264.

Abraham, N. B., Mandel, P., and Narducci, L. M. (1988). Dynamical instabilities and pulsations in lasers, *in* "Progress in Optics," Vol. XXV (E. Wolf, ed.). Elsevier, Amsterdam.

Abraham, N. B., Arecchi, F. T., and Lugiato, L. A., eds. (1988). "Instabilities and Chaos in Quantum Optics II" (lecture notes of a summer school). Plenum, New York.

Arecchi, F. T., and Harrison, R. G., eds. (1987). "Instabilities and Chaos in Quantum Optics" (collection of research reviews). Springer-Verlag, Berlin and New York.

Bandy, D. K., Oraevsky, A. N., and Tredicce, J. R. (1988). Laser instabilities, *J. Optical Society of America* B **5,** May.

Boyd, R. W., Raymer, M. G., and Narducci, L. M., eds. (1986). "Optical Instabilities" (proceedings of an international conference with tutorial reviews). Cambridge Univ. Press, London and New York.

Harrison, R. G. (1987). Dynamical instabilities and chaos in lasers, *Contemporary Physics*.

Harrison, R. G., and Biswas, D. J. (1986). Chaos in light, *Nature*, **321,** 394–401.

Harrison, R. G., and Biswas, D. J. (1985). Pulsating instabilities and chaos in lasers, *Progress in Quantum Electronics* **10,** 147–228.

Narducci, L. M., and Abraham, N. B. (1988). "Lecture Notes on Lasers and Laser Dynamics." World Scientific, Singapore.

Weiss, C. O. (1988). Chaotic laser dynamics, *Optics and Quantum Electronics* **20,** 1–22.

LASERS

William T. Silfvast *AT&T Bell Laboratories*

Glossary

Absorption: Extinction of a photon of light when it collides with an atom and excites an internal energy state of that atom.

Emission: Radiation produced by an atomic species when an electron moves from a higher energy level to a lower one.

Frequency: Reciprocal of the time it takes for a lightwave to oscillate through a full cycle.

Gain: Condition that causes a beam of light to be intensified when it passes through a specially prepared medium.

Linewidth: Frequency or wavelength spread over which emission, absorption, and gain occur in the amplifier.

Mode: Single frequency beam of light that follows a unique path as it grows in the amplifier and emerges as a beam.

Photon: Discrete quantum of light of an exact energy or wavelength.

Population inversion: Condition in which more atoms exist in a higher energy state than a lower one, leading to amplification, or gain, at a wavelength determined by electron transitions between those states.

Wavelength: Distance over which light travels during a complete cycle of oscillation.

A laser is a device that amplifies, or increases, the intensity of light, producing a strong, highly directional or parallel beam of light of a specific wavelength. The word "laser" is an acronym for "light amplification by stimulated emission of radiation." Stimulated emission is a natural process, first recognized by Einstein, that occurs when a beam of light passes through a medium and initiates or stimulates atoms of that medium to radiate more light in the same direction and at the same wavelength as that of the original beam. A specific laser device (see Fig. 1) consists of (1) an amplifying, or gain, medium that produces an increase in the intensity of a light beam and (2) an optical resonator or mirror arrangement that provides feedback of the amplified beam into the gain medium thereby producing the beamlike and ultrapure frequency or coherent properties of the laser. The optical cavity, or resonator, which typically consists of two highly reflecting mirrors arranged at opposite ends of an elongated amplifier, allows a strong beam of light to develop due to multiple reflections that produce growth of the beam as it bounces back and forth through the amplifier. A useful beam emerges from a laser either by making one of the laser mirrors partially transmitting or by using a mirror with a small hole in it. Some lasers have such a high gain that the intensity increase is large enough, after only a single pass of the beam through the amplifier, that mirrors are not necessary to achieve a strong beam. Such amplifiers produce a directional beam by having the gain medium arranged in a very elongated shape, causing the beam to grow and emerge from the amplifier in only the elongated direction.

Some of the unique properties of lasers include high beam power for welding or cutting, ultrapure frequency for communications and holography, and an ultraparallel beam for long-distance propagation and extremely tight focusing. Laser wavelengths cover the far infrared to the near infrared, the visible to the ultraviolet, and the vacuum ultraviolet to the soft X-ray region. Laser sizes range from small semiconductor lasers the size of a grain of salt, for use in optical

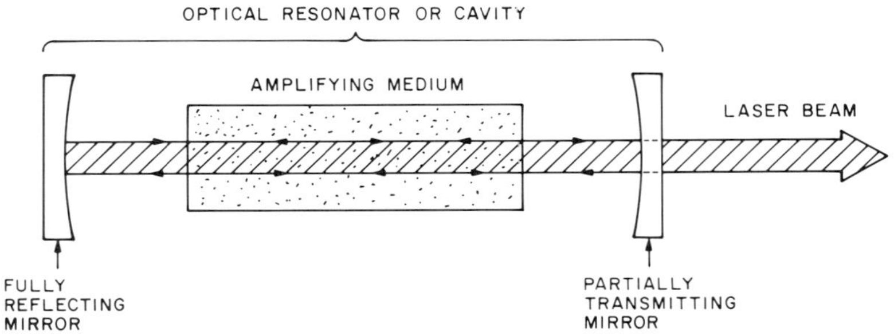

FIG. 1. Laser components including amplifying medium, optical cavity, and laser beam.

communications, to large solid-state and gas lasers the size of a large building, for use in laser fusion programs.

I. Laser History

Charles Townes was the first person to take advantage of the stimulated emission process as an amplifier by conceiving and constructing the first maser (an acronym for "microwave amplification by stimulated emission of radiation"). The maser produced a pure beam of microwaves that were anticipated to be useful for communications in a similar way to that of a klystron or a traveling-wave tube. The first maser was produced in ammonia vapor and the inversion occurred between two energy levels that produced gain at a wavelength of 1.25 cm. In the maser, the radiation wavelengths are comparable to the size of the device and therefore the means of producing and extracting the beam could not obviously be extrapolated to the optical spectrum in which the wavelengths of light are of the order of 100th the size of a human hair.

In 1958, Townes along with Arthur Schawlow began thinking about extending the maser principle to optical wavelengths. At that time they developed the concept of a laser amplifier and an optical mirror cavity to provide the multiple reflections thought to be necessary for rapid growth of the light signal into an intense visible beam. Townes later (1964) shared the Nobel prize in physics with A. Prokhorov and N. Basov of the Soviet Union for the development of the maser–laser principle.

In 1960, Theodore Maiman of the Hughes Research Laboratories produced the first laser using a ruby crystal as the amplifier and a flash lamp as the energy source. The helical flash lamp surrounded a rod-shaped ruby crystal and the optical cavity was formed by coating the flattened ends of the ruby rod with a highly reflecting material. In operation, an intense red beam emerged from the ends of the rod when the flash lamp was initiated.

Shortly after the ruby laser came the first gas laser, developed in 1961 in a mixture of helium and neon gases by A. Javan, W. Bennett, and D. Herriott of Bell Laboratories. At the same laboratories, L. F. Johnson and K. Nassau first demonstrated the now well-known and high-power neodymium laser. This was followed in 1962 by the first semiconductor laser demonstrated by R. Hall at the General Electric Research Laboratories. In 1963, C. K. N. Patel of Bell Laboratories discovered the infrared carbon dioxide laser which later became one of the most powerful lasers. Later that year A. Bloom and E. Bell of Spectra-Physics discovered the first ion laser, in mercury vapor. This was followed in 1964 by the argon ion laser developed by W. Bridges of Hughes Research Laboratories and in 1966 the blue helium–cadmium metal vapor ion laser discovered by W. T. Silfvast, G. R. Fowles, and B. D. Hopkins at the University of Utah. The first liquid laser in the form of a fluorescent dye was discovered that same year by P. P. Sorokin and J. R. Lankard of the IBM Research Laboratories leading to the development of broadly tunable lasers. The first of the now well-known rare-gas–halide excimer lasers was first observed in xenon fluoride by J. J. Ewing and C. Brau of the Avco–Everett Research Laboratory in 1975. In 1976 J. M. J. Madey and co-workers at Stanford University developed the first free-electron laser amplifier operating at the infrared carbon dioxide laser wavelength. In 1985 the first soft X-ray laser was successfully demonstrated in a highly ionized selenium plasma by D. Matthews and a large number of co-workers at the Lawrence Livermore Laboratories.

II. Laser Gain Media

A. Energy Levels and the Emission and Absorption of Light

All lasers (except the free-electron laser) result from electron energy changes among discrete energy levels of atomic species, including: (1) individual atoms or ions, (2) small uniquely bonded groups of atoms (molecules), (3) periodically arranged groups of atoms (semiconductors or crystalline solids), or (4) randomly arranged groups of atoms (liquids and amorphous solid structures). All of these species contain a lowest energy level (ground state) in which the electrons reside at low temperatures, and a spectrum of higher lying levels that are occupied when energy is pumped into the species either by heating or irradiating it with light or energetic particles such as fast electrons or fast atomic particles. Light originates from these species when electrons jump or decay from some of these high lying, or excited, energy levels to lower lying energy levels. The energy that is lost by the particular atomic material when the electron decays is given up in the form of a photon, a discrete particle of light. In order to satisfy the law of conservation of energy, the emitted photon must be of the exact energy corresponding to the energy difference between the higher lying level and the lower lying level, and the wavelength or frequency of the emitted photon is associated with that energy difference. Many photons together can form a beam or a wave of light.

Light, emitted when an electron decays, can occur either spontaneously, due to inherent interactions of the atomic structure, or by stimulated emission whereby the electron is forced or driven to radiate by an approaching photon of the appropriate energy or wavelength (see Fig 2). Absorption, the opposite process of stimulated emission, occurs when an atom having an electron in a low lying energy level absorbs and thereby eliminates an approaching photon, using the absorbed energy to boost that electron to a higher lying energy level.

B. Population Inversions

A laser amplifier is produced when conditions are created within the amplifying medium such that there are more atoms having electrons at a higher energy level than at a lower energy level for a specific pair of levels. This condition is known as a population inversion since it is the opposite or inverse of almost all physical situations at or near thermal equilibrium in which there are more atoms with electrons in lower energy levels than at higher levels. Under the conditions of a population inversion, when a beam of light passes through the amplifier more photons will be stimulated than absorbed thereby resulting in a net increase in the number of photons or an amplification of the beam.

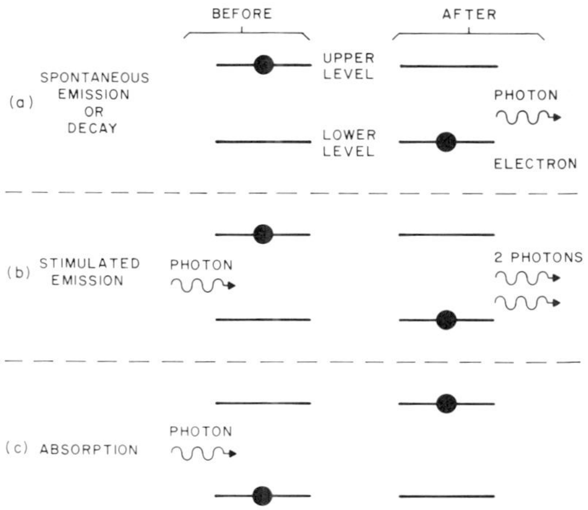

FIG. 2. Electronic transitions between energy levels depicting (a) spontaneous emission, (b) stimulated emission, and (c) absorption.

C. Excitation Mechanisms in Lasers (Energy Sources)

Since all laser emission involves radiation from excited states of atoms, the energy must be fed to those atoms to produce the excited states. This energy is provided in the form of highly energetic electrons (moving at rapid speeds of the order of 10^8 to 10^9 cm/sec), energetic heavier particles such as protons, neutrons, or even other atoms, or electromagnetic radiation (light) in the form of (1) a broad frequency spectrum of emission such as a flash lamp or (2) a narrow frequency spectrum provided by another laser. The most common excitation source is that provided by energetic electrons since they are easily accelerated by applying an electric field or voltage drop to an amplifier. Electrons are typically used in most gas and semiconductor lasers whereas light is most often used in liquid (dye) lasers and crystalline solid-state lasers. Electron excitation sources tend to be the most efficient since flash lamps are themselves generally excited by electrons before they are used to pump lasers. Heavier particles are generally less efficient as pumping sources since they are much more difficult to energize than either electrons or lamps.

D. Inversions in Gases, Metal Vapors, and Plasmas

Inversions in gases, metal vapors, and plasmas are generally produced by applying a voltage drop across the elongated gain region thereby producing an electric field that accelerates the electrons. These rapidly moving electrons then collide with the gas atoms and excite them to a wide range of excited energy levels. Some of those levels decay faster than others (primarily by spontaneous emission) leaving population inversions with higher levels. If the populations in the inverted levels are high enough, then the gain may be sufficient to make a laser. Typically if 1 in 10^5 or 10^6 atoms is in a specific upper laser level, that will be a sufficient fraction to produce enough gain to make a laser. Most gas lasers have relatively low gains and therefore amplifier lengths of the order of 25 to 100 cm are necessary. Since spontaneous emission rates are much faster for shorter wavelength transitions, power input for short-wavelength lasers is significantly higher than for visible and infrared lasers. Typical gas pressures for gas lasers range from 1/1000th to 1/100th of an atmosphere although there are some gas lasers that operate at atmospheric pressure and above and require very closely spaced electrodes (transverse excitation) in order to produce the necessary excited state populations.

E. Inversions in Liquids (Dyes)

Most excited states of liquids decay so rapidly by collisions with surrounding atoms or molecules (10^{-13} sec) that it is difficult to accumulate enough population in an upper laser level to make significant gain. Also, since it is difficult to use electron excitation in liquids, the primary energy source is optical excitation, either by flash lamps or by other lasers. Fluorescing dyes are the best liquid media for lasers. The fact that dyes fluoresce suggests that their excited energy levels stay populated long enough to lose their energy by radiation of light rather than by collisions with surrounding atoms or electrons. To help establish the population inversion, the lower laser level of a dye decays very rapidly by collisions.

F. Inversions in Semiconductors

Inversions in semiconductors are produced when a p–n junction is created by joining two slightly different semiconducting materials (in a similar way to that of a transistor). The n-type material has an excess of electrons and the p-type material has an excess of holes (missing electrons). When they are joined, the excess electrons of the n-type material are pulled over into the p region and vice versa by their charge attraction, causing the electrons and holes in that region to recombine and emit recombination radiation. This neutralizes the junction region, leaving a small, inherent electric field to prevent further recombination of the remaining electrons and holes near the junction. If an external electric field is applied in the appropriate direction, by applying a voltage across the junction, more electrons and holes can be pulled together, causing them to recombine and emit more radiation but also to produce an inversion. This inversion occurs on transitions originating from energy levels located just above the inherent energy band gap of the material. Semiconductor lasers operate in a similar way to light-emitting diodes except that the requirements for constructing the lasers are much more restrictive than the diodes, due primarily to the necessity for higher electric current densities that are essential to produce large gains, and also due to the need for better heat-dissipation capabilities to remove the heat produced by the higher current densities.

G. Inversions in Solids

Inversions in most solid-state lasers are obtained by implanting impurities (the laser species) within a host material such as a crystal or a glass in a proportion ranging from approximately 1 part in 100 to 1 part in 10,000. In most solid-state lasers the impurities are the form of ions in which the energy states are screened from the surrounding atoms so the energy levels are narrow, like those of isolated atoms or ions, rather than broad like those of liquids. In color center lasers the impurities are crystal defects produced by irradiating the crystal with X rays. In solids, as in liquids, electrons cannot easily be accelerated by electric fields to excite the laser energy levels of the impurity species so the energy must be fed to the medium via flash lamps or other lasers. The input lamp energy occurs over a broad wavelength region to a large number of excited energy levels. These levels then decay to the upper laser level which acts much like a temporary storage reservoir, collecting enough population to make a large inversion with respect to lower lying levels that have a rapid decay to the ground state.

H. Bandwidth of Gain Media

The frequency or wavelength spectrum (gain bandwidth) over which gain occurs in a laser amplifier is determined by a number of factors. The minimum width is the combined width of the energy levels involved in the laser transition. This width is due primarily to the uncertainty of the natural radiative decay time of the laser levels. This width can be increased by collisions of electrons with the laser states in high-pressure gas lasers, by interaction of nearby atoms and bonding electrons in liquids and solids, and by Doppler shifted frequencies in most gas lasers. This gain linewidth of the laser amplifier is only part of the contribution to the linewidth of the laser beam. Significant line narrowing due to optical cavity effects will be described in the next section.

III. Laser Beam Properties

A. Beam Properties

The beam properties of a laser, such as the direction and divergence of the beam and the wavelength or frequency characteristics that are not related to the bandwidth of the laser gain medium, are determined largely by the laser structure. The features of the structure affecting the beam properties include the width and length of the gain medium, the location, separation and reflectivity of the mirrors of the optical cavity (if the gain is low and the gain duration long enough to make use of mirrors), and the presence of losses in the beam path within the cavity. These features determine unique properties of the laser beam referred to as laser modes.

B. Shape of the Gain Medium

If a laser gain medium were in the shape of a round ball, then stimulated emission would occur equally in all directions and the only result might be a slight increase in the intensity of the light, for a slightly shorter duration than would occur if gain were not present, but the effect would probably not be noticeable to an observer. The goal of a laser designer is to cause most of the laser photons to be stimulated in a specific direction in order to produce a highly directional beam, at the expense of allowing those same photons to radiate in random directions by either stimulated or spontaneous emission (as was the case for the round ball). This is achieved by making the gain medium significantly longer in one dimension than in the other two.

C. Growth of the Beam and Saturation

When gain is produced in the amplifier and spontaneously emitted photons begin to be amplified by stimulated emission, photons that are emitted in directions other than the elongated direction of the amplifier soon reach the walls of the medium and die out. The photons that are emitted in the elongated direction continue to grow by stimulating other atoms to emit additional photons in the same direction until all of those photons reach the end of the amplifier. They then arrive at the mirror and are reflected back through the amplifier where they continue to grow. Finally, after a number of round trips, a beam begins to evolve. If the duration of the gain is long enough, amplification will lead to more photons in the beam than there are atoms available to stimulate, and growth can therefore no longer occur. The beam is then said to be saturated and the beam power reaches a steady value, determined by the amount of energy being fed into the upper laser level by the pumping source. If the population inversion can be maintained on a continuous basis in the amplifier, the laser-beam output becomes steady and the laser is referred to as a continuous wave, or cw, laser. If the gain only lasts for a short duration, the laser output occurs as a burst of light and the laser is referred to as a pulsed laser.

D. Optical Cavity (Optical Resonator)

The optical cavity or resonator, typically comprised of a mirror at each end of the elongated gain region (see Fig. 1), allows the rapidly growing beam to bounce back and forth or resonate between the mirrors. Although the first laser used flat mirrors, as suggested in the original Schalow–Townes paper, in 1961 Fox and Li suggested the use of slightly curved mirrors, especially for cavities where the amplifier consisted of a long narrow tube, in order to reconcentrate the beam in the center of the gain medium after each reflection from the mirrors thereby reducing the diffraction losses of the narrow tube. Stable modes of lower loss are possible for curved mirrors than for flat mirrors if the separation between the mirrors is less than twice their radius of curvature. Mirror reflectivities of 99.9% at the laser wavelength, using dielectric layered coatings, make possible laser operation under conditions of very low gain.

E. Stable and Unstable Resonators

The term resonator implies a wave that is in harmony or resonance with the device that is generating the wave, whether it be an organ pipe, a flute, or a microwave cavity. An optical wave can also have this property. The term "resonance" suggests that an exact integral number of wavelengths (a mode) of the wave fit between the mirrors of the resonator. A stable resonator refers to a mirror arrangement (usually one with a mirror at each end of the elongated cavity), producing modes that are continually reproducible during the duration that gain occurs in the amplifier (which could be a thousandth of a second or many days or longer). An unstable resonator is a mirror arrangement that is used to obtain modes when the amplifier gain is high and has a short duration (less than a millionth of a second) such that a normal mode would not have time to evolve. In that situation, the energy is extracted by using a mirror arrangement in which the beam begins to resonate in a small unstable region of the amplifier. Part of this beam is leaked into the larger portion of the amplifier where it rapidly grows and extracts most of the amplifier energy in a few passes. [*See* MODE-LOCKING OF LASERS.]

F. Laser Modes

Laser modes are wavelike properties relating to the oscillating character of a light beam as the beam passes back and forth through the amplifier and grows at the expense of existing losses. The development of modes involves an attempt by competing light beams of similar wavelengths to fit an exact number of their waves into the optical cavity with the constraint that the oscillating electric field of the light beam is zero at each of the mirrors. This is much like a vibrating guitar string which is constrained at each end by the bridge and a fret, but is free to vibrate with as many nodes and antinodes in the region in between as it chooses. As an example, a laser mode of green light having a wavelength of exactly 5.0×10^{-5} cm will fit exactly 1,000,000 full cycles of oscillation between laser cavity mirrors separated by a distance of exactly 50 cm. Most lasers have a number of modes operating simultaneously, in the form of both longitudinal and transverse modes, which give rise to a complex frequency and spatial structure within the beam in what might otherwise appear as a relatively simple, pencil-like beam of light.

G. Longitudinal Modes

Each longitudinal mode is a separate light beam traveling along a distinct path between the mirrors and having an exact integral number of wavelengths along that path. In the example of green light mentioned previously, three different longitudinal modes would have very slightly different wavelengths of green light (indistinguishable in color to the eye) undergoing respectively 1,000,000, 1,000,001, and 1,000,002 full cycles of oscillation between the mirrors while traveling exactly the same path back and forth through the amplifier (see Fig. 3). In this situation each mode would differ in frequency by exactly 300 MHz as determined by the velocity of light (3 ×

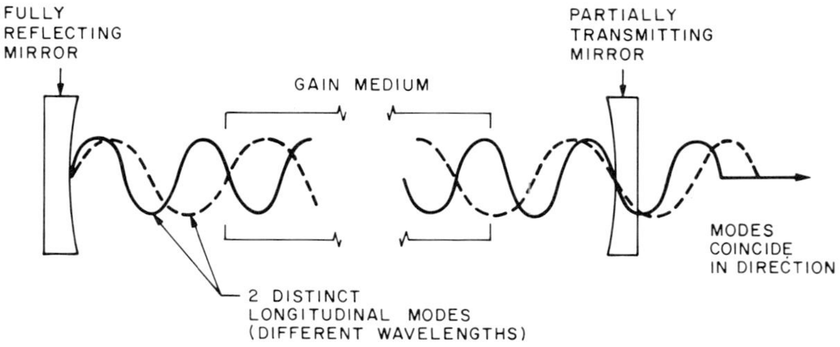

FIG. 3. Two distinct longitudinal modes occupying the same spatial region of the laser optical cavity.

10^{10} cm/sec) divided by twice the cavity length (2 × 50 cm). A gas laser amplifier having a relatively narrow gain width of 3 GHz could fit 10 longitudinal modes within the gain bandwidth whereas a liquid (dye) laser having a bandwidth covering up to one-fifth of the visible spectrum of light could have as many as 100,000 longitudinal modes all oscillating simultaneously.

H. Transverse Modes

Whereas longitudinal modes involve many light beams traveling exactly the same path through the amplifier, but differing in wavelength by an amount determined by the total number of wave cycles that fit between the mirrors, different transverse modes are represented by slightly different optical paths as they travel through the amplifier (Fig. 4). Thus each transverse mode traveling over its unique path could consist of several longitudinal modes oscillating along that path. In most instances, closely located transverse modes differ in frequency by a smaller value than do adjacent longitudinal modes that follow the same path through the amplifier.

IV. Laser Linewidth

A. Homogeneous Linewidth of Gain Media

All laser amplifiers have a finite frequency width or wavelength width over which gain can occur. This width is related to the widths of the energy levels involved in the population inversion. Single atoms or ions have the narrowest widths, determined by the very narrow energy levels inherent in the atomic structure. The gain linewidth for these amplifiers is the sum of the linewidths of the upper and lower laser levels. The linewidth is determined by both a homogeneous component and an inhomogeneous component. The homogeneous component includes all mechanisms that involve every atom in both the upper and lower laser levels of the gain medium in identically the same way. These mechanisms include the natural radiative lifetime due to spontaneous emission, broadening due to collisions with other particles such as free electrons, protons, neutrons, or other atoms or ions, or power broadening in which a high intensity laser beam rapidly cycles an atom between the upper and lower levels at a rate faster than the normal lifetime of the state. In each of these effects, the rate at which the process occurs determines the number of frequency components or the bandwidth required to describe the process, with faster processes needing broader linewidths. These rates can vary anywhere from 10^6 Hz in the infrared to 10^{10} Hz in the soft X-ray spectral region for spontaneous emission and up to 10^{12} Hz or more or rapid collisional broadening.

B. Inhomogeneous Linewidth of Gain Media

The inhomogeneous component of the broadening results from processes that affect different atoms in the upper and lower laser levels in different ways depending on unique characteristics of those atoms. The most common example of inhomogeneous broadening is Doppler broadening or motional broadening that results from the random thermal motion of the atoms due to their finite temperature. In this effect, atoms traveling in one direction would see an approaching lightwave as having a specific frequency and atoms traveling in the opposite direction would see that same lightwave as having a lower fre-

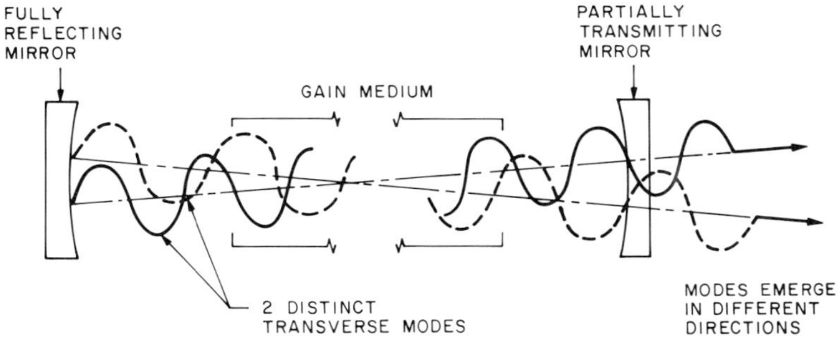

FIG. 4. Two distinct transverse modes oscillating over different spatial regions of the laser optical cavity.

quency. In a similar way, light emitted from each of those atoms would be seen by an observer as having different frequencies or wavelengths even though each atom emitted the same frequency. This Doppler effect is similar to that when a train approaches with its horn blowing and the pitch of the sound changes from a high tone to a lower tone as the train first approaches the listener and then moves away, even though the frequencies emitted from the horn remain the same.

C. Linewidth in Laser Amplifiers

The dominant broadening effect for most gas laser amplifiers is Doppler broadening which produces a linewidth of the order of 10^9 to 10^{10} Hz for visible and shorter wavelength amplifiers. Molecules have linewidths that are determined not only by the jumping of electrons between energy levels, as is the case of individual atoms, but also by the rotation of the atoms around a common center of gravity and by the vibrations of the atoms as though they were tied together by various springs. These rotations and vibrations produce a series of emissions of light over a relatively narrow range of wavelengths and in some instances these emissions can overlap in frequency to produce broad emission lines. If no overlap occurs, then the emission consists of an equally spaced series of narrow lines.

Liquids have their energy levels broadened due to the interaction of the closely packed atoms of the liquid. Such dense packing leads to a very rapid collisional interruption of the electronic states causing them to smear out into very broad energy bands thereby producing emission spectrum widths of the order of 10^{13} to 10^{14} Hz.

Solids, in addition to having closely located atoms (only slightly more dense than liquids) in many cases have a periodic structure due to the regularity of the atomic distribution (much as in the way eggs are lined up in an egg carton). This produces in many species a large energy gap between the lowest energy level and the first excited energy level. Emission from this excited level can have a very broad frequency spectrum similar to that of liquids; however, there also exist discrete levels within the bandgap, known as exciton states, that have a much narrower emission spectrum (of the order of 10^{12} Hz), due to electron–hole pairs bonding together to form atomiclike particles. Such exciton states are involved in some semiconductor lasers. Another class of emission and broadening in solids occurs when an atom like chromium is embedded in another solid material such as aluminum oxide (sapphire) to make a ruby crystal. In such a crystal, the outer electrons of the chromium atoms are shared with the surrounding aluminum oxide atoms while the inner electrons are screened from the neighboring atoms causing the atom to behave more like an isolated atom having narrow energy levels. These crystalline solids, containing specific impurities, can have narrow emission lines of the order of 10^{11} to 10^{12} Hz. The first laser was made in ruby using such levels.

D. Line Narrowing Due to Cavity Effects

A laser cavity tends to select specific wavelengths (Fig. 5) within the normal gain bandwidth of the gain medium as determined by the wavelengths of light that have an exact integral number of waves that fit between the mirrors (modes). These modes, which are equally spaced in frequency or wavelength, tend to be amplified at the expense of other wavelengths that suffer losses by not exactly "fitting" between the mirrors. In principal these modes can "narrow up" to widths of the order of a few hertz, but cavity stability problems tend to keep them from going much below 1000 Hz unless extremely stable environments and rigid cavity structures are available.

V. Laser Wavelengths

A. Range of Wavelengths

Wavelengths of electromagnetic radiation covering the spectral region where lasers occur are referred to in terms of fractions of meters. The two most common units are the micrometer (μm) or 10^{-6} m and the nanometer (nm) 10^{-9} m. Micrometers are used to designate the infrared region ranging from 0.7 μm to approximately 1,000 μm. Nanometers are used to cover the spectral range from the visible at 700 nm (0.7 μm) down to approximately 10 nm in the soft X-ray region. Each spectral region covers a specific wavelength range although the boundaries are not always exact. The infrared is broken up into three regions. The far infrared ranges from about 15 to approximately 1,000 μm (approaching the microwave region). The middle infrared covers from 2 to 15 μm and the near infrared ranges from 0.7 to 2 μm. The visible region in-

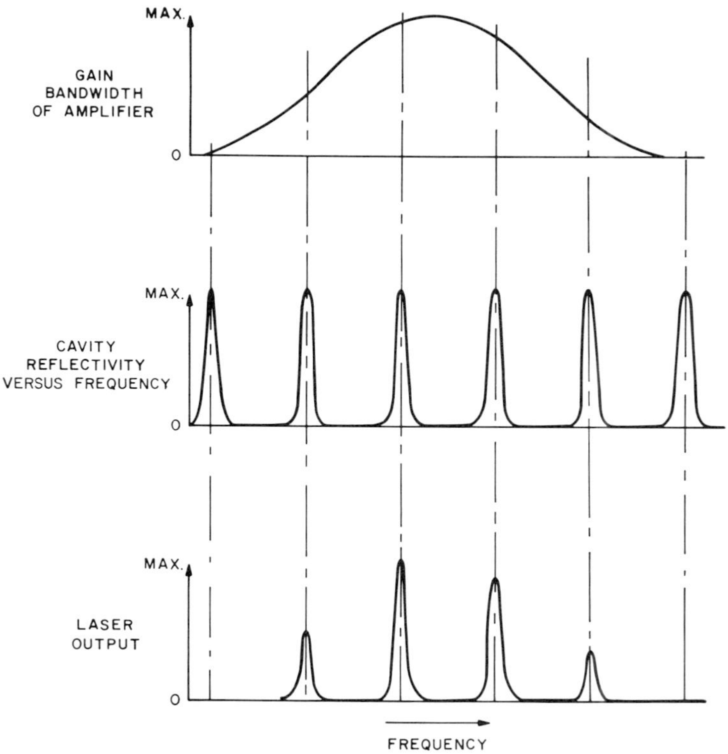

FIG. 5. Laser output resulting from effects of laser amplifier gain bandwidth and laser optical cavity modes.

cludes the rainbow spectrum ranging from the violet at 400 to 440 nm, the blue from 440 to 490 nm, the green from 490 to 550 nm, the yellow from 550 to 580 nm, the orange from 580 to 610 nm, and the red from 610 to 700 nm. The ultraviolet ranges from 400 to 200 nm with the 400- to 300-nm region termed the near ultraviolet and the 200- to 300-nm region the far ultraviolet. The vacuum ultraviolet covers the range from 100 to 200 nm, since it is the region where radiation can no longer transmit through the air (thus requiring a vacuum) because of absorption due to air molecules (mostly oxygen) and because transmission optics can still be used in this region. The shortest region is the extreme ultraviolet, which extends into the soft X-ray region, covering the range from 10 to 100 nm. In this region only reflection optics can be used and even then the reflectivities of the best materials are quite low (especially below 40 nm) when compared to those available in the visible. Free-electron lasers have the potential for operating at all wavelengths and will therefore not be singled out for any specific wavelength in this section.

B. Infrared Lasers

The most powerful lasers occur in the middle and near infrared, but a large number of lasers have been produced in the far infrared. These include the discharge excited water-vapor lasers with wavelengths ranging from 17–200 μm and the cyanide laser operating at 337 μm. The other principle far infrared lasers are the laser-pumped gases of methyl fluoride (450–550 μm) and ammonia (81 μm). In the middle infrared, the carbon dioxide laser is the most significant laser operating primarily at 9.6 and 10.6 μm. The other strong laser is the carbon monoxide laser which emits in the 5–6-μm region. There is also an important chemical laser, the hydrogen–fluoride laser, which operates at 3.7 μm. In the near infrared, many more lasers are available. The most significant laser is the neodymium laser, usually available in a yttrium–aluminum–garnet (YAG) host crystal referred to as the Nd:YAG laser, or in a glass host called a Nd:glass laser, both operating at 1.06 μm. Semiconductor lasers operate over the range from 0.7 to approximately 1.70 μm; their wavelengths being extended in both directions with continuing research. Color center lasers are tunable from 0.8 to 4.0 μm and the alexandrite laser is tunable from 0.7 to 0.8 μm. Tunable dye lasers also extend into the infrared to about 1.5 μm.

C. Visible Lasers

Visible lasers are primarily dominated by gas lasers and tunable dye lasers. The helium–neon laser at 633 nm is probably the most commonly seen laser. The argon ion laser covers the blue and green spectrum with the most prominent wavelengths at 488 and 515 nm. The krypton ion laser covers the spectrum from green to red with some of the most prominent wavelengths at 521, 568, and 647 nm. The helium–cadmium laser operates in the blue at 442 nm. Tunable dye lasers operate over the entire visible spectrum, generally pumped by a slightly shorter wavelengh laser such as the argon ion laser or the frequency doubled or tripled Nd:YAG laser. The rhodamine 6G dye has the lowest pump threshold and operates as a laser over a wavelength range from 570 to 630 nm.

D. Ultraviolet Lasers

There are fewer lasers available in the ultraviolet primarily because pump thresholds become much higher than for visible lasers and because cavity mirror reflectivities are lower and less durable. The two prominent continuous lasers are the argon ion laser, operating primarily at 351 nm and the helium cadmium laser at 325 nm. The rare-gas–halide excimer lasers produce high pulsed powers at 351 nm for xenon–fluoride, 308 nm for xenon chloride, and 248 nm for krypton fluoride. The pulsed nitrogen laser operating at 331 nm was extensively used for pumping dye lasers but this has now largely been replaced with the frequency doubled and tripled Nd:YAG laser and the excimer lasers. Tunable dye lasers as short as 310 nm are available but they are not easily pumped by commercial lasers and therefore frequency mixing and doubling of visible and infrared dye lasers is the most common technique for producing tunable laser radiation in this region.

E. Vacuum Ultraviolet Lasers

The molecular hydrogen laser was the first laser developed in this spectral region, operating in the 120- and 160-nm ranges but it never became a useful device. There are now only two readily available vacuum ultraviolet lasers. These are the argon–fluoride excimer laser operating at 193 nm and the fluorine excimer laser emitting at 153 nm. Much of the research requiring lasers in this spectral region is accomplished by frequency summing and mixing of various visible and ultraviolet lasers to produce coherent output, but such techniques are not yet readily available to the general laser community.

F. Extreme Ultraviolet and Soft X-Ray Lasers

Until 1984 there were no lasers to report in this spectral region. At that time stimulated emission was reported in krypton at 93 nm. In 1985 several highly ionized atoms provided laser output in the soft X-ray end of this spectrum, including twenty-fourth ionized selenium at 21 nm, fifth ionized carbon at 18 nm, twenty-ninth ionized yttrium at 15 nm and thirty-second ionized molybdenum at 13 nm. These lasers are so new that no experiments have yet been carried out with them. They are initiated with powerful neodymium and carbon dioxide lasers the size of large buildings and are therefore not easily duplicated in other laboratories.

VI. Types of Lasers

A. Gas Lasers

The most common types of gas lasers are the helium–neon laser, the argon and krypton ion lasers, the carbon dioxide laser, the rare-gas–halide excimer lasers, and the chemical lasers, most notably the hydrogen–flouride laser. Metal vapor lasers also fit into this category but are treated separately in Section V. With few exceptions these lasers receive their energy input via collisions of gas atoms with high-energy electrons. This energy is provided by applying a high voltage between electrodes located within the gaseous medium in order to accelerate the electrons to the necessary high energies. In some instances the electrons first excite a storage level in a separate species within the gaseous medium rather than directly pumping the laser state. The energy is subsequently transferred from that storage level to the laser level of the lasing species by direct collisional exchange of energy. [*See* LASERS, GAS.]

1. Helium–Neon Laser

The helium–neon laser was the first gas laser. The original laser transitions were in the near infrared but the most commonly used transition is the red laser at a wavelength of 632.8 nm. This laser, which has more units in use than any other laser, is available in sizes ranging from approximately 10 cm in length to over 100. It has continuous power outputs ranging from less than a milliwatt to over 100 mW and has a lifetime approaching 50,000 h for some commercial units. The excitation mechanism involves electrons colliding with helium atoms to produce helium metastable atoms, which then transfer their energy to neon laser levels. This laser is used in surveying, construction, supermarket checkout scanners, printers, and many other applications.

2. Argon and Krypton Ion Lasers

Argon and krypton ion lasers were discovered shortly after helium–neon lasers. They were the first lasers to operate in the green and blue regions of the spectrum and some versions provide ultraviolet output. These lasers have the capability of producing more than 20 W of continuous power for the largest versions. The size of the laser tubes range from 50 to 200 cm in length with a separate power supply. They are relatively inefficient and consequently require high input power and water cooling for most units. The high power requirements, which put great demands on the strength of the laser-discharge region, limit the lifetime of the high-power versions of these lasers. Some smaller, lower power versions of the argon ion laser are air cooled and offer lifetimes of 5000 h. The excitation mechanisms for these lasers involve electrons collisions first populating the ion ground states of the argon and krypton species with subsequent electron excitation to the upper laser level. Applications include phototherapy of the eye, pumping dye lasers, printing, and lithography.

3. Carbon Dioxide Laser

The carbon dioxide lasers are some of the most powerful lasers, operating primarily in the middle infrared spectral region at a wavelength of 10.6 μm. They range from small versions with a few milliwatts of continuous power to large pulsed versions the size of large buildings producing over 10,000 J of energy. They are among the most efficient lasers (up to 30%) and can produce continuous output powers of over 100 kW in room-size versions. Small versions of these lasers are referred to as waveguide lasers because the excitation region is of a cylindrical shape small enough to guide the beam down the bore in a waveguide type of mode. They can produce continuous power outputs of up to 100 W from a device smaller than a shoe box (with a separate power supply). The lasers typically operate in a mixture of carbon dioxide, nitrogen, and helium gases. Electron collisions excite metastable (storage) levels in nitrogen molecules with subsequent transfer of that energy to carbon dioxide laser levels. The helium gas acts to keep the average electron energy high in the gas-discharge region. This laser is used for a wide variety of applications including eye and tissue surgery, welding, cutting, and heat treatment of materials, laser fusion, and beam weapons. Figure 6 shows a carbon dioxide laser being used to drill a hole in a turbine blade. The white streamers are hot metal particles being ablated from the region of the hole.

4. Rare-Gas–Halide Excimer Lasers

The rare-gas–halide excimer lasers, relative newcomers to the laser industry, operate primarily in the ultraviolet spectral region in mixtures of rare gases, such as argon, krypton, or xenon with halide molecules such as chlorine and fluorine. They include the argon–fluoride laser at 193 nm, the krypton–fluoride laser at 248 nm, the xenon–chloride laser at 308 nm, and the xenon–flouride laser at 351 nm. These lasers typically produce short pulses of energy ranging from tens of millijoules to thousands of joules in pulse durations of 10 to 50 nsec and repetition rates of up to 1000 pulses per second. They range in size from an enclosure that would fit on a kitchen table top to lasers the size of a very large room. They are relatively efficient (1–5%) and provide useful energy in a wavelength region that has not had powerful lasers available previously. Their operating lifetimes are related to the development of discharge tubes, storage regions, and gas pumps that can tolerate the corrosive halogen molecules that are circulated rapidly through the gain region. Typical lifetimes are of the order of the time it takes to produce 10^6 to 10^7 pulses. The laser species are mixed with helium gas to provide a total pressure of 2

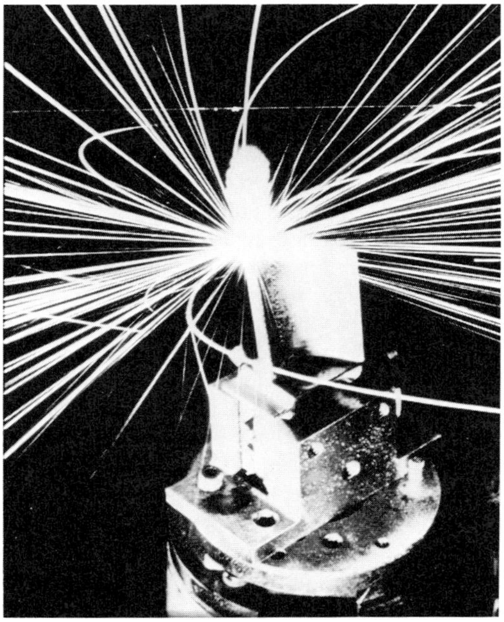

FIG. 6. Carbon dioxide laser used to drill holes in a turbine blade. White streamers are hot metal particles being ejected from the hole region.

atms. Excitation occurs by electron dissociation and ionization of the rare gas molecule to produce Ar^+, Kr^+, or Xe^+ ions. These ions then react with the halide molecules pulling off one of the atoms of that molecule to create an excited-state dimer (abbreviated as excimer) molecule. This excimer molecule then radiates rapidly to an unstable (rapidly dissociating) lower laser level. The very high operating pressures cause the molecules to react rapidly in order to produce the upper laser levels at a rate that can compete with the rapid decay of those levels. Applications include laser surgery, pumping of dye lasers, and lithography. [*See* LASERS, RARE GAS-HALIDE.]

5. Chemical Lasers

In these lasers the molecules undergo a chemical reaction that leaves the molecule in an excited state that has a population inversion with respect to a lower lying state. An example of this type of laser is the hydrogen–fluoride laser in which molecular hydrogen and molecular fluorine react to produce hydrogen–fluoride molecules in their excited state resulting in stimulated emission primarily at 2.8 μm. There are no commercially available chemical lasers but they have undergone extensive development for military applications.

B. Metal Vapor Lasers

Metal vapor lasers are actually a type of gaseous laser since the laser action occurs in the atomic or molecular vapor phase of the species at relatively low pressures, but the lasers have peculiar problems associated with vapors, such as having to vaporize a solid or liquid into the gaseous state either before or during the excitation and lasing process. These problems, along with the problems associated with controlling the condensed vapors after they diffuse out of the hot region in some designs, and with minimizing the corrosive effects of hot metal atoms and ions in other designs, have caused them to be classified in a separate category. The two most well-known types of metal vapors lasers are the helium–cadmium ion laser and the pulsed copper vapor laser.

1. Helium–Cadmium Laser

The helium–cadmium laser operates primarily at two wavelengths, in the blue at 441.6 nm and in the ultraviolet at 325.0 nm. It produces continuous power outputs of the order of 5–100 mW for the blue and 1–25 mW in the ultraviolet, in sizes ranging from 50–200-cm long. The cadmium vapor is obtained by heating the cadium metal in a reservoir located near the helium discharge. The cadmium vapor diffuses into the excited helium gas where it is ionized and the cataphoresis force on the cadmium ions causes them to move towards the negative potential of the cathode thereby distributing the metal relatively uniformly in the discharge region to produce a uniform gain. Typical operating life for the laser is of the order of 5000 h with the limiting factors being the control of the vapor and the loss of helium gas via diffusion through the glass tube walls. The laser levels are excited by collisions with helium metastable atoms, by electron collisions, and by photoionization resulting from radiating helium atoms. Applications include printing, lithography, and fluorescence analysis.

2. Copper Vapor Laser

This laser operates in the green at 510.5 nm and in the yellow at 578.2 nm. It efficiently (2%) produces short laser pulses (10–20-nsec duration) of 1 mJ of energy at repetition rates of up to 20,000 times per second yielding average powers of up to 20 W. The size is similar to that of an excimer laser. Commercial versions of this laser are designed to heat the metallic copper up to temperatures of the order of 1600°C in order to provide enough copper vapor to produce laser action. The lifetime associated with operating these lasers at such high temperatures has been limited to a few hundred hours before servicing is required. The excitation mechanism is primarily by electron collisions with ground-state copper atoms to produce upper laser states. Applications of these lasers include uranium isotope enrichment, large-screen optical imaging, and pumping of dye lasers. A gold vapor laser that is similar to the copper laser, but emits red light at a wavelength of 624.0 nm, is used for cancer phototherapy.

C. Solid-State Lasers

These lasers generally consist of transparent crystals or glasses as "hosts" within which ionic species of laser atoms are interspersed or "doped." Typical host materials include aluminum oxide (sapphire), garnets, and various forms of glasses with the most common lasing species being neodymium ions and ruby ions (the first laser). In color center lasers the host is typically an alkali–halide crystal and the laser species is an electron trapping defect in the crystal. The energy input in all of these lasers is provided by a light source that is focused into the crystal to excite the upper laser levels. The light source is typically a pulsed or continuously operating flash lamp, but efficient diode lasers are also being used to pump small versions of neodymium lasers and argon ion lasers are used to pump color center lasers.

1. Neodymium Lasers

Neodymium atoms are implanted primarily in host materials such as yttrium–aluminum–garnet (YAG) crystals or various forms of glasses in quantities of approximately one part per hundred. When they are implanted in YAG crystals, the laser emits in the near infrared at 1.06 μm with continuous powers of up to 250 W and with pulsed powers as high as several megawatts. The YAG crystal growth difficulties limit the size of the laser rods to approximately one centimeter in diameter. The YAG host material, however, has the advantage of having a relatively high thermal conductivity to remove wasted heat, thus allowing these crystals to be operated at high repetition rates of the order of many pulses per second. Glass hosts also produce Nd lasers in the 1.06-μm wavelength region but with a somewhat broader bandwidth than YAG. They can also be grown in much larger sizes than YAG, thereby allowing the construction of very large amplifiers, but glasses have a much lower thermal conductivity, thus requiring operation at much lower repetition rates (of the order of one pulse every few minutes or less). Thus Nd:YAG is used for continuous lasers and relatively low-energy pulsed lasers (1 J per pulse) operating at up to 10 pulses per second whereas glass lasers exist in sizes up to hundreds of centimeters in diameter, occupy large buildings and are capable of energies as high as 100 kJ per pulse for laser fusion applications. Neodymium lasers typically have very long lifetimes before servicing is required, with the typical failure mode being the replacement of flash lamps. Neodymium lasers are used for surgery applications, for pumping dye lasers (after doubling and tripling their frequencies with nonlinear optical techniques), as military range finders, for drilling holes in solid materials, and for producing X-ray plasmas for X-ray light sources, and for laser fusion and for making X-ray lasers.

2. Ruby Laser

The ruby laser, the first laser discovered, is produced by implanting chromium ions into an aluminum oxide crystal host and then irradiating the crystal with a flash lamp to excite the laser levels. Although ruby lasers were frequently used during the early days of the laser, the difficulties associated with growing the crystals, compared with the ease of making neodymium lasers, has led to their being used much less often in recent times.

3. Color Center Lasers

Color center lasers use a different form of impurity species implanted in a host material in quantities of one part per ten thousand. In such lasers the laser species is generally produced by irradiating the crystal with X rays to produce defects that attract electrons. These defect centers produce energy levels that absorb and emit light and are capable of being inverted to produce gain. Color center lasers typically operate in the infrared from 0.8–4 μm and are tunable within that range by using different crystals having different emission wavelengths. Their tunability makes them attractive lasers for doing spectroscopy. [*See* LASER, COLOR CENTER; ULTRAFAST LASER TECHNOLOGY.]

D. Semiconductor Lasers

Semiconductor or diode lasers, typically about the size of a grain of salt, are the smallest lasers yet devised. They consist of a *p–n* junction formed in an elongated gain region, typically in a gallium–arsenide crystal, with parallel faces at the ends to serve as partially reflecting mirrors. They operate with milliamps of current at a voltage of only a few volts. The entire laser package is very small and could be incorporated into an integrated circuit board if required. Heterostructure lasers, a more recently developed type of diode laser, include additional layers of different materials of similar electronic configuration, such as aluminum, indium and phosphorous on the sides of the junction to help confine the electronic current to the junction region in order to minimize current and heat dissipation requirements. Semiconductor lasers range in wavelengh from 0.7 to 1.8 μm with typical continuous output powers of up to 10 mW. By constructing a row of *p–n* junctions next to each other, all of the separate gain media can be forced to emit together in a phased array to produce an effective combined power output of over one watt. Applications for semiconductor lasers are primarily in the communications field in which the near-infrared beams can be transmitted over long distances through low-loss fibers. In addition, they have recently found a large market as the reading device for compact disc players. Figure 7 shows a diode laser array, consisting of 10 diode lasers, recording at a high data rate onto a multitrack optical disk.

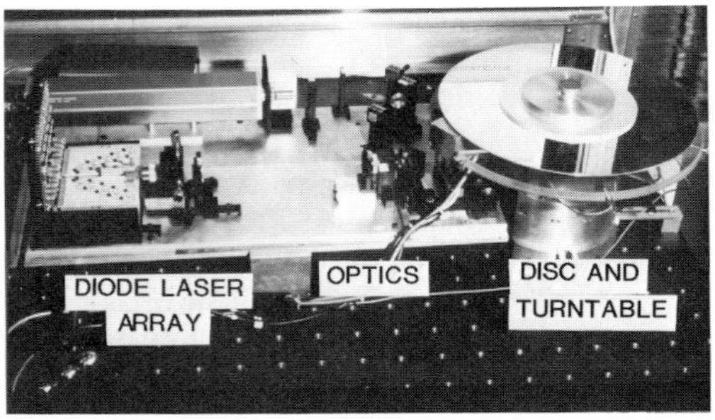

FIG. 7. High-data-rate multichannel optical recording using an array of addressable diode lasers. [Courtesy of RCA Laboratories.]

E. Liquid (Dye) Lasers

Dye lasers are similar to solid-state lasers in that they consist of a host material (in this case a solvent such as alcohol) in which the laser (dye) molecules are dissolved at a concentration of the order of one part in ten thousand. Different dyes have different emission spectra or colors thus allowing dye lasers to cover a broad wavelength range from the ultraviolet (320 nm) to the infrared at about 1500 nm. A unique property of dye lasers is the broad emission spectrum (typically 30–60 nm) over which gain occurs. When this broad gain spectrum is combined with a diffraction grating or a prism as one of the cavity mirrors, the dye laser output can be a very narrow frequency beam (10 GHz or smaller) tunable over a frequency range of 10^{13} Hz. Frequency tuning over even larger ranges is accomplished by inserting different dyes into the laser cavity. Dye lasers are available in either pulsed (up to 50–100 mJ) or continuous output (up to a few watts) in table-top systems that are pumped by either flash lamps or by other lasers such as frequency-doubled or -tripled YAG lasers or argon ion lasers. Most dye lasers are arranged to have the dye and its solvent circulated by a pump into the gain region from a much larger reservoir, since the dye degrades slightly during the excitation process. Dyes typically last for 3 to 6 months in systems where they are circulated. Dye lasers are used mostly for applications where tunability of the laser frequency is required, either for selecting a specific frequency that is not available from one of the solid-state or gas lasers, or for studying the properties of a material when the laser frequency is varied over a wide range. Most of these applications are in the area of scientific experiments. Another large application of dye lasers is for producing ultrashort optical pulses by a technique known as mode locking. In this process, all of the longitudinal modes of a dye laser (as many as 10,000) are made to oscillate together (in phase), causing individual pulses as short as 50 fsec (5×10^{-14} sec) to emerge from the laser, spaced at intervals of the order of 20 nsec. These short pulses are of interest in studying very fast processes in solids and liquids and may have applications for optical communications. [*See* TUNABLE DYE LASERS.]

F. Free-Electron Lasers

Free-electron lasers are significantly different from any other type of laser in that the laser output does not occur from discrete transitions in atoms or molecules of gases, liquids, or solids. Instead, a high-energy (of the order of one million electron volts) beam of electrons is directed to pass through a spatially varying magnetic field that causes the electrons to oscillate back and forth in a direction transverse to their beam direction, at a frequency related to the magnet separation in the transverse direction and also to the energy of the electron beam. This oscillation causes the electrons to radiate at the oscillation frequency and to stimulate other electrons to oscillate and thereby radiate at the same frequency, in phase with the original oscillating electrons, thereby producing an intense beam of light emerging from the end of the device. Mirrors can be placed at the ends of the magnet region to feed the optical beam back through the amplifier to stimulate more radiation and cause the beam to grow. The free-electron laser, although still more of a laboratory curiosity than a useful device, offers to produce very high-power output over a wide range of wavelengths from the far infrared to the vacuum ultraviolet.

VII. Applications of Lasers

A. Laser Properties Associated with Applications

Laser applications are now so varied and widespread that it is difficult to describe the field as a single subject. Topics such as surgery, welding, surveying, communications, printing, pollution detection, isotope enrichment, heat treatment of metals, eye treatment, drilling, and laser art involve many different disciplines. Before these individual topics are reviewed, the various characteristics or features of lasers that make them so versatile will be summarized. These properties include beam quality, focusing capabilities, laser energy, wavelength properties, mode quality, brightness properties, and pulse duration.

1. Beam Quality

When a laser beam emerges from a laser cavity, after having evolved while reflecting back and forth between carefully aligned mirrors, it is highly directional, which means that all of the rays are nearly parallel to each other. This directional property, if considered as originating from a single longitudinal mode emerging from a laser cavity, would have such a low beam divergence that a laser aimed at the moon would produce a spot on the moon only 5 miles in diameter after having travelled a distance of 239,000 miles! That is a very small divergence when compared to a flashlight beam which expands to five times its original size while traveling across a room.

2. Focusing Capabilities

Because of the parallel nature of the beam when it passes through a lens (of good quality) all of its rays are concentrated to a point at the focus of the lens. Since diffraction properties of the light must be taken into account, the beam cannot be focused to an infinitely small point but instead to a spot of a dimension comparable to the wavelength of the light. Thus a green light beam could be focused to a spot 5.0×10^{-5} cm in diameter, a size significantly smaller than that produced by focusing other light sources.

3. Laser Energy

The primary limitations on laser energy and power are the restrictions on the size of the amplifier and the damage thresholds when the beam arrives at the laser mirrors and windows. A 1 W continuous carbon dioxide laser beam, focused on a fire brick, will cause the brick to glow white hot and begin to disintegrate. A carbon dioxide laser has been made to continuously operate at a level 10^5 times that powerful! Similarly, a pulsed laser of 5.0×10^{-4} J, when focused into the eye, can cause severe retinal damage. A pulsed neodymium laser has been made that produces 10^8 times that energy!

4. Wavelength Properties

The capability of generating a very pure wavelength or frequency leads to many uses. It allows specific chemical reactions to be activated, wavelength sensitive reflective and transmissive effects of materials to be exploited, and certain atomic processes to be preferentially selected. Some of these processes can use the fixed frequencies of gas and solid-state lasers. Others require the broad tunability of dye lasers.

5. Mode Quality

The ultrapure frequency available from a single-mode output of a laser not only makes possible the concentrated focusing capabilities mentioned but it provides a very pure frequency that is capable of being modulated in a controlled way to carry information. Since the amount of information that is carried over an electromagnetic (light or radio) wave is proportional to the frequency of the radiation, a single-mode optical wave can carry over 10^4 times the information of a microwave and 10^9 times that of a radio wave. This realization is possible whether the optical wave is carried through space, through the atmosphere, or through a tiny glass fiber the size of a human hair.

6. Brightness Properties

The brightness properties are represented by the amount of light concentrated in a specific area during a definite amount of time in a specific wavelength or frequency interval. Such properties are applicable for use in holography and other coherent processes. The effective brightness temperature of a laser can be 10^{20} to 10^{30}°C, much higher than any other man-made light source.

7. Pulse Duration

The duration of a laser beam can vary anywhere from a continuous (cw) beam that will last as long as the power is supplied to the amplifier and as long as the amplifier keeps producing gain (50,000 h for some gas lasers and potentially many tens of years for some semiconductor lasers) to pulses as short as 6.0×10^{-15} sec for the shortest pulses from a pulse-compressed, mode-locked dye laser. Many applications require very short pulses, including high-speed digital signal transmission for communications and also surgical applications that would result in damage to surrounding tissue via heat conduction if longer pulses were used. Other applications require very long or continuous light fluxes to produce effects in materials that are relatively insensitive to the light beam but would be destroyed by shorter duration, higher-intensity beams.

B. Communications

One of the earliest recognized applications of the laser, because of its capability of producing a very pure frequency, was in the field of communications. Earlier developments using radio waves and then microwaves naturally led to thoughts of using optical frequencies in a similar manner to take advantage of the increased information carrying bandwidth that would be essential for the information age. This concept has now progressed to the point where the semiconductor laser with its small size, low power consumption, and high reliability, in conjunction with optical fibers as transmission media and rapidly developing product lines of optical connectors, couplers, modulating devices, etc., is a major component in communication systems. Using very short, discrete pulses of light to transmit digitally encoded signals is a more recent advancement that will most likely become the ultimate technique for both long and short-range communications.

C. Medical

Medical applications are often the most publicized uses of lasers primarily because they affect the general public more directly than other applications. The first applications were in the field of ophthalmology where the laser was used to weld detached retinas and photocoagulate blood vessels that had grown into the region in front of the retina, thereby blocking vision. In such instances the laser beam easily passes through the transparent portions of the eye, including the cornea and lens, to the region of its intended use where the laser energy is absorbed for treatment. Lasers were also developed as diagnostic tools in cell sorting devices for blood treatment and in fluorescent analysis of Pap smears. The more recent applications in laser surgery are perhaps the most far reaching applications of lasers in medicine. The ability of a laser beam to perform very localized cutting along with cauterization of the incision has produced a wide range of surgical procedures including eye operations (see Fig. 8), gynecologi-

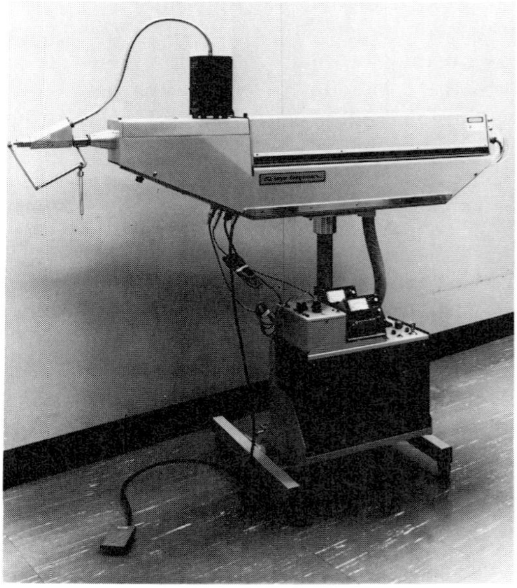

FIG. 8. Carbon dioxide laser eye surgery instrument showing articulated laser beam delivery arm on the left. [Courtesy AT&T Bell Laboratories.]

cal operations, throat and ear surgery, removal of birthmarks, and the most recent prospect of reaming out clogged arteries.

D. Materials Processing

The accurate focusing capability of the laser, allowing the concentration of high power into a small area, makes it a natural device for working with materials. Drilling accurate, tiny holes using a computerized control is now routine in many manufacturing centers, ranging from drilling holes in nipples of baby bottles to drilling holes through high-strength steel. Cutting and welding of high-temperature materials with a laser beam are also effective procedures due to the laser's ability to concentrate energy and power. Another use of lasers is in the heat treatment of metallic surfaces. Pistons of automobile engines, for example, were previously treated in ovens thereby requiring the heating of the entire piston, whereas now a high-power laser can be quickly scanned over specific locations of the piston, locally melting and resolidifying the surface in a short time without having to treat the entire piston.

E. Construction

The use of the laser in the construction industry primarily involves its effectiveness as a straight line reference beam. It is used in the construction of buildings by using a device that has three mutually perpendicular laser beams emerging to provide the reference lines for the sides and vertical alignment of the buildings. It is used as a reference beam for leveling and grading. In this procedure, a laser beam is arranged to continually scan a region under development so that the beam regularly provides a reference level for a grading tractor. Lasers are also used in surveying, as a horizontal reference level.

F. Information Processing

Information processing includes many applications involving reading information in one form and transmitting and converting it to another form. Supermarket bar code readers are probably the most well-known application of this type in which a laser beam scans the digitally encoded ''bar code'' on grocery items. The reflected, digitally encoded beam is then transmitted to a computer where the product is identified and the information is sent to the checkout register printout. In compact disc players, a diode laser is focused into the grooves on the disc and the reflected, modulated light is detected, converted to an electrical signal, and sent to an amplifier and speaker system. In holograms, the light that is reflected from an object is recorded on film in a way that denotes not only the intensity of the light from various portions of the object but also the relative phase of each of those portions. Reconstruction of the image then provides a three-dimensional image of the original object. Use of the laser in projection is accomplished by scanning various colors of lasers across a screen much as an electron beam is scanned in a television set. The light of the various laser colors is adjusted in intensity at each point on the screen to produce a realistic image of the original object.

G. Remote Sensing

A laser beam provides a unique opportunity to access a distant region without having to install sensing devices in that region. The region could be a hazardous or polluted area, a mine where poisonous gases are potentially located, or an ozone layer in the upper atmosphere. By various techniques the laser can scatter a small portion of its intense beam off of the impurity species, giving off characteristic radiation that is detected back at the source of the laser without requiring human access to the remote region. This technique makes it possible to do quantitative measurements in real time to provide valuable information that is often not available by other techniques.

H. Military

Military applications of lasers most often fall in the category of radar or ranging devices which determine accurate distances to specific targets or map out regions for future access. Lasers also can be directed onto specific targets (usually using an invisible infrared laser) to serve as an illuminating source that will guide infrared sensitive bombs or provide aiming of gunfire. More recently they have begun to be developed as a directed energy weapons; however, the size of such devices prevents them from becoming relatively portable field weapons.

I. Laser Fusion and Isotope Enrichment

Both of these processes involve the use of lasers in developing alternative energy sources for the future when oil supplies begin to dwindle. The laser fusion program is attempting to produce miniature hydrogen fusion reactions in which the fusion energy will be captured as heat that can be used to drive electric power generators. In a conceptual power plant, powerful lasers (1 MJ of energy) will be focused on tiny pellets of special hydrogen isotopes, compressing and heating them to temperatures as high as 10^8 degrees, densities 10^3 times that of solid densities and durations of the order of one billionth of a second (the conditions under which the fusion reactions occur). Laser isotope enrichment has already been shown to be an effective process for enriching concentrations of special isotopes of uranium for use in atomic fission reactors, in a way that is much less costly than the gaseous diffusion and centrifuge processes that have been used since World War II. This enrichment process is accomplished by using selective laser wavelengths that react with the desired rare isotope but not with the more common isotope of uranium.

J. Lithography and Printing

Lasers can be used as sources to expose paper in printing systems, to expose printed circuits for electronic circuit design, or to expose photoresist material to make electronic microchips. They can also be used to deposit circuit material in specific locations on microchips. This procedure is done by focusing the laser onto locations where deposition is required, thereby producing a localized chemical reaction that precipitates the solid material from a molecular gas or vapor containing that material.

K. Laser Art

Lasers are used in many artistic media. The laser light show is probably the most well known. In such a show, laser beams of various colors are directed around a dark room or on a screen in synchronization with a musical presentation. The complicated but artistic images provide a spectacular visual display. Laser are also used in etching or burning artistic patterns on various media.

L. Miscellaneous Applications

Several other applications that do not fall into the other categories are worth mentioning. Laser marking devices are used to put product labels, serial numbers, and other information on items that are difficult to permanently mark by other means, such as high-strength metal and ceramic materials. The laser beam actually melts or ablates the surface in the region where the marking is desired. In a similar way a laser is used to remove material from weights on automobile wheels as determined by computerized balancing instruments, while the wheels are still rotating, thus saving time and improving balancing precision. Lasers also serve as ultrasensitive reference beams in earthquake detection instruments.

Bibliography

Ready, J. F. (1978). "Industrial Applications of Lasers." Academic Press, New York.

Thyagarajan, K., and Ghatak, A. K. (1981). "Lasers—Theory and Applications." Plenum, New York.

Yariv, A. (1985). "Optical Electronics," 3rd ed. Holt, New York.

LASERS, CHEMICAL

Wayne C. Solomon *University of Illinois at Urbana–Champaign*

GLOSSARY

Beam quality: Measure of the excellence of the beam, that is, how closely it approaches the theoretical limit of 1.0.

Chemical laser: Laser operating on a population inversion produced (directly or indirectly) in the course of an exothermic reaction.

Efficiency: Effectiveness of conversion of chemical energy into laser energy output.

Optical cavity: Portion of the flowing system containing the gain medium.

Specific power: Power/mass flow rate, given in kilojoules per kilogram.

Spectral transitions: Energy spacing for the lasing lines.

Unstable resonator: Optical extraction system composed of two convex mirrors, allowing for resonance within the optical cavity.

Chemical lasers are normally divided into two classes, that is continuous wave (cw) flowing systems and various types of pulsed devices. These can be subdivided into direct chemical pumping and transfer lasers, depending on how the lasing species receives its energy. The laser systems of greatest potential for scaling to high average powers are the cw class; we will, therefore, direct this discussion to cw systems offering the most promise. There has been dramatic progress in chemical laser research in the past 25 years. Since the first pulsed chemical laser was discovered by J. V. V. Kasper and G. C. Pimentel in 1965, a very large body of scientific research and engineering data have been produced. The most comprehensive survey of the chemical laser field was accomplished by A. A. Steponov, R. W. F. Gross, and J. F. Bott several years ago.

I. Continuous Wave, Direct Pumping Chemical Lasers

A. EARLY WORK AND OPERATING CHARACTERISTICS

In 1967, K. G. Anlauf reported the first experiments capable of producing a steady stream of population-inverted active molecules. This demonstrated the *potential* for operation of a class of continuous wave chemical lasers. The excitation is provided by the simple rearrangement of the chemical bonds of the initial species undergoing exothermic chemical reaction. The development of the first *cw chemical laser* devices quickly followed these early experiments. In 1969, two independent groups almost simultaneously observed lasing from a supersonic diffusion flowing laser. The principle of operation for the flowing devices is based on the mixing of reagents at reduced pressure, chemical reaction, and the subsequent nonequilibrium distribution of energy within the product particle. When an optical system is provided, these purely chemical processes are nearly simultaneously followed by stimulated emission of radiation from the active lasing medium.

Continuous wave lasing has been achieved by direct pumping from a wide variety of chemical reactions. The HF/DF or DF/HF lasers, around which most of our discussion will center, have been highly developed in the United States. Other less-well-known cw chemical lasers include HCI, HBr, CO, and Hf overtone types. Many of these have been characterized by researchers in Europe and the Soviet Union. [*See* LASERS, NUCLEAR PUMPED.]

The supersonic diffusion HF[DF] laser employing fuel combustion is the most important example. An oft-studied derivative of this is an electric arc-heated device. Both will be discussed. Typically, these laser variants employ a one-step excitation process known as the "cold" reaction mechanism.

$$F + H_2[D_2] \rightarrow HF^*[DF^*] + H[D], \qquad \Delta H = -32 \text{ kcal/mole} \quad (1)$$

The existing lasers based on this chemistry are necessarily low-pressure devices due to the relatively short collisional lifetimes for the principal lasing species. The most efficient devices known have output energies (specific power) in the range 300–400 kJ/kg and corresponding chemical efficiencies of 5–20%. The higher chemical efficiencies are obtained at a lower range of optical cavity pressures. The HF laser radiates multiline at $\lambda = 2.5$–$3\ \mu m$, although for every process which we consider, there will be an analogous one governing the DF laser [$\lambda = 3.6$–$4.2\ \mu m$]. These wavelengths correspond to the vibration-rotation transitions in HF[DF].

Continuous wave lasers are designed with elements which can be best illustrated by considering a simple combustion-driven supersonic diffusion laser as an example. In this case, no external power supply is required; the laser operates purely on chemical energy. Figure 1 gives the main elements which make up this device. The laser combustor provides the appropriate thermodynamic conditions for the dissociation of the oxidizer (fluorine or fluorinated oxidizer). Diluent (helium) mixed with combustor fuel, D_2, is introduced into the combustor through a conventional gas-gas injector. Additional diluent plus an excess of F_2 enter through impinging jets, providing the complete mixture of combustion gases which undergo auto-ignition and rapidly achieve the desired equilibrium conditions. Combustion stagnation temperatures vary from 1500 to 2500 K, and stagnation pressures are in the range 30–300 psi in the subsonic flowing section. This short combustion zone has walls which are cooled with excess fuel or liquid coolant. The conditioned combustor gas containing the excess dissociated fluorine subsequently flows through an array of highly cooled small nozzles. These serve as the fine supersonic-supersonic mixing arrays which introduce the oxidizer stream into the optical cavity. These arrays of supersonic mixing nozzles are designed to be at their maximum efficiencies for particular operating conditions that produce flow at a temperature and pressure substantially lower than that in the combustor (optical cavity static temperatures are 200–400 K and pressures are 2–15 torr). Another function of the nozzle is to "freeze" chemically the F-atom mole fraction at or near its combustor value. The supersonic mixing nozzles thus establish appropriate pressure, temperature, and composition for the all important chemical reactions which proceed rapidly in the laser cavity. The cavity mixing and chemical excitation reaction stage takes advantage of the large cavity inlet velocity provided by the supersonic nozzles, which act to extend the lasing-zone length and fill the optical cavity.

A wide variety of laser optical systems are employed to extract a beam from the cavity. Typical of these is the unstable resonator in Fig. 1. In this system, there is a central region near the optical axis (of such a radius that its Fresnel number is near unity) within which all the laser radiation is closely coupled together by diffraction. Therefore, the laser emission produced by this central region is coherent. However, because the convex mirrors magnify the beam continually as it propagates through the optical cavity, this central or uniphase mode spreads out to fill the entire laser medium, eventually overflowing around one mirror to form the laser output shown exiting the beam extraction mirror (scraper mirror). One way to think of this unstable resonator is as a low-Fresnel-number oscillator region surrounded by a multipass amplifier. Since phase control of the output beam occurs within the central portion of the resonator, a high-quality output beam is usually obtained.

The output beam has the form of an annulus with a zero-intensity central region produced by the part of the beam that is blocked by the extraction mirror. Such an output beam, when passed through a conventional telescope designed to accommodate an unobscured beam, has an annular intensity distribution which departs from the ideal uniform intensity (such would give the minimum far-field beam width). However, in high-power lasers, it is frequently found that the annular beam departs so little in beam quality from the uniform beam that other factors, such as medium homogeneity, are more important than uniform intensity when optimization of laser system performance is conducted.

In the final stage of any flowing chemical la-

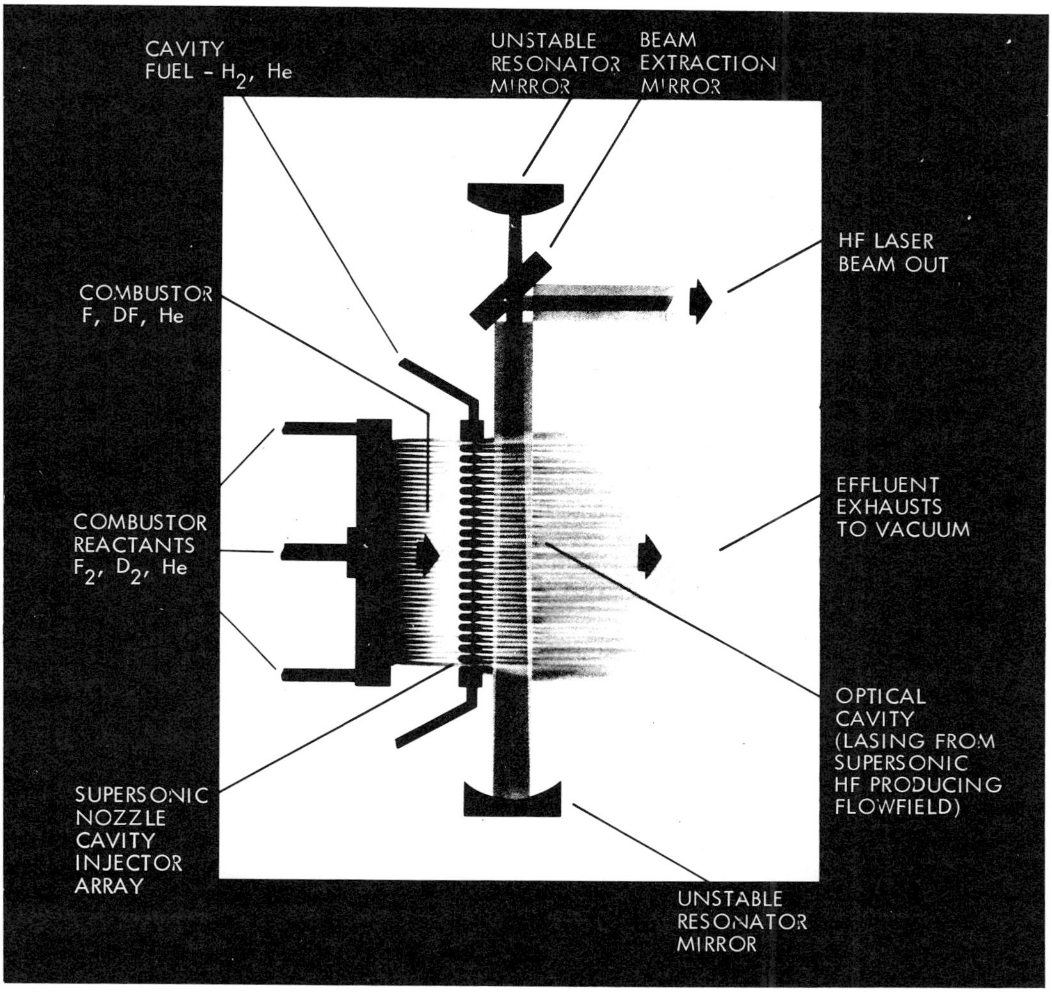

FIG. 1. Schematic of a cw HF chemical laser. (Courtesy of TRW, Inc.)

ser, the processing of the exhaust effluent must be considered. This is usually accomplished by a smooth transition of the cavity shroud into a diffuser designed to raise the pressure and accommodate the low entrance Reynolds numbers. Diffuser efficiency can be considered an integral part of the overall-design of the laser system. A common normal-shock diffuser model is usually adequate to optimize the performance of this section. Pumping of this effluent is subsequently accomplished after recovery of the available pressure within the system.

This completes our description of the generic cw chemical laser. The details and evolution of these systems will now be considered.

B. Experimental Results

Results obtained from arc-heated devices have been crucial in developing the required data base. Devices which can run for several hours, such as that illustrated in Fig. 2, have been used to guide the effort toward higher efficiencies. During these experiments, it was noted that the chemical reaction producing the excited HF is severely limited by diffusion and that fast mixing is the key to higher powers and better efficiencies. The gas generator unit illustrated here incorporates a successive arrangement of arc and plenum chambers to provide the source of atomic fluorine (eliminating the need for a

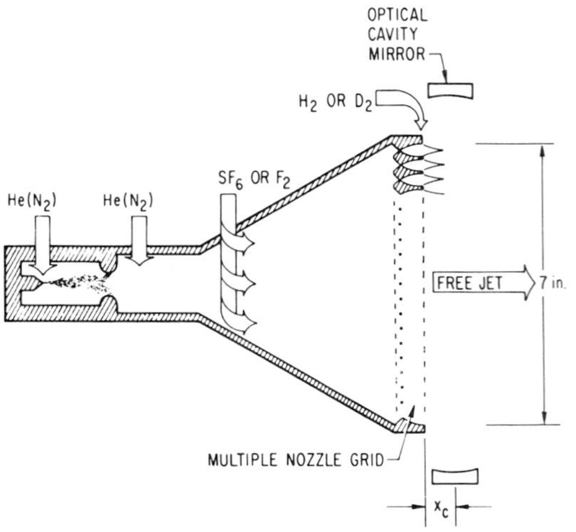

FIG. 2. Schematic of an arc-driven cw chemical laser. [Reprinted with permission from Gross, R. W. F., and Bott, J. F. (1976). "Handbook of Chemical Lasers." Wiley, New York.]

subsonic combustor). A stream of helium mixed with fluorine atoms is accelerated through a supersonic nozzle array into the laser cavity. At the exit of the nozzle, there is a secondary fuel injector system used to supply the fuel H_2 (or D_2). It quickly becomes apparent that short, minimum-length nozzles are required to expand and accelerate the gas flow to provide supersonic mixing of the oxidizer–diluent mixture with the secondary fuel jet. These nozzles are decidedly different from wind-tunnel nozzles or rocket nozzles, in which the main object is to produce a gas flow that is in equilibrium and in which all the energy introduced by the heater is recovered as kinetic energy and not frozen in the internal energy modes of the molecules. In contrast, the primary nozzle of a chemical laser generates only a nonequilibrium chemical composition. The high velocity of the supersonic jet is also an important feature of the chemical laser. This is because the very rapid deactivation of the HF* and, therefore, the very short effective lifetime of the lasing species result in short inversion zones even at supersonic velocities. Therefore, a premium is placed on the ability of a particular nozzle design to mix the fuel, H_2 (or D_2), rapidly into the supersonic flow. The special characteristics of arc devices have been particularly instructive in the effort to design proper supersonic mixing nozzles. Early experiments with these devices have provided the data base for rapid-mixing, two-dimensional, slit-nozzle arrays and large axisymmetric matrix nozzles. The latter led to the development of the fastest known supersonic mixing arrangement, which is the array of small circular axisymmetric nozzles in which the main fluorine jets are fully surrounded by fuel. In this design, the main jets are surrounded by hydrogen, and the distance the hydrogen has to diffuse is considerably shortened when compared to a slit-nozzle array of equal area ratio.

An analogous development with fine-scale axisymmetric nozzles has been conducted for combustion-driven low-pressure nozzles employing helium as a diluent (see Fig. 3). This has been followed by a number of sophisticated laboratory developments to provide integral two-dimensional, rapid-mixing nozzles for specific applications. This technology has been vastly expanded and demonstrated on a wide variety of combustion-driven lasers employing nitrogen diluent. However, experiments with a new technology eventually superceded these in what has proven to be a unique departure from these earlier integral nozzle arrays. The efficient fine-scale mixing obtained with the axisymmetric arrays in the presence of large boundary layers has been replaced by a clever hypersonic injection technique within the free stream. Several of these new arrays have been developed in such a way that highly efficient manufacturing methods are employed. The technology development referred to here is the employment of relatively large primary fluorine nozzles and injection of the H_2 (or D_2) by hypersonic wedges located across the nozzle exit plane. This method provides a well-established supersonic flow in the primary stream while allowing minimal boundary layer growth along the hypersonic wedges. Care is taken to ensure that the oblique shocks created by the hypersonic injectors do not block the large primary nozzle or create large optical path differences. This hypersonic wedge technology has been incrementally scaled up in the United States, utilizing modular devices such as the Multiple Purpose Chemical Laser and the Alpha verification module to provide the data base for the large engineering demonstration laser, Project Alpha, recently discussed by workers at TRW.

The Alpha cylindrical chemical laser is a high-power demonstration of several laser technologies. It provides the ability to wrap arrays of modules in the form of a large cylinder so that the fluorine and diluent flow passes radially out around the annulus which holds the hypersonic

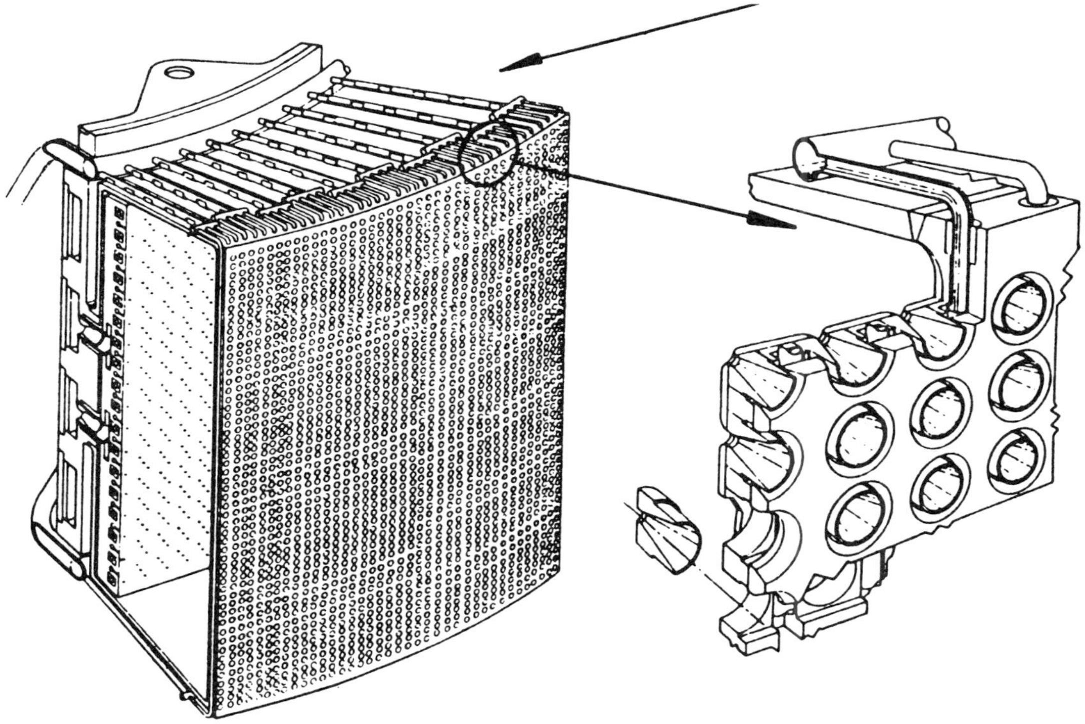

FIG. 3. Gain generator module with axisymmetric mixing nozzle. (Courtesy of Textron.)

hydrogen injectors (see Fig. 4). Mixing and chemical reaction occur in the annularly formed optical cavity. A specially designed annular resonator must be employed for mode control (see Fig. 5). Curvature in the radial direction on the annular mirrors allows mode control and intensity levels to be controlled in the compacted leg. The cylindrical configuration is preferred for very high powers because it allows for decreased gain length over that of conventional linear laser configurations. This provides many times the device output power without increasing the nozzle power flux, cavity injector length, or mode width. Such a resonator should also reduce effects from flow-field disturbances, diffraction losses, anomalous dispersion, and other optical loss mechanisms which might tend to produce a poor-quality beam.

Another trend has been toward improved mixing nozzles for the production of large linear lasers. Thus, a series of HF (or DF) chemical laser nozzle arrays have been developed for operation at high cavity pressure where mixing is likely to be slow and deactivation is rapid. These nozzles incorporate trips within the trailing edges of the arrays to enhance the stretching of the diffusion flame front. Several meters of individual banks of such nozzles can be coupled in a slightly tilted fashion (avoiding the alignment of repetitive flow disturbances) to achieve very high powers. Supersonic diffusers and ejectors have been developed for efficient recovery of pressure from such flows. The best example of a high power laser test device produced by scaling up the high-pressure trip nozzle technology is the Mid-Infrared Advanced Chemical Laser (MIRACL) system located at the White Sands Missile Range in New Mexico. The optical configuration for this system is a confocal unstable resonator similar to that illustrated in Fig. 1.

There have been a series of engineering demonstrations of large linear chemical lasers at TRW, leading to the development of the MIRACL. These demonstrations have been employed in exploring the beam characteristics, beam control technologies for pointing and tracking, DF laser beam propagation, and beam effects testing. In addition to the pure power-scaling effects with linear lasers, which do not appear to be of consequence, there are media- and hardware-induced degradations on the beam quality of these lasers at higher powers. The

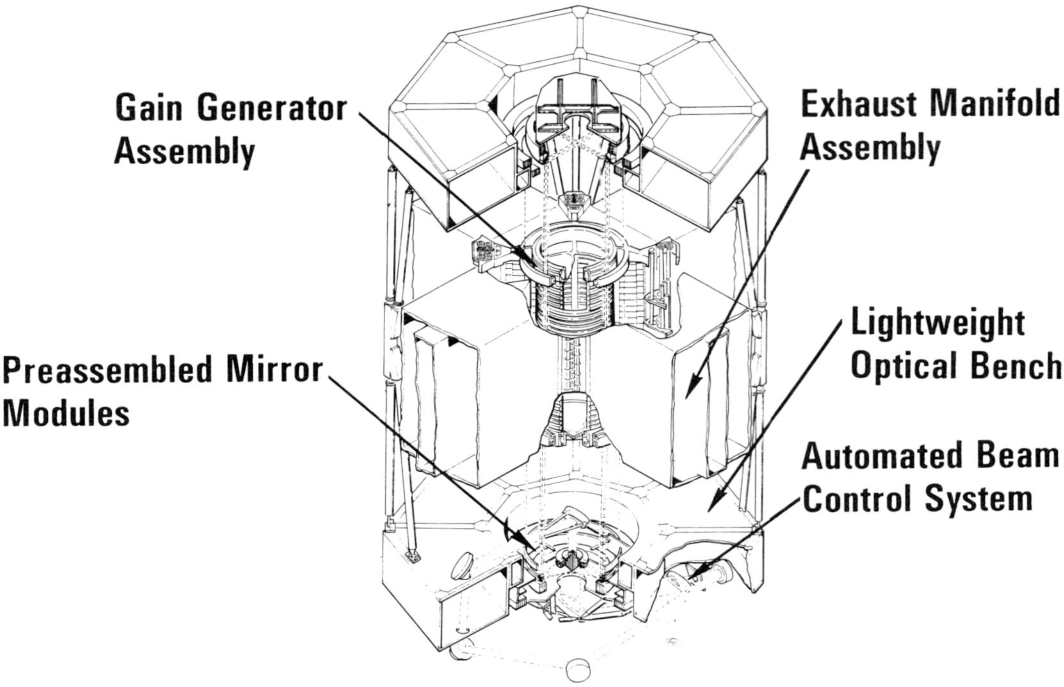

FIG. 4. Alpha HF chemical laser. (Courtesy of J. Miller, TRW, Inc.)

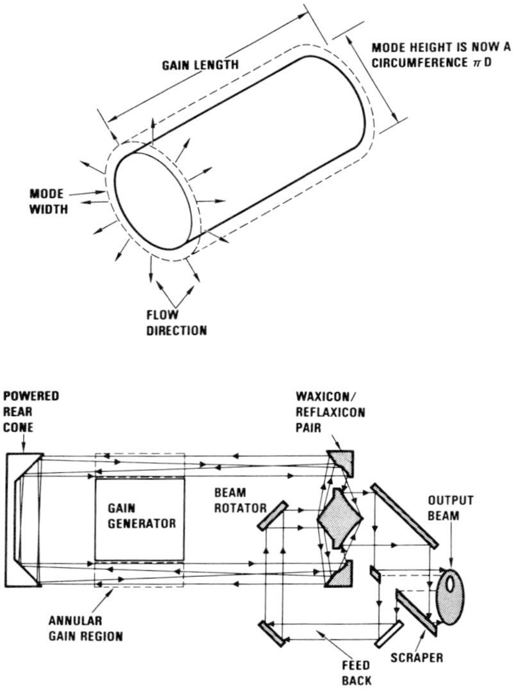

FIG. 5. Cylindrical laser resonator. (Courtesy of J. Miller, TRW, Inc.)

principal effects are repetitive flow-field disturbances, mirror distortion, and diffraction. At laser powers achieved so far, the most serious contributions to poor beam quality appear to be those which result in optical path differences within the cavity. Some of these are evidently due to design compromises, but even with the most rigidly designed linear devices, there will be dramatic benefits from optical devices which are designed to correct phase front distortions. The methods currently available include phase sensing and correction with a deformable mirror. Advances in this area are coming rapidly.

C. Recent Advances

New phase conjugation methods such as stimulated Brillouin scattering (SBS) might well be applied to HF lasers to improve the beam to attain very high quality and brightness. With further developments in this area likely, one can easily conclude that practical consideration of cw chemical lasers to tens of megawatts may be possible.

A completely different approach to scaling and beam projection for chemical lasers involves the combination of beams from separate resonators. Thus, phased arrays of laser beams can provide a means of increasing the power and aperture size of laser transmitters. D. J. Bernard has provided a good example of this technique in experiments with coupled multiline cw HF lasers. Here the larger aperture is synthesized by combining the outputs of several phase-locked laser systems. In a coupled device, part of the output from one laser is injected into a second laser in order to achieve phase locking between the two outputs. Phase locking here is defined as the achievement of mutual coherence between two outputs from every spectral line. Complete phase locking has now been achieved between each spectral line of two lasers employing unstable confocal resonators. The demonstrations have been impressive, since the corresponding far-field peak intensity enhancement and reduction in far-field spot size have been very near the theoretical limit.

Many attempts have been made to produce a purely cw chemical laser that is capable of operating at wavelengths shorter than 2.8 μm. The techniques proposed involve lasing on electronic transitions and have not been successful. However, a short wavelength laser concept which offers potential for scaling to very high powers has proven its capabilities in W. Q. Jeffers's laboratory. The concept is to operate an HF chemical laser on the first overtone transitions, thus shifting the output to several bands centered at 1.33 μm. The overtone chemical laser is produced by providing for the optical resonator to remain below threshold for the fundamental transition while lasing on the overtone transitions. It has been found that overtone efficiencies exceeding 30% of the available power on the fundamental of an HF laser can be obtained when the cavity mirror reflectivity at 2.8 μm is near 1% while maintaining a relatively high reflectivity (>98%) at the overtone wavelength, 1.3 μm. The potential for an even more efficient overtone device for utilization with smaller optical telescopes which transmit well through the atmosphere appears to be quite high, according to recent work by L. H. Sentman (private communication).

II. Continuous Wave Transfer Chemical Lasers

The operation of a cw transfer chemical laser depends on the transfer of energy from excited reaction products, which are produced in a mixing and reacting flow system, to host molecules or atoms which can undergo stimulated emission. Most of the work has been concerned with systems utilizing vibrational–rotational transitions in CO_2 and, more recently, in the development of chemical oxygen-iodine (COIL) cw chemical lasing utilizing electronic transitions. Recent work has focused on the utilization of new reagents to extend the spectral range of the emission.

A. The DF–CO_2 Transfer Chemical Laser

The most highly developed cw transfer chemical laser is the subsonic and supersonic DF-CO_2 laser. This laser depends on the chain reaction of fluorine and deuterium followed by the transfer of vibrational quanta from excited DF molecules to CO_2 molecules as seen in reactions (1′–3).

$$F + D_2 \rightarrow DF^* + D, \qquad \Delta H = -32 \text{ kcal/mol} \tag{1'}$$

$$D + F_2 \rightarrow DF^* + F, \qquad \Delta H = -100 \text{ kcal/mol} \tag{2}$$

$$DF^* + CO_2 \rightarrow DF[v-1] + \Delta CO_2[00^01] \tag{3}$$

The lasing occurs at 10.6 μm and corresponds to the usual P-20 transition, 00^01–100^0 band of the CO_2 molecule. This cw laser is undoubtedly the most versatile of all the known chemical lasers, having been operated successfully at multikilowatt powers over a range of cavity pressures of 10 to 250 torr, with extended lasing zones both subsonically and supersonically. Theory attributes this robustness to the large amount of chemical energy in storage, the rapid rate of reactions (1′-3), and the relatively low rate of deactivation of the upper state of CO_2. As a result of these factors, the chemical efficiency of these devices can be quite high.

B. The Chemical Oxygen-Iodine Laser

The chemical oxygen-iodine laser (COIL) is the only known chemically pumped cw laser utilizing electronic transitions. Overall processes involve the liquid phase generation and flow of excited metastable singlet oxygen, O_2 ($^1\Delta g$) into the gaseous phase. This is followed by a fast resonant electronic energy transfer to a metastable atomic iodine, $I(5^2P_{1/2})$ according to the following reaction set.

$$H_2O_2 + 2OH^- + Cl_2 \rightarrow O_2(^2\Delta g) + 2H_2O + 2Cl^- \tag{4}$$

$$2O_2(^1\Delta g) + I_2 \rightarrow 2O_2(^3\Sigma^- g) + 2I(5^2P_{3/2}) \quad (5)$$

$$O_2(^1\Delta g) + I(5^2P_{3/2}) \rightleftarrows O_2(^3\Sigma^- g) + I(5^2P_{1/2}) \quad (6)$$

$$I(5^2P_{1/2}) \rightarrow I(5^2P_{3/2}) + h\nu\ 1.315\ \mu m \quad (7)$$

In the first reaction (4), the chemical energy originally contained in the hydrogen peroxide is stored in the singlet oxygen. An alkaline solution is necessary to provide sufficiently rapid generation of the gaseous oxygen. The sound reaction (5) (although speculative in nature) is needed to generate sufficient quantities of atomic iodine species. The final chemical reaction (6) is a reversible process needed to generate the excited-state iodine atom for the upper laser state. Since this process is reversible, the ratio of excited-state oxygen to ground electronic state must be sufficiently high to ensure that a population inversion in iodine atoms obtains.

The state of development of this COIL device is inherently tied to the development of the singlet oxygen chemical generator. The usual two-phase flow-excited oxygen generation methods tend to operate best at very low pressures (1–5 torr), and this inherently narrows the operational characteristics available in supersonic flowing systems. The adverse reaction of water and hydrogen peroxide vapor in the process of quenching O_2 ($^1\Delta g$) and excited iodine atoms makes it necessary to remove these deactivating agents. Thus, cooling of the gas stream after generation but prior to entering the laser cavity is necessary to remove the condensibles. A number of clever laboratory generation/cooling techniques have been employed in an effort to increase the power and efficiency of supersonic COIL lasers; however, no completely acceptable solution for scaling the generator component is currently at hand, and the potential remains to be realized.

This laser has the shortest wavelength of any cw chemical laser. Such a device is of interest because it has been operated to maximum efficiencies of as much as 40% and offers the potential to reduce the size of the large optics used for high-power systems. The single-line laser wavelengh lends itself to good optical transmission through the atmosphere or silica fiber. In materials-processing applications, a coupling (absorption) of laser energy is also quite efficient at 1.3 μm. These same properties also permit some hope for application to the problem of controlled thermonuclear fusion.

BIBLIOGRAPHY

Airey, J. R., and McKay, S. F. (1969). *App. Phys. Lett.* **15,** 401.

Anlauf, K. G., Maylotte, C. H., Pacey, P. D., and Polanyi, J. C. (1967). *Phys. Lett. A* **24,** 208.

Bernard, D. J., Chodzko, R. A., and Mirels, H. (1988). *AIAA J.* **26,** 1369–1372.

Blauer, J. A., Hager, G. D., and Solomon, W. C. (1979). *IEEE J. Quantum Electron.* **QE-15,** 602.

Cool, T. A., and Stephans, R. S. (1970). *Appl. Phys. Lett.* **16,** 55.

Driscoll, R. J., and Tregay, G. W. (1983). *AIAA J.* **21,** 241.

Duignan, M. T., Feldman, B. J., and Whitney, R. B. (1987). *Opt. Lett.* **12,** 111.

Giedt, R. R. (1973). The Aerospace Corporation Tech. Rep., TR-0073(3435)-1, The Aerospace Corporation, Los Angeles, California.

Gross, R. W. F., and Bott, J. F. (1976). "Handbook of Chemical Lasers." Wiley, New York.

Jeffers, W. Q. (1989). *AIAA J.* **27,** 64–66.

Kasper, J. V. V., and Pimentel, G. C. (1965). *Phys. Rev. Lett.* **14,** 3529.

McDermott, W. E., Pchelkin, N. R., Bernard, D. J., and Bousek, R. R. (1978). *Appl. Phys. Lett.* **32,** 469.

Meinzer, R. A. (1970). *Int. J. Chem. Kinet.* **2,** 335.

Miller, J. (1986). Advances in chemical lasers, *Proc. Int. Conf. Lasers, 1985.* STS Press, McLean, Virginia.

Miller, J. (1988). *Proc. Int. Conf. Lasers, 1987.* STS Press, McLean, Virginia.

Spencer, D. J., Jacobs, T. A., Mirels, H., and Gross, R. W. F. (1969). *Int. J. Chem. Kinet.* **1,** 295.

Steponov, A. A., Schcheglov, V. A. (1982). *Sov. J. Quantum Electron.* (*Engl. Transl.*) **12,** 681–707.

Steponov, A. A., Schcheglov, V. A., and Yuryshev, N. N. (1985). *Sov. J. Quantum Electron.* (*Engl. Transl.*) **15,** 746–777.

Wilson, L. E., and Hook, D. L. (1976). *AIAA Pap.* **76–344.**

LASERS, COLOR CENTER

Clifford R. Pollock *Cornell University*

GLOSSARY

Cross section: Measure of the probability of a stimulated transition occurring. The larger the cross section, the more likely a photon will interact with the system.

Femtosecond: 10^{-15} second, abbreviated fsec.

Free spectral range (FSR): Frequency difference between adjacent resonances of an optical cavity.

Interstitial: Presence of an extra ion in the lattice at a site not normally occupied in a perfect crystal.

Quantum efficiency: Ratio of the number of emitted photons to the number of absorbed photons.

Stokes shift: Wavelength of the luminescence is generally greater than the wavelength of the stimulating radiation.

Threshold: Point where a laser has enough gain to begin to oscillate.

Vacancy: The absence of an ion at a lattice point that would normally be occupied.

Wave function: Distribution of the electron in space. This distribution is generally localized around a potential well.

Certain color centers in the alkali halides can be used to create broadly tunable, optically pumped lasers in the near infrared. These lasers may be operated in a continuous wave with output powers on the order of 1 W, or mode locked to yield pulses of less than 100 fsec duration. Laser-active color centers generally provide long-lived operation only when operated at cryogenic temperatures, although many of the centers can be stored at room temperature with no degradation. Operationally, color center lasers are analogous to dye lasers, except that instead of operating in the visible region, color center lasers cover the infrared tuning range from 0.8 to 4 μm. Their ability to generate tunable radiation in the near infrared has made color center lasers unique and indispensable in the study of guided wave optical devices, narrow bandgap semiconductors, and molecular spectroscopy.

I. Introduction to Color Center Lasers

Color centers are simple point defects in crystal lattices, consisting of one or more electrons trapped at an ionic vacancy in the lattice. These point defects are common in many crystalline solids and have been studied rather extensively in alkali-halide crystals (e.g., NaCl and KCl). Certain color centers have optical absorption and emission bands that make them suitable as laser gain media. The structure and physics of these centers and transitions will be reviewed in the next section. Lasers based on these color centers are closely analogous to organic dye lasers: they are optically pumped, can be broadly tuned, share a similar cavity design, and can generate ultrashort pulses. The significant difference between color center lasers and dye lasers is the tuning range: at present, through the use of several different types of centers and host lattices, the entire region between 0.8 and 4.0 μm can be covered. Tunable coherent radiation over this wavelength region is important for studies in optical communication, molecular and semiconductor spectroscopy, and various other specialized fields. It is this unique combination of broad wavelength tuning range and continuous wave power that makes the color center laser useful. [*See* LASERS.]

The laser-active color centers possess two characteristics ideal for efficient, tunable operation. First, their absorption and emission bands are homogeneously broadened: all the excited centers can contribute energy to a given laser mode, and all the centers will be equally well pumped by a single line laser operating within the pump absorption band. Homogeneous broadening allows efficient single-mode operation over the entire tuning range of the laser. Second, most of the transitions involved in laser emission are fully allowed. Such transition strengths when combined with broad homogeneous linewidths lead to large gains, quiet continuous wave (cw) operation, and the ability to generate ultrashort pulses ($\approx 10^{-13}$ sec duration). The single pass power in a 2-mm crystal containing a reasonable density of centers can exceed 100%. Such gains are in dramatic contrast to those obtained in solid state lasers that use transition metal ion impurities for the gain medium.

Color center lasers can be operated in pulsed, mode-locked, or cw fashion. In the cw mode, output powers exceeding 2 W have been achieved in certain crystals. Typical output powers and tuning ranges for the various color center lasers are summarized in the following sections of this article. In pulsed operation, output powers of 1 MW have been achieved, and it is reasonable to assume pulsed powers of many megawatts will be generated routinely in the future. [*See* MODE-LOCKING OF LASERS.]

The single frequency linewidth of the color center laser is truly exceptional in its purity. In single mode cw operation, linewidths below 4 kHz have been achieved. This performance is attributable to the solid state nature of the gain media: there are no moving parts in the laser cavity to perturb the phase of the laser. Such high frequency definition, coupled with broad tunability, has made the color center laser a powerful tool for spectroscopy and metrology.

It is perhaps the mode-locked operation of color center lasers that has been the most spectacular. Taking advantage of the broad emission bandwidth, the laser output can be transformed into a train of tunable picosecond and femtosecond duration pulses. The femtosecond color center laser was the first tunable subpicosecond pulse source, and is the only such source that has reasonable average output power (hundreds of milliwatts) and fast repetition rates ($\sim$100 MHz). Such short pulses are extremely useful for the investigation of ultrafast phenomena in semiconductor materials and optical fiber switches.

The laser active color centers are generally stable only when cooled to cryogenic temperatures. Although some center types allow for low-duty-cycle pulsed operation at room temperature, cw operation at room temperature usually leads to fading of the output power. At room temperature, the centers either thermally dissociate or become mobile and transform into nonlasing centers through attachment to other defects. Thermal degradation can be minimized or eliminated at reduced temperatures, hence the crystals are usually anchored to a cold finger maintained at liquid nitrogen temperature (77 K). Additionally, the radiative quantum efficiency for some of these centers increases significantly at reduced temperatures.

Due to the relatively short radiative lifetime of the color center, intense optical pumping from a laser source is necessary to achieve efficient laser operation. The pump laser depends on the crystal, but is usually a Nd:YAG laser operating at 1.06 or 1.32 μm, or an Ar- or Kr-ion laser operating in the visible. The color center laser cavity must contain dispersive elements such as a prism in order to facilitate tuning and line narrowing. Properly designed, a color center laser is usually capable of tuning over a range exceeding 25% of its central wavelength. Specific examples of the design and construction of the laser are described in this article.

II. Physics of Laser-Active Color Centers

A. Optical Emission Processes

While color centers exist in many different crystal lattices, most research to date has been done on point defects in alkali-halide crystals such as KCl. This review will concentrate on the alkali halide centers because they form the basis of practically all the useful color center lasers, and they are well understood. A representative sample of color centers in alkali-halide crystals is shown in Fig. 1. All laser-active color centers involve anion (halide ion) vacancies. The F center has the simplest structure, consisting of a single electron trapped at a vacancy surrounded by an essentially undisturbed lattice. If one of the neighboring alkali ions is a substitutional alkali impurity, say Li^+ in a KCl crystal, the cen-

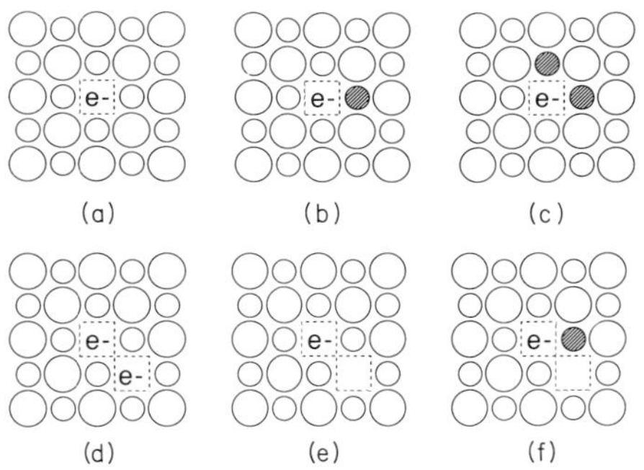

FIG. 1. A representative sample of color centers in alkali-halide crystals. The large and small circles represent negative and positive ions, respectively. Filled circles represent alkali impurities. (a) F center, (b) F_A center, (c) F_B center, (d) F_2 center, (e) F_2^+ center and (f) $(F_2^+)_A$ center.

ter is called an F_A center. Similarly, the F_B center consists of an F center beside two substitutional impurities. Two adjacent F centers along a [110] axis of the crystal form the F_2 center. Its ionized counterpart is called the F_2^+ center, which is an F_2 center with only one electron. Analogous to the F_A center, the $(F_2^+)_A$ center consists of an F_2^+ center adjacent to a substitutional alkali ion. Of the various centers described in Fig. 1, the F_A, F_B, F_2^+, and $(F_2^+)_A$ defects form color center lasers. Note that the simple F center does not lase. The reason for this will be discussed below.

There are also several types of laser-active color center not shown in Fig. 1. These include the $(F_2^+)^*$ and $F_2^+:O^{2-}$ centers, which consist of F_2^+ centers associated with an as yet unknown defect and with an oxygen ion, respectively. Also missing is the Tl°(1) center, which is schematically similar to the F_A center but is functionally more like a neutral Tl perturbed by an adjacent vacancy, and the N_2 center, which consists of three F-centers in a trigonal arrangement. Many other alkali-halide color centers are not shown, such as the larger aggregate centers (including F_4), but with few exceptions, these larger centers do not play a significant role in the physics of color center lasers. Laser-active color centers have also been reported in crystals other than the alkali halides, including the F^+ center in alkaline earth oxides and the H_3 and N_3 centers in diamond. These lasers have not been widely reproduced or studied, and there is still some doubt concerning the physics of their operation; hence they will not be discussed in this article.

The optical absorption and emission of the F center can be understood on a qualitative basis using a highly simplified quantum mechanical model, the particle-in-a-box. This model is based on the fact that F centers are essentially electrons trapped in a three-dimensional square well formed by the electrostatic potential of the surrounding positive ions. In this model, the energy between the ground state and first excited state is:

$$E_{2p} - E_{1s} = 3h^2/8ma^2$$

where 1*s* denotes the ground state, 2*p* the excited state, h is Planck's constant, a is the box dimension, and m is the mass of the electron. Note that the energy scales with the well dimension as a^{-2}. This model works amazingly well when applied to color centers. It is found experimentally that if distance a is taken as the nearest neighbor separation, the F-band energy can be related to a for most alkali halides as

$$E_F = 17.7a^{-1.84}$$

where a is in angstroms and E_F is in electron volts. This is known as the "Mollwo relation." As will be illustrated with examples below, many color centers follow a similar relation between the lattice constant and the energies of their absorption and emission bands. The model also predicts a strong coupling between the lattice dimensions and the transition energy. Lattice vibrations, called phonons, harmonically vary the actual dimensions of the square well in a period of less than 10^{-13} sec, causing the energy levels to vary on this time scale. Since this perturbation is random and occurs at all F centers at a rate faster than the excited state lifetime of the center, the absorption and emission bands of the center are homogeneously broadened.

B. F Centers

The F center is the most fundamental color center defect in the alkali-halide lattice. Although it is not laser-active, the optical properties of the F-center are important in understanding the laser physics of other color center lasers. The fundamental absorption band of the F center, called the "F" band, corresponds to a transition from the 1*s*-like ground state to the 2*p*-like first excited state of the square-well potential. The F band transition is very strong and dominates the optical spectrum of the alkali-halide crystal. In fact, the term *F center* comes from the German word *Farbe,* meaning color, and refers to the strong color imparted to the otherwise transparent alkali-halide crystals.

As noted above, the simple F center is not suitable for lasing. After excitation to the first excited state, the F electrons are very near the conduction band and can be easily ionized by thermal or optical energy. The strong possibility of self-absorption into the conduction band by photons emitted from other F centers also exists, destroying the potential gain mechanism as well as introducing loss. These deleterious effects result from an anomalous spatial relaxation following optical excitation, as illustrated in Fig. 2. After being excited, the electron is raised to the 2*p* state, where its spatial structure is more spread out than the 1*s* state. In response to this diffuse wave function, the lattice expands slightly, enlarging the dimensions of the potential well. This expanded lattice causes even further spreading of the excited-state wave function and lattice until lattice forces finally restrain the relaxed dimensions. The resultant wave function extends out several lattice constants and is called the relaxed excited state (RES). Due to the poor spatial overlap of the RES and the terminal state wave function, the emission dipole moment is relatively small, leading to a small gain cross section. No laser has ever been made based on simple F centers, and it appears unlikely that such a laser will ever exist. On the other hand, the F center is very useful for forming other varieties of color centers.

C. F_A(II) Centers and F_B(II) Centers

F_A centers are classified into two categories depending on their relaxation behavior after optical excitation. Type I centers, denoted F_A(I), behave almost identically to the simple F center just described. They display the same diffuse relaxed excited state, low gain cross section, and self-absorption. The other (and rarer) class of F_A centers are called type II. They are distinguished by a dramatically different relaxation

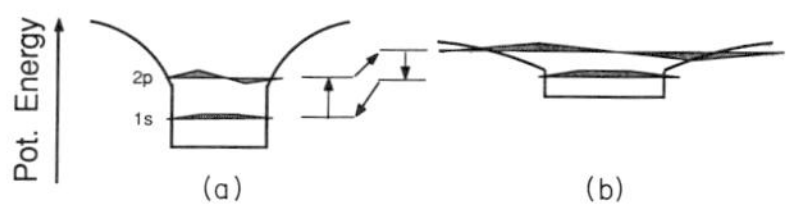

FIG. 2. Potential well and wave functions for the F center (a) before excitation (normal configuration) and (b) after excitation (relaxed configuration). The four-level energy scheme is shown between the wells. All energies are plotted with respect to the conduction band, hence the relaxed state appears to be at a higher energy than the first excited state.

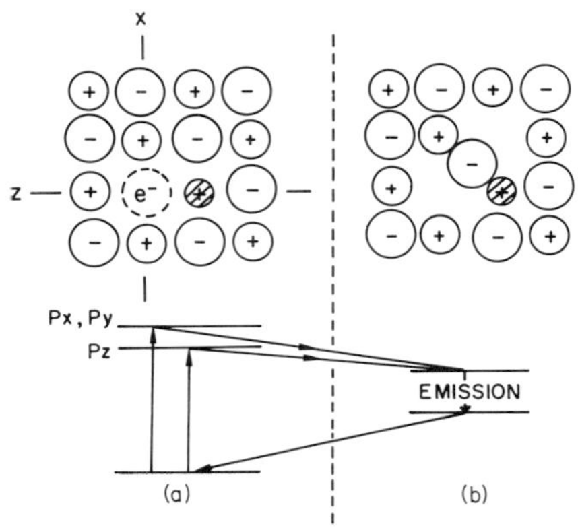

FIG. 3. Structure and energy-level diagram of the F_A(II) center (a) before optical excitation (normal configuration) and (b) after optical excitation (relaxed configuration).

process. After excitation, F_A(II) centers relax to a double-well configuration as shown in Fig. 3. A neighboring anion moves between the impurity and neighboring cation, creating a double-well potential. The resulting electronic wave functions remain localized and the transition moment is very strong. The resulting emission from this transition is Stokes shifted out to the 2–3 μm region.

The presence of the impurity ion in the F_A(II) system causes the P_z orbital to be distinguished from the $P_{x,y}$ orbitals (see Fig. 3). Transitions of the P_z orbital result in a longer wavelength absorption band that is often well resolved from the main band. In laser applications, this additional band considerably enhances the probability that a convenient pump source will overlap with the absorption.

Upon relaxation, the anion separating the two wells can move back into its original location or into the original vacancy. In the latter case, the F_A(II) center will have effectively rotated 90°. Such reorientation can lead to orientational bleaching of the band, where the center no longer absorbs light polarized along the original *z* axis. In practice, optimum power is achieved from F_A(II) crystals if a crystal ⟨100⟩ axis lies at 45° to the laser and pump polarization, so that either center orientation will have a component of the dipole moment aligned with the stimulating and pump fields.

F_A(II) centers have been found only in lithium-doped alkali halides, specifically KF, KCl, and RbCl. The lithium is incorporated into the crystal during growth in concentrations approaching 0.02 mol %. Lasers have been built using the KCl and RbCl centers and, except for different tuning ranges, their characteristics are similar. The quantum efficiency η of the F_A(II) luminescence in KCl: Li is about 40% at $T = 77$ K, and decreases slowly with increasing temperature until it approaches zero at $T \approx 300$ K. Efficient operation of F_A(II) center lasers thus requires that the crystals be maintained at cryogenic temperatures during use. Liquid nitrogen ($T = 77$ K) is commonly used, being inexpensive and readily available. Coupled with the large Stokes shift, the low quantum efficiency leads to a maximum conversion efficiency of about 10% for the F_A(II) laser.

F_B centers involve an F center beside two substitutional alkali impurities. Since the distribution of foreign alkali ions in an otherwise pure lattice is statistical, F_B centers are far fewer in number than F_A centers and are obtained in substantial quantities only when the impurity dopant concentration is fairly high (approximately 1%). Like the F_A center there are two types of F_B center, also classified by their relaxation behavior. The F_B(I) center is formed when the two substitutional impurities lie along a common ⟨100⟩ axis. The F_B(I) center has optical properties similar to the F center, which preclude the possibility of lasing action. The F_B(II) center is formed when the two alkali impurities are adjacent to one another along a ⟨100⟩ axis of the crystal (see Fig. 1).

The F_B(II) centers relax into a double-well configuration after excitation, similar to that shown in Fig. 3 for the F_A(II) center. Their emission is almost entirely quenched at temperatures of 4 and 300 K, but reaches a maximum around 100 K. Optimum laser performance can be obtained from the F_B(II) center with cw pumping, which raises the crystal temperature from 77 K to around 100 K. Pulsed operation is less effective in raising the crystal temperature, since the crystal has a chance to cool between pulses. One difficulty with F_B(II) centers is that they are accompanied by substantial quantities of F_A(I) and F_B(I) centers, all of which have overlapping absorption bands with the F_B(II) center. Consequently, the optical pump power suffers losses by these residual centers, diminishing the overall efficiency of the F_B(II) center laser.

The F_A(II) and F_B(II) are among the most stable color center lasers presently known, providing stable tunable laser radiation in the 2.2 to 3.6 μm region. The operational lifetime of these lasers is almost entirely determined by secondary effects, such as crystal fogging due to small vacuum leaks or water desorption in the dewar. Figure 4 shows the power and tuning range of an optimized color center laser using F_A(II) and F_B(II) centers. Other relevant details of these and the other color center lasers are tabulated in Table I.

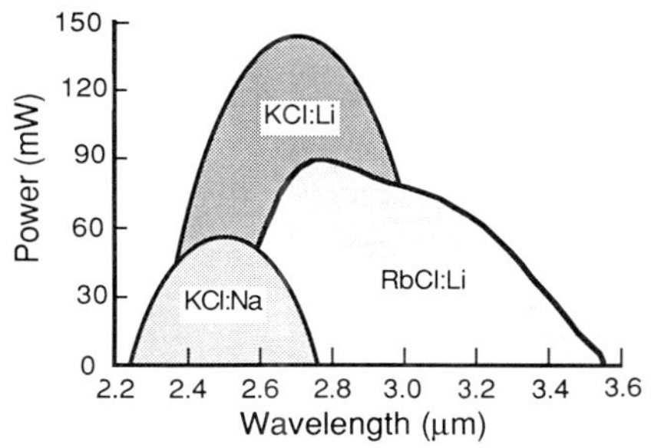

FIG. 4. Tuning range and output power from an optimized color center laser using F_A(II) and F_B(II) centers. (Adapted from German, 1986.)

D. F_2^+ Centers

A powerful but short-lived color center laser is based on the F_2^+ center. As indicated in Fig. 1, the F_2^+ center consists of two adjacent anion vacancies sharing one trapped electron. In contrast to the $F_{A,B}$(II) centers, the F_2^+ relaxation following excitation entails only a slight enlargement of the surrounding lattice.

The configuration of the F_2^+ center is suggestive of an H_2^+ ion imbedded in a dielectric continuum. The two lattice vacancies play the role of the protons. The energy levels of such an ion are related to the free space case by

$$E_{F_2^+}(r, K_0) = (1/K_0^2)\, E_{H_2^+}(R)$$

where $R = r/K_0$ is the proton separation in free space, r is the distance between the lattice vacancies, K_0 is the dielectric constant of the lattice, and $E_{H_2^+}(R)$ is the energy function of the molecular hydrogen molecule in free space, which has been calculated for various states and separations R. Figure 5 shows an F_2^+ energy level diagram. The levels are named after their molecular ion counterparts. The left side of the energy diagram shows the RES levels. Comparison of measured ground and excited state levels of the F_2^+ center in several alkali-halide lattices with predicted levels from the imbedded H_2^+ model show excellent agreement. Dotted lines indicate nonradiative transitions.

TABLE I. Peformance of Common Color Center Lasers

Host lattice	Center	Pump wavelength (μm)	Tuning range (μm)	Maximum power (W)	Operational lifetime
LiF	F_2^+	0.647	0.82–1.05	1.8	Days
NaF	$(F_2^+)^*$	0.87	0.99–1.22	0.4	Weeks
KF	F_2^+	1.06	1.22–1.50	2.7	Days
NaCl	F_2^+	1.06	1.4–1.75	1	Days
NaCl : OH	$F_2^+ : O^{2-}$	1.06	1.42–1.85	3	Years
KCl : Tl	$Tl^{\circ}(1)$	1.06	1.4–1.64	1	Years
KCl : Na	$(F_2^+)_A$	1.32	1.62–1.95	0.05	Months+
KCl : K_2O	$F_2^+ : O^{2-}$	1.32	1.7–1.85	0.06	Months+
KCl : Li	$(F_2^+)_A$	1.32	2.0–2.5	0.4	Months+
KI : Li	$(F_2^+)_A$	1.7	3.0–4.0	0.006 (pulsed)	?
KCl : Na	$F_B(II)$	0.514	2.25–2.65	0.05	Years
KCl : Li	$F_A(II)$	0.514	2.3–3.0	0.2	Years
RbCl : Li	$F_A(II)$	0.647	2.6–3.6	0.1	Years
KCl	N_2	1.064	1.27–1.35	0.04 (pulsed)	Months+

Since the alkali halides have a wide variety of lattice dimensions, r, and dielectric constants, K_0, one would expect the F_2^+ center to have a wide distribution of absorption energies in the various crystals. This is indeed the case, as was shown in Fig. 6, where the absorption bands of the $F_2{}^+$ center range from 0.67 μm in the tight LiF lattice up to 1.5 μm in the much larger KBr lattice. Similar to the F center, the broadening of individual absorption bands is caused by lattice phonons, and is homogeneous.

The transition of greatest interest for F_2^+ lasers is the $1S\sigma \rightarrow 2P\sigma$ transition between the ground state and first excited state. This transition has nearly ideal properties for laser operation: (1) the oscillator strength is large, allowing for a large gain cross section; (2) the quantum efficiency is 100% (3) the Stokes shift is just enough to prevent overlap of the emission and absorption bands, forming an ideal four-level system; and (4) there are no excited-state absorptions that overlap with the emission. Lasers based on this transition are among the most powerful and efficient color center lasers ever made. Figure 7 shows normalized tuning curves of some common F_2^+ lasers. The tuning range extends from 0.8 to 1.9 μm, a range important for optical communication. [The NaF* band shown in Fig. 6 belongs to the $(F_2^+)^*$ center described below.]

F_2^+ center lasers have two drawbacks: (1) they display a slow fading of output power with extended operation and (2) the crystals must be stored at cryogenic temperatures at all times. The mechanism for the decay is not totally understood, but it is probably associated with reorientation of the center. Excitation to the $2P\pi$ state is known to lead to a reorientation of the center's axis through nonradiative relaxation to one of the other ⟨110⟩ directions in the lattice. Figure 8 illustrates the reorientation of an F_2^+ center. Under the intense optical fields of laser operation, multiphoton excitation from the laser pump source may excite the $2P\pi$ state and lead to reorientation. Since there is nothing in the

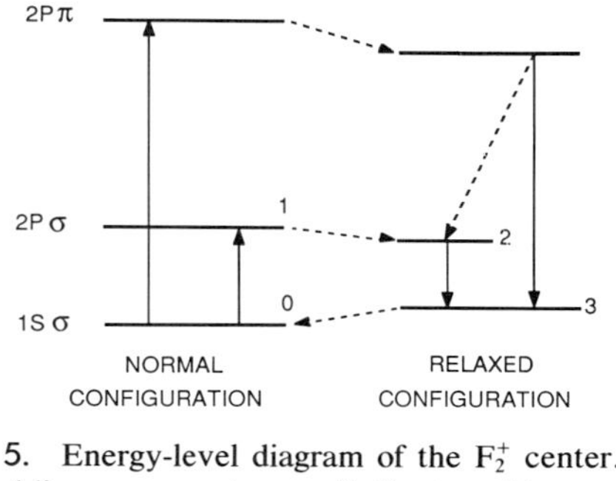

FIG. 5. Energy-level diagram of the F_2^+ center. The dotted lines represent nonradiative transitions.

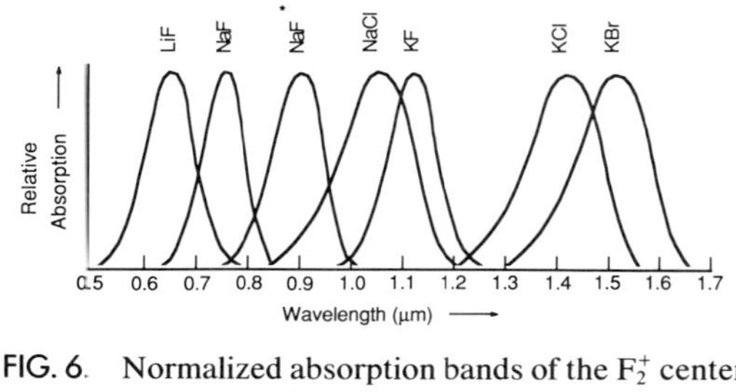

FIG. 6. Normalized absorption bands of the F_2^+ center in various alkali halides.

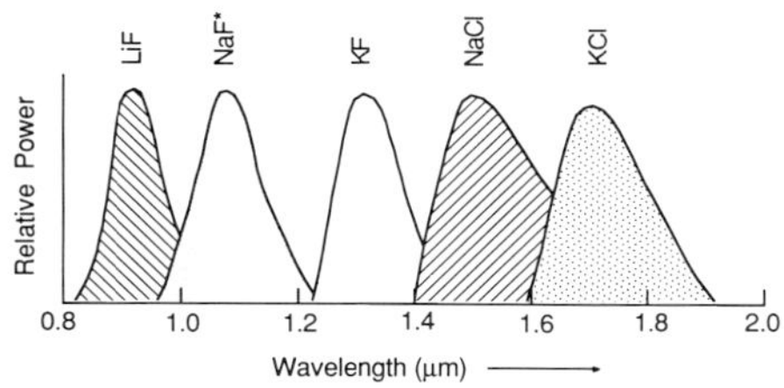

FIG. 7. Normalized tuning curves for some of the known F_2^+ lasers. The NaF* curve is from an $(F_2^+)^*$ laser.

lattice to pin the center to one location, repeated flipping of the $F_2{}^+$ centers causes them to take a random walk through the crystal. Eventually, it is likely they will run into other centers or defects, forming larger F-center aggregates.

The requirement of cold storage arises because the F_2^+ centers are formed through radiation damage. (Coloration techniques are described briefly in Section III.) At elevated temperatures the F centers and radiation by-products (such as interstitials) tend to annihilate one another through thermal motion. Storage at reduced temperature ($T < 170$ K) stops this aggregation. Cryogenic specimen dewars are generally used for both long-term storage and transporting crystals from the radiation source.

The operational lifetime of an F_2^+ laser depends on how long the crystal has been pumped. Under the best conditions a single crystal can be made to operate for only several days. This decay, coupled with the awkwardness of creating and storing the active crystals, and the discovery of more stable color center lasers, has virtually eliminated the use of F_2^+ lasers. However, the F_2^+ center laser was the first powerful color center laser, and in the hands of skilled experimenters it has been used to generate tunable near-infrared radiation.

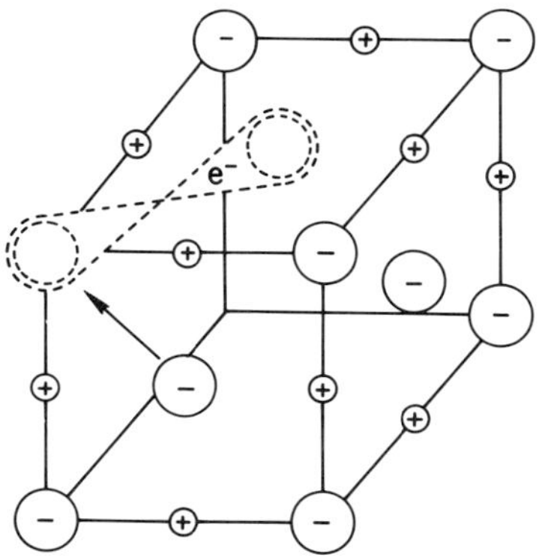

FIG. 8. Schematic representation of the reorientation of an F_2^+ center. A neighboring anion can move into one of the two vacancies, causing an effective rotation of the center.

E. Stabilized F_2^+ Centers

The F_2^+ centers can be associated with certain defects in the crystal lattice to form more stable color centers with output characteristics similar to the F_2^+ center. To date, four types of stabilized centers have been reported: the $(F_2^+)_A$, $(F_2^+)^*$, $(F_2^+)^{**}$ and $F_2^+ : O^{2-}$ centers. The $(F_2^+)_A$ center is an F_2^+ center located beside an alkali impurity (see Fig. 1). The $F_2^+ : O^{2-}$ center is an F_2^+ center beside a doubly negative anion impurity ion. The $(F_2^+)^*$ and $(F_2^+)^{**}$ centers are F_2^+ centers associated with an as yet undetermined defect in the lattice, most likely an interstitial halogen defect.

These stabilized centers display most of the advantages of the F_2^+ center, such as large cross sections and unity quantum efficiency, but they offer a number of additional benefits as well. First, the centers are pinned at one point in the lattice, and as a result they display reduced or no fading. Second, new and useful tuning ranges can be created because the stabilizing defect slightly perturbs the energy levels. Finally, the room temperature shelf life of the centers is usually increased to essentially infinite length with no degradation of ultimate laser performance.

1. $(F_2^+)^*$ and $(F_2^+)^{**}$ Centers

The $(F_2^+)^*$ center appears in NaF after a radiation-colored F_2^+ center crystal is allowed to sit at room temperature for several days in the dark. The F_2^+ band disappears and is replaced by a new band at a longer wavelength. Pumping this new band produces emission that is shifted to a longer wavelength relative to the F_2^+ emission band, but otherwise displays all the characteristics of an F_2^+ center. Strong evidence has been found linking the density of $(F_2^+)^*$ centers to the dosage of radiation used to introduce color centers.

The $(F_2^+)^{**}$ center is similar to the $(F_2^+)^*$ but is even further shifted in wavelength for both the absorption and emission band. In contrast to the $(F_2^+)^*$, the $(F_2^+)^{**}$ center is only generated in NaF crystals which contain OH^-, thus it is thought that the stabilizing defect for the "double star" center is an artifact of radiation damaged OH^- in the crystal.

The "star" centers can be stored at room temperature, and in NaF they cover an important spectral window around 1.1 μm. Figure 7 includes a tuning curve of the NaF $(F_2^+)^*$ laser. Unfortunately, like the F_2^+ laser, the $(F_2^+)^*$ and $(F_2^+)^{**}$ centers also display a slow fading of output power with use. This fading is an order of magnitude slower than that of the F_2^+ laser, so they represent an improvement from the user point of view. To this date, the actual structure of the "star" centers is not known, although it is likely that they are nearly identical to the $F_2^+ : O^{2-}$ center described in Section II,E,3, with the difference that the star centers are created with radiation damage and the $F_2^+ : O^{2-}$ center is created through additive coloration.

2. $(F_2^+)_A$ Centers

A stable laser based on the $(F_2^+)_A$ center has been demonstrated in several lattices and currently is the only color center laser able to tune beyond 3.6 μm. $(F_2^+)_A$ center lasers combine the best characteristics of the F_A and F_2^+ laser: (1) they are operationally stable with no fading, (2) they are room temperature storable because they are additively colored (see Section III), and (3) they are reasonably powerful.

The stability of the center arises from the trapping of the otherwise mobile F_2^+ center to one location in the lattice, stopping the debilitating migration. The impurity also affects the energy levels of the F_2^+ center: the absorption bands are only slightly shifted, but the emission bands are always shifted to longer wavelengths. The size of the shift depends on the substitutional impurity: a small ion in a large lattice causes a large shift, while similar sized substitutional ions cause a smaller shift. This new degree of freedom is a boon to the laser engineer: by choosing a suitable dopant, the energy bands of the F_2^+ center can be shifted to new wavelength ranges. Examples of these new ranges are shown in Fig. 9, where the laser tuning curves of several $(F_2^+)_A$ centers in KCl, KI, and RbCl are displayed. To illustrate the wavelength shift caused by the impurity, the emission band of the F_2^+ center in pure KCl is also displayed, along with the two known $(F_2^+)_A$ centers in KCl.

To date, $(F_2^+)_A$ lasers have been able to produce output powers of only several hundred milliwatts. This is a fraction of the power available from a comparable F_2^+ laser, and is due to the low density of $(F_2^+)_A$ centers that can be created in a given crystal. Typical $(F_2^+)_A$ crystals only absorb about 30% of the pump power, limiting the overall conversion efficiency. The low absorption is due to a low concentration of centers, which in turn appears to be due to a lack of suitable electron traps. The F_2^+ and $(F_2^+)_A$ centers are each ionized, so there must be one stable electron trap in the crystal for each active center. In the additively colored $(F_2^+)_A$ center crystals, the traps are other color centers, such as the F_A center which traps two electrons to become an F_A^- center. (In the F_2^+ center crystal, artifacts from radiation damage such as interstitial ions serve this function.) Typical of most negatively charged color centers, the lowest lying energy level of this extra electron is energetically near the conduction band of the crystal, so that only a small amount of energy (thermal or optical) is needed to ionize the center, again creating a free electron. The F_A^- electron traps are subsequently slowly discharged by the intense pump light from the laser. To counter this, all $(F_2^+)_A$ lasers use an auxiliary ultraviolet light to continually reionize the $(F_2^+)_A$ centers to form $(F_2^+)_A$ centers. A dynamic equilibrium between $(F_2^+)_A$ and F_A^- centers thus exists in the crystal during lasing. In Section IV, an example of an $(F_2^+)_A$ laser is shown (see Fig. 12) that uses a mercury lamp to maintain lasing. Typically, lasing ceases within 1 sec of blocking the UV illumination onto the crystal. In spite of the comparatively low power of the $(F_2^+)_A$ laser, for many applications a stable, reliable laser source with 200 mW output power is sufficient.

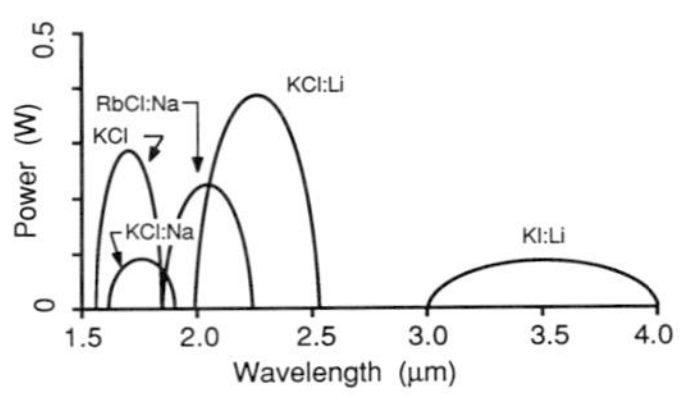

FIG. 9. Tuning curves of several $(F_2^+)_A$ lasers. The data from the KI : Li laser is extrapolated from pulsed data. The KCl tuning curve is for a pure F_2^+ laser and is shown for comparison to the other KCl systems.

3. The $F_2^+ : O^{2-}$ Center

The $F_2^+ : O^{2-}$ center forms one of the most stable and powerful color center lasers yet discovered. The center is an F_2^+ center adjacent to a doubly negative substitutional anion impurity, usually O^{2-} although S^{2-} has also been used. A schematic representation of the model is shown in Fig. 10. The structure is distinct from the

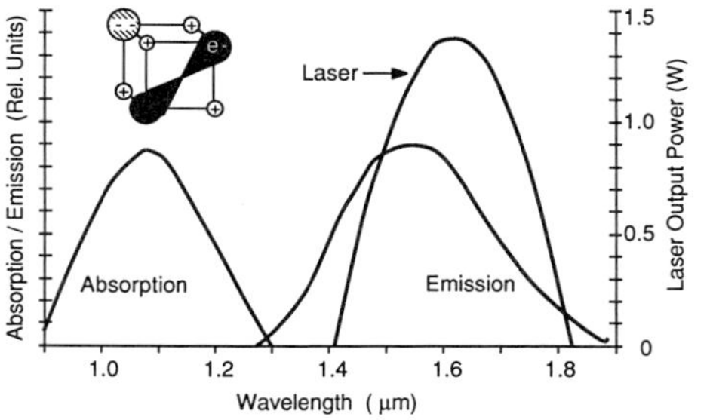

FIG. 10. Tuning curve for the NaCl F_2^+ : O^{2-} center laser. The absorption and fluorescent emission bands are shown in relative units. The insert shows a schematic representation of the F_2^+ : O^{2-} center. Note that the O^{2-} impurity is at an anion location, in contrast to the $(F_2^+)_A$ center.

$(F_2^+)_A$ center because the perturbing impurity is located at an anion site.

This new family of color center laser is operationally similar to the $(F_2^+)_A$ center in three ways: (1) the crystals are additively colored and can be stored at room temperature, (2) lasing is enhanced by an auxiliary light, and (3) the tuning range of each crystal is shifted to slightly longer wavelength than that of the F_2^+ center in the corresponding lattice. In addition, the center appears to be more robust than the $(F_2^+)_A$ center in terms of electron trapping and operating temperatures. Because the impurity ion is doubly negative (as opposed to the singly negative anion it replaces) the overall $F_2^+ : O^{2-}$ center is "charge neutral," so there is little tendency for a free electron to be attracted to and neutralize the laser-active center, as is the case with other F_2^+ systems. The $F_2^+ : O^{2-}$ center essentially has its own "built-in" electron trap.

The laser has been demonstrated in NaCl doped with O^{2-} and S^{2-}, in KCl and RbCl doped with O^{2-}, and will probably be found in other lattices as well. Best results to date have been obtained with the NaCl system, which conveniently operates over the 1.4 to 1.8 μm range. Figure 10 shows the absorption, emission, and laser tuning range of the NaCl system. Following additive coloration and room temperature exposure to UV light for 30 min, a stable absorption band forms near 1.09 μm, accompanied by a strong emission band centered at 1.6 μm. When cooled to 77 K and pumped by a cw Nd: YAG (neodymium-doped yttrium-aluminum-garnet) laser at 1.06 μm, the NaCl crystal has been made to lase with over 3 W of cw output power. Mode-locked operation of the NaCl laser has generated 4-psec pulses, which are at least a factor of two shorter than other stable color centers can produce. Using additive pulse mode-locking techniques (see Section V,C) 75-fsec pulses can be routinely generated with this laser.

Under the action of intense pumping, the $F_2^+ : O^{2-}$ center can reorient in the lattice. Only centers that are aligned with the pump polarization strongly interact with the radiation, so they are most likely to reorient. Unfortunately, once the center flips, it no longer is aligned with the driving polarization, so it no longer participates in the gain process. To counter this effect, an auxiliary light is simultaneously exposed onto the crystal during pumping. The auxiliary light acts to reorient the misaligned centers so that their dipole moment becomes aligned parallel to the pump- and laser-electric-field polarization. Commonly, the output of a HeNe laser or a frequency-doubled Nd: YAG laser is used. One milliwatt of auxiliary power is more than enough to counter the effects of intense pumping.

F. Tl°(1) Center

The Tl°(1) center consists of a neutral Tl atom perturbed by the field of an adjacent single anion vacancy. The superscript in the notation denotes that the Tl atom is neutral. The number in parentheses represents the number of vacancies that are adjacent to the atom. The Tl°(1) center has been demonstrated to lase in KCl and KBr lattices doped with Tl. The latter crystal has proven to be very difficult to grow, so most commonly the Tl°(1) center is used only in KCl. An F center trapped beside the Tl ion will find that its electron spends most of its time on the Tl^+ ion, effectively forming a neutral Tl atom that is perturbed by an adjacent positive vacancy.

The transition involved in the Tl°(1) laser is not related to other color center transitions discussed so far. This laser transition occurs between the perturbed $^2P_{1/2}$ and $^2P_{3/2}$ states of the free Tl atom. This transition is normally parity forbidden, but the strong odd symmetry perturbation caused by the positive ion vacancy mixes the ^2P states with higher lying states, and allows for a modest electric dipole to appear between these states. The absorption band caused by this transition is centered around 1.06 μm, and the emission band is centered at 1.5 μm. The Stokes shift comes about through lattice relaxation after excitation. The laser has a relatively narrow tuning curve, extending from 1.4 to 1.63 μm for the KCl host, and from 1.5 to 1.7 μm for the KBr host. This range is about half that expected for an F_2^+-type center. Output powers up to 1 W have been obtained from the KCl Tl°(1) laser. When mode locked, pulses as short as 9 psec have been directly generated.

The Tl°(1) center must be formed by radiation damage, usually using 2 MeV electron beams. Once formed, the center is operationally stable, but requires modest cooling ($T < 0°C$) for long-term storage. The laser properties of the crystal are destroyed if warmed above room temperature for short periods (days) or if pumped too hard in a laser. Due to these inconveniences, and since the NaCl $F_2^+ : O^{2-}$ offers more power, broader tuning, and easier handling, the Tl°(1) laser is slowly being displaced by NaCl.

G. N Centers

In most alkali halides a pair of absorption bands, called the N_1 and N_2 bands, exist at a wavelength slightly longer than the F_2 band. The structure of the N centers responsible for these bands has not been conclusively determined, even though the center has been the focus of many studies over the past two decades. The longer wavelength band, called the N_2 band, is usually attributed to the F_3 center in which the three point defects form a triangle in the lattice.

In KCl, the N_2 band overlaps the 1.06 μm line of the Nd : YAG laser, which forms a convenient pump for the center. The emission, shown in Fig. 11, spans from 1.1 to 1.5 μm. Lasing in a pulsed mode has been obtained from this center over the 1.23 to 1.35 μm range, making this the shortest wavelength stable color center laser yet reported. The laser only operates in a pulsed mode, however. The pulsed operation is probably (but not yet conclusively) due to multiplet formation of the electrons in the excited state. Unlike all the other lasers described in this article, the N center has more than one electron, which leads to possible triplet or multiplet formation upon relaxation. Such multiplet formation could lead to deleterious absorptions in the lasing region and to a general depletion of laser-active centers. Nonetheless, the N-center laser represents the first of a new class of aggregate center lasers which may open the door to new systems and applications in the future.

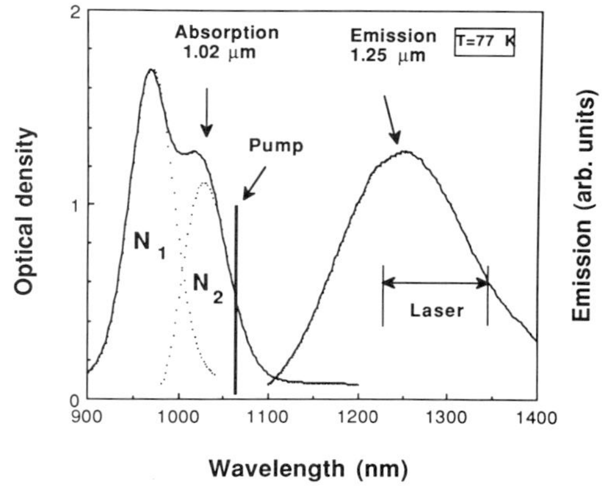

FIG. 11. Absorption and emission bands for the N center in KCl. When pumped by a Q-switched 1.06-μm laser, the N_2 center lases from 1.23 to 1.37 μm.

H. Summary of Laser Performance

Table I lists relevant data concerning the performance of the more common color center lasers. Since the operational lifetime is sometimes an issue with color center lasers, the approximate useful period of a single crystal is also listed. Lifetimes listed as "Months+" represent centers for which no fading has been observed, but observation periods have only been for periods up to 3 months. Unless otherwise noted, the powers are for cw operation.

III. Formation of Color Centers

A question often asked is "How are these color centers formed?" In this section, several proven techniques for forming laser-active crystals will be described.

The first step in generating laser-active centers is to create a population of ordinary F centers, either through additive coloration or radiation damage. Additive coloration is the preferred coloration technique because the F centers produced are very stable, whereas radiation damaged crystals usually require cryogenic storage at all times. However, some lasers, like the F_2^+ and the Tl°(1), can only be colored through radiation damage.

A. Additive Coloration

Additive coloration is achieved by diffusing a stoichiometric excess amount of alkali metal into an alkali-halide crystal. This diffusion process can be achieved by placing a crystal in a vapor bath of the alkali metal for a sufficient length of time. To get reasonable vapor pressures of metal requires temperatures on the order of 600°C. The equilibrium concentration for F centers is directly proportional to the metal vapor density.

An excellent apparatus for coloring crystals is the heat pipe. A detailed description of the heat pipe would be out of place in this article, but an excellent review of the method is given by Mollenauer (see the bibliography). Briefly, the heat pipe maintains a zone of pure alkali metal vapor at a precisely controlled pressure. An uncolored crystal is lowered into the alkali vapor for 30 to 60 min, during which time excess alkali ions diffuse into the crystal. To maintain charge neutrality, negative ion vacancies with electrons (F centers) must diffuse into the crystal in equal concentration. The ultimate density of F centers in the crystal is precisely controlled by adjusting the vapor pressure. The density of centers is often critical for optimized laser performance.

After coloration, the F centers are converted into the desired laser-active center through controlled aggregation. The F centers are made mobile by the illumination of the crystal with F-band light (light absorbed by the F center). This optical excitation is usually carried out with nothing more sophisticated than an unfiltered light bulb. The light ionizes some of the F centers, forming vacancies and free electrons. The free electrons become trapped elsewhere in the lattice, typically at another F center, forming F centers. The vacancies wander through the lattice until they combine with another color center or with a foreign metal ion. Recapture of an electron (from one of the F^- centers) by the new center leads to the formation of an F_2 or F_A center, respectively.

The end product can be controlled through proper doping and temperature control during processing. If F_A or F_B centers are the desired end product, the host lattice should have a higher density of foreign ions than it has F centers. The wandering anion vacancy will then most likely run into a trapping impurity before it runs into another F center. Temperature control is critical: if $T < -50°C$, the vacancies become immobile, while at $T > 0°C$, the vacancies will not attach once they meet an impurity. If the crystal temperature is kept within these limits, an equilibrium population of F_A or F_B can be formed in about 30 min.

To create a more complicated center, such as an $(F_2^+)_A$, a multistep process, which must be empirically determined for each lattice and center, is usually followed. In KCl doped with Li for example, a high density of F centers is first put into the crystal through additive coloration. Aggregation at $-20°C$ then leads to the formation of large populations of F_2 centers as well as F_A centers. The binding energy for F_{2A} centers (an F_2 center beside a substitutional impurity) is less than the thermal energy of the lattice at these temperatures, so few F_{2A} centers are formed in this first step. The crystal is then cooled to $-70°C$ and illuminated with F light. At this temperature, the F centers are nearly immobile, but the F_2 centers are excited by the F light and relax by reorienting (see Fig. 7). Subsequent excitation-relaxation cycles lead to a random walk of the F_2 centers through the lattice, and eventually they are trapped at individual impurity ions, forming F_{2A} centers. Cooling to 77 K and exposing the crystal to UV light ionizes the F_{2A} centers, forming the desired $(F_2^+)_A$ centers. The free electrons are conveniently trapped by the residual F_A centers.

Both the F_A and $(F_2^+)_A$ centers dissociate if the crystal temperature is raised to -300 K. In fact, if left at room temperature for a long time (days), the F centers will form large aggregate centers called colloids. The colloids are easily dispersed by briefly annealing the crystal at the coloration temperature for about 1 min. Due to this ability to be regenerated, additively colored crystals are considered to be room temperature storable for essentially infinite periods, with the proviso that the crystal may require annealing and reaggregation prior to use.

B. Radiation Damage

Radiation damage is a simple technique for creating color centers. No matter what source of radiation is used, whether it be X rays, γ rays, or high-energy electrons, the primary effect is to produce electron-hole pairs. In the alkali halides, the incident radiation strips the electron from a negatively charged halogen ion, Eventually the electron returns home, with 5–10 eV of kinetic energy. The released energy, in combination with thermal energy from the lattice, is usually enough to eject a halogen atom into an interstitial position in the lattice, leaving the electron behind in the vacancy to form an F center. If irradiation is carried out at low temperatures ($T < 170$ K), the vacancies and interstitials will remain frozen in place. But, if the temperature is raised sufficiently, the anion vacancies will migrate. Should it meet an interstitial, the two defects will annihilate each other, leaving a perfect lattice behind. Thus, radiation damaged crystals must be stored at cold temperatures during and after coloration.

Radiation damage is required only for F_2^+ and Tl°(1) lasers. To form the F_2^+ center, the crystal is irradiated at about −100°C, then allowed to warm to room temperature for a few minutes, during which time thermally mobile anion vacancies aggregate with F centers. This warm aggregation process conveniently occurs during the mounting of the crystal in the laser: the crystal must be warmed to room temperature to prevent condensation or frost forming on the crystal surfaces. After mounting, the crystal is cooled to 77 K for use. It must remain below 170 K from then on.

The Tl°(1) center is processed in a similar manner, except with less severe temperature restrictions. After irradiation, the crystal must be kept below 0°C, which can easily be achieved in a home freezer. The steps involved in warming the crystal to mount it are sufficient to aggregate the F centers beside the Tl ions. White light at −10°C for 30 min completes the aggregation process. From then on, the crystal must be stored below 0°C to ensure reliable laser operation.

IV. Optical Gain from Color Centers

A. Stimulated Emission Cross Section

Color centers form an ideal four-level system for laser operation. The energy level diagram of the F_2^+, center in Fig. 4 shows a good example of this. The relevant energy levels for laser operation are labeled 0 through 3, representing the ground state (0), the first excited state (1), the relaxed excited state (RES) (2), and the lower laser level (3). The laser depends on stimulated transitions between levels 2 and 3.

Optical gain is usually defined in terms of a stimulated emission cross section σ, which can be calculated from readily measurable quantities:

$$\sigma = \lambda^2 \eta/(8\pi n^2 \delta\nu \tau_{obs})$$

where π_{obs} is the measured radiative lifetime of the center, η the quantum efficiency of the emission process, n the index of refraction, λ the wavelength of emission, and $\delta\upsilon$ the full width at half maximum (FWHM) of the luminescence. For color centers, η is defined as the number of quanta emitted per quanta absorbed. A value less than unity implies that a nonradiative process is occurring in addition to spontaneous emission. Table II lists typical values of τ, η, $\delta\upsilon$, and σ for a few laser-active color centers.

The gain coefficient γ (cm^{-1}) for a laser medium is related to the cross section by

$$\gamma = \sigma(N_2 - (g_2/g_3)N_3)$$

where N_2 and N_3 are the population densities of the relaxed-excited and relaxed-ground state of the transition, respectively, and g_2/g_3 is the ratio of degeneracies for the two states. The population of the upper laser level N_2 depends on the pumping rate. For color center lasers, virtually all of the centers pumped from the ground state arrive in the relaxed-excited state. If we assume cw pumping and no saturation of the ground state (i.e., $N_0 > N_2$ at all times), simple rate equations show that the unsaturated population of N_2 is

$$N_2 = P\tau/h\nu$$

where P is the power per unit volume absorbed by the crystal, $h\upsilon$ the pump photon energy, and τ the lifetime of the upper state. Due to the relatively short radiative lifetime of the color center, the pump intensity required to achieve a useful population in level 2 must be in the 10^5 W/cm^2 range. Such large intensities can most readily be achieved using a tightly focused pump laser beam. Most color center lasers are pumped by the Ar^+ ion or Nd : YAG laser.

The population of the lower laser level, N_3, decays rapidly into the normal ground state, 0, through lattice contraction. Like the 1 → 2 transition, the 3 → 0 transition is nonradiative and occurs within 10^{-12} sec, so the residual population Na is essentially zero. The gain in a color center system thus depends primarily on the upper state population.

TABLE II. Laser Design Parameters

Center	λ_0 (μm)	τ_{obs} (nsec)	η (%)	$\Delta\nu$ (THz)	σ (10^{-16} cm^2)	I_{sat} (kW/cm^2)
F_A(II)	2.7	200	40	15	1.7	9.4
F_2^+	1.5	80	100	30	1.6	45
$(F_2^+)_A$	2.3	170	100	20	2.7	8.2
$F_2^+ : O^{2-}$	1.6	160	100	45	0.9	9.0
T1°(1)	1.5	1600	100	15	0.2	21
N_2	1.3	210	~100	20	0.4	18

Energy extraction from a laser crystal involves the key process of stimulated emission. High intensity is needed to induce stimulated transitions and overwhelm the spontaneous emission from level 2. The characteristic intensity for a stimulated emission process is called the saturation intensity I_{sat}, and is given by the equation

$$I_{sat} = h\nu/\sigma\tau$$

At $I = I_{sat}$, the stimulated emission rate just equals the spontaneous emission rate. I_{sat} values for several types of color center are given in Table II. A laser is usually designed to operate with an intracavity intensity I in the range $I_{sat} < I < 10\ I_{sat}$. The lower limit of I is obviously for efficiency. The upper limit comes about from the reducing marginal increase in extraction efficiency with increasing intensity.

A linear color center laser cavity is schematically shown in Fig. 12. The cavity has two arms, one with a tight beam-waist at which the color center crystal is placed and one with a nominally collimated beam where tuning elements may be inserted. The crystal is oriented at Brewster's angle to minimize reflective losses. The tight focus at the crystal establishes the high intensity needed for efficient saturation of the population inversion. The spot size at the beam focus, designated the beamwaist parameter ω_0, is typically in the range of 20 to 35 μm for color center lasers.

The beam size expands due to diffraction as the light propagates away from the waist. The characteristic distance over which the beam radius remains smaller than $\sqrt{2}\omega_0$ is called the confocal parameter b and is given by

$$b = 2\pi n\omega_0^2/\lambda$$

where n is the index of refraction and λ the wavelength of the beam. Because efficient stimulated emission requires high intensity, the gain media outside of the confocal parameter makes little contribution to the overall power. Therefore color center laser crystals are usually made no thicker than b, with typical values of b in the 1 to 3 mm range.

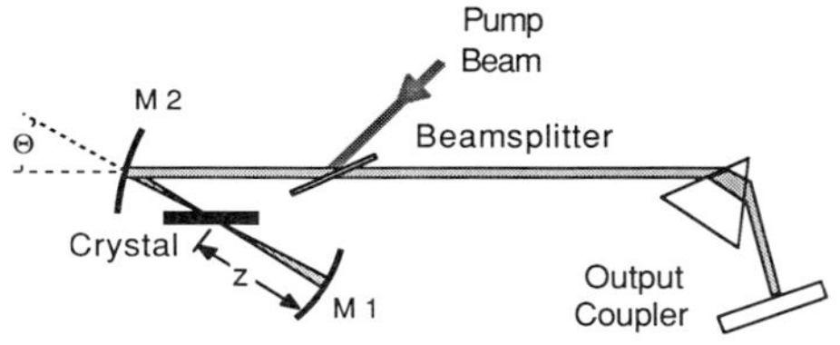

FIG. 12. Schematic of a linear color center laser. The beamsplitter is dichroic, reflecting the pump wavelength yet transmitting the color center wavelength. Tuning is accomplished by rotating the output coupler.

Pump absorption is determined by the Beer's law expression

$$P_{abs} = P_{in}(1 - e^{-\sigma_g N_0 l})$$

where σ_g is the ground state absorption cross section (which is approximately the same size as the emission cross section for the laser-active color centers), N_0 the ground state population, l the crystal thickness, and P_{in} and P_{abs} represent the input and absorbed pump power, respectively. Efficient pumping demands that most of the pump power be deposited in the crystal, namely $e^{-\sigma_g N_0 l} < 0.1$. However, if $N_0 l$ is too high, the pump power will be absorbed in a thin region, causing severe local heating problems. Good results have been obtained with $N_0 l$ set to give 80–90% absorption per pass.

A clever aspect of the folded cavity shown in Fig. 12 is that it is astigmatically compensated. A Brewster angle crystal introduces a certain amount of astigmatism that is exactly opposite in sign to the astigmatism introduced by the off-axis folding mirror. The total astigmatism can be eliminated by choosing the proper angle of incidence θ of the beam on the folding mirror.

B. Color Center Laser Cavity

Since the color center laser is operated at cryogenic temperatures, the crystal must be enclosed in a vacuum chamber to provide thermal insulation and to prevent condensation on the crystal surfaces. The focusing optics, M1 and M2 of Fig. 12, are usually located inside the vacuum chamber to avoid the astigmatism effects of windows. These mirrors must be carefully prealigned prior to operation. The crystal is usually mounted on a translatable cold finger so that the position of the beamwaist on the crystal can be adjusted. In this way, any local defects or scratches in the crystal can be avoided.

The collimated arm, sometimes called the "tuning arm," is directed out of the main vacuum chamber through a Brewster's angle window. Tuning elements can then be easily placed and adjusted in the tuning arm without disrupting the vacuum surrounding the crystal. The tuning arm is often separately evacuated as well in order to avoid absorptive losses from H_2O and CO_2 bands in the 2.7-μm region.

C. Optical Pumping Techniques

Due to the thickness of the gain media, it is necessary to pump the crystal coaxially with the cavity mode to achieve reasonable efficiency. Several schemes have been employed for injecting the pump beam into the cavity. One method involves the use of dichroic mirrors, where one of the cavity mirrors is given a coating which is transparent to the shorter wavelength pump laser, but reflective for the color center laser wavelength. An example of this technique is shown in the ring laser of Fig. 13. In this example, the pump beam enters the cavity through an end mirror, and the cavity lens focuses both the laser mode and pump beam onto the crystal.

A second popular method is to use a Brewster's angle beamsplitter with a special coating which transmits nearly 100% of the color center laser radiation, yet reflects nearly all of the pump radiation. This technique is shown in Fig. 12. The injected pump beam is focused onto the crystal by the curved mirror M1, and power that is not absorbed on the first pass through the crystal is reflected back by mirror M2 for a second pass. One advantage of this scheme is that the mirrors can be coated with broadband enhanced silver, which permits one set of mirrors to operate over a broad wavelength range.

V. Color Center Laser Operation

A. Broadband Tuning Techniques

Color center emission bands are homogeneously broadened by lattice vibrations. This broadening leads to the wide tuning range of the color center laser, and its homogeneous nature allows for straightforward single-mode operation. However, this same broad tuning range makes it nearly impossible to control the output wavelength with only one tuning element. Generally, a hierarchy of dispersive elements are required for single-mode operation. These elements include a coarse tuner for general wavelength selection, an intermediate dispersive element such as an etalon for individual mode

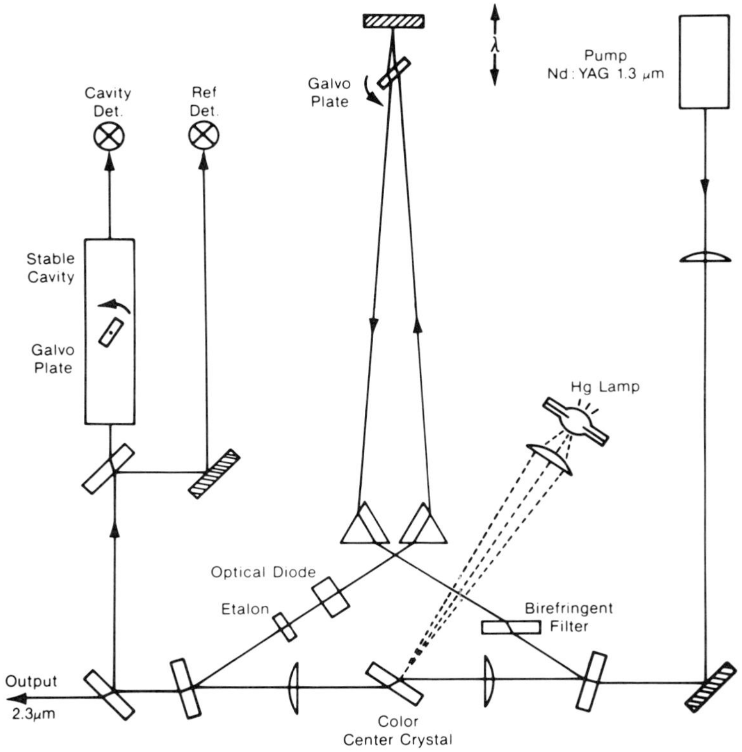

FIG. 13. Actively stabilized color center ring laser. The wavelength is adjusted by translating the top mirror. The mercury lamp is required for $(F_2^+)_A$ center operation.

selection, and a cavity length adjustment for continuous frequency scanning of the individual mode. For mode-locked operation, however, it is only necessary to use a coarse tuner.

A Brewster angle prism is often used as a simple and inexpensive tuning element. The prism has the advantage of being low loss and monotonic in wavelength transmission; however, it has the disadvantages of having relatively low dispersion and deviating the direction of the beam as the wavelength is changed. The prism is generally not used in favor of other elements such as the grating or birefringent tuner.

The Littrow mounted diffraction grating has very high dispersion. The Littrow orientation causes the refracted beam to retroreflect along the incident beam. If the blaze angles are chosen correctly, gratings can exhibit first-order retroreflections of >95%. A practical method of using a grating tuner is shown in Fig. 14. The first-order reflection feeds back into the laser and tunes it according to $\lambda = 2d \sin \theta$, where d is the groove spacing and θ is defined in the figure. The zeroth order reflection serves as the output coupling. The zeroth order reflection is bounced off a second mirror adjusted such that a constant deviation of 180° is achieved with respect to the input beam. A small pick-off mirror then directs the beam away from the cavity. The laser wavelength can be linearly scanned using a "sine bar," where motion in the x direction causes a linear change in $\sin \theta = x/h$. The dispersion of the grating is given by

$$\delta\lambda = 2d \cos \theta \, \delta\theta$$

where $\delta\theta$ is the laser beam diffraction angle. It has been found that a laser ceases to operate when the returning beam is misaligned by the angle $\Delta\theta = \lambda/40\omega$, where ω is the spot size of the beam. Assuming a 1-mm beam spot size, $\lambda = 1.5$

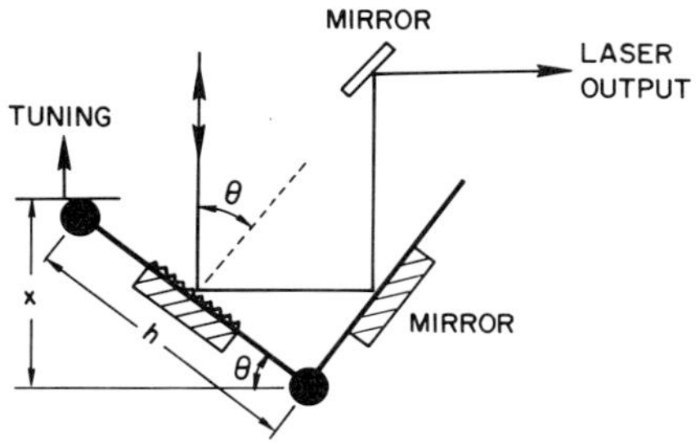

FIG. 14. Littrow-oriented diffraction grafting for tuning a laser. The zeroth order reflection is used as the output coupling, while the first order reflection is fed back into the laser.

μm, and $d = 600$ mm^{-1}, we find $\delta\lambda = 0.6$ Å, which is about 30 times narrower than the bandwidth of a prism.

An intermediate selectivity tuning element can be constructed using birefringent plates in the cavity placed at Brewster's angle to the beam. Tuning is accomplished by rotating the plates about their normal axis. A linearly polarized incident beam emerges in general as an elliptically polarized beam. This exit beam suffers substantial reflection losses at the Brewster surfaces of the cavity. However, for certain wavelengths the output polarization is linear and unrotated, and for these there is no loss. These eigenwavelengths vary with plate rotation angle θ as

$$\lambda = (\lambda_p/m)[1 - \cos^2\phi \sin^2\theta]$$

where $\lambda_p = (n_0 - n_e)t/\sin \theta$, m is an integer, t the plate thickness, and ϕ Brewster's angle. The bandwidth $\delta\lambda$ is a complicated function of the number of polarizing surfaces in the cavity but has a magnitude that falls somewhere between the dispersion of the prism and the grating. An advantage of the birefringent tuner is that it requires no displacement of the beam during tuning, in contrast to the prism or grating. One disadvantage of the birefringent tuner arises from the multiple orders that exist in a plate, making it possible for the laser to hop back toward line center when tuned to the extremes of the tuning curve.

B. Single Mode Operation

It is possible to operate a color center laser in a narrowline single mode that can be tuned to any wavelength within the tuning range of the crystal. Such capability has proven useful for molecular spectroscopists, where the excellent frequency of definition and tunability of the color center laser have allowed detailed studies of many important molecular species.

1. Standing Wave Linear Laser

Using a coarse tuning element, the homogeneously broadened standing wave laser oscillates in one primary mode and one or two secondary modes caused by spatial hole burning. The frequency spacing of the secondary modes from the primary mode is given by

$$\Delta\nu_{\text{hole}} = c/4z$$

where z is the distance between the end mirror and the active media (see Fig. 12). The physical

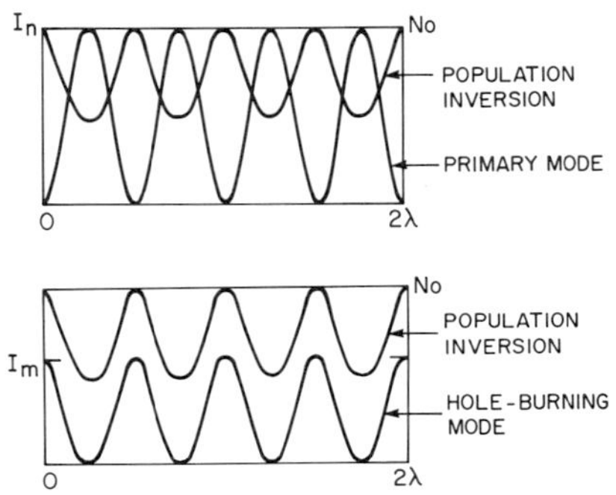

FIG. 15. Plot of the spatial gain profile in the grain medium of a standing wave laser. The antinodes of the standing wave saturate the gain, while at the nodes the gain remains high. A second mode can find gain at the nodes.

mechanism causing oscillation at the hole burning frequencies is illustrated in Fig. 15. The standing wave of the primary mode "burns" holes into the population inversion of the gain media, saturating the gain to the level where gain equals cavity loss. At the nodes of the standing wave, the gain is not saturated and remains at values well above that needed to exceed threshold. A second mode which is spatially $\pi/4$ out of phase with the primary mode will perfectly overlap this periodic gain and will see the excess gain. Unless mode selective losses are included in the cavity, this second "hole burning" mode will oscillate.

Single-mode operation in a linear laser is usually achieved by making the hole burning spacing large (small z) and using a combination grating and etalon. An etalon is a Fabry-Perot optical resonator consisting of two plane parallel mirrors separated by a distance l. The etalon has a "picket fence" of transmission peaks, equally spaced in frequency by the free spectral range (FSR)

$$\text{FSR} = c/2nl$$

where n is the refractive index between the mirrors. The etalon selects one cavity mode of the laser, and the grating selects one order of the etalon. The optimum FSR is chosen to be twice the hole burning mode spacing $\Delta\nu_{\text{hole}}$. The single-mode output power is $\approx 70\%$ that of the multimode laser. This power drop is due to the loss of the hole burning mode.

Scanning the etalon and coarse tuner in tandem, the laser will tune in steps of the cavity FSR, $c/2l_c$, where l_c is the cavity length. Typical cavity FSRs are 300 MHz. Tuning the laser frequency between adjacent cavity modes can be achieved by smoothly increasing the cavity length by $\lambda/2$. This is usually accomplished with a PZT driven cavity mirror or a tilted Brewster angle plate. To achieve smooth continuous scans, the three tuning elements must be synchronized.

2. Traveling Wave Ring Lase

The ring laser overcomes the hole burning limitations of the standing wave laser by operating in a traveling wave mode, allowing uniform saturation of the gain media. This has two advantages: first, single mode operation is more efficient, since one mode can extract all the power, and second, because there is no gain for other modes, low finesse optics can be used for tuning.

Figure 13 shows a schematic of a frequency stabilized ring laser. Instead of curved mirrors, two antireflection coated lenses are used for focusing the cavity mode into the color center crystal. In this scheme, the lenses serve both as focusing elements and as vacuum barriers for the evacuated region surrounding the crystal. Astigmatism is compensated by tilting the lenses at a small angle to the beam axis.

A unique property of ring lasers is that the direction of the traveling wave is not determined unless some form of biasing is introduced. Commonly, a combination of a "Faraday effect" rotator and an "optically active" plate is employed to force oscillation in only one direction. This combination is called an "optical diode." The Faraday effect is due to magnetically induced birefringence which nonreciprocally rotates the polarization of transmitted light through a small angle

$$\theta = VlH$$

where V is the Verdet constant of the material, l the length of the device, and H the strength of the magnetic field inside the material. At wavelengths longer than 1.5 μm, YIG (yttrium–iron–garnet) is used for the Faraday rotator because of its large Verdet constant. YIG becomes lossy below 1.5 μm, so SF-6 glass is used for the shorter wavelength applications. Following the Faraday device, an optically active plate is used as a reciprocal rotator. Depending on the direction of travel, the reciprocal device will either rotate the polarization to a further degree, or for oppositely directed waves, rotate the polarization back to its original state. Light whose polarization has been rotated will suffer loss at polarizing Brewster surfaces, while unrotated light will see no additional loss. This small direction dependent loss is enough to force the laser to oscillate in one direction only. Typical rotation values are ~2%.

The linewidth of the single-mode laser is determined by fluctuations in the optical path length of the resonator. These fluctuations are caused primarily by mechanical instabilities of the optical mounts and by temperature variations of the color center crystal. The mechanical system is perturbed by floor vibrations and acoustics, both of which can be minimized with proper design to yield a laser-linewidth of ~10 kHz. Pump power amplitude noise is a major source of frequency instability. Changes in pump power cause temperature variations which alter the index of refraction of the crystal, effectively modulating the cavity length. The magnitude of this thermal tuning has been measured to be around 20 kHz per milliwatt change of pump power. For example, a pump power of 1 W with 1/2% amplitude noise will have a minimum linewidth of 100 kHz.

Active frequency stabilization can be applied to color center lasers to yield spectacularly narrow linewidths. The ring laser in Fig. 13 shows one scheme for active frequency stabilization. A portion of the output is directed through a thermally and acoustically isolated Fabry-Perot optical resonator. Comparing the frequency of the laser with the stable transmission passband of the Fabry–Perot yields an error signal that is proportional to the frequency excursion. This error signal is electronically amplified and used to alter the laser cavity length through a PZT driven mirror and a Brewster angle plate. The PZT mirror compensates for small high-frequency excursions, while the Brewster plate is galvonometrically tilted to control low-frequency noise and drift, The laser in Fig. 13 achieved a stabilized linewidth of less than 4 kHz.

C. Mode-Locked Operation

Color center lasers are relatively easy to mode-lock by synchronous pumping. In view of the large homogeneous luminescence bandwidth, the ultimate limits on pulse width with mode-locked color center lasers are under 1 psec. Mode-locking refers to the phase-locking of hundreds of adjacent longitudinal cavity modes. In synchronous pumping, the cavity length L of the color center laser is adjusted such that the cavity round trip time $2L/c$ corresponds exactly to the period between pulses of the mode-locked pump laser. The dramatic temporal gain modulation produced by such pumping excites many sidebands, whose frequency separation corresponds to the color center cavity mode spacing. The sidebands build up in intensity through the homogeneous gain of the medium.

In practice, synchronous mode-locking is achieved by pumping with a mode-locked laser, such as an ion laser or Nd: YAG laser, and adjusting the cavity length of the color center laser until the above length condition is satisfied. It is generally necessary to add a low-dispersion tuning element to the mode-locked cavity in order to obtain transform limited pulses (i.e., the product $\Delta\nu\ \Delta\tau$, where $\Delta\tau$ and $\Delta\nu$ represent the FWHM of the temporal width and bandwith of the pulse, respectively, is a minimum for the pulse shape employed by the laser). With no tuning element, the pulses will have excess frequency bandwidth but will not necessarily be any shorter in duration. Such non-transform-limited pulses can lead to anomalous results and excess dispersion in applications. A prism or single plate birefringent tuner is thus often employed in mode-locked color center lasers. Typically, synchronous pumping mode-locking has generated 5–15 psec pulses from the various color center lasers.

Several new mode-locking techniques have recently been introduced which provide subpicosecond pulses from color center lasers. The first method uses passive mode-locking through the introduction of a suitable semiconductor saturable absorber in the laser cavity. To date, 200-fsec pulses have been generated at fixed wavelengths in the 1.5 and 2.7 μm region.

The second technique is called additive pulse mode-locking (APM). Figure 16 shows a schematic representation of an additively mode-locked laser. The laser consists of two coupled cavities, one with the color center gain media and the other containing a single mode optical fiber. A portion of the mode-locked output is coupled onto the optical fiber, where it experiences a nonlinear effect called self phase modulation (SPM). SPM effectively adds bandwidth to the pulse by "red-shifting" the leading edge and "blue-shifting" the trailing edge of the pulse. The two cavities are made equal length so that when the broadened pulse is coupled back

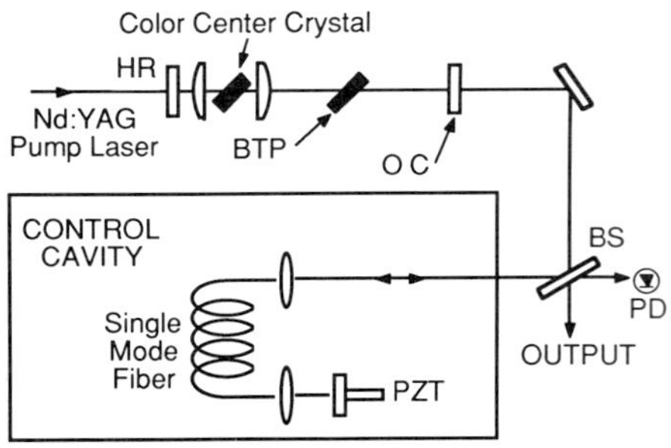

FIG. 16. Additive pulse mode-locked laser. The output of the color center laser is coupled to a nonlinear fiber. The combination produces tunable femtosecond duration pulses. (OC, output coupler; BS, beam splitter; BTP, birefringent tuner plate; HR, high reflector; PZT, Pb-doped zirconium titanate piezotransducer.)

into the laser it interferes with the cavity pulse. The two pulses destructively interfere in the wings, leading to a shorter pulse being reinjected back into the gain media. This shortening process repeats with every round trip until a bandwidth limitation is reached, such as due to a tuning element. To date, 75-fsec pulses have been generated that are transform-limited and tunable from 1.48 to 1.75 μm, making this the first tunable femtosecond source. APM techniques are now being extended to other sources, such as Ti : sapphire and Nd : YAG lasers.

VI. Future Developments

The color center's unique ability to generate broadly tunable light in the infrared ensures its continued usefulness, especially as a research tool for semiconductors, optical communication devices, and optical fibers. The recent development of tunable femtosecond pulses in the spectral region where optical fibers operate has made possible many new experiments that are likely to influence the communication systems of the future. It is likely that new color center sources will be developed which extend the coverage of stable lasers to new wavelength regions. Currently, there are no stable continuous wave color center lasers that operate below 1.4 μm, which is an important region for fiber optics research. Undoubtedly, new sources will be developed that provide convenient, useful tuning bands.

Bibliography

Farge, Y., and Fontana, M. P. (1979). "Electronic and Vibrational Properties of Point Defects in Ionic Solids," North-Holland Publ., Amsterdam.

Geogiou, E. T., Pinto, J. F., and Pollock, C. R. (1987). Optical properties and formation of oxygen-perturbed F_2^+ color center in NaCl, *Phys. Rev. B* **35,** 7636.

Geogiou, E. T., Carrig, T. J., and Pollock, C. R. (1988). Stable, pulsed, color center laser in pure KCl tunable from 1.23 to 1.35 μm, *Opt. Lett.* **13,** 987.

German, K. R. (1986). Optimization of F_A(II) and F_B(II) color center lasers, *J. Opt. Soc. Am. B: Opt. Phys.* **3,** 149.

Ippen, E. P., Haus, H. A., and Liu, L. Y. (1989). Additive pulse mode locking, *J. Opt. Soc. Am. B: Opt. Phys.* **6,** 1736.

Mollenauer, L. F. (1979). Color center lasers, *in* "Methods of Experimental Physics," Vol. 15B (C. L. Tang, ed.). Academic Press, New York.

Mollenauer, L. F. (1985). Color center lasers, *in* "Laser Handbook," Vol. 4 (M. Stitch, ed.). North-Holland Publ., Amsterdam.

Mollenauer, L. F., and Stolen, R. H. (1984). The soliton laser, *Opt. Lett.* **29,** 13.

Mollenauer, L. F., Vieira, N. D., and Szeto, L. (1983). Optical properties of the Tl°(1) center in KCl, *Phys. Rev. B* **27,** 5332.

Pinto, J. F., Georgiou, E. T., and Pollock, C. R. (1986). Stable color center laser in OH-doped NaCl tunable from 1.41 to 1.81 μm, *Opt. Lett.* **11,** 519.

LASERS, FREE ELECTRON

H. P. Freund *Science Applications International Corp.*
R. K. Parker *Naval Research Laboratory*

GLOSSARY

Amplifier: A device used to increase the amplitude of some input signal. The term *superradiant amplifier* is often used to describe a free-electron laser that is configured to amplify noise (i.e., random fluctuations) in the beam rather than an externally supplied signal. In contrast to oscillator configurations, there is no reflection of the signal, and the superradiant amplifier is a single-pass device.

Beat wave: A composite wave formed by the superposition of two waves having different angular frequencies (ω_1, ω_2) and wavenumbers (k_1, k_2). Beat waves form at the sum and difference frequencies ($\omega_1 \pm \omega_2$) and wavenumbers ($k_1 \pm k_2$).

Compton regime: This denotes operation in a free-electron laser in which the dominant mechanism is stimulated Compton scattering. In this process, the wiggler field (which appears to be a backwards-propagating electromagnetic wave in the rest frame of the electrons) produces secondary electromagnetic waves by scattering off the electrons.

Electrostatic accelerators: Include Van de Graaf and Cockcroft–Walton configurations. Van de Graaf accelerators accelerate charges by passing a moving belt through the coronal discharge from an array of points. The charge is then carried away by the belt to a field-free region where it can be extracted from the accelerator. The maximum voltages that can be achieved with electrostatic accelerators are in the range of from 10–30 MV.

Free-streaming: The free and unrestrained propagation of particles without hindrance by external forces. This is often used in a context that denotes trajectories that are unbounded.

Gain: A measure of the amplification of the input signal in an amplifier. The gain of an amplifier is often measured in decibels (dB), which is ten times the common logarithm of the ratio of the output power of the amplifier to the input drive power.

Linear induction accelerators (induction linacs): Linear accelerators that operate by inducing an electromotive force in a cavity through a rapid change in the magnetic field strength. In effect, the electron beam acts as the analog of the secondary winding in a transformer.

Larmor rotation: The circular rotation of charged particles in a uniform magnetic field. Also called *cyclotron* rotation.

Master oscillator power amplifier (MOPA): A shorthand notation for a power amplifier in which the source of the input drive signal is an external, or *master,* oscillator.

Microtrons: Cyclic accelerators in which the particles execute circular motion in a uniform magnetic field that carries the beam through an rf accelerating cavity, one in each cycle.

Modulators: A pulsed-voltage source that includes an energy storage element (such as a capacitor bank) and a switching system to discharge the energy through some load. [See *Pulse-line accelerators*.]

Oscillator: A device used to generate periodic (i.e., oscillatory) signals without the necessity of an external drive signal. Free-electron laser oscillators are constructed by the insertion of the wiggler/electron-beam system within a reflecting cavity in which the signal makes many passes through the interaction region. As a result, the signal grows from noise and is amplified during each pass. As a result, the signal can grow to high intensities without the need for a strong input (driving) signal.

Phase space: The multidimensional space formed by the position and momentum of a particle (or of an ensemble of particles).

Phase velocity: The speed of propagation for a single wave of angular frequency ω and wavenumber k. The phase velocity is determined by the ratio ω/k and defines the speed of a point of constant phase of the wave.

Ponderomotive wave: A slowly-varying wave formed by the beating of two waves.

Pulse-line accelerators: Draw an intense current from a diode by means of a transmission line from a high-voltage capacitor bank. The capacitor bank and transmission line form a distributed capacitance network. The diode acts as a load through which the energy is discharged. [See *Modulators*.]

Radio-frequency linear accelerators (rf linacs): A linear accelerator that employs radio frequency (rf) cavities for electron acceleration. The particles are accelerated in cylindrical cavities that require a high-power source for the rf fields. The rf fields in these cavities may be either traveling or standing waves. In the case of traveling-wave configurations, which are most often employed for electron accelerators, the phase velocity of the rf fields must be synchronized with the desired electron velocity.

Raman regime: This denotes operation in a free-electron laser in which the dominant mechanism is a three-wave scattering process. It occurs when the electron-beam density is high enough that the longitudinal (i.e., electrostatic) waves driven by the beam exert a greater force than the ponderomotive wave. In this process, as opposed to stimulated Compton scattering, the wiggler field scatters off the beam-driven longitudinal waves to produce the secondary electromagnetic waves.

Separatrix: The line or surface in the phase space of a particle that distinguishes between two classes of trajectories as, for example, between bounded and unbounded motion.

Storage rings: A toroidal configuration in which beams of electrons and/or positrons circulate for periods of the order of several hours. Short bunches of electrons and positrons are injected into the torus and guided around the ring by a system of bending and focusing magnets. Due to the curved trajectories of the beam, the particles lose energy during each circuit by means of synchrotron radiation. Two compensate for this loss, an rf accelerating cavity is included in the ring. The ring itself may be circular or polygonal; however, the straight sections in polygonal rings facilitate the insertion of the wiggler magnets required for free-electron lasers.

Undulator: See *Wiggler*.

Untrapped trajectories: Unbounded trajectories of particles under the influence of some external force. Examples include parabolic and hyperbolic trajectories of bodies subject to a central gravitational force or the unrestrained motion of a circular pendulum.

Wiggler: The periodic magnet used in free-electron lasers to generate an undulatory motion in the electron beam. The term *wiggler* is specifically used for the magnets employed to generate coherent radiation in free-electron lasers, as opposed to the similar periodic magnets (referred to as *undulators*) employed in synchrotron light sources to generate spontaneous, or incoherent, radiation.

In its fundamental concept, the free-electron laser is an extremely adaptable light source that can produce high-power coherent radiation across virtually the entire electromagnetic spectrum. In contrast, gas and solid-state lasers generate light at well-defined wavelengths corresponding to discrete energy transitions within atoms or molecules in the lasing media. Dye lasers are tunable over a narrow spectral range but require a gas laser for optical pumping and operate at relatively low power levels. Further, while conventional lasers are typically characterized by energy conversion efficiencies of only a few percent, theoretical calculations indicate that the free-electron laser is capable of efficiencies as high as 65%, while efficiencies of 40% have been demonstrated in the laboratory.

Applications of free-electron lasers to date

range from experiments in solid-state physics to molecular biology, and novel designs are under development for such diverse purposes as communications, radar, and ballistic missile defense. At the present time, however, free-electron lasers have been largely confined to the laboratory. Most have been built around available electron accelerators, and although they have the potential to emit light anywhere from the microwave to the ultraviolet, researchers have encountered difficulties in getting them to lase at visible and shorter wavelengths. Only recently have free-electron lasers begun to come into their own, as accelerators are designed for their specific needs, and user facilities are set up so that researchers in other disciplines can take advantage of this new source of intense and tunable light.

I. Introduction

The free-electron laser was first conceived almost four decades ago and has since operated over a spectrum ranging from microwaves through visible light. There are plans to extend this range to the ultraviolet. In a free-electron laser, high-energy electrons emit coherent radiation, as in a conventional laser, but the electrons travel in a beam through a vacuum instead of remaining in bound atomic states within the lasing medium. Because the electrons are free-streaming, the radiation wavelength is not constrained by a particular transition between two discrete energy levels. In quantum mechanical terms, the electrons radiate by transitions between energy levels in the continuum and, therefore, radiation is possible over a much larger range of frequencies than is found in a conventional laser. However, the process can be described by classical electromagnetic theory alone.

The radiation is produced by an interaction among three elements: the electron beam, an electromagnetic wave traveling in the same direction as the electrons, and an undulatory magnetic field produced by an assembly of magnets known as a *wiggler* or *undulator*. The wiggler magnetic field acts on the electrons in such a way that they acquire an undulatory motion. The acceleration associated with the curvilinear trajectory is what makes radiation possible. In this process, the electrons lose energy to the electromagnetic wave, which is amplified and emitted by the laser. The tunability of the free-electron laser arises because the wavelength of light required for the interaction between these three elements is determined by both the periodicity of the wiggler field and the energy of the electron beam.

Although the basic principle underlying the free-electron laser is relatively simple, the practical application of the concept can be difficult. In 1951 Hans Motz of Stanford University first calculated the emission spectrum from an electron beam in an undulatory magnetic field. At the time, coherent optical emission was not expected due to the difficulty of bunching the electron beam at short wavelengths: however, it was recognized that maser (microwave amplification through stimulated emission of radiation) operation was possible. Experiments performed by Motz and co-workers shortly thereafter produced both incoherent radiation in the blue-green part of the spectrum and coherent emission at millimeter wavelengths. The application of undulatory magnetic fields to the maser was independently invented by Robert Phillips in 1957 in search of higher power than was currently available from microwave tubes. The term ubitron was used at this time as an acronym for undulating beam interaction. Over the succeeding seven years, Phillips performed an extensive study of the interaction and pioneered many innovative design concepts in use today. Whereas the original microwave experiment at Stanford observed an output of 1–10 W. Phillips achieved 150 kW at a 5-mm wavelength. However, the full potential of the free electron laser was unrecognized, and the ubitron program was terminated in 1964 due to a general shift in interest from vacuum electronics to solid-state physics and quantum electronics.

A resurgence of interest in the concept began in the mid-1970s, when the term free-electron laser was coined in 1975 by John Madey to describe an experiment at Stanford University. This experiment produced stimulated emission in the infrared spectrum at a wavelength of 10.6 μm using an electron beam from a radio-frequency linear accelerator (rf linac). The first optical free-electron laser was built using the ACO storage ring at the Université de Paris Sud, and has been tuned over a broad spectrum. More recently, stimulated emission at visible and ultraviolet wavelengths has been reported using the VEPP storage ring at Novosibirsk in the Soviet Union. Visible wavelength free-electron lasers have also been built both at Stanford University and by a Boeing Aerospace/Los Alamos National Laboratory collaboration based on rf linacs, and there is interest in the use of an rf linac to drive a free-electron laser in the ultraviolet at Los Alamos National Laboratory. The rf linac has also been the basis for a longstanding infrared free-electron laser experimental program at Los Alamos.

In parallel with the work at Stanford, experimenters at several laboratories began work on microwave free-electron lasers, successors to the ubitron. Those projects, at the Naval Research Laboratory, Columbia University, the Massachusetts Institute of Technology, Lawrence Livermore National Laboratory, TRW, and the Ecole Polytechnique in France, differed from the original work of Phillips by using intense relativistic electron beams with currents of the order of a kiloampere and voltages in excess of a megavolt. The principal goal of this effort was the production of high absolute powers, and the results ranged from a peak power of the order of 2 MW at a wavelength of 2.5 mm at Columbia, through 70 MW at a 4-mm wavelength at the Naval Research Laboratory, to a maximum power figure of 1 GW obtained by Livermore at an 8-mm wavelength. This latter result represents an efficiency (defined as the ratio of the output radiation power to the initial electron-beam power) of 35% and was made possible by the use of a nonuniform wiggler field.

At the present time, free-electron lasers have been constructed over the entire electromagnetic spectrum. This spectral range is summarized in Fig. 1, in which we plot the peak power

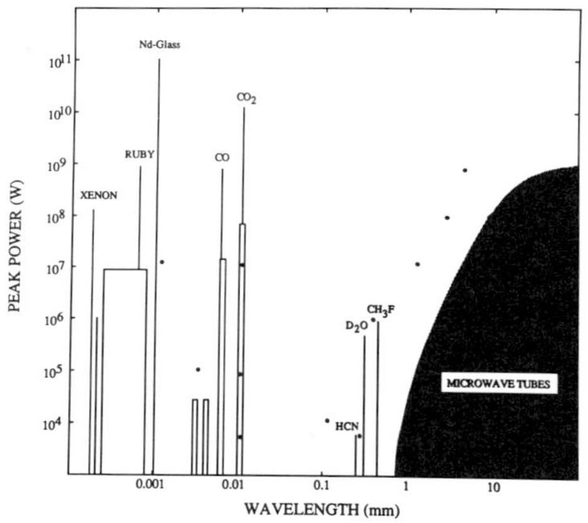

FIG. 1. An important criterion in the judgement of radiation sources is the peak power available at specific wavelengths. A comparison of free-electron lasers, represented by dots, with conventional lasers and microwave sources is shown.

of a sample of conventional lasers, microwave tubes, and free-electron lasers as a function of wavelength. At wavelengths above 0.1 mm, free-electron lasers already either match or exceed power levels obtainable from conventional technology. At shorter wavelengths, conventional lasers can be found with higher power than is currently available from free-electron lasers. However, free-electron laser technology is rapidly maturing, and this situation is likely to change in the future.

II. General Principles

An electron beam that traverses an undulatory magnetic field emits incoherent radiation. Indeed, this is the mechanism employed in synchrotron light sources. In conventional terminology, the periodic magnetic field in synchrotron light sources is referred to as an *undulator,* whereas that used in free-electron lasers is called a *wiggler,* although there is no fundamental difference between them. It is necessary for the electron beam to form coherent bunches in order to give rise to the stimulated emission required for a free-electron laser. This can occur when a light wave traverses an undulatory magnetic field such as a wiggler because the spatial variations of the wiggler and the electromagnetic wave combine to produce a beat wave, which is essentially an interference pattern. It is the interaction between the electrons and the beat wave that gives rise to the stimulated emission in free-electron lasers.

This beat wave has the same frequency as the light wave, but its wavenumber is the sum of the wavenumbers of the electromagnetic and wiggler fields. With the same frequency, but a larger wavenumber (and thus a shorter wavelength), the beat wave travels more slowly than the light wave; for this reason it is called a *ponderomotive* wave. Since the ponderomotive wave is the combination of the light wave and the stationary (or magnetostatic) field of the wiggler, it is the effective field experienced by an electron as it passes through the free-electron laser. In addition, since the ponderomotive wave propagates at less than the speed of light *in vacuo* it can be synchronous with the electrons limited by that velocity. Electrons moving in synchronism with the wave are said to be in *resonance* with it and will experience a constant field—that of the portion of the wave with which it is traveling. In such cases, the interaction between the electrons and the ponderomotive wave can be extremely strong.

A good analogy to the interaction between the electrons and the ponderomotive wave is that of a group of surfers and a wave approaching a beach. If the surfers remain stationary in the water the velocity difference between the wave and the surfers is large, and an incoming wave will merely lift them up and down briefly and then return them to their previous level. There is no bulk, or average, translational motion or exchange of energy between the surfers and the wave. But if the surfers "catch the wave" by paddling so as to match the speed of the wave, then they can gain significant momentum from the wave and be carried inshore. This is the physical basis underlying the resonant interaction in a free-electron laser. However, in a free-electron laser, the electrons amplify the wave, so the situation is more analogous to the surfers "pushing" on the wave and increasing its amplitude.

The frequency of the electromagnetic wave required for this resonant interaction can be determined by matching the velocities of the ponderomotive wave and the electron beam. This is referred to as the phase-matching condition. The interaction is one in which an electromagnetic wave characterized by an angular frequency ω and wavenumber k and the magnetostatic wiggler with a wavenumber k_w produce a beat wave with the same frequency as the electromagnetic wave but with a wavenumber equal to the sum of the wavenumbers of the wiggler and electromagnetic waves (i.e., $k + k_w$). The velocity of the ponderomotive wave is given by the ratio of the frequency of the wave to its wavenumber. As a result, matching this velocity to that of the electron beam gives the resonance condition in a free-electron laser

$$\frac{\omega}{k + k_w} \cong v_z$$

for a beam with a bulk streaming velocity v_z in the z-direction. The z-direction is used throughout this article to denote both the bulk streaming direction of the electron beam and the symmetry axis of the wiggler field. The dispersion relation between the frequency and wavenumber for waves propagating in free space is $\omega \cong ck$, where c denotes the speed of light *in vacuo*. Combination of the free-space dispersion relation and the free-electron laser resonance condition gives the standard relation for the wavelength as a function of both the electron-beam energy and the wiggler period

$$\lambda \cong \frac{\lambda_w}{2\gamma_z^2}$$

where $\gamma_z = (1 - v_z^2/c^2)^{-1/2}$ is the relativistic time-dilation factor related to the electron-streaming energy, and $\lambda_w = 2\pi/k_w$ is the wiggler wavelength. The wavelength, therefore, is directly proportional to the wiggler period and inversely proportional to the square of the streaming energy. This results in a broad tunability that permits the free-electron laser to operate across virtually the entire electromagnetic spectrum.

How does a magnetostatic wiggler and a forward-propagating electromagnetic wave, both of whose electric and magnetic fields are directed transversely to the direction of propagation, given rise to an axial ponderomotive force that can extract energy from the electron beam? The wiggler is the predominant influence on the electron's motion. To understand the dynamical relationships between the electrons and the fields, consider the motion of an electron subject to a helically symmetric wiggler field. An electron propagating through a magnetic field experiences a force that acts at right angles to both the direction of the field and to its own velocity. The wiggler field is directed transversely to the direction of bulk motion of the electron beam and rotates through 360° in one wiggler period. An electron streaming in the axial direction, therefore, experiences a transverse force and acquires a transverse velocity component on entry into the wiggler. The resulting trajectory is helical and describes a bulk streaming along the axis of symmetry as well as a transverse circular rotation that lags 180° behind the phase of the wiggler field. The magnitude of the transverse wiggle velocity, denoted by v_w, is proportional to the product of the wiggler amplitude and period. This relationship may be expressed in the form

$$\frac{v_w}{c} \cong 0.934 \frac{B_w \lambda_w}{\gamma_b}$$

where the wiggler period is expressed in units of centimeters. B_w denotes the wiggler amplitude in tesla, and

$$\gamma_b = 1 + \frac{E_b}{m_e c^2}$$

denotes the relativistic time-dilation factor associated with the total kinetic energy E_b of the electron beam (where m_e denotes the rest mass of the electron, and $m_e c^2$ denotes the electron rest energy).

Since the motion is circular, both axial and transverse velocities have a constant magnitude. This is important because the resonant interaction depends on the axial velocity of the beam. In addition, since the wiggler induces a constant-magnitude transverse velocity, the relation between the total electron energy and the streaming energy can be expressed in terms of the time-dilation factors in the form

$$\gamma_z \cong \frac{\gamma_b}{\sqrt{1 + 0.872\, B_w^2 \lambda_w^2}}$$

As a result, the resonant wavelength depends on the total beam energy and the wiggler amplitude and period through

$$\lambda \cong (1 + 0.872\, B_w^2 \lambda_w^2)\, \frac{\lambda_w}{2\gamma_b^2}$$

It is the interaction between the transverse wiggler-induced velocity with the transverse magnetic field of an electromagnetic wave that induces a force normal to both in the axial direction. This is the ponderomotive force. The transverse velocity and the radiation magnetic field are directed at right angles to each other and undergo a simple rotation about the axis of symmetry. A resonant wave must be circularly polarized with a polarization vector that is normal to both the transverse velocity and the wiggler field and that rotates in synchronism with the electrons. This synchronism is illustrated in Fig. 2 and is maintained by the aforementioned resonance condition.

To understand the energy transferase, we return to the surfer analogy and consider a group of surfers attempting to catch a series of waves. In the attempt to match velocities with the waves, some will catch a wave ahead of the crest and slide forward while others will catch a wave behind the crest and slide backward. As a result, clumps of surfers will collect in the troughs of the waves. Those surfers who slide forward ahead of the wave are accelerated and gain energy at the expense of the wave, while those who slide backward are decelerated and lose energy to the wave. The wave grows if more surfers are decelerated than accelerated, and there is a net transfer of energy to the wave. The free-electron laser operates by an analogous process. Electrons in near resonance with the ponderomotive wave lose energy to the wave if their velocity is slightly greater than the phase velocity of the wave, and gain energy at the expense of the wave in the opposite case. As a result, wave amplification occurs if the wave lags behind the electron beam.

This process in a free-electron laser is described by a nonlinear pendulum equation. The *ponderomotive phase* Ψ [$= (k + k_w)z - \omega t$] is a measure of the position of an electron in both space and time with respect to the ponderomotive wave. The ponderomotive phase satisfies

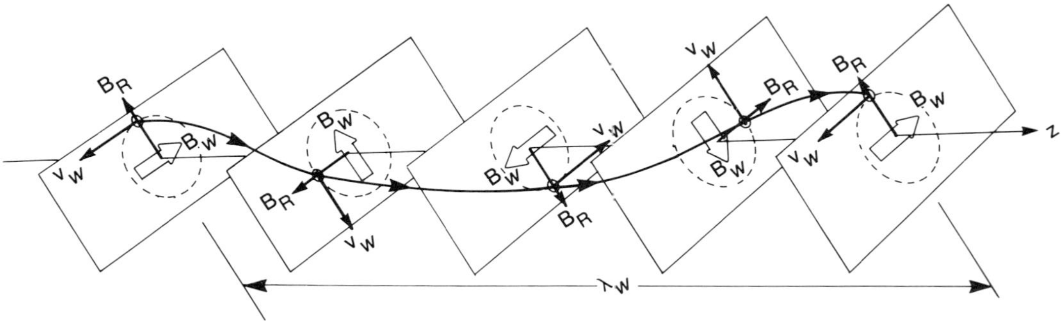

FIG. 2. The electron trajectory in a helical wiggler includes bulk streaming parallel to the axis of symmetry as well as a helical gyration. The vector relationships between the wiggler field B_w, the transverse velocity v_w, and the radiation field B_R of a resonant wave are shown in the figure projected onto planes transverse to the symmetry axis at intervals of one quarter of a wiggler period. This projection of the orbit is circular, and the transverse velocity is directed opposite to that of the wiggler. A resonant wave must be circularly polarized, with a polarization vector that is normal to both the transverse velocity and the wiggler field and which rotates in synchronism with the electrons. The electrons then experience a slowly varying wave amplitude. In addition, the transverse velocity and the radiation magnetic field are directed at right angles to each other and undergo a simple rotation about the axis of symmetry. The interaction between the transverse velocity and the radiation field induces a force in the direction normal to both that coincides with the symmetry axis.

the circular pendulum equation

$$\frac{d^2}{dz^2}\Psi = K^2 \sin \Psi$$

where the pendulum constant is proportional to the square root of the product of the wiggler and radiation fields

$$K \approx 8.29 \frac{\sqrt{B_w B_R}}{\gamma_b}$$

Here K is expressed in units of inverse centimeters and the magnetic fields are expressed in tesla. The pendulum equation can be reduced to

$$\frac{1}{2}\left(\frac{d\Psi}{dz}\right)^2 + U(\Psi) = H$$

where H has the form of the Hamiltonian or total energy of the system, and

$$U(\Psi) = K^2 \cos \Psi$$

is the ponderomotive potential. The electron trajectories through the wiggler, therefore, may be expressed as

$$\frac{d\Psi}{dz} = \pm \sqrt{2H - 2K^2 \cos \Psi}$$

Observe that the first derivative of the phase [i.e., $d\Psi/dz = (k + k_w) - \omega/v_z$] is a measure of the electron-streaming velocity; hence, this equation effectively describes the electron velocity as a function of the phase of the ponderomotive wave.

There are two classes of trajectory: trapped and untrapped. The *separatrix* describes the transition between trapped and untrapped orbits and occurs when $H = K^2$. Hence, the separatrix is defined by a pair of curves in the phase space for $(d\Psi/dz, \Psi)$

$$\frac{d\Psi}{dz} = \pm 2K \sin\left(\frac{\Psi}{2}\right)$$

Free-streaming, untrapped orbits are characterized by $H > K^2$ and occupy that region of the phase space outside of the separatrix,

$$\frac{d\Psi}{dz} > \left|2K \sin\left(\frac{\Psi}{2}\right)\right|$$

The trapped orbits are those for which $H < K^2$ within the bounds of the separatrix. The free-streaming orbits correspond to the case in which the pendulum swings through the full 360° cycle. The electrons pass over the crests of many waves, traveling fastest at the bottom of the troughs and slowest at the crests of the ponderomotive wave. In contrast, the electrons are confined within the trough of a single wave in the trapped orbits. This corresponds to the motion of a pendulum that does not rotate full circle, but is confined to oscillate about the lower equilibrium point. In the dynamical process, illustrated in Fig. 3, the pendulum constant evolves during the course of the interaction. Electrons lose energy as the wave is amplified: hence, the electrons decelerate and both the pendulum constant and separatrix grow. Ultimately, the electrons cross the growing separatrix from untrapped to trapped orbits.

In typical operation, electrons entering the free-electron laser are free-streaming on untrapped trajectories. The gain in power during this phase of the interaction increases as the cube of the distance z in the case of relatively low-current operation, in which the total gain is less than unity. This case is often referred to as the low-gain Compton regime, and the power gain in decibels is given by

$$G(\text{dB}) \approx 1.09 \frac{\omega_b^2}{c^2 k_w^2} \frac{v_w^2}{c^2} (k_w z)^3 F(\theta)$$

where

$$\omega_b = \sqrt{\frac{4\pi e^2 n_b}{\gamma_b m_e}}$$

is the so-called *electron plasma frequency*. Here e represents the charge of the electron, and n_b denotes the bulk density of the electron beam. The spectral shape of this gain is determined by

$$F(\theta) = \frac{d}{d\theta}\left(\frac{\sin \theta}{\theta}\right)^2$$

where $\theta = (\omega/v_z - k - k_w)z/2$. This spectral function is shown in Fig. 4 and exhibits a maximum at $\theta \approx -1.3$, for which $F \approx 0.54$; hence, the peak gain occurs at a wavelength

$$\lambda \approx \frac{\lambda_w}{2\gamma_z^2\left(1 + \dfrac{2.6}{k_w z}\right)}$$

This regime is relevant to operation at short wavelengths in the infrared and optical spectra. These experiments typically employ electron beams generated by radio-frequency linear accelerators, microtrons, storage rings, and electrostatic accelerators in which the total current is small.

In contrast, experiments operating at microwave and millimeter wavelengths often employ high-current accelerators, and the wave amplification is exponential. In these cases, two dis-

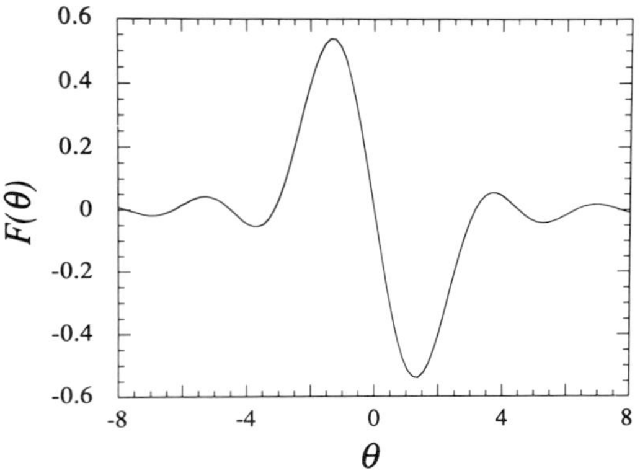

FIG. 4. The spectral function measures the strength of the interaction as a function of the detuning of the wave from resonance with the electron beam. The maximum gain is found at $\theta \approx -1.3$. In contrast, the wave is damped for $\theta \approx 1.3$.

tinct regimes are found. The high-gain Compton (sometimes called the *strong-pump*) regime is found when

$$\frac{\omega_b}{ck_w} \ll \frac{1}{16}\gamma_z^2\left(\frac{v_w}{c}\right)^2$$

In this regime, the maximum gain in the signal power over a wiggler period is given by

$$G(\text{dB}) \approx 37.5\left(\frac{v_w^2}{c^2}\frac{\omega_b^2}{c^2k_w^2}\right)^{1/3}$$

and is found at the resonant wavelength.

The opposite limit, referred to as the collective Raman regime, is fundamentally different from either the high- or low-gain Compton regimes. It occurs when the current density of the beam is high enough that the space-charge force exceeds that exerted by the ponderomotive

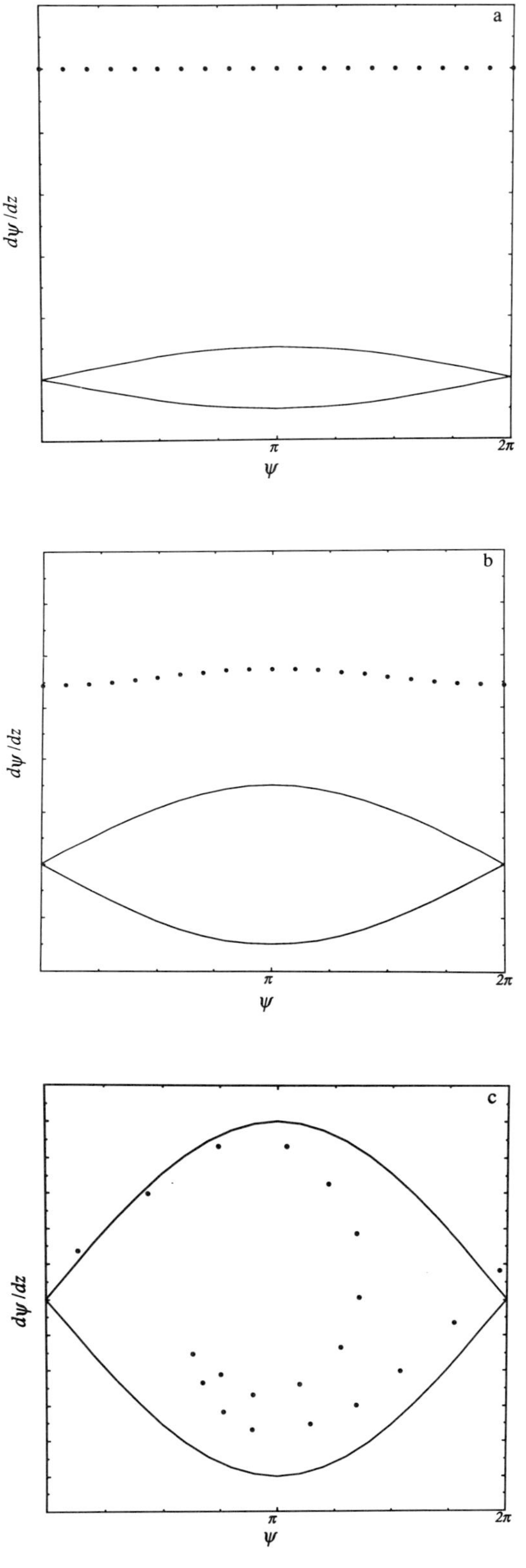

FIG. 3. The evolution of the phase space distribution of an electron beam is illustrated schematically for three general stages of the interaction. In the initial state (a), a monoenergetic electron population is located far from the separatrix. As the interaction progresses (b), the electrons lose energy to the wave, and the separatrix grows. Observe that the electrons are still on untrapped trajectories: however, the coherent bunching mechanism characteristic of the interaction has begun. In the final stage (c), the bulk of electrons have crossed the separatrix and become trapped. Electron trajectories after this point circulate about within the separatrix, alternately gaining from and losing energy to the wave. Saturation occurs when the net rate of energy transfer vanishes. Observe that all electrons do not become trapped.

wave. The gain in power over a wiggler period in this regime varies as

$$G(\text{dB}) \approx 27.3 \frac{v_w}{c} \sqrt{\gamma_z \frac{\omega_b}{ck_w}}$$

In this regime, the space-charge forces result in electrostatic waves that co-propagate with the beam and are characterized by the dispersion relations

$$\omega = k_{sc}v_z \pm \frac{\omega_b}{\gamma_z}$$

which describe the relation between the frequency ω and wavenumber k_{sc}. These dispersion relations describe positive- and negative-energy waves corresponding to the "+" and "−" signs, respectively. The interaction results from a stimulated three-wave scattering process. This is best visualized from the perspective of the electrons, in which the wiggler field appears to be a backwards propagating electromagnetic wave called a *pump* wave. This pump wave can scatter off the negative-energy electrostatic wave (the *idler*) to produce a forward-propagating electromagnetic wave (the *signal*). The interaction occurs when the wavenumbers of the pump, idler, and signal satisfy the condition $k_{sc} = k + k_w$, which causes a shift in the wavelength of the signal to

$$\lambda \approx \frac{\lambda_w}{2\gamma_z^2 \left(1 - \dfrac{\omega_b}{\gamma_z c k_w}\right)}$$

Observe that the interaction in the Raman regime is shifted to a somewhat longer wavelength than occurs in the high-gain Compton regime.

Wave amplification can saturate by several processes. The highest efficiency occurs when the electrons are trapped in the ever-deepening ponderomotive wave and undergo oscillations within the troughs. In essence, the electrons are initially freestreaming over the crests of the ponderomotive wave. Since they are traveling at a velocity faster than the wave speed, they come upon the wave crests from behind. However, the ponderomotive wave grows together with the radiation field, and the electrons ultimately will come upon a wave that is too high to cross. When this happens, they rebound and become trapped within the trough of the wave. In analogy to the oscillation of a pendulum, the trapped electrons lose energy as they rise and gain energy as they fall toward the bottom of the trough. As a result, the energy transfer between the wave and the electrons is cyclic, and the wave amplitude ceases to grow and oscillates with the electron motion in the trough. The ultimate saturation efficiency for this mechanism can be estimated from the requirement that the net change in electron velocity at saturation is equal to twice the velocity difference between the electron beam and the ponderomotive wave. This results in a saturation efficiency of

$$\eta \approx \frac{\gamma_b}{2(\gamma_b - 1)} \left(\frac{v_w^2}{2c^2} \frac{\omega_b^2}{c^2 k_w^2}\right)^{1/3}$$

in the high-gain Compton regime, and

$$\eta \approx \frac{\gamma_b}{\gamma_b - 1} \frac{\omega_b}{\gamma_z c k_w}$$

in the collective Raman regime.

However, this process places stringent requirements on the quality of the electron beam. The preceding formulas apply to the idealized case of a monoenergetic (or cold) beam. This represents a theoretical maximum for the gain and efficiency, since each electron has the same axial velocity and interacts with the wave in an identical manner. A monoenergetic beam is physically unrealizable, however, and all beams exhibit a velocity spread that determines a characteristic temperature. Electrons with axial velocities different from the optimal resonant velocity are unable to participate fully in the interaction. If this axial velocity spread is sufficiently large that the entire beam cannot be in simultaneous resonance with the wave, then the fraction of the electron beam that becomes trapped must fall. Ultimately, the trapping fraction falls to the point where the trapping mechanism becomes ineffective, and saturation occurs through the thermalization of the beam. Thus, there are two distinct operating regimes: the *cold* beam limit characterized by a narrow bandwidth and relatively high efficiencies, and the *thermal* regime characterized by a relatively broader bandwidth and sharply lower efficiencies.

The question of electron-beam quality is the most important single issue facing the development of the free-electron laser at the present time. To operate in the cold beam regime, the axial velocity spread of the beam must be small. It is convenient to relate the axial velocity spread to an energy spread to obtain an invariant measure of the beam quality suitable for a wide range of electron beams. In the case of the low-gain limit, this constraint on the beam thermal spread is

$$\frac{\Delta E_b}{E_b} \ll \frac{1}{N_w}$$

where ΔE_b represents the beam thermal spread, and N_w is the number of periods in the wiggler. In the high-gain regimes, the maximum permissible energy spread for saturation by particle trapping is determined by the depth of the ponderomotive or space-charge waves, which is measured by twice the difference between the streaming velocity of the beam and the wave speed. The maximum permissible thermal spread corresponds to this velocity difference, and is one-half the saturation efficiency for either the high-gain Compton or collective Raman regimes, that is,

$$\frac{\Delta E_b}{E_b} \ll \frac{1}{2}\eta$$

Typically, the energy spread must be approximately 1% or less of the total beam energy for the trapping mechanism to operate at millimeter wavelengths, and decreases approximately with the radiation wavelength. Hence, the requirement on beam quality becomes more restrictive at shorter wavelengths and places greater emphasis on accelerator design.

Two related quantities often used as measures of beam quality are the *emittance* and the *brightness*. The emittance measures the collimation of the electron beam and may be defined in terms of the product of the beam radius and the average pitch angle (i.e., the angle between the velocity and the symmetry axis). It describes a random pitch-angle distribution of the beam that, when the velocities are projected onto the symmetry axis, is equivalent to an axial velocity spread. In general, therefore, even a monoenergetic beam with a nonvanishing emittance displays an axial velocity spread. The electron beam brightness is an analog of the brightness of optical beams and is directly proportional to the current and inversely proportional to the square of the emittance. As such, it describes the average current density per unit pitch angle and measures both the beam intensity and the degree of collimation of the electron trajectories. Since the gain and efficiency increases with increasing beam current for fixed emittance, the brightness is a complementary measure of the beam quality. Although it is important to minimize the emittance and maximize the brightness in order to optimize performance, both of these measures relate to the free-electron laser only insofar as they describe the axial velocity spread of the beam.

Typical free-electron laser efficiencies range up to approximately 12%; however, significant enhancements are possible when either the wiggler amplitude or period are systematically tapered. The free-electron laser amplifier at Livermore, which achieved a 35% extraction efficiency, employed a wiggler with an amplitude that decreased along the axis of symmetry, and contrasts with an observed efficiency of about 6% in the case of a uniform wiggler. The use of a tapered wiggler was pioneered by Phillips in 1960. The technique has received intensive study of late. Tapered-wiggler designs have also been shown to be effective at infrared wavelengths in experiments at Los Alamos National Laboratory and, using a superconducting rf linac, at Stanford University.

The effect of a tapered wiggler is to alter both the transverse and axial velocities. Since the transverse velocity is directly proportional to the product of the amplitude and period, the effect of gradually decreasing either of these quantities is to decrease the transverse velocity and, in turn, increase the axial velocity. The energy extracted during the interaction results in an axial deceleration that drives the beam out of resonance with the wave; hence, efficiency enhancement occurs because the tapered wiggler maintains a relatively constant axial velocity (and phase relationship between the electrons and the wave) over an extended interaction length. The pendulum equation is modified in the presence of a tapered wiggler, and has the form

$$\frac{d^2}{dz^2}\Psi = K^2(\sin\Psi - \sin\Psi_{res})$$

where the resonant phase Ψ_{res} is determined by the wiggler taper. The wiggler taper can be accomplished either through the amplitude or period. However, it is technically simpler to taper the amplitude, and most tapered-wiggler experiments have employed this approach. In this case, the resonant phase varies as

$$\sin\Psi_{res} = \left(\frac{v_w}{v_z}\right)^2 \frac{k + k_w}{K^2} \frac{1}{B_w} \frac{d}{dz} B_w$$

Integration of the tapered-wiggler pendulum equation results in an equation similar to that found in the case of a uniform wiggler, with a ponderomotive potential

$$U(\Psi) = K^2(\cos\Psi + \Psi\sin\Psi_{res})$$

If the wiggler amplitude is a decreasing function of axial position, then sin $\Psi_{res} < 0$ and the average potential decreases linearly with the ponderomotive phase. The difference between the ponderomotive potential for a uniform and a tapered wiggler is illustrated in Fig. 5. As a result, the motion is similar to that of a ball rolling down a *bumpy* hill and accelerating as it falls.

The enhancement in the tapered-wiggler interaction efficiency is proportional to the decrement in the wiggler field of ΔB_w, and satisfies

$$\Delta\eta \approx \frac{0.872B_w^2\lambda_w^2}{1 + 0.872B_w^2\lambda_w^2}\frac{\Delta B_w}{B_w}$$

In practice, a tapered wiggler is effective only after the bulk of the beam has become trapped in the ponderomotive wave. In single-pass amplifier configurations, therefore, the taper is not begun until the signal has reached saturation in a section of uniform wiggler, and the total extraction efficiency is the sum of the uniform wiggler efficiency and the tapered wiggler increment. Numerical simulations indicate that total efficiencies as high as 65% are possible under the right conditions.

Once particles have been trapped in the ponderomotive wave and begin executing a bounce motion between the troughs of the wave, the potential exists for exciting secondary emission referred to as sideband waves. These sidebands are caused by the beating of the primary signal with the ponderomotive bounce motion. This bounce motion is at the pendulum period that depends weakly on the depth of the ponderomotive well and the amplitude of the bounce motion. For deeply trapped particles that oscillate near the bottom of the well, the pendulum equation can be approximated as a harmonic oscillator with a wavenumber equal to the pendulum constant K. The sidebands, therefore, occur at wavenumbers shifted both upward and downward from the radiation wavenumber by this value (i.e., $k_\pm = k \pm K$, where $k_\pm$ denotes the sideband wavenumber). Note that the bounce period is, typically, much longer than the radiation wavelength (i.e., $K \ll k$), and these sidebands are found at wavelengths close to the wavelength of the primary signal.

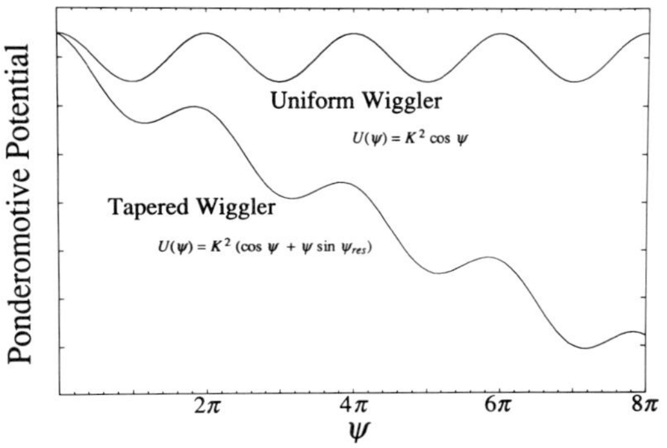

FIG. 5. A comparison of the ponderomotive potentials for uniform and tapered wigglers. The extraction efficiency of the free-electron laser can be enhanced by introducing a taper in the wiggler field. In particular a gradual reduction in either the amplitude or period of the wiggler will reduce the magnitude of the transverse velocity and accelerate the electrons in the axial direction. This is illustrated by the effect of the taper, for sin $\Psi_{res} < 0$, on the ponderomotive potential. In such a potential, an electron behaves in a manner analogous to a ball rolling down a *bumpy hill* and accelerating as it falls.

The difficulties imposed by the presence of sidebands is that they may compete with and drain energy from the primary signal. This is particularly crucial in long tapered-wiggler systems designed to trap the beam at an early stage of the wiggler and then extract a great deal more energy from the beam over an extended interaction length. In these systems, unrestrained sideband growth can be an important limiting factor. As a result, a great deal of effort has been expended on techniques of sideband suppression. One method of sideband suppression was employed in a free-electron laser oscillator at Columbia University. This experiment operated at a 2-mm wavelength in which the dispersion due to the waveguide significantly affected the resonance condition. As a consequence, it was found to be possible by proper choice of the size of the waveguide to shift the sideband frequencies out of resonance with the beam. Experiments on an infrared free-electron laser oscillator at Los Alamos National Laboratory indicate that it is also possible to suppress sidebands by (1) using a Littrow grating to deflect the sidebands out of the optical cavity or (2) changing the cavity length.

The foregoing description of the principles and theory of the free-electron laser is necessarily restricted to the idealized case in which the transverse inhomogeneities of both the electron beam and wiggler field are unimportant. This is sufficient for an exposition of the fundamental physics of the free-electron laser. In practice, however, these gradients can have important consequences on the performance of the free-electron laser. It is beyond the scope of this article to delve into these subjects in depth, and we will present only a simple sketch of the types of effects to be encountered. The most important effect that is found if the wiggler field varies substantially across the diameter of the electron beam is that the electron response to the wiggler will vary as well. In practice, this means that an electron at the center of the beam will experience a different field than an electron at the edge of the beam, and the two electrons will follow different trajectories with different velocities. As a result of this, the wave-particle resonance that drives the interaction will be broadened, and the gain and efficiency will decline. In essence, therefore, the transverse wiggler inhomogeneity is manifested as an effective beam thermal spread. The bounded nature of the electron beam also affects the interaction, since wave growth will occur only in the presence of the beam. Because of this, it is important in amplifier configurations to ensure good overlap between the injected signal and the electron beam. Once such overlap has been accomplished, however, the dielectric response of the electron beam in the presence of the wiggler can act in much the same way as an optical fiber to refractively guide the light through the wiggler.

III. Experiments and Applications

There are three basic experimental configurations for free-electron lasers: amplifiers, oscillators, and superradiant amplifiers. In an amplifier, the electron beam is injected into the wiggler in synchronism with the signal to be amplified. The external radiation source that drives the amplifier is referred to as the master oscillator and can be any convenient radiation source, such as a conventional laser or microwave tube. As a consequence, this configuration is often referred to as a master oscillator power amplifier (MOPA). Because amplification occurs during one pass through the wiggler, MOPAs require intense electron beam sources that can operate in the high-gain regime. Oscillators differ from amplifiers in that some degree of reflection is introduced at the ends of the wiggler so that a signal will make multiple passes through the system. The signal is amplified during that part of each pass in which the radiation copropagates with the electrons and allows for a large cumulative amplification over many passes, even in the event of a low gain per pass. Oscillators are typically constructed to amplify the spontaneous (i.e., shot) noise within the beam, and no outside signal is necessary for their operation. However, a long-pulse accelerator is required because a relatively long time may be required to build up to saturation. Superradiant amplifiers are devices in which the shot noise in the beam is amplified over the course of a single pass through the wiggler and, like amplifiers, require high-current accelerators to drive them. Since the shot noise present in the beam is generally broadband, the radiation from a superradiant amplifier is typically characterized by a broader bandwidth than a MOPA.

The optimal configuration and type of accelerator used in a free-electron laser design depends on the specific application, and issues such as the electron-beam quality, energy, and current are important considerations in determining both the wavelength and power. In general, however, each accelerator type is suited to the production of a limited range of wavelengths, as shown in Fig. 6. In addition, the temporal structure of the output light from a free-electron laser corresponds to that of the electron beam. Thus, either a pulsed or continuous electron-beam source will give rise to a pulsed or continuous free-electron laser. Free-electron lasers have been constructed using virtually every type of electron source, including storage rings, radiofrequency linear accelerators, microtrons, induction linacs, electrostatic accelerators, pulse-line accelerators, and modulators. Since the gain in a free-electron laser increases with current but decreases with energy, accelerators producing low-current/high-energy beams are generally restricted to the low-gain regime. Accelerator types that fall into this category include rf linacs, microtrons, storage rings, and electrostatic accelerators. In contrast, intense beam accelerators such as induction linacs, pulse-line accelerators, and modulators are suitable electron-beam sources for high-gain systems.

Storage rings are typically characterized by multiple electron pulses continuously circulating through the ring. Each pulse is several nanoseconds in duration, and the output light from a free-electron laser driven by a storage ring is a continuous stream of picosecond bursts. In addition, while storage rings produce high-quality and high-energy beams of low to moderate currents, the electron pulses are recirculated through both the ring and the wiggler, and the stability of the ring is disrupted by the extraction of too much energy. Hence, storage rings are feasible for applications that require uniform and continuous short-wavelength radiation sources but do not demand high output powers.

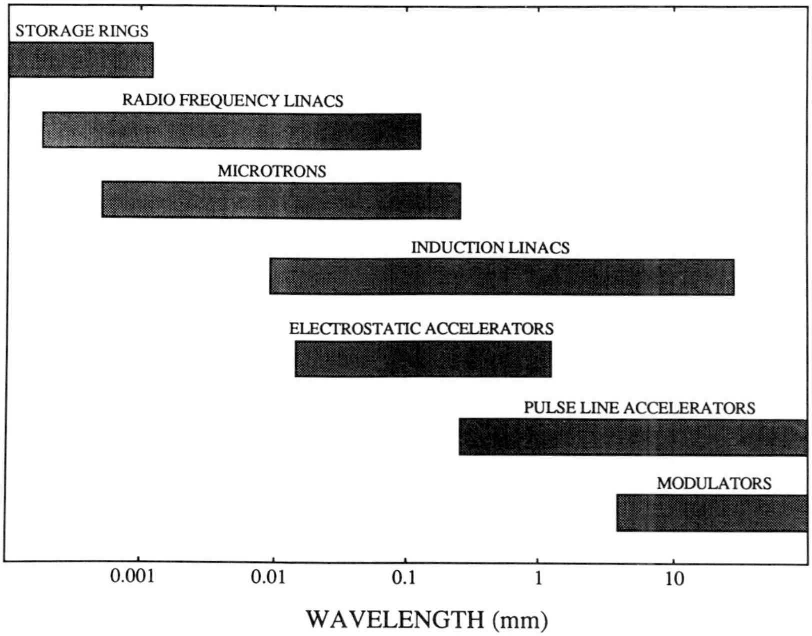

FIG. 6. The limits on the wavelengths possible with different accelerators depend both on the electron beam energies that may be achieved as well as on the state of wiggler development. The wavelength ranges that may be accessed by accelerators given the present state of accelerator and wiggler technology are shown.

The first successful operation of a storage ring free-electron laser was at the Université de Paris Sud at Orsay. This experimental configuration was that of an oscillator and made use of the ACO storage ring, which operates at energies and average currents in the range of 160–224 MV and 16–100 mA. The laser was tuned across a broad band of the visible spectrum, but was first operated at wavelengths in the neighborhood of approximately 0.65 μm. The peak output power from the oscillator was 60 mW over the 1-ns duration of the micropulses, which corresponds to an intracavity power level of 2 kW. The average power extracted from the system was typically of the order of 75 mW. Higher harmonic emission was also detected in the ultraviolet, however, which posed a problem since radiation at these wavelengths resulted in the ultimate degradation of the optical system.

An ultraviolet free-electron laser oscillator has also been achieved using the VEPP storage ring at Novosibirsk. This experiment employed an optical klystron configuration in which the wiggler was composed of two distinct sections separated by a diffusive drift space. In this configuration, the first section operates as a prebuncher for the electron beam, which subsequently enhances the gain in the second wiggler section. Operating the storage ring at 350 MV and a peak current of 6 A, experimenters were able to obtain coherent emission at wavelengths as short as 0.3 μm and average output power as high as 6 mW.

Radio-frequency linacs use a series of cavities that contain rapidly varying electromagnetic (rf) fields to accelerate streams of electrons. The beams they produce are composed of a sequence of macropulses (typically of microseconds in duration) each of which consists of a train of shorter picosecond pulses. Microtrons produce beams with a temporal structure similar to that of rf linacs but, unlike the rf linac, are composed of a single accelerating cavity coupled to a magnet that causes the electron beam to recirculate through the cavity many times. The output light from a free-electron laser built with these accelerators, therefore, is similar to the output from a storage ring. Recent experiments at Stanford University and Boeing Aerospace have also demonstrated the feasibility of the rf linac to produce visible light. In addition, rf linacs and microtrons are suitable for high-power free-electron lasers, since the electrons are not recirculated and the energy extraction is not limited by the disruption of the beam.

Free-electron lasers based on rf linacs have demonstrated operation over a broad spectrum extending from the infrared through the visible. The initial experiments conducted by Madey and co-workers at Stanford University resulted in (1) and amplifier that operated at a wavelength of 10.6 μm with an overall gain of 7%, and (2) a 3.4-μm oscillator that produced peak and average output power of 7 kW and 0.1 mW, respectively. In collaboration with TRW, the superconducting rf linac (SCA) at Stanford University has been used to drive a free-electron laser oscillator that has demonstrated efficiency enhancement with a tapered wiggler, operation at visible wavelengths, and beam recirculation. The significance of the latter point is that the overall wall-plug efficiency can be enhanced by recovery and reuse of the spent electron beam subsequent to its passage through the free-electron laser. The tapered-wiggler experiment operated in the infrared at a wavelength of 1.6 μm and peak power levels of 1.3 MW. This yields a peak extraction efficiency of approximately 1.2%, which constitutes an enhancement by a factor of three over the efficiency in the case of an untapered wiggler. Operation at visible wavelengths was also found at 0.52 μm and peak power levels of 21 kW. The superconducting technology embodied in the SCA can enable the rf linac to further compete with storage rings by operating in a near steady-state mode. Both energy recovery and enhancement of the extraction efficiency by means of tapered wiggler were also demonstrated at Los Alamos National Laboratory. Starting in 1981 with a tapered-wiggler free-electron laser amplifier that obtained an extraction efficiency of 4% at a wavelength of 10.6 μm, researchers went on to (1) extend that to a 5% extraction efficiency in an oscillator configuration, and (2) demonstrate a 70% energy recovery rate with beam recirculation.

The limitations that storage rings, rf linacs, and microtrons impose on free-electron laser design stems from restrictions on the peak (or instantaneous) currents that may be obtained and thus limits the peak power from a free-electron laser. High peak powers may be obtained by using induction linacs, pulseline accelerators, or modulators that produce electron beams with currents ranging from several amperes through several thousands of amperes, and with pulse times ranging from several tens of nanoseconds through several microseconds. Induction linacs operate by inducing an electromotive force in a cavity through a rapid change in the magnetic field strength. In effect, the electron beam acts as the secondary winding in a transformer. For example, the Advanced Test Accelerator (ATA) at Livermore is an accelerator of this type and can achieve energies and currents as high as 50 MV and 10 kA over a duration of 50 ns. At lower energies, pulse-line accelerators and conventional microwave tube modulators are available. Pulse-line accelerators produce beams with energies up to several tens of megavolts, currents of several tens of kiloamperes, and pulse times up to 50–100 ns. As a result, pulse-line accelerators and modulators have been applied exclusively to microwave generation.

Amplifier experiments employing induction linacs have been performed at the Naval Research Laboratory, Lawrence Livermore National Laboratory, and at the Institute for Laser Engineering at Osaka University in Japan and have demonstrated operation from the microwave through the infrared spectra. A superradiant amplifier at the Naval Research Laboratory employed at 650-kV/200-A electron beam and produced 4 MW at a wavelength of 1 cm. The Livermore experiments have employed both the Experimental Test Accelerator (ETA) and the ATA. The free-electron laser amplifier experiment at an 8-mm wavelength was conducted with the ETA operating at approximately 3.5 MV and a current of 10 kA. However, due to beam quality requirements, only about 10% of the beam was found to be usable in the free-electron laser. This ETA-based MOPA has been operated in both uniform and tapered-wiggler configurations. In the case of a uniform wiggler, the measured output power was in the neighborhood of 180 MW, which corresponds to an extraction efficiency of about 6%. A dramatic improvement in the efficiency was achieved, however, using a tapered wiggler. In this case, the total output power rose to 1 GW for an efficiency of 35%. The ATA has been used for a high-power MOPA design at a wavelength of 10.6 μm. Experiments are currently in progress at both Livermore and the Institute for Laser Engineering at Osaka on the use of induction linacs in high-power MOPAs at frequencies above 140 GHz for the purposes of radio-frequency heating of magnetically confined plasmas for controlled thermonuclear fusion.

An important consideration in the construction of free-electron lasers with the intense beams generated by these accelerators is that an additional source of focusing is required to confine the electrons against the self-repulsive forces generated by the beam. This can be accomplished by the use of additional magnetic fields generated by either solenoid or quadrupole current windings. Quadrupole field windings were employed in the 8-mm amplifier experiment at the Lawrence Livermore National Laboratory; the interaction mechanism in a free-electron laser is largely, though not entirely, transparent to the effect of the quadrupole field. In contrast, the solenoidal field has a deep and subtle effect on the interaction mechanism. This arises because a solenoidal field results in a precession, called Larmor rotation, about the magnetic field lines that can resonantly enhance the helical motion induced by the wiggler. This enhancement in the transverse velocity associated with the helical trajectory occurs when the Larmor period is comparable to the wiggler period. Since the Larmor period varies with beam energy, this relation can be expressed as

$$B_0 \approx 1.07 \frac{\gamma_b}{\lambda_w}$$

where the solenoidal field B_0 is expressed in tesla and the wiggler period is in centimeters. For fixed-beam energies, therefore, this resonant enhancement in the wiggler-induced velocity requires progressively higher solenoidal fields as the wiggler period is reduced.

The effect of a resonant solenoidal magnetic field is to enhance both the gain and saturation efficiency of the interaction. This was demonstrated in a superradiant amplifier experiment using the VEBA pulseline accelerator at the Naval Research Laboratory. In this experiment, the output power from the free-electron laser was measured as a function of the solenoidal field as it varied over the range of 0.6–1.6 T. The beam energy and current in the experiment were 1.35 MV and 1.5 kA, respectively, and the wiggler period was 3.0 cm. It should be remarked that, due to the high current in the experiment, the beam was unable to propagate through the wiggler for solenoidal fields below 0.6 T. The magnetic resonance was expected for a solenoidal field in the neighborhood of 1.3 T, and the experiment showed a dramatic increase in the output power for fields in this range. Other experiments that have demonstrated the effect of a solenoidal field have been performed at the Massachusetts Institute of Technology, Columbia University, and the Ecole Polytechnique in France.

The maximum enhancement in the output power in the experiment at the Naval Research Laboratory was observed for solenoidal fields slightly above the resonance. In this case, the nature of the interaction mechanism undergoes a fundamental change. In the absence of a solenoidal field (or for fields below the magnetic resonance), the axial velocity of the electrons decreases as energy is lost to the wave while the transverse velocity remains relatively constant. In contrast, the result of the strong solenoidal field is to cause a negative-mass effect in which the electrons accelerate in the axial direction as they lose energy to the wave. The bulk of the energy used to amplify the wave is extracted from the transverse motion of the electrons. Computer simulations of free-electron lasers operating in this strong solenoidal regime indicate that extremely high extraction efficiencies (in the neighborhood of 50%) are possible without recourse to a tapered-wiggler field. However, operation in this regime is precluded below submillimeter wavelengths. This is because the solenoidal field required to achieve this magnetic resonance varies directly with the beam energy and inversely with the wiggler period. Because of this, impractically high fields are required for wavelengths in the far infrared and below.

It is important to bear in mind that the high peak-versus-average power and oscillator-versus-MOPA distinctions between the different aforementioned accelerator technologies are becoming blurred by advances in the design of both rf and induction linacs. On the one hand, the development of laser-driven photocathodes at Los Alamos National Laboratory have dramatically increased both the peak (of the order of 400 A) and average currents achievable with rf linacs. As a result, a high-gain MOPA experiment is under design at Los Alamos National Laboratory. It is significant in this regard that a Stanford University collaboration with Rocketdyne Inc. has already achieved MOPA operation using the Mark III rf linac. On the other hand, new induction linacs are under development that may be fired repetitively at the rate of up to several thousand times per second. Successful completion of these development programs will enable high average power free-electron lasers to be constructed using this technology.

Although their average power is lower than that of linacs, electrostatic accelerators can produce continuous electron beams using charge recovery techniques. In such a process, the electron beam is recirculated through the wiggler and back into the accelerator in a continuous stream. Using this technology, the electrostatic accelerator holds promise as an electron beam source for a continuous or long-pulse free-electron laser. However, given practical restrictions on the size of such accelerators, which limit energies and currents, electrostatic accelerators have been restricted to the construction of free-electron laser oscillators that operate from the microwave regime through the infrared spectrum.

The breadth of free-electron laser experiments includes many different wiggler configurations and virtually every type of accelerator in use today. The wiggler has been produced in planar, helical, and cylindrical forms by means of permanent magnets, current-carrying coils, and hybrid electromagnets with ferrite cores. An example of a bifilar helical wiggler currently in use at the Naval Research Laboratory is shown in Fig. 7. Helical wiggler fields are produced by a current-carrying bifilar helical coil in which the field increases radially outward from the symmetry axis and provides magnetic focusing to confine the beam against the mutually repulsive forces between the electrons. In a planar wiggler, both the transverse and axial components of the velocity oscillate in synchronism with the wiggler. As such, the interaction is determined by the average, or root-mean-square, wiggler field. Because of this, planar wigglers require a stronger field to produce the same effect as helical wigglers. This is compensated for, however, by the ease of adjustment allowed by a planar design, in which the strengths or positions of the individual magnets can be altered to provide either a uniform or a tapered field. In contrast, the only adjustment possible for a bifilar helix is the strength of the field.

One practical constraint on the development of free-electron laser oscillators at the present time is mirror technology for infrared and shorter wavelengths; this constraint relates to both reflectivity and durability. The reflectivity is important since the net gain of an oscillator decreases as the mirror losses increase, and oscillation is possible only if the amplification due to the free-electron laser interaction exceeds the losses at the mirrors. The reflectivity is a measure of this loss rate, and must be kept sufficiently high that the energy losses at the mirrors do not overwhelm the gain. The issue of durability relates to the power level that any specific mirror material can endure without suffering optical damage. In this sense, optical damage refers to a decrease in the reflectivity. Note that the extreme case of the complete burning out of the mirrors might be described as a catastrophic drop in the reflectivity. Problems exist in finding materials with a high enough reflectivity and durability to operate in the infrared and ultraviolet spectra: even the visible presents problems. For example, the visible free-electron laser oscillator at the Université de Paris Sud experienced mirror degradation due to harmonic emission in the ultraviolet. At extremely high power levels, solutions can be found through such techniques as the grazing-incidence mirrors used by Boeing Aerospace in which the optical beam is allowed to expand to the point where the power density on the mirrors is low. In the infrared, oscillator experiments at Los Alamos National Laboratory originally employed a dielectric mirror material with a high reflectivity at low power levels. However, recent observations indicate that nonlinear phenomena occur in this material at high power levels that effectively reduce the reflec-

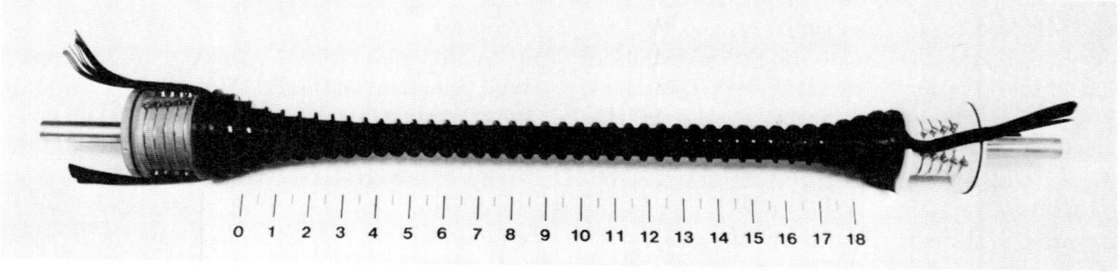

FIG. 7. One of the principal wiggler designs in use is the bifilar helical current winding. The example shown here exhibits flares at both the entrance and the exit to the wiggler, to facilitate the transition of the electron beam both into and out of the wiggler field. The scale shown is in centimeters.

tivity, and that the use of copper mirrors substantially improves performance. An additional problem occurs at high power levels due to thermal distortion of the optical surface. To combat this problem, actively cooled mirrors are under development.

The principal biomedical applications of the free-electron laser are surgery, photocoagulation and cauterization, photodynamic therapy, and the *in vivo* thermal destruction of tissue through a process called photothermolysis. The most common surgical technique is the thermal ablation of tissue, which requires a laser producing 10–100 W at a wavelength of approximately 3 μm. This corresponds to a strong absorption resonance of the water molecule characterized by relatively little scattering of the light by the tissues. In contrast, photocoagulation requires a shorter wavelength of approximately 1–1.5 μm, which is also strongly absorbed by the water molecule but exhibits a higher degree of scattering throughout the surrounding tissue. It is important to observe that the tunability of the free-electron laser holds the potential for a surgical laser that may be tuned in a single sequential process from 3 μm down to 1 μm to give both clean surgical incisions and cauterization. Another advantage is that the optical pulse can be tailored to meet specific requirements by control of the temporal structure of the electron beam. For example, short pulses are useful in ophthalmic therapy for the surgical disruption of pigmented tissue, while longer pauses are required for retinal photocoagulation.

Photodynamics therapies rely on the injection of photosensitive dyes that are preferentially concentrated in malignant tissue. Subsequent irradiation excites a photooxidation process that is toxic to the tumorous tissue. The principal dyes are photosensitive at wavelengths between 0.6–1.7 μm and are used to treat tumors of the lung, bladder, and gastrointestinal tract at early stages in their development and also as a palliative treatment at later stages of growth. At relatively high average powers (up to 100 W), a free-electron laser makes possible the simultaneous treatment of relatively large masses of tissue. However, the high-energy electron beams needed to produce these wavelengths also produce relatively large X-ray fluxes, and the entire facility including power supply, accelerator, wiggler, optical system, and X-ray shielding is likely to be rather bulky and complex. Hence, in consideration of the rapid development of conventional laser sources at these wavelengths, the long-term biomedical applications are envisioned to be in (1) the initial refinement of these therapeutic techniques, (2) large centralized facilities for tumor treatment, and (3) experimental research tools.

Applications to research are unimpaired by considerations of the bulk and complexity of a free-electron laser facility; the first user facility was established by Luis Elias at the University of California at Santa Barbara in 1984. This facility, shown in Fig. 8, employs a long-pulse 3-MV electrostatic accelerator. The free-electron laser produces a peak power of as much as 10 kW over a range in wavelengths of 390–1000 μm and is suitable for a wide range of experiments in the biomedical, solid-state, and surface sciences. In the field of photobiology, since the DNA molecule is sensitive to infrared wavelengths, the free-electron laser can study such behavior as the variation in the DNA mutation rate with wavelength. In addition, experiments have been conceived in the linear and nonlinear excitations of phonons and magnons, ground and excited-state Stark splitting, the generation of coherent phonons, phonon amplification by stimulated emission, induced phase transitions, and semiconductor band-gap structure. The latter application may prove relevant to the study of high critical-temperature superconductors.

More recently, two user facilities have been constructed at Stanford University based on both the Mark III rf linac and the SCA. The Mark III facility, established by John Madey and co-workers, is tunable over the range 0.5–10 μm and produces 60 kW over a pulse time of several microseconds. Due to the electron energies available from the Mark III, however, the fundamental operation occurs at wavelengths in the neighborhood of 1–3 μm. Shorter wavelengths are achieved through the use of frequency-doubling techniques common to laser engineering. In this case, the tunability, high power, and temporal structure offer a unique opportunity to study surgical applications. In particular, experiments have been conducted in the cutting of both bone and soft tissue with encouraging results. Since spot sizes of the order of 100–1000 μm and power densities as high as several megawatts per square centimeter are possible, the cutting mechanism is not thermal ablation but direct plasma formation of the irradiated tissue with extremely clean and localized incisions. In contrast to conventional lasers (which produce lower power levels over longer pulse times), the combination of high power and short

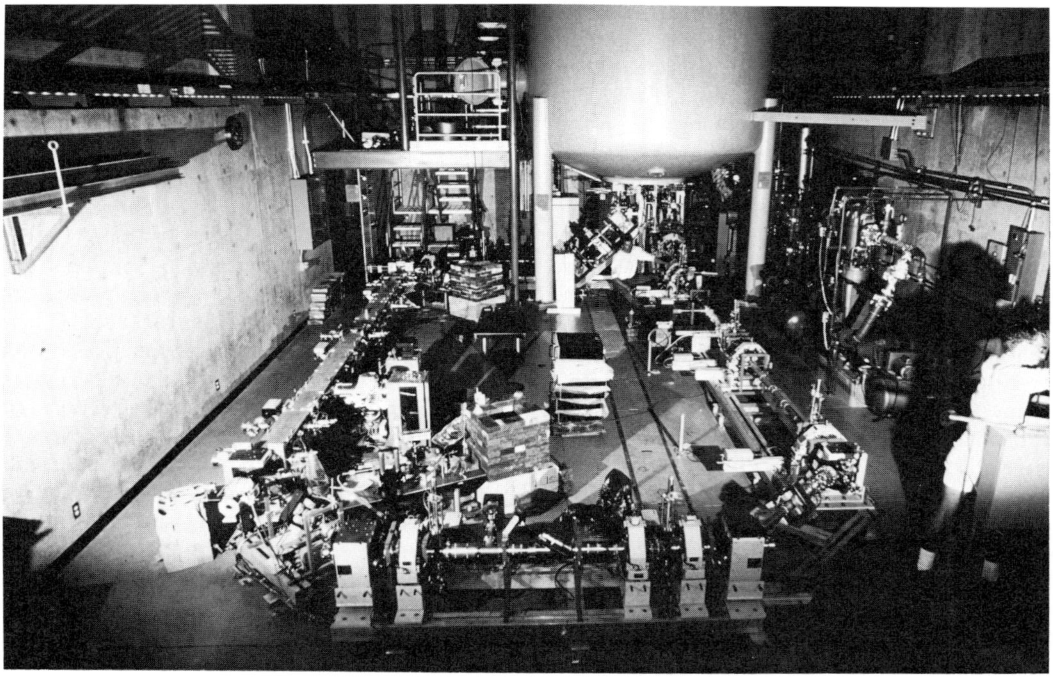

FIG. 8. The first free-electron user facility was established at the University of California at Santa Barbara. This device operates in the far infrared and employs an electrostatic accelerator, as shown in the background. A magnetically focused system of electron-beam optics is used to transport the beam from the accelerator through the wiggler (in foreground) and back to the accelerator. (Photo courtesy of Luis Elias.)

pulses results in less scar formation and more rapid healing. Indeed, the power densities available with this free-electron laser have raised concern that current optical fiber technology may ultimately prove inadequate to the task of directing the radiation, and research has begun in the development of optical fibers capable of handling higher intensities. In addition, experiments have been conducted to study semiconductor band-gap structure as well as the multiphoton spectroscopy of germanium and polyacetylene. The Mark III free-electron laser has been relocated at Duke University.

The SCA free-electron laser facility commonly operates in a continuous mode in which the macropulses are generated at a frequency of 20 Hz (that is, 20 macropulses per second) over a timescale of several hours. A typical macropulse is of 5-ms duration and is composed of a train of 3-ps micropulses separated by 84.6 ns. Average electron-beam currents over a macropulse can reach 200 μA with a peak current of 6 A over a micropulse. The peak voltage of the superconducting linac is 75 MV, but the recirculation system allows this to rise as high as 150 MV. The free-electron laser has operated over wavelengths ranging from 0.5–3.5 μm and is capable of operation in the ultraviolet. This range will soon be extended to 15 μm, using a wiggler supplied by Spectra Technologies, Inc.

Experiments to data have been concerned with dynamical processes on picosecond time scales in materials such as, for example, photon echoes in dye molecule/glass systems. To this end, the picosecond micropulses and the relatively large macropulse separation (which is long enough for conventional optical pulse selection techniques to be used) produced by the SCA are crucial. For a recent experiment, the free-electron laser was operated at a wavelength of 1.54 μm with a linewidth of 0.08% and was stable over a timescale of several hours. The output power was approximately 300 kW over a micropulse, 12 W averaged over a macropulse, or 1 W over the longer timescale.

The operation of the SCA is soon to be upgraded by the implementation of a novel electron injector acceleration scheme. In a conventional rf linac, the electron beam is accelerated by a single-frequency rf signal that varies sinusoidally over time. Since the amount of electron acceleration depends on the rf power, the electron pulse must be synchronized to the peak of the rf signal and its duration kept short. In general, the longer the electron pulse, the larger the variation in rf power over the pulse and the greater the energy spread of the electron beam. To minimize the beam energy spread, which degrades the performance of the free-electron laser, researchers at the SCA plan to use a composite rf signal composed of waves at multiple frequencies. In a manner analogous to the way in which a *square-wave* signal can be built up from a large composite spectrum of waves, this process will extend the duration of the peak rf signal. As a consequence, both the duration and power in the electron beam will increase at little or no cost to the beam quality. It is estimated that the peak and average beam currents will increase to approximately 50 A and 1 mA, respectively, with corresponding increases in the output of the free-electron laser.

As a measure of the impact of advances in accelerator technology on the free-electron laser, it should be noted that the Mark III linac was the accelerator used by Hans Motz in 1951, and that the present range of experiments was made possible by the continual improvement of the original design. Indeed, a user facility was under construction at Vanderbilt University late in 1989 based on a further improved Mark III linac. This free-electron laser was designed to operate over a spectral range of 0.2–10 μm, and experiments are currently envisioned to study wound healing and scarification after short-pulse laser surgery, neurosurgical shrinkage of irradiated tumors, the differential transport of molecules across membranes, Raman active normal modes of DNA, and high-intensity laser-induced damage in glasses and crystals.

In general, the principal advantages of the free-electron laser as a research tool are high intensity (relative to currently available sources), tunability, and a temporal structure controlled by the characteristics of the accelerator. Tunability permits the selection of specific energy states for study, while an appropriate tailoring of the temporal structure of the pulses allows the time evolution and decay of excited states to be investigated. In addition, it should be remarked that there are no good infrared sources available with wavelengths ranging from 2–5 μm. Important areas of investigation are the bulk and surface properties of semiconductors—in particular, the band-gap structure. Some of the most commercially important semiconductors exhibit band gaps in the range of 0.25–2.5 μm, and it is important to extend the spectral range of study to within 0.1 μm about this range. A high-intensity, tunable free-electron laser producing pulses of approximately 10–100-ps duration at a repetition rate of several megahertz would permit the study of the dynamic excitation and subsequent decay of electrons into unoccupied energy states.

Other applications include laser photochemistry and photophysics that require sources in the visible and ultraviolet spectra. Initial development of an ultraviolet free-electron laser is being conducted at Los Alamos National Laboratory using rf linac technology. Since the electron beam is composed of short bursts at high repetition rates, rf linacs produce radiation with the desired temporal structure. The principal competition in the ultraviolet comes from incoherent synchrotron light sources that also make use of undulator magnets. The advantage of a free-electron laser over synchrotron sources is the increased counting rates resulting from a larger photon flux, which would make practical a large number of currently marginal experiments. A nonexhaustive list of experiments possible with a coherent visible through ultraviolet source includes the multiphoton ionization of liquids, chemistry of combustion and of molecular ions, high-resolution polyatomic and fluorescence spectroscopy, time-resolved resonance Raman spectroscopy, spin-polarized photoemission and photoemission microscopy, magnetooptical studies of rare-earth elements, and studies of optical damage from high-intensity ultraviolet radiation.

Industrial applications are envisioned in materials production and photolithography. The requirements for materials production are sources in the near infrared (2.5–100 μm) and the ultraviolet through soft X-ray spectra, and involve the pyrolytic production of powders for catalysts, the near-stoichiometric production of high-value chemicals and pharmaceuticals, and the pyrolytic and photolytic deposition of thin films on substrates. In photolithography, the surface of a wafer is coated with a layer of a photoresisting substance of which a part is illuminated. The wafer is then processed by the removal of either the exposed or unexposed portions of the resist. Photolithography is primarily done with the optical lines of the mercury arc that occur over the spectral range of 436–357 μm: the excimer laser is under consideration for this purpose as well.

Three principal lithographic techniques are either in use or under consideration. Contact printing is performed by bringing a mask and wafer into contact, whereas in proximity printing a small space separates these two components. The preferred technique is that of projection printing in which the image of the mask is projected onto the wafer from a greater distance than in contact or proximity printing, which allows the use of larger masks and improves usable mask lifetime. Each of these techniques requires uniform and stable sources of illumination. The sources may be either continuous or pulsed; however, possible difficulties with pulsed sources (e.g., rf linac driven free-electron lasers) are that (1) the instantaneous pulse power necessary to give a sufficiently high average power may also be high enough to damage the wafer, and (2) extremely high uniformity from pulse to pulse is required. In addition, short wavelength sources may render the nonlithographic direct printing of wafers possible and eliminate the need for photoresists.

Applications also exist for high-power microwaves and submillimeter waves in the fields of communications, radar, and plasma heating. We continue the discussion to the heating of a magnetically confined plasma for controlled thermonuclear fusion. The reactor design of greatest interest is the Tokamak, which confines a high-temperature plasma within a toroidal magnetic *bottle*. A thermonuclear reactor must confine a plasma at high density and temperature for a sufficiently long time to ignite a sustained fusion reaction. In its original conception, the Tokamak was to be heated to ignition by an ohmic heating technique whereby a current is induced by means of a coil threading the torus. As such, the Tokamak acts like the secondary winding in a transformer. However, recent developments indicate the need for auxiliary heating, and the resonant absorption of submillimeter radiation has been proposed for this purpose. The frequencies of interest are the harmonics of the electron cyclotron frequency and range from about 280 GHz through 560 GHz. In the case of the Compact Ignition Torus, which is the proposed design of the next major Tokamak experiment in the United States, the applied magnetic field is 10 T and the resonant wavelengths are in the neighborhood of 1 mm and less. The estimates of the power requirements are, of necessity, relatively crude but indicate the need for an average power of approximately 20 MW over a pulse time of nearly 3 s. At present there are no sources capable of meeting this requirement. However, the free-electron laser has operated in this spectral region at power levels of this order, but over a much shorter pulse time. As such, it represents one of several competing concepts.

A more controversial application of high-power, long-pulse free-electron lasers is strategic defense against intercontinental ballistic missiles. In this regard, planners envision a large-scale ground-based laser that would direct light toward a target by means of both ground-based and orbiting mirrors. Designs based on both amplifier and oscillator free-electron lasers are being pursued.

In experiments during the late 1980s, a free-electron laser amplifier at Livermore amplified a 14-kW input signal from a carbon dioxide laser at 10.6 μm to a level of approximately 7 MW, a gain of 500 times. Boosting the input beam to 5 MW yielded a saturated power of 50 MW.

Boeing Aerospace has built an experimental free-electron laser oscillator in collaboration with Los Alamos National Laboratory based on a 5-meter-long planar wiggler and an advanced radio-frequency linac. The linac produces electron beams with energies as high as 120 MV. The oscillator has lased in the red region of the visible spectrum at a wavelength of 0.62 μm and at power levels a billion times that of the normal spontaneous emission within the cavity. The average power over the course of a 100-μs pulse is about 2 kW. The corresponding conversion efficiency is about 1%, but the peak power is a more respectable 40 MW. Even though oscillators typically generate short-wavelength harmonics that can damage the cavity mirrors, no degradation has been observed thus far. Work is underway to convert the uniform wiggler to a tapered configuration to increase the oscillator's efficiency.

Unclassified figures indicate that pulses of visible or near-infrared light at an average power of about 10–100 MW over a duration of approximately one second are required to destroy a missile during its boost phase. This means lengthening the pulses or increasing the peak power levels of existing free-electron lasers by a factor of a million or more. Depending on laser efficiency and target hardness, a collection of ground-based free-electron lasers would require somewhere between 400 MW and 20 GW of power for several minutes during an attack. (For comparison, a large power plant generates about 1000 MW.) For these and other reasons, it is not clear whether it will be practical to scale up free-electron lasers to the power levels required. Current and future experiments will help to resolve this question.

IV. Summary and Discussion

The aforementioned discussion includes a necessarily abridged list of recently conceived applications of the free-electron laser. The fundamental principles of the free-electron laser are understood at the present time, and the future direction of research is toward evolutionary improvements in electron-beam sources (in terms of beam quality and reliability) and wiggler designs. The issues, therefore, are technological rather than physical, and the free-electron laser can be expected ultimately to cover the entire spectral range discussed. In this regard, it is important to recognize that the bulk of the experiments to date have been performed with accelerators not originally designed for use in a free-electron laser, and issues of the beam quality important to free-electron laser operation were not adequately addressed in the initial designs. As a consequence, the results shown do not represent the full potential of the free-electron laser, although many of the experiments have produced record power levels. The only accelerators specifically designed for use with a free-electron laser are the rf linac at Boeing Aerospace, an induction linac at Lawrence Livermore National Laboratory, and the electrostatic accelerator at the University of California at Santa Barbara. At the present time, an intensive program at Los Alamos National Laboratory is directed toward adapting the technology of rf linacs to the design of short-wavelength free-electron laser oscillators. In particular, it is found that wakefields induced by pulses of high peak currents in the accelerator and beam transport system can result in serious degradation in beam quality, and that the minimization of these effects is an important consideration in the overall design of the beam line in free-electron lasers.

Another important direction for future research is the design of short-period wigglers that permit short-wavelength operation with relatively low-voltage electron beams. An alternate approach to the production of short-wavelength radiation with moderate-energy electron beams is the use of higher harmonic interactions. For example, if the third harmonic interaction is employed [i.e., $\omega = (k + 3k_w)v_z$], then the energy requirement for a fixed-wavelength output is reduced by a factor of approximately $\sqrt{3}$. Indeed, lasing has been achieved at the third harmonic in experiments at (1) Stanford University using the Mark III linac at a wavelength of 1.4–1.8 μm and (2) Los Alamos National Laboratory at a wavelength of 4 μm. The reduction in the voltage requirement has important practical implications in the simplification of accelerator design problems and the reduction in the production of secondary X-rays and neutrons. The combination of improved accelerators and short-period wigglers will reduce both the size and complexity of free-electron laser systems and open doors to a host of new practical applications of the technology.

Free-electron laser research and development at the present time is international in scope with a wide range of experiments either in operation or in the planning stages throughout the United States, Europe, Japan, China, and the Soviet Union. These projects include a wide range of designs based on all the accelerator types and cover a spectral range extending from microwaves through the ultraviolet. The technology can therefore be expected to make the transition from development in the laboratory to active exploitation over a range of applications during the next decade.

Bibliography

Brau, C. A. (1990). "Free-Elecron Lasers." Academic Press, Boston.

Deacon, D. A. G., Elias, L. R., Madey, J. M. J., Ramian, G. J., Schwettman, H. A., and Smith, T. I. (1977). First operation of a free-electron laser. *Phys. Rev. Lett.* **38**(16), 892.

Freund, H. P., and Parker, R. K. (1989). Free-electron lasers. *Sci. Am.* **260,** 84.

Jacobs, S. F., Pilloff, H. S., Sargent, M., Scully, M. O., and Spitzer, R., eds. (1980). "Physics of Quantum Electronics: Free-Electron Generators of Coherant Radiation." Vol. 7. Addison-Wesley, Reading, Massachusetts.

Jacobs, S. F., Pilloff, H. S., Sargent, M., Scully, M. O., and Spitzer, R., eds. (1982). "Physics of Quantum Electronics: Free-Electron Generators of Coherant Radiation." Vols. 8, 9. Addison-Wesley, Reading, Massachusetts.

Luchini, P., and Motz, H. (1990). "Undulators and Free-Electron Lasers." Clarendon Press, Oxford.

Marshall, T. C. (1985). "Free-Electron Lasers." Macmillan, New York.

Martellucci, S., and Chester, A. N., eds. (1983). "Free-Electron Lasers." Plenum Press, New York.

Motz, H. (1951). Applications of the radiation from fast electron beams. *J. Appl. Phys.* **22**(5), 527.

Phillips, R. M. (1988). History of the ubitron. *Nucl. Instrum. Methods Phys. Rev. Sect. A* **272**(1), 1.

Roberson, C. W., and Sprangle, P. (1989). A review of free-electron lasers. *Phys. Fluids B* **1**(1), 3.

Sessler, A. M., and Douglas, V. (1987). Free-electron lasers. *Am. Sci.* **75**, 34.

LASERS, GAS

W. W. Duley *York University*

GLOSSARY

Band: Grouping of spectral lines in the emission or absorption spectrum of a molecule.

Continuous wave: Refers to dc operation of laser; typically a steady (dc) output for 1 sec or more.

Excimer: Molecule that is strongly bound in an excited state but normally has a dissociative ground state. The term excimer comes from excited dimer. Excimers also include exciplexes (excited complexes).

Mode: Output characteristic of laser; normally refers to the intensity distribution of output light intensity.

Population: Subset of atoms or molecules in a particular energy level.

Pumping: Means of producing an inversion in a laser system.

Transverse excitation-atmospheric pressure (TEA): Excitation geometry where the discharge is applied transverse to the optical path; gas pressure is close to 1 atm.

Tunable: Having an output wavelength that can be adjusted over a range of 1 nm or more.

Vacuum ultraviolet: Region of the spectrum with wavelengths less than 200 nm.

Laser emission has been obtained from most elements of the periodic table in gaseous form as well as from a host of molecular species. Output wavelengths available from gas lasers span the spectrum from the far infrared to the X ray. Output powers are a function of the mode of excitation—either continuous wave or pulsed—as well as of the laser gas. Gas lasers may be pumped electrically, chemically, thermodynamically, or optically by other laser or light sources. Few gas lasers are tunable over an appreciable wavelength range.

I. Introduction

The first gas laser was operated in 1961, only one year or so after Maiman's demonstration of the feasibility of obtaining maser-type emission at optical frequencies. Gas lasers had been envisioned in fundamental patents for quantum electronic systems but difficulties associated with pumping of candidate systems inhibited the development of practical gas laser devices. The operation of an He–Ne laser at a wavelength of 1152.27 nm showed that these problems could be overcome and opened the door to the rapid development of the gas laser field. [*See* LASERS.]

The five or so years following the announcement of laser oscillation in He–Ne saw the development of gas lasers based on ionized rare gas atoms, a variety of neutral atoms, and simple molecules such as N_2 and CO_2. In recent years this pace of discovery has slackened somewhat, although the mid-1970s saw the development of excimer and gold lasers, and attention has focused instead on the commercialization of these and other gas laser systems (Table I). At the same time, interest has shifted to the use of gases as nonlinear media for the generation of tunable vacuum ultraviolet radiation. The free electron laser, which, in a sense, is also a gas laser, has been the subject of much recent development and offers the possibility of obtain-

TABLE I. History of Commercial Gas Lasers

Laser	First reported	Date commercialized
He–Ne	1961	1962
Far infrared	1963	1969
Iodine	1964	1983
CO_2	1964	1966
Rare gas ion	1964	1966
Nitrogen	1966	1969
Copper vapor	1966	1981
HF/DF	1967	1977
He–Cd	1968	1970
Excimer	1975	1976
Gold vapor	1978	1982

ing high-power laser radiation tunable over a wide range of wavelengths.

Today laser emission has been obtained at well over 1000 wavelengths from gaseous elements in atomic or ionic form. Most elements in the periodic table have been induced to lase when in gaseous form, generally via pulsed or continuous-wave (cw) discharge pumping. A multitude of molecular gases as well as radical and short-lived transient species have also exhibited laser emission. These molecular lasers emit at wavelengths extending from the vacuum ultraviolet (H_2 laser, excimer lasers) to the far infrared (HCN laser). The most important of these from the point of view of industrial applications is the CO_2 laser operating at 10.6 μm.

II. Helium—Neon Laser

Laser oscillation in a mixture of He and Ne gas was first reported in 1961 by Ali Javan and colleagues working at Bell Laboratories. Helium–neon has the distinction of being the first gaseous system to exhibit laser oscillation. Since 1961 the He–Ne laser has become widely available as a compact, reliable commercial product used in many industrial applications, primarily in the measurement and metrology fields.

The active medium in the He–Ne laser is a gaseous mixture of He and Ne with proportions of about 10:1 in a sealed Pyrex tube at a pressure of several torr. This gas is excited in a positive column discharge with a current of some 100 mA. Optimum operating parameters (e.g., discharge current, He:Ne ratio, total gas pressure) are functions of tube diameter and also depend on the output wavelength selected.

TABLE II. Wavelengths λ (in Air and Vacuum) for Important He–Ne Laser Lines

λ (air) (nm)	λ (vacuum) (nm)
543.364	543.515
632.816	632.991
1152.27	1152.59
3391.32	3392.24

The He–Ne laser can be made to emit at a variety of discrete wavelengths in the visible and infrared regions of the spectrum (Table II); however, dominant spectral lines lie at 632.8 nm (the He–Ne red line) and 3391.3 nm (see Fig. 1). For operation at 632.8 nm, emission at 3391.3 nm must be suppressed since the two lines share the same upper level. oscillation on the high-gain 3391.3 nm line depletes the excited state population for 632.8 nm emission. Discrimination against the infrared line can be accomplished by adjusting the reflectivity of the laser mirrors so as to have peak reflection at 632.8 nm together with low reflectance at 3391.3 nm. Alternatively, application of a longitudinal magnetic field has been shown to suppress oscillation at 3391.3 nm by Zeeman splitting. Magnetic fields of ~200 G are typically required.

The low gain of the 632.8 nm laser line in He–Ne makes for a relatively inefficient system with low output powers. While cw output powers of ~1 W are attainable from laboratory devices, standard commercially available He–Ne lasers offer powers of between 1 and 50 mW at 632.8 nm. Low-power He–Ne lasers are compact, with tube lengths of 20 cm or so, and emit either linearly polarized or randomly polarized light in a TEM_{00} mode. Higher-power He–Ne lasers may be 2 m or so in length. A summary of output characteristics is given in Table III.

TABLE III. Output Characteristics of He–Ne Lasers

Wavelength	632.82 nm
Power	0.5–50 mW
Beam diameter	0.5–2.0 mm
Beam divergence	0.5–2 mrad
Stability	5%/hr
Coherence length	0.1–0.3 m
Lifetime	10–20,000 hr

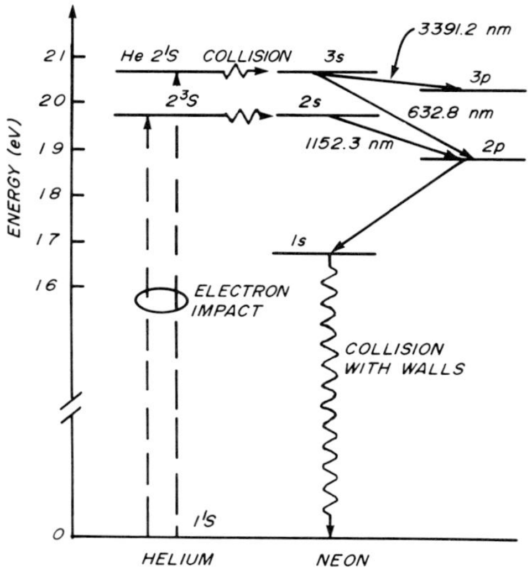

FIG. 1. Simplified energy level diagram for He–Ne laser showing laser transitions.

III. Rare Gas Ion Lasers

Laser emission has been observed under pulsed and cw excitation of the rare gases Ne, Ar, Kr, and Xe (see Table IV) in various ionization states. Rare gas ion lasers when operated in a cw mode provide up to 20 W of power at wavelengths in the spectral range 450–700 nm and up to several watts of power when oscillating in the 350 nm region. Lasers of the rare gas ion type therefore provide some of the highest cw powers available over the wavelength range between 350 and 700 nm (Table V). This is achieved at the expense of inefficient operation; the ArII laser, for example, has an efficiency of only about 0.1%. thus 10 kW of electrical power is required to obtain 10 W of laser output.

An energy level diagram showing some of the atomic and ionic states involved in the ArII laser is shown in Fig. 2. It is apparent that each 3-eV photon emitted by an excited ArII ion is the result of the ionization of a neutral Ar atom (ionization potential 15.76 eV) together with excitation of the resulting ion to states nearly 20 eV above the ground state of the ion. A number of mechanisms have been proposed for the excitation of the upper ArII levels in the laser discharge. Electron collisions may excite these states directly via a single step from the ArI level or indirectly by means of a two-step transition involving the ArII ground state as an intermediate level. Collisional excitation of higher ArII or ArIII states followed by radiative cascade back to the upper laser levels is probably also important.

TABLE IV. Rare Gas Ion Lasers—Primary Laser Wavelengths (cw Operation)

Ion	Wavelength in air (nm)	Ion	Wavelength in air (nm)
NeII	332.376	KrII	520.831
	334.552		530.865
	337.830		568.188
	339.286		647.088
	371.310		676.442
ArIII	351.112		752.546
	363.789	XeIII	345.424
ArII	454.504	XeIV	364.551
	457.935	XeIII	378.097
	465.789		406.041
	472.686		421.401
	476.486		424.042
	487.989		427.259
	496.508		460.302
	501.716		495.418
	514.531		500.778
KrIII	350.742		515.906
	356.422		523.893
	406.737		526.017
	413.132		526.189
KrII	468.041		535.288
	476.243		539.459
	482.517		541.915
			627.081

In general, the power P per unit length L emitted by the cw ArII laser is described by the expression

$$P/L = K(JR)^2$$

TABLE V. Output Characteristics of Ar and Kr Rare Gas Ion Lasers

Characteristic	Low power	High power
Wavelength[a] (nm)	457–530	457–530
Power[b] (W)	0.25	20
Beam diameter (mm)	2.0	1.9
Beam divergence (mrad)	1.5	0.40
Stability (%/day)	5	0.5
Beam amplitude noise[c] (% rms)	2	0.5
Lifetime	2000 hr	18 month

[a] 647–676 nm for Kr.
[b] Maximum 5 W for Kr operation.
[c] 0–100 kHz.

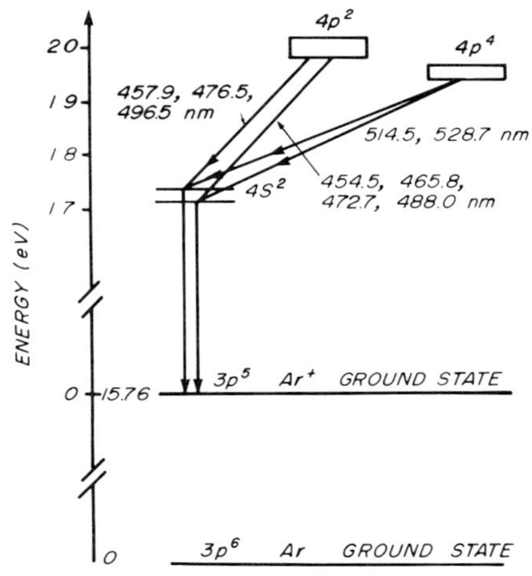

FIG. 2. Energy levels involved in the blue-green emission from the ArII laser.

where J is the current density in the laser discharge, R the radius of the discharge column, and K a constant which takes the value $2 \times 10^{-3} \leq K \leq 5 \times 10^{-3}$ when JR has units of amperes per reciprocal centimeter and P/L is in watts per meter. Typically, for a commercial ArII laser oscillating in the blue-green one has $p/L \sim 5 - 10$ W m^{-1} while $JR \sim 50$ A cm^{-1}. Optimum tube gas pressure depends on discharge current and discharge bore diameter. Pressures in the range 150–300 mTorr are usual, however.

The Doppler-limited linewidth of rare gas ion laser emission is generally in the range 5–10 GHz. With cavity stabilization the laser linewidth can be $\simeq$500 MHz with a drift of $\sim$100 MHz hr^{-1}. With a linewidth of 10 GHz, mode locking can produce pulse lengths of 100 psec. In ArII and KrII lasers mode locking yields pulses with a peak power of $\sim$1 kW at a pulse repetition frequency (prf) of $\approx$150 MHz. Cavity dumping can produce narrow pulses at a prf of $\geq$1 MHz with peak powers $\sim 10^2$ times the cw power. [*See* MODE-LOCKING OF LASERS.]

The large discharge current required for operation of Ar and Kr ion lasers places strong demands on bore materials. Current tube technology involves the use of segmented tungsten disk bores for high-power systems. Earlier technology centered on the use of graphite or beryllium oxide discharge channels. Beryllium oxide technology is currently used in several low-power air-cooled ArII lasers.

IV. Metal Vapor Lasers

Laser emission has been observed from vapors of a variety of metal atoms and their ions (see Fig. 3) under either pulsed or cw excitation. Most of these lasers have yet to be commercialized for one reason or another (low efficiency, competitive simpler system, etc.). For this reason, we limit the present discussion to two of the more important metal vapor systems—the He–Cd and Cu vapor lasers.

A. Helium–Cadmium Lasers

The two strong laser lines emitted by CdII in the He–Cd laser have wavelengths of 325.029 and 441.565 nm (in air). The cw output powers are typically 5–10 mW on the 325 nm line and 10–50 mW on the 441 nm line, both for fundamental mode (TEM_{00}) operation. Multimode powers are about 50% larger. Primary applications of the He–Cd laser have been in the electronic printing industry. The Xerox Company, for example, has used the He–Cd laser for high-speed writing on a selenium photoconductor.

The He–Cd laser operates with Cd vapor at a pressure of $\sim$2 mTorr maintained by evaporating metallic Cd. The He pressure is typically 4–6 Torr and a dc discharge is passed axially through the laser tube. Reliability problems are related to the consumption of Cd as the tube ages and to plating out of metallic Cd on tube windows. The overall lifetime of commercial He–Cd laser tubes is now in the 4000-hr range.

B. Copper Vapor Laser

The neutral Cu atom has two very high gain transitions at 510.554 and 578.213 nm that can be

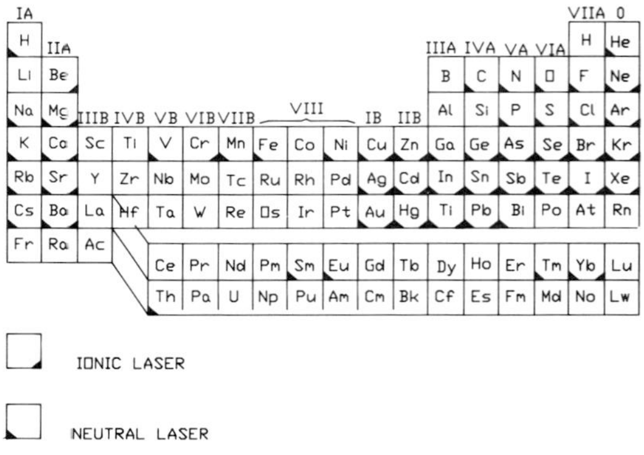

FIG. 3. Periodic table showing the elements that have exhibited laser emission in gaseous form.

pumped efficiently in pulsed discharges at very high repetition rates. Average powers of 40–50 W are available from commercial Cu vapor laser at prf's of up to 20 kHz. Laboratory systems have been pulsed at rates up to 150 kHz. Applications have centered on the use of these lasers to pump dye lasers, primarily for uranium enrichment.

The low vapor pressure of metallic Cu, together with the need to maintain a Cu pressure of ~0.5 Torr in the laser discharge, has hindered the development of these systems. Thermal evaporation of Cu metal requires that the metal be heated to 1400–1600°C, a severe constraint to operation. Recently, interest has focused on the use of excess heat from the laser discharge to maintain the requisite Cu vapor pressure.

V. Carbon Dioxide Laser

Laser emission from the CO_2 molecule was first observed by Patel in 1964. In Patel's early experiments, a pulsed discharge was passed through pure CO_2 and laser output powers were small. It was soon realized, however, that the overall efficiency of the CO_2 laser could be greatly increased by the incorporation of N_2. Nitrogen molecules that are vibrationally excited in the laser discharge collisionally excite the upper CO_2 laser level as follows:

$$N_2(X^1\Sigma_g^+, v'' = 1) + CO_2(00^01) \rightarrow$$
$$N_2(X^1\Sigma_g^+, v'' = 0) + CO_2(00^01) - 18 \text{ cm}^{-1}$$

where standard spectroscopic notation is used to designate molecular states. Infrared laser emission occurs from rotational levels of the CO_2 (00^01) excited vibrational state to rotational levels of either the $(10^00, 02^00)_{\text{I}}$ or $(10^00, 02^00)_{\text{II}}$ vibrational state (see Fig. 4). These transitions

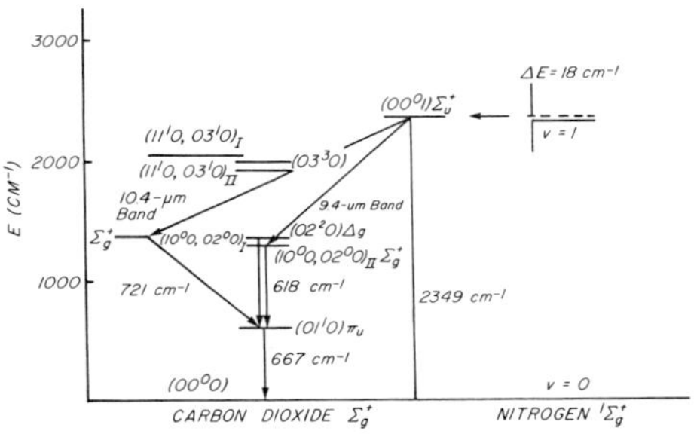

FIG. 4. Energy level diagram for CO_2 and N_2 molecules showing 10.4- and 9.4-μm bands.

form bands at 10.4 and 9.4 μm, respectively. Because rotational transitions are involved and many rotational levels are populated under discharge conditions, the CO_2 laser can be tuned to oscillate at a large number of discrete wavelengths within the 10.4- and 9.4-μm bands. In fact, at pressures of nearly 10 atm these lines broaden into a continuum. Under these conditions pulsed CO_2 lasers can be continuously tuned over a wavelength range of several micrometers near 10 μm.

Unless the CO_2 laser cavity contains a means by which individual wavelengths may be selected from within the 10.4- and 9.4-μm bands, oscillation occurs primarily on those lines that have the highest gain. Under most excitation conditions these are the $P(18)$, $P(20)$, and $P(22)$ lines of the 10.4-μm band. Their wavelengths (in vacuum) are $P(18)$, 10.5713 μm; $P(20)$, 10.5912 μm; and $P(22)$, 10.6118 μm. Since these three lines are near 10.6 μm, this is the emission wavelength that is usually quoted for the CO_2 laser.

Laser emission from CO_2 has also been observed at wavelengths in three bands near 4.3 μm as well as numerous bands between 11 and 18 μm. All are seen only under pulsed conditions.

The population inversion required to obtain laser emission from CO_2 may be established in a variety of ways. Excitation of the upper CO_2 laser level (00^01) can occur by inelastic collision with low-energy electrons or by a nearly resonant energy transfer from vibrationally excited N_2. Both mechanisms have been exploited in practical laser devices.

The CO_2 laser usually operate on a mixture of CO_2, N_2, and He gases. The optimum proportions of the three components depend on the mode of excitation, but generally for flowing cw systems the CO_2:N_2:He ratio is in the range 1:1:8 with a total gas pressure of 5–15 Torr. The role of He in the laser mixture is, in part, to quench the population that builds up in (01^10) and other low-lying levels of the CO_2 molecule after laser emission has occurred (see Fig. 4) and to stabilize the glow discharge. Helium atoms are translationally excited during such processes, and this heat must be removed from the laser gas for efficient operation. In practice, in slow-flow devices heat is removed by collisions with the walls of the laser tube. By increasing gas flow to the point where convective cooling occurs, the overall size of the laser may be reduced while maintaining high output power.

Typical values for the power per unit discharge length generated in a slow axial flow CO_2 laser is 75 W m^{-1}, while for fast-flow convectively cooled devices this ratio increases to 200–600 W m^{-1}.

Heat can also be removed by flowing the laser gas mixture transverse to the discharge direction (Fig. 5). This gas flow and excitation mode are now utilized in high-power (5–20 kW) commercial cw CO_2 lasers. Some properties of these and other cw CO_2 lasers are summarized in Table VI. Many cw CO_2 lasers can also be pulsed electrically or in Q-switching mode to obtain output pulses with peak power $\sim 10^2$ larger than the cw power. Pulse duration can extend from less than one microsecond to milliseconds. With intracavity modulation or mode locking pulse technique, pulse lengths as short as a few nanoseconds are obtainable in a high-pressure CO_2 laser.

The transverse excitation–atmospheric pressure (TEA) laser exploits a transverse discharge geometry to induce a uniform self-sustained avalanche discharge in the laser gas at high pressure. By employing a preionization technique to initially ionize CO_2 laser mixtures, arcing can be eliminated. The result is stable operation at high energy input and at high prf. Such TEA lasers exhibit a phenomenon known as gain switching. Here rapid pumping induces a large population in the upper laser level. When the electromagnetic fields builds up within the cavity the population inversion is already large, so rapid amplification occurs. The result is the emission of an intense gain-switched pulse lasting about 100–200 nsec (Fig. 6). After this pulse, populations in the upper and lower laser levels have been equalized. However, vibrationally excited N_2 molecules continue to pump the upper laser level, leading to the subsequent emission of a broad (1–10 μsec) pulse following the gain-switched pulse.

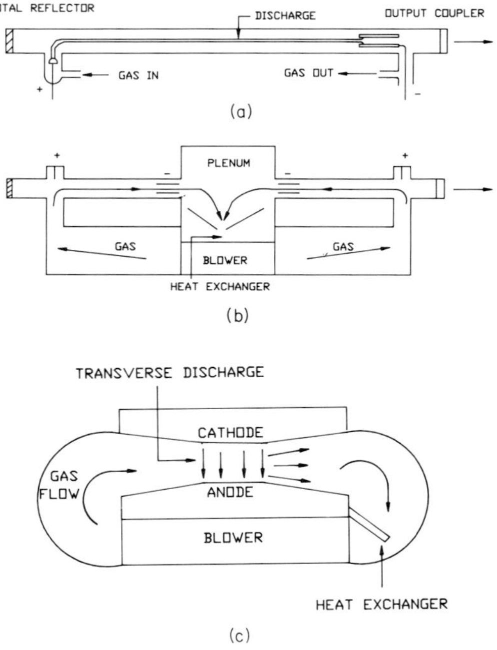

FIG. 5. Discharge and gas flow configurations for the CO_2 laser: (a) axial flow, (b) fast axial flow, and (c) transverse flow and discharge.

Commercial TEA lasers, of the sort used in laser machining applications, typically emit up to 3 J per pulse at prf's up to 50 Hz. The output beam of these lasers is rectangular in cross section with dimensions of $\sim 2 \times 3$ cm. High-energy TEA lasers are available that emit up to 2–3 $\times$ 10^3 J per pulse at low (0.05 Hz) prf.

Mode locking of the TEA laser output occasionally occurs spontaneously. Active mode locking yields -1-nsec pulses at atmospheric pressure. Operation at higher pressure can yield mode-locked pulses with durations as short as 100 psec.

TABLE VI. Continuous Wave (cw) CO_2 Lasers

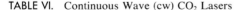

Configuration	Output power (W)	Beam diameter (mm)	Beam divergence (mrad)	Features
Waveguide	≤25	1.5–3	10	Sealed tube
Longitudinal excitation	≤75	5	3	Sealed tube
Slow axial flow longitudinal excitation	100–1000	5–30	1.5–3	Pulsed, line-tunable
Fast axial flow longitudinal excitation	500–3000	10–20	1.5–3	Compact size
Transverse flow transverse discharge	5000–15,000	>15	>3	High power

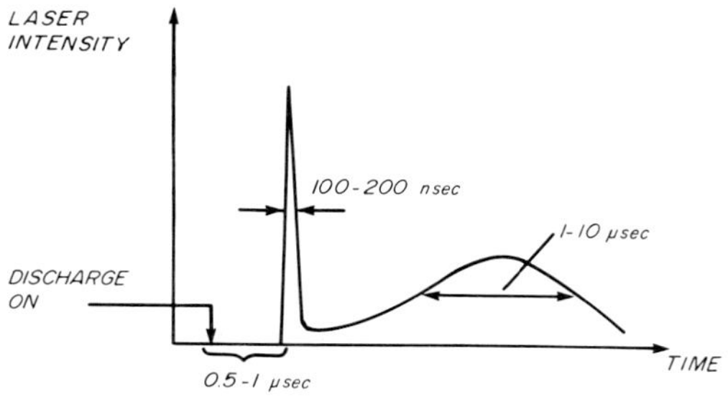

FIG. 6. Time dependence of TEA laser output. Both the gain-switched and broad pulses can contain comparable amounts of energy.

Large pulse energies can be extracted from electron beam-controlled CO_2 lasers. In these devices a high current of ~100-keV electrons is used to preionize the laser gas. When the preionization charge density is sufficiently large, a subsequent main electrical discharge can be operated at a lower field than that required for a self-sustained discharge. Hence the discharge field strength may be adjusted to optimize the CO_2 laser excitation and this laser output. In this way CO_2 laser pulse energies of 2×10^3 J with microsecond duration can be generated.

In the gasdynamic laser (GDL) a hot CO_2 gas mixed with hot N_2 and He with perhaps some added H_2O is allowed to expand supersonically through a nozzle. When the gas contains the right combination of quenching species (e.g., H_2O) the population of CO_2 molecules in the lower laser level can be reduced rapidly while still maintaining much of the population in the upper laser level. The overall result is the establishment of a population inversion between the two states. Large amounts of laser power can be extracted from such a system. Quasi-cw outputs of ~400 kW have been recorded from GDLs.

The GDL can also be operated on a pulsed basis with gas flow generated by the combustion of a mixture of CO, O_2, N_2, and H_2. Output pulses of millisecond duration and containing ~20 J have been reported.

VI. Excimer Lasers

Certain molecules such as ArF, KrF, and XeCl are strongly bound only in excited states. The ground state of these molecules, which are called excimers, are characterized by small dissociation energies or in some cases by repulsive potential energy curves. In the excimer laser electrical pumping creates atoms and ions that combine to form excimer molecules. Since the ground state of such molecules is essentially empty because of rapid dissociation, a population inversion between the excimer state and the ground state is easily obtained. Transitions between these states occur in most instances in the ultraviolet or vacuum ultraviolet. Thus excimer lasers emit primarily at wavelengths shorter than 350 nm (see Table VII). The high gain of excimer laser transitions leads to efficient operation—the ratio of average laser output power to electrical power into an excimer laser can be as large as 0.04. Furthermore, the short radiative lifetime of the excimer level (~10 nsec) yields short pulse operation at high prf's. Some excimer lasers have been operated at prf's up to 2000 Hz. Average powers up to 200 W can be obtained from commercial excimer lasers.

In excimer lasers operating on transitions involving molecules containing halogen atoms the halogen is obtained by electrical dissociation of a parent compound (e.g., HCl or F_2) that can be relatively easily introduced in the laser cavity by standard gas handling techniques. However, the reactive nature of these precursor gases and their dissociation products means that care must be taken to ensure that metal and glass surfaces in contact with the laser mixture are coated with materials that are chemically resistant. Nickel and brass have been found to be effective is electrode materials, while a coating of Teflon pro-

TABLE VII. Output Characteristics of Excimer Lasers—Values for Typical Commercial Lasers

Gas	F_2	ArF	KrCl	KrF	XeCl	XeF
Wavelength[a] (nm)	157	193	222	249	308	350
Pulse energy (mJ)	10	400	45	550	200	275
prf (Hz)	40	90	130	100	160	100
Average power (W)	0.5	30	6	45	30	20
Pulse length (nsec)	6	10	8	12	8	15

[a] Wavelength refers to the B → X transition.

tects the laser tube itself from corrosion. Despite these precautions, systems must be passivated by extended contact with halogen before stable operation can be obtained.

During operation of the laser, particulate matter and chemical impurities build up in the laser cavity. Particulate matter may deposit on the system optics and degrade output power, while molecular impurities and the reduction of the concentration of precursor halogen-bearing molecules reduce system gain. The overall result is a loss of output power. The limited lifetime of excimer gas mixtures was a major problem with early lasers. However, improvements in cavity design and electrical excitation have greatly extended the lifetime of excimer gas mixtures and reduced operating costs. In addition, the use of external gas processors that continually remove particulate matter and low vapor pressure impurities has extended operating times to up to several days on a single fill of laser gas. This makes the excimer laser one of the more economical lasers to operate, even though the cost of primary gases (e.g., Xe and Kr) can be high. The use of neon as a buffer gas in some systems (e.g., the KrF laser) can, however, be a major cost consideration.

VII. Other Molecular Lasers

A. Nitrogen Laser

Laser emission from the N_2 molecule can be excited at pressures of ~100 Torr in a transverse discharge geometry. The output wavelength of the N_2 laser lies at 337.1 nm and involves vibronic transitions within the $C^3\Pi_u \rightarrow B^3\Pi_g$ second positive band system. Nitrogen laser radiation consists of a single pulse of amplified spontaneous emission with a duration of ~10 nsec. Typical output powers are up to 1 MW with pulse energies of ≈10 mJ. Pulse repetition rates can be 100 Hz. Picosecond pulse widths are also possible with high-pressure, short-pulse excitation.

The short wavelength and narrow pulse width of the N_2 laser, together with an excitation geometry that yields an output beam with a rectangular cross section, have led to extensive use of these lasers as pumps for pulsed dye lasers. A major limitation, however, is the low energy per pulse—almost one to two orders of magnitude less than that from the excimer laser.

B. Carbon Monoxide Laser

The CO laser can be operated as a cw axial flow device, as a gas dynamic laser, and under TEA-type excitaton conditions. It can also be run as a chemical laser. Laser emission occurs between high vibrational levels of ground state CO molecules. The output wavelength is line-tunable between 5 and 7 μm. Highly excited vibrational levels are populated in a discharge via a collisional process known as anharmonic pumping:

$$\mathrm{CO}\ (v = i) + \mathrm{CO}\ (v = j) \rightarrow$$
$$\mathrm{CO}\ (i + n) + \mathrm{CO}\ (j - n)$$

where $n = 1, 2, \ldots, i \geq j$. In the anharmonic process CO molecules can be raised to vibrational states with v as high as 35. The laser emission involves the radiative cascade process

$$\mathrm{CO}\ (v, J) \rightarrow \mathrm{CO}\ (v - 1, J \pm 1) + hv$$

where J is the rotational quantum number. Output power of the cw CO laser is greatly enhanced by cooling the gas to 77 K. Output powers of 20 W are available from commercial cw devices. TEA-type excitation yields 10-mJ pulses of ~1-μsec duration at a prf of 10 Hz.

C. The HF/DF Laser

The exothermic chain reaction between H_2 and F_2 to yield vibrationally excited HF is the basis for an efficient chemical laser requiring little input of electrical power. Continuous-wave output powers of 2.2 MW at 2.7 μm (HF) and 3.8 μm (DF) have been produced in this way. In a pulsed mode, pulse energies of 5 kJ have been reported. The reaction between F atoms and H_2

$$\mathrm{F} + \mathrm{H_2} \rightarrow \mathrm{HF}\ (v) + \mathrm{H}$$

yields HF molecules in vibrationally excited states peaking at $v = 2$ for HF and $v = 3$ for DF. A population inversion with respect to lower vibrational levels can be established as the result of this selective excitation. The nonchain HF laser, for example, oscillates on lines of the $2 \rightarrow 1$, $1 \rightarrow 0$, and $3 \rightarrow 2$ vibrational bands, while the chain reaction HF laser typically oscillates on lines up to the $6 \rightarrow 5$ band.

To promote the reaction and then freeze in the high-temperature equilibrium, a mixture of H_2 and F_2 gases is heated in a high-temperature precombustor (Fig. 7). Extra F_2 is added downstream before the gaseous mixture is allowed to

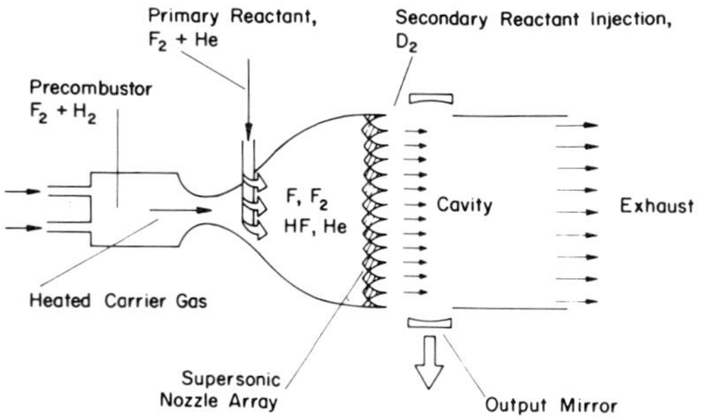

FIG. 7. Schematic diagram of the elements of a cw supersonic chemical laser. [From Cool, T. A. (1979). In "Methods of Experimental Physics," Vol. 158 (L. Marton and C. Marton, eds.), Academic Press, New York.]

expand through an array of supersonic nozzles. Supersonic expansion together with quenching of low vibrational levels results in the establishment of a population inversion downstream. Laser oscillation then occurs transverse to the direction of gas flow.

While more emphasis has been placed on the development of cw HF/DF chemical lasers for military applications, smaller versions are available as commercial products. Output powers of ~150 W can be obtained from such cw devices. High-power pulsed HF lasers initiated by intense electron beams have been developed as candidates for the inertial confinement fusion energy driver.

D. FAR-INFRARED LASERS

Molecular emission at wavelengths in excess of 10 μm are dominated by pure rotational transitions. Such transitions can be excited thermally, in glow discharges or via optical pumping. The latter technique has proved to be the most versatile in view of the availability of the CO_2 laser as a line-tunable pump. To date, more than 50 molecules have been pumped optically with the CO_2 or other mid-infrared lasers. Emissions occurs in the form of discrete lines at wavelengths extending to the millimeter region.

Optical pumping of selected rotational levels in a molecule such as NH_3 or CH_3OH leads to the establishment of a population inversion between the excited level and one or more rotational levels at lower energy. With the high power available from pulsed and cw CO_2 (or N_2O) lasers, the pump transition can be relatively easily saturated, yielding significant excited state populations. Where an exact resonance does not exist between the pump wavelength and a transition of the excited molecule, Stark shifting may be employed to bring the molecular transition into resonance.

VIII. Laser Radiation via Nonlinear Effects

The nonlinear electrical susceptibility of many gases when exposed to intense laser radiation has been exploited for some time in the generation of tunable vacuum ultraviolet (VUV) radiation. The polarization $\bar{P}(w)$ of a medium when exposed to an electrical field containing components at frequencies w_1, w_2, and w_3 contains the term

$$\bar{P}(w) = \sum_{123} X^{(3)}(w = w_1 + w_2 + w_3)\bar{E}(w_1) \cdot \bar{E}(w_2) \cdot \bar{E}(w_3)$$

where $\bar{E}(w_1)$ is the electric field at frequency w_1 and so forth. As a result, the system can generate radiation of frequency w which is the sum of individual applied components. Energy levels involved in such transitions are shown schematically in Fig. 8.

The third-order susceptibility can be written

$$X^{(3)}(w = w_1 + w_2 + w_3) = \frac{3e^4}{4\hbar^3} \times \frac{\mu_{01}\mu_{12}\mu_{23}\mu_{03}}{(\Omega_{30} - w_1 - w_2 - w_3)(\Omega_{20} - w_1 - w_2)(\Omega_{10} - w_1)}$$

where e is electron charge, $\hbar$ is Planck's constant/2Π, the μ_{ij}'s are dipole matrix elements, and Ω_{30} etc. are frequency differences between real states and the ground state. It is apparent that $X^{(3)}$ has resonances when $\Omega_{20} - w_1 = 0$ and so forth; however, those involving one- or three-photon processes are accompanied by strong ab-

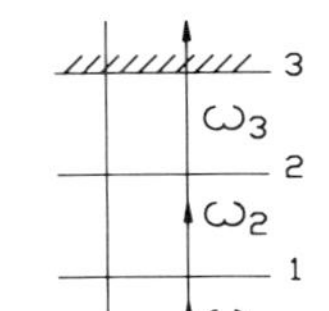

FIG. 8. Energy levels and transitions involved in four-wave sum mixing to generate radiation of frequency w.

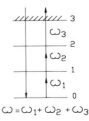

TABLE VIII. Atomic Vapor Used for Generation of Tunable VUV Laser Radiation via Four-Wave Sum Mixing

Vapor	Tunable wavelength range (nm)	Laser system
Sr	195–178	N_2–dye
Mg	174–140	N_2–dye
	129–121	KrF–dye
Zn	140–106	XeCl/KrF–dye
Hg	125–93	Nd:YAG–dye
Xe	206–160	Nd:YAG–dye
Ke:Kr	147–140	Nd:YAG–dye
Kr	130–110	Nd:YAG–dye
		Excimer–dye
Ar	102.7[a]	XeCl
Xe	83[a]	cw–dye, Kr–dye
H_2	79[a]	ArF–dye
Ar, H_2, Kr	64[a]	cw–dye, ArF–dye
Ar	57[a]	Xe_2

[a] Small tuning range.

sorption in the nonlinear medium. Hence, tunable radiation at frequency $w = 2w_1 \pm w_2$ is usually obtained by tuning $2w_1$ to resonate with a two-photon transition, preferably chosen such that $2w_1 + w_2$ resonates with an autoionizing state above the ionization limit of the absorber.

Fortunately, many atomic vapors satisfy the requirement of accessible two-photon states together with a strong autoionization resonance at high energy (Table VIII). Experimentally, the beam from a fixed-frequency dye laser (w_1) is combined with that of a tunable dye laser in a Glan prism to form a collinear beam that enters a cell containing the nonlinear vapor. When $2w_1$ is tuned to a two-photon resonance in the vapor, a beam at $w = 3w_1$ can be generated. However, when the laser emitting at w_2 is tuned into resonance or near resonance with an autoionizing level, then an enormous enhancement of coherent output at $w = 2w_1 + w_2$ is observed. Phase matching of output and input beams is required for optimum results. Conversion efficiencies for visible power to VUV power as high as 10^{-3} have been reported under pulsed excitation. Output (VUV) linewidths of 0.02 cm^{-1} have been obtained. Molecular gases can also be used for four-wave sum mixing.

BIBLIOGRAPHY

Bennett, W. R. (1979). "Atomic Gas Laser Transition Data." Plenum Press, New York.

Duley, W. W. (1976). "CO_2 Lasers, Effects and Applications." Academic Press, New York.

McIlrath, T. J., and Freeman, R. R. (1982). "Laser Techniques for Extreme Ultraviolet Spectroscopy" *American Institute of Physics,* **90.** New York.

Tang, C. L. (1979). "Quantum Electronics," **15** A,B. Academic Press, New York.

Weber, M. J. (1982). "CRC Handbook of Laser Science and Technology" CRC Press Inc. **II,** Boca Raton, Florida.

LASERS, NUCLEAR PUMPED

David A. McArthur *Sandia National Laboratories*

Glossary

Fast burst reactor (FBR): Produces neutron pulses about 0.1–1 msec in width, by rapid mechanical assembly of the critical mass in a neutron-free environment.

Nuclear device: Nuclear explosive which produces a single short pulse of intense gamma and fast-neutron radiation.

Nuclear device pumped laser (NDPL): Laser pumped by the very high radiation fluxes obtainable near an exploding nuclear device.

Range: Mass per unit area of a particular material which is sufficient to absorb all the kinetic energy of a charged particle having a well-defined initial energy (usually expressed in milligrams per square centimeter).

Reactor pumped laser (RPL): Laser pumped by a portion of the leakage neutrons or gamma rays produced by a pulsed or steady-state nuclear reactor.

Substrate: Mechanical support for a thin coating of fissile material in direct contact with the laser medium or nuclear flashlamp medium.

TRIGA: Zirconium-hydride-moderated research reactor with inherently safe operating characteristics which can be operated in a variety of modes (pulsed, steady-state, or multiple pulses).

Volumetric pump rate: The rate of energy deposition per unit volume of laser medium.

This work was supported by the U.S. Department of Energy under contract DE-AC04-76PD00789.

Nuclear pumped lasers (NPLs) are optical lasers operating at wavelengths ranging from the ultraviolet through the infrared which are excited directly or indirectly by high-energy charged particles resulting from nuclear reactions. This definition includes optically pumped laser media in which the pumping light source is produced by nuclear reactions, but it excludes lasers in which nuclear radiation is used merely to pre-ionize the laser medium to control a discharge which provides the primary excitation.

Ideas for NPLs were proposed shortly after the invention of the laser. Two broad categories of NPLs have been demonstrated, those pumped by nuclear explosives (NDPL) and those pumped by specialized (usually pulsed) research reactors (RPLs). Table I summarizes basic data on representative NPLs.

I. Examples of Nuclear Pumped Lasers

A. Nuclear Device Pumped Lasers

In 1974 two independent experiments in pumping of laser media by nuclear explosives were reported briefly. Lawrence Livermore Laboratory reported measurements of optical gain and directionally enhanced light emission in high-pressure Xe gas, and Los Alamos Laboratory simultaneously reported a chemical HF laser initiated by radiation. These were the first NPLs reported and demonstrated that nuclear radiation could produce lasing action.

In these studies the laser media were pumped at extremely high volumetric pump rates with an intense short pulse of gamma rays, resulting in laser pulses of about 10 nsec width. The laser cells themselves were small but efficiencies were reasonable. Great care was exercised to minimize radiation damage to the laser optics

TABLE I. Representative Nuclear Pumped Lasers

Laser	Wavelength (10^{-6} m)	Laboratory[a]	Date	Pump source[b]	Target nucleus	Volumetric pump rate (MW/m^3)	Laser energy[b] (J)	Laser efficiency[b] (%)
Xe_2^*	0.17	LLNL	1974	NDPL	gamma	1.5×10^9	N/A	N/A
HF	2.7	LANL	1974	NDPL	gamma	8.0×10^8	2.9	6.5
CO	5.4	Sandia	1975	FBR	^{235}U	1000	0.02	0.5
Xe	3.5	LANL	1975	FBR	^{235}U	200	10^{-6}	10^{-4}
N	0.86, 0.94	UI	1976	TRIGA	^{10}B	3.3	10^{-5}	10^{-4}
Hg^+	0.615	UI	1977	FBR	^{10}B	300	2×10^{-7}	10^{-6}
Xe	2.65	NASA	1980	FBR	$^{235}U/UF_6$	25	10^{-3}	0.05
Ar	1.79	NASA	1981	FRB	^3He	2100	0.12	0.02
Xe	1.73	USSR	1982	N/A	^{235}U	10	2–3	2–5
Cd^+	0.4416	USSR	1982	N/A	^3He	1.9	5×10^{-6}	0.007

[a] LLNL, Lawrence Livermore National Laboratory, Livermore, California; LANL, Los Alamos National Laboratory, Los Alamos, New Mexico; Sandia, Sandia National Laboratory, Albuquerque, New Mexico; UI, University of Illinois, Champaign, Illinois; NASA, NASA Langley Research Center, Hampton, Virginia; USSR, Soviet Union, laboratory not specified.
[b] N/A, not available.

and to construct an optical apparatus which was insensitive to radiation damage. It is likely that the laser apparatus was totally destroyed by the blast or at least made inaccessible by radioactivation. There are no other reports in the nonclassified literature of NDPL experiments, although other countries with nuclear weapons programs and access to underground test facilities may have performed similar experiments.

Although many laser media require such high pump rates that they can only be pumped with the high radiation fluxes from a nuclear device, the difficulty and cost of protecting the laser apparatus from the shock and blast effects of the nuclear explosion may limit NDPLs to single-shot systems. Since much of the cost of a large laser system may be associated with the laser optics, routine destruction of the laser may not be acceptable. The catastrophic effects of an accidental explosion of the nuclear device would also limit deployment of NDPLs to areas far from human activity. In light of these limitations, it is likely that NDPLs could only be deployed in space or in underground locations below the earth's surface. Because of the highly specialized nature of NDPLs and the small amount of published information, further discussion will emphasize the reactor pumped laser.

B. Reactor Pumped Lasers

The more typical NPL reported has been pumped by a pulsed or steady-state nuclear reactor. Reactor pumped lasers (RPLs) are in a sense "laboratory" laser devices, even though in practice there are only a few laboratories with the required reactor facilities. The relatively few workers in the RPL field is probably related to the scarcity of these facilities. In these RPL experiments an intense pulse of neutrons triggers a nuclear reaction, which emits heavy charged particles into a gaseous laser medium. This results in excitation processes qualitatively similar to those produced by an intense electron beam.

The first clear case of reactor pumped lasing was reported by Sandia National Laboratories in 1975 and occurred in CO gas cooled to 77 K (see Table I). Shortly thereafter, Los Alamos Scientific Laboratory reported lasing in He/Xe gas mixtures, and in 1976 the University of Illinois reported lasing in Ne/N_2 gas mixtures at the much lower volumetric pump rates obtainable with their pulsed TRIGA reactor. In all of these feasibility experiments, only a very small fraction of the leakage neutrons from a reactor facility was used to excite the laser media.

Figure 1 shows a representative reactor pumped laser experiment. The laser apparatus consists of a rectangular stainless steel chamber located adjacent to a pulsed reactor (the Sandia National Laboratories SPR-II fast burst reactor). The chamber is fitted with high-reflectivity mirrors which reflect the laser beam in a folded path through the spatial region which contains the highest neutron flux. The chamber is filled

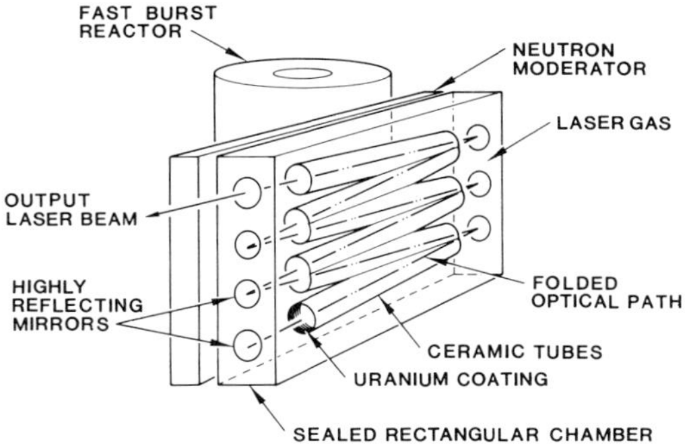

FIG. 1. Reactor pumped laser apparatus for use with a fast burst reactor (FBR).

with laser gas, and the laser gas along the "folded" optical path is excited by fission fragments emitted from the inner surfaces of hollow cylindrical ceramic tubes.

A slab of hydrogen-containing plastic is placed between the reactor and the chamber to slow the fast neutrons produced by the reactor (the process of "neutron moderation"). The slow neutrons are more readily absorbed by the uranium coatings on the inside of the cylinders, triggering the fission reaction. Fission fragments (energetic, highly charged heavy ions) emerge from the coatings to excite the laser gas. The excitation energy is stored in the ^{235}U nucleus, and the function of the neutron is to trigger the release of this fission energy. The energy deposition originates at the spatial location where the neutron is absorbed by the uranium nucleus and extends along the path of the fission fragment until it comes to rest. The volumetric pump rate is easily varied over a wide range by varying the energy released in the reactor pulse.

Figure 2a shows the time dependence of the fission fragment pulse which excites the laser gas, along with the laser pulse from a CO laser gas mixture. The laser action begins at a low excitation power but peaks before the excitation power peaks, and lasing ceases before the end of the excitation pulse. The volumetric pump power is about 1000 W/cm^3, and the total energy deposited is about 0.2 J/cm^3.

Termination of the laser pulse before the end of the excitation pulse is commonly seen for reactor pumped lasers. It may be related to gas heating which reduces the optical gain, to optical distortion of the laser medium by gas heating, or to creation of chemical species which absorb the laser light. In early measurements of optical gain in CO gas, severe focusing of a

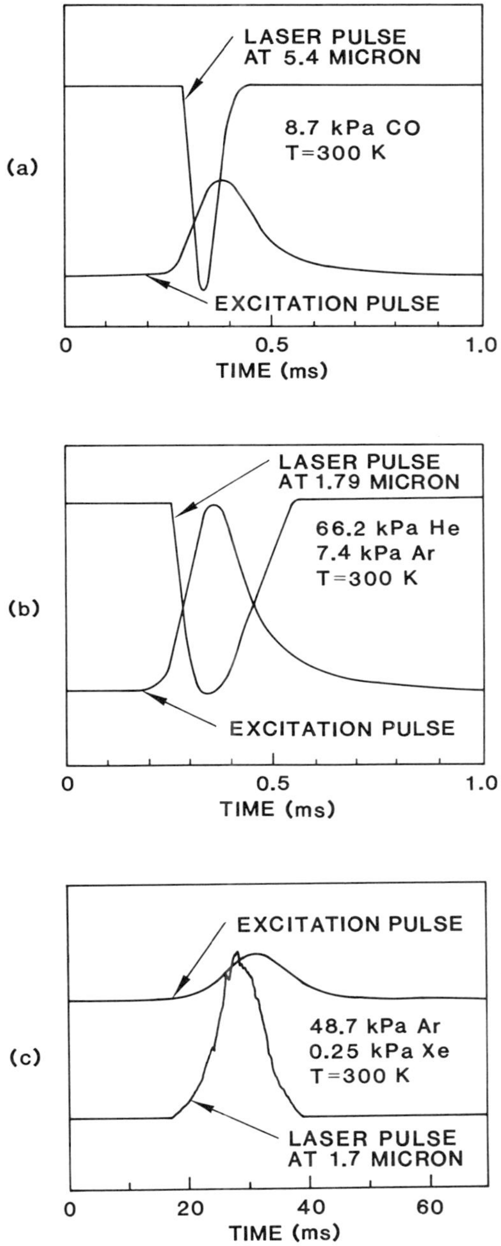

FIG. 2. Representative reactor pumped laser signals: (a) CO RPL excited by Sandia Labs SPR-II (FBR); (b) Ar RPL excited by Sandia Labs SPR-II (FBR); (c) Xe RPL excited by Sandia Labs ACRR (analogous to pulsed TRIGA reactor).

probe laser beam by optical aberrations in the excited medium was observed. More recent measurements have revealed details of this focusing tendency in the excited medium, and this is an active area of current research directed toward improving reactor pumped laser performance. In early experiments, evidence of chemical decomposition of the CO gas was also observed. A yellowish film (probably C_3O_2) accumulated on the laser mirrors. C_3O_2 is a well-known decomposition product observed when CO is irradiated with alpha particles.

Figure 2b shows a laser pulse at about 1.8 μm wavelength which is obtained with the apparatus shown in Fig. 1 when the CO laser mixture is replaced by a He/Ar mixture. The fact that lasing occurs over most of the excitation pulse indicates that laser pulse termination is not a property of the laser apparatus itself but results from differences between the two laser gas mixtures.

Figure 2c shows the excitation pulse and the resulting laser pulse at 1.7 μm wavelength from an Ar/Xe laser gas mixture excited by a reactor analogous to a pulsed TRIGA reactor (the Sandia National Laboratories ACRR). In this case, lasing continues over most of the excitation pulse, which is much longer than the pulse width of the reactor used to obtain the data of Figs. 2a and 2b.

II. Characteristics of Nuclear Pumped Lasers

A. Pumping Mechanisms

There are two types of pump sources: a source of intense gamma radiation or a source of intense neutron flux. The gamma rays can irradiate the laser medium directly and produce excitation. The neutrons ordinarily excite the laser medium indirectly by irradiating other "target" nuclei which undergo nuclear reactions and are the direct agents in exciting the laser medium. At present there are two practical sources: pulsed research reactors and nuclear devices.

The energetic charged particles which excite a nuclear pumped laser medium derive from three main sources: Compton-scattered electrons produced by energetic gamma rays; fission fragments (particles having atomic masses of about 95 and 140 amu, initial energies of 65 to 100 MeV, and initial charges of about +20e); and charged particles such as protons, tritons, and alpha particles produced in exothermic nuclear reactions involving absorption of a neutron.

Table II contains basic data for several nuclear reactions which may be used to pump an RPL. The energy released varies over more than two orders of magnitude, with the largest energy release provided by fissioning of ^{235}U. Among the reactions in Table II, the fission reaction is unique in being able to produce more neutrons to sustain the nuclear reactions.

The charged particles are sufficiently energetic that excitation of a broad range of atomic and molecular states is energetically allowed. There is also, in general, no mechanism for selective excitation of only a few excited states. This selectivity of excitation, which has frequently been used to produce laser action, is not generally available in nuclear pumped lasers.

An important practical limitation is that each laser medium requires a minimum volumetric pump rate to begin lasing and a somewhat greater volumetric pump rate to convert the pumping power to laser light efficiently. One limitation of RPLs is that reactors tend to produce lower volumetric pump rates (no more than 3000 MW/m^3) than can be obtained with some conventional laser excitation methods. This limit is set by temperature limitations of the reactor structure itself. In the case of nuclear explosive devices used as pump sources, much higher pump rates can be obtained, since the survival of the nuclear device and its immediate surroundings is not required.

B. Potential Advantages as Large Lasers

For laser applications that require a very large laser or a laser remote from conventional electrical or chemical power sources, a nuclear pumped laser may be an effective alternative to more conventional lasers. Commercial, power reactors routinely operate for months at total fission powers of 3000 MW, with corresponding electrical power outputs of over 1000 MW. Although a large RPL is not expected to resemble a power reactor in detail, conversion of a small fraction of such available fission energy to laser light would produce an extremely powerful, long-lived laser.

Such potential high output powers are possible because of the extremely compact and lightweight energy storage of the fissionable nucleus. Alternatively, the fuel for an electrical power source or the reactants for a powerful chemical laser must be stored in large tanks, in the form of highly corrosive or explosive liquids or gases with an energy storage per unit mass of about 1000 kJ/kg. By contrast, the energy stored in enriched uranium oxide (a dense, refractory ceramic) considerably exceeds 10^{10} kJ/kg. The ura-

TABLE II. Nuclear Reactions for Pumping RPL

Target nucleus	Cross section[a] (10^{-24} cm^2)	Energy release (MeV)	Particles released	Particle energy (MeV)	Range in 1 atm air (cm)
^{3}He	5330	0.76	^{1}H	0.6	1.0
			^{3}H	0.2	0.2
^{10}B	3838	2.79	^{4}He	1.8	1.0
			^{7}Li	1.0	0.5
^{235}U	585	165	^{93}Kr	100	2.3
			^{140}Xe[b]	65	1.8

[a] Thermal neutron energy.
[b] Representative nuclei from a broad spectrum of fission products.

nium "fuel" of an RPL thus represents a huge, compact, stable, self-sufficient energy source, even allowing for incomplete uranium fuel utilization.

Another potential advantage of the RPL is that the energy is deposited in the laser medium based on its density, and the initial steps of the energy deposition process are largely independent of details of the laser medium condition (such as electron density in the medium or chemical composition of the medium).

The long absorption length of the neutron also allows the excited laser medium to be scaled to volumes of about 100 m^3, while remaining well within the bounds of current reactor technology. This scaling process involves replication of mechanical reactor substructures, such as plates of ceramic neutron-moderator material coated with very thin uranium coatings. Proliferation of complex, relatively fragile high-voltage apparatuses is not required, nor is it necessary to separate the laser gas from adjacent high-vacuum regions with thin, relatively fragile foils. Although the close spacing of the RPL structure presents problems with the extraction of a high-quality optical beam, several potential solutions are being studied. These unusual scaling laws may be of significant advantage in constructing very large lasers.

III. Basic Physics of Reactor Pumped Lasers

A. Nuclear Aspects

1. Reactor Characteristics

A nuclear reactor normally is designed to operate for many years at its maximum output (pulsed or steady-state); so the practical limitation on the lifetime of an RPL is typically related to other factors, such as limitations on coolant supply or degradation of laser optics.

Fast burst reactors (FBRs) have the advantage of producing high pump power in the RPL in a short pulse which does not overheat the laser medium. FBRs are also typically housed in laboratory facilities which allow convenient access to the volume around the reactor for setup of laser apparatuses. However, FBRs have very low pulse repetition rates because of the need to cool a large compact mass of reactor fuel between pulses.

Another relatively common research reactor, the pulsed TRIGA reactor, operates by pulsing from a very low initial power level using control rods. The pulsed TRIGA reactor can be pulsed more frequently because it typically is located at the bottom of a tank of water which acts as both coolant and shield. The neutron spectrum of a TRIGA reactor also has a much lower average energy, which reduces or eliminates the need for neutron-moderator material in the laser apparatus.

The practical laboratory sources of intense neutron fluxes are pulsed or steady-state reactors fueled primarily by uranium. Since each ^{235}U fission event releases about 168 MeV of fission fragment energy and about 2.4 neutrons, the energy cost per neutron created in a reactor is at least 70 MeV/neutron. In fact, because some of the neutrons are absorbed in the reactor fuel to sustain the reaction, the energy cost per neutron is greater than 70 MeV per neutron. Thus the use of low-energy-release reactions from Table II severely reduces the efficiency of a large RPL system. However, for demonstration experiments any of the nonfission reactions in Table II may be used, in some cases with great practical advantages compared to use of the fission reaction.

There is typically some unavoidable waste energy deposited in the reactor structure itself, and the maximum temperature which it can withstand usually limits the obtainable pump rate in RPLs. For typical research reactors, pump rates of perhaps 3000 MW/m^3 can be obtained in pulses with minimum widths ranging from 0.2 to 10 msec. The neutron flux from high-flux steady-state reactors limits the laser pumping power per unit volume to about 10 MW/m^3.

2. Substrate Pumping

The least impact on the laser medium conditions is obtained by separating the target nucleus from the laser medium by using substrate pumping. In substrate pumping the target nuclei are chemically bound into a solid compound that is coated onto the surface of a substrate in contact with the laser gas. From Table II, the maximum path lengths of the charged particles in air at 1 atm pressure are typically a few centimeters. If substrate pumping is used, the pumping of the laser medium will be quite inhomogeneous if the source substrates are too far apart (so that the charged particles do not even reach the center of the laser medium, for example). A typical optimum separation between source substrates is approximately equal to the charged particle range. The energy deposition is also more uniform if the substrates are in the form of large parallel plates.

In all RPL experiments reported to date, a substrate has been used to support the target nuclei (with the exception of ^3He). This method has thus far been limited to excitation of gaseous laser media because of the extremely short range of charged particles in liquids and solids. The target nucleus compound is usually chosen for its chemical and mechanical stability and its adherence to the substrate material. The compound is deposited on the substrate in a thin layer, since the charged particles produced in the coating typically have ranges of a few milligrams per square centimeter of the coating material.

A portion of the energy of the charged particles is deposited in the coating and substrate material. This produces waste heat which does not contribute to laser excitation. For a given coating material and thickness, a constant fraction of the total energy created in the coating is emitted from the coating and is available to excite the laser medium. The output energy per unit area of coating increases as the slow neutron flux increases. For a typical uranium oxide coating of 1 μm thickness, the coating efficiency is about 32%. For neutron fluences at the edge of the core of the Sandia Laboratories ACRR reactor facility, volumetric energy depositions of 1.5 J/cm^3 and volumetric pump rates of 200 W/cm^3 are readily obtained for typical laser gases at about 1 atm pressure.

As the coating thickness increases, the coating efficiency decreases and the flux of energy from the coating approaches a constant value. In experiments it may be useful to maximize this energy flux to obtain the maximum excitation with a given fixed neutron flux. However, in a practical RPL system it would be important to maximize efficiency while maintaining the necessary pumping power and overall reactor characteristics desired.

3. Homogeneous Pumping

Dispersing the target nucleus throughout the laser medium (by choosing a gaseous compound containing the target nucleus and mixing it with the laser gas) normally produces the greatest spatial uniformity of pumping. Homogeneous pumping also uses essentially all the nuclear reaction energy at high pressures of the laser medium, since no energy is lost in a coating. However, the presence of the target nucleus in its host molecule may interfere with the processes which produce gain in the laser medium.

Experiments performed as part of the NASA RPL program have studied homogeneous pumping to the greatest degree, culminating in a 1 kW laser (Table I). Development of a large, efficient RPL system based on ^3He is, however, limited by the very small energy release and the very large neutron absorption cross section of the ^3He reaction (Table II). If the ^3He partial pressure in the laser mixture is several atmospheres, the neutron absorption length shortens to a few centimeters, and the uniformity of pumping will be limited by the neutron absorption length itself.

If a laser medium tolerant of gaseous uranium compounds could be developed, homogeneous pumping would be preferable to any other scheme. The report of lasing at 2.65 μm in Xe in the presence of a small pressure of $^{235}UF_6$ is therefore of considerable interest (Table I). Researchers at Los Alamos National Laboratory have also proposed liquid RPL media containing uranium compounds.

B. Laser Medium Aspects

The charged particles give up their kinetic energy to the laser medium by producing both ionization and excitation of the laser medium. Low-energy secondary electrons produce further ionization and excitation in the medium. The number of ions and excited atoms/molecules can be estimated by using measured properties of the laser gas, such as the average energy required to create an electron–ion pair. However, there is no obvious mechanism to produce highly selective excitation directly. Thus, population inversion relies on selective kinetic and photophysical processes which preferentially populate certain states.

The excitation of high-lying excited states may stimulate high chemical reactivity of the laser medium, making it necessary to replace the laser gas periodically or scrub it.

For substrate pumping, the relatively short range of charged particles requires a separation between the substrates of a few centimeters. This results in large, slablike gain regions separated by opaque barriers. Extraction of a laser beam with good beam quality and high efficiency from this type of system is the most challenging aspect of large-system RPL design. Relatively little work has been done thus far to deal with this optical complexity, which must be weighed against the potential advantages of the simpler RPL excitation structure.

Finally, the relatively low pumping power densities obtainable with reactor pumping requires that the laser medium possess long lifetimes for retaining excitation. The CO laser was initially chosen as a likely candidate for reactor pumping, based on the long lifetimes of the upper energy levels of the laser transitions ($\sim$30 msec). The Xe laser may also have a long effective lifetime for excitation because of energy recycling through a high-lying metastable level.

C. Medium Inhomogeneity

For the relatively long energy deposition times involved with typical pulsed reactors, the laser medium can move in response to spatial variations in the energy deposition. This gives rise to nonuniformities in the laser medium density and gradients of the index of refraction which cause distortion of the laser beam (tilt, focusing, defocusing, or higher order aberrations). To produce a very-high-quality laser beam, these distortions must be corrected.

In general, there are two possible causes of inhomogeneous pumping: charged-particle-range effects and effects from absorption of neutrons by the target nucleus. Charged-particle-range effects are a problem with substrate pumping, and neutron-absorption effects are a problem with homogeneous pumping.

For substrate pumping (assuming efficient usage of the fission fragment energy), the spatial scale of the nonuniform energy deposition is of the order of the separation between adjacent substrates. If the substrates are in the form of large parallel plates, a nearly one-dimensional density variation results. Wavefront distortion measurements have been reported for this excitation geometry. For intense pulsed excitation, the density can vary by as much as a factor of two, producing an effective focal length of less than 1 m for a cell only 30 cm long. Such time-dependent focusing can have significant effects on the modal stability of a laser. In fact, resonator stability transitions have been observed in the atomic Xe laser when energy depositions approach 1 J/cm^3.

D. Contrasts with Conventional Lasers

The RPL differs from electrically, optically, or chemically excited lasers in several respects.

1. The maximum excitation power per unit volume in the laser medium is lower than the comparable maximum for electrically excited lasers (assuming that specialized RPL designs based on existing reactor technology are used). However, the energy deposition per unit volume of laser medium is at least comparable to that obtained with electrical or electron-beam excitation.
2. The geometry of the laser excitation region is complex if substrate pumping is used, which demands accurate relative phasing of beams from many independent gain regions to produce a single coherent laser beam.
3. If substrate pumping is used, the excitation process itself gives rise to variations in laser medium density which severely affect beam quality unless the resulting laser beam aberrations are corrected.
4. The laser optics must operate reliably in a

relatively severe radiation environment, which consists primarily of high-energy gamma rays and fast neutrons.

5. The construction of the laser typically involves robust mechanical apparatus rather than electrical or chemical apparatus.

IV. Reactor Pumped Lasers

A. Technological Progress

About 20 RPLs have been discovered since the first report of an RPL in 1975. These are summarized in review articles mentioned in the bibliography.

In 1977 several concepts for constructing large RPL systems were analyzed and reported by Sandia workers. The concepts were based solely on substrate pumping and described specialized nuclear reactor designs which could excite large volumes of laser gas at efficiencies approaching the coating efficiency. These relatively efficient system concepts tended to resemble the TRIGA or ACRR reactors more than the FBR. These initial calculations showed that with a high intrinsic laser efficiency, perhaps 10% of the total reactor energy might be obtained as laser light, using current or near-term reactor technology. However, the problem of extracting a high-quality optical beam from the complex reactor structure was not addressed.

Experimental research directed toward discovery of new RPLs has continued at the University of Illinois. System studies of possible large-scale RPL applications and detailed measurements of radiation-induced absorption in optical materials have been reported. Several comprehensive review articles on RPL research and applications have been published [see Miley (1989) and (1984) in the bibliography].

The NASA program at Langley Research Center was broad and productive: New RPLs were discovered, homogeneous pumping with ^{3}He was developed, the volume limits of RPLs were studied, excitation processes were investigated theoretically, and a reactor pumped amplifier was demonstrated.

In 1979 researchers in the Soviet Union reported near-infrared RPLs using mixtures of noble gases pumped at very low volumetric pump rates, with surprisingly high efficiencies and high energy outputs (Table I). The combination of relatively short wavelength, high efficiency, relatively high pressure, and stable laser gases may make these lasers attractive for RPL applications.

Moderate-efficiency lasing was observed by Russian researchers in Cd vapor at 0.442 to 0.54 μm wavelength using very low volumetric pump rates. Thus, it is possible that high-power visible RPLs with reasonable efficiency can be developed.

Finally, alternate forms of substrate pumping were considered in some detail. The energy escape fraction is largest from small spheres of uranium metal or oxide. Such spheres cannot be incorporated directly into the laser medium because of the optical scattering loss they introduce, even if they were overcoated with a thin reflective coating. However, concepts have been developed to use such reflective aerosols to pump a fluorescer medium, which produces intense incoherent light usable for optically pumping a laser medium. Such nuclear flashlamp pumped RPLs have been investigated in some detail theoretically but have not been demonstrated experimentally.

B. Radiation Effects on Optics

One concern in early research on RPLs was the question of degradation of optics by the intense radiation field of the reactor environment. The radiation environment of the reactor consists of broad spectra of both neutrons and gamma rays ranging in energy up to several MeV.

In early experiments at Sandia in the FBR environment, it was found that no visible optical damage occurred to several convenient window materials, such as optical-grade NaCl, BaF_2, and CaF_2. Metallic mirrors showed almost no measurable change in reflectivity, perhaps because they are already highly conductive. In more recent experiments, dielectric-coated mirrors made of elements with low neutron absorption have also demonstrated very little change in reflectivity in intense pulsed radiation fields. Schlieren-grade fused silica also displays relatively low radiation-induced absorption for visible and near-infrared wavelengths, and is thus a convenient and versatile RPL optical material.

However, materials containing elements such as ^{10}B or ^{6}Li (such as borosilicate glass) should be avoided in optical components because of their large neutron-absorption cross sections. In these nuclei, absorption of a neutron creates tracks of intense ionization in the host material and atomic displacements which can act as defect centers for optical absorptions. Therefore, a basic step in optical design for RPLs is to avoid neutron-absorbing elements in window materials, coating materials, and substrate materials for mirrors.

Optical components can be protected from bombardment by low-energy neutrons by relatively thin sheets of materials such as Cd metal or B_4C suspensions in plastics. Very energetic neutrons cause damage by displacing lattice atoms in elastic collisions. A low-mass recoil atom may have enough energy to create ionization tracks in the material. High-energy neutrons can be moderated to low energies (for absorption in Cd or B) by scattering from shielding materials containing high densities of hydrogen (such as high-density polyethylene).

Gamma rays produce energetic Compton-scattered electrons which may cause significant damage even in optical materials which do not contain neutron-absorbing nuclei. The energetic Compton electrons degrade in energy by producing ionization in the optical material so that a weak transient conductivity is induced by the radiation. Complete shielding of the gamma rays requires thick layers of high-density materials such as Pb, but this is usually not practical in the vicinity of the laser apparatus.

C. Development Toward Applications

The unique characteristics of nuclear pumped lasers include the following: Essentially infinite energy storage; relatively straightforward scaling of the volume of excited laser medium; extremely high total excitation power with current reactor technology; no requirement for pulsed power systems or high-voltage electrical power; and robust mechanical construction.

However, these applications must be realized in the presence of the unique disadvantages of nuclear pumping: Low pump power per unit volume (for RPLs, not NDPLs); intense radiation fields; extraction of the laser beam from the complex reactor structure (for substrate pumping); and the health, safety, and proliferation concerns of nuclear technology in general.

Lasers with moderate total energies have found numerous practical applications. It may be that as applications for very large lasers emerge, the relatively robust "mechanical" nature of NPLs will have important system advantages. NPLs have been considered recently for specialized applications such as for space power, for large industrial chemical excitation, and as weapons. Several articles in the bibliography treat some of these potential applications in greater detail. [See, for example, Miley (1984) and Prelas and Loyalka (1988) in the bibliography.]

Bibliography

Fitaire, M., ed. (1978). *Int. Symp. Nucl. Induced Plasmas Nucl. Pumped Lasers [Pap.], 1st, 1978*. Les Editions de Physique, Orsay, France.

Jalufka, N. W. (1983). "Direct Nuclear-Pumped Lasers," NASA Tech. Pap. No. 2091. National Aeronautics and Space Administration, Washington, D.C.

McArthur, D. A., *et al.* (1988). Recent results on reactor-pumped laser studies at Sandia National Laboratories, *Laser Interact. Relat. Plasma Phenom.* **8,** 75.

Miley, G. H. (1982). Direct nuclear pumped lasers—status and potential applications, *Laser Interact. Relat. Plasma Phenom.* **4A,** 181.

Miley, G. H. (1984). Review of nuclear pumped lasers, *Laser Interact. Relat. Plasma Phenom.* **6,** 47.

Miley, G. H., *et al.* (1989). Fission reactor pumped lasers: History and prospects, *in* "50 Years with Nuclear Fission" (J. W. Behrens and A. D. Carlson, eds.), Vol. 1, p. 333. American Nuclear Society, La Grange Park, Illinois.

Prelas, M. A., and Loyalka, S. K. (1982). A review of the utilization of energetic ions for the production of excited atomic and molecular states and chemical synthesis, *Prog. Nucl. Energy* **8,** 35.

LASERS, RARE GAS-HALIDE

Minoru Obara and Fumihiko Kannari *Keio University*

GLOSSARY

Excimer: Molecule that is strongly bound in an excited state but normally has a dissociative ground state. The excited state has a very short lifetime of less than 10 nsec. The term excimer comes from "excited dimer." Excimer also includes exciplex (excited complex).

Pumping: Means by which an inversion is produced in a laser system.

Tunable: Describes a laser having an output wavelength that can be adjusted within a gain bandwidth.

Vacuum ultraviolet (VUV): Region of the spectrum with wavelength less than 200 nm.

Strong laser emission has been obtained from ArF, KrF, XeF, KrCl, XeCl, and XeBr excimers. Strong output wavelength of rare gas-halide lasers spans the spectrum from the near ultraviolet to the vacuum ultraviolet. Rare gas-halide lasers have been operated only in a pulsed mode. Their laser pulse length extends from picoseconds to a microsecond time domain. Rare gas-halide lasers may be pumped in a pulsed mode by electric discharges, intense electron beams, proton beams, or optical sources. These lasers are wavelength tunable over wavelength ranges of several nanometers.

I. Rare Gas-Halide Excimers

A. HISTORY

The first demonstration of an excimer laser was made by Basov, Danilychev, and Popov in 1971. They showed stimulated emission of Xe_2 at 172 nm using electron-beam pumping of cryogenic liquid Xe.

The first lasing of a rare gas-halide (RGH) excimer (XeBr) was reported by Searles and Hart in 1975. Shortly thereafter, lasing from XeF was reported by Brau and Ewing. Both XeBr and XeF lasers were pumped by intense electron beams. Subsequently, other RGHs shown in Table I were reported to lase. In addition to electron-beam pumping, researchers have also employed volume-uniform avalanche discharges with X-ray, UV, or corona preionizations, electron-beam controlled discharges, and proton beams successfully to pump a variety of excimer lasers. [*See* LASERS.]

Table I lists RGH lasers. The strong output wavelength of RGH lasers spans the spectrum from the near UV to the vacuum ultraviolet (VUV). Under normal operating conditions, excimer lasing occurs on the wavelength based on the B → X transition described in Section I,B.

In addition to the diatomic RGHs, triatomic RGH excimers can provide tunable coherent photon sources in the visible to the UV region of the spectrum. Table II shows a list of triatomic RGH excimers.

In addition to the triatomic RGHs, a new broad band emission from a fouratomic RGH excimer, Ar_3F at (430 ± 50) nm was reported by Sauerbrey *et al.* in 1986. A fouratomic Ar_3F RGH excimer emission (not lasing) was detected from electron-beam pumped Ar/F_2 and Ar/NF_3 mixtures.

B. SPECTROSCOPIC FEATURES OF RARE GAS-HALIDE EXCIMER LASERS

Figure 1 shows the schematic potential curves for the RGH excimers. The upper laser level is an ionically bound state while the ground state is covalently bound. The upper laser level is

TABLE I. A List of RGH Excimer Lasers

RGH	Wavelength (nm)	Author	Reported year
ArCl	175[a]	Waynant	1977
ArF	193	Hoffman, Hays, and Tisone	1976
KrF	248 (275)[b]	Ewing and Brau	1975
KrCl	222 (240)	Murray and Powell	1976
XeBr	282 (300)	Searles and Hart	1975
XeCl	308 (345)	Ewing and Brau	1975
XeF	351,353 (460)	Brau and Ewing	1975

[a] Wavelength due to B → X transition having the strongest gain coefficient.
[b] Wavelength due to C → A transition in parenthesis.

formed via ionic or neutral reactions. At close internuclear separation, the potential energy curve splits into the $^2\Sigma$ and $^2\Pi$ states as shown in Fig. 1. By convention the $^2\Sigma$ state is referred to as the B state. Under normal high-pressure operating conditions both the B ($^2\Sigma$) and C ($^2\Pi$) state are collisionally mixed.

The ground-state manifold consists of two states, of which the $^2\Sigma$ state has the lowest energy, and is referred to as the X state. This X state is generally nearly flat or weakly bound with the exception of an XeF excimer having a strong bound state with a 1065-cm^{-1} binding energy. The other manifold is the $^2\Pi$ state, which is always repulsive as shown in Fig. 1. This $^2\Pi$ state is referred to as the A state.

Figures 2 and 3 show the potential curves of KrF and XeCl excimers, respectively.

The emission spectrum of RGH excimers consists of two bands such as B ($^2\Sigma$) → X($^2\Sigma$) and C($^2\Pi$) → A($^2\Pi$). The B → X transition has a stronger stimulated-emission cross section than that of the C → A transition, indicating that the B → X transition usually gives intense lasing. The C → A band consists of relatively broad continua, which is attributed to the repulsive structure of the A state.

The stimulated-emission cross section of the B → X bands of RGHs like XeCl and KrF may be written as

$$\sigma = \frac{1}{4\pi c\tau}\sqrt{\frac{ln2}{\pi}}\,\frac{\lambda^4}{\Delta\lambda}$$

assuming that near the line center the line shape is approximately Gaussian, where c is the velocity of light, λ the wavelength at the line center, τ the lifetime of excimers, and $\Delta\lambda$ the bandwidth of the spectrum.

TABLE II. A List of Triatomic RGH Excimers[a]

RGH	Wavelength (nm)
Ar_2F	285 ± 25
Ar_2Cl	245 ± 15
Kr_2F	420 ± 35
Kr_2Cl	325 ± 15
Kr_2Br	~318
Xe_2F	610 ± 65
Xe_2Cl	490 ± 40
Xe_2Br	440 ± 30

[a] Wavelength and tuning range are based on the data by F. K. Tittel *et al.*

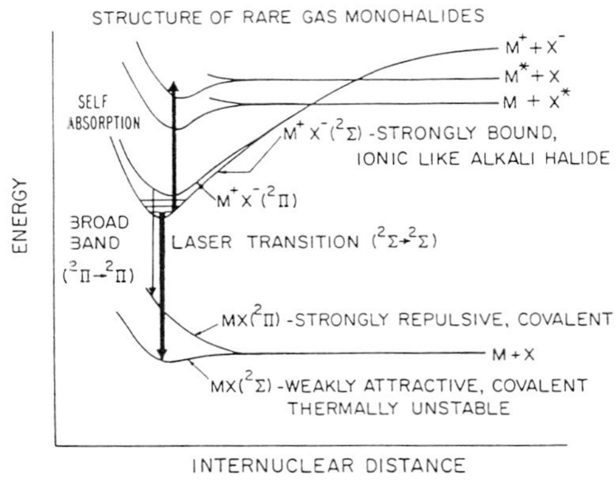

FIG. 1. Schematic potential energy diagram of rare gas halides. [Reproduced with permission from Ch. A. Brau (1984). Rare gas halogen excimers, *in* "Excimer Lasers" (Ch. K. Rhodes, ed.), Springer-Verlag, Berlin and New York.]

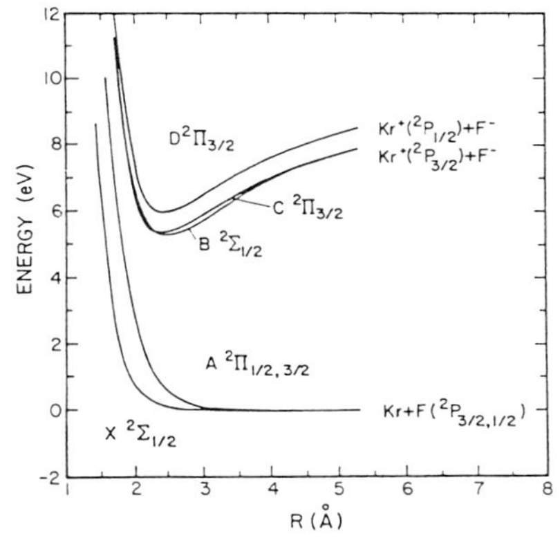

FIG. 2. Potential energy diagram of the KrF excimer. [Reproduced with permission from Ch. A. Brau (1984). Rare gas halogen excimers, *in* "Excimer Lasers" (Ch. K. Rhodes, ed.), Springer-Verlag, Berlin and New York.]

II. Rare Gas-Halide Excimer Laser Kinetics

The kinetic processes involved in a RGH laser are very complicated compared to those of discharge-pumped CO_2 lasers, because neutral reactions and ionic reactions, two-body and three-body reactions, superelastic reactions, and absorption reactions are all responsible for the RGH laser. The kinetic processes involved in the individual RGH lasers are to some extent similar with the exception of those of the XeF laser. Therefore, the kinetic processes for only the discharge-pumped XeCl laser and the e-beam-pumped KrF laser are presented here as an example.

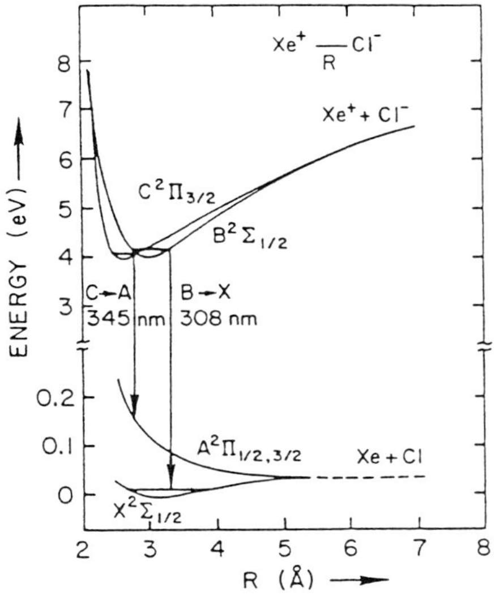

FIG. 3. Potential energy diagram of the XeCl excimer. [Reproduced with permission from D. L. Huestis, G. Marowsky, and F. K. Tittel (1984). Triatomic rare-gas-halide excimers, *in* "Excimer Lasers" (Ch. K. Rhodes, ed.), Springer-Verlag, Berlin and New York.]

A. Discharge-Pumped XeCl Lasers

A typical gas mixture for a self-sustained discharge-pumped XeCl laser is 3-atm mixture of Xe/HCl/Ne = 1/0.1–0.2/balance(%). A list of kinetic reactions responsible for XeCl lasers with their rate constants is shown in Table III. The electron energy distribution in the discharge mixture can be calculated using a Boltzmann equation code, an example of which is shown in Fig. 4. The case is treated of the above mixture pumped by a 100-nsec discharge pulse at an excitation rate of 3 MW/cm^3.

Formation reactions for XeCl(B) are shown in Fig. 5. The percent contribution of the XeCl formation is varied with the HCl concentration. Dominant formation reactions are $Xe^+ + Cl^- \rightarrow$ XeCl(B) (ion recombination reaction) and $NeXe^+ + Cl^- \rightarrow$ XeCl(B) + Ne. A little contribution comes from $Xe^* + HCl(v) \rightarrow$ XeCl(B) + H and $Xe_2^+ + Cl^- \rightarrow$ XeCl(B) + Xe. Over 23% of the electrical energy deposited into the discharge can be supplied to form XeCl(B).

Relaxation reactions for XeCl(B) are shown in Fig. 6. About 65% of the formed XeCl(B) con-

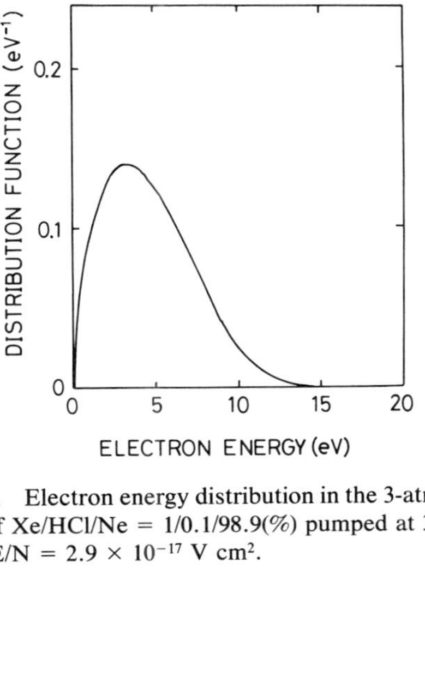

FIG. 4. Electron energy distribution in the 3-atm mixture of Xe/HCl/Ne = 1/0.1/98.9(%) pumped at 3 MW/cm^3. $E/N = 2.9 \times 10^{-17}$ V cm^2.

TABLE III. Kinetic Reactions Involved in the Discharge-Pumped XeCl Laser[a]

Reaction	Rate constant
Secondary electron process	
$e + Ne \rightarrow Ne^* + e$	
$e + Ne \rightarrow Ne^+ + 2e$	
$e + Ne^* \rightarrow Ne^+ + 2e$	
$e + Xe \rightarrow Xe^* + e$	Calculated by Boltzmann Eq.
$e + Xe \rightarrow Xe^+ + 2e$	
$e + Xe^* \rightarrow Xe^+ + 2e$	
$e + HCl \rightarrow HCl(v) + e$	
$e + HCl \rightarrow H + Cl^-$	
$e + HCl(v) \rightarrow H + Cl^-$	
$e + Cl_2 \rightarrow Cl^- + Cl$	1.1(−10) cm³/sec
Electron quenching	
$Ne^* + e \rightarrow e + Ne$	Calculated by Boltzmann Eq.
$Xe^* + e \rightarrow e + Xe$	
$Ne_2^* + e \rightarrow e + 2Ne$	Analogy to Ne*
$Xe_2^* + e \rightarrow e + 2Xe$	Analogy to Xe*
$Cl_2^* + e \rightarrow e + Cl_2$	3.0(−7) cm³/sec
$NeCl^* + e \rightarrow e + Ne + Cl$	2.0(−7)
$XeCl^* + e \rightarrow e + Xe + Cl$	2.0(−7)
HCl(v) quenching	
$HCl(v) + Ne \rightarrow HCl + Ne$	6.2(−17) cm³/sec
$HCl(v) + HCl \rightarrow 2HCl$	2.7(−14)
Neutral reaction	
$Ne^* + 2Ne \rightarrow Ne_2^* + Ne$	4.1(−34) cm⁶/sec
$Xe^* + 2Xe \rightarrow Xe_2^* + Xe$	8.0(−32)
$Xe^* + Xe + Ne \rightarrow Xe_2^* + Ne$	1.6(−32)
$Xe^* + HCl \rightarrow Xe + H + Cl$	5.6(−10) cm³/sec
$Xe^* + HCl(v) \rightarrow Xe + H + Cl$	5.6(−10)
$Xe^* + HCl(v) \rightarrow XeCl^* + H$	2.0(−10)
Penning ionization	
$Ne^* + Xe \rightarrow Xe^+ + Ne + e$	7.5(−11) cm³/sec
$Ne^* + Xe \rightarrow NeXe^+ + e$	1.8(−11)
$Xe^* + Xe^* \rightarrow Xe^+ + Xe + e$	5.0(−10)
$Xe_2^* + Xe_2^* \rightarrow Xe_2^+ + 2Xe + e$	3.5(−10)
Charge transfer	
$Ne^+ + 2Ne \rightarrow Ne_2^+ + Ne$	4.4(−32) cm⁶/sec
$Ne^+ + Xe \rightarrow Xe^+ + Ne$	1.0(−14) cm³/sec
$Ne^+ + Xe + Ne \rightarrow NeXe^+ + Ne$	1.0(−31) cm⁶/sec
$Ne_2^+ + Xe \rightarrow NeXe^+ + Ne$	1.0(−13) cm³/sec
$Ne_2^+ + Xe + Ne \rightarrow Xe^+ + 3Ne$	4.0(−30) cm⁶/sec
$Xe^+ + 2Xe \rightarrow Xe_2^+ + Xe$	3.6(−31)
$Xe^+ + 2Ne \rightarrow NeXe^+ + Ne$	2.5(−31)
$Xe^+ + Xe + Ne \rightarrow Xe_2^+ + Ne$	1.0(−31)
$NeXe^+ + Xe \rightarrow Xe^+ + Ne + Xe$	5.0(−10) cm³/sec
$NeXe^+ + Xe \rightarrow Xe_2^+ + Ne$	5.0(−12)
Ion-electron recombination	
$Ne_2^+ + e \rightarrow Ne^* + Ne$	3.7(−8)$Te^{-0.43}$ cm³/sec
$Xe_2^+ + e \rightarrow Xe^* + Xe$	2.2(−7)$Te^{-0.5}$
$NeXe^+ + e \rightarrow Xe^* + Ne$	2.0(−7)$Te^{-0.5}$
Ion-ion recombination	
$Ne^+ + Cl^- \rightarrow NeCl^*$	} ~2.0(−6) cm³/sec
$Ne_2^+ + Cl^- \rightarrow NeCl^* + Ne$	

(*continues*)

TABLE III. *(Continued)*

Reaction	Rate constant
$Xe^+ + Cl^- \rightarrow XeCl^*$	Pressure dependent rate $\sim 2.0(-6)$ cm³/sec
$Xe_2^+ + Cl^- \rightarrow XeCl^* + Xe$	
$NeXe^+ + Cl^- \rightarrow XeCl^* + Ne$	
$Cl^+ + Cl^- \rightarrow Cl_2^*$	$2.0(-6)$ cm³/sec
Radiation	
$Ne_2^* \rightarrow 2Ne + h\nu$	$3.6(+8)$ sec^{-1}
$Xe_2^* \rightarrow 2Xe + h\nu$	$6.0(+7)$
$Cl_2^* \rightarrow Cl_2 + h\nu$	$5.0(+7)$
$XeCl^* \rightarrow Xe + Cl + h\nu$	$2.5(+7)$
$XeCl^* + h\nu \rightarrow Xe + Cl + h\nu$	$1.25(-16)$ cm²
$Xe_2Cl^* \rightarrow 2Xe + Cl + h\nu$	$7.4(+6)$ sec^{-1}
Predissociation	
$NeCl^* \rightarrow Ne + Cl^+ + e$	$1.0(+10)$ sec^{-1}
$XeCl^*$ quenching	
$XeCl^* + Ne \rightarrow Xe + Cl + Ne$	$1.0(-12)$ cm³/sec
$XeCl^* + Xe \rightarrow 2Xe + Cl$	$3.2(-12)$
$XeCl^* + HCl \rightarrow Xe + Cl + HCl$	$1.7(-9)$
$XeCl^* + HCl(v) \rightarrow Xe + Cl + HCl$	$7.7(-10)$
$XeCl^* + 2Ne \rightarrow Xe + Cl + 2Ne$	$1.0(-33)$ cm⁶/sec
$XeCl^* + 2Xe \rightarrow Xe_2Cl^* + Xe$	$7.3(-31)$
$XeCl^* + Xe + Ne \rightarrow Xe_2Cl^* + Ne$	$1.5(-31)$
Xe_2Cl^* quenching	
$Xe_2Cl^* + Cl_2 \rightarrow 2Xe + Cl + Cl_2$	$2.6(-10)$ cm³/sec
$Xe_2Cl^* + Xe \rightarrow 3Xe + Cl$	$6.0(-15)$
Absorption	
$Ne_2^+ + h\nu \rightarrow Ne^+ + Ne$	$7.4(-18)$ cm²
$Xe_2^+ + h\nu \rightarrow Xe^+ + Xe$	$2.6(-17)$
$NeXe^+ + h\nu \rightarrow Xe^+ + Ne$	$1.0(-19)$
$Xe_2^* + h\nu \rightarrow Xe_2^+ + e$	$1.4(-17)$
$Xe^* + h\nu \rightarrow Xe^+ + e$	$6.0(-20)$
$Xe_2Cl^* + h\nu \rightarrow$ products	$2.6(-17)$
$Cl^- + h\nu \rightarrow Cl + e$	$2.1(-17)$

[a] T_e is electron temperature.

tributes to the stimulated emission as an intracavity laser flux due to its large stimulated-emission cross section. About 30% of the XeCl(B) is collisionally quenched and spontaneous emission is negligible during lasing. Collisional quenching processes concerned with the XeCl(B) excimer are shown in Fig. 7. At this high excitation rate of 3 MW/cm³, a large fraction is occupied by the discharge electron, which is called a superelastic collision process.

All the intracavity laser flux cannot be extracted because the RGH laser mixture contains many absorbers at the laser wavelength. The percent contribution of the absorption channel is shown in Fig. 8. Main absorbers seem to be Cl^- and Xe_2^+. The photon extraction efficiency, defined as the ratio of the extracted laser energy to the intracavity laser energy, is in excess of 70% here (see Fig. 6). This means that over 70% of the intracavity laser energy can be extracted as a laser output. Here, the maximum extraction efficiency can be written as

$$\eta_{\max} \simeq (1 - \sqrt{\alpha/g})^2$$

where g and α are small-signal gain and absorption coefficients, respectively. Therefore, the efficiency is increased with increasing values of g/α.

If the mixing ratio of Xe/HCl/Ne is varied, the electron energy distribution in the discharge plasma changes. As a result, formation of precursors Xe^+, Xe^*, Ne^+, and Ne^* is greatly affected. If helium is used as a diluent gas in place of Ne, the electron temperature also changes, resulting in a different pathway for the XeCl(B) formation and a less effective formation than that of the Ne diluent.

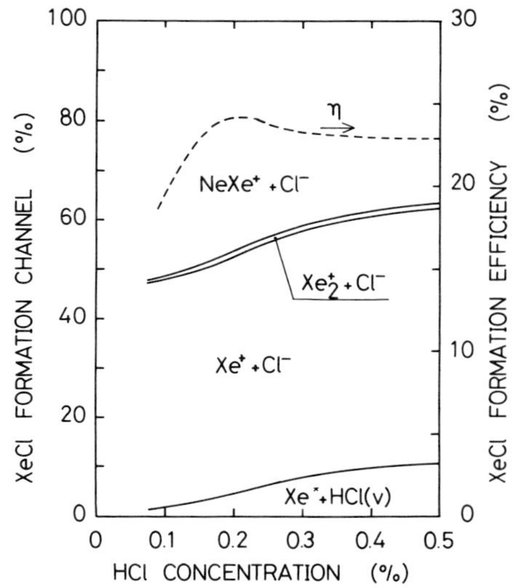

FIG. 5. Variation of percent contribution of the XeCl* formation channels and the XeCl* formation efficiency with the HCl concentration. The gas mixture is X% HCl/1% Xe/(99-X)% Ne. [Reproduced with permission from M. Ohwa and M. Obara (1986). *J. Appl. Phys.* **59**(1), 32.]

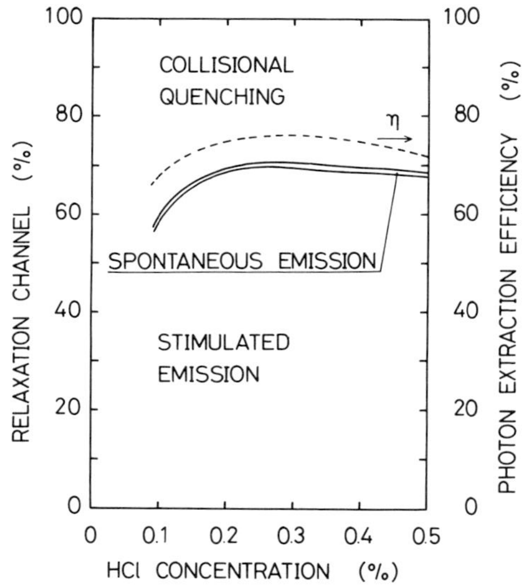

FIG. 6. Variation of percent contribution of the XeCl* relaxation channels and the photon extraction efficiency with the HCl concentration. [Reproduced with permission from M. Ohwa and M. Obara (1986). *J. Appl. Phys.* **59**(1), 32.]

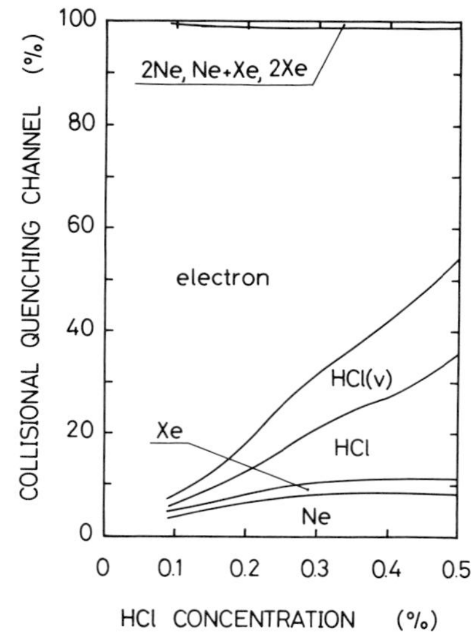

FIG. 7. Variation of percent contribution of the XeCl* collisional quenching channels with the HCl concentration. [Reproduced with permission from M. Ohwa and M. Obara (1986). *J. Appl. Phys.* **59**(1), 32.]

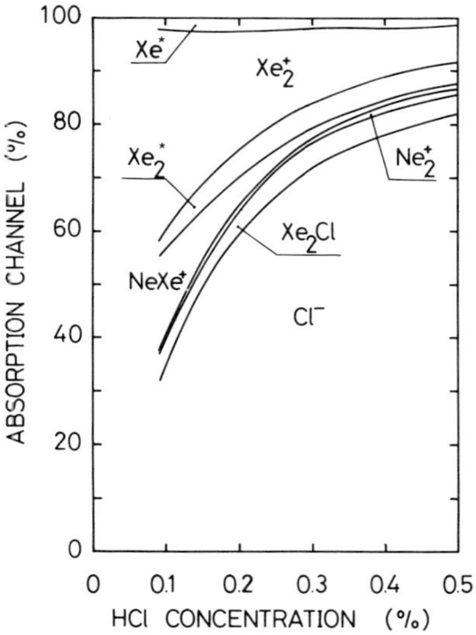

FIG. 8. Variation of percent contribution of the absorption at 308 nm with the HCl concentration. [Reproduced with permission from M. Ohwa and M. Obara (1986). *J. Appl. Phys.* **59**(1), 32.]

B. Electron-Beam Pumped KrF Lasers

A list of kinetic processes concerned with the e-beam-pumped KrF laser using a typical mixture of $Kr/F_2/Ar$ is shown in Table IV.

High-energy electrons of 300 keV to 2 MeV generated from a pulsed relativistic e-beam generator are deposited into the $Kr/F_2/Ar$ mixture to produce the precursors Ar^+, Ar^*, Kr^+, and Kr^*. A typical e-beam current density is from 10 A/cm^2 to 1000 A/cm^2, and its excitation rate ranges from 0.1 MW/cm^3 to 10 MW/cm^3, approximately, depending on the mixture pressure. The high-energy electrons can rapidly be thermalized in He, Ar, and Kr gases in the nanosecond time range, and as a result the secondary electrons reach a thermalized energy of around 1 eV. The initially formed Ar^+ and Ar^* are used to form ArF^*, and then KrF^* is formed via the reaction $ArF^* + Kr \rightarrow KrF^* + Ar$. Here Kr^+ is formed via the charge transfer reaction $Ar^+ + Kr \rightarrow Kr^+ + Ar$, and Kr^+ is also used to form

TABLE IV. KrF^* Kinetic Processes Involved in the e-Beam-Pumped KrF Laser[a]

Reaction	Rate constant
Neutral reaction	
$Ar^* + F_2 \rightarrow ArF^* + F$	7.5(−10)
$Ar^* + Kr + Ar \rightarrow ArKr^* + Ar$	1.0(−32) cm^6/sec
$Ar^* + 2Ar \rightarrow Ar_2^* + Ar$	1.14(−32) cm^6/sec
$Ar^* + Kr \rightarrow Ar + Kr^*$	6.2(−12)
$Ar^* + F_2 \rightarrow Ar + 2F$	3.1(−10)
$Ar^{**} + F_2 \rightarrow ArF^* + F$	4.7(−10)
$Ar^{**} + Ar \rightarrow Ar^* + Ar$	1.0(−10)
$Ar^{**} + F_2 \rightarrow Ar + 2F$	3.1(−10)
$Ar_2^* + F_2 \rightarrow Ar_2F^* + F$	2.5(−10)
$Ar_2^* + F \rightarrow ArF^* + Ar$	3.0(−10)
$Ar_2^* + Kr \rightarrow Kr^* + 2Ar$	4.0(−10)
$Ar_2^* + F_2 \rightarrow ArF^* + Ar + F$	3.0(−10)
$Kr^* + F_2 \rightarrow KrF^* + F$	8.1(−10)
$Kr^* + 2Ar \rightarrow ArKr^* + Ar$	1.0(−32) cm^6/sec
$Kr^* + Kr + Ar \rightarrow Kr_2^* + Ar$	2.7(−32) cm^6/sec
$Kr^{**} + F_2 \rightarrow KrF^* + F$	8.1(−10)
$Kr^{**} + Ar \rightarrow Kr^* + Ar$	1.0(−10)
$Kr_2^* + F_2 \rightarrow Kr_2F^* + F$	3.0(−10)
$Kr_2^* + F_2 \rightarrow KrF^* + Kr + F$	3.0(−10)
$Kr_2^* + F \rightarrow KrF^* + Kr$	3.0(−10)
$ArKr^* + F_2 \rightarrow KrF^* + Ar + F$	6.0(−10)
$ArKr^* + Kr \rightarrow Kr_2^* + Ar$	1.0(−10)
$ArKr^* + F_2 \rightarrow ArKrF^* + F$	3.0(−10)
$F + F + M \rightarrow F_2 + M$	1.0(−33) cm^6/sec
ArF^* relaxation	
$ArF^* + Kr \rightarrow KrF^* + Ar$	1.6(−09)
$ArF^* + 2Ar \rightarrow Ar_2F^* + Ar$	4.0(−31) cm^6/sec
$ArF^* + F_2 \rightarrow Ar + F + F_2$	1.9(−9)
$ArF^* + Ar \rightarrow 2Ar + F$	9.0(−12)
Ar_2F^* relaxation	
$Ar_2F^* + F_2 \rightarrow 2Ar + F + F_2$	2.0(−10)
$Ar_2F^* + Kr \rightarrow ArKrF^* + Ar$	1.0(−10)
$Ar_2F^* + Kr \rightarrow KrF^* + 2Ar$	1.0(−10)
$Ar_2F^* + Ar \rightarrow 3Ar + F$	1.0(−10)
KrF^* relaxation	
$KrF^* + Kr \rightarrow 2Kr + F$	2.0(−12)[b]
$KrF^* + Ar \rightarrow Kr + Ar + F$	1.8(−12)[b]
$KrF^* + 2Ar \rightarrow ArKrF^* + Ar$	7.0(−32) cm^6/sec[b,c]
$KrF^* + Kr + Ar \rightarrow Kr_2F^* + Ar$	6.5(−31) cm^6/sec[b,c]
$KrF^* + F_2 \rightarrow Kr + F + F_2$	7.8(−10)[b]

(*continues*)

TABLE IV. *(Continued)*

Reaction	Rate constant
$KrF^* + 2Kr \rightarrow Kr_2F^* + Kr$	$6.7(-31)$ cm^6/sec[b,c]
$KrF^* + F \rightarrow Kr + 2F$	$7.8(-10)$[b]
Kr_2F^* relaxation	
$Kr_2F^* + F_2 \rightarrow 2Kr + F + F_2$	$1.5(-10)$
$ArKrF^*$ relaxation	
$ArKrF^* + F_2 \rightarrow Ar + Kr + F + F_2$	$1.0(-09)$
$ArKrF^* + Kr \rightarrow Kr_2F^* + Ar$	$2.0(-11)$
$ArKrF^* + Ar \rightarrow Ar_2F^* + Kr$	$2.0(-11)$
Electron excitation, ionization, and attachment	
$Ar + e \leftrightarrow Ar^* + e$	$5.0(-09)Te^{0.74}\exp(-11.56/Te)$
$Ar + e \leftrightarrow Ar^{**} + e$	$1.40(-80)Te^{0.71}\exp(-13.15/Te)$
$Ar^* + e \leftrightarrow Ar^{**} + e$	$8.90(-07)Te^{0.51}\exp(-1.590/Te)$
$Ar + e \rightarrow Ar^+ + 2e$	$2.30(-08)Te^{0.68}\exp(-15.76/Te)$
$Ar^* + e \rightarrow Ar^+ + 2e$	$6.80(-09)Te^{0.67}\exp(-4.20/Te)$
$Ar^{**} + e \rightarrow Ar^+ + 2e$	$1.80(-07)Te^{0.61}\exp(-2.61/Te)$
$Ar_2^* + e \rightarrow Ar_2^+ + 2e$	$9.00(-08)Te^{0.70}\exp(-3.66/Te)$
$Kr + e \leftrightarrow Kr^* + e$	$9.00(-09)Te^{0.72}\exp(-9.96/Te)$
$Kr + e \leftrightarrow Kr^{**} + e$	$2.30(-08)Te^{0.72}\exp(-11.47/Te)$
$Kr^* + e \leftrightarrow Kr^{**} + e$	$9.00(-07)Te^{0.50}\exp(-1.51/Te)$
$Kr + e \rightarrow Kr^+ + 2e$	$2.70(-08)Te^{0.70}\exp(-14.00/Te)$
$Kr^* + e \rightarrow Kr^+ + 2e$	$7.00(-08)Te^{0.68}\exp(-4.04/Te)$
$Kr^{**} + e \rightarrow Kr^+ + 2e$	$2.00(-07)Te^{0.62}\exp(-2.53/Te)$
$Kr_2^* + e \rightarrow Kr_2^+ + 2e$	$9.00(-08)Te^{0.70}\exp(-3.53/Te)$
$ArKr^* + e \rightarrow ArKr^+ + 2e$	$9.00(-08)Te^{0.70}\exp(-3.60/Te)$
$F_2 + e -$ beam $\rightarrow F_2^+ + e -$ beam $+ e$:	32 eV/ion electron
$Ar + e -$ beam $\rightarrow Ar^+ + e -$ beam $+ e$:	26.2 eV/ion electron
$Kr + e -$ beam $\rightarrow Kr^+ + e -$ beam $+ e$:	24.3 eV/ion electron
$Ar + e -$ beam $\rightarrow Ar^* + e -$ beam:	$0.28 \times$ ionization rate
$Kr + e -$ beam $\rightarrow Kr^* + e -$ beam:	$0.28 \times$ ionization rate
$F_2 + e \rightarrow F^- + F$	$4.5(-09)$ ($Te = 1$ eV)
Penning ionization	
$Ar^{**} + Ar^{**} \rightarrow Ar^+ + Ar + e$	$5.0(-10)$
$Ar^* + Ar^* \rightarrow Ar^+ + Ar + e$	$5.0(-10)$
$Ar_2^* + Ar_2^* \rightarrow Ar_2^+ + 2Ar + e$	$5.0(-10)$
$Kr_2^* + Kr_2^* \rightarrow Kr_2^+ + 2Kr + e$	$5.0(-10)$
$Kr^* + Kr^* \rightarrow Kr^+ + Kr + e$	$5.0(-10)$
Charge transfer reaction	
$Ar_2^* + Kr \rightarrow Kr^+ + 2Ar$	$7.5(-10)$
$Ar^+ + Kr \rightarrow Kr^+ + Ar$	$3.0(-11)$
$Ar^+ + 2Ar \rightarrow Ar_2^+ + Ar$	$2.5(-31)$ cm^6/sec
$Ar^+ + Kr + Ar \rightarrow ArKr^+ + Ar$	$1.0(-31)$ cm^6/sec
$Kr^+ + 2Ar \rightarrow ArKr^+ + Ar$	$1.0(-31)$ cm^6/sec
$ArKr^+ + Kr \rightarrow Kr_2^+ + Ar$	$3.2(-10)$
$Kr^+ + 2Kr \rightarrow Kr_2^+ + Kr$	$2.5(-31)$ cm^6/sec
$Kr^+ + Ar + Kr \rightarrow Kr_2^+ + Ar$	$2.5(-31)$ cm^6/sec
Three-body ion–ion recombination reaction	
$Ar^+ + F^- + (Ar, Kr) \rightarrow ArF^* + (Ar, Kr)$	~$2.0(-6)$ cm^3/sec (effective two-body collision rate)
$Ar_2^+ + F^- + (Ar, Kr) \rightarrow ArF^* + Ar + (Ar, Kr)$	
$ArKr^+ + F^- + (Ar, Kr) \rightarrow KrF^* + (Ar, Kr)$	
$ArKr^+F^- + (Ar, Kr) \rightarrow ArKrF^* + (Ar, Kr)$	
$Kr^+ + F^- + (Ar, Kr) \rightarrow KrF^* + (Ar, Kr)$	
$Kr_2^+ + F^- + (Ar, Kr) \rightarrow KrF^* + Kr + (Ar, Kr)$	
$F_2^+ + F^- \rightarrow 3F$	$4.0(-8)$

(continues)

TABLE IV. *(Continued)*

Reaction	Rate constant
Desociative recombination reaction	
$Ar_2^+ + e \rightarrow Ar^* + Ar$	$0.6(-6)[Te(K)/300]^{-0.66}$
$Ar_2^+ + e \rightarrow Ar^{**} + Ar$	1.1(−07)
$Kr_2^+ + e \rightarrow Kr^* + Kr$	$1.2(-6)[Te(K)/300]^{-0.55}$
$Kr_2^+ + e \rightarrow Kr^{**} + Kr$	1.9(−07)
$ArKr^+ + e \rightarrow Kr^{**} + Ar$	$1.2(-6)[Te(K)/300]^{-0.55}$
Superelastic reaction	
$ArF^* + e \rightarrow Ar + F + e$	1.6(−07)
$Ar_2F^* + e \rightarrow 2Ar + F + e$	1.0(−07)
$Kr_2F^* + e \rightarrow 2Kr + F + e$	1.0(−07)
$KrF^* + e \rightarrow Kr + F + e$	2.0(−07)
$ArKr^* + e \rightarrow Ar + Kr + e$	1.0(−07)
$ArKrF^* + e \rightarrow Ar + Kr + F + e$	1.0(−07)
$Ar_2^* + e \rightarrow 2Ar + e$	1.0(−07)
$Kr_2^* + e \rightarrow 2Kr + e$	1.0(−07)
Radiative lifetime	
$KrF^*(B) \rightarrow Kr + F + h\nu$	1.43(08) sec^{-1}
$KrF^*(C) \rightarrow Kr + F + h\nu$	1.33(07) sec^{-1}
$ArF^*(B) \rightarrow Ar + F + h\nu$	2.50(08) sec^{-1}
$ArF^*(C) \rightarrow Ar + F + h\nu$	2.27(07) sec^{-1}
$Kr_2^* \rightarrow 2Kr + h\nu$	8.0(07) sec^{-1}
$Ar_2^* \rightarrow 2Ar + h\nu$	6.0(07) sec^{-1}
$Kr_2F^* \rightarrow 2Kr + F + h\nu$	5.6(06) sec^{-1}
$Ar_2F^* \rightarrow 2Ar + F + h\nu$	5.4(06) sec^{-1}
$ArKr^* \rightarrow Ar + Kr + h\nu$	8.0(07) sec^{-1}
$ArKrF^* \rightarrow Ar + Kr + F + h\nu$	5.0(06) sec^{-1}
248-nm absorption cross section	(cm^2)
$F_2 + h\nu \rightarrow 2F$	1.2(−20)
$F^- + h\nu \rightarrow F + e$	5.6(−18)
$Kr_2^+ + h\nu \rightarrow Kr^+ + Kr$	1.6(−18)
$Ar_2^+ + h\nu \rightarrow Ar^+ + Ar$	1.3(−17)
$Ar^{**} + h\nu \rightarrow Ar^+ + e$	6.0(−18)
$Kr^{**} + h\nu \rightarrow Kr^+ + e$	6.0(−18)
$Ar^* + h\nu \rightarrow Ar^+ + e$	4.5(−18)
$Kr^* + h\nu \rightarrow Kr^+ + e$	1.0(−19)
$Kr_2F^* + h\nu \rightarrow 2Kr + F$	6.0(−18)
$Ar_2F^* + h\nu \rightarrow 2Ar + F$	1.0(−18)
$KrF^* + h\nu \rightarrow Kr + F + 2h\nu$	2.6(−16)
$ArKr^+ + h\nu \rightarrow Ar^+ + Kr + h\nu$	1.5(−17)
$Kr_2^* + h\nu \rightarrow Kr_2^+ + e$	1.8(−18)

[a] Units are in cm^3/sec unless otherwise noted. T_e is electron temperature.

[b] These quenching rate constants were experimentally evaluated from the product of quenching rate constant k and radiative lifetime of $RgX^*(B)$ state $\tau(B)$. Considering the mixing process of $RgX^*(B)/(C)$ at a finite rate, these quenching rate constants were modified using the effective radiative lifetime, $\tau(B/C)$. Reduction factors for ArF^* quenching rate constants and KrF^* quenching rate constants are 0.418 and 0.433, respectively.

[c] Expressed for 300 K gas temperature.

KrF^* via $Kr^+ + F^-$. The negative ion F^- is formed via an electron attachment process with the thermalized slow electron $e + F_2 \rightarrow F^- + F$.

The percent contribution to the KrF^* formation as a function of excitation rate is shown in Fig. 9. The $Kr/F_2/Ar$ mixture of 1.5 atm is treated as a typical system. The KrF^* excimer is mainly formed through $Kr^+ + F^-$, $ArF^* + Kr$, and $Kr^* + F_2$. The KrF^* formation efficiency reaches roughly 20%

The percent contributions of the KrF^* relaxation channels are shown in Fig. 10. Sixty to

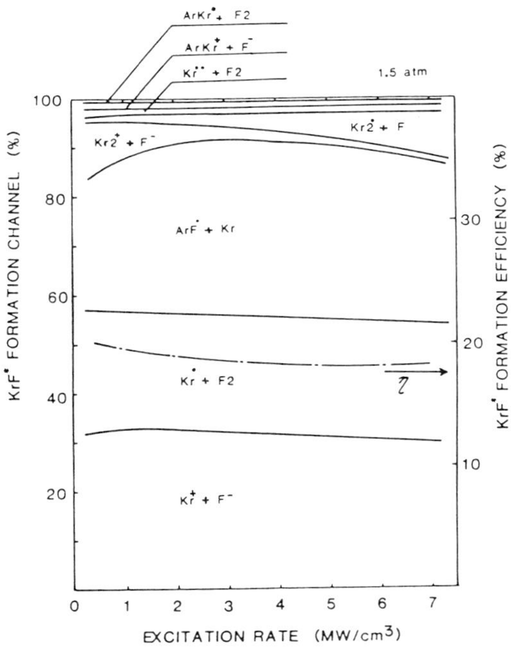

FIG. 9. Variation of percent contribution of the KrF* formation channels and the KrF* formation efficiency with the excitation rate for the 1.5-atm mixture with argon diluent pumped by a 70-nsec e-beam. [Reproduced with permission from F. Kannari *et al.* (1983). *IEEE J. Quantum Electron.* **QE-19**(2). Copyright © 1983 IEEE.]

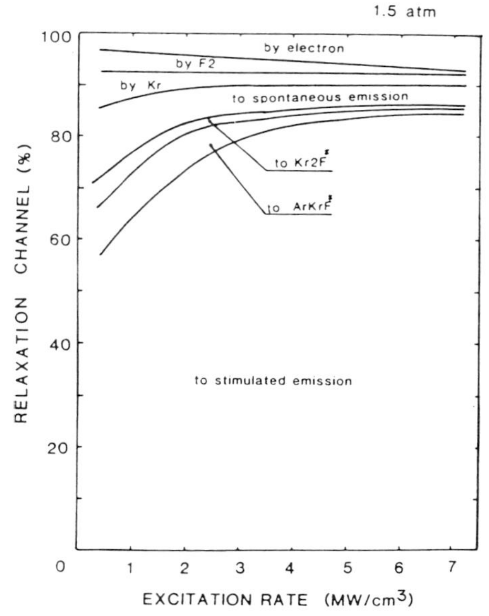

FIG. 10. Variation of percent contribution of the KrF^* relaxation channels with the excitation rate for the 1.5-atm mixture. [Reproduced with permission from F. Kannari *et al.* (1983). *IEEE J. Quantum Electron.* **QE-19**(2). Copyright © 1983 IEEE.]

eighty percent of the KrF^* excimers can contribute to the stimulated emission as an intracavity laser flux, depending on the excitation rate. Other relaxation processes are by a slow electron, F_2, Kr, and Ar. In these collisional relaxation reactions the reaction $KrF^* + Kr$ forms the Kr_2F^* trimer, and the reaction $KrF^* + Ar$ forms the $ArKrF^*$ trimer.

About 85% of the intracavity laser flux can be extracted as a laser output energy, as shown in Fig. 11. The rest of the energy is lost in the cavity by absorptions due to F_2, F^-, Ar_2^+, Kr_2^+, and Kr_2F^*, etc.

III. Rare Gas-Halide Excimer Laser Technology

Typical gas mixtures of rare gas-halide lasers are high-pressure (approximately 1–5 atm) rare gas mixtures containing a small amount of halogen donor. High excitation-rate pumping of several 100 kW/cm^3 to several MW/cm^3 is necessary to efficiently produce high gain of the excimer

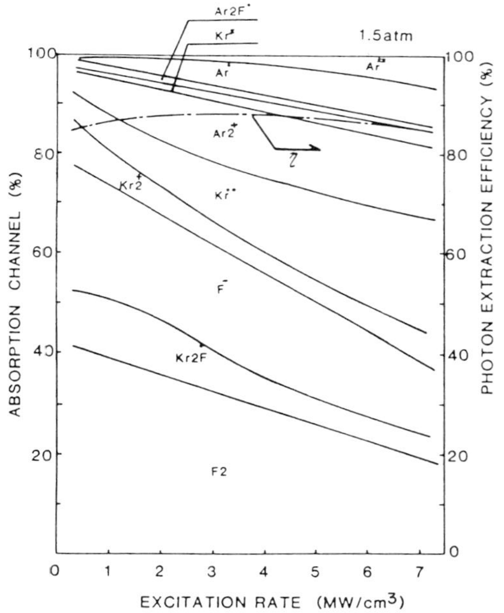

FIG. 11. Variation of percent contribution of the 248-nm absorption channels and the photon extraction efficiency with the excitation rate for the 1.5-atm mixture. [Reproduced with permission from F. Kannari *et al.* (1983). *IEEE J. Quantum Electron.* **QE-19**(2), 232. Copyright © 1983 IEEE.]

laser of interest in relation to the absorption. For this purpose, pulsed e-beam pumping and self-sustained discharge pumping have been mainly employed, while proton-beam pumping, nuclear pumping, e-beam sustained discharge pumping, and rf discharge pumping have also been tried.

Shown in Fig. 12 is a plot of the laser output energy as a function of the pulse repetition rate for various reported RGH lasers. The oblique lines show the average RGH laser output power (laser energy per pulse multiplied by pulse repetition rate). It is understood that the recent RGH laser power level lies in the power region less than 1 kW, although the laser power level is rapidly being increased. Discharge-pumped RGH lasers capable of producing laser output up to 100 W are now commercially available. Region A in Fig. 12 shows the regime in which the average laser power is gained not by pulse energy but by pulse repetition rate. These lasers are predominantly discharge pumped. Region B indicates the regime in which the average power is increased by both pulse energy and pulse repetition rate. Finally, Region C shows the regime in which low-repetition-rate or single-pulse lasers are operated with high-energy laser output. These lasers are mainly pumped by intense relativistic e-beams. The high-repetition-rate technology for these lasers is not a current issue, but energy-scaling technology for single pulse operation is currently a rather urgent issue. The lasers concerned in this region are e-beam-pumped high-energy KrF and XeF lasers for inertial confinement fusion applications and for military applications, respectively. The world's largest KrF laser reported to date is the system called LAM (large aperture module), developed at Los Alamos National Laboratory, and is used as an inertial confinement fusion driver. In 1985 this laser could produce ~10 kJ per pulse output. The highest-energy XeCl laser of 60-J level output pumped by discharges was developed at the US Naval Research Laboratory in 1985.

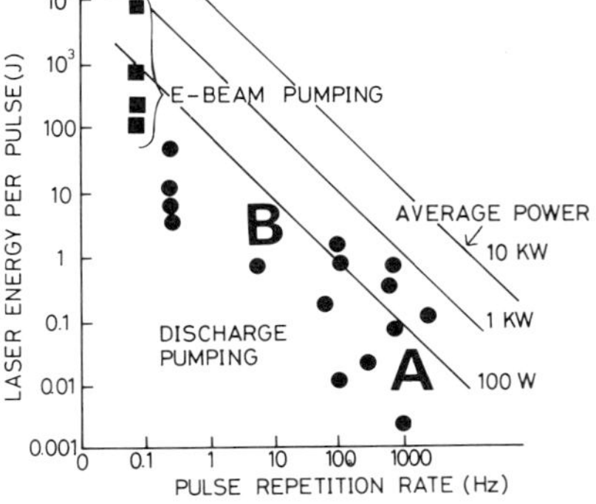

FIG. 12. Plots of the RGH laser energy as a function of pulse repetition rate for various RGH lasers reported.

A. Electron-Beam Pumping

The pulsed-power technology involved in the efficient and spatially uniform generation of intense (high current-density) relativistic e-beams from relatively large aperture diodes has advanced recently for single shot operation. The e-beam generation technology is so scalable in energy that high-energy RGH excimer lasers are more readily realizable than discharge-pumped lasers.

The relevant components of a cold cathode-type e-beam diode suited for RGH laser pumping are shown schematically in Fig. 13. The e-beam diode consists of a cold cathode to which the pulsed high voltage (negative polarity) of 30 to 1500 nsec is applied, a thin foil anode, and a pressure foil separating the high-pressure laser gas mixture from the vacuum diode chamber. These foils are made of a half-mil to three-mil-thick titanium foil or aluminized polyimide (e.g., KAPTON®) film. The support structure is placed between the foils like a Hibachi assembly to withstand the pressure of the laser gas mixture. The diode chamber is typically evacuated to low pressures less than 10^{-3} torr. An intense relativistic e-beam with a current density of 10 to 1000 A/cm^2 and an electron energy of 0.3 to 2 MeV has been used to pump RGH lasers. This high current-density e-beam can be generated only from a cold cathode-type diode made of carbon felt, or multi-blades of tantalum or titanium foils, which can enhance the local electric

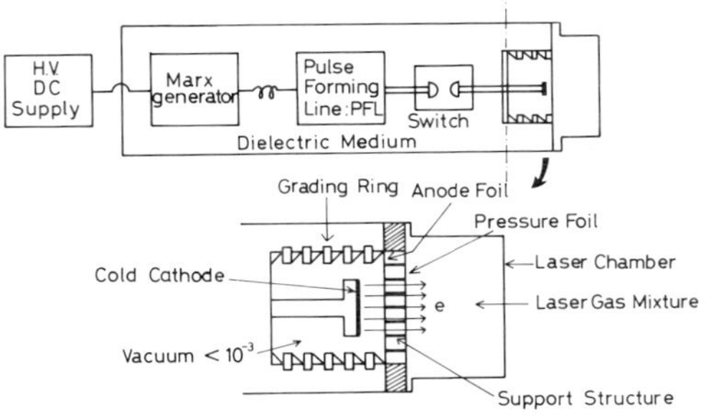

FIG. 13. Schematic diagram of a typical e-beam pumping system for excimer lasers.

field strength up to typically 1 MV/cm. The operational characteristics of the cold cathode-type diode approximately obey the Child–Langmuir law (space-charge-limited electron flow). Therefore, the e-beam current density can be approximately written as

$$J_{eb} = \frac{\sqrt{2}}{9\pi}\left(\frac{e}{m_0}\right)^{1/2}\frac{V^{3/2}}{d^2}$$

$$= 2.3 \times 10^3 \frac{V^{3/2}}{d^2}\ \text{A/cm}^2$$

where J_{eb} is the current density in A/cm^2, V the applied voltage in MV, and d is the anode–cathode spacing in cm. Here e and m_0 are the electron charge and mass, respectively. This expression is accurately the nonrelativistic expression. In the region of $V > \sim 0.5$ MV some relativistic correction is required. Thermionic electron emitters (hot cathode) are not used for direct e-beam pumping of RGH lasers (except for indirect e-beam pumping, such as an e-beam-sustained discharge pumping), due to their inherent characteristic of low current-density e-beam generation.

The axial magnetic field is in some cases applied to ensure uniform e-beam generation if total e-beam current is larger than the critical current for self pinching, and also to improve the e-beam utilization.

A variety of e-beam-pumped RGH laser layouts have been successfully tried. Four major geometries are shown schematically in Fig. 14. The merits and demerits of these layouts should be discussed in terms of the energy scaling, the aspect ratio of the pumped region, uniform pumping, e-beam utilization, and output performance of an available pulsed high-voltage generator. To improve the e-beam energy deposition into the laser mixture, the external magnetic field is applied in some cases as shown in Fig. 14. The depth of the pumped region is determined by the electron penetration depth at a given accelerating voltage of electrons. The variation of the electron range in one atmospheric pressure of various rare gases commonly used for RGH lasers is shown in Fig. 15. As can be seen in Fig. 15, a higher-Z rare gas can deposit more e-beam energy because of its shorter propagation distance. Actually, a typical KrF mixture is a 2–3 atm mixture of $Kr/F_2/Ar$ = 10/1/89(%). In 1983, low pressurization of the KrF laser mixture was proposed and successfully tried by increasing a higher Z krypton content

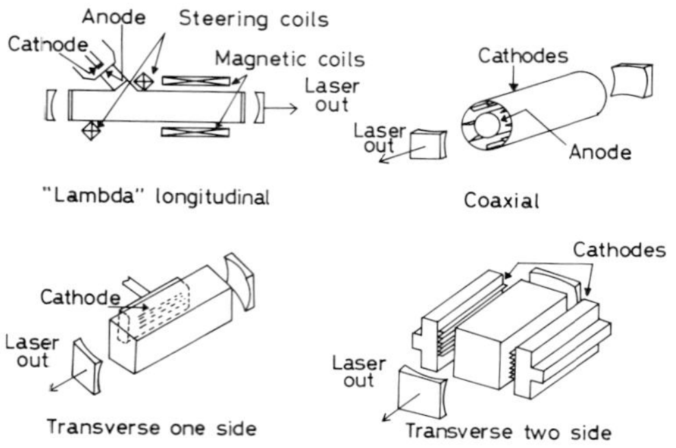

FIG. 14. Schematic of four major layouts for e-beam pumped RGH lasers.

than argon or by using an argonless mixture of Kr/F_2 to keep the e-beam deposition constant.

Under the high-excitation-rate pumping, the precursor for a RGH excimer is a rare gas ion, as mentioned previously. Some typical values of the average energy (eW_i) to produce an ion pair of rare gas by an e-beam are shown in Table V along with their ionization potentials. If the energy deposited into the rare gas mixture is calculated, or measured, the net rate of ion-pair production can be calculated. The secondary electrons can rapidly cool down to around 1 eV in pure rare gases such as He, Ar, Kr, etc. In Ne gas the electrons cannot be thermalized rapidly. The e-beam energy deposited into the rare gases can be measured by a calorimetric and pressure-jump method. This energy measurement is re-

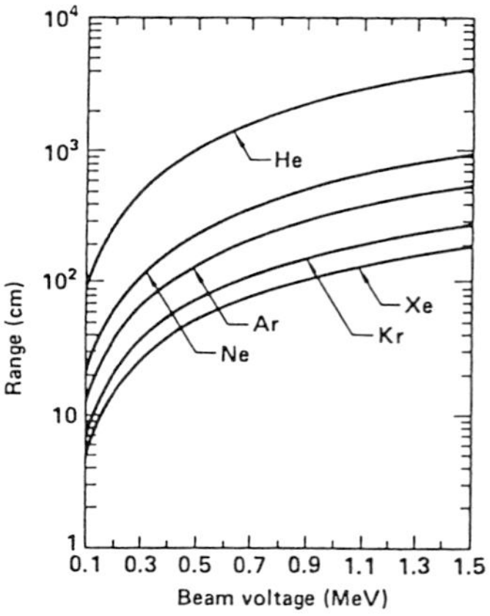

FIG. 15. Berger and Seltzer range for commonly used rare gases at 1 atm. [Reproduced with permission from J. J. Ewing (1979). Excimer lasers, *in* "Laser Handbook" Vol. 3 (M. L. Stitch, ed.), North-Holland Publ., Amsterdam.]

TABLE V. Comparison of Average Energy to Ionize Rare Gases and Their Ionization Potentials

Rare gas	eW_i (eV)	Ionization potential (eV)
He	42	24.6
Ne	36	21.6
Ar	26	15.8
Kr	24	14.0
Xe	22	12.1

quired to estimate the intrinsic efficiency for e-beam-pumped lasers, defined as a ratio of the laser output energy to the deposition energy. Experimentally, intrinsic efficiencies for KrF and XeCl lasers are typically 6–12% and around 5%, respectively. As a single shot, or low-repetition-rate device several companies can supply complete e-beam accelerators for RGH laser pumping.

The world-wide KrF lasers pumped by e-beams are shown in Fig. 16. It is understood that the scaling-up of the laser energy is done experimentally by increasing laser pulse width (in other words, pumping pulse width). These large-scale KrF laser systems have all been constructed to be used as a power amplifier in a fusion laser system. The SPRITE laser employed a four-sided transverse excitation scheme, while RAPIER and LAM employed two-sided transverse excitation schemes as shown in Fig. 14. The size of LAM in Los Alamos National Laboratory is as large as 2 × 1 × 1 m^3. The repetitive operation of the e-beam-pumped RGH laser is mainly limited by the heating of the anode foil. By specially cooling the anode foil, the repetitive operation is realizable at thermal loadings of up to several hundreds of watts per square centimeter onto the anode foil.

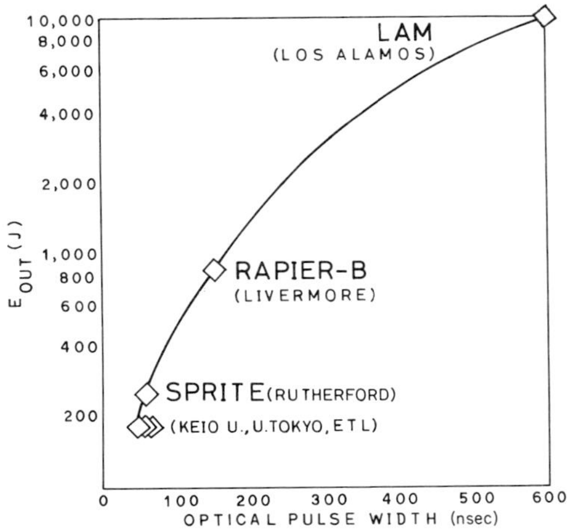

FIG. 16. World-wide KrF lasers pumped by e-beams. [Adapted with permission from L. A. Rosocha (1985). A short-pulse multikilijoule KrF inertial fusion laser system, presented at CLEO'85 (Conference on Lasers and Electro-Optics), May, LA-UR-85-1506.]

B. Discharge Pumping

The discharge pumping technology is well suited to excite high-repetition-rated RGH lasers, which can operate so far with laser output energies of several milijoules per pulse to a joule level at a repetition rate up to several kHz.

Applying an X-ray preionization to a high-pressure mixture of Xe/HCl/Ne, an energy scaling study of discharge-pumped XeCl lasers has also been done since 1979 and in 1985 a high-energy laser of 60-J level output has been successfully demonstrated as a single pulse device at the U.S. Naval Research Laboratory.

A pumping rate on the order of 1 GW per liter of discharge volume is necessary to efficiently produce RGH laser gains. The discharge resistance of the RGH discharge load is typically around 0.2 ohms. Therefore, the typical voltage of 20 kV gives discharge current as high as 100 kA. This high current cannot be switched by thyratron switches due to the heavy loadings of the switch. Hence, the primary low power and long pulse is produced in a primary circuit and then this pulse is compressed in the secondary circuit into the secondary high power and short pulse, which can efficiently pump the RGH lasers. Discharge pumping circuits developed so far are mainly classified into capacitor transfer circuit, pulse forming line (PFL) circuit, magnetic pulse compressor circuit, and spiker sustainer circuit, which are shown schematically in Fig. 17.

1. Pumping Circuits

a. Charge Transfer Circuit. The charge transfer circuit is a circuit widely used in relatively small-scale repetition-rated RGH lasers and commercially available RGH lasers. Among this type of excitation circuit, the resonant charge transfer mode ($C_1 = C_2$ in Fig. 17) is mostly employed, because the charge transfer effi-

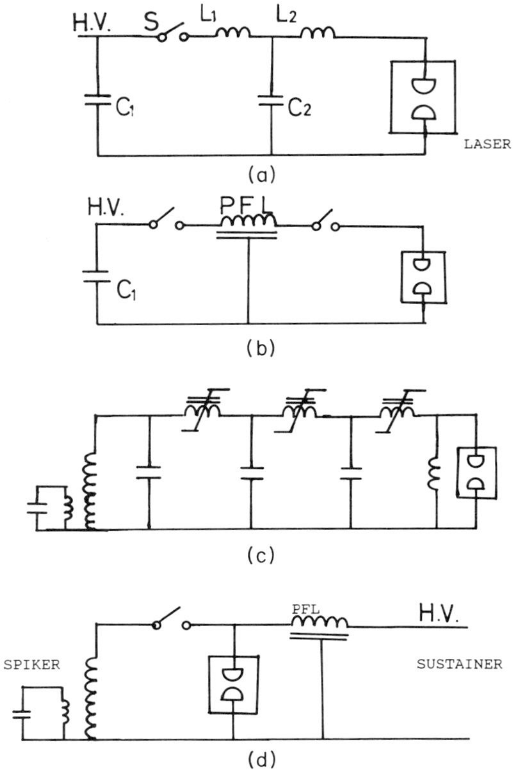

FIG. 17. Schematic of widely used RGH laser excitation circuits. (a) Charge transfer circuit, (b) pulse forming line (PFL) circuit, (c) magnetic pulse compressor circuit, and (d) spiker sustainer circuit.

ciency from C_1 to C_2 is maximized. Figure 18 shows a set of typical values for this type of excitation circuit used to pump RGH lasers. When operating the circuit shown in Fig. 18, the operating characteristics of the XeCl laser can be numerically analyzed by computer simulation, the results of which are shown in Fig. 19. A 4-atm mixture of Xe/HCl/Ne = 1.3/0.1/98.6(%) is assumed as an optimum gas mixture. Peak value of the primary current I_1 is less than 5 kA, which is within the current ratings of thyratrons widely used for RGH lasers. While peak value of the secondary current I_2 is increased up to about 18 kA. This increase is attributed to the fact that L_2 is much less than L_1 as shown in Fig. 18. The corresponding excitation rate is ~1.6 MW/cm^3, which gives a specific laser energy of 3 J/liter. The excessive excitation rate will result in the low laser efficiency mainly due to the excimer deactivation by discharge electrons.

Using this type of excitation circuit, a maximum laser efficiency of nearly 3% for both XeCl

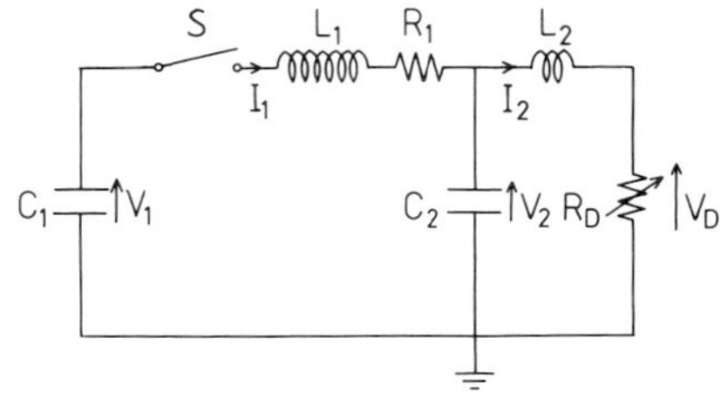

FIG. 18. Equivalent circuit of the capacitor transfer circuit. C_1 = 60 nF, L_1 = 200 nH, R_1 = 0.2 Ω, C_2 = 60 nF, L_2 = 5 nH, and V_D = laser discharge voltage. Discharge volume is 2.0(H) × 1.0(W) × 6.0(L) = 120 cm^3.

and KrF lasers was obtained with output energies of around 300 mJ, while only a 1.3% laser efficiency was obtained for the ArF laser. It is noted that laser efficiency and output energy are experimentally traded off. This is attributed to the fact that the breakdown voltage is determined not by the charging voltage V_1 but by the laser gas mixture. This laser is mostly equipped with the UV spark array preionization, which is directly and simultaneously driven by the main discharge circuit because of its simplicity.

b. Pulse Forming Line (PFL) Circuit. The PFL circuit uses a low-impedance (typically less

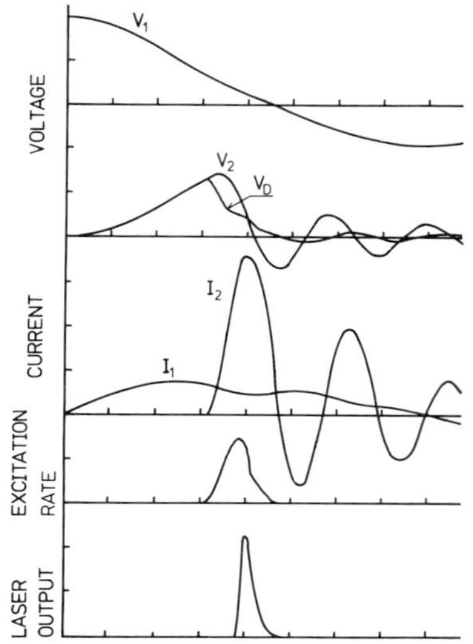

FIG. 19. Temporal histories of voltage, current, excitation rate, and XeCl laser output at a charging voltage of 20 kV. The inductance L_2 of the secondary loop is 5 nH. Each ordinate is as follows: voltage; 10 kV/div.; current, 10 kA/div.; excitation rate, 1 MW/cm^3/div.; and laser output; 5 MW/div.

than 1 ohm) PFL consisting of solid or liquid dielectric materials in place of capacitor C_2 in the capacitor transfer circuit in Fig. 17. Solid dielectric materials include Mylar® (polyamide) and epoxy sheets, while liquid materials are deionized water or deionized ethylene glycol. Coaxial-type, parallel-plate-type, and Blumlein-type PFLs were used for the RGH laser excitation.

The advantage of this circuit is that it makes it possible to inject a quasi-rectangular waveform pulse into a discharge load. The pulse duration and output impedance are simply selected by changing the length and geometry of the PFL, respectively. This pumping system is well suited for high-energy XeCl lasers of in excess of several joules per pulse.

Figure 20 shows a schematic of a PFL discharge-pumped XeCl laser together with measured and theoretical time histories of discharge voltage and current. The scaling-up of the PFL circuit is readily realizable. However, establishment of large-volume uniform self-sustained discharge in a RGH laser mixture is a state of the art technology. As an output switch in this scheme, rail gaps, UV-laser-triggered rail gaps, or magnetic switches, which will be described below, are used instead of thyratrons.

In 1985 a maximum output of 60 J in an XeCl laser was obtained with X-ray preionization at the U.S. Naval Research Laboratory. An X-ray preionized XeCl laser of 100 W at 100 Hz is commercially available that is pumped by a PFL discharge.

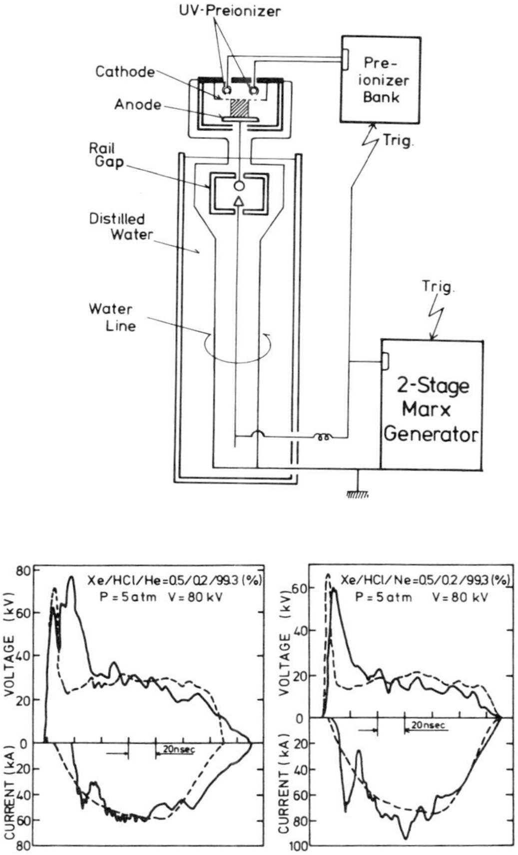

FIG. 20. Schematic of a PFL discharge pumped XeCl laser (top) together with measured (solid line) and theoretical (dashed line) time histories of the discharge current and voltage (bottom). [Reproduced with permission from H. Hokazono *et al.* (1984). *J. Appl. Phys.* **56**(3), 680.]

c. Magnetic Pulse Compressor (MPC) Circuit. A magnetic switch (MS) is a new switch consisting of a magnetic core made of ferromagnetic materials, being completely different from a gas-discharge switch such as thyratron. A magnetic core is completely saturated in an ON phase. If these MSs are connected in series, the primary pulse is successively compressed only by decreasing the saturated inductance of the magnetic coils. A three-stage MPC is schematically shown in Fig. 17. A typical MPC circuit is shown in Fig. 21, together with each voltage and current. An 8-μsec pulse is compressed to a 100 nsec pulse. The MS is a long-life or endless-solid-state switch because it experiences no erosion, and it can act reliably at high-repetition frequency. An XeCl laser operating at 150 W in average laser output at 500 Hz is commercially available.

d. Spiker Sustainer Circuit. The spiker sustainer circuit is an advanced excitation circuit for RGH lasers. The low-impedance PFL sees initially the discharge load being an open load so that the reflection of the voltage pulse may occur due to the impedance mismatch. To eliminate this unfavorable voltage reflection, the high-voltage high-impedance pulser initially breaks down the laser gas mixture and then the other power supply maintains the discharge plasma to condition the electron energy distribution for efficient pumping of the RGH laser. In this scheme, the former is called a spiker, the latter being a sustainer. This scheme is more complicated than the PFL circuit alone, but higher overall electrical efficiency is expected, because of sufficient impedance matching. Using this

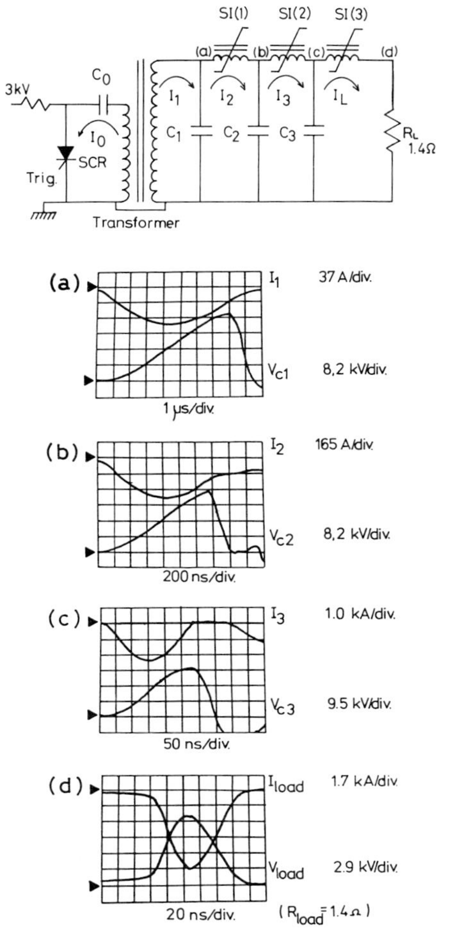

FIG. 21. A typical MPC circuit (top) together with each voltage and current (bottom). $C_0 = 2.5\ \mu F$ and $C_1 = C_2 = C_3 = 13.6$ nF. (a) First stage, (b) second stage, (c) third stage, and (d) load. [Courtesy of Tsutomu Shimada.]

scheme, an XeCl laser of 4.2 J has been realized with a high efficiency of 4.2%.

2. Preionization Technology

To initiate a volumetrically uniform avalanche discharge in the 2–4 atm rare gas–halogen mixture, preionization of the high-pressure mixture prior to the initiation of the main discharge is indispensable. Spatial uniformity of the preionization in the rare gas-halogen mixture is the most important issue. Especially, its uniformity perpendicular to the discharge electric field is of importance. The preionization electron number density on the order 10^6 to 10^{12} #/cm^3 is experimentally utilized, and is dependent on the preionization strength employed and gas mixtures.

A variety of preionization technologies developed so far are shown in Fig. 22. The simplest and most convenient preionization technology is a UV photo-preionization using a photo-electron emission process. The UV photons are generated by the use of a pin-arc discharge and a dielectric surface discharge, both of which are induced in the laser gas mixture, and UV RGH laser beams. UV preionization via pin-spark discharge is widely used in commercially available RGH lasers.

X-ray preionization technology was successfully applied in 1978 to high-pressure RGH lasers, and has been used preferably in large-scale RGH laser devices. A high-energy XeCl RGH laser of 60-J level output employed the X-ray preionization. By masking the X-ray beams by Pb plates as shown in Fig. 23 to determine the preionized volume, only the preionized (X-ray irradiated) volume can be discharge pumped with less effect of the nonuniformity of the electric field induced by main electrode geometries than that with noncollimated UV preionizers.

The effect of the preionization electron number density is large and it is experimentally revealed that the RGH laser energy and laser pulse width are increased in logarithmic form with increasing initial electron number density. An example for the KrF laser is shown in Fig. 24.

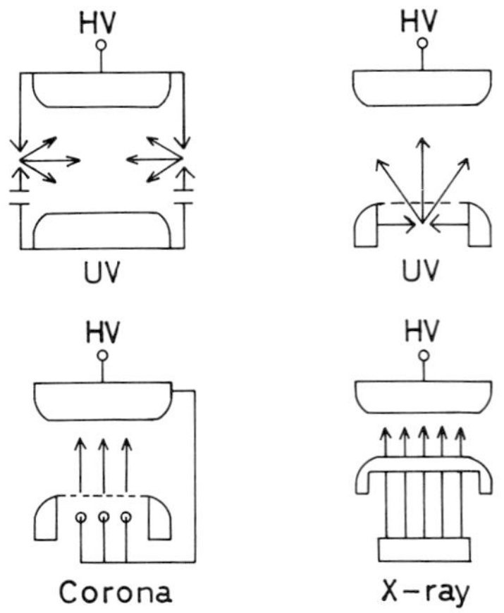

FIG. 22. A variety of preionization technologies developed to date. UV and corona preionization are suitable for high repetition rate and relatively small lasers. The X-ray preionization is suitable for large-scale discharge lasers.

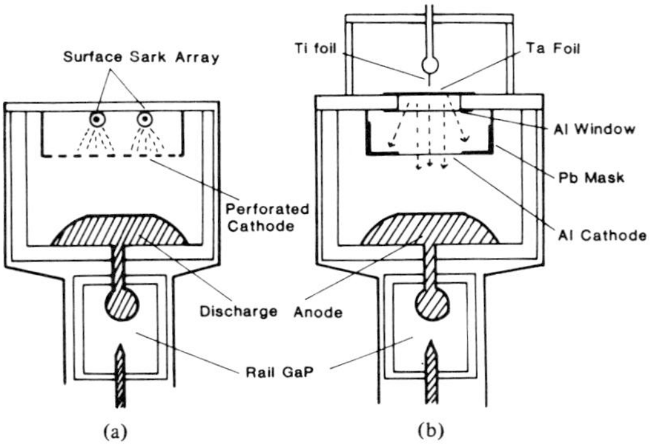

FIG. 23. Comparison of (a) noncollimated UV and (b) collimated X-ray preionizers. [Reproduced with permission from K. Midorikawa *et al.* (1984). *IEEE J. Quantum Electron.* **QE-20**(3), 198. Copyright © 1984 IEEE.]

3. Long Pulse Operation

Long pulse operation of the RGH lasers pumped by a self-sustained discharge is interesting in view of gaseous electronics and ultrashort pulse generation via mode-locking technology. Many RGH lasers have so far been operated in a short pulse (10–50 nsec) regime. In 1985, long pulse oscillations of 1.5-μsec XeCl lasers were demonstrated by conditioning the discharge in a sophisticated manner. Long pulse RGH lasers with reduced intensity can efficiently deliver their energies through quartz fibers so that they can be used in photomedicine such as laser-angioplasty and laser surgery.

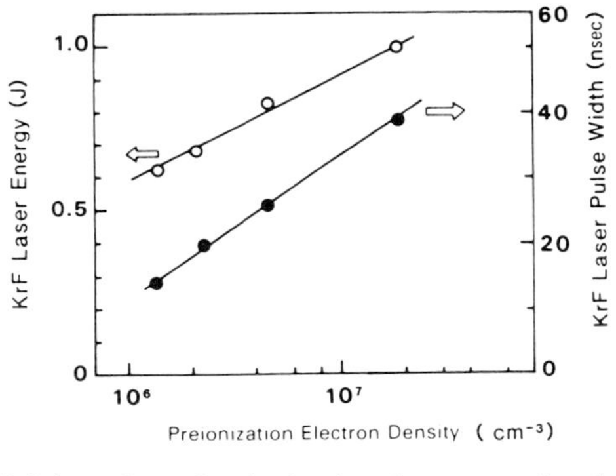

FIG. 24. Effect of preionization electron number density on KrF laser energy and pulse width. [Reproduced with permission from K. Midorikawa *et al.* (1984). *IEEE J. Quantum Electron.* **QE-20**(3), 198. Copyright © 1984 IEEE.]

4. High-Repetition-Rate Operation

High-repetition-rate operation of RGH lasers is desirable for high average-power generation. For this purpose thyratrons have been commonly used as a switching element. The operational performance of the used switch is one of the repetition-rate limiting issues.

The relationship of high-repetition-rate RGH lasers to the switching elements used is shown in Table VI. Because of rapid progress in both the pulsed power technology involved in the modulator and laser gas purification, operations at repetition rates of up to 2 kHz and an average laser power of up to 300 W have been demonstrated separately. Using a single thyratron an average laser power of up to 55 W is obtained and an average laser power of in excess of 120 W is obtained using multi-thyratrons in parallel, a thyratron with a magnetic assist, or spark gaps. The magnetic assist means that using a saturable inductor in series with a thyratron switch the current-rise rate through the thyratron is reduced so as to decrease the energy dissipated in the thyratron. The allowable rise rate of the current for thyratron is less than 10^{11} A/sec, while that of a gas-insulated spark gap reaches 10^{13} A/sec. However, their operational lifetime be-

TABLE VI. Relationship of High Repetition Rate RGH Lasers and the Switching Elements Used

Year reported	RGH	Repetition rate (Hz)	Average power (W)	Switch[a]
1976	KrF	20	16×10^{-3}	G
1977	XeF	200	50×10^{-3}	T
	KrF	1000	40	T
1978	KrF	1000	10	T
	XeF	500	1.5	T
1979	KrF	1000	55	T
	XeF	2000	24	4 × T
1980	KrF	1000	200	2 × G
	ArF	250	6	2 × T
	KrF	400	28	2 × T
	XeCl	600	45	2 × T
	XeF	250	5	2 × T
1982	XeCl	750	3.5	T + M
1983	XeCl	1500	130	T + M
	XeCl	300	120	2 × T
	XeCl	400	180	G
1984	XeCl	500	150	T + M
	XeCl	250	40	S + M
1986	XeCl	500	300	T + M

[a] G: Spark Gap, T: Thyratron, M: Magnetic Switch, S: Semiconductor Switch.

comes extremely short under the heavily loaded conditions required for efficient RGH laser excitation.

For attaining the nearly endless lifetime of a RGH laser exciter, an all-solid-state circuit is the state of the art and appears to be promising. At present, commercially available high-power semiconductor switches have been well developed, but maximum ratings such as hold-off voltage, peak current, and current-rise rate cannot fulfill the switching requirements necessary for efficient RGH laser excitation. Therefore, additional voltage transformer circuits and a magnetic pulse compression circuit are needed, as shown previously in Fig. 21.

In addition to the high-repetition-rate exciter, gas purification and aerodynamic technologies such as a fast gas circulation system and an acoustic damper at repetition rates exceeding the multi-kilohertz range are required to realize long-life high-repetition-rated operation of the RGH lasers. A long operational shot life of up to 10^8 shots has been demonstrated to date.

C. Control of Laser Properties

1. Spectral Properties

The fluorescence from the rare gas-halides with bound lower states (e.g., XeF and XeCl) typically contains line structure originating from the transitions from the lowest vibrational level of the upper laser state to various vibrational levels of the ground electronic state. When these lasers are operated without wavelength tuning elements in the resonator, the laser emission consists of radiation on the two or three strongest vibrational transitions. For the rare gas-halides with unbound lower electronic states (e.g., KrF and ArF), the fluorescence shows a weakly structured band. The untuned laser emission typically consists of a band approximately 100 cm^{-1} wide near the peak of the fluorescence.

The linewidth of the RGH lasers can be reduced and the tunability of the RGH lasers can be realized using gratings, prisms, etalons, or some combination of these elements in the laser resonator. The lowest level of frequency selection is usually obtained with a grating used in a Littrow geometry at one end of the resonator or with one or more prisms for the tuning element. This technique provides tunability over the emission band of the RGH lasers and realizes selection of single vibrational transition in lasers such as XeF or XeCl. Narrow linewidths of 80 cm^{-1} for KrF and 5 cm^{-1} for ArF have been demonstrated with two prisms in the resonator.

Narrower linewidths of RGH lasers are needed especially for the photolithography of the ultra-large-scale integration (ULSI) devices. With intracavity etalon, either alone or with a grating, narrower linewidths are achievable. A combination of three etalons has been used in a XeCl laser to produce a linewidth of 220 MHz and single-mode operation with a linewidth of 30 MHz. Narrower linewidths can also be obtained by expanding the intracavity laser beam cross section to cover the large number of grooves on the grating, which is used especially in dye lasers. This configuration includes grazing-incidence gratings and Littrow gratings with a prism beam expander. Linewidths of 0.3 cm^{-1} for KrF and 0.5 cm^{-1} for ArF and XeCl have been achieved by the use of a grazing-incidence grating.

2. Spatial Properties

Because of the high gain and wide gain bandwidth of RGH lasers, high-Fresnel-number stable resonators, which are commonly used to efficiently extract the available laser energy, produce a laser output with high spatial divergence. A low divergence laser beam from RGH lasers can be obtained by using a confocal unstable resonator with a large magnification or by simply using a low-Fresnel-number stable resonator. The use of an unstable resonator can efficiently extract laser output with high beam quality, while the use of low-Fresnel-number stable resonators results in a substantial decrease in the available laser energy. Rare gas-halide laser beams with divergencies within a factor of one or two of their diffraction limits are obtainable without any difficulty by the use of high-magnification confocal unstable resonators. Typical

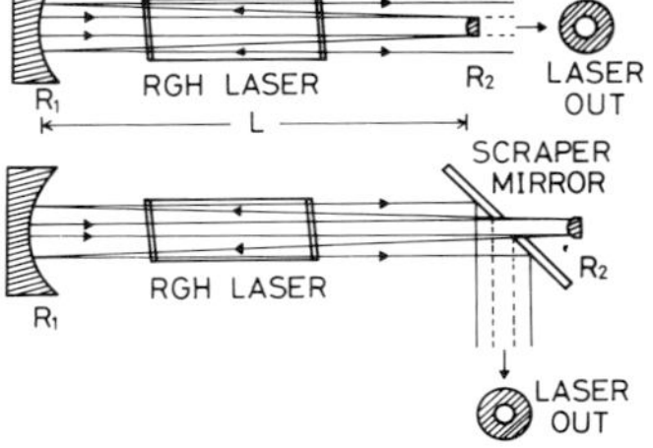

FIG. 25. Typical output coupling methods for confocal unstable resonators.

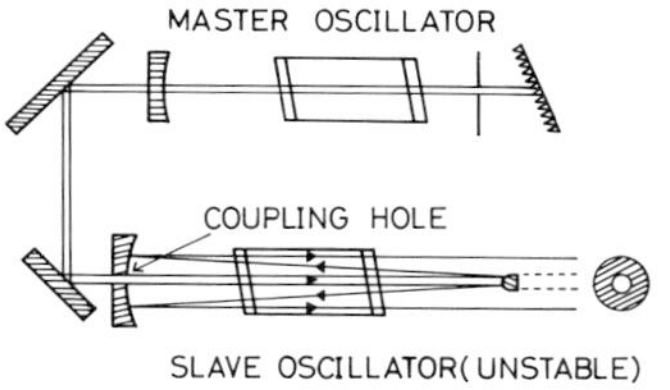

FIG. 26. Schematic of an injection-locked resonator (unstable).

output coupling methods of confocal unstable resonators are schematically shown in Fig. 25.

3. Injection Locking

For some applications, it is necessary to produce RGH lasers at a reasonable output power level with low spatial divergence and narrow bandwidth. To fulfill these requirements, use of either a master oscillator/power amplifier system or an injection-locked resonator is the most convenient method. Figure 26 shows a schematic of an injection-locked resonator. In this scheme the slave oscillator is an unstable resonator that can control the output energy and spatial mode quality. Input pulse can be made by a master oscillator typically consisting of a cavity with a line-narrowing function. An input power level on the order of 10^{-3} or less of the output laser level is effective. When a phase-conjugate mirror employing an effective stimulated Brillouin scattering (SBS) material in the UV wavelength (such as C_6H_{14} or SF_6) is used as a back mirror of an amplifier, phase front distortion induced on the laser beam in the amplifier can be eliminated, and then the highly controlled properties of the input laser can be realized on the amplified beam. High-power laser extraction is more readily achievable as a by-product with injection locking than without injection because the injected seed pulse assists the build-up of the intracavity flux and reduces energy loss. This effect is more remarkable in shorter duration lasers.

In injection-locked RGH lasers, an input pulse can be made by an entirely different kind of laser. When radiation generated from a visible dye laser chain pumped by a flashlamp, an Ar ion laser, a frequency-doubled YAG laser, or an RGH laser is injected into the RGH amplifier after one or more stages of frequency conversion, a highly controlled laser pulse with desirable spectral, spatial, and temporal beam quality can be amplified to high energy level. The use of a cw single-mode dye laser provides a narrow band seed signal whose wavelength is tunable over the bandwidth of the RGH laser. A system of this type has also been adapted for an e-beam pumped XeF(C-A) laser, and the extremely wide bandwidth of 80 nm was continuously tuned with a linewidth of less than 0.001 nm and an intrinsic efficiency of 1.5%. Beam divergencies within a factor of three of the diffraction limit were achieved.

D. Ultrashort Pulse Amplification

The broad bandwidth afforded by RGH lasers makes these systems promising candidates for constructing ultrashort pulse laser systems. Although direct generation of ultrashort RGH laser pulses by using either active or passive mode locking is limited to its pulsewidth on the order of or slightly shorter than 1 nsec due to the short gain duration, successful ultrashort pulse generation using visible dye lasers and their wavelength conversion technologies have made it possible to generate high-power subpicosecond UV lasers using RGH gain media for an amplifier. The shortest pulses and highest powers achieved by various RGH lasers are listed in Table VII. The highest laser peak power of 4 TW in a 390 fsec pulse has been obtained by amplifying a frequency tripled short pulse dye laser generated in a synchronously pumped dye

TABLE VII. Ultrashort Pulse RGH Lasers

Excimer	Bandwidth (cm^{-1})	Bandwidth-limited pulsewidth (fsec)	Saturation energy (mJ)	Present status: Output energy	Present status: Pulsewidth
XeCl	120	88	1.35	300 mJ	310 fsec
			(<3 psec)	12 mJ	160 fsec
KrF	325	32	2.0	1.5 J	390 fsec
				4 mJ	45 fsec
ArF	400	26	3.0	30 mJ	10 psec

laser stage by three discharge pumped KrF amplifiers and an e-beam pumped KrF amplifier. The shortest RGH laser pulse of 45 fsec was obtained by amplifying a frequency doubled short pulse dye laser which was generated in a distributed feedback dye laser cavity pumped by a cavity quenched dye laser pulse.

Since the storage times of RGH lasers are typically 1–2 nsec, saturation energy is typically 1–2 mJ/cm^2, which is much lower than the values of other high-power lasers. Therefore, an amplifier with large aperture is required to amplify a laser pulse to very high energy levels. In such a system, amplified spontaneous emission (ASE) generated from the final large aperture amplifier tends to reduce the aspect ratio of the output laser pulse. At 248 nm wavelength, acridine dye dissolved in ethanol acts as an effective saturable absorber.

When focusing a subpicosecond RGH laser pulse generated in these systems, intensity reaches well over 10^{17} W/cm^2. High-order harmonic generation of these short pulse RGH lasers can decrease their wavelength down to the XUV wavelength region. At 14.6 nm pulse was obtained by 17th-harmonic generation with a picosecond KrF laser. An ultrashort UV probe continua was also generated through self-phase modulation (SPM) induced in high peak power RGH lasers focused into high-pressure gases. A TW-level RGH laser will be able to generate continuum pulse in the XUV spectral range.

Bibliography

Bass, M. and Stitch, M. L. (1985). "Laser Handbook," Vol. 5, North-Holland, Amsterdam.

Kannari, F., Obara, M., and Fujioka, T. (1985). An advanced kinetic model of electron-beam-excited KrF lasers including the vibrational relaxation in KrF*(B) and collisional mixing of KrF*(B,C), *J. Appl. Phys.* **57**(9), 4309–4322.

Midorikawa, K., Obara, M., and Fujioka, T. (1984). X-ray preionization of rare-gas-halide lasers, *IEEE J. Quantum Electron.* **QE-20**(3), 198–205.

Ohwa, M., and Obara, M. (1986). Theoretical analysis of efficiency scaling laws for a self-sustained discharge pumped XeCl laser, *J. Appl. Phys.* **59**(1), 32–34.

Rhodes, C. K., Egger, H., and Pummer, H. (1983). "Excimer Lasers—1983" American Institute of Physics, Vol. 100, New York.

Rhodes, C. K. (1984). "Excimer Lasers," 2nd ed., Springer-Verlag, Berlin and New York.

Stitch, M. L. (1979). "Laser Handbook," Vol. 3, North-Holland, Amsterdam.

Suda, A., Obara, M., and Noguchi, A. (1985). Properties of a KrF laser with atmospheric-pressure Kr-rich mixture pumped by an electron beam, *J. Appl. Phys.* **58**(3), 1129–1134.

LASERS, SEMICONDUCTOR INJECTION

Peter J. Delfyett and Chang-Hee Lee *Bell Communications Research*

GLOSSARY

Auger recombination: Three-body collision involving two electrons and a hole (or two holes and an electron). The energy released by the recombination of an electron and a hole is immediately absorbed by another electron (or hole), which then dissipates the energy by emitting phonons.

Band gap energy: Energy difference between the conduction and valence bands in a semiconductor material, which also corresponds to the energy required to promote an electron from the valence band to the conduction band.

Conduction band: Band of energy levels above the valence band which can support the conduction of electrons.

Degenerate doping: Amount of doping required to bring the Fermi energy level to a level comparable to the conduction band energy for electrons and the valence band energy for holes.

Direct band gap semiconductor: Semiconductor in which the valence band maximum and the conduction band minimum occur at the same position in momentum space.

Dopant: Material which is incorporated into a semiconductor material which adds excess electrons (*n*-type dopant) or excess holes (*p*-type dopant).

Electron-hole recombination: Radiative (or nonradiative) process in which an electron in the conduction band recombines with a hole in the valence band. In the radiative recombination process, photons are generated, while in the nonradiative recombination process, phonons are generated.

Fermi level: Energy level which represents a 50% chance of finding a state occupied by an electron.

Indirect band gap semiconductor: Semiconductor in which the conduction band minimum and the valence band maximum do not occur at the same place in momentum space. In these semiconductors, electrons in the conduction band minimum require a change in momentum in order to recombine with a hole at the valence band maximum. The recombination process in this case usually requires a phonon.

Nonlinear gain: Nonlinear part of the gain in semiconductor lasers, which manifests itself in the gain versus photon density curve. In this case, the gain decreases with an increasing photon density, due to finite intraband scattering and dynamic carrier heating.

***p–n* junction:** Region which joins two materials of opposite doping. This occurs when *n*-type and *p*-type materials are joined to form a continuous crystal.

Population inversion: Necessary condition which must exist for the stimulated emission process to occur. This condition exists when the population of the upper lasing level exceeds the population of the lower lasing level.

Q-switching: Method for producing a high power pulse from a laser system. This is usually accomplished by inserting an optical shutter in the cavity to control resonant Q or quality factor.

Quantum well: Material structure which can spatially confine electronic charges to spatial dimensions on the order of tens of angstroms (10^{-10} m). These dimensions are comparable to the de Broglie wavelength of the electron/hole.

Schawlow–Townes equation: Equation which theoretically predicts the linewidth of the lasing transition of a single mode laser. The linewidth predicted from this equation is inversely proportional to the output power and the cavity quality factor (Q-factor).

Valence band: Energy band corresponding to the valence electrons of a semiconductor crystal. This energy band is normally filled and as a result does not allow the conduction of electrical current.

Window structure: Modification to the standard laser facets of a semiconductor injection laser. The modification involves processing the laser facets so that the energy gap of the laser facet material is larger than the emitted photon energy. This reduces optical absorption at the laser facets and prevents irreversible facet damage.

Semiconductor injection lasers are highly efficient laser light emitting devices which are extremely small, with typical linear dimensions being on the order of a few hundred micrometers (1 μm = 10^{-6} m). These lasers belong to a specific class of solid state lasers which are constructed from semiconductor materials, as opposed to conventional solid state lasers which are made from insulating crystals doped with active ions. The semiconductor injection laser derives its input power from an electrical current which is directly passed or injected through the device. The typical threshold currents for initiating lasing in these devices is on the order of a few milliamperes, with conversion efficiencies between the injected electrons and the generated photons exceeding 90%. Other methods of excitation are possible, such as optical pumping and electron beam pumping. However, these methods of pumping are considered to be less attractive because they do not take advantage of the compactness of the diode laser, due to the relatively large size of the pumping sources, and the pumping scheme is normally less efficient. Semiconductor injection lasers are normally constructed from several semiconductor material systems, most notably the gallium arsenide/aluminum gallium arsenide system and the indium phosphide/indium gallium arsenide phosphide system. The material system used is dependent on the desired emission wavelength of the laser. The field of semiconductor injection lasers began in 1962, just three years after the first laser was invented. These early devices were very crude; however, during the past 29 years, tremendous advances have been made in the development of these devices. Now, many scientific, industrial, and commercial applications rely on the existence of these devices. The present article reviews the basic principles of light generation in semiconductor injection lasers, surveys several important semiconductor laser structures and their applications in the scientific and commercial communities, and contemplates the future directions and trends in this rapidly growing and exciting field of research.

I. Brief Historical Overview

The first semiconductor laser devices were made from chips of gallium arsenide (see Fig. 1). The gallium arsenide was grown such that a *p–n* junction, or diode, was formed inside the crystal. The chip had a metallic base with a wire contact attached to the top to allow the injection of the electrical current. Smooth end faces were formed on the diode and acted as mirrors to provide the optical feedback necessary to attain laser oscillation, while the side walls of the laser chip were roughened to prevent laser oscillation in the direction perpendicular to the desired direction of lasing. These devices had very high threshold currents and could not be operated at very low temperatures. The light output characteristics from these laser chips were far from what their solid state and gas laser counterparts could produce. The laser emission from the chips suffered from a lack of coherence due to the wide spectral bandwidth inherent in all semiconductor light emitting devices, and the output

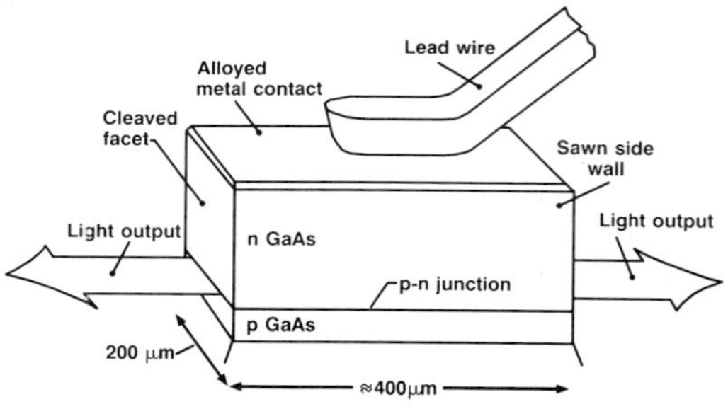

FIG. 1. Broad contact semiconductor injection laser mounted on a heat sink, with a wire contact. [From Thompson, G. H. B. (1980). "Physics of Semiconductor Laser Devices." Wiley, New York.]

beam emission was contained in a very broad far-field pattern. Despite these initial drawbacks, it was apparent that semiconductor lasers would have a very promising future. Twenty-eight years later, semiconductor lasers have been developed to the point where they have easily overcome the drawbacks which plagued them in the early days. [*See* LASERS, SOLID-STATE.]

The techniques used today for developing semiconductor lasers are identical to the technology which is used for manufacturing electronic devices. This fact means that semiconductor lasers can be mass-produced with a comparable reliability as standard electronic components. As a result of this link in processing technology, electronic devices can be integrated with semiconductor lasers on the same wafer. This feature has had a tremendous impact on the fields of integrated optoelectronics, optical communications, and optical data storage, and it is what makes semiconductor lasers very attractive for technological and commercial applications.

II. Basic Principles

The basic principles involved in the light generation process of semiconductor injection lasers can most easily be described by examining the energy level diagram of a p–n junction made from a direct band gap semiconductor. Indirect band gap semiconductors are not used for semiconductor lasers due to the nonradiative processes which are the dominant mechanism for electron-hole recombination. These processes generate lattice vibrations, or phonons, which are mechanisms for generating sound and heat and are not useful for light generation. In Fig. 2, an energy level diagram of a p–n junction is shown. Two semiconductor layers with opposite doping are grown in contact with each other. The n-doped side has an excess number of electrons; the p-doped side has an excess number of holes. The doping levels are typically 10^{18} cm^{-3} and assure that the Fermi level, shown as the dotted line in Fig. 2a, lies within the upper level or conduction band on the n-doped side and the lower level or valence band lies on the p-doped side. When this occurs, the doping is said to be degenerate.

In thermal equilibrium, electrons and holes can not recombine with each other due to the potential barriers which exists between the p–n junction. As a forward bias voltage is applied

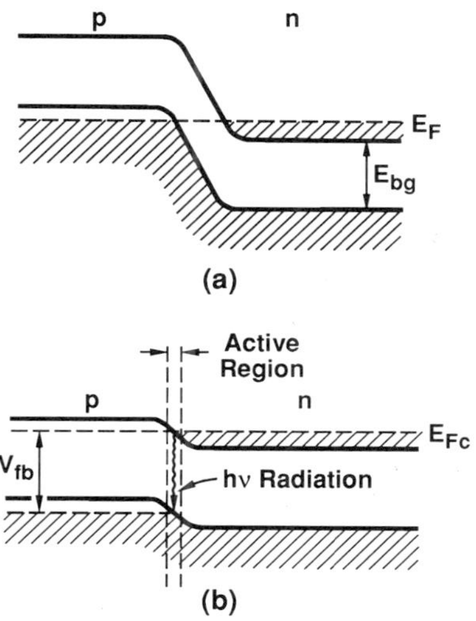

FIG. 2. (a) Degenerate p–n junction at zero bias. (b) Junction with a forward bias voltage comparable to the band gap energy. [From Yariv, A. (1975). "Quantum Electronics," 2nd ed. Wiley, New York.]

across the junction, the potential barrier is lowered. If the forward bias voltage is increased to a level which is nearly equal to the band gap energy, as in Fig. 2b, that is,

$$V_{fb} \leq \frac{E_{bg}}{e}, \tag{1}$$

then both electrons and holes are injected into the active region of the p–n junction. In the above equation, V_{fb} is the forward bias voltage, E_{bg} the band gap energy of the host semiconductor in units of electron volts, and e the electron charge. This biasing condition produces a population inversion in the active region, which is a necessary condition for the lasing process. The electrons and holes are now allowed to recombine with each other directly, emitting photons which experience a gain that satisfies the relation

$$E_{bg} < h\nu < E_{Fc} - F_{Fv} \tag{2}$$

In the above equation, E_{Fc} and E_{Fv} are the quasi-Fermi levels of the conduction and valence bands, respectively, h is Planck's constant, and ν is the optical frequency of the laser emission. Once the light has been generated and amplified, the optical feedback is provided by the cleaved end facets of the semiconductor. The cleaved end facets act as mirrors which reflect the light back and forth inside the semiconductor, initiating laser oscillation. The gain inside the semiconductor laser can approach 100× in a single pass. Due to this large gain factor, relatively low reflectives from the cleaved facets are sufficient to initiate lasing. The typical reflectivity of the cleaved facets is approximately 30% as compared to 60–99% for solid state and dye laser mirrors.

A. Optical and Electronic Confinement: Transverse Confinement

The first semiconductor injection lasers developed were called homostructures. This is because the *p–n* junction was made from one type of semiconductor material, for example GaAs (gallium arsenide). In these lasers, there is no mechanism to confine the injected carriers or created photons. As a result, these lasers suffered from high threshold currents and a poor quality output beam. These problems, however, were overcome with the development of heterostructure lasers, that is, a semiconductor laser made from different semiconductor materials, such as gallium arsenide (GaAs) and aluminum gallium arsenide ($Al_xGa_{1-x}As$). In this notation, x is the fractional content of aluminum and is typically 30%.

The most common type of heterostructure laser is the double heterostructure laser, illustrated in Fig. 3. This laser is made from a combination of semiconductor materials which have different band gap energies for current confinement and different optical indices of refraction for optical confinement. The double heterostructure laser is made of three types of semiconductor materials; a layer of *p*-type low band gap material, such as GaAs, sandwiched between a *p*-type and an *n*-type material with higher band gap, such as $Al_xGa_{1-x}As$. The value of aluminum content is chosen such that the AlGaAs regions will have a higher band gap energy and a lower optical index of refraction than the GaAs active region.

With the design of the band gaps of the double heterostructure laser, as depicted in Fig. 3a, it is possible to understand the current confinement by considering the injected carriers being trapped inside a potential well. Electrons and holes are injected into the active region from the high band gap material, AlGaAs. The electrons and holes become trapped in the potential well created by the low band gap material, GaAs. This potential well acts to confine the carriers in the active region of the laser. As a result, the electrons and holes cannot diffuse out of the active layer and are forced to recombine with each other in the GaAs material, contributing to the light generation.

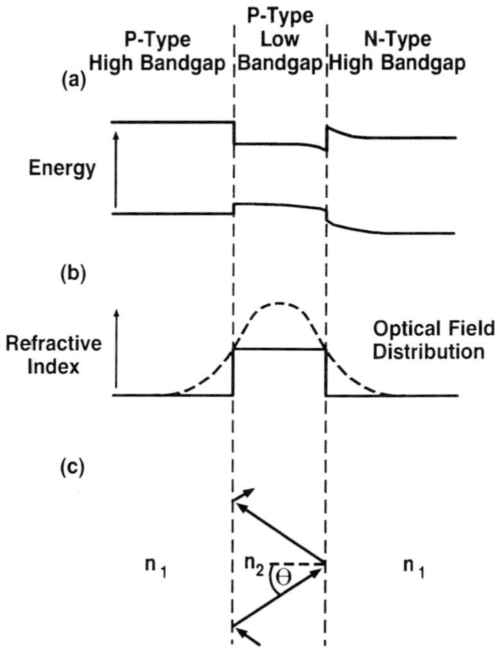

FIG. 3. Schematic of a double heterostructure laser. (a) Band diagram under forward bias. (b) Refractive index profile and optical field distribution. (c) Waveguiding effect produced by total internal reflection and the index profile shown in (b). [From Kapon, E. (1989). *In* "Handbook of Solid State Lasers" (P. K. Cheo, ed.), Marcel Dekker, New York.]

The optical beam confinement is provided by the waveguiding properties of the AlGaAs/GaAs/AlGaAs material structure depicted in Figs. 3b and 3c. The AlGaAs layers have a lower optical index of refraction than that of the GaAs (Fig. 3b). This type of spatial index profile leads to the confinement of an optical beam inside the higher index material. This is because of the total internal reflection experienced by an optical beam inside of the GaAs material (Fig. 3c). The minimum angle of incidence which an optical beam can have and still undergo total internal reflection is given by

$$\sin \theta = \frac{n_1}{n_2}, \tag{3}$$

where θ is the critical angle of incidence and n_1 and n_2 are the indices of refraction of the AlGaAs and GaAs materials, respectively.

III. Laser Structures

The optical and electrical confinement just discussed provides confinement of the injected carriers and the optical beam in a direction which is parallel to the growth direction of the layered structure. Optical and electrical confinement are also needed in the lateral direction, that is, in a direction parallel to the layers. This can be provided by two means: (1) gain guiding and (2) index guiding. The physics describing the operation of these two general classes of semiconductor injections lasers can best be understood by considering some specific laser structures as described in the next section.

A. Gain-Guided and Index-Guided Laser Structures: Lateral Confinement

Gain guiding is one method of providing electrical and optical confinement of the injected carriers and the generated photons in a direction which is perpendicular to the direction of growth of the layered structure. It is most easily accomplished by fabricating a narrow electrical opening in an otherwise normally insulating region, forming a stripe on the top of the laster structure. The carriers are injected and confined into the active layer directly under the contact stripe. This provides optical gain only under the stripe contact, thus giving the name gain-guided laser. Some specific laser structures which utilize the gain-guiding principle are the oxide stripe laser and the proton implanted laser. These lasers are depicted schematically in Fig. 4.

The oxide strip laser in Fig. 4a has a narrow opening on the order of several micrometers

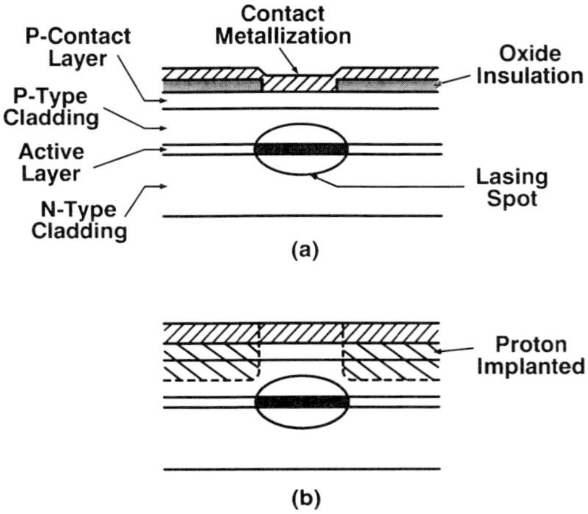

FIG. 4. Schematic cross sections of two types of gain-guided laser structures. (a) The oxide stripe laser. (b) The proton implanted laser. [From Kapon, E. (1989). *In* "Handbook of Solid State Lasers" (P. K. Cheo, ed.), Marcel Dekker, New York.]

which is created in an electrically isolating oxide layer. A metallization layer is then deposited on top of the oxide layer to create the stripe contact. The layers located above the active region are made sufficiently thin so that the injected carriers are confined in a narrow stripe in the active region.

The proton implanted laser in Fig. 4b has a contact stripe which is created by implanting protons into the metallization layer, leaving only a small stripe which has not been implanted. The implanted regions become highly resistive to current injection, while the unimplanted region has a low resistivity which serves as the electrical stripe contact. Using this method, it is possible to control the amount of current confinement by varying the depth of proton implantation.

In gain-guided structures, the unpumped regions on both sides of the stripe are lossy at the lasing wavelength. This leads to a quasi-gaussian lateral gain profile. The peak of the gain profile is located directly under the stripe, while the wings of the gain profile extend into the lossy regions. This leads to guidance of the optical field in a direction along the laser stripe. The features of the gain-guided optical field are not only determined by the gain distribution. Additional guiding is naturally provided by the index change due to local lateral temperature gradients and carrier density gradients in the active layer.

Alternative methods of providing lateral electrical and optical beam confinement can be seen by examining index-guided structures. Index-guided structures provide optical lateral confinement by fabricating a refractive index distribution which is parallel to the laser's active layer. This, in combination with the double heterostructure configuration, gives a two-dimensional confinement of the optical field. The electrical confinement can be provided by a small opening in an electrically isolating layer, as in the gain-guided structures, or by employing reversed biased p–n junctions which sandwich the lasing region in the lateral direction. Some types of index-guided structures are the ridge wave guide laser and the buried heterostructure (BH) laser. These laster structures are depicted schematically in Fig. 5.

In the ridge waveguide structure (Fig. 5a), the top of the laser device is etched down to be very close to the active layer. Only a small part of the diode is not etched. This produces a type of plateau above the active layer, which ultimately becomes the lasing region. The evanescent field of the propagation wave extends into the plateau

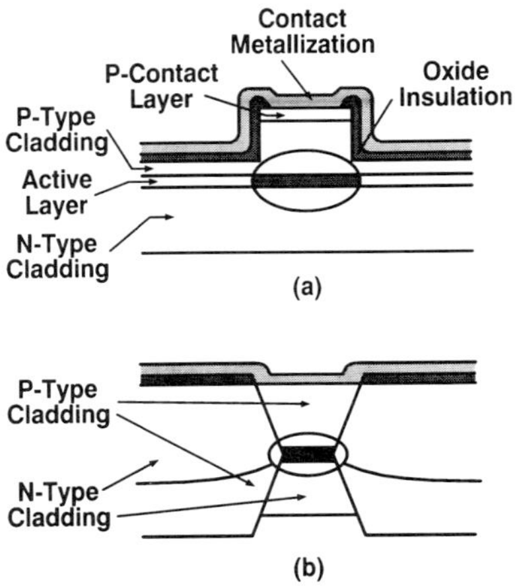

FIG. 5. Schematic cross sections of two types of index-guided lasers. (a) The ridge waveguide laser. (b) The buried heterostructure laser. [From Kapon, E. (1989). *In* "Handbook of Solid State Lasers" (P. K. Cheo, ed.), Marcel Dekker, New York.]

region and is efficiently guided in this process. In this structure, the electrical confinement is provided by the opening in the insulating oxide layer.

The buried heterostructure laser in Fig. 5b is designed so that the active region is completely surrounded by material which has a lower optical index and also a higher energy band gap. As a result of this two-dimensional index profile, the optical beam is tightly confined in both transverse and lateral directions to the direction of propagation. This structure employs two reversed biased p–n junctions so that the current also becomes laterally confined to the lasing region. With this type of optical and current confinement, threshold currents of less than 1 mA have been achieved.

As we have seen, there are several methods for confining both the injected electrical current and the generated optical beam. The gain-guided structures are easier to fabricate than the index-guided structures, however, gain-guided structures have higher threshold currents and an inferior output beam as compared to index-guided lasers. As a general rule, by properly designing the optical and electronic properties of the semiconductor laser, the injected carriers and generated photons can be confined into a well-defined region, yielding the maximum interaction, which leads to lower threshold currents and a high quality output beam.

B. High Power Semiconductor Lasers

Typical optical power output levels in standard single-stripe diode lasers are on the order of several milliwatts. These power levels are adequate for many commercial applications which use diode lasers, for example, fiber communications and optical disks. However, for many other applications, such as optical pumping, optical time domain reflectrometry, laser radar, and nonlinear optics, these power levels are not sufficient.

The most obvious way of increasing the output power of a semiconductor laser is to increase the driving current of the laser. This method works up to the point where the output power damages the facets of the laser or until the heat generated in the active region starts to degrade the performance of the laser diode.

Other methods of increasing the output power of the laser diode rely on increasing the volume of the active region. This is typically done by either increasing the width of the thickness of the active area. Increasing the length of the laser only reduces the threshold current. The output power in this case is still limited by the catastrophic facet damage.

By increasing the active region stripe width, one produces what is termed a broad area laser. These devices have very wide active areas typically ranging from 10 μm to over 250 μm. These lasers are capable of providing large output powers on the order of a few watts with several amperes of driving current. These lasers can be used as an optical pump in solid state laser systems or in other applications which require a compact, high output power laser. The problems associated with these lasers are that they usually require large biasing currents. This leads to potentially damaging thermal effects in the active region, ultimately leading to device failure. Another problem associated with broad area lasers is that the laser tends to operate in a multispatial mode pattern. The poor beam quality which is produced makes it difficult to focus the beam to a small spot, making the device unsuitable for fiberoptic applications. Another serious limitation to broad area lasers is due to beam filamentation. The filamentation is caused by a nonlinear optical effect called self-focusing. Self-focusing is caused by an increase of the optical index of refraction which is proportional to the optical intensity of a laser beam. An optical beam which has spatial nonuniformities in the intensity of the transverse beam profile causes a spatial distribution of varying refractive index. This causes the beam to collapse or self-focus into a filament which causes damage to the laser and, ultimately, device failure.

To overcome these difficulties, new device structures were developed. The problem of high driving currents was addressed by the development of quantum well lasers. These lasers rely on properties of the electron which occur when the electron is confined to small region in space. The active area thickness of typical quantum well lasers is approximately 100 Å. Broad area lasers which utilize a quantum well as the active area can have threshold currents as low as 80 mA with a stripe width of 100 μm, and have output powers as high as 1 W with 1 A of driving current.

The problem of beam filamentation has been addressed by the development of laser arrays. A typical laser array structure is shown in Fig. 6. Several laser stripes are formed by proton implantation of an initially wide stripe. This is shown by the shaded areas of the p^+ GaAs region. The disordered regions become highly resistive to current flow, while the unimplanted regions become the lasing stripes. The stripes which define the width of the active region are kept small, typically a few micrometers. This forces each individual laser to operate in the single fundamental transverse mode, which eliminates the problem of the beam filamentation. The individual stripes are positioned close enough to the neighboring stripes to allow the evanescent fields of the individual stripes to overlap and interact. This interaction allows coupling of the spatial modes of the individual stripes, forcing the laser array structure to operate coherently. Utilizing a structure with 10 single emitters with 10-μm wide stripes in an external cavity configuration, output powers in excess of 700 mW have been produced in a single lobed beam.

These one-dimensional array structures can be stacked on top of each other to produce a two-dimensional laser array. However, at the present stage of development, it is difficult to achieve coupling of all of the individual stripes without the use of external optics. The highest power produced from this type of two-dimensional laser array structure has exceeded 100 W. Although the emitted energy is not totally coherent, due to the inability to couple all of the individual emitters, the output power is sufficient to allow the device to be used as an optical pump to excite a solid state laser material, such as Nd:YAG. This type of application is very promising for semiconductor laser array structures.

C. High Modulation Frequency Lasers

The direct modulation property of semiconductor injection lasers is one of its most unique characteristics, and this feature provides the potential for many scientific and commercial appli-

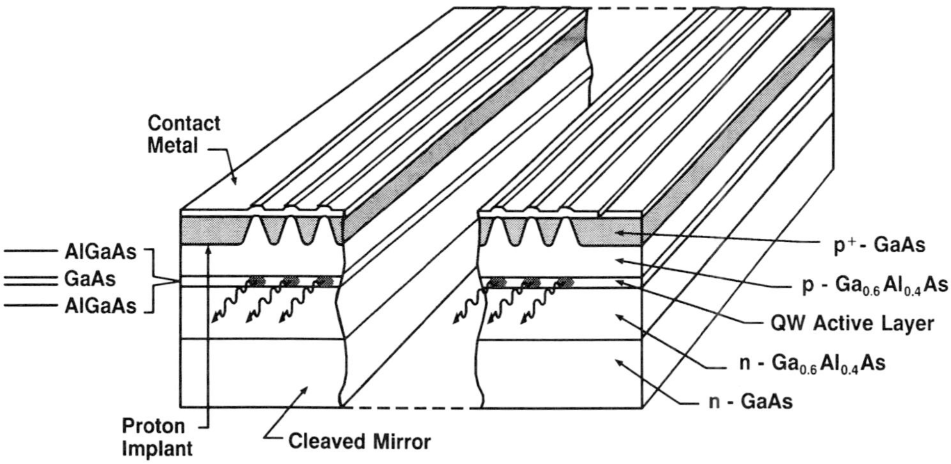

FIG. 6. Schematic cross section of a multiple laser array. [From Streifer, W., Scifres, D., Harnagel, G., Welch, D., Berger, J., and Sakamoto, M. (1988). Advances in diode laser pumps, *IEEE J. Quantum Electron.* **QE-24,** 883.]

cations. Unlike other solid state and liquid lasers, the optical output of the semiconductor injection laser can be controlled directly by modulating the injection current.

The modulation dynamics of semiconductor injection lasers can be described by the rate equations for the laser, which have been derived from the Maxwell–Bloch equations after adiabatically eliminating the atomic polarization. These equations are

$$\frac{dN}{dt} = \frac{I}{eV} - \frac{N}{\tau_s} - g(1 - \varepsilon S)(N - N_a)S \quad (4a)$$

and

$$\frac{dS}{dt} = g(1 - \varepsilon S)(N - N_a)S - \frac{S}{\tau_p} + \beta\frac{N}{\tau_s} \quad (4b)$$

In these equations, N is the electron density in the active region, S the photon density, V the active region volume, τ_s and τ_p the electron lifetime and photon lifetime, respectively, N_a the carrier density at transparency, β the spontaneous emission coupling coefficient, g the differential gain coefficient, ε the gain saturation coefficient, and e the electron charge.

By employing a small signal analysis of the laser rate equations above the lasing threshold, one can derive the resonance frequency f_r and the damping constant α_d for the modulation response of the photon density to the injection current. This yields

$$f_r = \frac{1}{2\pi}\sqrt{\frac{gS_0}{\tau_p}} \quad (5)$$

for the resonance frequency and

$$\alpha_d = \frac{1}{\tau_s}(1 + gS_0\tau_s) + \frac{\tau_s}{\tau_p}\left[\beta\frac{1 + g\tau_p N_a}{g\tau_s S_0}\frac{1}{\tau_s} + egS_0\right] \quad (6)$$

for the damping constant, where S_0 is the steady state photon density.

In Fig. 7, typical modulation response curves which have been experimentally measured for several values of output power are shown. The circuit diagram shows how the measurement is performed. The modulating signal $i_1(\omega)$ is applied to the laser diode and varied from a low modulation frequency of ~200 MHz to a high modulation frequency of ~10 GHz. In this notation, ω denotes the applied frequency. The current $i_2(\omega)$ is measured from a wide bandwidth photodiode, and the ratio of the output current to the input current is plotted on a logarithmic scale. These curves show three salient features which are characteristic of the modulation response of semiconductor laser diodes. For quasi-static modulation, the modulation frequency applied to the laser is much less than the laser resonance frequency. In this region, the optical output of the laser follows the modulating current, and the modulation efficiency is equal to the slope efficiency of the steady state light output versus dc current input curve of the laser diode. At the high frequency limit, the coupled electron–photon system can not follow the modulation current, and the modulation efficiency decreases rapidly. The interesting feature, that is, the resonant enhancement of the modulation response, is observed when the modulating current is at or near the resonance frequency of the laser. This resonance peak in the modulation response is indicative of a damped oscillation of the photon density after being perturbed from the steady state.

The peak in the modulation response can be described by a strong two-way interaction between the populations of injected carriers and photons. The stored energy of the system can swing between the two populations with a natural resonance frequency which depends on particular circumstances but is normally in the vicinity of a few gigahertz. Little damping is supplied by the optical resonator since under laser conditions its Q-factor is very large and the main contribution to damping comes from the spontaneous recombination time of the carriers, giving a decay time on the order of 5 nsec. The resonance manifests itself as a transient oscillation during laser switching and also as an enhancement of the modulation response to a small sinusoidal current in the relevant frequency range.

The modulation bandwidth of the semiconductor injection laser, given by Eq. (5), is determined by the gain coefficient, photon lifetime, and the steady state photon density. These parameters are influenced by the structure of the laser, the operating temperature, and the laser diode material system. For a given laser, the bandwidth can be increased by increasing the injection current as shown in Fig. 7. However, the maximum current is limited by the catastrophic facet damage for AlGaAs lasers and by nonlinear gain. Auger recombination, and current leakage in InGaAsP lasers. By fabricating a window structure near the facets in AlGaAs lasers, the damage threshold can be increased due to the decrease in the optical absorption occur-

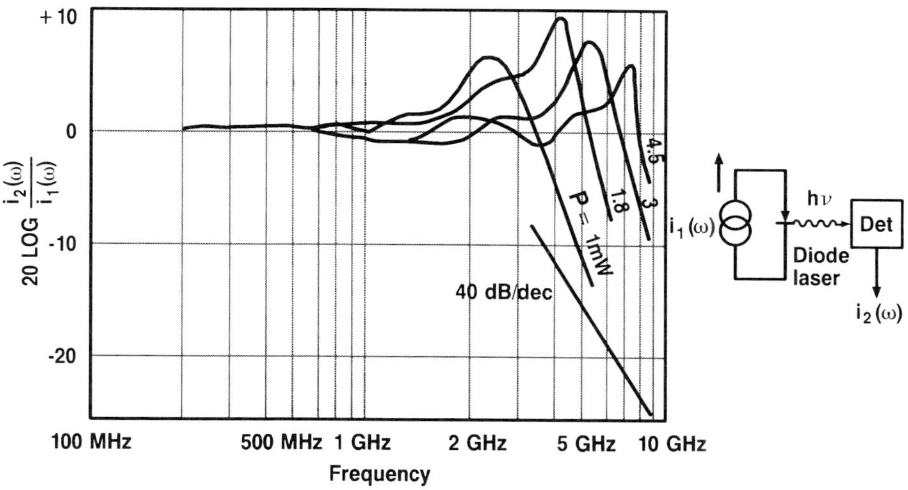

FIG. 7. Experimentally measured continuous wave output power versus current characteristic of a laser of length 120 micrometers. The inset shows the method of measurement. [From Lau, K., Bar-Chaim, N., Ury, I., and Yariv, A. (1983). Direct amplitude modulation of semiconductor GaAs lasers up to X-band frequencies, *Appl. Phys. Lett.* **43,** 11.]

ring at the facets. These lasers have been demonstrated to have modulation bandwidths in excess of 11 GHz at room temperature.

Another method of increasing the modulation bandwidth is to decrease the photon lifetime. This is most easily accomplished by decreasing the laser diode cavity length. This, however, increases the laser threshold current level and therefore lasers with extremely low threshold current levels are required for this method. Utilizing a 40-μm-long AlGaAs multiple quantum well laser, a modulation bandwidth of 24 GHz has been achieved.

In addition to excessive current pumping and shortening the laser diode cavity length as a means to increase the modulation bandwidth, the differential gain coefficient can be increased. This can be achieved by lowering the operation temperature of the laser diode. For example, the bandwidth of a GaAs buried heterostructure laser which is 7 GHz at room temperature (25°C) can be extended to 9.5 GHz at −50°C for a 175-μm-long cavity length. Similarly, the bandwidth of an InP constricted mesa laser can be increased from 16 GHz at 20°C to 26.5 GHz at −60°C. The drawback with this method is that there is a decrease in the modulation efficiency due to an increase in the series resistance of the diode which occurs at low temperatures.

Higher differential gain coefficients can also be obtained by utilizing semiconductor quantum well structures. Due to the confinement of carriers in a direction of the quantum well growth, the density of states becomes stepwise and increases the differential gain coefficient. This staircase density of states distribution increases the modulation bandwidth by a factor of 2. It is expected that another factor of 2 increase in the modulation bandwidth will be obtainable with quantum wire structures, which have a quasi-discrete density of states distribution.

Other phenomena which influence the modulation dynamics of semiconductor lasers include the spontaneous emission, gain saturation, and the external electrical connections to the device. These effects normally manifest themselves as a suppression of the relaxation oscillations which reduces the peak of the modulation response and also reduces the modulation bandwidth.

D. Narrow Linewidth Lasers

The spectral linewidth of standard Fabry–Perot semiconductor lasers is typically on the order of 100 MHz. For many applications, such as holography, spectroscopy, and coherent optical communication systems, these broad linewidths are unsatisfactory. The main difficulty of obtaining narrower linewidths in semiconductor lasers is that there is a modulation of the index of refraction due to fluctuations of the excited population caused by spontaneous transitions. This has an effect of broadening the spectral linewidth of the lasing transition which is predicted by the Schawlow–Townes formula by a factor of $(1 + \alpha_l^2)$. The parameter α_l is called the linewidth enhancement factor and is defined as

$$\alpha_l = \frac{\chi_r^{(3)}}{\chi_i^{(3)}} = \frac{\partial \chi_r / \partial N}{\partial \chi_i / \partial N} \qquad (7)$$

where $\chi_{r/i}^{(3)}$ is the real/imaginary part of the third-order nonlinear susceptibility, χ the linear plus nonlinear components of the susceptibility, and N the population density. In most gas and solid state lasers, the lasing gain spectrum is symmetric due to a single atomic transition. This implies that α_l is zero for these laser systems, and the linewidth is correctly predicted by the Schawlow–Townes equation. In semiconductor injection lasers, the gain spectrum is not symmetric due to the density of states and the Fermi–Dirac statistics of electrons and holes. This leads to a nonzero value for α_l in semiconductor lasers and thus a broader spectral linewidth of the lasing transition. The typical value of α_l is ~5 for bulk semiconductor injection lasers and ~2.5 for quantum well and semiconductor injection lasers.

Because of this difficulty in obtaining inherently narrow spectral linewidths, there has been great interest in developing new laser structures and techniques which can yield linewidths less than a few megahertz. The most promising method for reducing the linewidth of a semiconductor laser incorporates a grating structure inside the semiconductor chip itself or utilizes a grating in an external cavity configuration.

The two most popular laser structures which utilize gratings as an integral part of the laser structure are (1) the distributed feedback (DFB) laser structure and (2) the distributed Bragg reflector (DBR) laser structure. In these laser structures, part of the semiconductor waveguide is fabricated to include a corrugated region. This region acts as a diffraction grating which couples a narrow spectral portion of the total spontaneous emission back into the laser diode. The relationship between the corrugation period and the laser emission wavelength must satisfy the relation.

$$m\Lambda \cong \frac{\lambda}{2n} \qquad (8)$$

where Λ is the grating period, λ the laser wavelength, n is the index of refraction, and m an integer.

In the DFB laser, the grating structure is distributed along the entire length of the laser diode, just slightly above the gain region. This is shown schematically in Fig. 8. Due to the frequency selective feedback provided by the grating, lasing occurs at a single longitudinal frequency defined by the laser cavity. The power contained in the longitudinal modes that have frequencies which do not correspond to the Bragg condition [(Eq. (8)] is lower by 1000 times that in the lasing mode. Another attractive feature of the DFB laser is that the cavity is defined by the grating structure, not by cleaved facets. This allows the DFB laser to be incorporated directly into an integrated optoelectronic device.

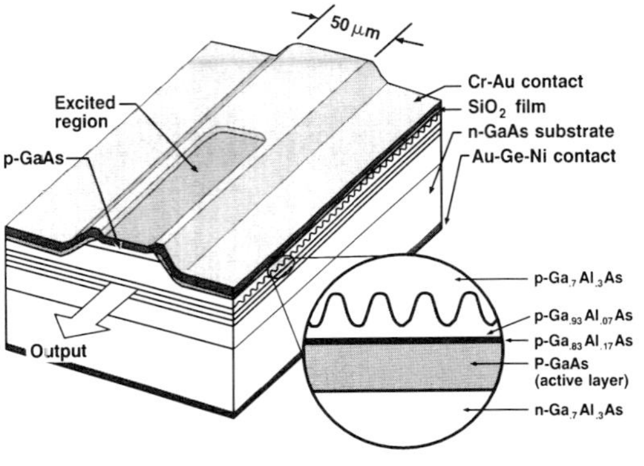

FIG. 8. Schematic of a GaAs–GaAlAs distributed feedback laser. The inset gives a detailed illustration of the laser layers and the corrugated structure. [From Yariv, A. (1988). "Quantum Electronics," 3rd ed. Wiley, New York.]

The distributed Bragg reflector laser is similar to the DFB laser. Both lasers incorporate grating structures directly into the waveguiding path of the laser mode. The difference between these two structures in that the DBR laser utilizes a passive waveguiding region to contain the corrugated structure. The main advantage of this type of structure is that it does not require epitaxial growth over the grating structure and, hence, is easier to fabricate. The disadvantage is that the coupling efficiency between the grating structure and the active region is lower, due to the waveguide discontinuity between the active and passive regions. Both of these laser structures provide lasing emission linewidths on the order of 1 MHz, which is two orders of magnitude narrower than the conventional Fabry–Perot laser structure.

Narrower linewidths can be obtained by utilizing an external cavity. Typical cavities include an objective lens for collecting and collimating the laser emission and a reflecting diffraction grating or etalon for frequency selection. When the optical feedback from the external cavity is strong, an antireflection coating is required on the laser facet which is inside the external cavity and faces the frequency selective element. The antireflection coating is necessary because it eliminates the longitudinal modes of the Fabry–Perot structures. If the antireflection coating is not employed, there will be competition between the longitudinal modes defined by the external cavity and the cleaved facets. With external cavity semiconductor lasers employing a diffraction grating, linewidths as narrow as 1 kHz have been achieved. The disadvantage of external cavity lasers is due to the relatively large dimensions, typically on the order of several centimeters.

IV. Applications

Since the development of semiconductor lasers there has been an increasing desire for their utilization in many applications. This is due to their compact size, efficient electrical-to-optical conversion, and extremely low cost. In this section, several scientific and commercial applications of semiconductor injection lasers are reviewed.

A. Diode-Pumped Solid State Lasers

The advances of semiconductor laser arrays has recently caused a resurgence of research activity in the solid state laser community. This is mainly because diode laser arrays have the potential to be used as an efficient optical pump for these laser systems. The advantages of a semiconductor laser array pump as compared to a conventional flashlamp pumped system are numerous. The semiconductor laser arrays are compact, efficient, robust, and potentially inexpensive. The emission wavelength of the laser arrays can be controlled by varying the material composition during the wafer growth. As a result, the emission wavelength can be made to coincide precisely with the peak absorption lines of the solid state laser crystal, thus making the laser array a much more efficient optical pump as compared to a broadband flashlamp. In addition, diode pumps produce less undesirable heating of solid state laser crystal and less potential for damage than a flashlamp pumped system, due to the high energy photons present in a flashlamp source. Another attractive feature of a semiconductor laser array pump is that the light emitted is partially coherent, enabling the light to be efficiently focused or mode-matched to the solid state laser system.

Specific examples of a semiconductor laser array pump would include devices made from the AlGaAs, material system. The emission wavelength can be varied from 700 to 900 nm by varying the Ga/Al composition. These emission wavelengths can be made to coincide with absorption bands of several important solid state lasing ions, such as neodymium, chromium, holmium, erbium, and promithium.

Solid state lasers can be made to operate in various manners and geometric configurations, all of which can utilize a diode array as the pump source. The solid state laser can be an optical fiber, a slab, or a standard cylindrical rod. The solid state laser may operate as a continuous wave (CW), quasi-CW or pulsed, or Q-switched device, and the emission may be single- or multispatial and longitudinal mode. Each operating condition and geometry places different requirements on the pump source. Longitudinal or end pumping is most efficient for optical fiber and rod active mediums, whereas transverse or side pumping is particularly suitable for slab active mediums.

Presently, the diode laser arrays which are used as the pump source in a longitudinally pumped solid state laser system are typically 100–200 μm wide and rated to operate ~5 years with 1 W of CW output. The pumping is normally coupled by optical fibers or bulk optics so that there is mode matching between the diode pump and the solid state laser. The advantages of this geometry are the long absorption path of the pump light and the efficient utilization of the pump light resulting from a mode-matched system.

Figure 9 illustrates a typical longitudinally, diode-pumped solid state laser system. The diode array is made from AlGaAs material system and is mounted on a thermoelectric cooler which controls the operating temperature and the emission wavelength of the laser array. The coupling optics collect the light emission from the laser array and spatially manipulate the beam shape so that the transverse spatial mode patterns of the diode pump and the Nd : YAG laser cavity are matched. The laser rod is an Nd : YAG crystal which has high reflecting (HR) and antireflecting (AR) coatings to allow the reflection and transmission of the desired wavelengths. The 95% reflecting curved mirror serves as the output coupler of the complete Nd : YAG laser.

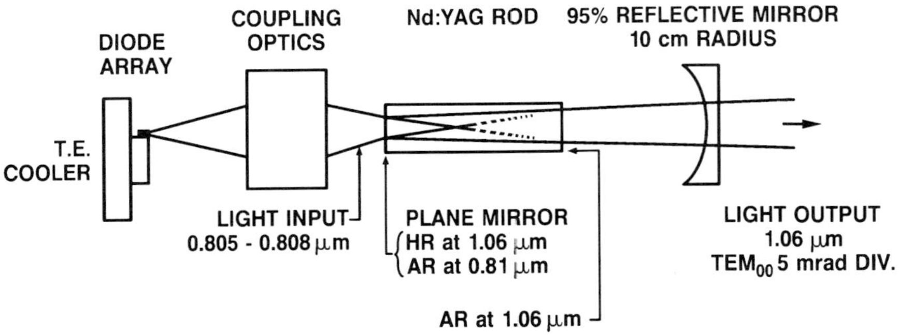

FIG. 9. Schematic of a longitudinally, diode-pumped Nd : YAG laser. [From Streifer, W., Scifres, D., Harnagel, G., Welch, D., Berger, J., and Sakamoto, M. (1988). Advances in diode laser pumps, *IEEE J. Quantum Electron.* **QE-24,** 883.]

This configuration has been used to produce over 450 mW of CV output power with approximately a 10% electrical-to-optical conversion efficiency.

The longitudinally pumped scheme is limited in output power by the diode output power per unit width. Higher power can be obtained by overdriving the laser arrays, which ultimately reduces the operating lifetime of the array. One simple solution is to use several arrays, each coupled into an optical fiber. The fiber is then combined into a bundle and used as the pumping source. Utilizing this method, ~1 W of TEM_{00} power was produced from an Nd : YAG laser emitting at 1.06 μm. Intracavity frequency doubling was also employed, which produced ~200 mW of light at 530 nm.

Transverse pumping can be utilized in both rod and slab geometries. The advantage of this method is the large area available for pump light illumination, with the disadvantage being inferior mode-matching capabilities. Utilizing a quasi-CW pumping scheme in Nd : YAG, a 0.4 cm^2, 13-bar, two-dimensional stack laser array was employed, emitting 90 W of pumping power into the laser crystal. Particularly noteworthy are the intracavity frequency doubling results, which produced ~3 W of green light at 532 nm with this pumping configuration.

The field of semiconductor laser arrays is still a new and developing technology. With future advancement in achieving higher output power and higher efficiencies, their use in increasingly larger solid state laser systems will be unavoidable. In addition, as manufacturing volumes and yields increase, the cost of these pump sources will decrease with an improvement of diode quality. Even with the present state of technology, it is apparent that semiconductor laser arrays will be an important player in the field of compact solid state laser systems.

B. Optical Communications

Semiconductor lasers have a tremendous potential for use in optical communication systems, due to their high efficiency, small size, and direct modulation capability. Because of their small size, they become the ideal source for optical radiation to be utilized in an optical fiber transmission system. The reason for developing an optical communication system is that these systems can take advantage of the large bandwidth that optics has to offer. For example, in a conventional copper wire communication system, the bandwidth of the transmission channel (i.e., the coaxial cable) is limited to approximately 300 MHz. In a normal telephone conversation, frequency components up to 3 kHz are required for the listener to understand the conversation. By multiplexing many telephone conversations on different carrier frequencies, approximately 100,000 conversations can be sent through a single conventional coaxial cable without interference between conversations. However, in an optical fiber communication system, the bandwidth of the fiber is typically several terahertz. Thus by multiplexing the conversations with a suitable optical carrier signal, more than one billion conversations can be sent over a single optical fiber. This example clearly shows the potential advantage of utilizing an optically based communication system.

Communication systems have three main components: the transmitter, the receiver, and the transmission path. Each component has certain characteristics which ultimately define how the communication system is to be designed. An example of this is seen clearly in the early designs of an optical communication system. These systems were based on the GaAs semiconductor laser wavelengths. The main reason for this was due to the availability of these devices. However, due to the dispersion and absorption losses of the transmission channel (i.e., the optical fiber), this wavelength region was considered to be appropriate only for short distance communication networks. Long distance communication networks which were based at this wavelength would be costly, due to the losses of the transmission channel and the necessity of a short repeater spacing. With the development of longer wavelength semiconductor injection lasers from the InP/InGaAsP material systems, communication systems can take advantage of special properties which are characteristics of glass optical fibers.

In most optical communication systems, the information is encoded onto a beam of light and transmitted through an optical fiber. In an ideal system, the information is undistorted by the transmission path. However, in a real optical fiber, the power level of the signal is decreased as it is transmitted, due to absorption and scattering losses in the fiber. As a result, the signal needs to be regenerated along the transmission path in order for the signal to be detected at the receiver side. Another detrimental effect caused by the fiber is due to the chromatic or group velocity dispersion. This has an effect of broadening bits of information, causing them to overlap in time. These detrimental effects are minimized by utilizing specific wavelengths which take advantage of special physical properties of optical fibers. For example, optical fibers have a minimum loss window at 1.55 μm, typically 0.2 dB/km, and a minimum dispersion window at 1.3 μm, typically 3 psec/km/nm. By utilizing semiconductor lasers which emit in these wavelength regions, the problems can be minimized. The InP/InGaAsP semiconductor lasers emit in these wavelength regions and have been developed sufficiently so that long distance communication systems are being designed to take advantage of these optical windows.

The most basic type of optical communication system utilizes an intensity modulation scheme to encode information onto an optical beam. In these schemes, the coherent properties of the laser are not employed. For detection, the detector simply counts the number of incident photons during a given amount of time in order to recover the modulation signal. Although the intensity modulation scheme does not utilize the coherent properties of the semiconductor laser output, many applications still require single longitudinal mode lasers in order to reduce the effects of chromatic dispersion in an optical fiber. These effects are most important for long distance fiber communications.

Many of the advantages of an optical communication system exploit the coherent properties of the laser output. As in a conventional radio communication system, coherent optical communication systems have a local oscillator at the receiver side. By employing a local oscillator, the detected signal sensitivity is increased by an order of magnitude. This ultimately translates into a longer repeater spacing. This feature is very important for ultralong distance communications (i.e., transoceanic optical communication links). Figure 10 shows a typical coherent optical communication system. The transmitter consists of a semiconductor injec-

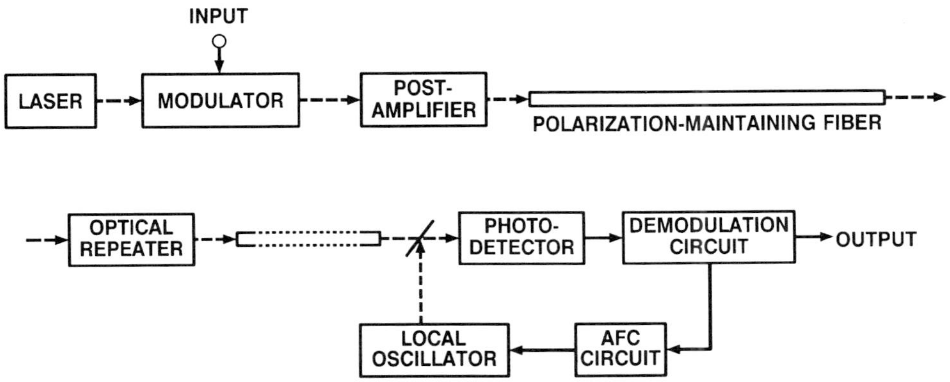

FIG. 10. Schematic of a coherent optical communication system.

tion laser, an external modulator, and an amplifier which amplifies the modulated signal before it is launched into the transmission channel. The transmission channel consists of an optical fiber and an optical repeater, which regenerates the transmitted signal. On the receiver end there is a photodetector, which detects the transmitted signal along with the local oscillator signal. The demodulation circuit demodulates the signal from the photodetector to produce the desired received information. The demodulation circuit also provides a feedback signal to the automatic frequency control circuit. This circuit controls the frequency of the local oscillator so that it can track the fluctuation of the input frequency.

There are numerous modulation schemes that depend on which parameter of the electric field is modulated, that is, amplitude shift keying (ASK), frequency shift keying (FSK), and phase shift keying (PSK). Since the coherent properties of the laser output are utilized in these systems, the bandwidth of the transmitted signal can be reduced to the bandwidth of the modulation signal. Thus by appropriately multiplexing many signals together, whether time division multiplexing (TDM) or frequency division multiplexing (FDM), the communication system can take full advantage of the channel capacity that the optical fiber has to offer.

V. Directions and Trends

The field of semiconductor lasers is only 29 years old. Since its development, it has revolutionized the science of laser optics and given birth to the field of integrated optoelectronics. The field is growing at a tremendous rate, with new laser structures yielding lower threshold currents and higher output power being reported in the technical journals each month. With advances such as these, it is apparent that the future will be even more exciting than the fields' development up to the present. It is difficult to predict the future; however, recent trends point to areas in which tremendous progress will be made. Next, a few areas of semiconductor research which will play an important part in the future development of the field are highlighted.

New semiconductor laser structures will rely on the physics of quantum wire and quantum box effects. This will enable the devices to operate with only a few microamperes of injection current. In addition, these devices will have tunable bandwidths spanning several tens of nanometers.

Two-dimensional surface emitting lasers are another area which will contribute to future semiconductor laser development. These devices have the potential to impact fields of high power semiconductor laser arrays, optical storage, and optical computing.

Semiconductor lasers have certainly advanced to the stage where, in the near future, they will replace the more common and solid state and gas lasers which have been the workhorses in both the scientific and industrial arenas. Semiconductor lasers will be successfully mode locked and the resultant ultrashort optical pulses will be amplified to peak power levels approaching the kilowatt region. This will have a tremendous impact on the ultrafast laser community, by providing an inexpensive, efficient, and compact source for ultrafast nonlinear optical studies. In addition, real-time optical signal processing and optical computing will take one step closer to reality with this advancement.

New wavelengths will become available by utilizing strained layer semiconductor material. The key difficulty to overcome in this area is to make the devices thermodynamically stable on a time scale equivalent to the human life span. These new material structures will not only provide wavelengths previously unattainable from semiconductor injection lasers, but will undoubtedly uncover new physics resulting from the combined interaction of quantum well structures and strained layer materials.

Visible diode lasers are now becoming available with wavelengths in the 600-nm regime. Utilizing the wide band gap II–VI material systems, such as ZnSeTe, ZnCdTe, and CdSSe, wavelengths extending to 480 nm will be available. The major hurdle in this field is that p–n junctions of sufficiently high quality are difficult to fabricate, due to the out-diffusion process of the p-type dopant. However, present research indicates that this, problem will soon be overcome.

Semiconductor injection lasers are also having a major impact in the area of optical amplification. By simply modifying the device structure, a semiconductor injection laser can be transformed into an amplifying device. This type of device is of paramount importance in integrated optical receivers, optical repeaters, and high power amplifiers for semiconductor mode-locked lasers.

Terabit communication systems will undoubtedly be a part of the future communication networks. This will come about with the continued development of multisegmented semiconductor injection lasers. In these devices, the laser, a modulator, and a frequency selective element are integrated on a single chip. With the continued advancements in high speed electronics, these devices will directly emit pulses on the order of a trillionth of a second, with repetition rates exceeding 100 GHz.

From this brief look into the future, it is apparent that semiconductor injection lasers will have a tremendous impact on the telecommunications, medical, scientific, and industrial communities. The advances in device technology have far exceeded the expectations of the early researchers. We can only assume that the past advances will continue into the future, bringing devices and technologies, which at this time can only be dreamed of, into reality. How these new technologies will shape the development of the world and what impact they will have on society remains to be seen.

Acknowledgments

The authors wish to thank A. M. Weiner and E. Kapon for reading the manuscript.

Bibliography

Kapon, E. (1989). *In* "Handbook of Solid State Lasers" (P. K. Cheo, ed.). Marcel Dekker, New York.

Lau, K., Bar-Chaim, N., Ury, I., and Yariv, A. (1983). Direct amplitude modulation of semiconductor GaAs lasers up to X-band frequencies, *Appl. Phys. Lett.* **43,** 11.

Streifer, W., Scifres, D., Harnagel, G., Welch, D., Berger, J., and Sakamoto, M. (1988). Advances in diode laser pumps, *IEEE J. Quantum Electron.* **QE-24,** 883.

Thompson, G. H. B. (1980). "Physics of Semiconductor Laser Devices," Wiley, New York.

Yariv, A. (1975). "Quantum Electronics," 2nd ed. Wiley, New York.

Yariv, A. (1988). "Quantum Electronics," 3rd ed. Wiley, New York.

LASERS, SOLID-STATE

Stephen A. Payne
Georg F. Albrecht *Lawrence Livermore National Laboratory*

Glossary

Active medium or active ion: Material or dopant ion responsible for the lasing.

Energy storage: Capability of a laser material to store energy in the inverted population.

Flash lamps: High-current plasma discharges contained in a fused silica envelope whose light outputs pumps a laser.

Fusion driver: Laser system of sufficient power to initiate nuclear fusion on a laboratory scale.

Host material: Crystal or glass which is host to the ion whose energy transitions make the lasing possible.

Inversion: Amount of population density by which the upper laser level population exceeds that of the lower laser level.

Laser transition: Electronic change in the state of an active ion that gives rise to the emission of a photon at the lasing wavelength.

Optical switch: Device used to control the pulse format generated by a laser.

Pumping: Process intended to drive a laser medium to or above the threshold inversion density.

Sensitizer ion: Impurity ion used to enhance the absorption of pump light by the laser medium and then transfer this energy to the active ions.

Tunable laser: Laser for which the output wavelength may be tuned to different values.

A solid-state laser is a device in which the active medium is based on a solid material. While this material can be either an insulator or a semiconductor, semiconductor lasers are covered elsewhere in this encyclopedia. Solid-state lasers based on insulators include both materials doped with, or stoichiometric in, the laser ions and materials which contain intrinsic defect laser species, known as F-centers. F-center lasers, however, are considered elsewhere in this encyclopedia as well. Thus, the designation solid-state lasers is intended to denote those laser systems which are based on crystalline or glassy insulating media, in which a stoichiometric component or extrinsic dopants incorporated into the material serve as the laser species.

The physics and engineering of solid-state lasers is both a mature field and an area burgeoning with new activity. While there are many concepts and laser designs that have been established, each year continues to bring remarkable discoveries that open new avenues of research. This article is not only intended to provide an accounting of the known physics of solid-state laser source but also to convey a sense of the enormity of the field and the likelihood that many new laser materials and architectures will be discovered during the next decade.

I. Introduction

The principle of laser action was first demonstrated in 1960 by T. H. Maiman. This first system was a solid-state laser; a ruby crystal served as the active element and it was pumped with a flash lamp. With this report of laser action, the main concepts on which solid-state lasers are based became established (see Fig. 1). The idea

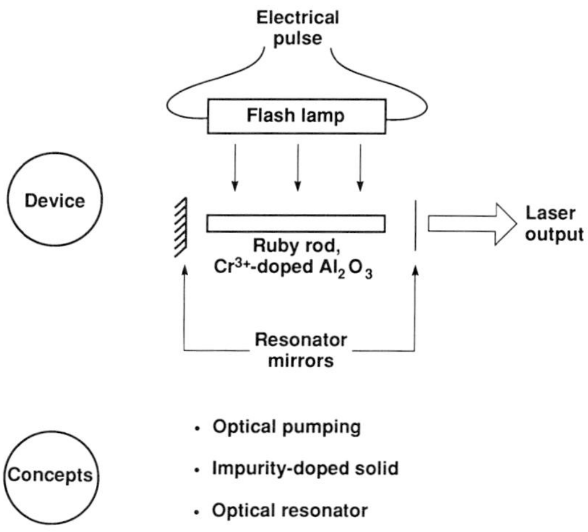

FIG. 1. Schematic desorption of the ruby system for which laser action was first reported and a listing of the fundamental concepts that were introduced.

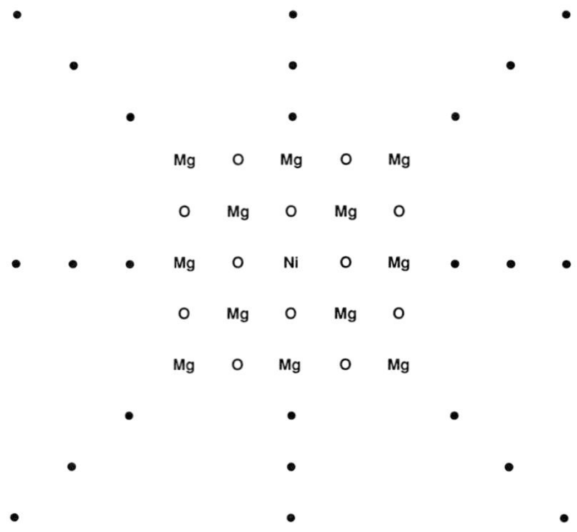

FIG. 2. Example of an impurity-doped host, $MgO:Ni^{2+}$.

of optically pumping the laser rod was realized, as well as the use of an impurity-doped solid is the laser medium. Lastly, the concept of a laser resonator, as adapted from the work of Townes and Schalow, was experimentally demonstrated. Much of this article is essentially an exposition of the extensive technical progress which has occurred in each of these three areas. Optical pumping has evolved considerably by way of optimization of flash lamps and through the additional use of laser-pumping techniques. The number of impurity-doped solids that have now been lased stands at over 200. Optical resonators have also become remarkably sophisticated in terms of the manipulation of the spatial, temporal, and spectral properties of the laser beam. [*See* LASERS.]

II. Solid-State Laser Materials

A. Laser-Active Ions in Solids

Solid-state lasers are based on a wide variety of materials. All of these materials are conceptually similar, however, in that a laser-active impurity ion is incorporated into the solid material, referred to as the host. In nearly all cases of interest to us, the host is an ionic solid (e.g., MgO), and the impurity carries a positive charge (e.g., Ni^{2+}). As a simple illustration of this situation, a two-dimensional view of the $MgO:Ni^{2+}$ system is pictured in Fig. 2. Here, a small fraction of the Mg^{2+} sites are substituted by Ni^{2+} ions. While the pure MgO crystal is clear, the NiO doping leads to green coloration. It is the impurity ions that are responsible for the laser action. The host medium nevertheless profoundly affects the electronic structure of the impurity and is, of course, responsible for the bulk optical, thermal, and mechanical properties of the laser medium.

1. Ions in Crystals and Glasses

On the basis of the introduction and a cursory glance at the periodic table of the elements, it may seem that the number of potential impurity–host systems is virtually limitless. The reported laser ions are indicated in Table I, along

TABLE I. Laser Ions and Abbreviated Listing of Host Materials

Laser ions
Transition metal ions: Ti^{3+}, V^{2+}, Cr^{4+}, Co^{2+}, Ni^{2+}
Trivalent rare earth ions: Ce^{3+}, Pr^{3+}, Nd^{3+}, Pm^{3+}, Sm^{3+}, Eu^{3+}, Gd^{3+}, Tb^{3+}, Dy^{3+}, Ho^{3+}, Er^{3+}, Tm^{3+}, Yb^{3+}
Divalent rare earth ions: Sm^{2+}, Dy^{2+}, Tm^{2+}
Actinide ion: U^{3+}
Examples of laser hosts
Fluoride crystals: MgF_2, CaF_2, LaF_3, $LiYF_4$, $LiCaAlF_6$
Oxide crystals: MgO, Al_2O_3, Y_2O_3, $BeAl_2O_4$, $YAlO_3$, $CaWO_4$, YVO_4, $Y_3Al_5O_{12}$, $Gd_3Sc_2Ga_3O_{12}$, $LiNdP_4O_{12}$
Glasses: ZrF_4–BaF_2–LaF_3–AlF_3, SiO_2–Li_2O–CaO–Al_2O_3, P_2O_5–K_2O–BaO–Al_2O_3

with a very abbreviated list of host crystals. While 22 laser ions are reported in Table I, it should be noted that these ions lase with varying degrees of proficiency, and generally possess both advantages and disadvantages. For example, Ti^{3+} has a wide tuning range but lacks the ability to store energy, Pm^{3+} is predicted to lase quite efficiently but is radioactive, Sm^{2+} lacks good chemical stability, and so on.

Each of the laser host materials possesses certain attributes and handicaps. The ease of crystal growth is important, as is the "meltability" of glassy materials. It is also noted that only certain impurity ions will be compatible with a particular host. Generally, the size and charge of the substitutional host metal ion must be similar to that of the impurity ion. For example, Ni^{2+} can be incorporated into the Mg^{2+} sites of MgF_2 and MgO, and Nd^{3+} into the Y^{3+} sites of $LiYF_4$, Y_2O_3, $YAlO_3$, and $Y_3Al_5O_{12}$.

2. Energy Levels

The nature of the energy levels and dynamics of the impurity–host system determine the character and effectiveness of the laser. A generic representation of the impurity energy levels and the energy flow appears in Fig. 3. An ideal laser crystal or glass would efficiently absorb the light from the pump source (step 1). The energy then relaxes to the lowest excited state (step 2). This level typically has a lifetime that is long enough to "store" energy. Gain occurs in the next step, as the impurity undergoes a transition between the upper and lower laser levels. While there are many potential loss mechanisms in a laser material, two that are fundamental in nature are noted in Fig. 3. One is excited-state absorption,

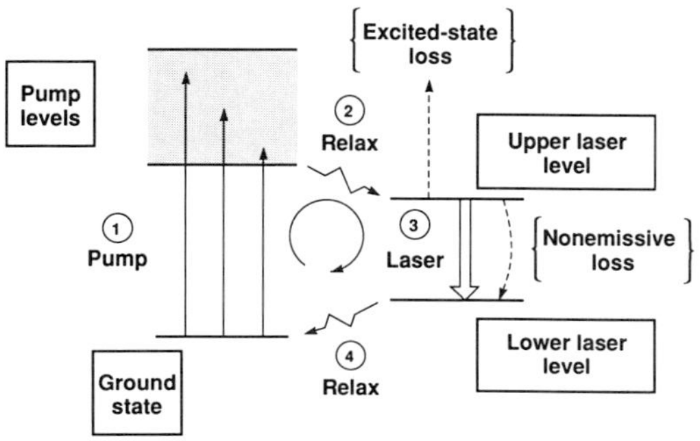

FIG. 3. Generic representation of the energy levels and energy flow (steps 1–4) for an idealized impurity laser ion. The dashed arrows illustrate two fundamental loss mechanisms.

where the upper level "sees" some amount of loss, rather than gain, due to the excitation to a higher lying excited state. A second loss involves the degradation of the energy of the upper laser level into heat, resulting in nonemissive loss. Step 4 shows the lower laser level relaxing back to the ground state. This last step is critically important since a system in which this process is absent (known as a 3-level laser) requires considerably more energy in order to lase. The advantage of the 4-level scheme depicted in Fig. 3 is that the lower laser level is unoccupied and therefore cannot absorb the laser light (thereby introducing ground state absorption loss into the system).

B. Host Materials

The host materials that are utilized in laser systems must exhibit adequate transparency, mechanical strength, and thermal properties. In addition, the material must be able to sustain a precise optical polish and be cast or grown adequately within reasonable economic and time constraints. The host must afford the impurity ions the type of spectroscopic properties that are appropriate for good laser performance. As a result of the numerous requirements, not many materials turn out to be useful in practical circumstances. Next, the nature of glasses and crystals is discussed, and the important physical properties are briefly outlined.

1. Glasses

Most laser glasses fall into one of several categories, including silicates, phosphates, and fluorides. These glasses may also be mixed, yielding fluorophosphates, silicophosphates, etc. In all cases, the glass is imagined to consist of two components: the network former and the modifiers. The network is a covalently bonded three-dimensional system, while the modifiers are ionically bonded and are imagined to disrupt the network structure. The silicate glasses provide the simplest description of the interplay between the network and the modifiers. First, consider crystalline quartz, or SiO_2, as illustrated in Fig. 4. Here, every oxygen bridges between two silicons. Fused silica is similar although it is glassy, meaning that the highly ordered nature of the system has been eliminated. If modifiers such as Na_2O are added, some of the oxygens become "nonbridging." There are some favorable features afforded to the glass by the modifier ions:

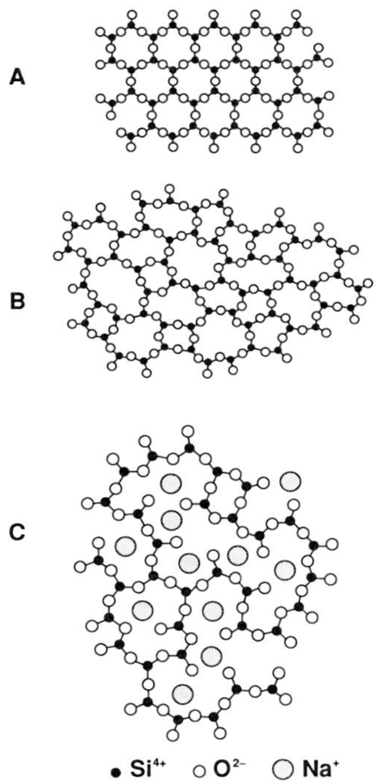

FIG. 4. Two-dimensional view of the structure of SiO_4 tetrahedrons in (A) quartz crystal, (B) fused silica, and (C) sodium silicate glass.

the melt acquires a much lower viscosity and may be easily poured and cast, and the glass is able to dissolve rare earth ions much more effectively than fused silica.

A similar situation exists for other types of glasses as well. For example, the P_2O_5 in phosphate glasses forms the network, and alkali and alkaline earth oxide compounds are added as modifiers. For the case of fluoride glasses, ZrF_4, ThF_4, or BeF_2 may serve as the network former.

2. Crystals

The growth of most crystals turns out to be considerably more difficult than is the case for melting and casting glassy materials. Crystals provide important advantages, however, since a precisely defined site is available to the laser ion rather than the broad distribution of sites that characterize a glass. Crystals often have more favorable thermal and mechanical properties as well. For example, the thermal conductivity tends to be much higher and oxide crystals tend to be very strong mechanically compared to glasses. As a result, it is often advantageous to generate the crystalline media.

Crystals may be grown in many different ways, two examples of which are shown in Fig. 5. The Bridgman method typically involves slowly lowering a crucible through a zone in which the temperature abruptly drops from above to below the melting point of the crystal. A seed crystal is sometimes placed at the bottom of the crucible to initiate the growth. Also shown is the Czochralski method, in which a seed is dipped into the melt and then slowly raised as it is rotated. Most crystals are grown at the rate of 0.1–10 mm/hr. It is important to note that there are many other methods of crystal growth that have not been discussed here (solution and flux growth, flame-fusion, etc.). All methods are based on the concept of slowly enlarging the seed crystal.

3. Physical Properties

The physical properties of the host material, in part, stipulate the architecture of the laser system. The properties of several types of host materials, including glasses and crystals, are

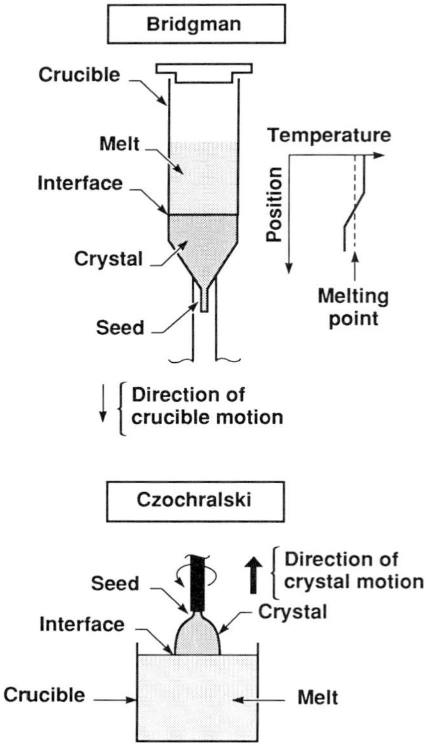

FIG. 5. Schematic drawing of two common crystal growth methods.

outlined in Table II. The qualitative trends evidenced in the table can be enumerated as follows: (a) The high-melting oxides tend to provide the highest mechanical strengths, as noted by the magnitudes of Young's modulus (the "stiffness") and the fracture toughness (a measure of the material's resistance to breaking). (b) The thermal conductivity of crystals is much higher than glasses. This permits the rapid cooling of the laser material when deployed in a system. (c) The temperature difference between the surface and center of a laser material gives rise to a thermal lens. The magnitude and sign of the change of refractive index with temperature, dn/dT, partially determines the extent of thermal lensing, which is typically smallest for fluorides and largest for oxides. (d) The nonlinear refractive index, n_2, is smallest for fluorides. The value of n_2 determines the power at which self-focusing occurs. In this process the power of the beam itself creates a lens in the material, which may result in catastrophic self-focusing of the light.

C. Rare Earth Ion Lasers

As mentioned above, 13 of the rare earth (RE) ions have been lased. In passing from Ce^{3+} to Yb^{3+} the $4f$ shell becomes filled with electrons, $4f^1$ to $4f^{13}$. It is the states that arise from the $4f^n$ shell that give rise to nearly all of the RE laser transitions. In this section a few specific systems will be discussed in detail in order to provide representative examples of the nature of RE lasers.

1. Nd^{3+} Lasers

All of the relevant absorption and emission features of Nd^{3+} are due to $4f \rightarrow 4f$ transitions. Dozens of electronic states arise from the $4f^3$ electronic configuration of Nd^{3+}, many of which are indicated in Fig. 6. The ground states consist of the ^4I_J manifold, where the ^4I designation describes the spin ($S = 3/2$) and orbital ($L = 6$) angular momenta, and the $J = 9/2, 11/2, 13/2, 15/2$ indicate the coupling between these two momenta. Absorption transitions occur from the $^4I_{9/2}$ ground state to the indicated energy levels, and each of these transitions are manifested in the absorption spectrum. Figure 7 contains the absorption spectrum of Nd^{3+} in a phosphate glass known as LG-750. The appearance of the spectrum for Nd^{3+} is similar in any host, since it is primarily due to the free-ion properties of Nd^{3+}. The main effect of the host glass (crystal) is to split and broaden the atomic transitions into bands (lines).

Following excitation into any of the absorption bands shown in Figs. 6 and 7, the energy rapidly relaxes to the metastable $^4F_{3/2}$ excited state and generates significant heat during this process. The $^4F_{3/2}$ state, on the other hand, decays in a radiative manner to all the states of the ^4I manifold. The $^4F_{3/2} \rightarrow {}^4I_{11/2}$ transition produces an emission band which peaks at 1054 nm (see Figs. 6 and 7). It is the transition that provides the strongest gain for Nd^{3+}-doped laser glasses and crystals. Nd^{3+} lasers are by far the most technologically important type of lasers. The three main materials that are routinely utilized

TABLE II. Summary of Some Thermal, Mechanical, and Optical Properties for Several Laser Hosts

	Thermal		Mechanical		Optical	
Material	Melting (softening) points, T (°C)	Thermal conductivity, κ (W/m °C)	Young's modulus, E (GPa)	Fracture toughness, K_{IC} (MPa/m$^{1/2}$)	Index change, dn/dT (10^{-6}/°C)	Nonlinear index, n_2 (10^{-13} esu)
Glasses:						
ED-2 (silicate)	(590)	1.36	92	0.83	+3.8	1.4
LG-750 (phosphate)	(545)	0.62	52	0.45	−5.1	1.1
Crystals:						
Al_2O_3	2040	34	405	2.2	+1.6	1.3
$Y_3Al_5O_{12}$	1970	13	282	1.4	+8.9	2.7
CaF_2	1360	9.7	110	0.27	−11.5	0.4
$LiYF_4$	820	5.8, 7.2	75	0.31	−2.0, −4.3	0.6

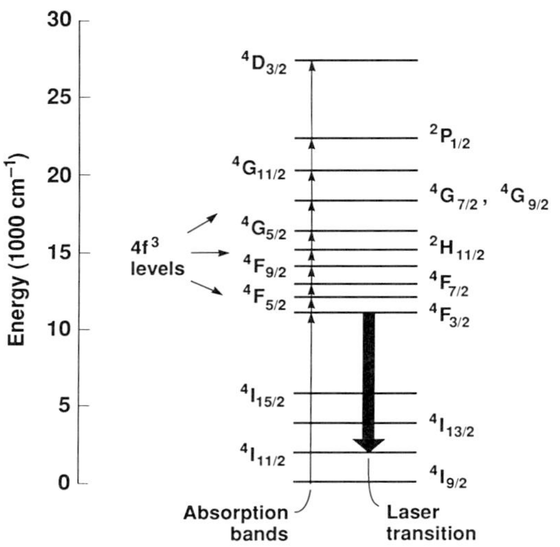

FIG. 6. Energy levels of Nd^{3+} showing the transitions responsible for the absorption bands and the laser action. Note that for clarity of presentation only the major states involved in the transitions have been indicated.

with Nd^{3+} are $Y_3Al_5O_{12}$ and $LiYF_4$ (known as Nd : YAG and Nd : YLF, respectively) and several kinds of glass.

2. Er^{3+} Lasers

The Er^{3+} ion has been lased in many crystals and glasses, and this ion has in fact been reported to lase on 13 different transitions. The relevant energy levels and the wavelengths of the laser transitions are shown in Fig. 8. Of all

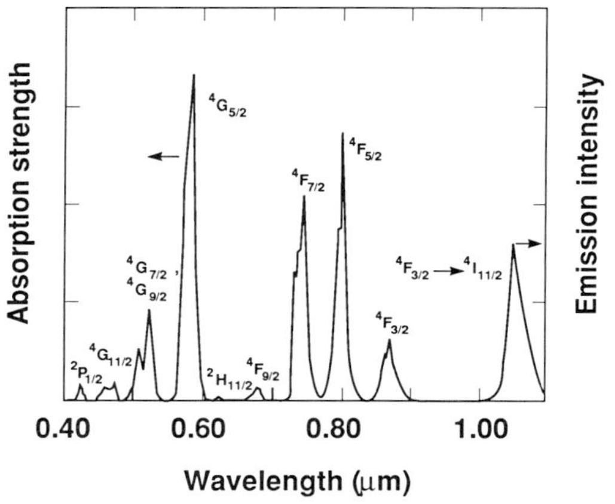

FIG. 7. Absorption and emission spectra of Nd^{3+} in phosphate glass (LG-750). The final states of the absorption transitions are indicated.

the laser lines, however, only the $^4I_{13/2} \rightarrow {}^4I_{15/2}$ transition is utilized in a commercial system. The Er^{3+} laser ion illustrates the wide gap between demonstrated laser transitions and those that are suitable for technological application. This disparity may be taken as an indication of the progress in laser physics and design that is likely to occur in the coming years.

One question that may come to the reader's mind is "why does all the energy relax to the $^4F_{3/2}$ metastable level for Nd^{3+} irrespective of which state is excited, while so many of the higher lying states of Er^{3+} are found to emit sufficiently to allow for laser action?" The answer to this question lies in the "energy gap law." Simply put, it states that the rate of nonemissive decay between two energy levels of a rare earth ion is solely dependent on the energy gap between them. Since the energy gaps are generally larger for Er^{3+} than for Nd^{3+} (compare Figs. 8 and 6), more of the energy levels are able to emit in the case of Er^{3+} and therefore many potentially be able to lase.

3. Other Rare Earth Lasers

As noted above, there is a great disparity between the number of RE ions that have been lased and the relatively small number of materials that are actually used in practical applica-

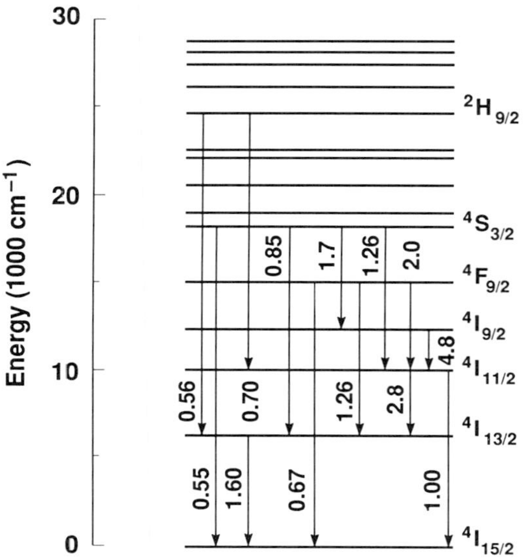

FIG. 8. Energy levels and demonstrated laser transitions of Er^{3+}-doped materials. The wavelengths of the laser action are indicated in micrometers.

tions. Nevertheless, great potential exists for the future. A summary of all the wavelengths that have been generated by RE ions appears in Fig. 9. (Note that the particular transitions involved have not been indicated on the figure.) The wavelengths span the range from 0.18 to 5.2 μm, and both divalent and trivalent RE ions are represented. The efficiencies of many of these systems are extremely low, however, and may never prove to be useful in practical circumstances.

D. Transition Metal Ion Lasers

1. Ti^{3+} Lasers

The optical properties of transition metal ions are fundamentally different from the rare earth species. This is primarily because the $3d \rightarrow 3d$ electronic transitions that are responsible for the absorption and emission features of transition metal ions interact strongly with the host, in contrast to relative insensitivity of the rare earth $4f \rightarrow 4f$ transitions. The type of situation that

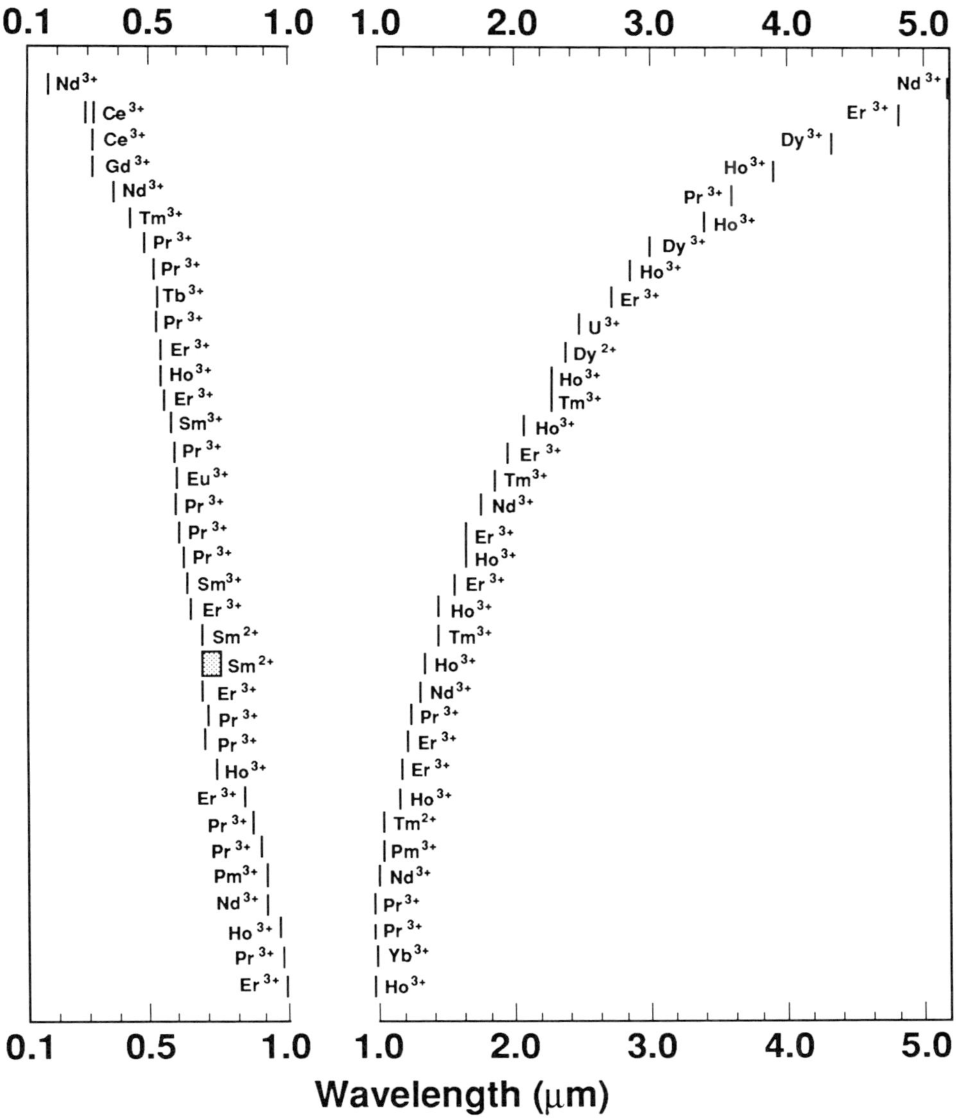

FIG. 9. Summary of all the wavelengths that may be generated by RE ions. Each line indicates a particular transition for a RE ion that may have been lased in numerous host materials.

arises is depicted in Fig. 10 in terms of a "configuration coordinate" model. The Ti^{3+} ion in Al_2O_3 has been selected for illustrative purposes because its valence shell contains only a single *d* electron, $3d^1$. The 3*d* electron is split into two states, the ^2E and $^2T_2$, by the six nearest-neighbor oxygen anions surrounding the Ti^{3+} ion. (The splitting is much larger than that experienced by the 4*f* electrons of RE ions.) As depicted in Fig. 10, the average Ti–O distance is slightly larger in the ^2E state than in the $^2T_2$ state. This difference is particularly important because it produces wide absorption and emission features.

The configuration coordinate diagram of Fig. 10 explains how the different Ti–O distances in the ground and excited states give rise to broad spectral features. The gaussian curve drawn on the ground state potential energy surface indicates the probabilistic distribution of Ti–O distances that occurs. Since the electronic transition to the excited state occurs rapidly compared to the motion of the Ti–O atoms, this ground state Ti–O distance distribution is simply "reflected" off the rising side of the upper state energy surface, thereby producing a broad absorption feature. A similar argument applies to the emission process.

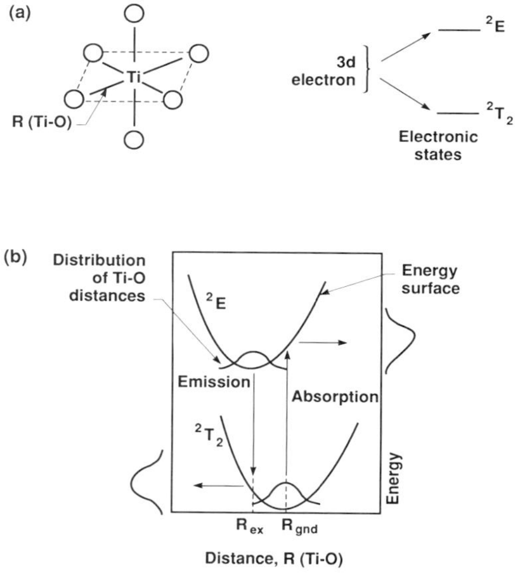

FIG. 10. (a) Splitting of the 3*d* electron of Ti^{3+} into the ^2E and $^2T_2$ states due to the interaction with the six nearest-neighbor oxygen anions of Al_2O_3, (b) Configuration coordinate model of the Ti^{3+} impurity depicting how the displacement between the $^2T_2$ and ^2E states results in broad absorption and emission features.

The actual absorption and emission spectra of $Al_2O_3 : Ti^{3+}$ are shown in Fig. 11. This material (known as Ti : sapphire) may be optically pumped with a doubled Nd : YAG laser, an Ar^+ laser, or a flash lamp. The output of the laser can be tuned from 0.66 to 1.2 μm. Ti : sapphire operates efficiently and is not adversely impacted by the detrimental loss mechanisms indicated in Fig. 3.

2. Cr^{3+} Lasers

Cr^{3+} lasers are similar to Ti^{3+} lasers in that these crystals exhibit broad spectral features. Cr^{3-}-doped systems possess an important advantage, however, in that they have three absorption bands rather than one and therefore absorb flash lamp light more efficiently. Furthermore, because the trivalent oxidation state is very stable, Cr^{3+} may be incorporated into a wide variety of hosts. A summary of the tuning ranges achieved by Cr^{3+}-doped materials appears in Fig. 12, where it is seen that wavelengths from 0.70 to 1.25 μm can be covered with different host materials. It is crucial to emphasize, however, that many of the reported Cr^{3+}-lasers are flawed in various ways, such as by having low efficiency or perhaps by permanently coloring under the influence of ultraviolet flash lamp light. The two most promising lasers are Cr^{3+}-doped $BeAl_2O_4$ and $LiCaAlF_6$ (known as alexandrite and Cr : LiCAF, respectively).

Another important distinction between Ti^{3+} and Cr^{3+} lasers pertains to the lifetime of the metastable excited state, which is typically near 1–10 μsec for Ti^{3+} and 100–300 μsec for Cr^{3+}. As a result, Cr^{3+} lasers can be arranged to "store" more energy than Ti^{3+} lasers.

3. Other Transition Metal Ion Lasers

There are, in total, 30 transition metal ions, including the first, second, and third row ions. In addition, several oxidation states exist for each of these ions. In spite of this diversity, only four ions other than Ti^{3+} and Cr^{3+} have been lased, they are V^{2+}, Cr^{4+}, Co^{2+}, and Ni^{2+}. These ions exhibit laser output in the 1–2.3 μm region and, of these materials, $MgF_2 : Co^{2+}$ crystals seem to have the most promise.

The limited number of transition metal ion lasers is related to a combination of factors. First, many of the ions do not have stable oxidation states and tend to vaporize rather than dissolve in the host material. Second, many ions turn out either to be nonemissive or to have serious ex-

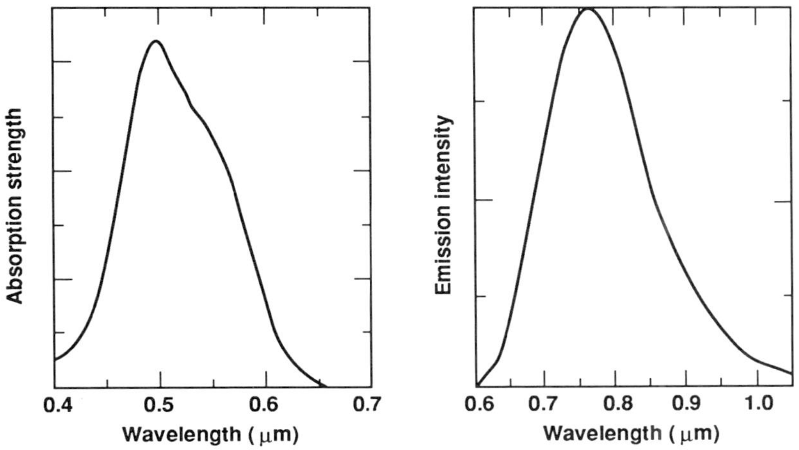

FIG. 11. Absorption and emission spectra of Ti^{3+}-doped Al_2O_3 at 300 K.

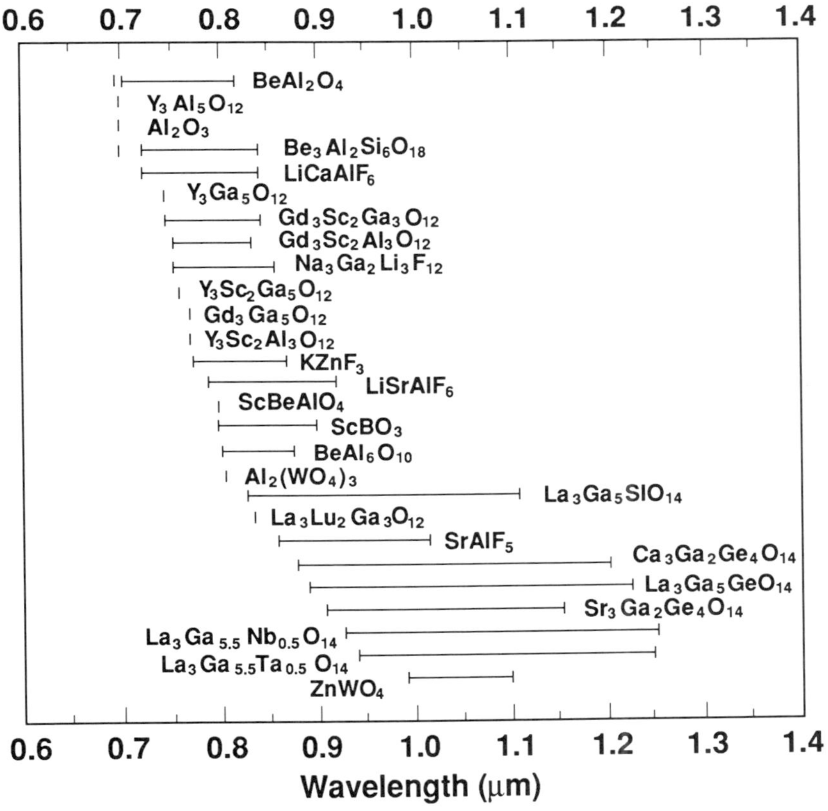

FIG. 12. Reported tuning ranges of Cr^{3+}-doped crystals.

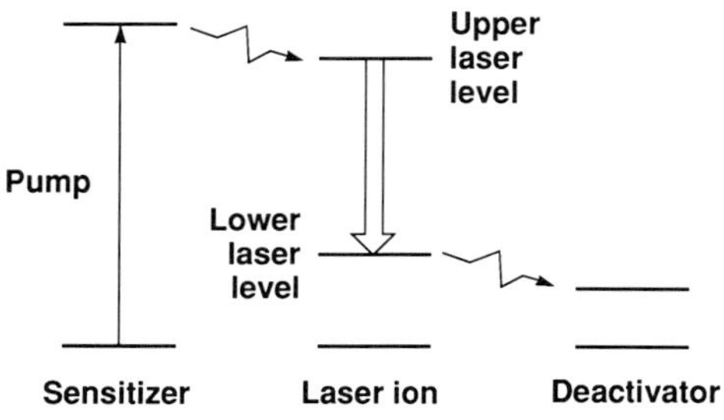

FIG. 13. Illustration showing the role of a sensitizer to excite the upper laser level or that of a deactivator to depopulate the lower laser level.

cited state absorption losses, rendering them useless as laser ions.

E. Energy Transfer in Laser Materials

1. Background

The performance of a laser material may be enhanced by the presence of additional impurity ions. Figure 13 illustrates two possible roles for these extra ions. A sensitizer increases the level of pump-light absorption by the laser material, by absorbing in spectral regions where the laser ion normally does not absorb. The sensitizer then efficiently transfers energy to the upper level of the laser ion.

Another role that the additional ions may play is that of "deactivating" the lower laser level. As discussed above, a four-level laser has important advantages since the lower laser level remains unpopulated. If this level does not rapidly drain following the laser action, it will become populated. The deactivator serves to funnel this energy away from the laser ion.

2. Examples of Sensitized Laser Materials

There are several sensitized laser materials that have proved to be useful. As an example, consider the case of Cr^{3+} and Nd^{3+} doped together into $Gd_3Sc_2Ga_3O_{12}$ (GSGG), where Nd^{3+} serves as the laser ion and Cr^{3+} as the sensitizer. The absorption spectrum of GSGG : Cr^{3+}, Nd^{3+} is shown in Fig. 14. Since the sharp features are due to the Nd^{3+} ion and the broad bands to Cr^{3+}, it is clear that the Cr^{3+} ion provides greatly enhanced absorption for the flash-lamp-pumped system. (The flash lamp output is essentially a quasi-continuum throughout the ultraviolet–visible–infrared regions.) It is also crucial to note that the Cr → Nd energy transfer is extremely efficient (>90%). GSGG : Cr^{3+}, Nd^{3+} and re-

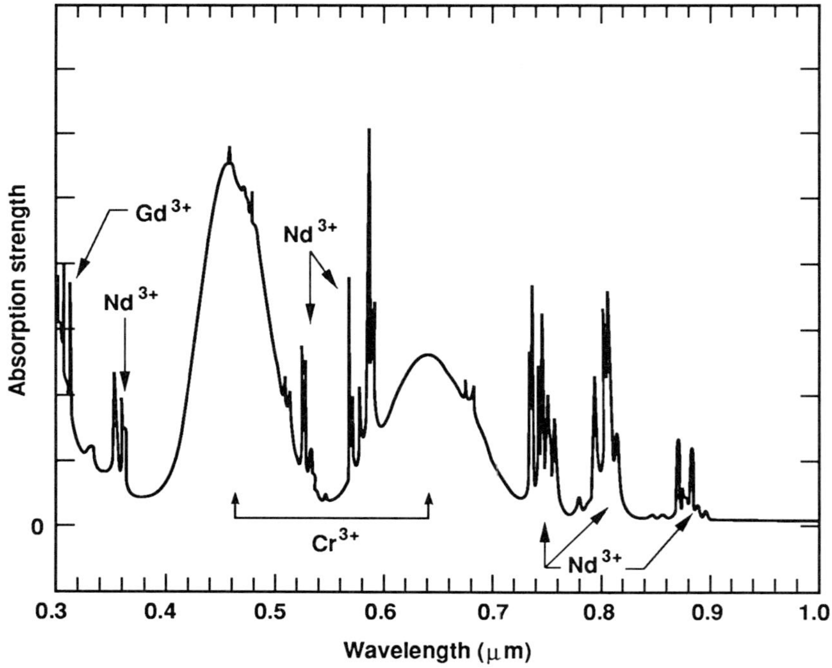

FIG. 14. Absorption spectrum of Cr^{3+} and Nd^{3+} doped into $Gd_3Sc_2Ga_3O_{12}$. The Cr^{3+} sensitizers provide for more efficient flash lamp absorption and then rapidly transfer their energy to the Nd^{3+} laser ions.

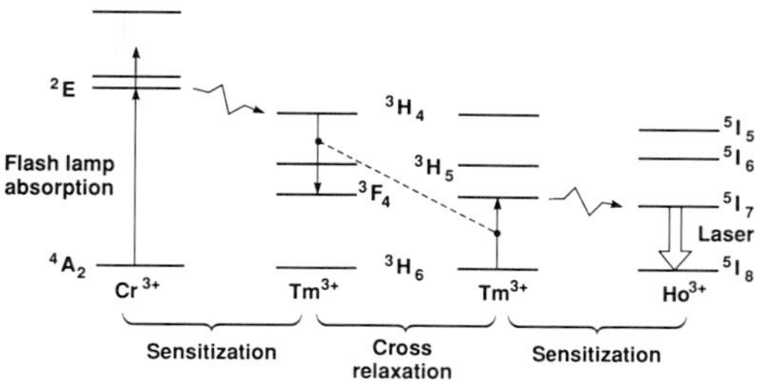

FIG. 15. Energy-transfer dynamics of the Cr^{3+}, Tm^{3+}, Ho^{3+} : YAG laser crystal. The Cr^{3+} impurities initially absorb the light and transfer the energy to Tm^{3+}. The Tm^{3+} ions then cross-relax to produce two excited states for each ion initially excited. Lastly the energy is transferred to the Ho^{3+} laser ions.

lated systems have provided the highest flash-lamp-pumped efficiencies measured to date.

The energy transfer of the Cr^{3+}, Tm^{3+}, Ho^{3+} : YAG crystal is a striking example of an elegant new laser system. The Cr^{3+} ions efficiently absorb the flash lamp light. The energy is then transferred to the Tm^{3+} ions, as shown in Fig. 15. The Tm^{3+} ions are doped at high concentration to allow for efficient cross-relaxation in which two Tm^{3+} ions are generated in the $^3F_4$ excited state for each Tm^{3+} ion initially in the $^3H_4$ state. Lastly, the energy is transferred to the Ho^{3+} ions, which exhibit gain near 2.1 μm. Each of the concentrations of the ions must be chosen carefully to optimize the energy transfer steps.

F. Practical Laser Materials

A myriad of issues impact the effectiveness of a laser material. The issues range from the laser parameters to the thermal-optical-mechanical factors to the raw materials costs and the ease of fabrication. A listing of some viable solid-state laser materials appears in Table III. Nd : YAG is by far the most widely used material. It offers high gain and has a long storage time of 240 μsec. The R_T value, a measure of the material's resistance to thermal stress-induced fracture, shows that YAG is a strong crystal. Nd : YLF is mechanically weaker than YAG (low R_T value) because it is a fluoride rather than an oxide. The main advantages of Nd : YLF are that it generates significantly weaker thermal lensing and that it stores energy about twice as long. The main advantage of Nd : glass is that it can be fabricated in large sizes with excellent optical quality. By contrast, the size of crystals is usually much more limited. The sensitization of Nd^{3+} by Cr^{3+}, as has been accomplished for the GSGG host, results in a material that gives flash-lamp-pumped efficiencies that are about twice as large as can be obtained for Nd : YAG.

While Nd^{3+} is probably the most important laser ion, the Ti^{3+}, Cr^{3+}, Ho^{3+}, and Er^{3+} ions are also useful dopants for laser materials (see Table III). The Ti : sapphire and alexandrite crystals allow for broadly tunable output from the laser, while Ho^{3+} and Er^{3+} are capable of generating infrared light.

III. Solid-State Laser Architectures

The many different laser materials described in the previous section are complemented by a similarly large variety of oscillator and amplifier configurations. On one end of the extreme are

TABLE III. Properties of Some Common Laser Materials

Name	Material	Laser wavelength, λ (μm)	Upper level lifetime, τ (μsec)	Thermal stress resistance, R_T ($W/m^{1/2}$)	Type of pumping[a]
Nd : YAG	$Y_3Al_5O_{12}:Nd^{3+}$	1.064	240	1100	FL, DL
Nd : YLF	$LiYF_4:Nd^{3+}$	1.047, 1.053	480	140	FL, DL
LG-750	Phosphate glass : Nd^{3+}	1.054	350	70	FL
Cr, Nd : GSGG	$Gd_3Sc_2Ga_3O_{12}$: Cr^{3+}, Nd^{3+}	1.061	250	660	FL
Ti : sapphire	$Al_2O_3:Ti^{3+}$	0.66–1.2	3.2	3400	ArL, D-YAG
Alexandrite	$BeAl_2O_4:Cr^{3+}$	0.70–0.82	250	2350	FL
Cr, Tm, Ho : YAG	$Y_3Al_5O_{12}:Cr^{3+}$ Tm^{3+}, Ho^{3+}	2.1	8000	1100	FL
Er : glass	Er^{3+}-doped silicate	1.54	10,000	200	FL

[a] FL, flash lamps; DL, diode laser; ArL, argon ion laser; D-YAG, double neodymium YAG laser.

the minilasers, which can be about the size of a sugar cube and deliver microwatts of power. On the other end of the scale is the Nova laser at the Lawrence Livermore National Laboratory with a light output pulse that delivers terrawatts of peak power, more than the total power consumption of the entire United States at any one instant (see Fig. 25). Solid-state lasers are used in a large variety of applications, and the following examples are only an indication of the possibilities. The smallest lasers are used for memory repair in integrated circuits and for a multitude of alignment tasks. As the power of the laser increases, applications such as ranging and wind velocity measurements become important. Somewhat larger lasers enable activities involving marking medical, and military applications. Some of the most powerful systems are designed for cutting, drilling, and welding at high rates of throughput. A modern automotive production line now includes many robot-controlled solid-state lasers. The largest lasers are quite unique and serve special research purposes. On the top end of the list is the fusion driver Nova, which, as the name suggests, generates enough energy and power to initiate the same process of thermonuclear fusion which powers the stars.

Regardless of the size of the laser, one always has to start out with an active medium which is pumped by either some lamp or another laser. This creates an inversion which is then extracted by amplification of a signal or spontaneous emission. This process takes place in a resonator cavity which consists of two or more mirrors and which may contain optical switches as well. Such an assembly is referred to as an oscillator, and the basic processes are discussed by W. T. Silfvast elsewhere in this encyclopedia. There are a multitude of ways to arrange the optical switches in a cavity to change the temporal format of the laser output; several of these will be discussed in this section. One significant difference between solid-state lasers and other types is that they are storage lasers. The word *storage* refers to the fat that the typical fluorescent lifetime of an inversion is very much longer (several microseconds to milliseconds) than the time it takes for the lasing process to extract the inversion (microseconds to nanoseconds). Hence, as the active medium is excited by the pump, the inversion can be accumulated over time (it can be stored) and, by use of an electro-optic switch, can be extracted at a chosen instant. To get increased amounts of power or energy one can, up to a point, make larger oscillators. Eventually, however, one has to build external amplifiers to further increase the output of a system. We will discuss amplification toward the end of this section.

A. Methods of Pumping

1. Flash Lamp Pumping

There are three methods with which an inversion can be created in a solid state laser. The cheapest and most common method uses flash lamps (Fig. 16). A flash lamp essentially consists of a fused silica tube of suitable diameter and length with an electrode at each end. Once triggered with a short high-voltage spike, a plasma discharge occurs between the electrodes and converts the supplied electrical power with high efficiency to power radiated as light in the infrared, visible, and ultraviolet. Some of this light is absorbed by the active ion with which the host medium is doped and, by virtue of its energy levels and decay dynamics, an inversion is created. Pulsed lasers operated in a storage-type mode use different kinds of flash lamps than continuous wave (CW) or quasi-CW systems (pulse duration is long compared to the fluorescent lifetime of the laser ion). The flash lamp used for a CW Nd : YAG laser is filled with several atmospheres of Kr gas. In this case the plasma radiates around 800 nm, which is a wavelength readily absorbed by the neodymium ion. If one wants to pump a pulsed laser, the gas of choice tends to be Xe. In that case the electrical pulse applied to the lamp is on the order of or shorter than the lifetime of the upper laser level. The energy delivered to the lamp electrodes can be in the range of many kilojoules in a pulse-width of several hundred microseconds. The plasma radiation pumping the laser is approximately described with a blackbody spectrum which extends from the ultraviolet to the infrared spectral regions. As a result, only a small fraction of it is actually absorbed by the active medium. Nevertheless, the peak power densities possible with such pulsed Xe flash lamps are sufficiently intense that high-power pulsed lasers can be constructed in this way. Excessive loading of the flash lamp will eventually result in explosive failure of the component.

2. Diode Pumping

The pumping of small solid-state lasers with laser diodes has attracted great interest within the last few years. This method allows for very

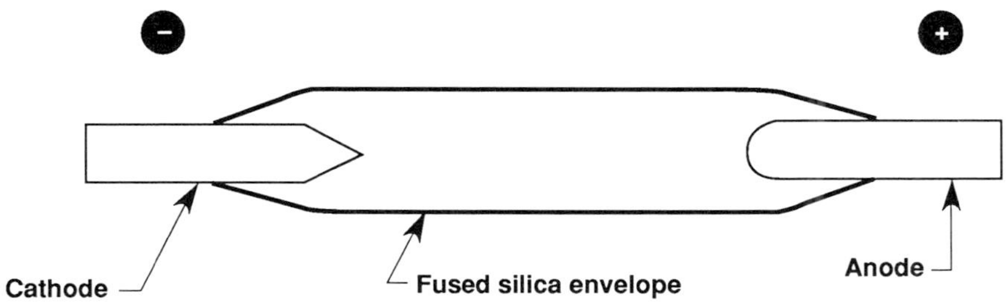

FIG. 16. The basic elements of a flash lamp. The envelope is typically made from fused silica and the electrodes from a tungsten alloy. The shape of the cathode helps to increase lamp life.

efficient solid-state lasers, because the diode lasers themselves convert electrical power to radiated power very efficiently (see the article "Semiconductor Injection Lasers" in this encyclopedia), and the light output by the diode laser can be accurately tuned to the absorption line of the active medium of the solid-state laser. Although diode pumping is at present far more expensive than flash lamp pumping, it is the method of choice where efficiency is a premium, as is the case for most military applications. Diode-pumped lasers are, nevertheless, likely to become cheaper in the future through increased volume of production. Since laser diodes are limited by their peak power, the total energy output necessarily decreases with a shorter pump pulse duration. The single shot intensity of a two-dimensional diode array is on the order of several kilowatts per square centimeter. As a consequence, laser ions with a long fluorescent lifetime are easier to diode pump efficiency than ions with a short fluorescent lifetime. Presently, the most common device involves the use of GaAs diode lasers to pump the Nd^{3+} absorption band near 810 nm in various hosts.

3. Laser Pumping

It is also possible (and the diode pumping mentioned above is a case in point), to pump a laser with another laser. With the exception of diode pumping, this is mostly done for scientific applications. A typical example is the pumping of Ti:sapphire with frequency-doubled Nd:YAG lasers. Here, the upper level lifetime of Ti:sapphire (3.2 μsec) is too short to easily apply conventional flash lamp pumping techniques, whereas the wavelength of frequency-doubled Nd:YAG ideally matches the absorption band of Ti:sapphire and has a suitably short pulsewidth. Furthermore, when compared to flash lamp pumping, a pump laser can deliver considerably higher fluence at the absorption line of the active ion than flash lamps.

A quantity known as the saturation fluence F is given by

$$F = h\nu/\sigma \tag{1}$$

and is an important characteristic parameter for various aspects of laser behavior. In Eq. (1), h is Planck's constant, ν is the frequency of the light, σ is, in this example, the absorption cross section of the active ion. This last item is the enabling factor in so-called "bleach-pumped" solid-state lasers. As a specific example, an alexandrite laser pulse may be used to pump the 745 nm absorption line of Nd^{3+} in Y_2SiO_5 with a sufficient fluence to put nearly all of the Nd^{3+} ions present in the host crystal into the upper laser level. With essentially no Nd^{3+} ions left in the ground state, the active medium becomes transparent to further pump radiation, hence the name bleach pumping. This method of pumping makes it possible to achieve efficient laser action on transitions on which the active ion would otherwise not lase due to ground state absorption. Although a new development, the number of useful wavelengths for solid-state lasers is greatly extended by this method, and outputs of 0.5 J at several hertz repetition rates have been demonstrated on transitions which could not be lased at such output levels with conventional flash lamp pumping methods.

B. Optical Switches

The aligned mirrors that surround the active medium and permit repeated passes of laser light through the inversion form the resonator cavity. The basic resonator physics is described elsewhere in this encyclopedia (see "Lasers"). Aside from the active medium one can also place a variety of electro-optic switches inside the cavity, including Pockels cells, acousto-optic switches, and saturable dyes. It is these switches which contribute to the great versatility of solid-state lasers and the different output pulse formats that they can generate.

1. Pockels Cell

Figure 17 explains the basic functioning of a very commonly used device known as the Pockels cell. Such a cell often consists of an electrooptic crystal called KD*P (deuterated potassium dihydrogen phosphate) fitted with electrodes to create an electric field within the crystal. The presence of a strong electric field (typically about 3 kV) changes the refractive index of the KD*P crystal for a particular direction of polarization. Since voltages can be switched rapidly, one can also abruptly switch the polarizing properties of the KD*P crystal. For the case of a setup with zero voltage applied to the crystal, the incident beam with vertical polarization passes through the KD*P switch unaffected; this beam will also pass through an appropriately oriented polarizer on the exit side of the crystal. With a voltage applied, however, the KD*P crystal will rotate the direction of polarization of the incident beam by 90°, so that the transmitted beam will now reflect off the polarizer (see Fig. 17). Although the intrinsic response time of the crystal is in the range of tens of femtoseconds, practical rise and fall times are limited by the circuitry to switching times on the order of nanoseconds. Hence a Pockels cell can be used as a very fast polarization switch with a good degree of synchronization between the applied high-voltage pulse and the switched light beam. A switching contrast of 1000:1 with a single Pockels cell and good polarizers is readily achievable.

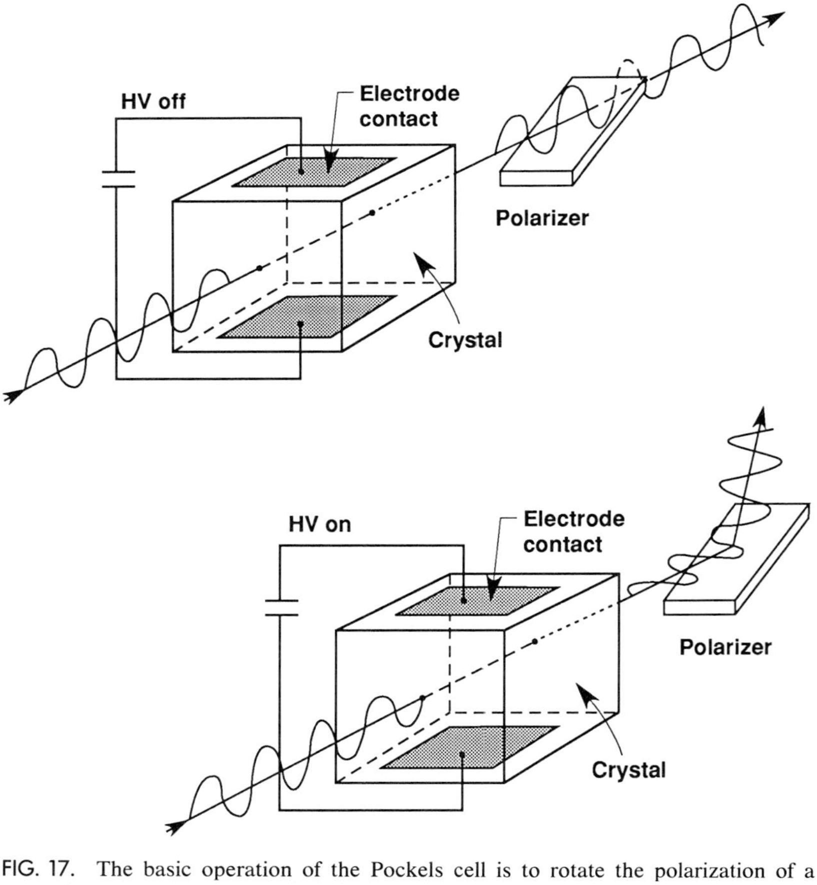

FIG. 17. The basic operation of the Pockels cell is to rotate the polarization of a transmitted beam on application of a high-voltage signal. In conjunction with one or two polarizers, Pockels cells are widely used inside of resonator cavities as Q-switches or cavity dumpers and outside of resonators as fast switchout systems.

2. Acousto-Optic Switch

Another common switch, based on the acousto-optic effect, is sketched in Fig. 18. A piezoelectric transducer driven by a radio-frequency (typically tens of megahertz), low-voltage signal launches an acoustic wave sets up a sinusoidal refractive index grating in accordance with the photoelastic effect. This refractive index grating then scatters the incident beam out of its original direction with good efficiency, introducing a corresponding loss in the transmitted beam. There are two typical applications of this technique. For a traveling acoustic wave of a given duration, the transmitted beam is switched off while the acoustic wave is present in the beam aperture. Turn-on and turn-off speeds are equal to the time it takes the leading or falling edge of the radio-frequency (RF) train to travel across the beam diameter (a few microseconds for typical intracavity applications). For the case of Q-switching, it is important that the acoustic wave be terminated without reflection from the surface of the quartz block in order to achieve fast switching speeds, (see Section III, C, 3). In comparing this technique to switching an optical beam with a Pockels cell, one finds that the Pockels cell method is much faster and provides better contrast but requires considerably higher voltages and also has more severe limits with respect to the maximum repetition rate that can be obtained.

The other typical application of acousto-optic switching is based on generating a standing (or stationary) wave in a fused silica block which is explicitly configured to form a resonant cavity for the acoustic wave. The resonant acoustic wave will then create a refractive index grating which oscillates at twice the RF drive frequency, thus periodically scattering the beam from its original direction. An acousto-optic device utilized this way inside of a laser cavity is called a mode-locker (see Section III, C, 5).

3. Saturable Absorber

The last switching method to be discussed involves the use of a saturable absorber. The optical beam enters a cell which contains a material that absorbs at the wavelength of the incident light pulse. If the beam enters above several saturation fluences for the absorption transition [see Eq. (1)], the beginning of the pulse will bleach through the cell, making it transparent for the rest of the pulse. Hence such a saturable absorber solution acts more like an intensity

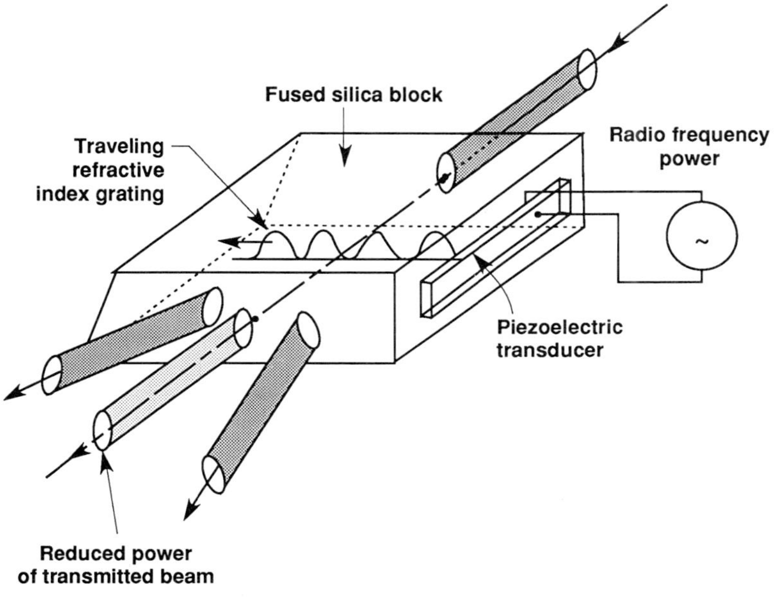

FIG. 18. The basic operation of an acousto-optic device is to reduce the intensity of a transmitted beam by diffraction from a refractive index grating which is generated, via the photoelastic effect, by the RF power supplied to the transducer. The device is depicted is used for Q-switching and cavity dumping. If configured as a resonator for the acoustic wave, it serves as a mode-locker.

threshold filter than an actual switch. The cell can contain a solution of an appropriate dye, or it can be a crystal containing suitable F-centers. Switching light by this method is very popular as a simple and cheap Q-switching and mode-locking technique in the laboratory. But the statistics of the bleach process, the lack of timing control, and the chemical stability of the dyes make it unsuited for lasers which either need to be switched precisely and with good repeatability or need to be maintenance free.

C. Modes of Operation

The different switches may be configured in various ways in the resonator cavity such that many modes of operating a solid-state laser become possible. A wide variety of output pulse durations and formats can be achieved, ranging in duration from picoseconds to a continuous mode of operation, although some pulse durations are easier to produce than others. The availability of different pulse durations, in conjunction with variable output energies and wavelengths, contributes to the versatility of solid-state lasers. Other intracavity elements include wavelength-tuning or wavelength-narrowing devices such as prisms, birefringent tuners and etalons, and apertures to control the transverse mode behavior. In addition, frequency converters outside the resonator cavity can double the optical frequency of output pulses having sufficient peak power. For example, a large fraction of the output of a 1.06-μm Nd^{3+} laser may be shifted to the visible wavelength of 0.53 μm. Medical application provide an example of the diversity of the wavelength and pulse duration requirements that arise. For example, a CW output may be used at one particular wavelength to cut tissue and at another wavelength to coagulate blood, while long pulses may be used to break apart kidney stones and short pulses to spot-weld loose retinas in the eye.

1. CW Operation

The simplest mode of operating a laser is with no switches in the cavity, so that the resonator only contains the active medium. For a continuous pump, the laser operates in a CW mode. If no transverse or longitudinal mode control is implemented, the output will fluctuate due to the complex ways in which the longitudinal and transverse modes beat and couple to each other via the active medium. Other output fluctuations will come from fluctuations in the power supply. A laser with full mode control will operate only on a single longitudinal and transverse mode. After stabilizing the power supply, such lasers can have output fluctuations of less than 1%. Continuous wave lasers have many applications, depending on the degree to which they are stabilized and their output power. These range from small alignment lasers (milliwatt range) to medical lasers used for surgery (watt range) to lasers used for cutting steel (kW range).

2. Free Running

The term *free running* is generally used to describe a laser which runs CW for times that are long compared to the storage time of the laser, which is typically greater than several milliseconds. Figure 19 shows the pump pulse, the gain and loss in the active medium, and the output power. As the active medium is pumped sufficiently to exceed threshold, lasing starts with a few output spikes after which it settles down to the CW output level. The output of lasers is often temporally shaped by tailoring the current pulse to the flash lamps. The most frequent application of such lasers is for materials working, industrial drilling, and welding applications.

3. Q-Switching

This mode of operation requires the addition of a Pockels cell and a polarizer into the resonator as sketched in Fig. 17. Figure 20 shows the

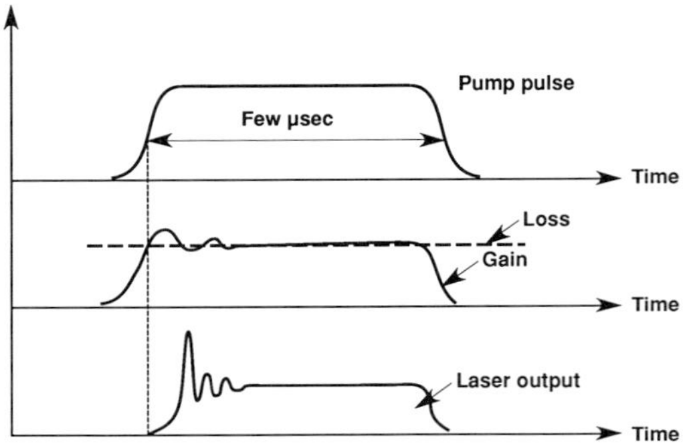

FIG. 19. Timing diagram for a free-running, pulsed oscillator. Depending on how fast the pump pulse causes the gain to rise above the loss initially, the gain and laser output will react with overshoots which will damp out. The loss level includes that of the active medium and the transmission of the resonator mirror, through which the laser light exits the resonator cavity. IN CW and quasi-CW lasers the steady-state gain equals the loss, and the excess pump power is converted to laser output.

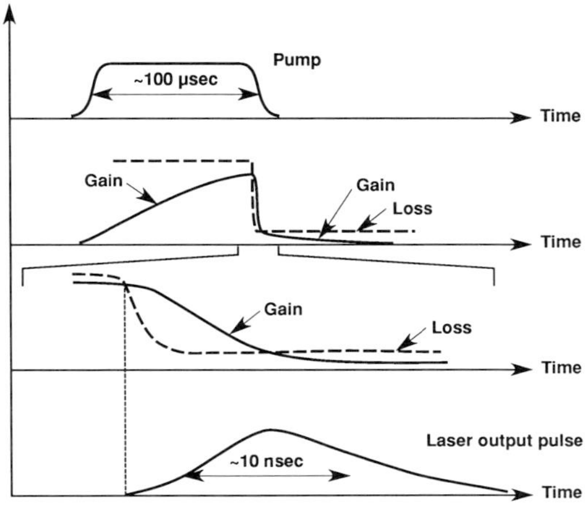

FIG. 20. Timing diagram for a Q-switched oscillator. Initially, the Pockels cell causes a high loss in the cavity so that lasing is inhibited and the pump power is integrated as inversion in the upper laser level. When the pump pulse is over, the Pockels cell loss is switched off, lowering the loss in the resonator cavity to a value corresponding again to the transmission of the mirror through which the laser light leaves the cavity. The laser pulse will build up rapidly (note the much expanded time scale) and reach the peak at the time where the gain is equal to the loss.

timing sequence of the pump pulse from the flash lamp, the impact of the Pockels cell voltage on the transmission of the resonator cavity, and the laser output. At first the Pockels cell blocks the light from traveling back and forth between the mirrors. As the active medium is pumped with flash lamp light, the inversion in the upper laser level accumulates, thereby storing the inversion until the pump pulse is nearly over. Note that far larger inversions are built up in this way than are possible for the free-running case. Once the peak inversion density is reached, the Pockels cell is switched to transmission. The net gain in the resonator cavity suddenly becomes very high so that the energy of the output pulse rapidly builds up and the inversion is extracted efficiently. Note that the pulse duration depends on the amount of inversion just before switching and that the generation of short pulses requires that a large initial inversion be stored. Typical Q-switched oscillators produce 100-mJ pulses in tens of nanoseconds.

4. Cavity Dumping

A mode of operation closely related to Q-switching is cavity dumping. The essential architecture is the same as that for Q-switching; the timing diagram is given in Fig. 21. The first phase of cavity-dumped operation is similar to that of Q-switching in that energy is stored. Both of the resonator mirrors are selected to be 100% reflective, such that the amplified light remains trapped within the cavity. As the peak intracavity intensity is reached, the Pockels cell rapidly switches the cavity transmission off again. This ejects the light circulating in the cavity by reflection off the polarizer in a pulse whose duration is equal to the two cavity passes. This technique is used to produce pulses of a few nanoseconds duration, since the pulsewidth now depends on the length of the resonator cavity and not on the amount of inversion stored before switching. The peak power output is significantly limited in this method since the light circulating inside the resonator can become intense enough to destroy critical components of the laser.

An architecture very closely related to the cavity-dumped oscillator is the regenerative amplifier. The principle difference is that the laser oscillation in a regenerative amplifier does not build up from spontaneous emission but is initiated by a signal injected into the resonator from the outside as the Pockels cell is switched to transmission. This injected signal is then trapped in the cavity and amplified until it has reached maximum intensity, at which point it is ejected (dumped) from the cavity.

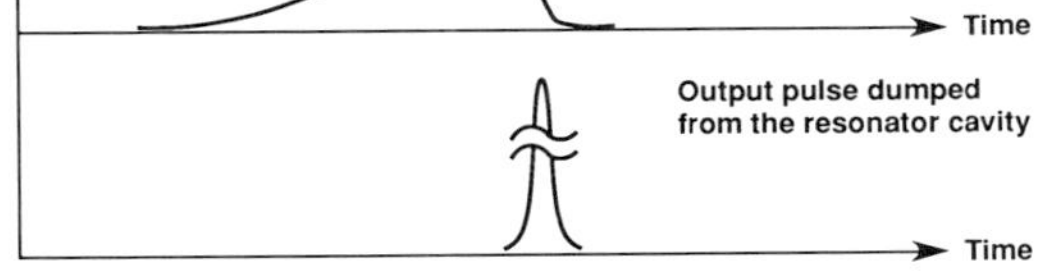

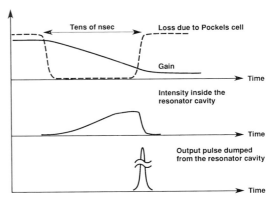

FIG. 21. In the pump phase, the timing diagram for the cavity-dumped case is identical to the Q-switched case. After switching the Pockels cells to enable lasing, the cavity loss now is very small since, for a cavity-dumped architecture, the reflectivity of both resonator mirrors is 100%. Once the intensity in the cavity has reached the maximum value, the Pockels cell is again switched and ejects the intracavity intensity from the laser in a pulse equal to the round-trip time of the resonator cavity.

5. Mode-Locking

By inserting an acousto-optic mode-locker in the cavity it is possible to produce very short pulses in an oscillator. With a mode-locker in the cavity and the transverse modes suitably constrained, the oscillator can be operated quasi-CW to produce a steady stream of short pulses. It is also possible to add a Pockels cell and a polarizer to produce an output which has the pulse envelope of a Q-switched pulse but which is composed of individual short pulses from the mode-locking process. External to the cavity one can then pick out a single pulse by placing an additional Pockels cell between two polarizers and applying a short high-voltage pulse at just the instant when the desired pulse is at the Pockels cell. Such an arrangement is commonly called a *single-pulse switchout*. This is a standard way to produce individual pulses with durations from 100 psec to 1 nsec and energies on the order of 100 μJ. [*See* MODE-LOCKING OF LASERS.]

D. Types of Oscillators

In this section representative examples of frequently used solid-state lasers are described, starting with the smallest lasers and proceeding to lasers of increasing power and energy. These lasers are practical embodiments of the pumping and operating schemes described above.

1. Minilasers

Figure 22 is a sketch of a generic diode-pumped minilaser. The diode or array of diodes is focused with suitable optics through one of the resonator mirrors into the active medium (typically Nd:YAG). This "end-pumping" method allows the precise matching of the pumping volume to the lasing volume of the lowest order transverse mode, thereby contributing to the good efficiency of minilasers. Output powers are typically in the milliwatt range. The mode of operation ranges from CW to repetitively Q-switched (requiring the addition of a small Pockels cell to the resonator cavity). These lasers offer a stability of a few percent and are extremely rugged; the entire device fits comfortably in the palm of the hand.

2. Watt/Joule Level Laser

This heading encompasses lasers with outputs in the range of a few watts, and with pulsed energies of 0.1 to 1 J. Continuous wave systems as well as pulsed systems are characterized by a great variety of resonator configurations and make up the majority of solid-state lasers sold today. These lasers typically contain a rod with a diameter on the order of 6 mm and a length of 10 cm, which is pumped with one or two flash lamps. The resonator cavity is generally 30 cm to 1.5 cm long, depending on whether there is a mode-locker, a Pockels cell, or another combination of switches. The cavity may be made from low thermal expansion materials for more demanding applications. The power supply operates in the kilowatt range and typically is a floor unit occupying a few cubic feet of space. A photograph of a representative 200-W system appears in Fig. 23. Various CW versions are used for medical applications, such as cutting tissue and coagulating blood, and for marking and scribing in industrial settings. The CW mode-locked laser is an important component of many ultrafast pulse setups. Free-running, pulsed, and Q-switched systems have other uses

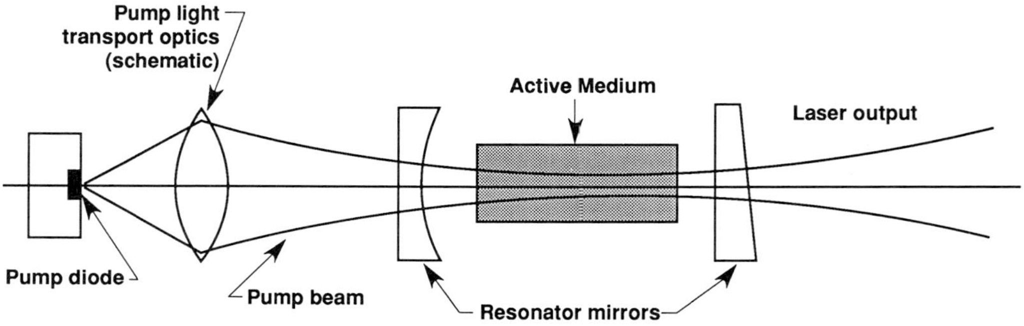

FIG. 22. The essential elements of a diode-pumped minilaser as explained in the text. In practice, the pump light transport optics is a sophisticated array of lenses to change the spatial characteristics of the diode output to those optimally suited to pump the minilaser.

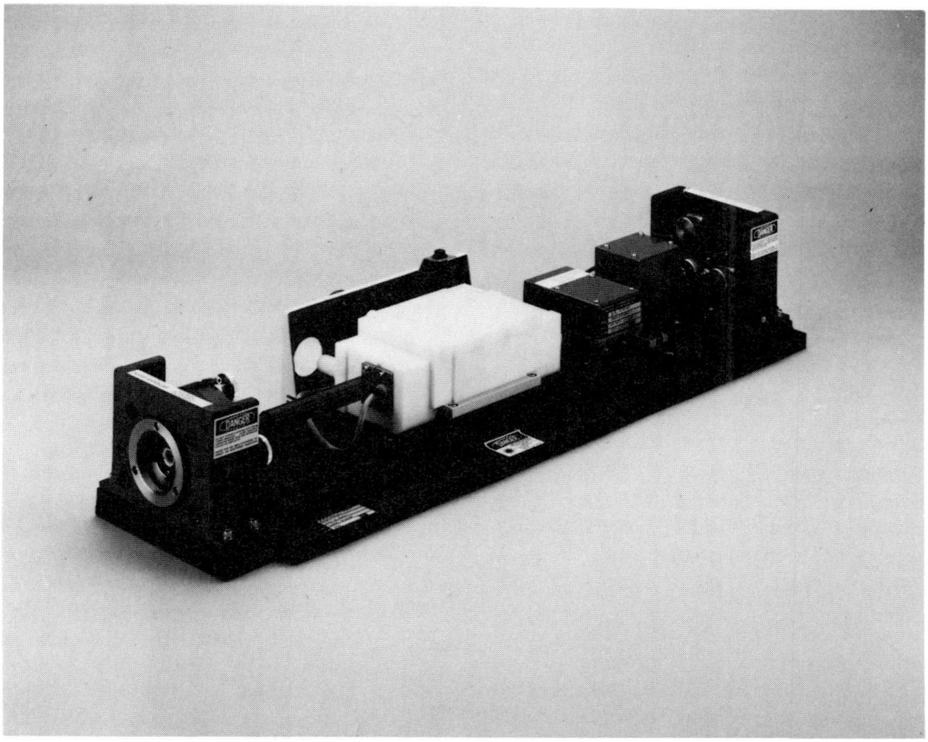

FIG. 23. A 250-W Nd : YAG laser used in the semiconductor industry. (Courtesy of Quantronix Corp.)

in the medical field (e.g., breaking up kidney stones without intrusive surgery). Industrial applications include semiconductor processing and working with thin metal films. Many lasers for scientific applications operate in this range as well. Commercial laser companies offer a variety of resonators and modes of operation for the scientific market, and further variations can be seen in the laboratory.

3. Materials Working Lasers

These lasers operate mostly in the CW or free-running pulsed mode and deliver output powers up to and exceeding 1 kW. They are configured as oscillators but often have two or three laser rods in the resonator cavity. The resonator cavity is still approximately 1 m long, although the power supply may be significantly larger. Furthermore, these lasers, as well as some of the smaller lasers described above, often incorporate sophisticated beam delivery systems which allow the use of one central laser system on several work stations. Larger systems are used for demanding welding and drilling application (e.g., components for jet engines).

A more recent development is the slab laser (Fig. 24). As opposed to the rod-shaped active media typically used in conventional solid-state lasers, the active medium of slab lasers is in the form of a thin plate or slab. The beam enters and exits through tilted surfaces and zigzags through the active medium in such a way that the optical distortions, which a beam experiences by passing through the material, can largely be eliminated. A slab laser can generate increased output power by employing a larger volume of the active medium, and the beam that is delivered can be brought to a tighter focus. Slab lasers involve a number of complex technological issues but have experienced a large development effort in recent years. A slab laser with 1-kW output has been demonstrated by General Electric Corporation.

E. Laser Scaling

We have thus far primarily described laser oscillators. To achieve higher energies, amplifica-

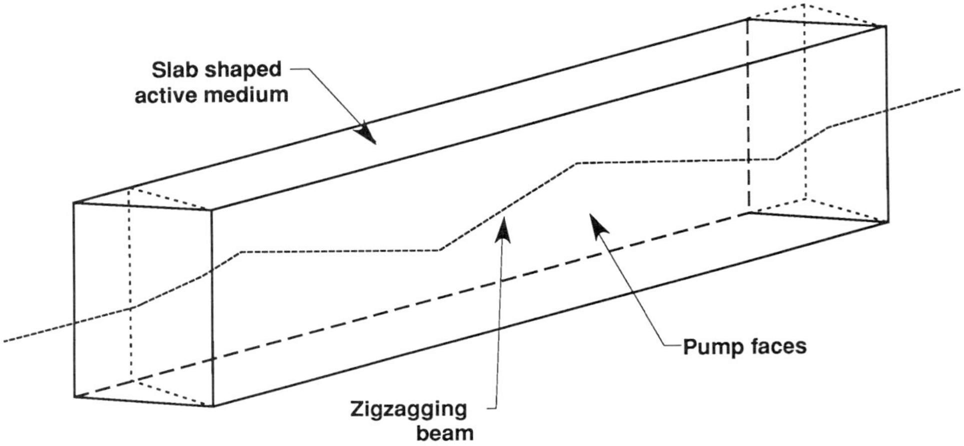

FIG. 24. The basic idea behind a slab laser is to zigzag the beam through the active medium and thus greatly reduce the thermal distortions of the beam. The dotted lines are meant to indicate where perpendicular edges would lie. The actual slab laser has entrance and exit surfaces which are inclined with respect to the incident beam.

tion of the pulse from the oscillator is required. The regenerative amplifier was already mentioned in the section on cavity dumping. In comparison to a single-pass amplifier, the regenerative amplifier is a far more complex setup, although it provides for very efficient extraction of energy from the medium and is favored for short pulse amplifiers in the laboratory. To get to higher energy, further amplification stages are required. One would, of course, like to make the most efficient use of the inversion stored in such an amplifier, while avoiding the potentially destructive consequences of propagating a high peak power pulse through the amplification medium. Consider a pulse making a single pass through an amplifier in which an inversion is stored. The key parameter to describe the amplification process is again the saturation fluence, of Eq. (1), where σ is now the stimulated emission cross section (rather than the absorption cross section, as noted earlier). If the input fluence to the amplifier remains small compared to the saturation fluence of the transition (called the small signal gain regime), the amplification G proceeds in an exponential manner according to:

$$G = \exp(N_i \sigma\, x) \tag{2}$$

where N_i is the inversion density and x is the pathlength in the amplifier. In this regime the amplification factor G is high but the extraction of the inversion is consequently low, since saturation of the inversion does not occur. The other extreme is that the input fluence is much larger than the saturation fluence. In this case extraction of the inversion will approach 100%, and the energy stored in the amplifier is simply added to the energy in the input beam. Generally, the best place to operate is in between the two extremes, where there is a desirable degree of signal amplification at an acceptable extraction efficiency of the energy originally stored in the amplifier. The basic equation which describes this amplification process is the Frantz–Nodvik equation.

There are a variety of effects that limit the energy which may be generated in a large-scale amplifier chain. First, the amplifier medium cannot be made arbitrarily large since it will lose its storage capability. Spontaneous emission, generated by fluorescence decay of the inverted ion population inside the amplifier, can be trapped inside a large amplifier module and deplete the inversion before the extraction beam arrives. This process is called *parasitic oscillation*. Second, as the peak power in the amplified pulse increases its intensity, it becomes large enough that the electric field of the amplified light wave itself changes the refractive index of the medium through which it travels. This can induce a process called *self-focusing*, where the amplified beam destroys the active medium by creating tracks and bubbles inside the amplifier. Finally, amplifier surfaces and other optics are often covered with dielectric coatings to increase, or decrease, their reflectivities. These coatings can be destroyed by a light pulse which has too high a peak power, often at power levels below that at which self-focusing sets in. The resistance of

FIG. 25. Nova, the biggest laser in existence. Note the people and automobile shown for scale.

such coatings to this effect is described by a *damage threshold* which characterizes the fluence the coating can withstand at a given pulse duration.

As the ultimate example of a laser which can only be built if all of these types of processes are well understood, Fig. 25 shows the Nova laser at the Lawrence Livermore National Laboratory. It has delivered pulses with 120,000 J of energy in durations of several nanoseconds.

IV. Future Directions

There are three clear areas where solid-state laser architectures will advance significantly in the next few years. The first is to take diode-pumped lasers from the minilaser scale to the level of tens of watts. This requires development of high-average power, two-dimensional diode arrays, which is now well underway. The second is to utilize slab laser technology to operate lasers at the 1–10 J/pulse level at repetition rates of about Hz. Finally, large fusion lasers may ultimately operate at several hertz, and produce average output powers in the megawatt regime.

The new laser materials that are developed will be deployed in systems to generate new wavelengths, operate more efficiently, be produced at lower cost, and have optical properties that are tailored to meet specific technical objectives. Solid-state lasers that operate efficiently in the ultraviolet-blue region are likely to be developed. Many new transition metal lasers having optical properties that are useful may be discovered in the next decade. One change that may occur will involve the advent of tailoring some types of laser materials for a specific application. (This has already occurred in the case of Nd-doped glass for fusion lasers.) This process of designing, rather than discovering, laser materials will be enhanced by a better understanding of the physics and chemistry of solid-state media.

Acknowledgment

This research was performed under the auspices of the Division of Materials Sciences of the Office of Basic Energy Sciences, U.S. Department of Energy, and the Lawrence Livermore National Laboratory under Contract No. W-7405-ENG-48.

Bibliography

Adair, R., Chase, L. L., and Payne, S. A. (1989). Nonlinear refractive index of optical crystals, *Phys. Rev. B*. **39,** 337.

Albrecht, G. F. (1990). Average power slab lasers with garnet crystals as the active medium, *in* "YAG and Other Garnet Lasers" (De Shazer, ed.). Wiley, New York.

Ballhausen, C. J. (1962). "The Theory of Transition Metal Ions." McGraw-Hill, New York.

Belforte, D., and Levitt, M. (1989). "The Industrial Laser Annual Handbook." PennWell, Tulsa, Oklahoma.

Berger, J., Welch, D. F., Scifres, D. R., Streifer, W., and Cross, P. S. (1987). High power, high efficiency Nd : YAG laser end pumped by a laser diode array, *Appl. Phys. Lett.* **51,** 1212.

Brown, D. C. (1981). "High Peak Power Nd : Glass Laser Systems," Springer Series in Optical Sciences, Vol. 25, Springer-Verlag, New York.

Dieke, G. M. (1968). "Spectra and Energy Levels of Rare Earth Ions in Crystals." Wiley (Interscience), New York.

Izumitani, T. S. (1986). "Optical Glass." American Institute of Physics, New York.

Kaminskii, A. A. (1981). "Laser Crystals." Springer-Verlag, New York.

Koechner, W. (1988). "Solid State Laser Engineering," Springer Series in Optical Sciences, Vol. 1. Springer-Verlag, New York.

Krupke, W. F., Shinn, M. D. Marion, J. E., Caird, J. A., and Stokowski, S. E. (1986). Spectroscopic, optical and thermo-mechanical properties of neodymium- and chromium-doped gadolinium scandium gallium garnet, *J. Opt. Soc. Am. B* **3,** 102.

Moulton, P. F. (1986). Spectroscopic and laser characteristics of Ti : Al_2O_3, *J. Opt. Soc. Am. B* **3,** 4.

Payne, S. A., Chase, L. L., Newkirk, H. W., Smith, L. K., and Krupke, W. F. (1988). $LiCaAlF_6 : Cr^{3+}$: a promising new solid-state laser material, *IEEE J. Quantum Electron.* **QE-24,** 2243.

Pfaender, H. G., and Schroeder, H. (1983). "Schott Guide to Glass." Van Nostrand Reinhold, New York.

Siegman, A. E. (1986). "Lasers," University Science Books, Mill Valley, California.

Walling, J. C., Heller, D. F., Samelson, H., Harter, D. J. Pete, J. A., and Morris, R. C. (1985). Tunable alexandrite lasers: Development and performance, *IEEE J. Quantum Electron.* **QE-21,** 1568.

Weber, M. J., ed. (1982). "Handbook of Laser Science and Technology." CRC Press, Boca Raton, Florida.

Yariv, A. (1975). "Quantum Electronics." Wiley, New York.

LASERS, TUNABLE DYE

T. F. Johnston, Jr. *Coherent, Inc.*

GLOSSARY

Amplified spontaneous emission (ASE): Background light from dye fluorescence, which in high-gain short-pulse dye lasers limits the achievable gain and must be suppressed between amplifier stages to leave a spectrally pure laser output.

Autocorrelation, background-free: Method of measuring mode-locked laser pulse lengths, in which the pulse train is split into two beams, one of which is delayed, and in which the two beams are focused to overlap in a crystal whose phase-matching conditions permit frequency summing only when one photon is taken from each beam. The summed or doubled power, versus path delay, is proportional to the autocorrelation in time of the pulse with itself and so gives the pulse length, if the functional form of the pulse shape is known.

Brewster's angle: That singular angle of incidence (the angle between the ray direction and the normal to the surface of a dielectric plate of index n) given by $\tan \theta = n$ for which there is 100% transmission (no reflection) of light whose electric field vibrates in the plane of incidence. This low-loss property makes Brewster angle windows and entrance faces very common in intracavity laser optics.

Cavity dumper: Device for coupling single pulses out of the resonator of a mode-locked laser, consisting of an acousto–optic cell situated at a beam focus in the cavity. A transducer bonded to the cell receives a short burst of radiofrequency (rf) energy timed to the pulse, setting up sound waves that diffract the pulse at a slight angle to dump it out of the cavity. This is used both to reduce the pulse repetition rate to a manageable value and increase the energy per pulse.

Chromophore: Series of alternating single and double bonds in a dye molecule (be it linear, branched, or cyclic linkages), which through chemical resonance give rise to laser states, strong visible absorption and color, and delocalized mobile electrons, making the dye molecule a good "antenna" for visible light.

Etalon: Fabry–Perot or parallel-plate interferometer of fixed plate separation (often the coated, parallel sides of a plate of glass), which when tipped at an incidence angle greater than the beam divergence acts in transmission as an intracavity frequency (or longitudinal mode) selecting filter.

Free spectral range (FSR): Frequency spacing between adjacent transmission peaks of a parallel-plate interferometer and, by extension, between orders of other multiply ordered frequency filters.

Jitter: Average residual frequency excursion or linewidth of a single-mode laser, due to residual environmental perturbations of the cavity length.

Mode locking: Formation of a high-peak-power, repetitive train of short-output pulses from a laser of cavity length d by the imposition of constant or "locked" phases for the difference or beat frequencies (nominally $c/2d$) between adjacent longitudinal modes. Here c is the speed of light, and a modulator (mode locker) or saturable absorber placed in the cavity forces the phase locking. The Fourier transform to the time domain of this locked-mode spectrum gives a pulse of period $2d/c$, the round-trip transit time for a circulating pulse in the cavity, and pulse length equal to the inverse of the locked bandwidth.

Modes, longitudinal and transverse: Terms for the discrete frequencies and associated intensity distributions supported by a laser resonator. At a mode frequency, an integral number of wavelengths fits in the path distance of a round trip in the resonator, for then the multiply reflected waves from many transits add up in phase, and oscillation will be fed back there. The integral number of on-axis wavelengths defines the *longitudinal mode* number q, and there are intensity distributions possible peaking off-axis, adding path length, altering the frequency, and producing interference nodes in the two directions transverse to the axis, whose integer numbers m, n label the *transverse mode*. As light waves are transverse electromagnetic waves, by analogy with the designations for modes in microwave cavities, the full designation for a laser cavity mode is TEM_{mnq}, although by convention the q is often suppressed, the lowest-order transverse mode (a single spot of Gaussian intensity profile) being designated the TEM_{00} mode.

Phase matching: Process of adjusting the extraordinary refractive index relative to the ordinary refractive index of a nonlinear crystal either by changing the temperature (temperature-tuned matching) or the direction of propagation of a laser beam relative to the crystal's optic axis (angle-tuned matching), to make the indices of the fundamental beam and its orthogonally polarized harmonic precisely match, within a few parts per million. Then the harmonic frequencies radiated from the microscopic volume elements along the path of the fundamental beam all add up in phase in the forward direction to produce a macroscopic harmonic beam.

Saturation intensity: Intensity producing a sufficiently rapid stimulated transition rate to reduce the level population difference to half its initial value (and thus reduce the absorption or gain on the transition to half its initial value); the scale parameter in saturated absorption or gain saturation.

Singlet and triplet states: Terms referring to the net or total electronic spin of a molecular state, a singlet being a spin of zero, and a triplet a spin of one quantum unit of angular momentum. (In a magnetic field the unity spin can be oriented parallel, antiparallel, or perpendicular to the field, giving rise to the term "triplet.") The distinction is important in dyes that have a singlet ground state, because the optical selection rules forbid strong transitions where the spin changes (spin is conserved), making the excited triplet state metastable and troublesome in designing dye lasers.

Spatial hole burning: Gain saturation by a single-frequency standing wave field proceeds primarily locally at the antinodes of the standing wave, reducing the gain there or "burning spatial holes," a process of importance in mode selection in single-frequency lasers.

Spectral condensation: Efficient spectral narrowing that occurs when a wavelength-selective filter is added to a dye laser cavity; the oscillating linewidth may be reduced many orders of magnitude, while the output power or energy is reduced typically by less than half.

Synchronous pumping: Method of mode-locking a laser (here the dye laser) by gain modulation or repetitive pulsed pumping, where the round-trip transit time in the cavity of the pumped laser is adjusted to be precisely equal to (synchronous with) the period of a mode-locked pumping laser (here, usually an argon laser or doubled Nd : YAG laser).

Wave number: The number $1/\lambda$ of wavelengths in a centimeter (units of cm^{-1}), a convenient spectroscopic unit of frequency because the free spectral range of an interferometer of plate spacing t (cm) is just $1/2t$ (cm^{-1}). To convert the wave number of a photon to its energy in joules, multiply by $hc = 1.99 \times 10^{-23}$ (h is Planck's constant, c the speed of light).

Dye lasers are the light energy convertors of the scientific world, converting input pump light from flashlamps or fixed-wavelength pump lasers into tunable-output wavelengths, broad pumping bandwidths into narrow-linewidth outputs, and short pumping pulses into ultrashort-output pulses. To make these conversions they use optically excited molecular antennas—the conjugated double bonds of the strongly absorbing and fluorescing organic substances commonly called dyes, the same substances that color clothes, photographic emulsions, and Easter eggs. Among the widely variable and highly desirable properties of the output beams from dye lasers are the broadest range of wavelengths from any laser (ultraviolet to infrared), the narrowest linewidths of common spectroscopic sources (10^2 Hz at center frequencies near 10^{15} Hz), and the shortest electrical pulses directly generated in a human-made device (10^{-14} sec).

I. Introduction

A. Dye Laser Types

Laser action in dyes takes place between the broad, diffuse energy bands characteristic of complex molecules in condensed liquid solvents. The tunability of the dye laser—the ability to smoothly vary the output wavelength over a broad range, much as the receiving wavelength of a radio may be continuously tuned—is a result of these broadened electronic states. A large number of organic dyes exist (more than 200 are actively in use as laser dyes), each fluorescing in a specific wavelength region, giving overlapping tuning ranges from which the laser's broad overall spectral coverage is constructed. The tunability of the dye laser is the basic attribute from which its other desirable properties are derived.

The diffuseness of the energy bands is evidence of the short lifetimes of the laser states, due both to the strongly allowed nature of the laser electronic transition and to the frequent collisions of each dye molecule with its neighbors. To invert such states takes large pumping rates, so far only achieved by optical means, with input light from a high-intensity flashlamp or a second, pumping laser. Pump lasers occur most commonly in scientific applications (the focus of this article), since with them the widest range of dye laser output properties are provided; flashlamps were important in the development of the dye laser and are still the most economical pump sources. [*See* LASERS.]

The three main branches of the family of scientific dye lasers are distinguished by the types of their pump sources and by the applications appropriate to their resultant outputs. Pulsed dye lasers take advantage of the active laser medium being a liquid, to scale to large pumped volumes readily cooled by flowing the dye. From pulsed pump laser inputs, they produce high-output energies per pulse, typically tens of millijoules in a 10-nsec pulse, in a beam a fraction of a centimeter across. The resultant peak intensities, exceeding a megawatt per square centimeter, are large enough that the nonlinear terms may dominate in the response function of a dielectric sample placed in the beam. The intense electric field time modulates the index of refraction of the sample, to produce new light frequencies or other effects in the interaction revealing the structure of matter, and making up the body of applications termed nonlinear optics. [*See* NONLINEAR OPTICAL PROCESSES.]

Continuous-wave (cw) dye lasers, pumped by continuous output lasers, take advantage of the efficient spectral narrowing that occurs in a dye laser when a dispersive element is added to the feedback cavity for wavelength control. In the first observation of this effect, a diffraction grating was substituted for an end mirror in an early pulsed dye laser. The term "spectral condensation" was coined to describe the result, that the bandwidth of the output beam shrank to 1% of the original bandwidth, while retaining 70% of the original output energy. The spectral filters for today's cw dye lasers are designed to select and allow oscillation only on a single mode of the dye laser cavity. The narrowness of the spectrum of output frequencies is then determined by how stable is the frequency of that cavity mode, and frequency stabilization servos are employed to produce condensation factors smaller than 10^{-8}. These output bandwidths are less than 10^{-3} of the Doppler broadening width of a typical spectral line in a gas. When incident on a gaseous sample, this light will produce a velocity-selected, "saturated" absorption—an absorption only by those atoms with the proper velocity component to be Doppler-shifted into resonance with the frequency of the laser beam. The selected absorption can be read with a second, probe laser beam. By looking inside the Doppler width, spectral resolutions are reached that are finer by factors of 10^{-1} to 10^{-3} than was possible before, making up the body of applications termed high-resolution laser spectroscopy.

Mode-locked dye lasers take advantage of the broad spectrum over which the dye molecules can lase, to assemble a short pulse of light from oscillations at many dye cavity mode frequencies (tens of thousands of modes are made to oscillate with their phases locked together). The dye cavity or feedback resonator nominally supports oscillations only at the cavity mode frequencies $q(c/2d)$ (where q is a large integer of order 10^6, c is the speed of light, and d is the optical path distance between the cavity end mirrors). These are just the frequencies where the multiply reflected waves, generated in multiple transits of the cavity, reinforce and add up in phase. The frequency differences between adjacent cavity modes are all nominally $c/2d$, but ordinarily the phases of these difference (or mode-beating) frequencies are random. If the phases can be made constant, or *locked,* the Fourier sum of the phase-locked frequencies will produce a repetitive, high-peak-power spike of duration the inverse of the locked bandwidth, and of period of $2d/c$, (the cavity round-trip transit time) corresponding to a short pulse of light circulating back and forth in the cavity. Phase- or mode-locking is produced in two different ways. In passive mode-locking (which uses a cw pump laser), an absorber is introduced into the dye cavity (generally, this is a second dye), whose absorption lessens (saturates) at high input intensities. This favors a form of oscillation that maximizes the peak power incident on the absorber, to produce the greatest saturation, and pulse formation and mode-locking ensue. In active mode-locking, most commonly today of the form called synchronous mode-locking, the dye laser is pumped with a mode-locked pump laser. The optical cavity length of the dye laser is adjusted to precisely equal that of the pump laser, matching the transit times in the two cavities. This favors the formation of that short pulse in the dye cavity that optimally saturates the repetitive, pulsed gain from the pump pulse, and again mode-locking ensues. With the short pulses assembled in this way, it is possible (by saturation and probe techniques) to measure molecular reorientation times and trace energy flow paths in the photochemistry of molecules of biological or chemical interest. This body of applications is termed time-domain laser spectroscopy. [*See* MODE-LOCKING OF LASERS; ULTRAFAST LASER TECHNOLOGY.]

The dye laser has well fulfilled the spectroscopist's wish, expressed soon after the laser was invented, for an almost infinitely malleable laser whose wavelength, bandwidth, or pulse length could be varied as desired. Since its invention, the dye laser has evolved with or caused each advance in pump laser technology, in a 20-year record of increasing malleability. Practical, commercial dye laser systems convert 20–50% of the input light energy into variable, controlled-output light energy—an efficiency record that does not leave much room for other competing nonlinear optical processes to displace the use of dyes. As long as this historical trend of coevolution persists, it is likely that the dye laser will remain the premier instrument bringing a gleam to the spectroscopists' eye.

B. Historical Overview

The evolution of the scientific dye laser family tree is outlined in Fig. 1, which shows the year of introduction of each of the major ideas to be discussed in this article. The figure may serve as a guide in further literature study, to help find an early paper where the idea (then new) is thoroughly discussed. On the margins, indications are given of the pump lasers predominately in use, and on the right edge of each branch the performance specifications available by year are listed. For the linewidths (in hertz) shown for the cw branch, and pulse lengths (in seconds) shown for the mode-locked branch, these specification represent the best performance published through that year, as researchers generally could reproduce these results once the details were published. The average power specification (in watts) given for the pulsed branch is more problematical. For some experiments the energy per pulse is most important, in others it is the pulse repetition rate, and researchers (whose lasers may excel in only one regime, and not the other) do not always report both. Therefore this specification axis gives the average power available from commercial pulsed lasers by year. Flashlamp pumped dye lasers are obviously pulsed lasers, but are shown as a transition leading into the column to which they gave rise, the cw branch. The years 1966–1970, when the three main types were differentiated, are discussed here. A brief sketch is then given of the trends each branch subsequently followed, with more details in later sections.

Several publications in the first years of the 1960s suggested that lasing might be possible in optically excited organic dyes. The first experimental attempt to demonstrate a dye laser was in 1964, where a dye cell positioned between two cavity mirrors and filled with a solution of

FIG. 1. The historical development of the three main types of dye lasers used as scientific instruments today. The year of introduction in the literature is shown of ideas discussed in this text, along with an indication of the types of pump lasers predominately in use and the output specifications available from each type of dye laser.

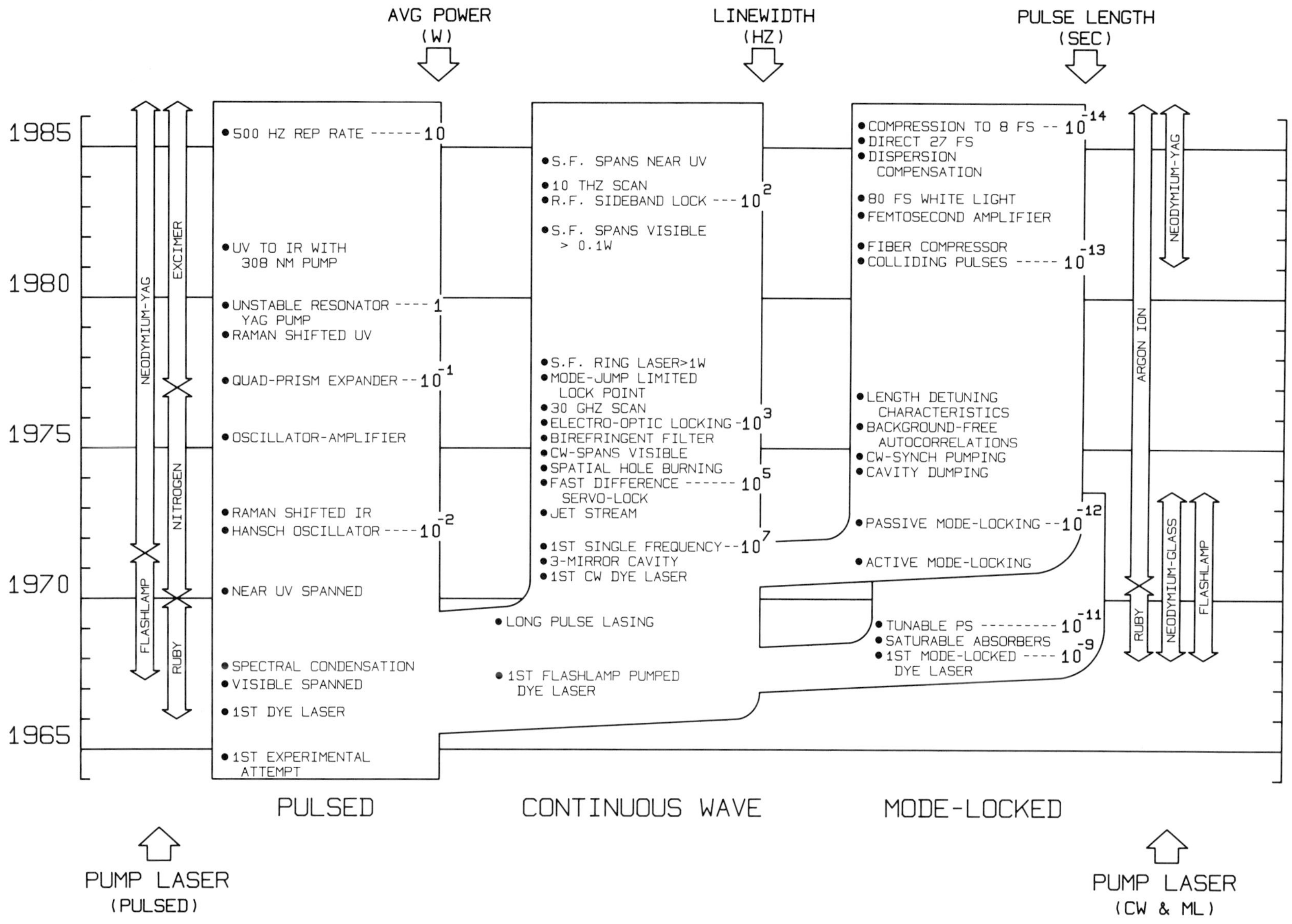
AVG POWER (W)
LINEWIDTH (HZ)
PULSE LENGTH (SEC)
1985
1980
1975
1970
1965
NEODYMIUM-YAG
FLASHLAMP
EXCIMER
NITROGEN
RUBY
500 HZ REP RATE ------10
UV TO IR WITH 308 NM PUMP
UNSTABLE RESONATOR ---- 1
YAG PUMP
RAMAN SHIFTED UV
QUAD-PRISM EXPANDER --10^-1
OSCILLATOR-AMPLIFIER
RAMAN SHIFTED IR
HANSCH OSCILLATOR ----10^-2
NEAR UV SPANNED
SPECTRAL CONDENSATION
VISIBLE SPANNED
1ST DYE LASER
1ST EXPERIMENTAL ATTEMPT
S.F. SPANS NEAR UV
10 THZ SCAN
R.F. SIDEBAND LOCK ---10^2
S.F. SPANS VISIBLE > 0.1W
S.F. RING LASER>1W
MODE-JUMP LIMITED LOCK POINT
30 GHZ SCAN
ELECTRO-OPTIC LOCKING-10^3
BIREFRINGENT FILTER
CW-SPANS VISIBLE
SPATIAL HOLE BURNING
FAST DIFFERENCE ------10^5
SERVO-LOCK
JET STREAM
1ST SINGLE FREQUENCY--10^7
3-MIRROR CAVITY
1ST CW DYE LASER
LONG PULSE LASING
1ST FLASHLAMP PUMPED DYE LASER
COMPRESSION TO 8 FS -- 10^-14
DIRECT 27 FS
DISPERSION COMPENSATION
80 FS WHITE LIGHT
FEMTOSECOND AMPLIFIER
FIBER COMPRESSOR
COLLIDING PULSES ----- 10^-13
LENGTH DETUNING CHARACTERISTICS
BACKGROUND-FREE AUTOCORRELATIONS
CW-SYNCH PUMPING
CAVITY DUMPING
PASSIVE MODE-LOCKING --10^-12
ACTIVE MODE-LOCKING
TUNABLE PS ---------10^-11
SATURABLE ABSORBERS
1ST MODE-LOCKED ----10^-9
DYE LASER
ARGON ION
NEODYMIUM-YAG
RUBY
NEODYMIUM-GLASS
FLASHLAMP
PULSED
CONTINUOUS WAVE
MODE-LOCKED
PUMP LASER (PULSED)
PUMP LASER (CW & ML)

the dye perylene was illuminated by a flashlamp. This dye is now known to have high losses from excited-state absorptions, and this attempt was ended when there was no clearly positive result.

The first certain dye laser action was in 1966 in the work of Sorokin and Lankard at the IBM Research Center, Yorktown Heights, New York. They were interested in the spectral properties of the phthalocyanine dyes, a class of dyes then in use in *Q*-switch solutions for ruby lasers. (The normal temporally spiking output from a ruby laser may be converted to a single giant pulse, by adding a saturable absorber dye cell, or "*Q*-switch," to the ruby cavity.) When the dye chloroaluminum phthalocyanine was excited by the output of a giant-pulse ruby laser at 694 nm, Sorokin and Lankard observed an anomalous darkening of their spectral plate at 755 nm. This, they suspected, was due to stimulated emission as this wavelength coincided with a peak in the dye fluorescence curve, and they quickly confirmed this by adding resonator mirrors around the dye cell to generate an intense, well-collimated beam. By the end of the year, the same discovery had been made independently three more times, again in the United States by Spaeth *et al.*, in Germany by Schafer *et al.*, and in the Soviet Union by Stepanov *et al.*, all workers also studying *Q*-switch dyes stimulated by ruby laser giant pulses.

Dyes fluoresce and lase only at wavelengths longer than their excitation wavelength; thus, to extend the infrared emission of these first dye lasers to the visible required a shorter-wavelength pump source than the direct ruby laser. This was obtained by doubling the output frequency of ruby or of neodymium–glass (Nd : glass) lasers in the nonlinear crystals potassium dihydrogen phosphate (KDP) or ammonium dihydrogen phosphate (ADP), to give 347-nm (near ultraviolet) or 532-nm (green) pumping beams. Nearly two dozen new lasing dyes were quickly demonstrated with these new pump sources, spanning the visible spectrum with pulsed dye outputs by the end of 1967. These dye lasers were tuned by varying the concentration of the dye in the cell.

The spectral condensation effect was discovered that same year. A diffraction grating in the Littrow orientation replaced one mirror of a two-mirror cavity, to reflect a dispersed fan of color back along the general direction of the incident light. Only a small band of wavelengths lay in the solid angle of the modes of the dye cavity defined by the grating and the second mirror. Not only was most of the original energy retained in the resulting narrow band output, but the wavelength of this output could be tuned (over seven times the previous range) by merely rotating the grating, a vast improvement in ease of tuning.

The requirements for successful flashlamp pumping of a dye could be determined from measurements on laser-pumped dye lasers, and this significant step followed in 1967 as well, making dye lasers accessible to many more scientists. What had not been sufficiently appreciated in 1964 was that the absorption overlapping the lasing wavelengths, arising from the excited, metastable triplet state of the dye molecule, could be largely avoided if the rise time of the flashlamp pulse were fast enough (less than a few tenths of a microsecond instead of the typical 10 μsec). Then lasing could occur before the build-up of an appreciable triplet population. Perylene was made to lase in 1972 with 20-nsec pump pulses from a *Q*-switched, doubled ruby laser.

The large-gain bandwidths demonstrated by the tuning ranges of these dyes prompted efforts to mode-lock the dye laser to produce tunable ultrashort pulses. Mode-locking was achieved in 1968 first by synchronously pumping with a mode-locked, doubled, Nd : glass laser, and then by introducing an absorber dye cell in the cavity of a flashlamp-pumped dye laser. The pulse lengths of these first systems were reported as being "detector limited," less than a half nanosecond, the rise time of a fast oscilloscope. By the end of that year the pulses had been shown by the two-photon fluorescence technique to be 10^{-11} sec in length, and the substitution of the diffraction-grating end reflector had shown these short pulses to be tunable.

There also was interest in generating longer pulses from dye lasers to approach cw operation, by removing the limits imposed by the absorbing triplet states. Careful measurements on long-pulse flashlamp-pumped dye lasers led to the conclusion that in some dyes, notably the rhodamines, the triplet population could be sufficiently quenched (returned to the ground state) by chemical interaction with oxygen from the air dissolved in the dye mix, that the residual triplet absorption did not in principle prevent cw operation. (Other chemical triplet-state quenchers were subsequently discovered.) What terminated the lasing of the dye before the end of the pump pulse, it was then realized, were the losses due to optical inhomogeneities in the heated dye. Peterson, Tuccio, and Snavely, at the Kodak Research Laboratories (Rochester, N.Y.), designed a dye cell and pumping geometry to deal with these thermal problems after carefully evaluating the pump power that would be required to exceed cw laser threshold. They used a 1-W, 514-nm argon laser pump beam critically focused into a near-hemispherical dye cavity 4.5 mm long with a minimum transverse mode diameter, or waist, of only 11 μm. Water was used to dissolve the dye, because of its excellent thermo-optic properties, and the solution was circulated in a fast flow of 4 m sec^{-1} velocity across the pumped spot. Each dye molecule effectively saw a flash, since the transit time through the pumped volume was only 3 μsec. With this apparatus they successfully operated in 1970 the first cw dye laser, in rhodamine 6G dye.

Thus by the end of 1970 the three main branches existed. Developments in the following years carried the pulsed-branch lasers through a sequence of adaptions to ever more versatile and powerful pump lasers. First the nitrogen gas laser, with a 337-nm pumping wavelength, gave access to dyes lasing from the near ultraviolet (UV), through the blue and into the red, with one pump laser. This was then supplanted by the doubled and tripled Nd:YAG pump laser, giving higher pump energies per pulse (hundreds instead of a few millijoules) and the excimer pump laser, giving higher pulse repetition frequencies (hundreds instead of tens of pulses per second). In cw dye lasers, the technology first became easier with the introduction of the three-mirror cavity and free-flowing dye jet stream, which eliminated the critically toleranced and damage-prone dye cell, and then became harder again as frequency servo and control electronics of increasing sophistication were brought in to scan the single-frequency oscillation of ever narrower residual linewidths, over ever broader scan widths. Mode-locked lasers adopted the cw-type pumping format once this became available. The steady conditions allowed for a better characterization and definition of the regime where the mode-locked circulating pulse compresses on each transit of the cavity, and shorter pulses were produced. In this regime, the brevity of the pulse length is limited by the residual pulse-stretching effects in all of the optical elements the pulse sees, and the subsequent history is one of finding these and eliminating them ever since.

It is clear from Fig. 1 that the dye laser is still in a state of rapid evolution. What is also important in the figure, but is not perhaps immediately evident, is that the history of the dye laser gives a splendid example of the way a rich technology evolves. A new idea brings additional new ideas by extrapolation (and laser-pumped dye lasers led to flashlamp-pumped ones, which ushered in cw dye lasers). Improvements make the end device more useful, which leads to a component development allowing further improvements (excimer lasers, argon lasers, and Nd:YAG lasers have all experienced a decade of improving specifications through the demands made for better dye pump lasers). Performance only gets better, as to be adopted, each new idea must produce results that surpass the old. After grasping more of the details of Fig. 1 (in what follows), it is worth looking again on the figure from these points of view.

II. Quantum Chemistry and Physics of Dyes

A. Conjugated Double Bonds as Chromophores

The fundamental properties of a dye laser derive directly from the molecular structure of the dyes. Figure 2 shows the chemical structure in solution of the chloride salt of the most common laser dye, rhodamine 6G. Two equally probable forms [Figs. 2(a) and 2(b)] are shown, differing only in the location of the trivalent nitrogen atom. One form is obtained from the other by transferring an electron from one side of the molecule to the other, along the connecting chain of conjugated carbon bonds (alternating single and double bonds) in the ring structures. To maintain the correct +4 valence of each carbon atom in this transfer, the locations of four of the six double bonds in the three connecting rings must also be changed. In classical theories of dyes, the chain of shifted bonds was called the chromophore, and the light absorption and color of the dye were attributed to this oscillating dipole formed by the transfer of charge—the chromophore was a "molecular antenna." These theories arose from the empirical fact that essentially all organic dyes were found to contain conjugated double bonds, or, equivalently, were represented by a chemical "resonance" between nearly identical structures, differing only in the placement of the double bonds.

The important features of this type of bonding are best grasped by building up to a complicated

RHODAMINE 6G WAVE FUNCTIONS

$$\Psi_g = \frac{1}{\sqrt{2}}(\phi_1 + \phi_2)$$
$$\Psi_e = \frac{1}{\sqrt{2}}(\phi_1 - \phi_2)$$

(a) where ϕ_1 = (b) and ϕ_2 =

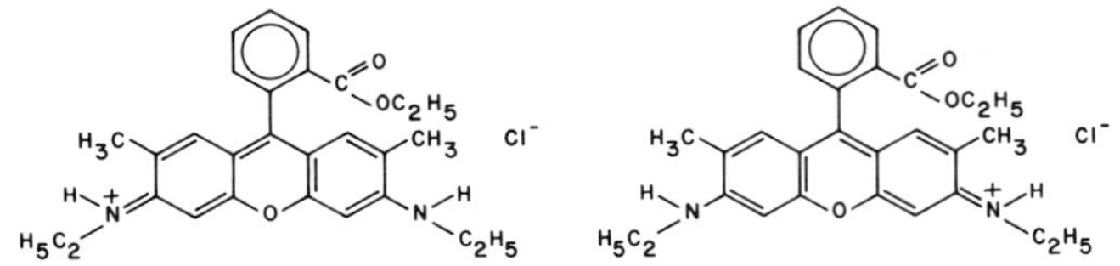

FIG. 2. Chemical symbols for two "resonant" forms of the structure of the rhodamine 6G dye molecule and the wave functions to which this resonance gives rise.

dye structure like Fig. 2, through the simpler molecules shown in Fig. 3. Ethylene, $H_2C{=}CH_2$, illustrates the character of the double bond in carbon (Fig. 3a). To "prepare" the carbon for bonding, three of the four $2s^22p^2$ outer electrons are hybridized into three sp^2 trigonal orbitals, having lobes of the wave function lying 120° apart in a plane (like a clover leaf). The fourth electron remains as a p electron with a wave-function node at the nucleus and the positive- and negative-phase lobes of the p orbital projecting perpendicularly from this plane. The first bond of the double bond is formed by overlapping one sp^2 orbital from each carbon atom, making a bond rotationally symmetric about the nuclear axis, called the σ bond. The remaining four sp^2 orbitals in ethylene are filled by making σ bonds to hydrogen atoms. The second bond in the double bond is formed by overlapping the two remaining p orbitals. The molecular π bond thus formed retains the node, giving a pair of sausage-shaped lobes (of opposite phases) floating above and below a nodal plane containing all the nuclei and the center lines of all the σ bonds (Fig. 3a). The binding energy of the π bond is greatest when the atomic p orbitals overlap most (when their lobe axes are parallel). This explains the absence of free rotation about the double bond, and this and the sp^2 hybridization explain why the characteristic forms of dye molecules are planar structures built up from zigzag chains and hexagonal rings with 120° bond angles.

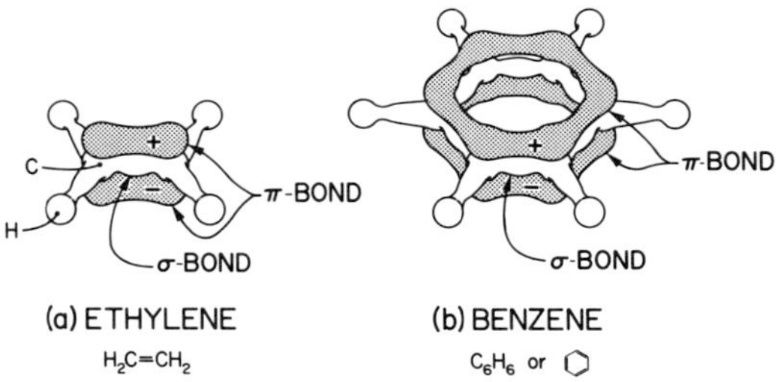

FIG. 3. Chemical symbols and schematic three-dimensional representations of the electron density distributions, for (a) a double bond system, ethylene, and (b) a conjugated double bond system, benzene. The shapes show the surfaces of constant electron density except for distortions necessary for clarity in depicting the overlapping σ-bond and π-bond electron clouds.

As a prototype conjugated molecule, consider benzene, C_6H_6 (Fig. 3b), six sp^2 carbons joined in a plane. X-Ray data shows that all the carbon bond lengths in benzene are equal, and of intermediate length (0.139 nm) between a single (0.154 nm) and double (0.134 nm) carbon bond. By definition, there are only enough p-orbital electrons (one per conjugated atom) to make a second bond over half of the σ-bond carbon linkages. What happens, by symmetry, is that the six available p electrons are *shared equally* by the six carbons, linking them by six "half bonds." They form two ring-shaped lobes or π-bond electron clouds in which the π electrons freely move, floating above and below the molecular skeleton of σ bonds lying in the nodal plane as shown in Fig. 3b. The characteristic of the conjugated bonding found in dyes is that it gives delocalized, mobile π-orbital electrons.

In quantum mechanics this resonance or sharing between possible structures is described by taking for the wave function of the actual structure a linear combination of the wave functions for the resonant possibilities. The energy of the system is calculated with the combined wave function, and the linear coefficients are determined as those that they give stationary values for the system's energy. For example, in combining the equally likely structures in Figs. 2a and 2b, this produces from the old wave functions Φ_1, Φ_2, each associated with the energy E, the two new sum and difference wave functions Ψ_g, Ψ_e of the figure, one associated with an energy less than E and one greater than E. The square of the absolute value of the wave function gives the spatial electron density in the molecule. In the additive combination $\Phi_1 + \Phi_2$, there results an averaging of the positions of the double bonds of the resonant forms, essentially placing an extra half bond everywhere along the chromophore. This reduced spatial specificity, by the uncertainty principle, implies a lower electronic kinetic energy, and the additive combination Ψ_g is the lower-energy state. The amount the energy is lowered over the nonresonant state is called the delocalization energy. Since the molecular energy is lowered, this combination it is termed a *bonding* state, or π state. In the subtractive combination $\Phi_1 - \Phi_2$, the nodes and antinodes of the wave function along the chromophore are emphasized, corresponding to localized electron density peaks and higher kinetic energy for the π electrons, and this is the higher-energy (excited) state. Since the molecular energy is increased, this is termed an *antibonding* state, or π^* state. Electronic states of stable molecules usually correspond to having more electrons in bonding states than in antibonding states.

By similar quantum-mechanical rules, starting with N conjugated atoms in a dye chromophore, each contributing one electron to the π system, it can be shown there will result N separate energy states for π electrons, each capable of holding up to two electrons (in a filled state the electrons must be paired due to the Pauli exclusion principle, with antiparallel spins). Half of these states will be bonding states and the other half antibonding states. The π states in large unsaturated molecules are usually the highest-lying bonding levels and the π^* states the lowest-lying antibonding levels. Thus the normal electronic ground state for a dye uses the available N electrons, to just fill the $\frac{1}{2}N$ bonding π states with two paired electrons each. This gives a resultant zero spin to the system, and the ground state in dyes is a singlet state. The lowest-lying empty state is the first antibonding π^* state, the $\frac{1}{2}N + 1$ level of the system. The characteristic absorption and fluorescence of dyes, which is the working electronic transition in the dye laser is this $\pi(\frac{1}{2}N) \rightarrow \pi^*(\frac{1}{2}N + 1)$ transition.

The energies of these levels, and thus the center wavelength for that dye in a laser, may be calculated successfully with a surprisingly simple model, called the free-electron model. This assumes that the σ-bond framework of the conjugated chain provides a line or confining box of constant electrostatic potential along which the π electrons move freely. The important variables are the size of the box (number of conjugated atoms) and its topology (whether the bonding network is linear, branched, or ring structures). At the ends of the chromophore, the constant potential gives way to a steeply rising Coulomb potential, so the π electrons have the properties found in the quantum-mechanical problem of "a particle in a one-dimensional box." Their wave functions are sinusoidal standing waves with an integral number of half wavelengths fitting into the length of the box, with their energies increasing quadratically with their quantum number (the number of half wavelengths). The electrons with more antinodes in their wave functions thus have larger kinetic energies. From these solutions, correct first-order values are obtained not only for the wavelength of the peak of the dye absorption (which increases with the length of the chromophore in a linear molecule) but also for many other properties. Some of these are the oscillator strength of the transition (which is large, of order unity), the polarization dependence of absorption (which peaks for the incident electric field aligned along the chromophore), and the shift of peak absorption wavelength with atomic substitution in the molecule, or with change of solvent.

It was shown already that the ground state for a dye molecule has zero spin and is a singlet. In the first excited state there are two unpaired electrons (one in the $\frac{1}{2}N$ bonding level, and the other in the $\frac{1}{2}N + 1$ antibonding level). The Pauli exclusion principle does not restrict the spins of these electrons to be antiparallel, since they are in different levels, and a triplet state (parallel spins, for a total spin of unity) is possible in the excited electronic state. The free-electron wave functions can be used to show that due to spatial correlation effects between these unpaired electrons, the energy of the excited triplet state will lie below that of the singlet level. This gives rise to the problem of accumulation of dye molecules after optical pumping in the metastable triplet level, which was of such great importance in the historical development of dye lasers. (The triplet state is metastable or requires a collision to deactivate it, because a change in spin is not allowed in a radiative transition).

To summarize this, the quantum theory substantiates the classical view of mobile electrons, free to move along the chain of conjugated atoms in dyes, giving rise to oscillating dipoles and strong absorption and fluorescence. These are shown to be π-bond electrons, arising from the "resonance" or ambiguity in placement of the double bonds in the chain, which splits the electronic energy into a set of delocalized bonding levels and a set of localized antibonding levels. Laser operation and the strong color of the dye are due to the transition between the highest member of the low-lying set and the lowest member of the high-lying set, and are seen to be phenomena deeply imbedded in the quantum properties of matter.

B. Dye Absorption and Fluorescence Spectra Derived from Potential-Energy Curves

The basic spacing of the levels discussed above is about 20,000 cm^{-1} in rhodamine 6G dye. These levels are broadened by molecular vibration, rotation, and collisions with solvent molecules. Vibration produces sublevels, spaced by up to several hundreds of wave numbers, which in some dyes are sufficiently resolved to give secondary peaks in the absorption spectrum. Rotational and collisional (homogeneous) broadening smears these sublevels into overlapping bands to make the tunable continuum.

Vibrational broadening in molecular spectra is interpreted with a potential energy diagram such as is shown, somewhat schematically, for rhodamine 6G in Fig. 4a. A potential diagram has a clear interpretation for a simple diatomic molecule, where the structural coordinate R (the horizontal axis) is the separation between the two atomic nuclei. The characteristic shape of the potential energy curve is a dip or potential well, as the nuclei approach from infinite separation, by the amount of the binding energy (reached at separation R_0) before rising steeply as the nuclear Coulomb repulsion takes over at smaller separations. The ground-state separation R_0, at the potential minimum, fixes the normal linear dimension in a diatomic molecule. In a complex dye molecule, there are many nuclear separations that change in various directions with different modes of vibration, and the concept of a potential energy depending on a structural coordinate must be generalized. The ideas are the same as in the diatomic case, but the diagram becomes somewhat schematic. For Fig. 4a, the dimension for the structure coordinate axis was chosen (arbitrarily) as the distance between the nitrogen atoms in rhodamine 6G. The measured spectra (for wavelengths less than 700 nm) for rhodamine 6G are plotted in Fig. 4(c), and the schematic nature of the potential diagram is unimportant in this discussion since it was constructed to be consistent with this spectral data.

Each electronic state (ground state S_0, first excited singlet S_1, triplet T_1, and so forth) has a separate potential curve $E(R)$. As the molecular dimensions generally swell in the excited states, larger values for the structural coordinate R are found at the potential minima of the higher curves (a fact having important consequences for laser operation).

Vibrational energy in a molecule is quantized, giving a set of discrete levels shown in Fig. 4a as horizontal lines drawn between the boundaries of the potential wells. The square of the wave function for each of these levels gives the probability the nuclei will be found at a given value of R; three of these, for energies E_0, E_2, and E_3, are shown. These probabilities peak near the potential boundaries that correspond to the classical turning points in the vibratory motion, where the nuclear velocity is near zero and reverses direction. The intermediate points are passed through relatively quickly; the vibrating nuclei are likely to be found near their maximum or minimum positions.

Light absorption or emission is governed by the Franck–Condon principle, which states that the change in electronic energy occurs so much more rapidly than the vibrational motion that neither the position nor the momenta of the nuclei can change appreciably. Thus, on the potential-well diagram, the absorption (or emission) of a photon is represented by a vertical line, which, by the weighting of coordinate values, begins and ends near a potential-curve boundary for the strong transitions. (Transitions to endpoints well away from the curve boundaries are prevented by the second part of the Franck–Condon principle—there can be no discontinuous changes in nuclear kinetic energy.) The length of the vertical line is given by the photon energy (which matches the difference in electronic energy) hc/λ, where h is Planck's constant, c the velocity of light, and λ the photon wavelength, or, if

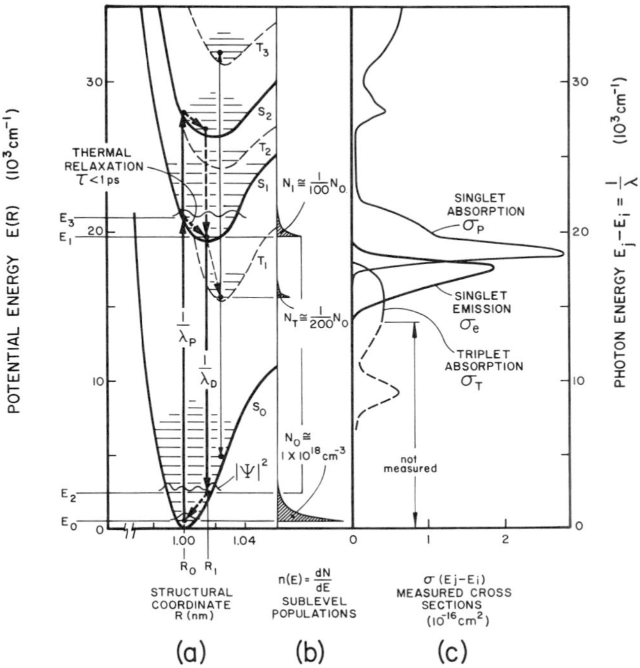

FIG. 4. Schematic potential-energy wells constructed to be consistent with the measured spectra for the rhodamine 6G dye molecule. (a) The potential energy versus generalized structural coordinate (nuclear separation) for the first three singlet and first three triplet energy bands. Laser light absorption and emission (at pump and dye laser wavelengths) are indicated by heavy arrows, and nonradiative (collision) processes by dashed arrows. (b) Thermal equilibrium sublevel population distributions in these six bands (only the lowest three are appreciably populated). (c) Absorption and emission cross sections measured for this dye (except that the triplet absorption between 5000 and 14,000 cm^{-1} is inferred from spectra on similar dyes).

energy is measured in wave numbers as in Fig. 4, the length is directly $1/\lambda$. The line strength for the transition is given by quantum mechanics as an overlap integral, calculated with the two end-point vibrational wave functions.

The intensity of the transition is also weighted by the sublevel population density $n(E)$, the number of molecules per unit volume in the initial vibrational sublevel at energy E. The collisional and rotational broadening at room temperature spans the vibrational level spacing, so this sub-level population density has the form appropriate for Boltzmann (thermal) equilibrium (Fig. 4b) or $n(E)$ decreases sharply (falling exponentially) with energy above the bottom of the potential well. The product of this Boltzmann factor and the quantum-mechanical line strength is taken and plotted versus the energy difference of the potential curves, to produce the dye absorption and fluorescent emission curves (Fig. 4c).

These spectra are presented as cross sections for molecular absorption σ_p, or its inverse, stimulated emission σ_e. These are defined by Beer's law, which for example in the case of absorption of pump light from the ground state is

$$I_p(z) = I_p(0) \exp(-N_0 \sigma_p z) \quad (1)$$

Here a plane light wave of uniform intensity I_p (watts per square centimeter) and wavelength λ_p (nanometers) has been assumed, incident on a sample of dye of thickness z (centimeters) with a ground-state dye concentration of N_0 (molecules per cubic centimeter). A cross section has units of centimeters squared and represents in the case of σ_p, for example, the absorbing area per molecule in the ground state. Because these cross sections are defined by an average over the Boltzmann population distribution in the initial state, they are temperature and solvent-dependent.

The total molecular population density N is the sum over all the populated states, which is for Fig. 4 where only the ground state, first singlet, and first triplet are appreciably populated:

$$N = N_0 + N_1 + N_T \quad (2)$$

(Each of these state populations is the integral of the sublevel population density $n(E)$, over the energy range of several kT that the level populations are spread, k being Boltzmann's constant, T the absolute temperature, and $kT = 200\ cm^{-1}$ at room temperature. In Fig. 4b the energy spread is exaggerated to about twice this range, to allow the exponential fall-off to show). The assumption of a wave of uniform intensity here and in what follows simplifies the equations, and real devices with nonuniform waves can be treated later by integrating these results over the intensity variation within the active volume.

The two most striking features of the curves of absorption and emission versus photon energy are their asymmetric shapes and the fact that these are nearly mirror images of each other (Fig. 4c). These are consequences of the offset $R_0 < R_1$ between the potential minima of the S_0 and S_1 singlet states. The absorption from the ground state (labeled $1/\lambda_p$ in Fig. 4a) proceeds from the populated sublevels near the bottom of that well, to high-lying sublevels at points of minimum R along the steep inner boundary of the upper potential well. Hence, the σ_p spectrum shows a sharp rise, then falls with a more gradual tail, with increasing photon energy. Conversely, the fluorescence decay (5 nsec time constant) or stimulated transition (labeled $1/\lambda_D$ in Fig. 4a) arises from populated sublevels near the bottom of the upper well. These transitions go to the high-lying sublevels at points of maximum R along the descending outer boundary of the ground-state potential curve. Hence the σ_e spectrum rises sharply, then falls with a more gradual tail, with decreasing photon energy.

Other processes shown in Fig. 4a may be listed that compete with the main dye laser cycle of absorption at λ_p and emission at λ_D. Higher-energy pump photons can excite π electrons to the second singlet state directly ($S_0 \rightarrow S_2$, depicted as an extension of the arrow for the $1/\lambda_p$ transition, and as the second, higher-energy peak of σ_p). This excitation relaxes to S_1 by fast *internal conversion* processes (shown as dashed lines; these are collision-induced energy transfers on a picosecond time scale, without radiation). Internal conversion on $S_2 \rightarrow S_1$ allows pumping of the rhodamines and other visible dyes by ultraviolet pump lines such as the 308-nm line from the xenon chloride excimer laser. Internal conversion on $S_1 \rightarrow S_0$, which reduces laser efficiency, is also possible.

Some collisions produce *intersystem crossing,* converting the excited population in S_1 to that in the triplet state T_1 (indicated by a light dashed arrow). The triplet is a long-lived metastable state, as the radiative decay to the ground state $T_1 \rightarrow S_0$ is forbidden by selection rules that do not allow a change in spin in an electronic transition. Interactions with solvent molecules and torsional bending of the dye molecule produces a weak mixing of spin states, allowing a weak, delayed phosphorescence on this transition (thin solid arrow downward in Fig. 4a). Because this state is long-lived (microsecond to millisecond lifetimes), even a slow pump rate from S_1 due to collisions can result in an appreciable T_1 population, and thus also $T_1 \rightarrow T_3$ absorption, which overlaps the lasing wavelengths (thin solid arrow upward in Fig. 4a and absorption spectrum σ_T in Fig. 4c). Estimates of the triplet population can be made by various means, among them by noting the power increase in a dye laser by the addition of the liquid cyclooctatetrane (COT) to the dye mixture. This is a molecule with acceptor states lying below the first triplet level of many visible dyes, which by collisions relaxes (or quenches) the dye triplet population back to the ground state, reducing the deleterious absorption. From a typical cw laser output power increase of +30% in rhodamine 6G, this method estimates the T_1 state population to be half that of S_1. Another well-known triplet-state quencher is oxygen (O_2) dissolved from the air into the dye solution. These processes are described by a set of quantum efficiencies (branching ratios) φ, φ_T, φ_{IC} whose sum is unity, and that give the probabilities for a molecule put into S_1 to decay by each of the three channels. For good laser dyes, the fluorescence efficiency $\varphi = 1 - \varphi_T - \varphi_{IC}$ will exceed 85%, making these competing pathways unimportant (so long as the triplet absorption is quenched). With these definitions, if τ is the spontaneous emission lifetime for fluorescent $S_1 \rightarrow S_0$ decay, the total decay rate out of the first singlet state is $1/\tau\varphi$.

C. Spectral Condensation, Gain Saturation, and Laser Output Power

Referring to Fig. 4a, dye molecules optically pumped from the ground state to E_3 above the singlet potential minimum thermally relax to E_1 by collisions giving up heat energy to solvent molecules in a time on the order of a picosecond. This relaxation is faster than the optical absorption or stimulated emission rates in actual dye lasers. It is this thermal equilibrium process that, by maintaining the population distribution among the sublevels of each state at the Boltzmann values despite the perturbing optical transitions, allows the pumped dye molecules to exhibit gain and work as a laser medium. The fluorescent decays labeled $1/\lambda_D$ into the ground state are into high-lying depopulated vibrational sublevels (near E_2), which remain so because of the ground-state Boltzmann equilibrium. This greatly reduces the pumping rate needed to establish gain in the dye. A pump rate sufficient to produce a singlet population N_1 of only 1% of that of the ground state N_0 is all that is needed to establish a population inversion between sublevels $n(E_1) > n(E_2)$, and gain in rhodamine 6G dye (see Fig. 4b). The thermal equilibrium process works in the laser for the pump absorption labeled in $1/\lambda_p$ as well, by rapidly removing population from the terminal sublevel E_3 to prevent stimulated emission at λ_p back to the ground state. This makes it possible to totally invert the working states in a dye laser (i.e., put all of the dye molecules into the excited state, $N_1 \gg N_0 \approx 0$). The Boltzmann equilibrium creates a classical four-level laser system out of the two broadened states.

It is also responsible for the spectral condensation effect. When broadband, nonselective feedback is provided in the dye laser, stimulated emission occurs from all occupied sublevels in the upper band S_1. The higher-lying sublevels (in the high-energy tail of the population distribution) emit primarily to higher sublevels in the ground state, (i.e., at longer wavelengths) than do those molecules near the potential minimum E_1. In this case the spectral bandwidth of the emission is broad, 10–20 nm in a pulsed dye laser. When a spectrally selective element is added to the dye feedback cavity, the threshold is raised for all emissions but those in the narrow selected wavelength band, say, the wavelengths emitted from level E_1, which are all that lase. The population in the entire upper state S_1 drains through this channel as the thermal collisions maintaining the Boltzmann equilibrium attempt (successfully) to fill the hole in the depleted sublevel population distribution. The same argument holds if the selective feedback is tuned for lasing at shorter or longer wavelengths, but the higher energy of the draining sublevel permits access only to the higher-energy tail of the Boltzmann distribution, and the process is not as efficient.

How much less efficient may be seen by calculating the steady-state laser output power for the case of a spectrally narrow tunable filter with center wavelength λ_D selecting the oscillation wavelength. The idea of gain saturation is the basis for an output power calculation. Assume uniform plane waves once again, with later integrations over the active volume accounting for intensity spatial variations in real devices. Initially, before lasing begins, the population inversion and the (small signal) gain per pass k_0L are at a maximum. Here k_0L is the exponential gain constant in Beer's law, and L is the dye optical thickness along the resonator axis.

This initial gain must decrease, or saturate, because as the lasing intensity I_e builds up, it causes stimulated transitions at rates comparable to the spontaneous fluorescent transition rate $1/\tau\varphi$, and the population inversion is depleted. Thus the gain constant $k(I_e)L$ is a decreasing function of I_e. In the steady state after the buildup transient, the laser intensity inside the resonator is the intensity that decreases the gain per pass to just balance the cavity losses, as then the laser intensity suffers no net change in a cavity round trip. For a ring (or traveling-wave) laser, the dye gain is traversed once per round trip of the resonator (of mean reflectivity r), so that balance is achieved if $re^{kL} = 1$, or

$$k(I_e)L = \ln(1/r) \tag{3}$$

This is the implicit equation for the steady-state laser intensity. Once it is solved for I_e, the output power P_{out} is given by

$$P_{out} = t(\pi w_D^2)I_e \tag{4}$$

Here πw_D^2 is the area of the laser beam of (uniform) radius w_D in the dye medium. The resonator losses consist of the output coupling loss t (transmission of the output mirror) and the dissipative losses a due to light absorption and scatter in the intracavity optics, and the insertion losses of the wavelength selective filter. As t and a are usually small, $\ln(1/r) = \ln[1 - a - t]^{-1} = a + t$ in Eq. (3).

The form of the gain decrease may be found by solving rate equations for the level populations, which balance in the steady state the rate of transitions into S_1 from pump absorptions ($S_0 \rightarrow S_1$) against the rate out of S_1 due to stimulated laser transitions and spontaneous fluorescent decays. The broadening of the laser states is included by the Boltzmann average in the cross-section definitions, so the rate equations deal with the total state populations N_1 and N_0. (Care must be exercised in the definitions and averaging to arrive at a consistent set of rate equations. Additional terms describing intersystem crossing, triplet and excited singlet state absorptions, and so forth, are not included here. In particular, it is assumed that the triplet population is quenched, $N_T = 0$.)

The essential physics is illustrated with just these four terms, in the time-independent, plane-wave, longitudinal pumping case. (The pump light propagates along the same axis as the dye laser beam.) The gain constant is given by

$$\begin{aligned} k(I_e)L &= (N_1\sigma_e - N_0\sigma_a)L \\ &= [N_1(\sigma_e + \sigma_a) - N\sigma_a]L \end{aligned} \tag{5}$$

since $N = N_1 + N_0$ by Eq. (2). Here σ_a is the singlet absorption cross section, evaluated at the lasing wavelength λ_D. The steady-state balance of the transition rates into and out of the upper laser state gives a value $N_1(I_e)$ for that population density that is dependent on the laser intensity I_e. When used in Eq. (5), there results a saturated gain equation of the form expected for a homogeneously broadened laser,

$$k(I_e)L = \frac{k_0 L}{1 + I_e/I_s} \tag{6}$$

where the initial or small signal gain is

$$k_0 L = NL\left(\frac{\sigma_e\sigma_p I_p - \sigma_a(hc/\lambda_p)(1/\tau\varphi)}{\sigma_p I_p + (hc/\lambda_p)(1/\tau\varphi)}\right) \tag{7}$$

[Equation (7) corrects an error in the corresponding equation in the Johnston article.] The saturation intensity, which by Eq. (6) is the value of I_e dropping the gain to half its initial value, is

$$I_s = \frac{\lambda_p}{\lambda_D}\left(\frac{\sigma_p I_p + (hc/\lambda_p)(1/\tau\varphi)}{\sigma_e + \sigma_a}\right) \tag{8}$$

Setting the saturated gain equal to the resonator losses (asumed small) as in Eq. (3), solving Eq. (6) for I_e, and putting this into Eq. (4) gives the expected form for the output power (valid above threshold, when the expression in the last bracket is positive):

$$P_{out} = t(\pi w_D^2)I_s\left(\frac{k_0 L}{a + t} - 1\right) \tag{9}$$

The output increases linearly with the excess above unity or threshold value of the small-signal gain-to-loss ratio. Since the denominator of Eq. (7) is the same as the numerator of Eq. (8), it is convenient to consider the form the output power takes when the laser is pumped well above threshold (where these factors cancel in the product $I_s k_0 L$), and as a further simplification, at dye wavelengths in the middle of the tuning range or longer where the ground-state reabsorption may be neglected.

Then

$$P_{out} \approx \left(\frac{t}{a + t}\right)\frac{\lambda_p}{\lambda_D}(NL\sigma_p)\rho P_{in} \tag{10}$$

for $k_0 L/(a + t) \gg 1$ and $\sigma_a = 0$. Here $\rho = w_D^2/w_p^2$, the ratio of dye beam area to pumped area, is introduced and $\pi w_p^2 I_p$ is recognized as the input power in the longitudinal pumping case.

As a first use of these results, note the direct connection they establish between the experimental behavior of a dye laser and the underlying molecular physics. In using the laser, the ease of operation is greatest when well above threshold, and differences in behavior at opposite ends of the tuning range of a dye are immediately apparent. On the short-wavelength end of the range, there is a wide tolerance of output to mirror misalignment, dirty optics, etc., which persists even as the short-wavelength oscillation limit is approached and the output abruptly dies. The opposite is true as the long-wavelength limit is approached, where cavity alignment and losses are critical, and there always seems to be some output available at even longer wavelengths if only the critical adjustments can be maintained. The excess gain may be thought of as a measure of the tolerance to cavity losses, while by Eq. (9) the saturation intensity is a weighting factor, giving the value of this gain in determining output power. The behavior just described is thus due to the mirror-image and asymmetry properties of the absorption and emission cross sections. The short-wavelength end of the range is near the peak where the emission cross section σ_e is slowly varying, and the tuning limit is determined by the sharp rise in absorption cross section σ_a with decreasing λ_D. The rise in σ_a both decreases the saturation intensity [Eq. (8)] and adds a cavity loss term due to laser photon reabsorption in the dye itself [Eq. (7)]. The long-wavelength end of the range is determined by the asymmetric slow falloff of σ_e with increasing λ_D. This drops the gain towards the threshold (resonator) loss value, there is negligible reabsorption ($\sigma_a = 0$), and the rise in I_s [with $1/\sigma_e$, Eq. (8)] allows the output power to persist. An example where the k_0L and I_s parameters were measured as a function of λ_D in a cw dye laser is given in Section IV.

This linking of the macroscopic laser properties with the microscopic dye ones may be enhanced by further consideration of these results. In the gain expressions Eqs. (5) and (7), neglect the reabsorption term in σ_a, as is permissible in the middle of the tuning range. Then the small signal gain per pass of the dye medium is

$$k_0L = N_1L\sigma_e = NL\sigma_e\left(\frac{\sigma_pI_p}{\sigma_pI_p + (hc/\lambda_p)(1/\tau\varphi)}\right) \quad (11)$$

which is the product of the gain a uniform beam traversing the medium would see if all the dye molecules were in the upper state, at total inversion (NL being the molecular density in the beam cross section, σ_e the emitting area per molecule), times the fraction of molecules in the upper state (bracketed term). The interpretation of the bracketed term comes from Eq. (11), or directly from the rate equation and particle conservation equation from which it is derived.

The term $(hc/\lambda_p)(1/\tau\varphi)$ is the pump power dissipated (by all spontaneous decay processes) per molecule in the upper laser S_1. It is useful to estimate from Eq. (11) the minimum pump intensity needed to reach threshold in a dye laser. This will be when the pump power density absorbed by all ground-state molecules, $N_0\sigma_pI_p$, balances against the power density dissipated by upper-state decays, $N_1(hc/\lambda_p)(1/\tau\varphi)$, to give that excited-state fraction producing gain equal to the resonator losses.

From Eq. (11), this is:

$$I_p^{th} = \frac{(1/\sigma_p)(hc/\lambda_p)(1/\tau\varphi)}{[NL\sigma_e/(a + t)] - 1} \quad (12)$$

For typical values $\sigma_p = \sigma_e = 1 \times 10^{-16}$ cm^2, $\lambda_p =$ 500 nm, $\tau\varphi = 5 \times 10^{-9}$ sec, $N = 1 \times 10^{18}$ cm^{-3}, $(a + t)/L = 10$ cm^{-1}, this gives a threshold pump intensity of 90 kW cm^{-2}, clearly showing the need for bright flashlamps or a laser to pump a pulsed dye laser, and a coherent pump beam focusable to a small spot to pump a cw one. Note that in the example given, the pump power absorbed per ground-state molecule, σ_pI_p, is one-ninth the spontaneously dissipated power per molecule in the upper state. Gains and pump intensities 10 times the threshold value or more are realized in practical dye lasers.

The interpretation of the saturation intensity result, Eq. (8), contains a subtlety. In the conservative two-state system under discussion, a molecule removed from the upper state by laser-stimulated emission at the rate $\sigma_eI_e/(hc/\lambda_D)$ per molecule must appear in the lower state. There it immediately is subjected to a pump rate (per molecule) of $\sigma_pI_p/(hc/\lambda_p)$ returning it to the upper state. Thus for stimulated emission to produce a reduction of the small-signal upper-state population by half, it must be at a transition rate per molecule equal to the sum of the spontaneous decay rate plus the return rate, yielding Eq. (8). This makes the saturation intensity a linear function of the pump intensity; at high pump rates, the dye bleaches, the small-signal gain saturates at the total inversion value $NL\sigma_e$, and the output power increases with pump rate solely through the I_s term in Eq. (9).

Turning now to Eq. (10), the first term is recognized as the coupling efficiency $\eta_C = t/(a + t)$ found in all lasers, expressing the fact that a finite circulating power must be left in the resonator to stimulate emission (not all of the power represented by the initial population inversion can be coupled out of the resonator). High-gain dye lasers with optimized output transmission t have $\eta_C \approx 0.8$. The next term is the Stokes efficiency $\eta_S = \lambda_p/\lambda_D$, accounting for the power lost (for a quantum efficiency of unity) due to the dye photon being of lower energy than the pump photon. The term $NL\sigma_p$ is the fraction of the pump light absorbed in the dye in this uniform plane-wave case, where this factor must be small to maintain the assumption of uniformity. When the pump intensity is allowed to vary along the axis of propagation, this becomes the fraction of pump intensity absorbed in the transit of the dye medium, $\eta_A = [1 - \exp(-N\sigma_pL)]$ by Eq. (1). The ratio ρ of lasing to pumped areas accounts for any pumped volume left unutilized and is replaced by an average value sometimes called the filling factor η_F, equal to a volume integral of this ratio over the pump and dye beam intensity variations in describing actual devices. The threshold term may be restored to

Eq. (10), so that in its general form this may be rewritten to give the slope efficiency or ratio for conversion of pump power in excess of threshold to tunable dye laser output power:

$$P_{out}/(P_{in} - P_{th}) = \eta_C \eta_S \eta_A \eta_F \qquad (13)$$

Typical values, in the case of the rhodamine 6G cw single-frequency ring laser at the peak of the tuning curve and 6 W of input power, for the last three efficiency factors are $\eta_S = 0.85$, $\eta_A = 0.80$, and $\eta_F = 0.80$, giving a theoretical slope efficiency of 44%. Experimental values for this case reach 35%.

The question of the efficiency of the dye laser convertor and of spectral condensation in particular at wavelengths away from the maximum emission cross section is answered by Eq. (13). As long as the dye is pumped hard enough to create a gain well above threshold, the lasing conversion process occurs at fixed slope efficiency essentially independent of center wavelength or lasing bandwidth.

The most serious omission in the treatment given so far is the neglect of the triplet-state terms in Eqs. (7)–(13). The power loss due to triplet-state absorptions is treated by Peterson, who shows that the laser types are usefully separated by a demarcation time of $(K_{ST})^{-1} \approx 100$ nsec in rhodamine 6G, the inverse of the intersystem crossing rate filling the triplet state from the first excited singlet. This order of time is required to build up the equilibrium triplet population. For short pulse dye lasers (laser-pumped, pulsed lasers) the pump pulses are typically 10 nsec in length and the triplet absorption terms can be neglected. The largest effect is for the cw type, where, for example, in the rhodamine 6G ring laser considered earlier, inclusion of triplet losses would reduce the theoretical small signal gain by 34%, increase the saturation intensity by 17%, and reduce the output power by 30%. To compute these changes requires knowledge of the triplet absorption cross section σ_T, which is known in this case but has not been measured for most other dyes.

In short-pulse dye lasers there is insufficient time for triplet-state buildup and the results above are usable without correction. In flashlamp-pumped dye lasers, not only are triplet terms significant, but often the full time-dependent rate equations are needed, requiring numerical integrations in modeling their behavior. In mode-locked dye lasers the resonator losses are deliberately time-dependent, requiring further discussion (see Section V).

The dye lifetime, or stability against photo decomposition, is another important dye property not in these equations. All dye molecules eventually decompose under repeated pump excitations. In the more stable molecules this occurs after 10^6–10^7 photon absorptions, corresponding to about 10^4 J absorbed energy per cubic centimeter of dye solution, with perhaps a minimum of 1% of this lifetime required for a dye to be usable. In practice, a large volume of a liter or more of dye is circulated through a laser to give several hundred hours of operation between dye changes. Dye concentrations are adjusted to give the desired pump beam absorption depth, in matching the pumped volume to the dye beam diameter (fixed by the dye resonator). Dye concentrations are generally limited to less than 10^{-2} mol/liter, where the limit of solubility for some dyes occurs, and where aggregation (dimer formation) in others alters the dye spectra.

The main intent of the remainder of this article is to give a picture of the art of dye laser design in the three main scientific instrument categories, at the 1986 stage of their evolution.

III. Short-Pulse Dye Lasers

A. Status of Flashlamp-Pumped Dye Lasers

The high threshold pump intensity given by Eq. (12) means that flashlamps for dye laser pumping must be driven hard, blackbody temperatures above 6000 K being required, which results in short-lived, frequently replaced lamps. Much of the lamp radiation is in a broad ultraviolet band at these plasma temperatures, leading to relatively rapid photodecomposition of the dye if the lamp light is unfiltered, and inefficient operation if it is filtered. Lamp pulse lengths of 1–50 μsec are long enough that triplet-state quenching and thermal lensing of the dye must be dealt with. These pulses are too long (compared to the 5- to 30-nsec pulse lengths from pump lasers) to reach the peak dye powers most useful in nonlinear optics and available from laser-pumped dyes. These are the disadvantages of flashlamp-pumped dye lasers.

Nevertheless, because the flashlamp laser has the economy of eliminating the pump laser, many special-purpose lamp designs and dye lasers to go with them have been developed to fill special-purpose needs. There is also a considerable history of contributions to the dye laser art made with flashlamp pumping, ranging from the first demonstration of lasing in a large number of dyes, to clarifying the mechanisms of pulse formation in mode-locked dye lasers. But because of the disadvantages already listed, there are today few flashlamp pumped scientific dye lasers, and no widespread general example of this type in the same sense that these exist for the three types represented as the three main branches (Fig. 1) of the dye laser family tree. The review article by Peterson expertly and extensively covers many flashlamp systems. Here only the short-pulse category of pulsed dye lasers will be discussed.

B. Short-Pulse Oscillators

Dye fluorescent lifetimes are too short (4–8 nsec) to provide energy storage, and for a high small-signal gain, a high-intensity pump pulse (but not a high energy one) is required. Short pump pulses (less than 100 nsec duration) offer the necessary intensity without adding extensive cooling demands and have the advantages of being too fast for triplet-state absorption or thermal lens distortions to develop in the dye. (The index of refraction of a liquid is dominated by its density, and a relatively high change of refractive index with temperature is a consequence of a relatively high rate of thermal expansion—which has a time constant on the order of 10 μsec, however, to develop.) The dye in a short-pulse system is simply circulated or stirred fast enough (about 1 m/sec) to remove energy-deposition temperature gradients in the few milliseconds between shots.

In the early development of pulsed dye lasers these reasons made the nitrogen (N_2) lasers then available attractive as dye pumps. The nitrogen laser has 4- to 10-nsec pulse lengths, 100-kW peak powers, a near-UV wavelength of 337 nm, and a repetition rate of 100 Hz, high enough to complete spectroscopic experiments in hours, (unlike the alternative doubled ruby laser pump at 1 Hz). The design principles for a narrowband spectroscopic short-pulse dye laser were first worked out by Hänsch in 1972 with this pump laser (Fig. 5a). The dye laser market thus established stimulated development of the more powerful Nd : YAG and excimer lasers for pumping use, which were to later displace the nitrogen laser (Fig. 1).

Hänsch realized that the low ratio of pump pulse length to round-trip transit time in the laser cavity dictated the design of the short-pulse oscillator. In a cavity long enough (here 40 cm)

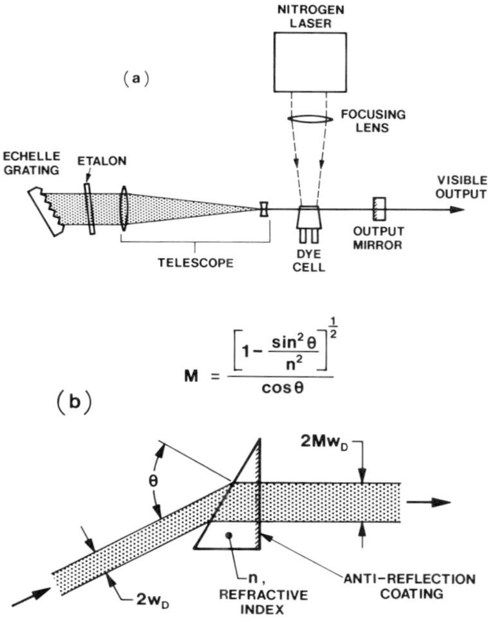

FIG. 5. The original short-pulse tunable dye oscillator. (a) The layout by Hänsch, with an intracavity telescope to increase the resolution of the grating. (b) One-dimensional beam expansion in a prism with high incidence angle on the input face and normal incidence on the exit face. A series of four prisms, arranged for no net dispersion, makes up the "quad-prism expander" that has replaced the Hänsch telescope. [Adapted with permission from Klauminzer, G. K. (1977). *IEEE J. Quantum Electronics* **QE-13,** 103. © 1977 IEEE.]

to accommodate a tuning device, a circulating, spontaneously emitted photon has only a few round trips during the excitation to replicate in an avalanche to $\sim 10^{15}$ photons (0.3 mJ at 600 nm), an output representing about 0.5 quantum efficiency of conversion of input photons. This necessitates a high gain in the dye, but nitrogen laser pumping permits this, as unsaturated gains of 10^3 in a few millimeters path had already been demonstrated. (Such gains correspond to nearly total inversion in Eq. (11). To achieve them, Hänsch transversely pumped an $L = 1$ cm long dye cell transversely (from the side) as shown in Fig. 5a. The nitrogen laser beam was focused into a narrow line of 0.15 mm width along the inner cell wall, with a dye concentration adjusted for a symmetrical 0.15 mm absorption depth). The output linewidth in such an avalanche is only a little smaller than the narrowest filter in the cavity, but very narrow filters (even though inevitably lossy) could be used because of the high gain, which also gives a high transmission for the output coupler. This widens the cavity mode widths to be comparable to their spacing, eliminating discrete longitudinal mode structure and allowing the laser to be smoothly tuned without servo control of the cavity length. The laser's frequency stability is determined just by that of the narrowest spectral filter. This short-pulse oscillator is essentially a few-pass amplifier of filtered spontaneous emission.

An appropriate filter set in this design is a grating in Littrow mounting (equal incidence and diffraction angles) plus a high-finesse etalon. An etalon is a pair of parallel reflecting surfaces (often the two sides of a plate of glass), which makes a wavelength filter by interference of the multiply reflected beams. The relative narrowness or half-transmission width of the filter ratioed to the spacing of adjacent orders, called the finesse, usually is determined by and increases with the reflectivity of the two surfaces. The grating resolution is determined by the number of lines illuminated, times the grating order. To increase the number of lines (or equivalently, to decrease the beam divergence on the grating), the cavity contains a beam-expanding telescope of magnification 25 (Fig. 5a). This also reduces the intensity incident on the grating to avoid damaging its aluminum coating, and reduces the etalon losses that are due to walk-off or incomplete overlap of the interfering beams. A coarsely ruled or echelle grating (600 lines/mm) is actually an advantage in that it allows the grating to work over a large surface area at high incidence angles, while keeping only one dye tuning range per grating order. With this design, Hänsch achieved 5-nsec pulses of 0.1 mJ energy and 0.1 cm^{-1} spectral width without the etalon, and 0.01-mJ, 0.01-cm^{-1} pulses with the etalon, tunable with several dyes over the visible spectrum.

The basic Hänsch design is used today with one major change—the telescope is replaced by a set of half-prism beam expanders (Fig. 5b). (As the exit face is used at normal incidence, this is "half" of a normal prism, used with symmetrical entrance and exit angles.) To increase resolution, expansion is required only in the dispersion plane of the grating; by expanding in one dimension only with prisms, the grating tilt in the orthogonal plane is made noncritical. Typically four prisms are used in pairs with substractive dispersions to give an in-line achromatic arrangement, constituting a quad-prism expander (see Fig. 6 in the next section). The magnifica-

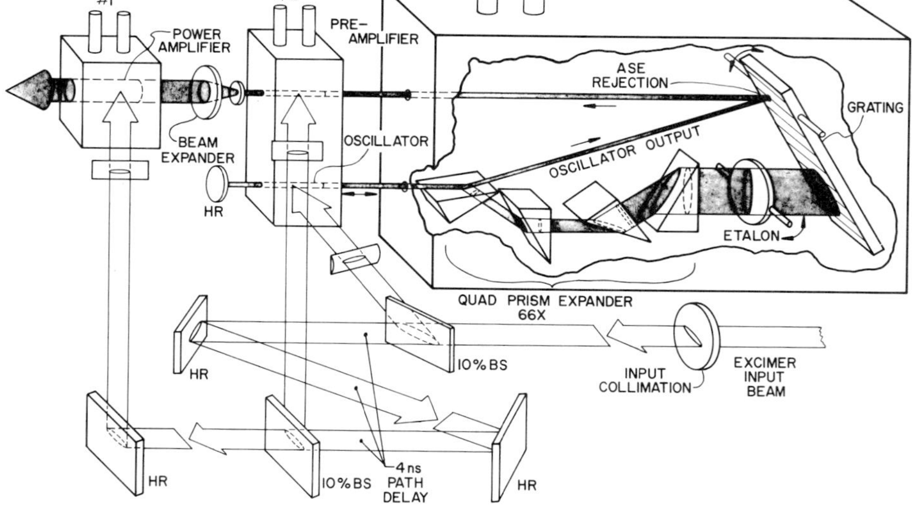

FIG. 6. Schematic diagram of a narrow-linewidth short-pulse dye laser of current design, for pumping by an excimer laser. Two stages of amplification and features increasing resolution and rejecting amplified spontaneous emission are shown. Highly reflecting mirrors are labeled as HR and beamsplitters as BS. (Placement of dye cells, optics, and angles between beams are altered for purposes of clarity.) (Courtesy of Lambda Physik, Göttingen, West Germany.)

tion given by a single prism (Fig. 5b) is large only at very high incidence angles, creating a large entrance-face reflection loss. By using several prisms, the incidence angle can be brought nearer to Brewster's angle to drastically reduce this loss; to produce the 66 times expansion of Fig. 6 with four symmetrical prisms, the incidence angle would be about 74° and the transmission 70% (through all four prisms) for the favored polarization direction lying in the incidence plane. The prisms automatically polarize the dye laser beam and are more economical than an achromatic telescope. Most importantly, large beam expansions are possible in a shorter length, allowing more transits during the excitation pulse and more efficient extraction of the oscillation input energy.

C. Excimer Laser-Pumped Dye Lasers and Oscillator/Amplifier Configurations

As more powerful short-pulse pump lasers were developed, the dye-laser designs evolved to make use of them. The limit on the small-signal gain per pass in a short-pulse oscillator is due to the growth of amplified spontaneous emission (ASE). This will be greatest for wavelengths near the peak of the emission cross section σ_e, and the intensity reached in a single pass must be kept well below one saturation intensity I_s [which by Eq. (8) varies inversely with σ_e] to prevent depletion of the gain at the desired, fed back wavelength λ_D. Calculation of the growth of ASE for a cylindrical geometry shows this will be true if a conservative rule of thumb is followed, that the gain per pass $G = (\exp k_0 L)$ be kept below $(L/w_p)^2$, the square of twice the aspect ratio of the pumped volume (w_p is the pump beam radius). (The spectral separation between the ASE and λ_D at the ends of the dye tuning range means the ASE can be spectrally filtered outside the resonator here; in mid tuning range, the heavy gain saturation at λ_D reduces the ASE.)

High gains in one pass thus require a long, thin pumped volume, leading to small total volumes and ineffective use of a powerful pump laser. A better route to high-output energies in a tunable narrowband source is to use an oscillator–multiple-stage amplifier configuration. Here the inefficiency of the oscillator (from lossy spectral filters and the cavity length to contain them) can be ignored, as most of the pump energy is put into the following amplifier cells. By spectral filtering between stages, and timing (with path delays) the arrival of the pump pulse at the amplifier cell, ASE can be minimized. The amplifiers work in the partially saturated regime, which smooths out intensity fluctuations. The beam can be expanded between stages (with the dye concentration adjusted in each cell) to achieve a large active volume and a balance between amplifier extraction efficiency and absorption losses from the excited singlet state, a problem in high-gain systems with a large percentage of inverted molecules.

These features are evident in the modern design for a short-pulse, narrow-linewidth dye laser shown in Fig. 6. (Other designs also in use are the Littmann grating mount, a high-incidence grating with back-up mirror, and sometimes three amplifier stages.) This shows an excimer laser-pumped laser, but the designs for doubled Nd : YAG laser pumping are very similar. The 308-nm line from the xenon chloride excimer is used to pump some 20 dyes covering 332–970 nm. In the longer-wavelength dyes, this is by absorption to higher singlet states, which nonradiatively relax to the upper laser state (see Section II,B). (There is usually reduced photochemical stability with UV pumping of low Stokes efficiency dyes, however.) Pump beams of 100 W average power (0.4 J energy in 28-nsec pulses at 250 Hz rate) are available.

An excimer is a molecular species that is stable only in the excited state. In a XeCl excimer laser, a high-current pulsed discharge in a mixture of xenon and chlorine gas makes Xe^+ and Cl^-, which attract to form the excited $XeCl^*$ molecule, the upper laser state. After radiative decay, the molecule dissociates back to Xe and Cl, so there is no laser lower-state bottleneck to be concerned with in this laser. The discharge channel in an excimer laser is rectangular, giving an oblong cross section to the pumping beam (entering from the right in Fig. 6), making transverse pumping the most convenient. Ten percent of this beam is split off and focused into the dye cell (number 2) of the Hänsch type oscillator whose resonator mirrors are the grating on the right and the high reflector to the left of the dye cell. In the design shown, the first prism of the 66× quad-prism expander is placed at a higher incidence angle to make the reflection off its input surface serve as the oscillator output coupler. This output beam is directed at the grating at a small incidence angle, smaller than the angular width of the diffraction lobe for the unexpanded beam. This second diffraction off the grating thus acts as a spectral filter (that tracks automatically), reducing the amount of oscillator ASE that enters the preamplifier stage. An intracavity etalon with a finesse of 30 and order spacing of 1 cm^{-1} gives an 0.03-cm^{-1} linewidth, scannable either by microprocessor-controlled tilting of the grating and etalon (30 cm^{-1} range before resetting the etalon order) or by changing the gas pressure in the sealed oscillator housing. The 4-nsec path delay of the pump beam, before the 10% split off to pump the preamplifier dye, allows an appropriate oscillator buildup time before gating "on" the amplification of the next stage. The remaining 80% of the pump beam is weakly focused into the enlarged active volume of the final power amplifier stage, which is filled by the appropriately enlarged dye beam (about eight diameters expansion). This dye cell has a separate dye circulation system to allow the concentration to be adjusted for a longer absorption depth.

At 90-W average 308-nm input power, this system has generated, at a 250-Hz pulse rate with fast flows of coumarin 102 dye to avoid burning the dye cells, an average output power of 16 W at 475 nm. This is at 0.2 cm^{-1} linewidth (no etalon), with less than 1% ASE and a beam divergence of twice the diffraction limit. At 22 nsec pulse length this is 2.9 MW peak power. With an etalon giving 0.04 cm^{-1} linewidth, the average power was 13 W. At the time this article is being written, only a few dyes have been characterized at this high an input power, an example of a point in the evolutionary race between short-pulse pump and dye lasers where the pump laser is a little ahead.

D. Dye Lasers Pumped and Mixed With Harmonics of the Nd: YAG Laser

For the highest peak powers (at lower pulse repetition rates and average powers), the dye laser is pumped (and mixed) with harmonics of the *Q*-switched neodymium–YAG laser. Higher peak powers result from a more efficient pump wavelength (green, 532 nm) for rhodamine dyes, coupled with a shorter pump pulse length (of 5–9 nsec).

Pump energy is stored in the optically excited solid-state YAG laser rod over the upper-state lifetime of 200 μsec, and an intracavity electro-optic *Q*-switch dumps this stored energy at a fixed repetition rate, usually 10 Hz, to form these short pulses. (The fixed rate allows the thermal lens in the thermally loaded rod to be accounted for in optimizing the YAG resonator design.) High-power YAG systems consist of an oscillator rod followed by a larger-diameter amplifier rod. For dye pumping, the fundamental wavelength of 1.064 μm must be doubled in a phase-matched nonlinear crystal to the green wavelength. For shorter-wavelength spectral coverage, the green beam is sum-frequency mixed with the unused portion of the fundamental in a second nonlinear crystal to generate a 355-nm ultraviolet pump beam, the third harmonic. Mixing is like doubling, but with photons of unequal energies. Amplitude noise on the fundamental is carefully controlled as the noise level multiplies in these nonlinear conversions.

The same processes of doubling and of mixing with the 1.06-μm fundamental beam, are performed with the strong outputs of the green pumped dyes as well as to achieve spectral coverage into the ultraviolet. These nonlinear conversions are most efficient for beams in the lowest-order transverse intensity profile, or TEM_{00} Gaussian mode. It was the development of low-order-mode YAG lasers, based on unstable resonators with diffraction or polarization output coupling, that made pumping dyes with YAG lasers practical. This is also the reason for the main difference in dye laser design for use with YAGs, namely, that for the green-pumped dyes the final power-amplifier stage is pumped longitudinally, with the round, Gaussian profile pump beam folded in and overlapped along a common axis or at a small angle with the dye beam. The dye laser then replicates the low-order mode of the pump beam, enhancing the subsequent nonlinear conversions.

A 10-Hz YAG–dye system with 532-nm pump pulses of 360 mJ energy produces 120-mJ output pulses at 560 nm with rhodamine 6G dye, in a 5-nsec pulse of 0.3 cm^{-1} linewidth (no etalon), and less than 1% ASE. That is a 33% conversion efficiency, a 24-MW peak power, and 1.2 W average power with a beam divergence of four times the diffraction limit. With an etalon, 90-mJ pulses are produced at 0.05 cm^{-1} linewidth. Linewidths increase in the nonlinear conversions with the number and bandwidths of the photons involved.

E. Short-Pulse Dye Laser Tuning Spectrum

Dye output tuning curves for the two pump sources are compared in Fig. 7. This shows the output energy per pulse versus dye and output wave number, with only that portion shown of a dye's tuning range where the output exceeds

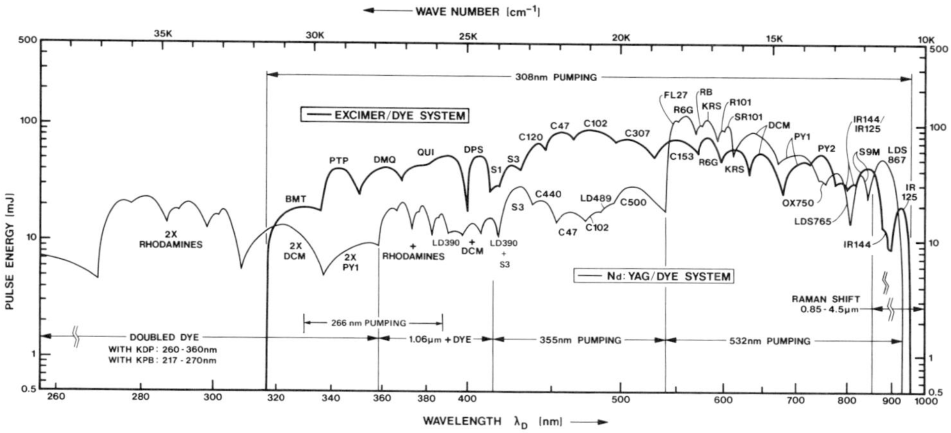

FIG. 7. Output tuning curves in energy per pulse at low repetition rates for excimer laser-pumped (heavy line) and Nd : YAG laser-pumped (light line) short-pulse dye lasers. Only the upper portion of a dye's tuning curve (above that of the adjacent dyes) is shown. Alternative pumping schemes to those shown are also possible for the YAG system, with the 266-nm fourth harmonic to pump dyes with outputs of 334–387 nm and with the 1.06-μm fundamental to pump dyes with outputs of 1.09–1.32 μm. (Excimer data, courtesy of Lambda Physik, Göttingen, West Germany; Nd:YAG data, courtesy of Quanta-Ray, Mountain View, Calif.)

that of the adjacent dyes. To obtain these results, the pump systems are configured to maximize the energy per pulse. This is at low repetition rates (<10 Hz), giving 0.5 J energy per 308-nm pump pulse for the XeCl system, and for the YAG system, 0.36 J per 532-nm pump pulse, 0.15 J per 355-nm pump pulse, and the undoubled portion of the initially 0.8-J, 1.06-μm mixing pulse. At higher rates both systems show a decreasing energy per pulse (but an increasing average power) as the lasers must dissipate more heat. The YAG system reaches a plateau of constant average power at about 15 Hz and is not designed to be used above 30 Hz. The excimer system pulse energy decreases more slowly, to 80% of the single pulse energy at a 250-Hz repetition rate, giving the excimer system the capability for nearly an order of magnitude higher average power. The difference in efficiency of the pump wavelength and in the shorter pulse width gives the YAG system the capability in the rhodamine dye region for nearly an order of magnitude higher peak power, and in this sense the two pumping systems are complementary.

Other features of Fig. 7 are also readily related to differences in the pump sources. For the strong green-absorbing dyes, the lower conversion efficiency of the excimer system is nearly accounted for by the lower Stokes efficiency η_S, which makes the 0.5-J UV input equivalent to 0.29 J of green input. Conversely, the UV excimer efficiently pumps the dyes lasing in the blue, where conversion to the third harmonic cuts the YAG pump power to less than half. In the red output region where there are common dyes, notice the shift to longer wavelengths for the excimer system. This is due to the overlapping σ_a absorption at the higher dye concentration, adjusted for a short transverely pumped absorption length and a more weakly absorbed pump wavelength. (The dye codes either are listed in the next section or are cross-referenced in laser dye manufacturers' literature.)

The YAG system propagates its strength in the red lasing dyes (using appropriate crystals and steering optics) by sum-frequency mixing these outputs with the YAG fundamental to cover the 358-to-413-nm span and doubling these dyes for the 270-to-358-nm span. Thus the characteristic pattern of the red dye tuning peaks appears three times in the YAG/dye spectrum. In both systems, doubling the coumarin and stilbene dye outputs reaches shorter UV wavelengths (only the YAG results are shown in Fig. 7), to 217 nm with two crystals. Output wavelengths are extended into the infrared to about 4.5 μm with both systems by directing the dye beam into a Raman shifter, a long (1 m) high-pressure (30 atm) cell filled with hydrogen gas. The hydrogen molecules are driven in coherent vibrations by the high-intensity input light scattered in the Raman process, and they radiate coherent beams shifted in wave number from the input beam in increments of the hydrogen vibrational level spacing of 4155 cm^{-1} at conversion efficiencies exceeding 20% for the first Stokes wave (light frequencies downshifted by one vibrational spacing) and 2% for the first anti-Stokes wave (upshifted frequencies, used to extend outputs deeper into the ultraviolet). In the days before lasers, the Raman effect was considered a weak process, as hours of exposure time with a several-kilowatt mercury arc source were required to register a Raman-shifted line on a spectrographic plate. With little more electricity taken from the wall than required by the old arc source, the short-pulse dye laser system produces, by stimulated Raman scattering, Raman-shifted beams of a megawatt peak power. Thus the wavelength extension techniques employed with short-pulse dye lasers serve quite well as examples of the nonlinear optics applications for the beams these systems generate.

IV. Continuous-Wave, Single-Frequency Dye Lasers

A. Dye Cells, Dye Jets, and Focusing Cavities

The first continuously operated dye laser focused the pump light from an argon ion laser into a cell of flowing dye to a spot diameter of around 10 μm, an active cross-sectional area of only 10^{-6} cm^2. By Eq. (12), this brought down the pump power needed to be comfortably above threshold to less than a watt, and the dye flow took care of cooling and triplet-state relaxation by exchanging the dye in this tiny active volume every few microseconds.

Focusing the coherent pump beam to this diameter was no problem, but building a stable dye laser resonator with a minimum area or beam waist diameter this small to overlap the pump spot was another matter. The necessity for matching the two beam diameters comes from a calculation of the filling factor η_F of Eq. (13) for the cw case of longitudinal pumping. A Gaussian TEM_{00} mode pump beam of $1/e^2$-radius w_p is assumed, whose axis and waist location overlaps that of a TEM_{00} mode dye beam of radius w_D. As previously defined, the ratio of beam areas is $\rho_0 = w_D^2/w_p^2$, where in this case the subscript zero has been added to indicate that the beam radii are to be taken as their minimum values, at their waists. The results are that the incremental gain constant for the dye beam is reduced from the plane wave result of Eq. (7) (where I_p is taken as the peak pump intensity at the center of the Gaussian profile) by a factor of $1/(1 + \rho_0)$, the threshold pump power in Eq. (13) is increased by a factor $(1 + \rho_0)$, and the filling factor η_F in Eq. (13) becomes $\rho_0/(1 + \rho_0^2)^{1/2}$. The output power is still a linear function of the input power above threshold, as given by Eq. (13), but the slope of this conversion increases only asymptotically with ρ_0, while the threshold power subtracted from the pump power increases linearly. Consequently there is in practice an optimum value of $\rho_0 \approx 1.2$–1.3 (giving $\eta_F \approx 0.8$), namely, that the dye beam diameter should be only slightly larger than the pump beam diameter.

The necessary small beam diameter was achieved with a resonator consisting of a flat and curved mirror (radius R), whose mirror separation d was critically adjusted around $d \approx R$ (but with $d < R$) to be near the stability limit. A resonator is said to be stable when multiply reflected paraxial rays stay within the structure; for this case, as d approaches R, a multiply reflected ray makes increasingly steep angles with the axis as it propagates, until at $d > R$ the ray walks out of the structure, as a ray tracing in the unfolded resonator (an equivalent sequence of lenses) will readily show. As this unstable condition is approached, the beam diameter at the flat mirror shrinks toward vanishing, and at the curved mirror it blows up to exceed the mirror aperture diameter. The first cw dye laser used $R = 4.5$ mm, and the spacing difference $R - d$ was set to 20 μm, to within ± 0.3 μm to keep the dye beam area within $\pm 20\%$ of the desired size. If the curved-mirror radius were made larger in such a resonator (to accommodate a wavelength tuning device), the tolerance on the required mirror spacing would become proportionally smaller. Clearly, a less critical assembly than a two-mirror resonator is needed for a cw dye laser.

A three-mirror or focusing resonator consisting of two curved mirrors and a flat provides this (Fig. 8b). This has a long arm of length $d \approx 0.6$ m where the beam is collimated and of a relatively large diameter $2(2d\lambda/\pi)^{1/2} \approx 1$ mm. The beam is then brought to a small focus of diameter $R(\lambda/2\pi d)^{1/2} \approx 40$ μm by the internal focusing mirror of radius $R \simeq 0.1$ m. A rhodamine 6G wavelength of $\lambda = 0.6$ μm has been assumed here.

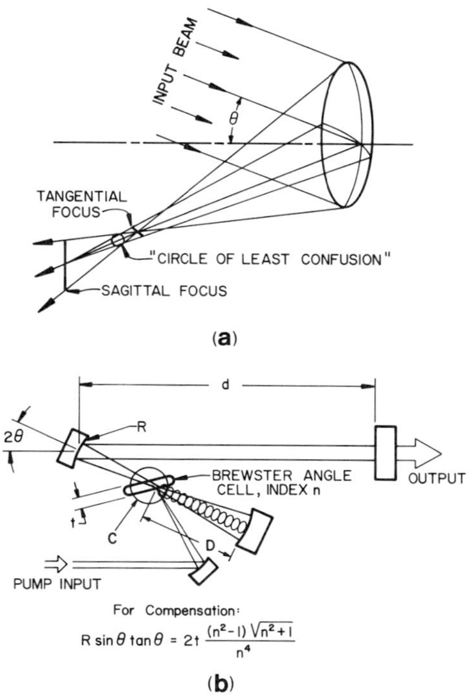

FIG. 8. (a) Astigmatism of an off-axis spherical mirror and (b) its compensation by a Brewster plate in a three-mirror focusing cavity, as originally used for standing-wave cw dye lasers.

(These dimensions are appropriate to the cw laser discussed below, which is pumped with a 6- to 24-W input and so works with a proportionally larger focal area than the earlier cw laser.) A new problem is introduced with this solution, which is fortunately readily solved. A spherical mirror used off-axis like the internal folding mirror in Fig. 8b generates an astigmatic focus, as shown in Fig. 8a. The rays lying in the incidence plane see the mirror's curvature foreshortened into a tighter arc and come to an out-of-plane line focus (the tangential focus) ahead of the on-axis focal length; rays lying in a plane orthogonal to the incidence plane see no foreshortening and reach a line focus (the sagittal focus) lying in the incidence plane beyond the on-axis focal length. In between the line foci, the beam shape becomes round (the "circle of least confusion") but at a considerably larger focal area.

Fortunately, an astigmatism of the opposite sense results when a flat plate is placed in the focused beam in the same plane of incidence but at an angle off normal incidence. In the dye laser this will be the dye cell, and it can compensate the fold-mirror astigmatism and restore the small (round) focus. The incidence angle chosen for the plate will be Brewster's angle θ_B (where $\tan \theta_B = n$, the index of refraction of the plate) for low loss. [Minimizing the nonuseful resonator losses a in Eq. (9) is very important in cw dye lasers that operate at low gain; this accounts for the abundance of Brewster angle faces found on cw intracavity wavelength control devices—which then serve to polarize the beam as well.] For a dye cell of thickness t, the correct fold angle 2θ between the collimated and focused beams that achieves compensation is calculated in Fig. 8b; for a 3-mm-thick glass cell in the example above, the result is a 9° fold angle.

The stability limits for a three-mirror resonator are computed as in the two-mirror case after forming from the combination of the output and fold mirror an optically equivalent single mirror, which has a small radius of curvature $R' = R^2/2(2d - R) = 4.5$ mm in the example. In aligning the dye laser, as the spacing between the two curved mirrors of Fig 8b is varied plus or minus half this distance off the central focus position, the dye spots on the curved mirrors blow up to fill the mirror aperture as the resonator reaches its limits of stable focus. The spot at the focus, in the dye, correspondingly shrinks toward vanishing, which gives a way to adjust ρ_0 downward and experimentally find the optimum value. Since the resonator for a laser must be stable in both the tangential and sagittal planes, if the astigmatism compensation is not correct, this range of stable focus adjustment is reduced by the amount of residual astigmatism (distance between the line foci of Fig. 8a), and the output beam is not round (except for the one adjustment where the circle of least confusion lies in the plane of the dye). For the resonator of the example, assuming perfect compensation, the adjustment range over which the dye beam area stays within ±20% of the central focus size is ±1.5 mm, a manageable tolerance and a vast improvement over the two mirror case. Note in Fig. 8b that the pump beam enters the dye cell at a slight angle to the dye beam (called noncollinear pumping), which is permissible as by the Beer's law absorption profile a good overlap of the two beams is only essential in the first third of the path length in the dye, where over half of the pump beam is absorbed (for a total absorption of 80–85% as normally employed).

The improved ease of operation made by the focusing resonator soon led from milliwatt-level to watt-level cw output powers (at higher input powers), accentuating another problem. No

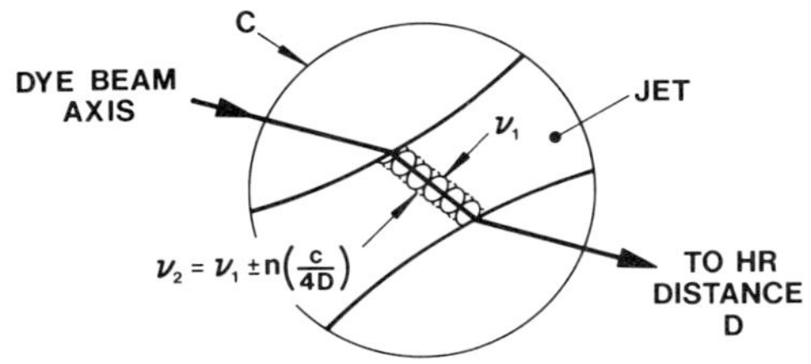

FIG. 9. Enlarged view of the jet, replacing the dye cell inside the circle C of the three-mirror cavity of Fig. 8b, showing the standing waves of the first frequency to lase locally depleting the gain or "burning spatial holes." This leaves gain regions unaddressed and allows a second frequency to lase.

matter how clean or carefully filtered the dye solution was made, something that would burn and stick always seemed to pass through the focused pump spot after a few hours of operation, forcing shutdown and realignment of the system on a clean position on the dye cell. The answer to this was to eliminate the dye cell! It was realized that good optical quality in the region of the dye was needed over an area only a few times larger than the small area of the focus. Experimentation with free jets of dye dissolved in a viscous solvent like ethylene glycol, squirted at 10 m $\sec^{-1}$ from a nozzle with a slotted tip and caught in an open tube returning the solution to a fluid pump, showed this jet stream to give adequate surface flatness, stability, and dye velocity. (The flat jet actually necks down near the middle of its cross section as shown in Fig. 9, and is translated during set-up to find the mid position where the two surfaces are parallel.) A jet and catch tube are shown in Fig. 10. In addition to solving the burning problem, nozzles are much more economical than optical quality cells. Astigmatism can be so reduced by closing up the fold angle (possible because of the small jet dimensions, only 4 mm wide by 0.1 mm thick in section at the incidence plane) that compensation is no longer necessary.

B. Spatial Hole Burning and Ring Cavities

To fulfill its promise as a light source for high-resolution spectroscopy, the cw dye laser had to be operated with a single-frequency output (i.e., in a single longitudinal and transverse mode), which led to the development of tunable intracavity selective filters or "filter stacks" capable of supressing oscillation in all but one such resonator mode. These are considered in the next section; here the phenomenon of spatial hole burning is discussed. This limits the single-frequency power obtainable in the resonator of Fig. 8b to small values.

The three-mirror cavity shown is called a

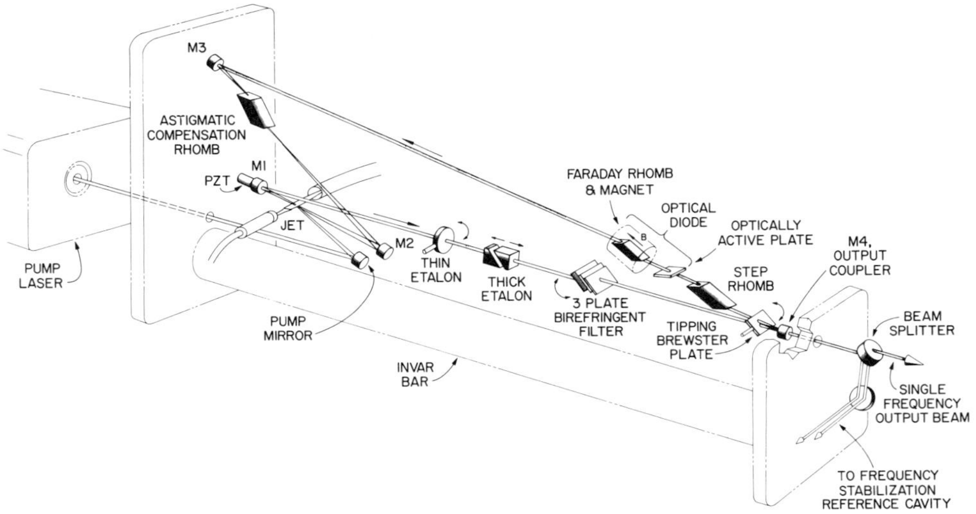

FIG. 10. Tunable single-frequency ring (traveling-wave) dye laser of current design. Spherical folding mirrors M1 to M3 and flat output coupler M4 fold the beam in a figure-eight path, which is traversed in the direction shown by arrows due to the biasing action of the optical diode element. Elements in the horizontal arm lying between M1 and M4 constitute the tunable filter stack, and the output frequency is controlled and the linewidth narrowed by a frequency stabilization servo (whose elements are not shown). (Courtesy of Coherent, Inc., Palo Alto, Calif.)

standing-wave or linear resonator, because the right-going and left-going dye beams in the resonator coincide and transform into each other at the normal incidence reflections at the two end mirrors. The superposition of these two traveling waves produces standing waves in the cavity that have nodes at the reflecting end surfaces. The allowed resonant frequencies or longitudinal modes of the cavity are precisely those that fit an integer number of half wavelengths into the optical path between the two end mirrors, as this condition gives constructive interference of the multiply reflected waves and results in the standing waves shown over length D in Fig. 8b. The oscillation in this resonator is at a single frequency, say the frequency ν_1. By counting half wavelengths from the nearest end mirror (the curved mirror at distance D from the jet), it is seen that inside the jet (see the magnified view of Fig. 9, inside the circle C of Fig. 8b) the standing waves occupy only part of the pumped volume. A second cavity mode with a frequency near $\nu_2 = \nu_1 \pm n(c/4D)$, where n is an integer, will have antinodes where the first mode has nodes and hence will not be suppressed by the gain saturation due to the first mode—the two modes in the same jet interact with spatially separated dye molecules. The first mode is said to "burn spatial holes" in saturating the gain medium, and the second mode utilizes the gain left between the holes made by the first. When a standing-wave, initially single-frequency dye laser is pumped well above threshold in an attempt to increase the single-frequency output power, at a fairly low input power a second frequency ν_2 begins to oscillate and destroys the single-frequency operation.

This limit is removed by going to the contemporary form of single-frequency dye laser in a traveling-wave or "ring" resonator (Fig. 10). The optical elements of the laser are shown here in their actual positions, with their support structure (invar bar and end plates) indicated in phantom lines. The dye beam is folded in a loop by mirrors M1 to M4, avoiding normal incidence end reflections and standing waves. (Actually, the folded path is more of a figure eight, to keep the fold angles on spherical mirrors M1 to M3 and their astigmatism small and compensable by the thick Brewster plate, or compensating rhomb, between M2 and M3.) Since the pumped volume is wholly utilized by a traveling wave, the first direction to oscillate (right- or left-going) will suppress the other possible one, and a single-frequency (s.f.) ring laser runs stably and naturally in one direction only. But cw dye lasers are subject to having their oscillation very briefly but often interrupted and restarted (due to microscopic particles or bubbles in the jet stream passing through the focal volume). A means to bias favorably one direction is required, or the output beam switches randomly and uselessly in exit angle from the output coupler.

The biasing device is called an "optical diode" and consists of a Faraday rhomb (a glass plate in a magnetic field) and an optically active plate. Considerations of time-reversal symmetry in Maxwell's equations dictate that any one-way or nonreciprocal light wave device be based on the Faraday effect, or the rotation of the direction of a linear polarization in transit of a material in a longitudinal magnetic field. The sense of the rotation depends only on the sign of the magnetic field B; for instance, for B pointing away from M4 in Fig. 10, the electric field of *either* a right-going or left-going beam is tipped away from the observer in a transit of the Faraday rhomb. When this is combined with a *reciprocal* polarization rotator (the Brewster incidence crystal quartz plate cut with optic axis along the ray propagation direction, to show optical activity), the forward or favored wave suffers substractive rotations, resulting in no tip of polarization out of the incidence plane of the remaining Brewster plates in the cavity and no reflection loss there. The backward wave suffers additive rotations and subsequent reflection losses; experimentally, a small differential loss of only 0.4% between these waves was found to be sufficient to always select the forward wave. The Faraday and optically active rotations are made to match over the desired spectral region by appropriate choice of magnetic field, rhomb material, and quartz plate thickness.

In addition to giving an order of magnitude increase in single-frequency output power, ring cavities enhance the intracavity second-harmonic generation process. By having all of the fundamental intracavity power traveling in one direction, the power of the doubled output, which extends single-frequency spectroscopy into the near ultraviolet, is increased an automatic factor of four.

C. Tunable Filter Stacks for Single-Frequency Lasers

Most of the remaining intracavity elements of Fig. 10 comprise the single frequency filter stack, a series of frequency filters of progressively narrower bandwidths, with overlaid center frequencies that tune together, designed to allow oscillation in but a single longitudinal mode of the ring cavity. (The transverse TEM_{00} dye mode is selected by the overlap with a TEM_{00} mode pump beam; this is called "gain aperturing.") Aside from the coarsest element (the lasing bandwidth of the dye itself), these filters all use the constructive interference between a first beam, and a second beam split off and delayed by a path length of an integer number of wavelengths, to generate a transmission peak. Each integer labels an order number of the multiply peaked filter, the spacing in frequency between orders is called the free spectral range (FSR), and the bandwidth of a transmission peak is given as the full width at half-maximum (FWHM). To minimize the intracavity losses [a in Eq. (9)], the FWHM of each element in the stack is made just narrow enough to select a single order of the next finer element of the stack, and spectral condensation plays a considerable role in this selection process.

The filter stack must be designed to span an enormous range. The two parts of Fig. 11 showing the filter stack at low and high resolution are therefore drawn with the expansion of the horizontal scale of 300 times between them directly indicated to help visualize this. The parameters of the figure are appropriate for rodamine 6G dye at its peak 580-nm wavelength. The gain bandwidth of this dye, determined largely by the emission cross section $\sigma_e(\lambda_D)$ derived in Fig. 4c,

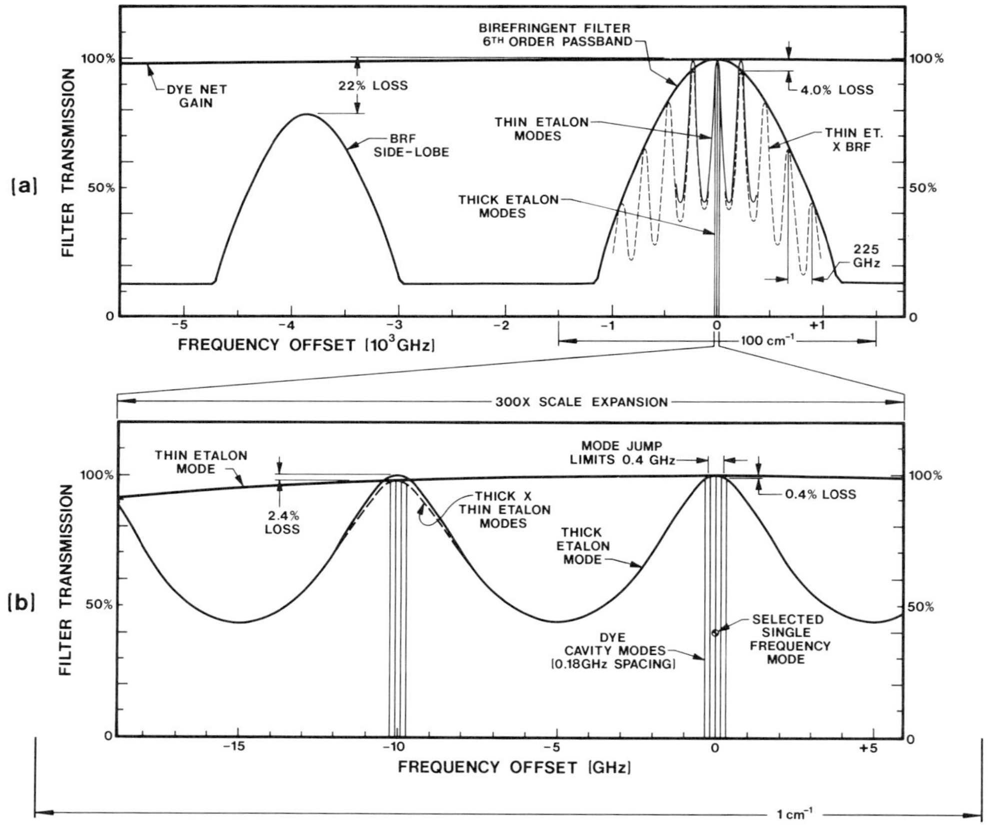

FIG. 11. Transmission functions of the filters in the tunable single frequency ring laser filter stack (a) at low resolution and (b) at 300 times higher resolution. Solid lines are for a filter element used alone, and dashed lines are for the composite stack. The curvature of the dye tuning curve is barely noticeable in (a) and the separation of the selected mode to the next adjacent cavity mode is barely visible in (b), emphasizing the enormous span of frequency over which the filter stack must work to select one mode out of 400,000. (Courtesy of Coherent, Inc., Palo Alto, Calif.)

is about 3×10^3 cm^{-1}, making the curvature of the gain curve (scaled up here slightly to fit a 0–100% axis) just noticeable on the 250-cm^{-1} span of Fig. 11a.

The FSR of the birefringent filter or BRF, the next finer element in the stack, is chosen to be 3×10^3 cm^{-1} so that only the sixth order falls within the region of strong lasing of this dye. Birefringent crystal quartz plates oriented at Brewster's incidence are each cut with their optic axis lying in the face of the plate but rotated about 45° out of the incidence plane. The linearly polarized dye beam is split upon entry into the crystal into orthogonally polarized components, the extraordinary and ordinary rays. These recombine at the exit face back into light linearly polarized in the incidence plane for the central pass frequency, but for other frequencies into elliptically polarized light (which is partially reflected at intracavity Brewster surfaces). Like an etalon where $2nt$ is the second beam path delay (n is the index, t the physical thickness) producing a multipeaked filter of FSR $= 1/2nt$ wavenumbers, this arrangement may be thought of as a two-beam interferometer with an $(n_0 - n_e)t$ path delay. In crystal quartz the ordinary–extraordinary index difference is about 0.01, so the birefringent filter acts like an etalon of thickness 1% of the physical thickness and is a convenient way to make a low-resolution interference filter. (An etalon of thickness of only 1 μm would be required to give the same FSR.) Three plates with precisely aligned axes and thicknesses in the exact ratios 1 : 4 : 16 produce an intracavity FWHM of 56 cm^{-1}, about half the width the same filter would produce extracavity between full polarizers. Gain saturation and spectral condensation are very effective in a cw dye laser, and this filter alone in the cavity ("broadband operation") will give an output spectral width of 0.03 cm^{-1}. The filter is tuned by rotation of the three plates together about their face normal, which varies the extraordinary index (and second beam path delay) while keeping Brewster's low-loss angle of incidence. Side lobes or frequency leaks in the filter transmission function correspond to polarizations that emerge from one or more (but not all) of the plates near the low-loss linear polarization. A BRF is not as positive as a grating for rejecting frequencies, because of these side lobes, but it is much lower in loss for the selected frequency (0.1% instead of 2–10%), which is what is important in cw dye lasers. It was the introduction of the low-loss BRF tuner in 1974 that allowed the cw dye laser to first span the visible with the low cw UV power then available to pump the blue lasing dyes.

A pair of low-reflectivity etalons (finesse of 1.8) reduces the BRF oscillating bandwidth to that of a single longitudinal cavity mode, the "thin" etalon of 7.5 cm^{-1} FSR or $\frac{1}{2}$ mm physical thickness, and the "thick" etalon of 0.33 cm^{-1} FSR and 10 mm physical thickness. Two etalons of low finesse give less loss for the selected mode than a single high-finesse etalon, due to a more complete overlap of the interfering beams (less "walk-off" loss). In Fig. 11a the thin-etalon transmission functions for the three central orders are shown as solid lines, and the products of the BRF and thin etalon functions (the composite filter) for several more orders are shown as dashed. The BRF suppresses the thin-etalon orders adjacent to the selected one by adding an extra 4% loss at the frequency offset of these orders. In Fig. 11b, the frequency scale is expanded 300 times to show the selection of a thick-etalon mode by the selected mode of the thin etalon. Here the curvature of the thin-etalon function is just noticeable, and a central thick etalon mode is selected by an extra 2.4% loss at adjacent orders. Finally, the thick etalon selects a single mode of the ring cavity to complete the filter stack, by inserting an additional 0.4% loss at adjacent cavity modes split off from the central one by a $c/P = 0.18$ GHz frequency offset (P is the path length around the ring perimeter). The total absorption and scatter loss per round trip at the selected mode frequency for the whole filter stack of Fig. 11, the a of Eq. (9), is 2.5%, with the walk-off loss of the thick etalon at 0.7% the largest component.

The center frequencies of this stack of filter elements must track together during scanning to tolerances that maintain proper mode selection. An offset of a coarse element, no greater than one-third of the FSR of the higher-resolution element whose order it selects, is acceptable. The basic continuous scan width of the system is 1 cm^{-1} (30 GHz); longer scans are pieced together from 1-cm^{-1} segments, and over this width the tracking tolerances and means of achieving them are as follows. The BRF need not be tuned at all but is stepped between segments. The thin etalon is tilt tuned with a rotational galvanometer and must stay within 3 GHz (or 10% of the scan range) of the linearly scanning frequency. This is done with a preprogrammed square-root drive to the galvo (the path-length change and hence center-frequency offset of a tilted etalon, goes as the square of the tilt angle away from normal incidence). The thick etalon must track to 60 MHz or 0.2% of the scan range, requiring a servo to meet this tolerance. The thick etalon is made up of two Brewster-surfaced prisms (essentially a solid etalon with a thin slice of air in the middle as shown in Fig. 10), so that its thickness may be tuned by piezoelectric translation. A small dither at a rate of a few kilohertz is added to the thick etalon drive voltage, generating a small-amplitude modulation of the output beam. This is phase-sensitively detected, giving a discriminant signal to lock the thick etalon center frequency to the scanning cavity mode frequency (standard dither-and-track circuit). To scan the cavity mode, a Brewster plate (on another rotational galvanometer) is tipped slightly ($\pm 2°$) off Brewster's angle. This introduces only slight reflection losses ($<0.4\%$) and linearly varies the path length through the plate by 120 μm, enough to scan the cavity frequency over the desired 1-cm^{-1} range. To avoid misaligning the ring cavity, this tipping plate is mounted near the beam vertex at the output coupler M4 and is traversed by both beams, in the design of Fig. 10. It was the introduction of the tipping Brewster plate as the cavity-mode scanning element that first allowed a 1-cm^{-1} or 30-GHz continuous scan range, due to the improvement in linearity and repeatability of this method over the older use of a mirror mounted on a piezoelectric element for the long-range scan.

D. The Narrowest Linewidths—Frequency Stabilization Servomechanisms

The intrinsic linewidth of the oscillation at the frequency of the selected single dye cavity mode, limited by spontaneous emission noise, can be found by the well-known Schawlow–Townes formula to be something less than 10^{-3} Hz. The observed linewidth is much larger and is determined not by this intrinsic width but by the stability of the cavity mode frequency given by $\nu_q = q(c/P)$ (where q is an integer of the order 3×10^6). The optical path P around the ring is subject to random environmental perturbations, a one-wavelength or 0.6-μm change in P, changing the cavity frequency by c/P or 0.18 GHz. The effective linewidth or frequency jitter produced by these perturbations will be (without stabilization) about 15 MHz rms, due to environmental noises, vibrations, and particularly due to the jet stream, whose thickness varies with pressure surges in the dye fluid circuit. This linewidth is reduced with a frequency stabilization servo that locks the dye cavity mode frequency to that of a stable reference interferometer, transferring the frequency stability properties of the output beam from that of the generating cavity, to that of the reference. The reference cavity, which can be compact and need not enclose a jet, is built to be stable by employing low-expansion materials in a temperature-stabilized housing, isolating the structure from vibrations, and sealing it against air-pressure changes.

A frequency servo consists of three parts: a *discriminator,* or error signal that changes sign when the perturbed output frequency passes through that of the reference; gain to boost this signal; and path-length transducers in the dye cavity driven by the amplified signal to bring the output frequency back to the reference value. The responses of the various transducers in this loop are included in the (complex) loop gain $M(f)$, which varies with the servo response rate or Fourier frequency f (the inverse of servo response time). The loop gain can be measured by breaking the loop, terminating the ends with the same impedances that were there before the gap, injecting a sinusoidal signal at frequency f into one end, and measuring the signal [$M(f)$ times as large] returned by the loop to the other end. Circuit analysis of the servo shows that a free-running or open-loop frequency deviation of the dye beam is reduced in magnitude when the loop is closed by the factor $1/[1 - M(f)]$. It is thus desirable to keep $M(f)$ large at high response rates f to correct excursions in P that occur even at rapid rates, to most reduce the output frequency jitter.

In doing this, however, the servo design must manage the phase shifts from all elements in the loop to keep the servo stable. The phase of $M(f)$ must be controlled over the full servo bandwidth where the magnitude of M is greater than unity, in order to keep the feedback negative and corrective and avoid oscillations of the loop, which correspond to a zero in the denominator of the feedback factor. All stable servos thus roll off the loop gain with increasing Fourier frequency to get and keep M less than 1 at high rates where phase shifts become uncontrollable. The two sources of phase shift of main concern are transducer resonances and the roll-off rate of M with f.

All path-length transducers have some form of inertia, and thus, when driven at a sufficiently high Fourier frequency f, they will resonate or reach large excursions at a drive frequency where the phase of their response is 90° relative to their low-f response. This resonance may span a narrow range of response rates, be highly nonlinear, and be critically dependent on small dimensions in the transducer (like the wall thickness of a piezoelectric element). Thus an inverse electrical filter (or "trap") added to the loop can generally only null out a transducer resonance to first order, and a servo designer's rule of thumb is to use gain roll-off to provide attenuation and a stability margin at the resonance by keeping the unity-gain frequency considerably smaller than the frequency of the lowest transducer resonance (no larger than one-third).

This upper bound on the unity-gain frequency is especially restrictive when phase shift due to the smooth, controlled roll-off of the loop gain itself is taken into account. This phase shift may be derived by interpreting mathematically the requirement of causality, that the response of the loop not precede its cause. The simplest case (most often used in practice) is for a constant roll-off slope S on a plot of log M versus log f, where S is constant over a minimum seven-octave span around unity gain (i.e., over frequencies from one-tenth to 10 times the unity-gain frequency). Then servo theory gives that this phase shift is proportional to S and reaches 180° (instability) at a slope of 12 dB/octave. A second designer's rule of thumb is thus to keep the roll-off rate less than 10 dB/octave, a painfully slow rate that limits the loop gain over much of the working servo bandwidth at Fourier frequencies below the unity-gain frequency, but such is the price for stability.

To summarize the basic design of a servo loop; the unity-gain frequency is usually dictated by the lowest resonant frequency of the path length transducers; the loop gain is made to rise at 10 dB/octave from unity gain toward lower response rates, reaching a maximum loop gain at a corner frequency determined by the drift rate of the reference [where generally $M(f)$ is leveled off, since it is pointless to provide more gain, and a tighter lock, good only at response rates where the reference is in error].

Usually, it is desirable to provide several length-control elements of different response rates in the dye cavity because the slow transducers will have larger correction ranges than the fast ones, and there is a corresponding correlation of speed with range among the forces perturbing the cavity length. The system of Fig. 10 connects the dc to 100-Hz components of the error signal to the galvo of the tipping Brewster plate, the slow (800 Hz first resonance) but long-range (30 GHz) transducer, to correct for room-temperature and air-pressure changes. With a crossover network it connects the 0.1-Hz to 10-kHz error information to the mirror M1 mounted on the piezoelectric transducer (PZT), the fast (30–60 kHz first resonance) but limited-range (1 GHz) element, to correct for bubbles or pressure fluctuations in the dye jet. The crossover network allows the first design rule to be followed in both the slow loop and the fast loop, to keep the servo stable. A convenient check that the servo is operating in the ring laser of Fig. 10 is to lightly push on a mirror end plate with a finger; when the servo is connected, the reflected spot off the tipping Brewster plate will reveal a proportional plate rotation, countering the direction of push and keeping P constant.

Frequency servos designed for dye lasers must address the fact that the dye oscillation is subject to brief (but frequent) momentary interruptions, or frequency excursions too fast for the servo transducers to follow due to bubbles in the jet stream. If the frequency servo can be made to automatically and rapidly relock the laser frequency to the original lock point after such an interruption, then the effect of the brief excursion can be made insignificant in the use of the laser, since this is generally to acquire time-averaged spectroscopic signals. The problem posed for the servo designer, since the laser oscillation may jump to a new dye cavity mode upon interruption (a "mode jump"), is how to unambiguously steer this arbitrary new frequency back to that of the original reference cavity mode.

Fortunately, the highest-resolution filter in the filter stack (the thick etalon) operates through a "mode-jump cycling" effect at optical rates as an optical frequency limiter and allows a relocking servo to be built. Figure 12 illustrates the relocking concept used for the laser and filter stack of Fig. 10 and 11. A discriminator is generated here by the "fast differencing" method (also called a "fringe-side" discriminator). This, one of the simplest discriminators, was the earliest type to be widely used, and is found today in commercial s.f. ring systems. A beamsplitter picks off from the output beam of Fig. 10 two low-intensity beams, one of which is transmitted through the reference cavity, the other attenuated an adjustable amount, and then the beams are detected with photocells connected to the input terminals of a fast differencing amplifier.

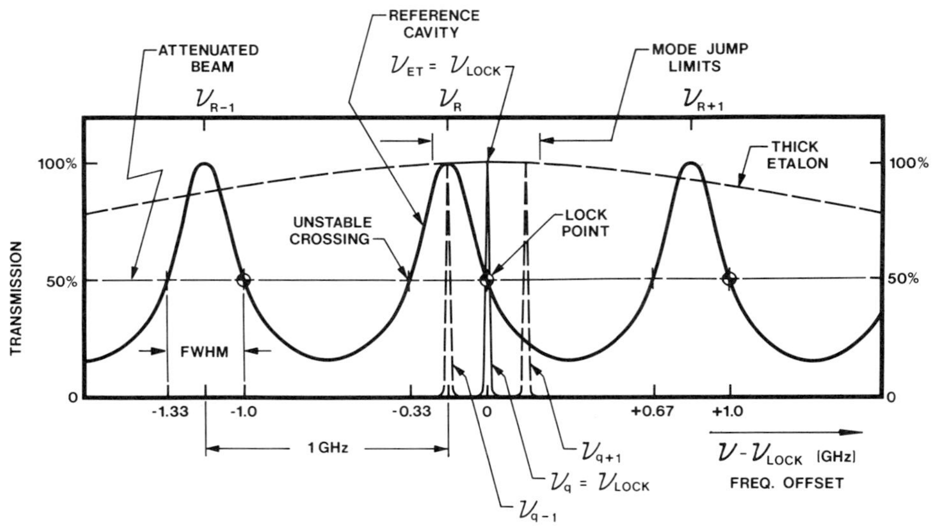

FIG. 12. Design for an automatic relocking servo with the "fringe-side" (fast difference) discriminator used with the ring laser of Fig. 10. The mode-jump limiting frequencies defined around the lock point (the zero-crossing frequency with a negative slope) must lie within that point's acquisition range (the frequency span between positive-slope zero crossings) to insure relocking to the original reference cavity mode after a momentary interruption of lasing. (Courtesy of Coherent, Inc., Palo Alto, Calif.)

The attenuation is adjusted to put the zero point of this difference signal at about the half-transmission point of a reference interferometer transmission peak (or half-way up the "side of the fringe"), as shown as a horizontal line labeled "attenuated beam" in Fig. 12. This level signal (independent of optical frequency) functions to prevent the mapping of intensity fluctuations into the difference, or frequency, error signal. The difference between this line, and the reference cavity transmission signal (at the negative slope zero crossing at 0 GHz frequency offset) is negative for frequencies above the zero crossing and positive below that lock point; taking the difference has generated a discriminator. There are additional potential lock points (negative-slope zero crossings) at -1.0 GHz, $+1.0$ GHz, and so forth, corresponding to adjacent reference cavity modes. These are separated by positive-slope, unstable zero crossings (at -1.33 GHz, -0.33 GHz, $+0.67$ GHz, and so forth) representing the boundaries or limits of the acquisition range of each stable lock point. The "mode-jump cycling" effect is used to contain the oscillating dye frequency within the acquisition range of the original lock point (of the reference cavity mode labeled ν_R) despite the interruption. Then when the perturbation has subsided, since there is only the original stable lock point (and no crossings to adjacent lock points) within the frequency range accessible to the dye oscillation, the servo will automatically relock as desired.

To understand mode-jump cycling, consider Fig. 12 and imagine the dye cavity modes ν_{q-1}, ν_q, ν_{q+1}, etc., being swept rapidly up in frequency by a fast perturbation, so rapidly that the thick-etalon tracking circuit cannot respond and the etalon peak is frozen in place. Originally the oscillating qth mode (at ν_q) is at the frequency of the etalon peak, but when this mode reaches an offset from the peak of $+\frac{1}{2}(c/P)$, it suffers a loss due to the etalon equal to that of the (nonoscillating) $(q - 1)^{st}$ mode at $-\frac{1}{2}(c/P)$ offset, and a mode-jump of the oscillation backward by $-c/P$ in frequency becomes possible. Due to the hysteresis introduced by gain saturation, the original oscillation will generally persist out to offsets greater than $\pm\frac{1}{2}(c/P)$ (both signs occur if downsweeps are considered as well as upsweeps). Nevertheless, observations have shown there are definite limits for the actual optical frequency change after the fast perturbation has subsided, regardless of the number of wavelengths of path change the perturbation contained. Measurements for the ring laser of

Fig. 10 over the visible dyes (and over the gain variation within the tuning range of each dye) give a maximum mode-jump limit span of less than $3(c/P)$ around the etalon peak (see Fig. 12). Once these limits are known, a relocking servo is constructed by choosing the parameters of the reference cavity such that when the system is normally locked and the thick-etalon frequency is aligned with the lock frequency, only one lock point is accessible from within this mode-jump limit span. For the fast-differencing discriminator of Fig. 12, the nearest unstable crossing point is at one fringe width (or FWHM, the full width at half maximum of the reference cavity peak) lower in frequency than the lock point. For symmetrical mode-jump limiting frequencies about the lock point, a relocking design is thus achieved with a reference cavity for which the FWHM is greater than half the mode-jump limit span.

A logical problem may exist in this relocking design, in that at the first turn-on of the servo, before the thick etalon frequency and reference cavity lock points are aligned, there may be no lock point within the mode-jump limit span. (For example, the etalon frequency could be at +0.33 GHz upon turn-on in Fig. 12). What happens then is that the fast length control element (the PZT mounted mirror) is driven to a limit of its range by mode-jump cycling and saturates, or ceases momentarily to function (until a lock is acquired, and the charge is bled from the capacitance of the PZT drive circuit). The servo response rate thus momentarily drops to that of the slow loop (the galvo response rate), which by design is comparable to the response rate of the thick-etalon dither-and-track circuit. Thus, the thick-etalon frequency can move on initial turn-on to allow acquisition of a lock point.

With other discriminators the details are different but the ideas are the same. A logical trail must be built, such that recovery from a momentary interruption leads only into the acquisition range of the original reference cavity mode. For servos with unity-gain frequencies in the megahertz range (attained with electro-optic path-length transducers), the bubble interruption may last several servo response times. This makes it necessary to clamp various transducer drive voltages within certain bounds and wait out the interruption. The response times and sequencing of elements during the recovery from the clamped state must then be tailored, to stay within the desired acquisition range.

Two other methods are also commonly employed for generating frequency discriminators. The first, due to Hänsch and Couillaud, generates a symmetrical, dispersion-shaped discriminator with relatively large signal amplitudes at large offsets from the lock point, which results in prompt relocking. It derives from a frequency-dependent elliptical polarization induced in the beam reflected from a reference cavity containing a Brewster plate with an incidence plane inclined to the plane of the linear input polarization. The second method, developed for lasers by Drever, Hall, Bjorklund, and their co-workers, is termed the "rf sideband lock," because the input beam to the reference cavity is modulated at a radio frequency with an electro-optic phase modulator. The upper and lower out-of-phase rf sidebands that this generates are split off from the central carrier by the modulation frequency, chosen to be greater than the width of the reference cavity resonance. When the laser (carrier) frequency is on resonance with a reference cavity mode, there is a buildup inside the cavity of standing-wave energy at the carrier frequency but not at the sideband frequencies. A discriminator is formed by heterodyning in a fast detector the fields reflected from the cavity, and phase-sensitively detecting the beat frequencies against the rf modulation source. Analysis of this signal shows it to be the optical analog of the Pound or "magic-tee" stabilizer for microwave sources, and to have the property of acting as an optical phase detector on resonance due to the phase memory of the buildup field leaking out of the cavity.

The linewidths produced by these systems are a function of the speed of the path-length transducers and the resultant unity-gain frequency or Fourier bandwidth of the servo. The commercial system of Fig. 10 with a tipping Brewster plate and a PZT mounted mirror as transducers, using a fast-differencing discriminator, achieves a 5- to 10-kHz servo bandwidth and an optical frequency jitter of 200–500 kHz rms measured over a 1-sec sampling time with a 10-kHz detector bandwidth. The laboratory system with the best reported performance adds an intracavity AD*P electrooptic phase modulator to the list of path-length transducers (a crystal whose index of refraction depends on an applied high voltage) and, using an rf sideband lock with a 40 MHz rf frequency, achieves a servo bandwidth of 3–4 MHz. The resulting jitter was so small that special techniques were required to measure it. A helium–neon laser was similarly rf sideband locked to an adjacent mode of the same reference cavity, so that problems with drift and isolation of the reference would not mask the measurement of the locked frequency jitter. The beat note between these two independently locked lasers was examined and found to be less than 100 Hz in width—only 2 parts in 10^{13} of the dye laser's output frequency. Such systems offer enormous opportunities for precision measurements in physics and other sciences.

The ability of a relocking system to rapidly and automatically recover from a momentary perturbation is what makes electronic control of an s.f. dye laser effective. This ability is put to good use in the most recently evolved version of this instrument, where the laser is coupled to a wavemeter and computer-driven over a 10-THz or 333-cm^{-1} scan width. Such a long scan is done by piecing together many shorter scans stored in memory, where the endpoints of the short scans are abutted by the computer to the wavelength precision of the coupled wavemeter to present seamless output spectra. All of the filter stack elements must be moved to cover this long scan, and reset each in turn after each has been scanned over its free spectral range. To do this, the computer is simply programmed to introduce a "momentary perturbation" of its own by clamping the drive signal for each element at its nominal value, opening the loop, resetting the appropriate element, and again closing the loop. The system then reacquires the original lock point just as though this had been an external perturbation.

E. Single-Frequency Dye Laser Output Tuning Spectrum

The argon and krypton ion pump lasers for the s.f. cw dye laser offer a wide span of pump wavelengths, and the dye laser performs best where the absorption maxima of efficient dyes can be matched to strong pump lines. The overlapping tuning ranges of the 11 combinations giving the highest reported output powers over the fundamental tuning range (the visible spectrum) in a single-frequency laser are shown in Fig. 13. Additional data for this figure are listed in Table I. All of the tuning curves are for the ring laser of Fig. 10, with the exceptions of the short-wavelength half of the stilbene 1 curve and all of the IR 140 curve. For these two ends of the fundamental spectrum, the laser was set up in a standing-wave (three-mirror) configuration, as a ring configuration was not needed for these low-gain combinations and the elimination of the optical diode losses gave better performance there.

Table I gives the pump powers used for these curves. The pump wavelengths or bands (groups of lines that lase simultaneously) from the argon ion laser are identified as UV for the ultraviolet (333–368 nm) pump band, BG for the blue-green

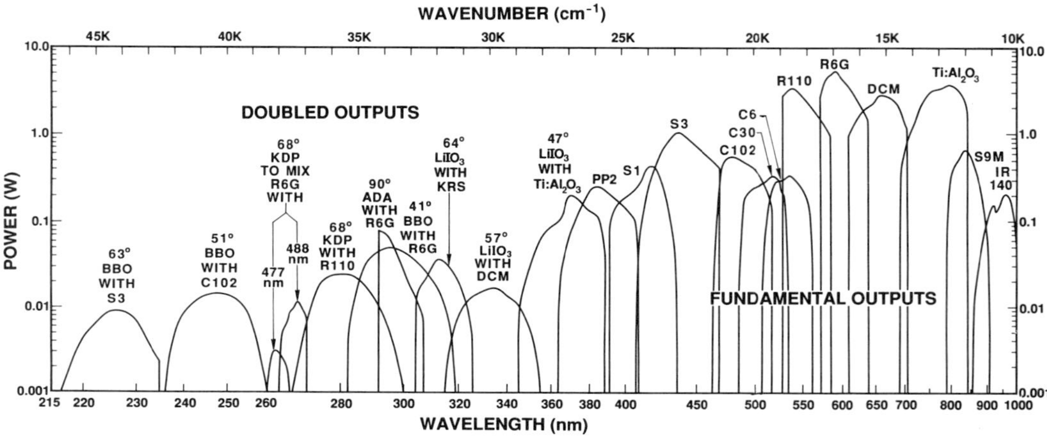

FIG. 13. Output tuning curves for the single frequency laser, pumped with the ion laser inputs listed in Table I. The fundamental outputs are extended into the ultraviolet by adding nonlinear crystals to the cavity to produce doubling and mixing. For discussion of the updated results in the media PP2, S1, S3, Ti : Al_2O_3, and doubling with BBO, see the discussion of recent developments in Section IX at the end of the article. [UV data and Ti : Al_2O_3 results courtesy of Coherent, Inc., Palo Alto, California, and visible data adapted with permission from Johnston, T. F., Jr., Brady, R. H., and Proffitt, W., (1982), *Appl. Optics* **21,** 2312.]

TABLE Ia. Fundamental Single-Frequency Outputs

Gain medium symbol	Molecular weight (amu)	Common name	Peak output λ_D (nm)	Peak output P_{max} (W)	$n\pi w_D^2$ (10^{-6} cm^2)	Optimum coupling t_0 (%)	Gain k_0L (%)	I_s (MW/cm^2)	Pump laser P_{in} (W)	Pump laser λ_p[a]
PP2	542	Polyphenyl 2	383	0.25	5.7	1.9	8	2.2	3.4	SUV
S1	569	Stilbene 1[b]	415	0.42	6.2	2.7	11	1.8	6.0	UV
S3	562	Stilbene 3	435	1.0	6.5	3.9	18	2.0	7.0	UV
C102	255	Coumarin 102	477	0.58	7.1	2.9	12	2.4	4.8	V
C30	347	Coumarin 30	518	0.38	7.7	2.4	10	2.1	4.6	V
C6	350	Coumarin 6[c]	535	0.35	8.0	3.8	16	0.8	6.0	B
R110	367	Rhodamine 110[c,d]	540	3.6	14	10	60	0.6	23	BG
R6G	479	Rhodamine 6G[c,d]	593	5.6	16	11	70	0.8	24	BG
DCM	303	Dicyano-methylene[c,d]	661	2.9	17	5.1	23	1.6	20	BG
Ti : Al_2O_3	—	Titanium-sapphire single crystal	790	3.6	94	5.3	23	0.4	20	BG
S9M	529	Styryl 9M	835	0.65	12	4.5	21	0.6	7.5	G
IR 140	779	Infrared dye 140[b]	960	0.2	6.2	~1	—	—	3.0	IR

TABLE Ib. Mixed and Doubled Single-Frequency Outputs

Crystal symbol	Match angle	Crystal name	Peak output λ_{UV} (nm)	Peak output P_{max} (mW)	Gain medium	Ion laser mixing line (nm)	Pump laser P_{in} (W)	Pump laser λ_p[a]
BBO	62°	Beta-barium borate	228	9	S3	—	7.1	UV
BBO	53°		248	15	C102	—	5.5	V
KDP	80°[e]	Potassium dihydrogen phosphate	262	3	R6G	477	7.5	BG
KDP	74°[e]		268	10	R6G	488	7.5	BG
KDP	68°		280	24	R110[c]	—	6.8	G
BBO	41°	Beta-barium borate	295	48	R6G[c]	—	8.5	G
ADA	90°	Ammonium dihydrogen arsenate	292	77	R6G	—	6.0	G
$LiIO_3$	65°	Lithium iodate	313	36	Kiton Red S	—	7.5	G
$LiIO_3$	57°		332	16	DCM	—	7.5	BG
$LiIO_3$	47°		370	200	Ti : Al_2O_3	—	20	BG

[a] Codes for the pump wavelengths are explained in the text, except for SUV, which is the 300–336 nm pump band.
[b] The IR 140 curve used a standing wave laser configuration; all others are for a ring laser. (The standing-wave portion of the S1 curve in the earlier edition is here replaced by ring laser data.)
[c] The triplet-state quencher COT was added here to the dye mix.
[d] Special water-based solvent AMX used (see the text).
[e] The crystal for R110 dye (cut for a match angle of 68° at Brewster incidence) was used here at large tip angle.

(455–514 nm) band, B for the blue (488 nm) wavelength, and G for the green (514 nm) wavelength; these last two are the two strongest individual lines and are often used singly. Similarly, for the krypton ion laser, V indicates the violet (407–415 nm) band, R the red (647–676 nm) band, and IR the infrared (753–799 nm) band. The prime example of a strong combination is the high-gain dye rhodamine 6G, which is efficiently pumped either by the blue-green argon band or single-line (for the best dye transverse mode control, important in intracavity doubling) with the 514-nm line, the highest-power line of all ion laser outputs. A single-frequency stabilized output of 5.6 W has been attained with this dye.

The dye laser was fully optimized for these fundamental tuning curves, making the available input power be the limit to the output reached. With the weaker pump lines, the radius of the fold mirror (M1 of Fig. 10) was decreased to tighten the dye and matching pump focal areas and keep the gain well above the 2.5% s.f. cavity losses. (The 10-cm radius for the red dyes became 7.5 cm for the stilbenes, coumarins, and S9M, and 5.0 cm for IR140). The transmission of the output coupler was also optimized across the span of each dye (the breaks on several of the tuning curves are places where a different output coupler was substituted). For the BG pumped dyes, a special dye solvent (called AMX by Johnston) consisting of three parts ammonyx LO and one part ethylene glycol, chilled to 10°C, replaced the normal ethylene glycol jet. This reduced the optical distortion of the jet from thermal lensing, which otherwise would limit the output at these input powers of 20 W or more. The ammonyx LO is mostly water, which has a low refractive index change with temperature and a high specific heat, yet due to the remaining component (a soap, lauryl amine oxide) has a high viscosity at this temperature and can form a stable jet. The additive COT (cyclooctatetraene), which relaxes the triplet state of the dye and enhances output, was used with this AMX solvent and in three other cases identified by footnote *c* in Table I. Small amounts of dissolving agents permitted dye concentrations sufficient for 80–90% pump beam absorption in the 0.1-mm jet thickness. For all of the Fig. 13 dye recipes, the observed locked jitter was less than 0.5 MHz rms, although when COT is added it must be fresh (stored in a vacuum ampule or nitrogen-purged container to avoid contact with oxygen, which turns it oily and immiscible). The vertical drops at the ends of some of the tuning curves are birefringent filter "break points," where the oscillation jumps from the main BRF transmission lobe to a side lobe closer to the peak of the dye gain curve. Tuning can be extended slightly beyond these breaks, by substituting a cavity optic coated to have a high transmission at the side-lobe wavelength.

Just as in the short-pulse dye laser case, these fundamental outputs are extended into the ultraviolet by doubling and mixing. In the short-pulse case, because of the high peak powers, high conversion efficiencies for the nonlinear processes are reached easily and the problem there is one of limiting the peak powers to less than the damage thresholds of the nonlinear crystals. The converse problem exists in the s.f. cw case, that of how to raise the fundamental power incident on the crystal sufficiently to reach a usable conversion efficiency. This is solved by placing the nonlinear crystal inside the dye laser cavity and replacing the output coupler with a high reflector, to reach circulating fundamental powers in the range 20–60 W and s.f. ultraviolet outputs of several milliwatts. The circulating intensity I_e at the focus in the dye jet is proportional (neglecting the threshold term) to the inverse of the cavity dissipative losses a, as shown by solving Eqs. (4) and (9) for I_e and setting $t = 0$, to give $I_e = I_s k_0 L / a$. The crystal absorption and scatter losses contribute to a and must be quite low (less than 1%) to reach the desired circulating powers. Therefore, high-quality, well polished crystals are used in the cavity at Brewster's incidence angle.

The high-power dyes R110 to LD700, for which doubling is attractive, span a broad fundamental wavelength range, best covered without gaps by angle-tuned phase matching. Angle matching produces a lower conversion efficiency to the ultraviolet than the alternative, temperature-tuned matching (with a fixed matching angle of 90°). But unlike this alternative, angle matching is insensitive to temperature gradients in the crystal and requires no slow, high-hysteresis temperature servo. (Temperature-tuned matching was the first method used for intracavity doubling in s.f. ring lasers, and it is still employed to double the long-wavelength half of the rhodamine 6G spectrum. Matching this half spectrum is done by heating an ADA crystal substituted for the astigmatic compensation rhomb of Fig. 10, from room temperature to ~100°C, producing the results in Fig. 13 and Table I).

The angle-matched conversion efficiency is lower because at input beam propagation directions other than 90° (or 0°) to the optic axis the harmonic beam is doubly refracted, or separates ("walks off") at a slight angle from the fundamental beam. This separation that develops between the beams effectively limits the interaction length, or distance over which the harmonic radiation is most efficiently produced, to the distance it takes for harmonic light generated at the crystal input face to be displaced by a beam diameter from the fundamental. This interaction length is the beam diameter divided by the walk-off angle. The conversion efficiency still rises with lengths longer than this, but the rate of increase slows and most of the additional harmonic power goes to make the UV beam progressively more elliptical and distorted in transverse mode profile.

Thus the angle-matched nonlinear crystals used with the dye laser, which must generate a clean beam profile to be usable in spectroscopy, are chosen to have a length of one interaction distance. This choice has the interesting consequence that the nonlinear crystal need not be placed in a beam focus in the cavity. If the crystal is placed in the collimated arm of the cavity where the fundamental beam is of large diameter (0.7 mm), there is no loss in conversion efficiency if the crystal length is scaled with the beam diameter to still be one interaction distance. This amounts to 1-cm-long $LiIO_3$ crystals and 4-cm-long KDP crystals for placement between M3 and the optical diode in the upper arm of the cavity of Fig. 10. This placement is chosen because of its mechanical convenience and because in a parallel beam the crystal may be made to produce negligible interference with the single-frequency filter stack. The doubled beam is coupled out of the resonator with a Brewster-angle dichroic beam splitter.

For most angular orientations in the cavity, the nonlinear crystal would act as a fourth plate of the birefringent filter, and when angle-tuned would surely disrupt the s.f. filter stack. This is avoided if the dye beam sees only one (pure) refractive index, which for the two crystals above is the pure ordinary index. The crystal is oriented so that the electric field of the refracted dye beam is perpendicular to the crystal optic axis, then the dye beam is "resolved" as a pure ordinary wave, and the crystal acts then as would a plate of glass instead of as a doubly refractive material. Setting up this perpendicular condition uses one of a total of two angular degrees of freedom; orienting the crystal for Brewster incidence (to maintain the high circulating fundamental beam power) uses the other. One of these conditions must be relaxed to permit angle-phase matching; for this adjustment the crystal is rotated about an axis parallel to the electric field direction, maintaining the "no-disruption" perpendicular condition. This gives smooth tuning (normal action of the s.f. filter stack) but produces cavity reflection losses that increase from zero as the square of the crystal tip angle away from Brewster's incidence. Several different cuts of crystal are used to minimize these reflection losses, each cut putting the Brewster incidence no-loss point at a wavelength in mid-tuning range of each dye to be doubled, with the results shown in Fig. 13 and Table I. These ultraviolet doubled-dye outputs scan over twice the range that the fundamental is scanned and have twice the jitter.

Tunable ultraviolet s.f. outputs extending to even shorter wavelengths, which still take advantage of the strong red dyes, can be generated by nonlinear mixing of the dye beam with a shorter-wavelength, single-frequency beam from an ion laser, to make the sum frequency. Mixing is just like doubling, but with unequal energies for the input photons; this merely requires slightly different phase-matching angles. For the results of Fig. 13, an ion laser cavity was folded to intersect and include in the ion beam cavity, the 68° KDP crystal in the dye cavity. The collimated-arm crystal placement permits this; the ion and dye beams must be collinear inside the crystal for the summing interaction, but at the Brewster angle faces of the crystal the two wavelengths are refracted differentially and separate with an angle between them of five times the beam divergence. The throw distance to the nearest dye cavity mirror in the collimated arm is large enough for the ion beam to clear the edge of the dye mirror, and on the other side of the crystal for the dye beam to clear the edge of an inserted ion cavity end mirror. The only common element in the two cavities is the KDP crystal. The ion laser is operated in a standing-wave cavity as the phase-matching condition with the traveling wave dye beam picks out the desired running wave ion beam component in the summing interaction. The mixed and doubled dye outputs of Fig. 13 allow single-frequency, high-resolution spectroscopy over the range 260–400 nm. Sum-frequency mixing has been used to generate even shorter UV tunable s.f. outputs, down to 194 nm, in scattered wavelength bands appropriate for particular experiments. The beam at the sum frequency has the scan range of the dye laser and a jitter equal to the sum of the ion laser and dye laser jitter.

F. Gains and Saturation Intensities for Common Dyes

The tuning curve data of Table I may be analyzed to give gains and saturation intensities for these dyes, under the listed pumping conditions. This permits an experimental check on the uniform plane-wave theoretical analysis of Section II.

The analysis uses the optimum output coupling values $t = t_0$ determined experimentally with the tuning curves and the estimate of the single-frequency cavity dissipative losses $a = 2.5\%$ for the ring laser of Fig. 10. Differentiating Eq. (9) with respect to t to find the output mirror transmission that maximizes the output power gives

$$t_0 = a[(k_0L/a)^{1/2} - 1] \tag{14}$$

from which

$$k_0L = a[(t_0/a) + 1]^2 \tag{15}$$

The gain values computed from Eq. (15) are listed in Table Ia for all the dyes (except IR 140, where lasing was too close to threshold to determine an optimum coupling). The output power with this optimum coupling is

$$P_{max} = n\pi w_D^2 I_s (t_0^2/a) \tag{16}$$

which shows that the maximum output is proportional to the inverse of the cavity losses a. The factor of $n = 1.4$, the index of refraction of the dye jet (at λ_D), did not appear in Eq. (9) for the plane-wave, longitudinally pumped case. It is appropriate in expressions like Eqs. (9) or (16) containing a focal area in a Brewster angle dye medium (the present case), because a beam of cross-sectional area πw_D^2 (normal to the beam direction) is expanded in area upon refraction at the Brewster surface to $n\pi w_D^2$. The prism expanders of Figs. 5 and 6 illustrate this expansion. [Note also that this factor of n was erroneously omitted in Eq. (6) of Johnston *et al.*, which resulted in saturation intensities reported there being 1.4 times too large.] Table Ia lists the correct beam focal areas. When the output power was measured using an optimum output coupler, inverting Eq. (16) gives the saturation intensity:

$$I_s = \frac{P_{max}}{n\pi w_D^2}\left(\frac{a}{t_0^2}\right) \tag{17}$$

and if a nonoptimum transmission t was used, Eq. (9) (including the factor of n) is solved for I_s, yielding the values in Table Ia.

The same analysis can be applied over a dye's full tuning range, to show experimentally the wavelength dependence of the gain and saturation intensity. This was done for the high-power tuning curve of rhodamine 6G, by determining the optimum transmission at seven points over the tuning range (Fig. 14b). The Fig. 14a tuning curves show as well the high conversion efficiency from broadband output (~2 GHz linewidth without etalons) to single-frequency operation of a ring laser. These curves were taken with a single output coupler to produce smooth full-range tuning data (this coupler gave a slightly lower peak output than the one that gave the peak power listed in Table Ia). Also, the t_0 values plotted were chosen (within the range of experimental error) to give smooth curves for k_0L, I_s [labeled EXPT in Fig. 14c and d] when put into Eq. (15) or Eq. (17).

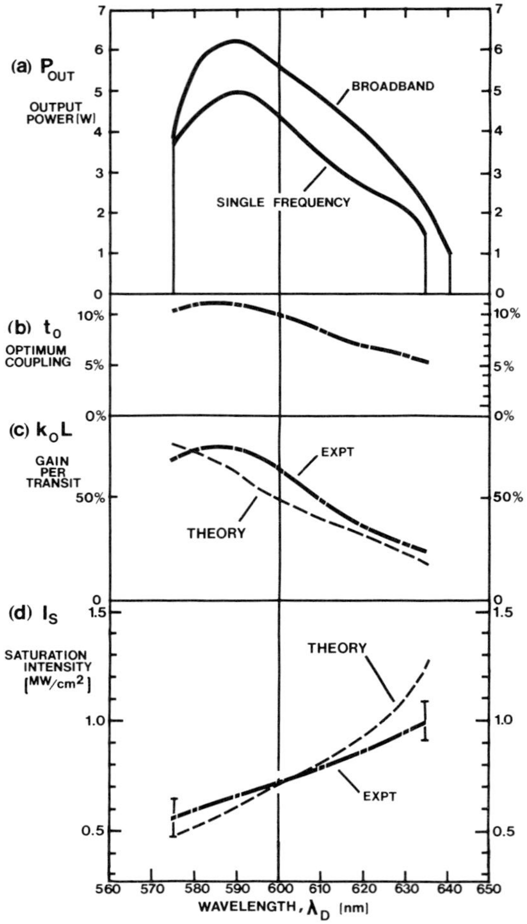

FIG. 14. Comparison of the gain and saturation intensities derived from measurements of optimum coupling (EXPT), with the theoretical plane-wave expressions using spectroscopic cross sections (THEORY) for rhodamine 6G dye in AMX solvent at 24 W pumping. [Adapted with corrections and permission from Johnston, T. F., Jr., Brady, R. H., and Proffitt, W. (1982). *Appl. Optics* **21,** 2311.]

These experimental values measure the response of the dye medium to changes in resonator loss, and as such represent the average over the active volume of the microscopic inversion variations in the dye. A direct comparison with theory would thus involve a (numerical) integration of the plane-wave equations over the focal volume, a procedure more complex than is warranted in view of the moderate accuracy of the measured t_0 values (about $\pm 10\%$ of their means). A simpler approximate treatment is to first establish upper bounds for I_s and k_0L by putting into the plane-wave Eqs. (8) and (11) the maximum pump intensity reached in the experiment (the intensity at the center of the Gaussian mode profile, on the input side of the jet). This saturation intensity upper bound is then reduced by an estimate of the ratio of the average pump intensity to this maximum value. This gain upper bound is then reduced by the factor $1/(1 + \rho_0)$ quoted earlier (in Section IV,A) derived from the overlap integral at the focus in longitudinal pumping of a dye beam of Gaussian waist radius w_D and pump beam of Gaussian waist radius w_p, where $\rho_0 = w_D^2/w_p^2$. The upper bounds are evaluated for $\lambda_D = 590$ nm, at the peak of the experimental gain curve.

The stimulated pumping rate $(\lambda_p/hc)\sigma_p I_p$ (transitions per second) appearing in Eq. (8) is replaced for a multiline pump beam by the sum of such terms over the wavelengths present. When weighted by the appropriate pump cross sections (Fig. 4), the 24-W BG pump is found to be equivalent to 15 W of 514-nm pumping. To convert power to intensity, note that a TEM_{00} mode beam of total power P and Gaussian $1/e^2$-radius w has a maximum intensity on axis of $2P/\pi w^2$ and an average intensity of *half* this, if the beam cross-sectional area is taken to be πw^2. The calculated pump focal area in the jet was $n\pi w_p^2 = 6.7 \times 10^{-6}$ cm^2, giving $\rho_0 = 2.3$, and a maximum pump intensity of $I_p = 4.4$ MW/cm^2. The spontaneous decay rate for rhodamine 6G is $1/\tau\varphi = 0.2$ GHz; the green-equivalent pump intensity above yields a maximum pumping rate of 1.6 GHz, and Eq. (8) gives an upper-bound saturation intensity of $I_s = 4.0$ MW/cm^2. Because this pump rate is much larger than the spontaneous decay rate, the saturation intensity is proportional to pump intensity and the upper bound can be cut in half to account for the radial, off-axis falloff of the pump intensity. It is cut again by a factor ranging from 0.32 to 0.39, the ratio of the maximum to the average on-axis intensity, to account for exponential absorption along the axis to a 5–10% transmission through the jet. This gives theoretical I_s estimates for the cw laser case of 0.6–0.8 MW/cm^2. These agree satisfactorily (within the error estimates) with both experimental values at this wavelength, 0.8 MW/cm^2 from the data of Fig. 13 and 0.65 MW/cm^2 from the data of Fig. 14.

The gain upper bound, for $N = 1.3 \times 10^{18}$ cm^{-3} (from the estimated dye concentration of 2×10^{-3} M), $L = 0.012$ cm, and a maximum inversion fraction (calculated from the relative transition rates above) of 0.88, is given by Eq. (11) as 210% per pass. Applying the Gaussian beam reduction factor of 0.30 for the 2.3 focal area ratio gives a theoretical gain estimate of 64% per pass, which agrees satisfactorily with the two experimental results of 70% and 73%.

The large inversion fraction implies that the dye jet was bleached on the pump input side, violating the Beer's law absorption profile assumed in deriving both reduction factors and showing the roughness of the present approximations. Thus, the best test of the plane-wave theory is probably the comparisons of the predicted and observed wavelength dependencies of Fig. 14(c) and (d), which involve fewer assumptions. Here the theoretical curves are scaled from the $\lambda_D = 590$ nm results according to Eqs. (7) and (8) by the measured cross sections of Fig. 4. Using the smaller of the two theoretical saturation intensity values gave the best overlap with the experimental curve. The plane-wave analysis is seen to predict satisfactorily the variation of I_s and k_0L over the tuning range observed in an actual cw single-frequency dye laser.

Figure 15 is an example of sub-Doppler saturated absorption spectroscopy, the basic application of the scanning single-frequency dye laser. This example was chosen to display the connection of laser spectroscopy with the older,

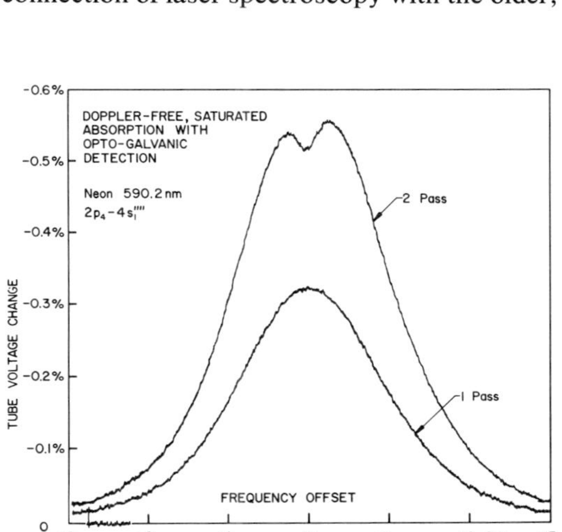

FIG. 15. Doppler-free and Doppler-limited laser spectroscopy compared on a neon absorption line, using opto-galvanic detection. The change in voltage across a helium–neon discharge tube was recorded as the single frequency of a coaxial dye laser beam (passed either once or twice through the discharge) and was scanned through the 590.2-nm resonance. [Adapted with permission from Johnston, T. F., Jr. (1978). *Laser Focus* **Mar.,** 58–63.]

Doppler-limited spectroscopy, and consequently is at a low resolution (not at all near the 1-MHz limit imposed by the frequency jitter of this stabilized laser). The laser beam was passed (through end windows) along the axis of a narrow-bore discharge tube run at constant current in a mixture of helium and neon gas. As the frequency of the dye laser scanned through the frequencies of neon spectral lines, power was absorbed from the laser beam, and proportional changes in the discharge power were recorded. This has been appropriately named optogalvanic (current-producing light) detection and is a detection scheme with a wide dynamic range and a good signal-to-noise ratio that is often used with spectral calibration lines for dye laser wavemeters.

The lower trace of Fig. 15 shows the absorption signal when the beam was passed once through the tube and shows a classical Doppler line profile, obtainable before the existence of lasers by high-resolution interferometry. This Gaussian line shape reveals the velocity distribution of the moving atoms in the gas and not the underlying homogeneous width of the spectral line (due to the finite lifetimes of the absorbing states). For laser frequencies below line center (negative offsets in Fig. 15), atoms with an on-axis velocity component along the laser beam (but in an opposed direction) see the laser frequency up-shifted into resonance and absorb the light. Since the atoms in the gas are moving in all directions with a finite average speed, the most likely axial velocity component in the distribution is zero, and the absorption increases (according to the Gaussian weighting function) as the laser frequency moves toward line center. The process is reversed as the laser frequency scans above line center, where the laser light is absorbed by a decreasing number of atoms seeing a down-shifted laser frequency.

If now the transmitted beam is retroreflected to make a second pass in the opposite direction through the tube, the absorption is doubled as expected for off-line center laser frequencies (as shown in the upper trace of Fig. 15), as both a right-going velocity group and a left-going velocity group of atoms have the correct Doppler shifts for absorption from one of the beams. But when the laser scans to line center, the two distinct velocity groups coalesce into a degenerate "zero-axial-velocity" group and there is a saturated absorption dip of width equal to the homogeneous width, marking the center of the line. The appearance of the dip requires sufficient laser power to perturb the velocity profile; a saturation intensity for absorption on the spectral line must be reached. Gas-phase spectral lines are typically 10^{-5} times narrower than the tuning range of a dye and the saturation intensities are correspondingly smaller than those of dyes, so the required intensities are readily reached (40 mW was the input here) even in an unfocused dye laser output beam. The improvement in ability to locate the central position of the line in Fig. 15 is only about an order of magnitude but is still enough to show, by the asymmetry of the dip, the presence of an isotope shift for the 9% of ^{22}Ne in the natural neon gas fill, to the high-frequency side of the line center of the main (91%)^{20}Ne component. For molecular absorption lines, the improvement in resolution reaches a factor of 10^3. This ability to see inside the classical Doppler limit throughout the dye tuning spectrum has revolutionized modern spectroscopy.

V. Ultrashort-Pulse (Mode-Locked) Dye Lasers

Of the three scientific dye laser types, the mode-locked branch is evolving most rapidly at present, as shown by the density of accomplishments in recent years in Fig. 1. This section covers the basics of the mode-locking of dye lasers. [*See* MODE-LOCKING OF LASERS.]

A. Pulse Formation by Phase-Locking of Cavity Modes

In TEM_{00} transverse mode operation, the mode frequencies ν_q of a standing-wave dye laser with resonator optical path length d are given by the longitudinal-mode values $\nu = q(c/2d)$. Here the integer q (of order 10^6) differs by 1 for adjacent modes, making the beat or difference frequencies between nearest neighbors in multimode oscillation all nominally $c/2d$. The beats are generally not precisely at this value, because of mode pulling and pushing effects. Associated with a gain peak at some center frequency there is an index of refraction variation given by the Kramers–Kronig relations tending to pull the mode frequencies slightly toward the center frequency; mode frequencies are slightly repelled from an absorption dip. The homogeneous-width "holes" in the gain curve caused by the competition between modes in a multimode laser thus normally cause a slight random shifting of nearest-neighbor beat frequencies away from the nominal value. This situation is best described by saying that the phases of the beat frequencies are normally random and uncorrelated.

By Fourier's theorem, however, if the phases could all be made constant (or "locked"), then the sum of the many mode amplitudes spaced regularly in frequency by differences of $c/2d$ would produce a periodic function, of period $T = 2d/c$. If initially these locked-mode amplitudes were phased for maximum constructive interference at some point in the cavity (producing a high peak power there), at time intervals of T they would return to this state at that location. The laser's steady multimode output would be converted to a repetitive train of pulses, with an interpulse spacing of T, corresponding to a circulating pulse striking the output coupler at intervals of the cavity round-trip transit time T. The width τ_D (FWHM) of this dye output pulse by Fourier's theorem would be given by a constant divided by the width $\Delta\nu$ (FWHM) of the spectral distribution of amplitudes of the locked modes, the constant being always of order unity but dependent on the form of the pulse shape.

To produce this locking of phases requires a small gain (or loss) term sufficient to overcome the random mode pulling effects; to establish the constructive initial phase distribution, this term should favor a high peak power pulse. Such a term is provided in the argon ion and Nd : YAG pump lasers by placing at one end of their resonators an acoustooptic loss modulator, or mode-locker. A sinusoidal radiofrequency voltage drives an acoustic wave in the mode-locker cell, giving a diffraction loss of the laser beam varying in time at a frequency precisely adjusted to equal the mode spacing frequency of the resonator. In frequency-domain terms, the sidebands introduced on a longitudinal mode carrier frequency by this amplitude modulation produce zero beats with the adjacent mode frequencies to lock the modes. In time-domain terms, the same result occurs because the formation of a short pulse allows oscillation with the least loss, as the pulse can pass through the loss modulator at the times of zero diffraction loss. Because input energy (other than that of the laser beam itself) is required to drive the mode-locker, this is called "active" mode-locking. Typically, a long pump laser is used giving a mode spacing of 76 MHz and a period of 13 nsec. The green pumping pulses from a mode-locked argon laser are about 120 psec long and from a mode-locked, doubled YAG laser are about 70 psec long, the difference reflecting the different gain bandwidths for these lasers.

The dye laser is similarly mode-locked by pumping synchronously (with the cavity round-trip transit times matched as will be described) with a mode-locked pump laser, producing repetitive gain modulation. Alternatively, mode-locking is produced (with constant cw pumping) by adding a second dye jet to the cavity, containing a saturable absorber dye. This adds a loss term that is least (saturates the most) for a high peak-power circulating pulse. This method is called "passive" mode-locking since the absorber is driven by the laser energy itself. Both mode-locking methods may be used together in a "hybrid" mode-locked laser as shown in Fig. 16.

To match the dye cavity length to that of the long pump laser, while keeping the dye laser compact, the beam in Fig. 16 is folded in a zigzag path by the two flat mirrors. The focal diameters produced in the gain jet by the mirrors M1 and M2 and in the absorber jet by mirrors M3 and M4 are given as in the cw case by the three-mirror analysis of Fig. 8. A translation stage (not shown) on the output end of the laser allows precise length adjustment. In the figure, a cavity-dumper assembly (which can be translated) is shown in place of an output mirror. This device is a time-gated output coupler, driven in synchronism with the mode-locker of the pump laser, and is often used to reduce the repetition rate of the train of output pulses while increasing the energy per pulse. An acoustic wave is turned on to generate a diffraction grating in the Brewster cell at the M5 and M6 focus for several nanoseconds at the time of passage of the light pulse. The interference of the diffracted and direct beams returned by M6 is phased in the second diffraction to couple nearly 100% of the pulse energy into the diffracted beam direction, where it is directed out of the laser by the take-out prism. Compared to a transmitting mirror, the use of all high reflectors and this large coupling factor in cavity-dumped operation gives 10 or more times the output energy per pulse, at one-twentieth the repetition rate.

B. Pulse-Shaping by Saturable Gain and Absorption

The number of modes phased together in the dye laser is so large (10^4 in a picosecond pulse) that the process is most conveniently described in the time domain as the shaping of the pulse in

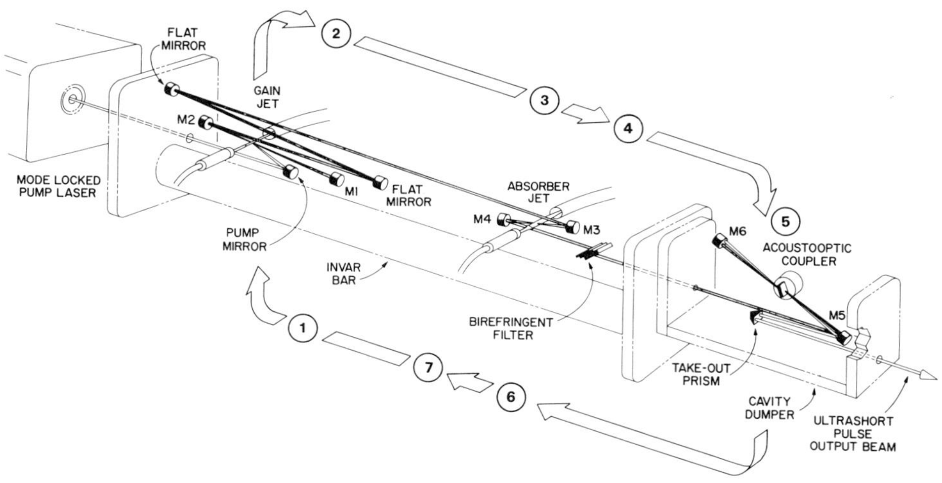

FIG. 16. Ultrashort pulse dye laser of current design for "hybrid" mode-locking (employing both synchronous pumping and a saturable absorber). Shown in place of an output mirror is a cavity dumper assembly, which is driven in synchronism with the circulating pulse to couple out a reduced number of pulses, at higher energy per pulse. (Courtesy of Coherent, Inc., Palo Alto, Calif.)

passage through the elements of the cavity. A picosecond pulse is spatially only 0.3 mm long and interacts sequentially with each element. In Fig. 17, the circulating pulse is moving to the right (time increases to the left), and the effect of each (numbered) passage in Fig. 16 is shown schematically.

In passage through the gain jet (1, 2) the leading edge of the pulse is amplified, which increasingly depletes the gain over the remainder of the pulse, since on the time scale of the dye pulse the rates of pumping transitions and spontaneous decays are slow. This steepens the leading edge and advances the timing of the peak of the pulse. For good mode-locking, the focal area in the absorber jet is made smaller than in the gain jet (note the shorter-focal-length mirrors in Fig. 16) to ensure faster saturation in the absorber (3, 7) to further steepen the leading edge (and slightly retard the peak). The uniform, linear loss of an output coupler (5) leaves the pulse shape unchanged, but the attenuation of the trailing edge here, in combination with the growing middle and attenuated leading edge, means a net pulse shortening in passage through these three elements. What keeps the pulse width from collapsing to zero is the finite spectral bandwidth of the frequency filter used in the cavity to tune the center wavelength of the pulse. In Fig. 16, this is shown as a three-plate birefringent filter (whose transmission function is shown in Fig. 11), but broader two- and one-

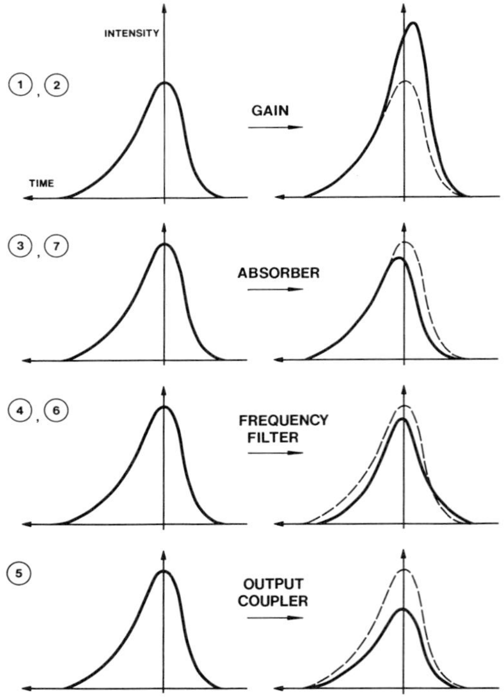

FIG. 17. Schematic diagram of the shaping of the pulse that occurs in the transit of the cavity elements (indicated by the circled numbers) of the laser of the preceding figure. The peak of the pulse is advanced by the interaction with the gain jet and retarded by the absorber; the pulse width is increased in the filter, and left unchanged (though the amplitude is attenuated) at the output coupler.

plate filters are also used for shorter pulses. By Fourier's theorem, the clipping by the filter of the highest and lowest frequencies in the pulse spreads the pulse shape and balances the compression.

The frequency filter functions in the mode-locking process to clean up the frequency noise and give transform-limited pulses. Pulse formation starts from noise bursts, spontaneous amplitude fluctuations that are limited in rate only by the dye gain bandwidth and that can be quite rapid. These are amplified and filtered in the "good mode-locking" regime, but can persist as temporal substructure in a nonoptimum pulse. The quality of a mode-locked pulse train is judged by measuring both its temporal and spectral widths and by checking that the product of these is close to the Fourier transform constant (implying a consistent pulse shape).

The pulse-shaping process just described applies directly to passive mode-locking, where the gain gradually recovers with cw pumping over a cavity transit time, and the gain seen by the dye pulse does not depend critically on its arrival time back at the gain jet. By contrast, in synchronous mode-locking, the gain rises as the integral of the pump pulse over the ~100-psec pulse width, and the shaping of the dye pulse critically depends on its arrival time (relative to the pump pulse) at the gain jet. This is discussed in Section V,C, after the method of measuring pulse shape is explained. To conclude here note that the smaller linear losses in cavity-dumped operation during the pulse shaping process accounts for output pulses 1.5–2 times greater in pulse width observed in that mode.

To measure the shape of the dye pulse requires optical techniques, since the $\sim 10^{14}$-Hz bandwidths involved far exceed the capabilities of conventional circuitry. While a variety of techniques has been developed, the standard today is "background-free autocorrelation"—an average (over interference terms) of the overlap of the pulse train with a delayed sample of itself is recorded as a function of the path delay. The setup is a modified Michelson interferometer where the incoming pulse train is divided at a beamsplitter into two beams, which follow different paths down the two arms of the interferometer and emerge as parallel separate beams. The length of one arm can be varied in a precise manner to give a calibrated path delay. A lens focuses the parallel beams to cross at the same spot on a thin nonlinear crystal oriented to phase match for second harmonic generation only when one photon is taken from each of the two crossing beams. An aperture can be centered to pass only the doubled light as this beam emerges between the two crossing beams, and together with a UV transmitting filter over the photomultiplier detector gives a "background-free" signal. Mathematically this is proportional to the autocorrelation of the pulse shape with itself. By its nature, an autocorrelation signal must be symmetric about zero path delay, and to deconvolve this signal trace to give the width of the original pulse, a prior knowledge of the functional form of the pulse shape is required. Consequently, the autocorrelation width itself is often quoted, which is adequate for many experiments. Table II gives the relationship of the pulse width τ_D, to the width of the autocorrelation trace τ_C (both FWHM) for several functional forms. The squared hyperbolic secant form (sech^2) is the shape predicted for dye laser pulses in first-order, linearized mode-locking theories. The Fourier transform "pulse width–spectral width" product $\tau_D\,\Delta\nu$ used to check for

TABLE II. Autocorrelation Widths and Spectral Bandwidths for Several Transform-Limited Pulse Shapes

Functional form of pulse shape	Ratio of pulse to autocorrelation width, τ_D/τ_C	Fourier transform product, $\tau_D\Delta\nu$
Square	1	0.886
Gaussian	0.707	0.441
sech^2	0.648	0.315
Lorentzian	0.500	0.221
One-sided exponential	0.500	0.110
Symmetric two-sided exponential	0.413	0.142

incomplete mode-locking is also listed. Another indication of partial mode-locking is the appearance of a "coherence spike" at zero time delay on the autocorrelation trace, where the noisy substructure in a pulse will have its maximum self overlap. For dye pulses of a few picoseconds or longer, where some dispersion in the autocorrelator apparatus can be tolerated, a convenient instrument is the "rapid scanning" type using a rotating glass block to generate a repetitive path delay scan at 60 Hz, permitting display of the trace on an oscilloscope. For subpicosecond pulse lengths, a stepping motor-driven translation stage with micrometer resolution gives the calibrated path delay and a thin doubling crystal (100 μm KDP) gives adequate detection bandwidth.

C. Pulse-Shape Dependence on Cavity Length in Synchronous Mode-Locking

In synchronous pumping, mismatching the two cavity lengths varies the relative arrival times at the gain jet of the dye and pump pulses, which has a strong pulse-shaping effect. The nature of this effect was revealed in a clever experiment by Firgo, Daly, and Mahr, using what they called an "optical up-conversion light gate." They used rhodamine 6G dye with 514-nm argon laser pumping in a three-mirror cavity equivalent to Fig. 16 without an absorber jet or cavity dumper. Using a lens that collimated fluorescent light from the gain jet, they collected a sample of both the dye and pump beams reflected from the same point at the jet and sent this "signal" beam into one arm of an autocorrelator, with the dye output pulse train incident along the other, variable path-delay arm. After being collinearly combined at a beamsplitter, all of these beams were focused into an angle-matched ADP crystal, and the sum-frequency ("up-converted") UV light from any pair of one of the three signals and the dye beam was detected through a filter monochrometer. This cross correlation of the dye pulse with either the argon pump pulse or the fluorescence signal became in this way a waveform sampling apparatus with high time resolution. All three signals originated at the same point on the jet, and the spatial arrangement of the experiment preserved the relative signal timing as shown in Fig. 18. (This is a fine example of time-domain spectroscopy, the main application of the mode-locked dye laser.)

The chronology of the pulse-forming process

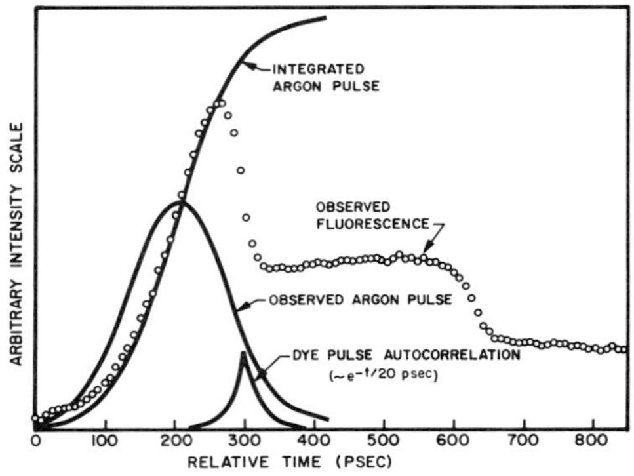

FIG. 18. Results of the optical up-conversion light gate experiment of Mahr *et al.* that measured the arrival time of the dye pulse relative to the pump pulse in synchronous pumping and demonstrated that synchronism is maintained by pulse shaping over the mode-locking range of cavity length. [Reprinted with permission from Frigo, N. J., Daly, T., and Mahr, H. (1977). *IEEE J. Quantum Electronics* **QE-13,** 103. © 1977 IEEE.]

demonstrated here is as follows. The gain (and fluorescence) is expected to rise as the time integral of the pump pulse, since the dye's spontaneous decay time far exceeds the time scale of the figure. Indeed, the fluorescence signal closely follows the integrated argon pulse (computed from the measured pump pulse shape) except in three places. First, there is a sharp drop in fluorescence coinciding with the time the dye pulse strikes the jet at 300 psec, due to the gain saturation (loss of upper-state population) in amplifying the dye pulse. The dye pulse here was traveling in a direction equivalent to that from M2 to M1 [passage (1)] in Fig. 16. Second, a fluorescence dip occurs 300 psec later, the propagation time from the jet to M1 and back, so this drop is due to the (reduced) amplification of the dye pulse on passage (2). Third, at zero time there is a residual fluorescence signal, due to incomplete spontaneous decay of the inversion produced 10 nsec earlier by the preceding pump pulse and left after the two passes of the preceding dye pulse.

The effect on these signals of mismatching the two cavity lengths was then studied. It was found that the optimum dye cavity length (that giving the shortest pulses) was slightly less than the length setting of Fig. 18. For this optimum length the dye pulse moved some 80 psec closer to the peak of the pump pulse, close enough that there was some gain recovery (rise in observed fluorescence) after the first passage of the dye pulse. This gain rise followed the shape of the integrated argon pulse. The cavity length change that caused this 80-psec time shift was equivalent to only a 0.25-psec cavity transit time change. The circulating dye pulse satisfies two conditions: that its round-trip transit time is precisely equal to the period of pumping pulses (after accumulated advance and retardation adjustments due to pulse shaping), and the "steady-state" condition, that the shape of the pulse is reproduced at each location in the cavity in each transit. To accommodate the shorter cavity length, the pulse position moved down the integrated fluorescence curve to a position of less gain. The pulse shape evolved into a shorter shape having 0.25 psec less net advance per round trip in the cavity. For a further 0.25-psec shortening of the transit time, the dye pulse position moved another 30 psec down the gain curve, and at this position the gain recovery was large enough after the first passage that a second dye pulse began to form.

Examples of this typical pulse-shape behavior for three cavity length settings are shown in Fig. 19, taken with the laser of Fig. 16 in 3.8-MHz pulse repetition rate (cavity-dumped) operation, with rhodamine 6G dye, a three-plate birefringent filter, and 1 W of doubled YAG pumping. The vertical axis is the signal from a rapid scanning autocorrelator, and the horizontal is the calibrated path delay. A display like this is used in setting up the laser to locate the optimum cavity length setting. In this laser, the absorber jet would then be turned on, the three-plate filter exchanged for a one-plate, and the new optimum cavity length setting would be found, yielding shorter pulses of 1 psec autocorrelation trace width, 18 nJ energy per pulse, and 18 kW peak dye power.

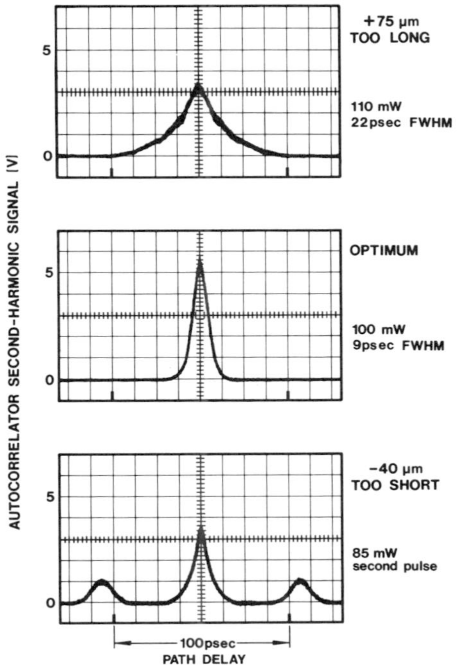

FIG. 19. Autocorrelation traces taken during setup of the cavity-dumped laser of Fig. 16, showing changes in the pulses with cavity length adjustment. A three-plate birefringent filter and a 1-W 532-nm pump beam were used without an absorber jet for this data. (Courtesy of Coherent, Inc., Palo Alto, Calif.)

D. The Shortest Pulses—Colliding-Pulse Ring Lasers and Pulse Compression

This picture of pulse formation in mode-locked dye lasers was sufficient for the generation of subpicosecond pulses and stood as the state of the art until the early 1980s, when two ideas were introduced, one that was new and one that then became widely appreciated, to permit the generation of even shorter pulses. The new idea was that of colliding-pulse mode-locking, due to Fork, Greene, and Shank. Here cw pumping of a ring laser was used, with a thin saturable absorber jet position at one-quarter the perimeter of the ring away from the gain jet. Two pulses circulate in this cavity, one clockwise and one counterclockwise, and collide in the absorber jet to produce interference fringes and a high degree of saturation there. The spacing of the two jets in the cavity ensures that each beam sees the gain jet at half a transit time after the last passage of a dye pulse, to give equal-intensity beams for maximum interference in the absorber. This laser produced 90-fsec pulse widths—a pulse only 0.03 mm long.

The second idea that awoke the scientists' imagination was the demonstration by Nikolaus and Grischkowsky of the compression by a factor of 12 of a 5-psec pulse to 450 fsec with a fiber-grating pulse compressor (Fig. 20). These experimentors realized that the spatially uniform (non-Gaussian) intensity distribution that results when a light beam is coupled into a single-mode optical fiber would result in spatial uniformity of the nonlinear optical effect known as self phase modulation (SPM). The refractive index of the fiber material is time-modulated by

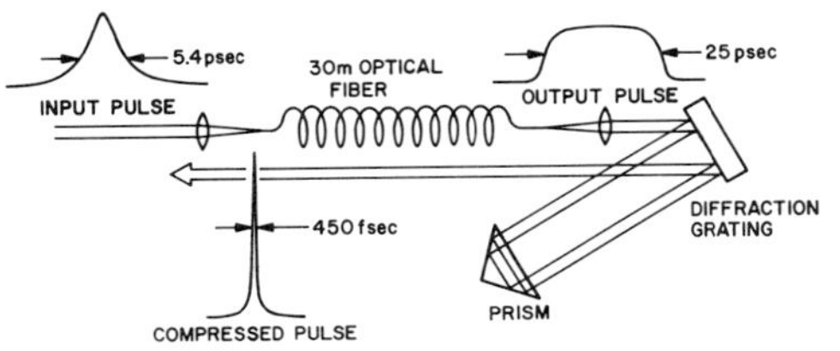

FIG. 20. The pulse compression experiment of Grischkowsky *et al.*, in which self phase modulation and group velocity dispersion of a pulse in an optical fiber are balanced to produce a linear frequency chirp in the output pulse. The two passes off the diffraction grating constitute a dispersive delay time, which compresses this pulse to one-twelfth the width of the input pulse. [Reprinted with permission from Nikolaus, B., and Grischkowsky, D. (1983). *Appl. Phys. Lett.* **42,** 1.]

the large electric field amplitude of the cavity-dumped dye pulse coupled into the fiber. This phase modulation increases the bandwidth of the pulse. (In fact, SPM has been used to generate a femtosecond white-light continuum by the focusing of ultrashort dye pulses into dielectric media.) In traveling through the fiber, the ordinary group velocity dispersion for this broadened spectral content linearly chirps the pulse—the redder wavelengths emerge first, followed linearly in time (in a longer pulse) across the pulse spectrum by the bluer wavelengths. A dispersive delay line (like the two passes off the grating of Fig. 20) provides a path length proportional to the wavelength and compensates this chirp to produce a compressed pulse.

These results showed that femtosecond-width pulses were possible in mode-locked dye lasers, revitalized the search for the processes limiting the pulse lengths, and led to the present evolutionary burst in this field. Dispersion-compensating delay lines were added intracavity in the dye laser. This looks like the quad-prism expander of Fig. 6 when placed in-line in an arm of a ring laser (only with "full" Brewster prisms instead of the "half" prisms in that figure), or equivalently is a pair of prisms placed in front of an end mirror of a linear laser. One prism is laterally displaced to adjust the relative spectral delay to compensate linear chirp from other intracavity elements. To date, pulses have been generated of 55-fsec width from a linear hybrid mode-locked laser, 27-fsec width from a colliding-pulse ring laser, and the shortest of all (as of 1985), a train of pulses of 8-fsec width was produced by compression from a 40-fsec source.

The molecular relaxation times measured with these ultrashort pulses in time-domain spectroscopy are as diagnostic of the system studied to a chemist or biologist as are atomic energy levels to a physicist. By modeling the chemical interaction and matching the calculated decay times to the observed ones, the actual molecular structure is revealed, and these new laser tools should keep these fields of study active for many years to come.

VI. Specialized Dye Lasers

The majority (in numbers) of dye lasers in existence is represented by the three scientific types already discussed, but these by no means represent the diversity of ways that lasers with a dye gain medium have been built. In this concluding section, four additional dye lasers are briefly discussed as a better indication of the breadth of this laser type and of its potential impact on future technology.

Vapor-phase dye lasers were initially investigated in the hope that the efficiency of the dye laser (plus pumping system) could be improved with excitation by a discharge directly in the dye vapor. This proved not to be the case. While molecular densities comparable to solution dye lasers were reached in the vapor state (by heating to ~400°C nonionic dyes sealed in silica glass cells), and spectra comparable to dye spectra in solution were observed (with slight broadening and a shift to shorter wavelengths), the inevitable result of running a discharge in the vapor was the rapid decomposition of the dye molecules. Several vapor-phase dyes were made to lase as short-pulse oscillators by optical pumping with a pulsed nitrogen laser, with results comparable to the same dyes in solution. The initial goal, however, is still well worth emphasizing. The applications of most lasers are limited by their high consumption of input power (their inefficiency), and the dye laser is one of relatively few lasers with an intrinsically efficient inversion mechanism (described in Section II). Thus, means to improve efficiency by eliminating another laser as the pump source, as in these vapor-phase experiments, are well worth seeking.

The distributed feedback dye laser first demonstrated the tunable, narrow-band output from a very compact structure that would be desired in a light source for integrated optical devices. The optical feedback in these mirrorless lasers is provided by Bragg scattering from a periodic spatial variation of the refractive index or the gain itself in a thin-film gain medium. The first such laser used a holographic phase grating, which was exposed and developed in a dichromated gelatin film on a glass substrate, before the film was dyed by soaking in a solution of rhodamine 6G. This was transversely pumped with a nitrogen laser to produce a 630-nm beam (of 0.05 nm linewidth) from the 0.1 × 0.1 × 10-mm total laser volume. To show a distributed feedback dye laser that was externally tunable, a dye cell was side-pumped with intersecting, interfering, 347-nm beams (from a beam-split, doubled ruby laser) to produce fringes and a periodic gain variation in the sheet of dye. The rhodamine 6G dye output wavelength tuned 70 nm for a 48–56° change in incidence angle for each of the two pump beams. In the tiny volumes of these lasers, if the dye molecules are immobilized in gelatin or plastic, the small number of molecules are recycled so frequently that photodecomposition limits the dye lifetime to a few seconds or less. The actual distributed feedback lasers that are candidate sources for integrated optical circuits, the inheritors of these dye laser results, will be analogs fabricated in semiconductor materials.

On the other end of the size and output power scale are the specialized dye laser oscillator and amplifier devices built for the atomic vapor laser isotope separation (AVLIS) process planned as the prime means in the United States for the enrichment of uranium-235 for nuclear reactor fuel rods near the turn of this century. In this process, the uranium raw stock is vaporized in a vacuum with an electron beam, and the streaming atomic vapor is exposed to dye laser radiations tuned to selectively photoionize (in three absorption steps) only ^{235}U atoms. These charged ions are deflected out of the stream by electrostatic fields to achieve separation. (Unlike the ^{20}Ne to ^{22}Ne isotope shift of Fig. 15, the ^{235}U to ^{238}U isotope shift for spectral lines of interest is greater than a Doppler width.) The general scale and specifications of the three laser beams (at three visible wavelengths) required in the separator are about the same as the design goal reported for the selective step, namely, ~1 J/pulse, ~10^4 Hz pulse repetition rate (or ~10 kW average power), in about a 1-GHz bandwidth locked onto the center of the uranium line. This high average power will be reached with massive banks of copper-vapor lasers (a short-pulse laser like the nitrogen laser but with emissions in the green and yellow) as pumps for short-pulse dye oscillator and amplifier chains. The copper-vapor lasers have a few percent electrical-to-optical efficiency, which is important in the economics of the process, and the yellow-green pump lines are efficient both in pumping red dyes and in giving long dye photodegradation times. Thus, dye lasers in about two decades may be responsible for a sizable fraction of the world's electric power generation.

Continuous-wave dye lasers have also been the basis in experimental investigations for the cure of cancer (Fig. 21). In this work, termed photodynamic therapy, the patient with a tumor is first injected with a drug (hermatoporphyrin derivative, HpD) that has the property of being selectively retained in rapidly dividing tissue (the tumor) and of photodegrading to release free oxygen when exposed to a measured dose of light of the proper color. After a waiting period of 2–3 days for the drug to clear from healthy tissue, the patient is given the light dose

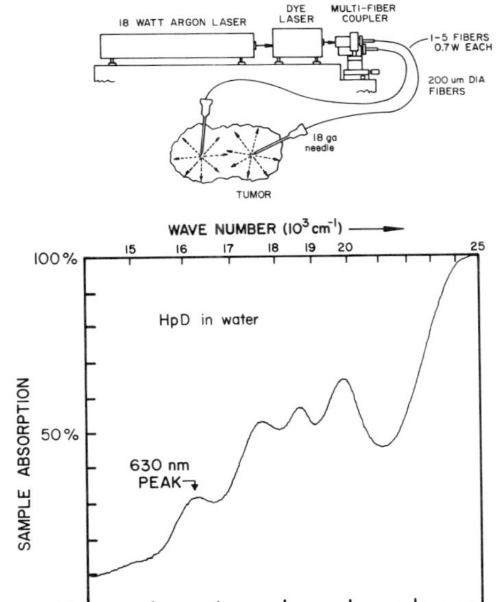

FIG. 21. Schematic diagram of the destruction of cancerous tumors by the activation of the experimental drug HpD (hermatoporphyrin derivative). A dose of dye laser light, tuned to a specific absorption band of the drug, is administered through fiber optic guides to photodecompose the drug and kill the tumor. The absorption spectrum shown is for an early form of the drug in water; the peaks shift somewhat in tissue and with the newer forms of the drug. (Courtesy of Coherent, Inc., Palo Alto, Calif.)

through fiber optic guides slipped into needles implanted into the tumor. The released oxygen burns up the tumor but has no effect (and leaves a sharp line of demarcation) on the healthy tissue. In principle, the drug can be activated by ordinary light sources, filtered to give the proper wavelengths (corresponding to an appropriate absorption peak). In practice, the only activating wavelength with enough penetration depth for coverage of a few cubic centimeters volume per implant in most bodily tissue is the one in the red, which requires a 630 ± 5 nm wavelength. A laser source is dictated by the convenience of delivery through fibers (a coherent source focuses efficiently into the fiber's input end) and by the large total dosage of ~40 J cm^{-3} needed in this narrow bandwidth. The cw dye laser is the laser of choice for this application. Experimental medicine using the tunability of the dye laser to selectively absorb in different tissues without drugs is also being done in photocoagulation inside the eye and in other laser surgical procedures. These examples show that the future importance of the dye laser can be expected to extend much beyond today's useage as a research tool.

VII. Recent Developments

Two new crystals have recently become available in high optical quality form to the benefit of the tunable lasers discussed in this article. The first, beta-barium borate (BBO), is a doubling crystal with transparency to slightly below 200 nm that has extended tunable outputs down into this wavelength region. The second, titanium : sapphire ($Ti:Al_2O_3$), is an optically pumped crystal which has been substituted for the dye medium in single-frequency and mode-locked laser cavities to produce tunable outputs at higher power in the near infrared than previously available. Increased powers from the pump lasers in all three types of scientific dye lasers have boosted tunable outputs as well, particularly in the case of the UV pump lines from argon ion lasers. The pump powers of the standard UV-line mix now are twice as great, and shorter UV pump lines have become available, making possible cw tunable lasing in the UV directly from new dyes. In ultrafast lasers the shortest-pulse record (done by extracavity pulse compression) is now 6 fsec; tains of pulses of 29 fsec duration have been generated directly in the hybrid mode-locking geometry by the addition of prism pairs to the laser cavity to compensate the intracavity group-velocity-dispersion; and commercial systems now attain and maintain sub-100 fsec pulse lengths by incorporating servo systems in their design.

A. Single-Frequency and Short-Pulse Lasers

The resulting changes in wavelength coverage for the single-frequency lasers have been illustrated in the tuning spectrum of Fig. 13. Beginning on the long wavelength end of the spectrum, the solid-state crystal titanium-doped sapphire has produced the highest reported single-frequency output over the 690–840 nm fundamental tuning range, with a peak of 3.6 W at 790 nm (replacing the 2.0 W peak at 740 nm of the dye LD700). This is a crystalline optically pumped gain medium and not a dye, but due to the homogeneous line broadening at the active Ti^{3+} ion sites, titanium : sapphire shows spectral condensation and tunability like a dye and is used as an alternate gain medium in the same laser as shown in Fig. 10 (now termed a Ti : dye laser). The 2 cm long crystal replaces the astigmatic compensation rhomb in the cavity (just as this position was used earlier for the temperature-tuned ADA doubling crystal, see Section IV.E), and the dye jet is turned off. The argon ion laser pump beam is folded to enter the cavity through the mirror M2, after striking a 30 cm radius fold mirror placed behind M2, to focus into the crystal in the colinear pumping geometry needed with a long gain medium. The same single-frequency filter stack and frequency servo system used with a dye produce with the crystal <500 kHz rms frequency jitter as described in the text. Titanium : sapphire is pumped by the blue-green band of lines from the argon ion laser. By clamping the crystal in a water-cooled block it withstands a full 20 W pump power, which accounts for the high output power (the LD700 dye used a red pump beam from a krypton ion laser, for which only 5 W pump power is available). The tunability of this crystal extends to 1000 nm and it would be expected with additional work to replace as well the next two longer wavelength dyes.

Improvements in argon ion lasers have raised the UV-band pump power to 7 W, and added a short-ultraviolet wavelength (300–336 nm) pump band (SUV in Table I) of about 3 W power. The first improvement has increased by a factor of three the blue wavelength outputs from the stilbene 1 and stilbene 3 dye lasers to 0.42 W and 1.0 W, and the second has permitted single-frequency ultraviolet lasing from the dye polyphenyl 2 over the range 364–408 nm with a 0.25 W peak output at 383 nm. Other UV-lasing dyes are under development. An output comparable to the directly UV-lasing dyes was produced by doubling titanium : sapphire radiation intracavity in an angle-matched lithium iodate crystal as described in Section IV.E. This high output (0.20 W at 370 nm with 345–388 nm tunability) was due to the low crystal absorption of <1% at the fundamental wavelengths and to the ability of this crystal to sustain high pump powers.

Advantage could be taken of the improved output powers in the blue dyes as the angle-matched crystal beta-barium borate for doubling this region became available at the same time. When used in the cavity (Fig. 10) of the stilbene 3 and coumarin 102 dye lasers, this extended the single-frequency tuning spectrum over most of the range from 215–260 nm. The small 235–238 nm gap of Fig. 13 is expected to be closed by doubling in stilbene 3 using the technique explained in Section IV.E for pushing the tuning range past a tuning curve break point. In R6G dye, BBO doubling has produced five times more second harmonic power than the earlier angle-matched result with KDP, and it is anticipated that the tuning curves remaining in the figure between the doubled R6G and C102 results will be superceded by BBO doubling results when this crystal is tried in the intervening dyes. To be useful for cw intracavity doubling a crystal must have an absorption of <1% over the length of the crystal (one aperture length of 7 mm here); the excellent results of Fig. 13 demonstrate that the crystals available now are of this high quality. This crystal also has a high damage threshold, permitting it to be used in doubling the blue wavelength outputs from short-pulse dye lasers, which has been done to produce ten times the previously available deep UV pulse energies.

B. Ultrashort-Pulse Lasers

An important recent result in the area of ultrafast lasers was the demonstration of pulses of 29 fsec duration directly genrated in a hybrid mode-locked linear dye cavity (like Fig. 16 of the text), to which a set of four prisms were added and arranged to compensate group-velocity-dispersion as discussed in Section V.D. This nearly matches the shortest pulse (27 fsec) so far generated directly in a colliding pulse mode-locked cavity and favors the use of hybrid mode-locking which has produced considerably higher output power (350 mW versus 50 mW) and considerably greater tunability. But since the pulse-width, shape, and noise of the pulse train from a synchronously mode-locked cavity are strong functions of the cavity length as discussed in Section V.C, for reproducible sub-100 fsec pulses the cavity length must be held stable to within about 100 nm. Holding this tolerance requires a cavity length servo. From among several possibilities, commercial systems use a length-discriminant based on the output power of the dye laser, which rises linearly through the cavity length region that gives the shortest pulses. With an autocorrelator to identify the desired pulse width and shape, the optimum cavity length and corresponding output power is found and a proportional reference voltage subtracted from the detected power to generate the discriminant. The advantages of this error signal are that it is reproducible over the whole tuning range and in different dyes, and its use simultaneously stabilizes the output power. However, it presumes that the only source of power fluctuation is the dye cavity length. In order to make this assumption true, a fast amplitude noise reduction servo based on acoustooptic diffraction (called a "noise eater") is used on the pump beam, and the pointing fluctuations of the pump beam are stabilized by sensing its positional error at the dye laser and feeding back adjustments to steer the pump laser output mirror. Routine optimization of these interacting servo systems is done by microprocessor control. In generating sub-100 fsec pulses a preference has come about for the doubled Nd : YLF (neodymium–yttrium–fluoride) laser as a pump source instead of the doubled Nd : YAG laser, due primarily to the lower noise characteristics of the former host crystal.

The new shortest pulse record of 6 fsec (compared to the former 8 fsec result) was produced from a train of 50 fsec pulsewidth amplified pulses, linearly chirped in a 0.9 cm length of single-mode quartz fiber, then compressed in a dispersion compensating delay line similar to that discussed in Section V.D except that the two pairs of prisms were preceded by two pairs of gratings in a similar folded geometry. The extra degree of freedom given by adjustment of both gratings and prisms permitted compensation of both the square and cubic terms in the Taylor expansion of the optical phase versus optical frequency offset from the center of the pulse spectrum, with the shorter compressed pulse being the result. The ultrashort pulse (ultrafast) laser area continues to be one of rapid evolution with the results discussed in this section merely suggestive of the types of many such changes occurring in this field.

Bibliography

Bradley, D. J., and New, G. H. C. (1974). Ultrashort pulse measurements. *Proc. IEEE* **62,** 313–345.

Couillaud, B., and Fossati-Bellani, V. (1985). Mode-locked lasers and ultrashort pulses. *Lasers and Applications* **Jan.,** 79–83, **Feb.,** 91–94.

Drever, R. W. P., Hall, J. L., Kowalski, F. V., Hough, J., Ford, G. M., Munley, A. J., and Ward, H. (1983). Laser phase and frequency stabilization using an optical resonator. *Appl. Phys. B* **31,** 97–105.

Duarte, F. J. (1990). "Dye Laser Principles with Applications." Academic Press, San Diego.

Fork, R. L., Shank, C. V., Yen, R., and Hirlimann, C. A. (1983). Femtosecond Optical Pulses. *IEEE J. Quantum Electronics* **QE-19,** 500–505.

Hänsch, T. W. (1972). Repetitively pulsed tunable dye laser for high resolution spectroscopy. *Appl. Optics* **11,** 895–898.

Ippen, E. P., and Shank, C. V. (1978). Sub-picosecond spectroscopy. *Phys. Today* **May,** 41–47.

Johnston, T. F., Jr., Brady, R. H., and Proffitt, W. (1982). Powerful single-frequency ring dye laser spanning the visible spectrum. *Appl. Optics* **21,** 2307–2316.

Mason, S. F. (1970). Color and the electronic states of organic molecules. *In* "The Chemistry of Synthetic Dyes," Vol. III (K. Venkataraman, ed.), pp. 169–221. Academic Press, New York.

Peterson, O. G. (1979). Dye lasers. *In* "Methods of Experimental Physics," Vol. 15A (L. Marton, ed.), pp. 251–359. Academic Press, New York.

Ryan, J. P., Goldberg, L. S., and Bradley, D. J. (1978). Comparison of synchronous pumping and passive mode-locking of CW dye lasers for the generation of picosecond and subpicosecond pulses. *Optics Commun.* **27,** 127–132.

Scavennec, A. (1976). Mismatch effects in synchronous pumping of the continuously operated mode-locked dye laser. *Optics Commun.* **17,** 14–17.

Schafer, F. P. (ed.) (1977). "Dye Lasers," Vol. 1 of "Topics in Applied Physics," 2nd revised ed. Springer-Verlag, New York.

Shank, C. V. (1975). Physics of dye lasers. *Rev. Modern Phys.* **47,** 649–657.

Sorokin, P. (1969). Organic lasers. *Sci. Am.* Feb., 30–40.

Valdmanis, J. A., and Fork, R. L. (1986). Design considerations for a femtosecond pulse laser balancing self phase modulation, group velocity dispersion, saturable absorption, and saturable gain. *IEEE J. Quantum Electronics* **QE-22,** 112–118.

LASERS, X-RAY

Raymond C. Elton *Naval Research Laboratory*

GLOSSARY

Amplified spontaneous emission (ASE): Amplification of internal spontaneous emission from a transition throughout the medium on a single pass.

Coherence: Correlation between instantaneous amplitudes and phase angles of two or more waves.

Holography: Formation of three-dimensional images by recording and then reconstructing amplitude and phase distributions of a wave disturbance.

***jj* coupling:** Coupling of the total angular momenta j for multiple bound electrons in an atom or ion, where $j = l + s$ for coupled orbital l and spin s electron momenta.

Photolithography: Photographic formation of relief structures in semiconducting materials for electronic microcircuitry.

Metastable state: Excited energy state in an atom or nucleus whose lifetime is unusually long.

Plasma: Ionized gaseous medium in which the net charge is zero because of a balance between the total charges of ions and electrons present.

Self-terminating laser: Laser in which the population inversion terminates naturally when the lower state becomes sufficiently populated from the upper state to destroy the inversion.

X-ray lasers are devices that amplify very short wavelength radiation along a well-defined direction in order to obtain an intense, collimated, and coherent beam of monochromatic and penetrating emission. Such a radiation source can be used for photolithography of microcircuitry, holographic microscopy of cellular structure in biology, plasma diagnostics, and many other scientific and technical purposes.

I. Introduction

In principle, a *laser* (light amplification by stimulated emission of radiation) is not limited to wavelengths normally associated with "light," that is, the visible wavelength range of approximately 380–780 nm (see Fig. 1). In fact, the first device demonstrating such amplification operated in the microwave region (millimeters to centimeters in wavelength) as a "maser." However, the availability of high quality reflecting mirrors for resonant cavities has resulted in the development of powerful and useful coherent beams of collimated radiation in the infrared, visible, and near ultraviolet spectral regions. From the very earliest experiments and publications on lasers, there has been anticipation of the eventual further extension into the extreme ultraviolet (xuv) and X-ray spectral regions (see Fig. 1). This might occur either by a giant leap or by a gradual advance through the vacuum ultraviolet (vacuum-uv or vuv) region, in which material penetration and optical properties are generally poor compared to the visible region. In either case, it was recognized that the challenges would be formidable. This was basically because of what were recognized to be four somewhat-associated difficulties, discussed in the following paragraphs. [*See* LASERS.]

(a) The first difficulty is a generally unfavorable scaling of the cross section σ_{stim} (and hence the probability) for stimulated emission with the square of the lasing wavelength λ, i.e.,

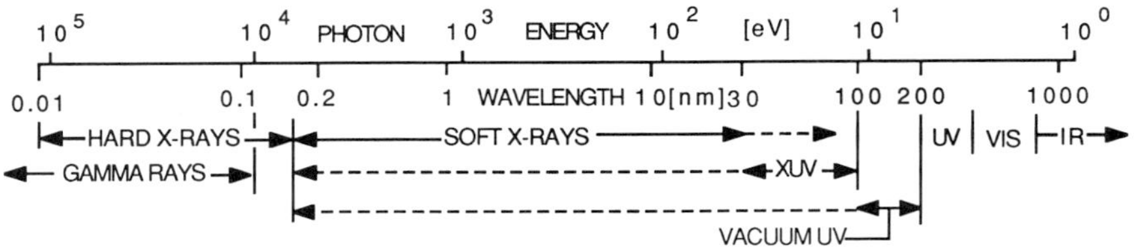

FIG. 1. Wavelength and photon-energy ranges and designations. [From R.C. Elton (1990), "X-ray Lasers," Academic Press, San Diego.]

$$\sigma_{\text{stim}} = \frac{nr_0cf\lambda^2}{\Delta\lambda} \cdot \frac{g_l}{g_u} \tag{1}$$

where $r_0 = e^2/mc^2 = 2.8 \times 10^{13}$ cm is the classical electron radius, $\Delta\lambda$ is the lasing-line width, f is the oscillator strength of the lasing transition, and g_u, g_l are the statistical weights of the upper and lower energy levels, respectively, for the laser transition. From the product of this cross section and the upper state density N_u is obtained the net gain coefficient $G = N_u\sigma_{\text{stim}} - N_l\sigma_{\text{abs}}$, where the latter product represents absorption on the lower laser state "l." Then, in the simplest case of a photon transversing an amplifying medium of length L, the net amplification achieved is given by $\exp(GL)$.

(b) The second difficulty is an inefficiency of reflecting mirrors for cavities, because vacuum-uv normal-incidence reflectivities decrease with shorter wavelengths and are generally less than 50%, compared to 99+% for the visible and/or infrared spectral regions. This generally has meant that amplification must be achieved on a single pass through the inverted medium ("lasant") by the amplification of spontaneous emission (ASE), rather than through ~100 multiple passes in an efficient cavity. To compensate for the lack of a cavity, directionality (collimation) and some coherence are achieved by forming the medium as a thin filament. Furthermore, the density of amplifying atoms with inverted level populations must be scaled up accordingly in order to achieve a similar overall amplification.

(c) The third difficulty is the large power required to generate (pump) and maintain the required large population density of inverted atomic states. At a minimum it is necessary to compensate for the spontaneous radiation power P_r per unit volume V losses, i.e.,

$$\frac{P_r}{V} = N_u \sum_j A_{uj} \cdot \frac{hc}{\lambda_{uj}}, \tag{2}$$

where A_{uj} and λ_{uj} are the transition probabilities and wavelengths, respectively, for a transition from the upper-laser state u to an arbitrary lower state j over which the summation is performed. For single-pass gain conditions this loss alone can be as high as 10^{11} W/cm^3 for a laser wavelength of 10 nm. Furthermore, for fixed gain it can be shown that this scales approximately as λ^{-4} and hence reaches 10^{15} W/cm^3 at a wavelength of 1 nm, still in the "soft" X-ray region (see Fig. 1). Such high power densities in the tenuous medium required to transmit the X radiation automatically generates a high temperature and degree of multiple ionization and, hence, an overall-neutral ionized gas or "plasma" lasing medium.

(d) The final difficulty is the short pulse required. There were early concerns that X-ray lasing would necessarily have to operate on traditional deep-innershell transitions after the creation of, for example, K-shell vacancies. Even if population inversions were so created, these vacancies would be filled and the lasing action would "self-terminate" on a femptosecond (10^{-15} sec) time scale. This seemed impossible in the 1960s, even though lasers now exist in this range.

Hence, a considerable degree of early pessimism existed. However, as known in astrophysics and plasma physics, there are associated with high temperature plasmas multiply (but not completely) ionized atoms which closely mimic neutral atoms with the same number of bound electrons. Such a group of ions is called an "isoelectronic sequence" and labeled H-like, He-like, Li-like, etc., for 1-, 2-, and 3-bound electrons, respectively. This in principle makes it possible to transfer atomic and ionic lasing at long wavelengths to vacuum-uv and shorter wavelengths with ions of increasing nuclear charge Z. The wavelengths of all transitions become increasingly shorter as Z increases along the sequence. For example, in the simplest case of the one-electron H-like sequence the wavelength scales as Z^{-2}, so that a transition from principal quantum number 3 to 2 at 656.2 nm in neutral hydrogen translates to 18.2 nm in five-times ionized C^{5+} ions. Conversely, a laser wavelength of 0.2 nm in the penetrating hard X-ray region could in principle be obtained on the same H-like 3-2 transition in a Ba ($Z = 56$) plasma. The scaling along other isoelectronic sequences is similar but more complicated because of the screening of additional bound electrons.

More importantly for X-ray lasers, it was realized that quasi-continuous-wave (cw) laser operation ("quasi" in the sense that lasing is limited only by the duration of the pumping impulse) could be achieved at short wavelengths using outershell "optical" transitions in such multiply ionized atoms in a high-temperature plasma medium. In this cw mode, typically lasting for tens of nanoseconds, the population inversion is maintained by rapid depletion of the lower-state density, usually accomplished through radiative decay to the ground state. The price paid is in efficiency lost in generating the highly ionized ions at the high densities required for short wavelength gain.

Indeed, success to date in generating ultrashort wavelength ASE has come about by using highly ionized, high density plasmas as the lasing medium. A typical geometry is a thin (~100–200 μm diameter) filament of several centimeters in length. Such a plasma is created by line-focusing a high power infrared or visible laser onto a target of the material desired for the plasma. X-ray lasing is then observed along the plasma axis, transverse to the driving-laser beam direction. An absolute value for the gain is determined either by varying the length and measuring an exponential increase in emission or by comparing axial amplified emission with transverse spontaneous emission. These methods are particularly convenient for such a transverse-driven geometry, because both ends of the plasma are readily accessible.

An alternative method of lasant creation is to use a linear electrical discharge, either free or confined (e.g., a capillary), to create the plasma; and there are preliminary reports now arriving of some success in this method (see Table II and footnote *a* to Table II). Instabilities in such discharge plasmas have led to axial inhomogeneities and a less than satisfactory X-ray laser medium. Hence, most of the experimental gain results collected in Tables I and II are based on more uniform laser-produced plasmas as lasants.

II. Pumping Modes and Experimental Results

As with any laser, it is necessary to "pump" electrons into an upper bound state of the lasing transition in order to establish therein a net population density exceeding that for the lower bound state, that is, a "population density inversion." Then stimulated emission from the former will exceed absorption from the latter as photons traverse the length of the plasma.

Self-contained in a high temperature high density plasma is the electron thermal energy per unit volume $N_e kT_e$ (N_e and T_e are the electron density and temperature, respectively). This intrinsic energy has been tapped very successfully for pumping X-ray laser transitions through inelastic collisions of free electrons with ions. Excitation, recombination, and (innershell) ionization are all possible electron-induced processes for effective pumping. The first two have proven to be most successful to date.

Electron-collisional excitation pumping of X-ray lasers, perhaps more than any other method, has evolved as an isoelectronic extrapolation of ion lasers from the ultraviolet spectral region (where efficient cavities exist). The pumping arises from the inelastic collision of a free electron with a ground-state ion in the plasma, resulting in a loss of free-electron energy and an excitation of a bound electron. The rate of pumping increases with electron temperature and hence is naturally compatable with the high temperature plasmas in which the ions exist. Indeed, $2p^{n-1}3p$-$2p^{n-1}3s$ $\Delta n = 0$ lasing transitions (n = 1–6), pumped from a $2p^n$ ground state are abundant in the ultraviolet region and have proven to be widely successful for the soft X-ray region. This is shown both in Fig. 3 and Table I for $n = 6$ neonlike ions (and for $3d^{10}$ ground state nickel-like ions), where the levels are indicated in *jj*-coupling notation which is the most accurate for the medium atomic weight elements involved. ASE measurements have been published for selected ions extending from Ti^{12+} through Mo^{32+} in the soft X-ray spectral region (Table I). Agreement between theory and experiments for the wavelengths of the lasing transitions shown is very good. However, calculated gains for the $3p$ ($J = 0$) to $3s$ ($J = 1$) "A" lasing transitions continue to exceed those from experiments by factors of 2–3. In this regard, it has been suggested that the pumping may not be pure collisional excitation from the $2p^6$ ground state and perhaps includes some innershell ionization and recombination contributions.

TABLE I. Wavelengths and Gain Coefficients for e-Collisional Pumping[x]

Ne-like Ions $3p$-$3s$ Transition:	A[a]	B[b]	C[c]	D[d]	E[e]	F[f]	Source[s]
Wavelength (nm):							
Ti^{12+}	32.65				508		LLE,RIKEN
Cu^{19+}	22.111	27.931	28.467				NRL
Zn^{20+}	21.217	26.232	26.723				NRL
Ga^{21+}		24.670	25.111				NRL
Ge^{22+}	19.606	23.224	23.626	24.732	28.646		NRL
As^{23+}		21.884	22.256				NRL
Se^{24+}	18.243	20.638	20.978	22.028	26.294	16.92	LLNL
	18.244	20.635	20.973				NRL
Sr^{28+}	15.98	16.41	16.65	17.51	22.49		LLNL
Y^{29+}		15.50	15.71	16.5	21.8		LLNL
Mo^{32+}	14.16	13.10	13.27	13.94		10.64	LLNL
Gain Coefficients (cm^{-1}):							
Ti^{12+}	2.7[r]						LLE,LLNL
Cu^{19+}	2.0	1.7	1.7				NRL
Zn^{20+}	2.3	2.0	2.0				NRL
Ge^{22+}	3.1	4.1	4.1	2.7	4.1		NRL
	1.0	2.1	2.2		2.8		LLNL
	1.5	2.5	2.5	1.0	1.8		LLE
	2.7	3.7	3.8	2.2	3.0		RAL
	2.3	3.3	3.4	2.3	3.2		SLL
As^{23+}			5.4				NRL
Se^{24+}	<1–2.7	4.0	3.8	2.3	3.5	≤1	LLNL
	2.6	4.9	4.9				NRL
Sr^{28+}		4.4	4.0				LLNL
Y^{29+}		4	4				LLNL
Mo^{32+}		4.1	4.2	2.9		2.2	LLNL

Ni-like Ions: Transition:	G[g]	H[h]	I[i]	J[j]	
Wavelength (nm):					
Eu^{35+}	10.039	10.456	7.100	6.583	LLNL
Yb^{42+}	8.10[y]	8.440	5.609	5.026	LLNL
Ta^{45+}	7.442	7.747	5.097	4.483	LLNL
W^{46+}	7.240	7.535	4.924[y]	4.318	LLNL
Re^{47+}				4.157[y]	LLNL
Au^{51+}				3.56	LLNL
Gain Coefficients (cm^{-1}):					
Eu^{35+}	0.08	(−0.07)	1.11	1.1	LLNL
Yb^{42+}		(−1)	(−0.4)	2.2	LLNL
Ta^{45+}	(−1)	1.3	(−1)	3.0	LLNL
W^{46+}	(−0.6)	0.8		2.6	LLNL
Au^{5+}				2.0	LLNL

[a] $(2p^5_{1/2},3p_{1/2})_0$-$(2p^5_{1/2},3s_{1/2})_1$ [b] $(2p^5_{3/2},3p_{3/2})_2$-$(2p^5_{3/2},3s_{1/2})_1$

[c] $(2p^5_{1/2},3p_{3/2})_2$-$(2p^5_{1/2},3s_{1/2})_1$ [d] $(2p^5_{3/2},3p_{3/2})_1$-$(2p^5_{3/2},3s_{1/2})_1$

[e] $(2p^5_{3/2},3p_{1/2})_2$-$(2p^5_{3/2},3s_{1/2})_1$ [f] $(2p^5_{3/2},3p_{3/2})_0$-$(2p^5_{3/2},3s_{1/2})_1$

[g] $(3d^9_{5/2},4d_{5/2})_2$-$(3d^9_{5/2},4p_{3/2})_1$ [h] $(3d^9_{5/2},4d_{5/2})_1$-$(3d^9_{5/2},4p_{3/2})_1$

[i] $(3d^9_{3/2},4d_{3/2})_0$-$(3d^9_{5/2},4p_{3/2})_1$ [j] $(3d^9_{3/2},4d_{3/2})_0$-$(3d^9_{3/2},4p_{1/2})_1$

[r] Pumping may be enhanced by resonance absorption (see text).

[s] LLE: U. Rochester; LLNL: Lawrence Livermore Nat'l Lab.; NRL: Naval Research Laboratory; RAL: Rutherford Laboratory, U.K.; RIKEN: Inst. Phys. Chem. Res., Japan.; SLL: Shanghai Laser Lab., PRC

[x] All values are measured except: [y] Calculated wavelengths.

TABLE II. Measured Wavelengths and Gains for Recombination Pumping

Species	Transition	Target[a]	Wavelength(nm)	Gain Coef(cm^{-1})	Source[b]
Hydrogenic:					
C^{5+}	3–2	Fi	18.2	25	HULL
	⋮	M	⋮	6.5	PPL
	⋮	Fo	⋮	3	NRL,SLL
	⋮	Fi	⋮	4.1	RAL
	⋮	Fo	⋮	2.0	ILE
	⋮	S	⋮	8	PPL
	⋮	C	⋮	1.2–1.7	RUHR
	⋮	Fo/C	⋮	2.0	ILE
O^{7+}	3–2	Fo	10.2	~0.5	LLNL
	3–2	Fo	10.2	2.3	ILE
F^{8+}	3–2	Fi	8.1	5.5	RAL
	⋮	Fi	8.1	4.4	RAL
	⋮	Fo		2.0	ILE
Na^{10+}	3–2	Fi,Fo,R	5.4	5.3	ILE
Mg^{11+}	3–2	R	4.5	1.5	ILE
$Al^{12}{}_{+}$	3–2	R	3.9	0.3	ILE
He-like:					
Al^{11+}	3d–2p	S	4.5	9.8	UTJ
	3s–2p	S	4.6	7	UTJ
	3p–3s	S	4.2	4.4	UTJ
Li-like:					
O^{5+}	4f–3d	M	5.20	1.8	PPL
Al^{10+}	5d–3p	Fo	10.4	1.0	ILE
	5d–3p	Fi	10.4	1.5	LSAI
	5f–3d	S	10.6	2–2.5	LSAI
	⋮	S	⋮	3.4	RIKEN
	⋮	S	⋮	3.1	SLL
	⋮	Fi	⋮	3	RAL
	⋮	Fo	⋮	1.5	ILE
	⋮	Fo	⋮	3.5	UMD
	⋮	Fi	⋮	1.5	LSAI
	⋮	S	⋮	2.2	LLE
	4d–3p	Fo	15.1	4.5	UMD
	⋮	Fi	15.1	1.4	LSAI
	4f–3d	M	15.5	3–4	PPL
	⋮	Fo	⋮	4.1	UMD
	⋮	Fi	⋮	2–3	RAL,LSAI
	⋮	S	⋮	4.5	RIKEN
	⋮	S	⋮	2.0	LLE
Si^{11+}	4f–3d	M,S	13.0	0.9–2	PPL,RIKEN
	5f–3d	S	8.9	1.5–1.7	SLL,RIKEN
	5d–3p	S	8.7	1.4	SLL
	6f–3d	S	7.6	1.7	SLL
	6d–3p	S	7.5	1.3	SLL
S^{13+}	5f–3d	S	6.5	1.3	LSAI
Cl^{14+}	4f–3d	Fi	8.0	3.5	RAL
Ti^{19+}	4f–3d	S	4.7	2.7	LLE
Be-like:					
Al^{9+}	5d–3p	S	12.3	3.4	RIKEN
	4f–3d	S	17.8	3.5	RIKEN
Si^{10+}	5f–3d	S	10.2	0.9	RIKEN
	4f–3d	S	14.8	0.6	RIKEN
Na-like:					
Cu^{18+}	6g–4f	S	7.2	2	SSL

[a] Targetrs: S, slab; M, magn. conf.; Fi, fiber; Fo, foil; R, ribbon; C, capillary

[b] See Table I footnote *s*, and:
ILE: Inst. Laser Engr., Osaka, Japan;
PPL: Princeton Plasma Lab.;
UMD: Univ. of Maryland;
HULL: Hull Univ., U.K.;
LSAI: Lab. Spect. Atom. Ion., France;
RUHR: Ruhr Univ., Bochum, Germany;
UTJ: Univ. Tokyo, Japan.

Collisional-recombination pumping is also an inelastic free-electron collisional-induced process that, in contrast to collisional excitation, requires considerable "unnatural" plasma cooling to be effective. Sometimes referred to as "three-body recombination," the process involves a free electron interacting both with an ion and simultaneously with another free electron such that one electron is captured into a highly excited bound state in the atom. (This may be thought of as the inverse process of electron collisional ionization of a bound electron from an excited state.) From there it cascades downward in energy. For certain pairs of levels the lower bound state depopulates more rapidly than the higher state, so that there is a net population density inversion and gain. The rate for this pumping process is largest at high electron density ($\propto N_e^k$ $k \approx 2$) and low electron temperature ($\propto T_e^{-2}$), so that again sudden and significant cooling is desired once the plasma is created at a high temperature and density. Such conditions often exist in very limited regions of parameter space for an expanding plasma. There have been numerous reports of measured gain associated with recombination pumping (see Table II and Fig. 3). In fact, the most "efficient" X-ray lasers produced to date are associated with recombination pumping, as discussed below in relation to Fig. 3. Numerical modeling tends to underestimate the magnitude of the gain compared to measurements, sometimes by as much as 100 times for certain transitions. Hence, there is a strong suggestion that the pumping is much less restrictive and more effective than explained by present recombination theory.

Pumping by photon collisions is also a possibility. Broadband flashlamps (most familiar from long-wavelength lasers) of sufficient power for pumping lasers in the X-ray spectral range do not exist at present. However, photoionization has been used for initiating the laser process for long wavelengths in the vacuum ultraviolet region (~100 nm, see "Auger" in Fig. 3). Here the removal of a tightly bound innershell electron by X-ray photoionization creates an ion sufficiently excited that Auger (or autoionization) processes can occur at a very rapid rate. When such processes more rapidly populate an upper laser state than lower, a population inversion and amplification are achieved. With the development of higher power drivers, photoionization pumping for the X-ray region may become a reality in the future. Also, very narrow-band photoexcitation pumping using the emission from an intense single spectral line of one ion of almost precisely the same photon energy as that of an absorbing excitation transition in a second lasant ion has been proposed as a form of flashlamp pumping. At least 112 such wavelength coincidences between spectral transitions have been identified for pumping X-ray lasers. To date, however, there is only one experiment in which there is evidence of such pumping of gain in the soft X-ray region, as noted in Table I, footnote *r*.

III. Characteristics of Plasma X-Ray Lasers

The quality of the beam from a present ASE-type X-ray laser is considered poor by usual laser standards, again because of the lack of high quality cavities. It is hoped that this will improve with further development. Vital operating parameters, present values, and crystal-ball projections for the near future are discussed in the following paragraphs.

Wavelengths extending from the present soft X-ray range of 4-30 nm to, say, 0.1-2.5 nm will require pumping powers continuing to scale up approximately as λ^{-4}, as previously discussed. Also, concerning *size,* much smaller diameters will be required at such shorter wavelengths in order to reduce radiative trapping on the transition connecting the lower laser level with the ground state. Smaller diameters also serve to reduce the number of transverse modes and hence increase the spatial coherence, as discussed below. The angular beam spread θ (the opposite of *collimation*) is determined for a single-pass ASE device by the length L and diameter d of the lasant plasma, i.e., $\theta = d/L \approx 10$ mrad at present. This is much larger than that for a diffraction limited perfectly coherent laser beam, where $\theta_d \approx 0.1$ mrad. The collimation can be expected to improve dramatically when efficient cavities are developed.

The *output power* will increase exponentially with length until saturation occurs, that is, until the stimulated emission rate competes with other rates and depletes the population inversion density. This occurs for $GL \gtrsim 14$. Largely because of expected monochromaticity, the *brightness* of the X-ray laser in units of photons $\cdot \text{cm}^{-2} \cdot \text{s}^{-1} \cdot \Delta\nu^{-1}$ is extremely high and advantageous for appropriate applications (ν is the photon frequency). This is illustrated in Fig. 2, where the a comparison is made to other popular

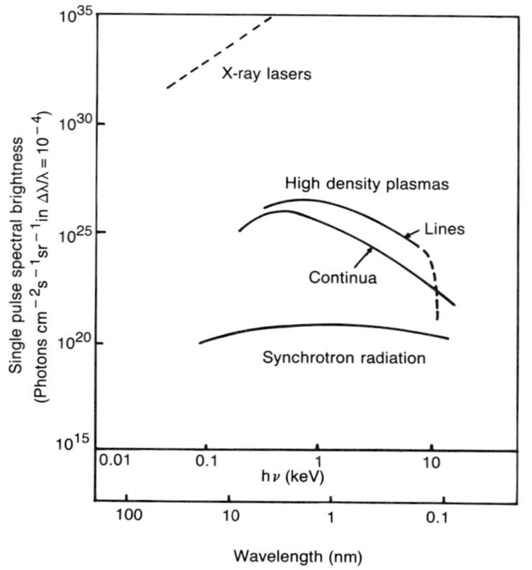

FIG. 2. Comparison of absolute spectral brilliance of various xuv and X-ray sources. [Adapted from M. H. Key (1988), *J. de Physique* **49,** C1-135.]

pulsed X-ray sources. Decreasing the *pulse length* leads to higher power for a given energy output. For applications requiring maximum power, this is most desirable. However, for pulse durations less than $L/c \approx 300$ psec (or even longer for multiple passes through a cavity), traveling wave pumping synchronized with the travel of the gain packet through the medium has been demonstrated, with additional complexity.

An important measure of the quality of any laser beam is the degree of *coherence*. Of primary interest for lasers are the transverse and longitudinal spatial coherence parameters, which are more-or-less independent. These characteristics are related to the focusing and holographic capabilities of the beam, as well as the spectral purity, or monochromaticity. The *transverse spatial coherence* across the X-ray laser beam is the extent D_{coh} over which a particular mode is coherent. At long wavelengths in more conventional lasers, a high degree of coherence and single transverse mode operation is achieved with high quality cavities and other optics not yet available for the vacuum ultraviolet and X-ray regions. Hence, values for present ASE systems would be considered quite poor by normal laser standards. This coherence is given by $D_{coh} = L_v\theta_d = L_v\lambda/d$, where L_v is the viewing distance from the laser and $\theta_d = \lambda/d$ is the diffraction limited beam spread for a perfectly coherent beam of diameter d or for a particular mode in a multimode beam. Hence, if a beam diameter of $d = 30$ μm can be created, the transverse coherence size at a viewing distance of 1 m is $D_{coh} = 300$ μm, so that holograms of objects as large as 1 mm might be possible. However, with ~1000 transverse modes present, the intensity in a single mode will be greatly reduced, thereby putting a great demand on the brightness delivered by the X-ray laser.

The Doppler broadened spectral *line width* in a high temperature plasma is typically 3×10^{-4} times the wavelength. Narrower lines are an advantage in producing higher gain [Eq. (1)] as well as improved monochromaticity and temporal (and longitudinal-spatial) coherence (discussed in Section IV). Such a decreased bandwidth might be obtained in very cold laser media or by so-called gain narrowing near saturation. Directly related to the line width is the *temporal coherence*. This is the interval t_{coh} during the passage of a wavefront over which coherence is maintained and is given simply by the inverse of the spectral bandwidth $\Delta\nu$ in frequency units, i.e., $t_{coh} = (\Delta\nu)^{-1}$. It follows that the more monochromatic the beam the longer the coherence time, as desired. As a plasma X-ray laser example, for a typical Doppler profile with $\Delta\nu/\nu \approx 3 \times 10^{-4}$ and for a laser wavelength of $\lambda = c/v = 10$ nm, the coherence interval is $t_{coh} \approx 0.1$ psec. This increases to ~0.3 psec for already reported narrowed lines of $\Delta\nu/\nu \approx 1 \times 10^{-4}$ and projected to ~1 psec for even further narrowing. A temporal coherence of 0.3 psec translates into a *longitudinal spatial coherence* of axial distance $L_{coh} = ct_{coh} \approx 100$ μm for the same conditions. This already is reasonable for holographic imaging of biological objects and microlithography, two specific applications discussed in Section V.

The overall *efficiency* is poor for present X-ray lasers, largely because of the power required to produce and sustain a significant population density in a high temperature, high density plasma. Unfortunately, there have been insufficient measurements of the output power from X-ray lasers to make meaningful comparisons of the output–input energy ratios and thereby overall efficiency. However, a figure-of-merit ratio GL/P achieved is obtainable from published data (see Table I), where P represents the pumping power used to create the plasma. This parameter is plotted in Fig. 3 and labeled for various dominant pumping processes. Many of

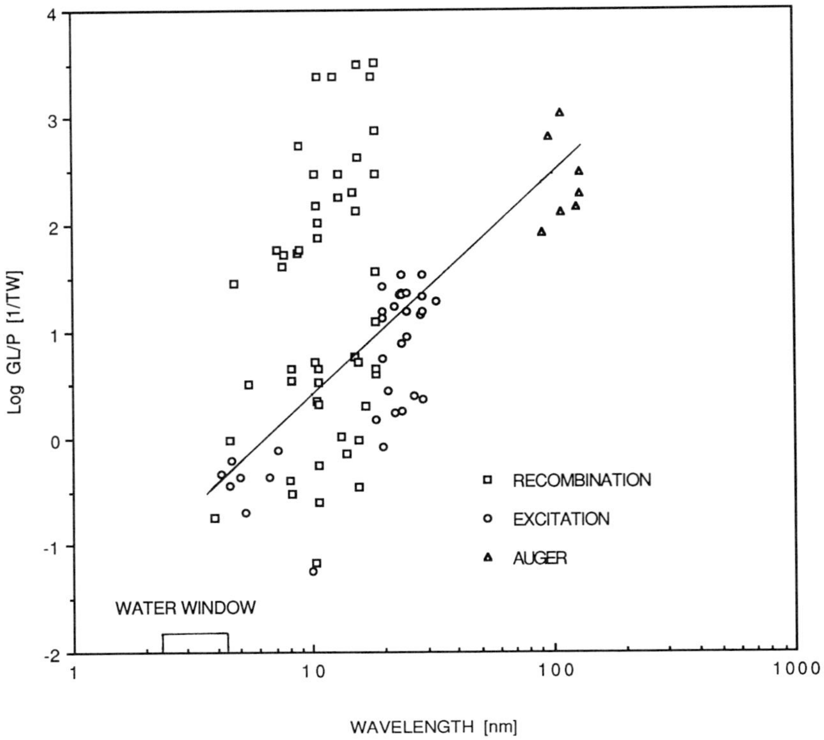

FIG. 3. Survey of measured gain products (*GL*) divided by input power *P* versus wavelength for various pumping mechanisms. The biological water window is indicated. The λ^2 line is somewhat arbitrary. [Expanded from M. H. Key (1988). *J. de Physique* **49,** C1-135.]

the data are seen to fall near a somewhat arbitrary λ^2 line. Some data associated with recombination pumping show phenomenally large figures-of-merit. It must be said that none of the experiments giving these unusually high values has been duplicated to date, whereas many of the collisional excitation results have been reproduced independently in a number of laboratories. Nevertheless, these apparently anomolously high values for GL/P are very encouraging for future compact and efficient X-ray lasers.

IV. Alternative (to Plasmas) and Complimentary Approaches

Besides direct amplification in a plasma medium, other novel X-ray laser approaches have been proposed. Most are still in the conceptual stage of development; some are complimentary to plasma amplifiers as master oscillators.

A prominent example of the latter is *harmonic generation* or frequency up-conversion. Here, a high quality long wavelength laser beam is converted to the soft X-ray region through the nonlinear response of certain transmitting materials to electromagnetic waves. This is analogous to the nonlinear response of audio and microwave electronic circuit elements, which results in harmonic distortion, parametric amplification, modulation, and rectification. For vacuum-uv conversions, gases, vapors, and even plasmas are possible nondestructive media of high transmission. Typical higher-order nonlinear processes used include odd-harmonic generation and the associated frequency mixing interactions, sometimes with resonant enhancement. Wavelengths throughout the vacuum-uv region reaching the 20–30 nm range have been generated. Anti-Stokes Raman scattering has also been successful at the longer vacuum-uv wavelengths. An advantage of this approach is that coherence and tunability at long wavelengths is preserved in the conversion. A disadvantage is the generally low efficiency for conversion ($\leq 10^{-5}$). Hence the proposed coupling to a plasma amplifier to increase the output power.

Free-electron lasers (FELs) are essentially an outgrowth and extension of modern synchrotron light sources. The amplification and radiation are achieved by a beam of free electrons forced into transverse oscillations by a spatially periodic wiggler magnetostatic field, thereby emitting magnetic bremsstrahlung radiation in the forward direction. They are sometimes advocated to combine the best of both broadband synchrotron sources and monochromatic, coherent lasers. FELs share with synchrotron sources the technologies of low-divergence electron beams and periodic magnetic structures. The major advantages of FELs over conventional lasers is the broad and continuous (over a band) tunability offered, even with diffraction-limited beam quality. [*See* LASERS, FREE ELECTRON.]

The wavelength in the laboratory frame of reference is approximately proportional to the spatial period of the wiggler and inversely to the electron beam energy squared. Hence, for operation in the vacuum-uv spectral region a very short wiggler period and/or high beam energy is required. For the former, even substitution of an optical wiggler (perhaps laser) is proposed. This is projected to provide amplification at a wavelength near 0.5 nm with a 5 MeV electron beam. Plasma and solid state wigglers are also under discussion. Once again, efficient cavities are required to achieve the level of operation expected from success with FELs in the infrared and visible spectral regions. In general, near-uv FELs are now a reality and vacuum-uv FELs are on the horizon, but operation in the X-ray region is still quite remote and faces many similar problems associated with present plasma X-ray lasers.

For wavelengths shorter than 1 nm, nuclear *gamma-ray* emitting transitions in solids are usually considered. Gamma-ray laser ("graser") design revolves around self-terminating transitions between the ground and first excited isomeric states. It has been projected that output powers as large as 10^{21} W might be possible. Certain aspects of the energy storage, inversion, and gain mechanisms are considerably more challenging than for X-ray lasers.

The threshold density for a graser is proportional to the product of the line width and the lifetime of the excited isomeric state. Hence, if the line width can be reduced, the density and overall pumping power can be kept reasonable with the long lifetimes typical of forbidden isomeric transitions. Indeed, operation on very narrow lines may be possible for certain Mössbauer recoilless transitions. In this mode, pumping must be "gentle" in order not to overheat or vibrate the crystal. Because of these problems, excited isomers must first be prepared slowly and gently into extremely metastable storage states. The next step in pumping involves the actual segregation of the excited isomeric nuclei from others, followed by crystallization in a recoilless lattice of a cooled slender thread or whisker. From there lasing would be initiated by various schemes, depending on the upper state lifetimes. For example, in the very slow mode, isomers are pumped to a metastable state and lasing is initiated by a change in environment, for example, by rapid cooling to reduce the line width and increase the stimulated emission above the losses in the medium. In a faster mode, the broadening limits are within the range of Mössbauer narrowing. One pumping approach uses X-ray line emission to pump a short-lived excited intermediate state in a three-level system, either from a ground state or a nearby long-lived preformed excited isomeric state. This storage state then rapidly decays to fill the upper-laser level.

The challenge to developing grasers continues to be the contradictory requirements of an intense pump and a relatively undisturbed solid host material. Efforts are currently aimed at laying the groundwork for future experiments. The current consensus seems to be that basic studies of the structure and properties of nuclear excitation must precede a true estimate of the feasibility of a gamma-ray laser, with a reasonable time scale for operation a couple of decades.

There is a continual need for new approaches for X-ray lasers. Several somewhat speculative ideas have been suggested. One category involves solid lasants in the form of crystals, with which both high densities and low temperatures are available for high gain. One major problem is absorption of the X-rays in the crystal. It has been suggested that certain diffraction effects may effectively offset some of this absorption. One proposed approach for lasing in a crystal involves photon pumping by the absorption of localized bremsstrahlung fluorescent radiation by a doped lasant substance. It is also proposed that the crystal lattice serve as the resonant cavity. Another crystal approach involves channeled radiation in a specific direction, which results from the interaction between the field in an aligned crystal and charged particles. The radiation from the oscillatory motion of the particles may be Doppler shifted from a few electron volts in photon energy to the kiloelectron volt or even megaelectron volt regions. It has been suggested also that X-ray lasing may be induced for channel radiation under certain circumstances. One approach considers the field as a very short-period undulator for a solid-state free-electron laser; the second involves more conventional transitions between channeling states.

Stimulating transitions of free electrons in the Coulomb field of a nucleus to make an X-ray laser would in principle result in tunability, because of the spread in energy for electrons in nonbound states. Transitions into other free-electron states results in *stimulated bremsstrahlung* emission. *Stimulated recombination* into bound states has also been proposed for pumping an X-ray laser. The central problem for achieving high gain in either case is a lack of sufficient free-electron density in a specific energy interval. These concepts are likely to become practical candidates for X-ray lasing only if a nonequilibrium situation can be generated at high density.

Another approach involves *Compton scattering,* in which photons injected into an oncoming relativistic electron beam are scattered back at greatly increased energies. The additional energy derives from the electron beam. Again, it may be possible to reach the X-ray spectral region starting with a long-wavelength laser. In addition, the output wavelength would be tunable by varying the acceleration of the electron beam. For 5 MeV electrons, 200 nm photons then emerge as 0.5 nm X rays. Shorter wavelengths are conceivable with gigaelectron volt accelerators. It also has been proposed that the relativistic electron beam used in Compton scattering be replaced by a beam of multiply ionized atoms. The population inversion created by optical pumping could lase with tunability in the X-ray region because of the Doppler shift.

V. Applications

While there has been continual "crystal ball" reflection on potential applications for X-ray lasers, the general attitude in the scientific community is that probably the most important applications will develop after a useful device has arrived, depending upon the characteristics. With a brilliance of $\sim 10^8$-times that of state-of-the-art pulsed X-ray sources now known (see Fig. 2), such a device could not possibly remain unappreciated for any significant period. The most exciting applications most likely will be as revolutionary in the X-ray region as they have been with visible and infrared lasers. Numerous (nonprioritized) potential X-ray laser applications are discussed in the following paragraphs.

In the scientific arena, photoexcitation and photoionization are applicable to pumping other laser transitions, both for other wavelengths and for investigating atomic kinetics. Photoionization may be used also to generate multicharged ions for accelerator sources. Photoexcitation also can produce resonance-fluorescence pumping of atoms and ions into excited states for quantitative studies of further excitation and ionization by either photons or electrons. Resonance absorption and fluorescence can also be used for measuring ground-state population densities as well as excitation temperatures in atoms and plasma ions. In the surface science electron spectroscopy for chemical analysis (ESCA) technique, one or more core electrons is photoionized by X rays or released by Auger emission, and the kinetic energy distribution is analyzed to determine the elemental composition and chemical state of the surface of a specimen. Also, nuclear processes can be influenced by X-ray lasers through the surrounding electrons. The responsible processes are internal conversion and K-electron capture. In addition, the impact of high energy radiation on matter eventually leads to chemical changes. This field involves in part photolysis as well as radiolysis on very short time scales. Finally, miniature electron accelerators have been conceived as a possible centimeter-long version of the 2 mile Stanford linear accelerator.

Moving from pure science to technical applications, the formation of diffractive gratings with sub-100 nm spacings may be possible using X-ray lasers. Also, high-resolution (<1 μm) photolithography is one of the more promising applications. X-rays are preferred to ultraviolet radiation to reduce diffraction, scattering, and reflection effects. Line-widths on the order of 20 nm have been reported using conventional X-ray sources with exposures of up to hours. Microelectronic devices appropriate for X-ray lithography include integrated circuits, diffraction gratings, magnetic bubbles, transistors, surface acoustic wave devices, gratings for distributed-feedback lasers, and Josephson junction cryogenic devices.

In surface science, photoelectron spectroscopy is a versatile probing technique for studying intrinsic and absorbate surface states in solids. Photons are used to release electrons from the surface, and their energy distribution is measured with an electron energy analyzer. The intensity and monochromaticity of an X-ray laser are decided advantages here. X-ray lasers in the 1 nm range also will be useful in metallurgy for ion implantation, surface alloying, laser annealing, wear, friction and corrosion detection, mirror surface evaluation, and phase transformation.

For biology, it is desirable to study cellular organelles with high spatial and millisecond-to-picosecond temporal resolutions in a natural and dynamic fluid state. Some vital questions that can be addressed are the locations of soluble enzymes in the cytoplasm and the presence of protein-associated aggregated structures. Since proteins in a live biological sample are more absorbing than the water present for wavelengths shorter than 4.4 nm (the K-absorption edge for carbon) and longer than the corresponding K-edge for oxygen at 2.3 nm wavelength, this particularly useful range has been dubbed the "water window" of high contrast (noted in Fig. 3). This has served to set one of the most important goals in terms of short wavelengths. Some gain in this wavelength region has already been achieved (see Tables I and II and Fig. 3), but the output power is still quite low for applications. With a high brightness, single-mode spatially coherent X-ray laser, biological holography becomes possible, thereby providing time-resolved three-dimensional images of the live cell. Also, three dimensional images of macromolecules and atoms may become a reality. In the field of biomolecular crystallography, micrometer scale imaging with an X-ray laser could immensely simplify the task of growing crystals free of irregularities. With added coherence it also may be possible to use X-ray scattering to determine the electron distribution in a crystal.

In the radiological medical field, some angiographic applications using X-ray and gamma-ray lasers are suggested. Differential absorption can be used to ascertain the distribution of heavy elements in organs *in vivo* with improved contrast, in a situation in which a pathological condition has led to a change in elemental composition. Some familiar examples are iodine in the thyroid gland and osteoporosity in bones. Holographic X-ray imaging could have tremendous clinical potential for the diagnosis of abnormal anatomical situations caused by congenital abnormalities or disease, such as the location and analysis of tumor masses.

VI. Summary and Prognosis

X-ray laser research and development has advanced to the success that it enjoys today through a series of spurts of interest and progress, with a periodicity of ~3–5 years, beginning around 1970. Some of the periodically renewed interests have arisen with the availability of new and more powerful drivers; some have followed a breakthrough in thinking and progressive experiments. Mostly, however, they have resulted from changes in policies and emphasis at various levels.

Now that lasers exist in the xuv and soft X-ray spectral regions of useful output power, the next logical step is to "institutionalize" this area of research, rather than continuing it as an adjunct to laser fusion and pulsed power programs. Fully dedicated, worldwide cooperative facilities are needed. Likely research areas of fruitful pursuit include shorter wavelengths, increased output, cavity capability, improved beam quality, reduced size, enhanced efficiency, and improved convenience and accessibility. We are on the threshold of acceptance of X-ray lasers as practical and useful tools. Clearly the promise is exciting for X-ray laser research, development, and application in the coming years. The truly revolutionary capabilities and applications are limited only by our imaginations and resources.

Bibliography

Baldwin, G. C., Solem, J. C., and Gol'danski, V. I. (1981). *Rev. Mod. Phys.* **53,** 687.

Brau, C. (1990). "Free Electron Lasers." Academic Press, San Diego.

Elton, R. C. (1990). "X-Ray Lasers." Academic Press, San Diego.

J. Quant. Spectros. Rad. Transfer (1988) **40,** n. 40.

Marshall T. C. (1985). "Free-Electron Lasers." Macmillan, New York.

Reintjes, J. F. (1985). Coherent ultraviolet and vacuum ultraviolet sources. In "Laser Handbook," (M. Bass and M. L. Stitch, eds.). North-Holland, New York.

Skinner, C. H. (1991). Physics of Fluids B **3,** 2420.

LIGAND FIELD CONCEPT

Günter Gliemann *University of Regensburg*

GLOSSARY

Absorption: Absorption of light quanta (electromagnetic radiation) by an atom, molecule, or solid. The strength of absorption is described by the extinction coefficient ε.

Central ion: Transition metal ion surrounded by ligands.

Charge transfer transition: Change of the electronic state of a complex ion by the transfer of an electron from the central ion to the ligand system or vice versa.

Coordination number: Number of ligands bound at the central ion.

Electron spin: Intrinsic angular momentum vector of the electron. A quantum phenomenon, which has no analog in classical mechanics.

Emission: Emission of light quanta (electromagnetic radiation) by an atom, molecule, or solid.

Excited state: State of less stability (higher energy) than the ground state.

Ground state: Most stable state of an atom, molecule, or solid (state of lowest energy).

Ligand: Atomic ion, molecular ion, or molecule coordinated at the central ion of a complex.

Octahedral complex: Complex with six ligands at the corners of an octahedron, surrounding the central ion.

Orbital angular momentum: Mechanical vector quantity perpendicular to the orbit of a particle. Its magnitude depends on the orbit diameter and the mass and velocity of the particle.

Term: Entity of states of equal energy.

Transition metals: Elements with incompletely filled *d* orbitals: scandium, titanium through copper (3*d* series); yttrium, zirconium through silver (4*d* series); lanthanum, hafnium through gold (5*d* series).

The ligand field concept is the basis of a quantum theoretical model developed in the 1950s for describing the electron systems of transition metal complexes. A transition metal complex is composed of a transition metal ion (central ion) surrounded by a system of ligands (atomic ions, molecular ions, or molecules). The ligands produce an electrical field (the ligand field) acting on the electron system of the central ion. As the ligand field theory shows, the optical, magnetic, and stability properties of transition metal complexes strongly depend on the symmetry and strength of the ligand field.

I. Basic Experimental Findings

Crystallized salts of metal complexes have an amazing variety of brilliant colors, which are expressed by such prefixes as violeo-, praseo-, luteo-, purpureo-, and roseo- (Table I). Investigations of the underlying chemical structures reveal a close relationship between color and composition, an immediate challenge for the spectroscopist. Therefore, after the foundation of coordination theory by A. Werner (1907) several of his students began to study the absorption spectra of solutions of complexes.

After about 1915 spectroscopic work on restricted areas of the wide field of complex compounds was done by Y. Shibata, R. Tsuchida, A. V. Kiss, R. Samuel, and co-workers with the aim of deriving relations between the number and the position of absorption bands and the na-

TABLE I. Nomenclature Describing the Colors of Some Transition Metal Complex Ions

Compound	Color	Prefix
cis-$[Co(NH_3)_4Cl_2]^+$	Violet	Violeo-
trans-$[Co(NH_3)_4Cl_2]^+$	Green	Praseo-
$[Cr(NH_3)_6]^{3+}$	Yellow	Luteo-
$[Co(NH_3)_5H_2O]^{3+}$	Rose	Roseo-
$[Co(NH_3)_5Cl]^{2+}$	Purple red	Purpureo-

ture of the central ion and the ligands. Some of these early experimental results were misleading, because the technique and apparatus for measuring absorption spectra were still rather undeveloped; the real state of the complex ions in solution, depending on the conditions of concentration and acidity, had received little attention; and sometimes the substances studied were not sufficiently pure. Endeavors to interpret the spectra according to the theory of electrons remained unsatisfactory until the 1940s, but it was soon recognized that the existence of *d* electrons is significant for the color of transition metal ion complexes.

The outstanding work of M. Linhard and coworkers, starting in 1944 with the investigation of Co^{3+} and Cr^{3+} complexes, set the standard for the utmost precision of absorption spectroscopy of dissolved complexes. One of the main results of Linhard's work is indicated schematically in Fig. 1. The absorption spectra of transition metal complexes can be divided into two spectral regions. In the long-wavelength region ($\lambda \gtrsim$ 350–400 nm) one finds one or more weak bands

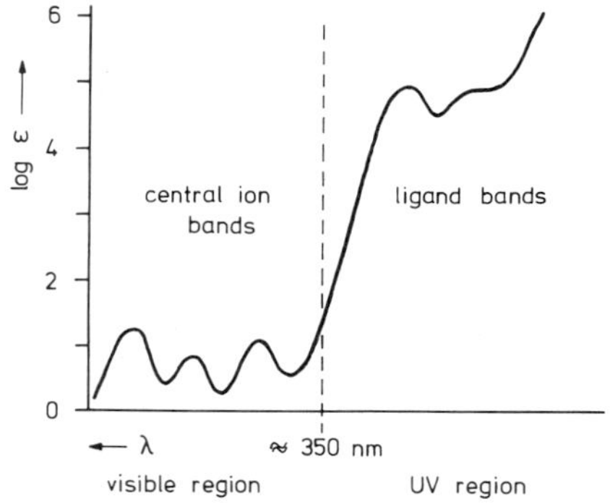

FIG. 1. Absorption spectrum of a transition metal complex ion (schematic). The central ion bands correspond to $d \rightarrow d$ transitions; the ligand bands correspond to charge transfer transitions and/or to intraligand transitions.

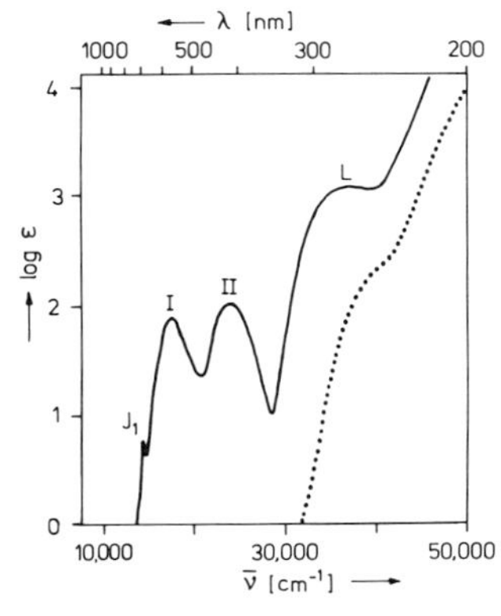

FIG. 2. Absorption spectra of $[Cr(C_2O_4)_3]^{3-}$ (full line) and $[Al(C_2O_4)_3]^{3-}$ (dotted line).

(value of the molar decadic extinction coefficient $\varepsilon \approx 1\text{–}10^2$ liters mol^{-1} cm^{-1}). These bands do not appear when the central ion is not a transition metal ion (e.g., Al^{3+} instead of Cr^{3+}; see Fig. 2). Therefore, these weak bands were assigned to transitions involving *d* electrons of the central ion (central ion bands, *d–d* bands). In the short-wavelength region ($\lambda \lesssim$ 350–400 nm) strong absorption bands ($\varepsilon \approx 10^4\text{–}10^5$ liters mol^{-1} cm^{-1}) are observed. These strong bands (ligand bands) are usually charge transfer bands, due to electron transfer between the central ion and the ligand system, or intraligand bands, caused by excitation of the electron system of the ligands. [*See* MOLECULAR OPTICAL SPECTROSCOPY.]

Stimulated by Linhard's work, F. E. Ilse and H. Hartmann formulated in 1946 the ligand field concept, based on the classical ionic model of transition metal complexes (W. Kossel and A. Magnus) and on appropriate group theoretical methods (H. Bethe).

II. Model and Theory

A. Complex Models and the Concept of Ligand Field

In the 1920s and 1930s two apparently contrary models had been developed to explain the binding between the central ion and the ligands. Kossel and Magnus described the central ion and the ligands by rigid, inpenetrable spheres with specific radii. The distribution of electrical charge within the complex components was represented by point charges and point dipoles fixed at the centers of the spheres (Fig. 3a). In a

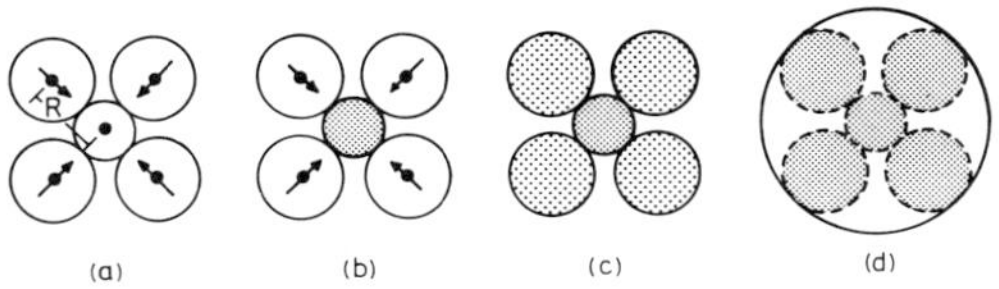

FIG. 3. Models of transition metal complex ions (schematic). (a) Ionic model (after Kossel and Magnus); (b) extended ionic model (after Ilse and Hartmann); (c) system of separated components; (d) covalent model (after Pauling).

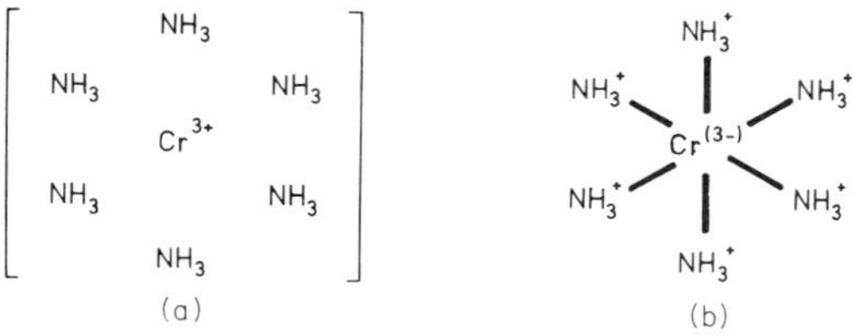

FIG. 4. Electrovalent (a) and covalent (b) forms of the $[Cr(NH_3)_6]^{3+}$ complex ion. In the covalent form each valence dash represents one bonding electron pair.

refinement of the model mutual electrical polarization of the complex components was taken into account, such as considering induced electrical dipoles. According to Kossel and Magnus the binding of the components of the complex is due to the electrostatic forces between the components.

This ionic model explains several phenomena in complex chemistry. For example, it gives the heats of formation of complexes (as a function of charges, dipole moments, and radii of the complex components) and the maximum size of the coordination number. The ionic model, however, does not explain the existence of *anomalous* coordination types (e.g., the square planar configuration instead of the *normal* tetrahedral configuration for the coordination number 4) and of certain "low-spin" complexes [e.g., diagmagnetism of octahedral Co(III) complexes; see Section IV].

N. V. Sidgwick and L. Pauling have formulated an essentially covalent model. According to this model the binding between the central ion and the ligands is accomplished by electron pairs. To get the correct number of equivalent bonds a certain number of electrons are transferred from the ligands to the central ion, forming covalent bonds with the unpaired electrons remaining on the ligands. [*See* ELECTRON TRANSFER REACTIONS, GENERAL.]

As an example Fig. 4 shows the ionic (electrovalent) and the covalent forms of a $[Cr(NH_3)_6]^{3+}$ complex ion. In the ionic model the triply positively charged chromium ion is surrounded by six NH_3 molecules provided with electrical dipoles. The bond arises from ion–dipole interaction. In the covalent model each bond is generated by an electron pair (valence dash). One electron from an electron pair on each NH_3 molecule is transferred to the central ion, which assumes the charge -3. This electron forms a bonding electron pair with the electron remaining on the NH_3^+ molecule ion.

On the basis of Pauling's covalent model the appearance of anomalous coordination types and of "low-spin" complexes can be explained.

Neither the ionic model nor the covalent model provided an interpretation of several optical properties, since these models were concerned primarily with the electronic ground state of the complex ions. Optical properties, such as the absorption and emission of light, however, involve both the ground state and excited states. By its nature, the ionic model of Kossel and Magnus is restricted to the ground state. Pauling's model is based on the valence bond theory. Because of the complexity of the quantum mechanical covalent scheme, for a long period the calculation of the excited states necessary for the analysis of optical spectra appeared to be a hopeless task.

As shown above, for a large number of complexes certain spectral regions of the absorption spectra can be assigned alternatively to the different components of the complex (central ion, ligand system), especially to the electron systems of these components. On this account a model that starts in a first rough approximation with the assumption of separated electron systems for the central ion and for the ligands will be appropriate for a theoretical treatment.

At first sight Pauling's covalent model stands in contrast to this concept, because the binding electron pairs belong to both the central ion and the ligands. One can speak only of an electron cloud for the entire complex (Fig. 3d). The ionic model of Kossel and Magnus, however, yields a basis for a model of separated electron systems. It can be developed by a consistent modification. The components are to be substituted by separated entities of nuclei and moving electrons, and the mutual coupling of the components is due to the electric forces between the charged particles (Fig. 3c).

If one is interested primarily in the electronic states of the central ion bound in the complex, one has to consider the electric field generated by the system of the surrounding ligands, the so-called ligand field, and the effect of this ligand field on the electronic states of the transition metal ion used as the central ion. The theory treating this concept of ligand field is the ligand field theory. To a first approximation the charge distribution of the ligands is represented by point charges and/or point dipoles in their centers (extended ionic model; see Fig. 3b).

The designation *ligand field theory* is used by several authors when the electronic structure of the ligand system is taken explicitly into account (see Section II,D). These authors denote the aforementioned theory based on the extended ionic model as crystal field theory.

The starting point of the ligand field theory is the description of the electronic states of the free, isolated transition metal ion that can function as the central ion in a complex. Information on the electronic ground state and the excited states of the free ions is available from the analysis of the corresponding emission spectra and (approximately) from quantum mechanical calculations.

The electronic states of a free ion can be characterized by their energy and by their angular momentum, composed of the orbital angular momenta and the spins of the electrons involved. For atoms that are not too heavy the Russell–Saunders coupling is a good approximation. In this approximation the orbital angular momenta of the electrons are added vectorially to the total orbital angular momentum **L** and the spins of the electrons are coupled to the total spin **S**:

$$\sum_j \mathbf{l}_j = \mathbf{L}; \qquad \sum_j \mathbf{s}_j = \mathbf{S}$$

where $\mathbf{l}_j$ is the orbital angular momentum and $\mathbf{s}_j$ is the spin of the jth electron. As shown by quantum mechanics the absolute values of the vectors **L** and **S** are restricted to certain discrete amounts,

$$|\mathbf{L}| = \hbar\sqrt{L(L+1)}, \qquad L = 0, 1, 2, 3, \ldots$$

$$|\mathbf{S}| = \hbar\sqrt{S(S+1)},$$

$$S = \begin{cases} 0, 1, 2, 3, \ldots & \text{for even number of electrons} \\ \frac{1}{2}, \frac{3}{2}, \frac{5}{2}, \frac{7}{2}, \ldots & \text{for odd number of electrons} \end{cases}$$

where $\hbar \equiv h/2\pi$ (h is Planck's constant); L and S are the quantum numbers of the total orbital angular momentum and the total spin of the system of electrons, respectively. For the numerical values $L = 0, 1, 2, 3, \ldots$ it is conventional to use the letters S, P, D, F, ... By quantum mechanical rules a spin **S** with quantum number S can take $2S + 1$ different spatial orientations with respect to a given direction (Fig. 5). The $2S + 1$ is denoted as multiplicity M. Correspondingly, an orbital angular momentum **L** with quantum number L can assume $2L + 1$ different spatial orientations. Therefore, to a given set of quantum numbers L and S, in total $(2L + 1)(2S + 1)$ states with different orientations of orbital angular momentum and/or spin belong. These states form a Russell–Saunders term, symbolized by ^{2S+1}L. For atoms that are not too heavy all $(2L + 1)(2S + 1)$ states of the same term have equal energies. They are energetically "degenerate." Usually, different terms have different energies. By Hund's rule the term with the highest multiplicity M and the highest L value is the ground state term (energetically most stable term).

For example, for a d^2 ion (two d electrons), various states with multiplicity 1 (singlet: spin configuration with the two electron spins antiparallel ⇅) and 3 (triplet: ⇈) result. In total there are two triplet terms and three singlet terms: ^{3}P, ^{3}F, ^{1}S, ^{1}D, ^{1}G. By Hund's rule the ^{3}F [composed of $(2 \times 3 + 1)(2 \times 1 + 1) = 21$ states] is the ground term. The five Russell–Saunders terms of a d^2 ion are shown in the energy-level diagram of Fig. 6. The complete sets of Russell–Saunders terms for the d^N ions with $N = 1, 2, \ldots, 9$ are given in Table II.

In the course of forming a complex the central ion is influenced by the ligand field (electrical field of the ligands), and thereby the motion

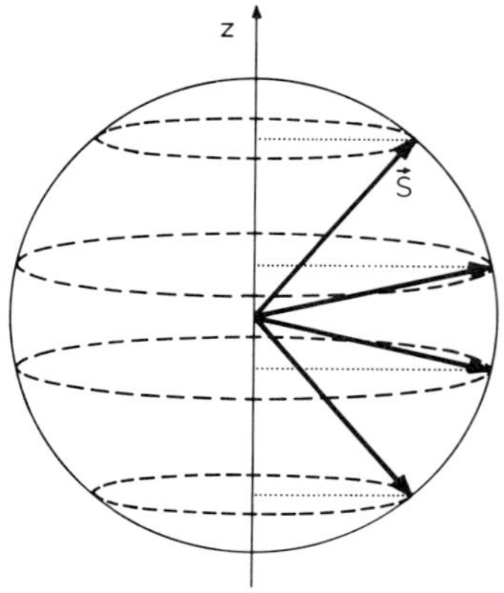

FIG. 5. Spatial orientations of a spin vector **S** with $S = \frac{3}{2}$. There are $2S + 1 = 4$ different values of projection on the z axis allowed.

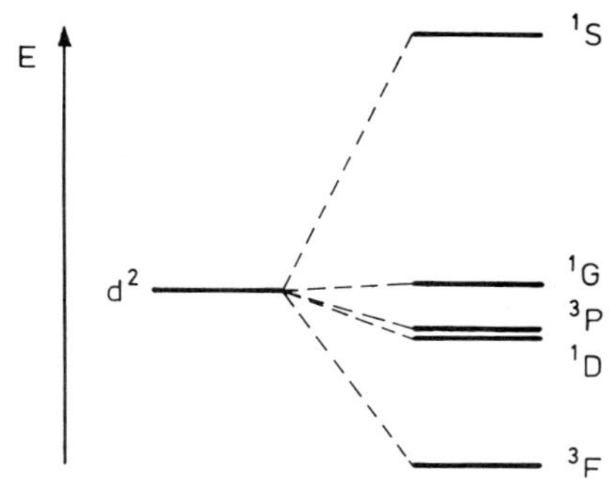

FIG. 6. Russell–Saunders terms of a d^2 ion (schematic).

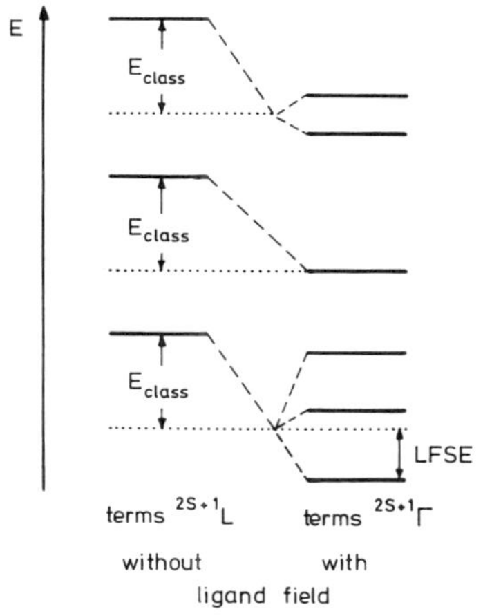

FIG. 7. Splitting of the Russell–Saunders terms of a central ion by a ligand field (schematic). E_{class}, electrostatic binding energy after Kossel and Magnus; LFSE, ligand field stabilization energy.

modes of the electrons of the central ion will be perturbed. Accordingly, the term system of the central ion will be changed, as shown schematically in Fig. 7. Some terms ^{2S+1}L of the free ion are energetically merely shifted, while others are split into progeny terms $^{2S+1}\Gamma_i$, $i = 1, 2, \ldots$, with different energies (intracomplex Stark effect). The symbol Γ_i describes the orbital state of the ith progeny term.

The number of the progeny terms $^{2S+1}\Gamma_i$ can be *exactly* determined by the methods of group theory. It depends on the L value of the (parent) term ^{2S+1}L and on the symmetry of the ligand system:

$$\text{Number of progeny terms } {}^{2S+1}\Gamma_i = f(L, \text{symmetry})$$

This general group theoretical result can be illustrated by simple model systems. First we consider a system of six ligands (represented by electrical negative point charges) at the corners of a regular octahedron. The central ion within this system is to be varied with regard to its orbital angular momentum (quantum number L). To simplify the problem the central ion may contain only one electron, either a p electron ($L = 1$) or a d electron ($L = 2$). The corresponding probability distributions of the electron charge known from the theory of atoms are shown in Figs. 8 and 9. The p electron can occupy three different orbital states ($2L + 1 = 3$). All three distributions are in equivalent positions with regard to the ligands (Fig. 8). Therefore, the energies of the three states will be shifted by the

TABLE II. Russell–Saunders Terms for Free d^N Ions[a]

Occupation of the *d* shell	Russell–Saunders term
d^1, d^9	$^2\underline{\mathrm{D}}$
d^2, d^8	$^3\underline{\mathrm{F}}$, ^{3}P
	$^1\underline{\mathrm{G}}$, $^1\underline{\mathrm{D}}$, ^{1}S
d^3, d^7	$^4\underline{\mathrm{F}}$, ^{4}P
	^{2}H, ^{2}G, ^{2}F, a^{2}D, b^{2}D, ^{2}P
d^4, d^6	$^5\underline{\mathrm{D}}$
	^{3}H, ^{3}G, a^{3}F, b^{3}F, ^{3}D, a^{3}P, b^{3}P
	^{1}I, a^{1}G, b^{1}G, ^{1}F, a^{1}D, b^{1}D, a^{1}S, b^{1}S
d^5	$^6\underline{\mathrm{S}}$
	^{4}G, ^{4}F, ^{4}D, ^{4}P
	^{2}I, ^{2}H, a^{2}G, b^{2}G, a^{2}F, b^{2}F, a^{2}D, b^{2}D, c^{2}D, ^{2}P, ^{2}S

[a] If for a d^N ion ($N = 1, \ldots, 9$) several terms with the same L value and the same S value exist, they are distinguished by prefixes a, b, c. Terms with underlined L symbols are the ground terms.

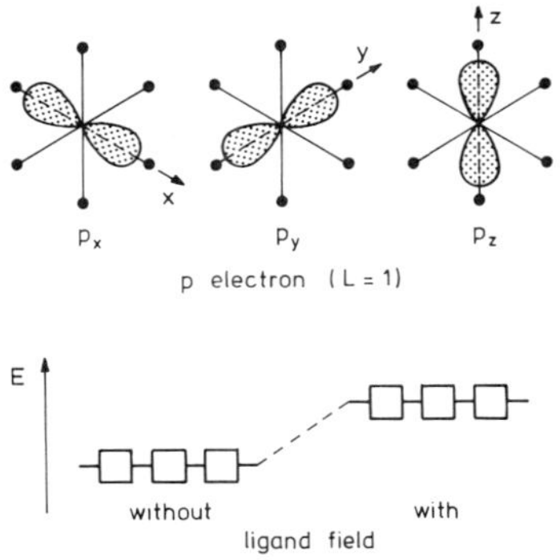

FIG. 8. Probability distributions and energy states of a p electron ($L = 1$) in an octahedral ligand field induced by six negative point charges (schematic).

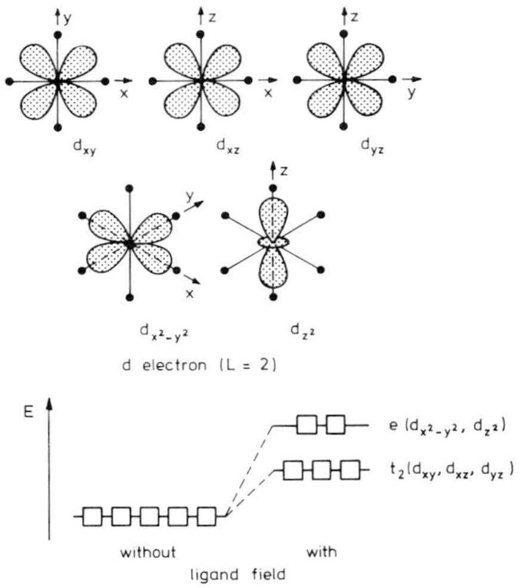

FIG. 9. Probability distributions and energy states of a d electron ($L = 2$) in an octahedral ligand field (schematic).

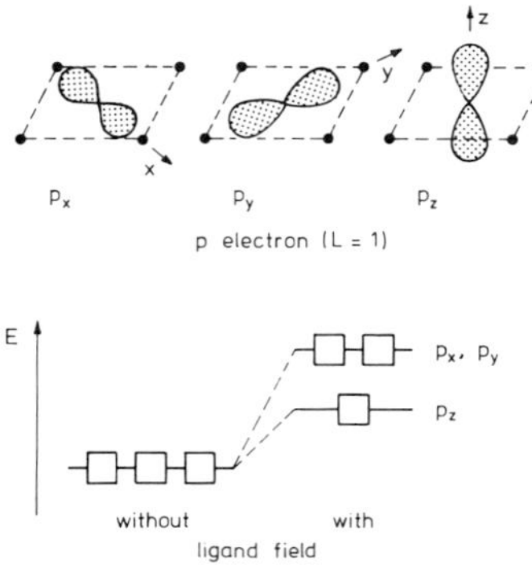

FIG. 10. Probability distributions and energy states of a p electron ($L = 1$) in a tetragonal ligand field (schematic).

same amount when the ligand field is acting on the central ion. No splitting will be observed. For a d electron ($2L + 1 = 5$), however, there are distributions that are obviously not equivalent with regard to the ligands (Fig. 9). The maxima of the distributions d_{xy}, d_{xz}, and d_{yz} are directed equivalently into the angular bisectors between the bonds. Therefore, these three states will have the same energy. The distribution $d_{x^2-y^2}$ has maxima along the bonds to the ligands located on the x and the y axes. It follows that the $d_{x^2-y^2}$ state will have a higher energy than the three states mentioned above because of the stronger repulsion between electron and ligands. The d_{z^2} distribution has a form different from the other d distributions. A d_{z^2} electron will strongly interact with the ligands on the z axis. Quantitative calculations show that the d_{z^2} state is energetically degenerate with the $d_{x^2-y^2}$ state. Therefore, the fivefold D term of a d^1 ion is split into a threefold state t_2 and a twofold state e (Fig. 9). From these examples we see that for the *same symmetry* of the ligand field the number of progeny terms depends on the quantum number L of the orbital angular momentum of the electron system.

On the other hand, for the same quantum number L of the orbital angular momentum the number of progeny terms depends on the *symmetry* of the ligand system, as shown graphically in Fig. 10 for a p electron ($L = 1$). The octahedral symmetry of the ligand system as given in Fig. 8 is reduced by canceling the ligands on the z axis. As a consequence the p_z distribution has a weaker coupling with the remaining four ligands than the distributions p_x and p_y have: Lowering of the symmetry yields a term splitting.

The *amount* of the energetic splitting or shifting can be (approximately) determined by the methods of quantum mechanical perturbation theory. Since the perturbation comes from the electrical interaction between the electrons of the central ion and the charge distribution within the ligand system, the magnitude of energetic splitting or shifting will depend on the central ion–ligand distances R and on the charges q and electrical dipole moments μ of the ligands:

$$\text{Magnitude of energetic splitting and/or shifting} = F(R, q, \mu)$$

Since the charge distributions within the ligands are not known exactly, an absolute calculation of these energetic effects is virtually impossible. In practice these magnitudes (as functions of R, q, and μ) are taken as parameters in the calculations and are fit to experimental data.

The energetic order within the system of progeny terms $^{2S+1}\Gamma_i$ determines important properties of the complex ions:

1. Optical properties. The energetic differences between the ground state and the energetically lowest excited states correspond to the absorption bands in the spectral region with $\lambda \gtrsim$ 350–400 nm, determining the color of the compound (Section III).
2. Magnetism. The spin multiplicity $M = 2S + 1$ of the ground term determines roughly

the magnetic behavior of the complex ion (Section IV).

3. Stability. The stabilization of the ground term by the ligand field stabilization energy represents an increase in the binding energy of the complex ion, in addition to that obtained by the ionic model of Kossel and Magnus (Section V).

B. Term Splitting under Octahedral Symmetry

Octahedral symmetry of the ligand field is realized, at least approximately, in the large family of six-coordinate transition metal complex ions. As shown in the preceding section, P terms ($L = 1$) are merely shifted under the influence of an octahedral field, whereas D terms ($L = 2$) are split into a twofold and a threefold term. Corresponding considerations yield the behavior of terms with $L = 0$ and $L > 2$ under octahedral fields. Table III summarizes the resulting term splittings for L values up to 4. The numbers in parentheses give the orbital degeneracy of the terms. A_1, A_2, E, T_1, T_2 symbolize different orbital symmetries of the terms, where A_1 and A_2 represent nondegenerate, E twofold degenerate, and T_1 and T_2 threefold degenerate terms.

Figure 11 shows schematically the term splitting of the ground states of d^N complexes with $N = 1, \ldots, 9$ in an octahedral ligand field. The d^N and d^{10-N} ions exhibit equivalent splitting diagrams, but the energetic order of the progeny terms is inverted. This is a consequence of the so-called electron-hole equivalence.

C. Weak- and Strong-Field Methods, Term Diagrams, *Dq* Values, and Spectrochemical Series

There are two methods for finding the term system of a transition metal complex when the

TABLE III. Splitting of Orbital States with $L = 0, 1, 2, 3, 4$ in an Octahedral Ligand Field

Orbital state of the free ion: Quantum number L	State symbol[a]		Orbital states in an octahedral ligand field (Mulliken notation)[a]
0	S(1)	→	$A_1(1)$
1	P(3)	→	$T_1(3)$
2	D(5)	→	$E(2) \oplus T_2(3)$
3	F(7)	→	$A_2(1) \oplus T_1(3) \oplus T_2(3)$
4	G(9)	→	$A_1(1) \oplus E(2) \oplus T_1(3) \oplus T_2(3)$

[a] The numbers in parentheses give the orbital degeneracy of the states.

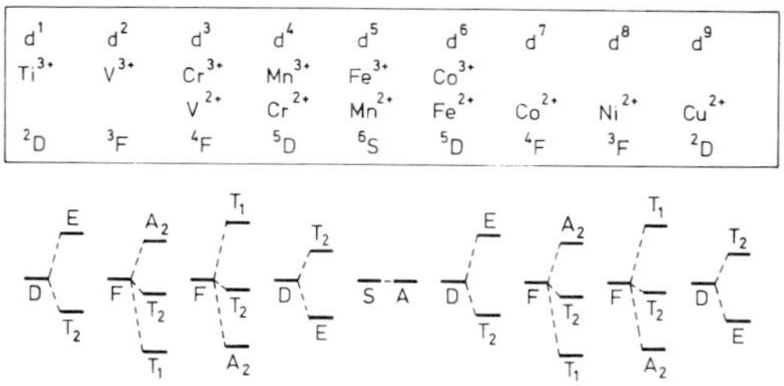

FIG. 11. Term splitting of the ground states of the ions Ti^{3+} to Cu^{2+} in an octahedral ligand field (schematic).

central ion contains two or more d electrons. Both methods start with the free d^N ion for which the electron–electron repulsion is not yet taken into account. They differ in the order in which the electron–electron interaction and the influence of the ligand field are treated. According to the expected relative amounts of these energetic quantities, the weak-field method is employed when the effect of electron–electron interaction dominates, whereas the strong-field method is appropriate when the influence of the ligand field is dominant. Complete treatments of a complex ion by both methods will ultimately yield the same results.

The weak-field method is described by the following scheme:

$$d^N \xrightarrow[\text{electron interaction}]{\text{step 1}} {}^{2S+1}L \xrightarrow[\text{ligand field}]{\text{step 2}} {}^{2S+1}\Gamma$$

The first step considers the electron–electron interaction. From this step the energies of the Russell–Saunders terms ${}^{2S+1}L$ of the free ion result. In the second step the splitting of these terms by the ligand field is determined, following the procedure given in Section II,A.

The two steps of the strong-field method have the opposite order:

$$d^N \xrightarrow[\text{ligand field}]{\text{step 1}} t_2^n e^{N-n} \xrightarrow[\text{electron interaction}]{\text{step 2}} {}^{2S+1}\Gamma$$

In the first step the splitting of one-electron states of the d shell in the ligand field is considered. For the octahedral ligand field, the five states of the d shell split energetically into a family e of two degenerate states $\{d_{x^2-y^2}, d_{z^2}\}$ and a family t_2 of three degenerate states $\{d_{xy}, d_{xz}, d_{yz}\}$ (Fig. 9). By quantum mechanical perturbation theory the energy difference between e and t_2 is calculated as $\Delta \equiv 10Dq$. For a given central ion the field strength parameter Dq depends on the central ion–ligand distance and on the charge distribution within the ligands. The value of Dq is determined from experimental data. The N d electrons can occupy the levels e and t_2 observing Pauli's principle: Each orbital $d_{x^2-y^2}$, d_{xy}, ... can be occupied by no more than two electrons, and these two electrons must have their spins opposed. In the second step of the strong-field method the electron–electron interaction is taken into account.

The results can be conveniently presented in the form of diagrams showing the term energies as functions of the strength of the ligand field. For systems with octahedral symmetry the energies of the terms ${}^{2S+1}\Gamma$ depend on the single parameter $\Delta \equiv 10Dq$ defined above. Figure 12 shows as an example the term diagram for Cr^{3+} in an octahedral environment. For $Dq = 0$ (vanishing ligand field strength) the term energies of the free Cr^{3+} ion are plotted. With increasing Dq value the terms are shifted and terms with $L > 1$ are split. By comparison of the optical absorption data of octahedral complex ions with the term diagram, the corresponding Dq values can be determined. The Dq values for several transition metal complexes are given in Table IV. The value of Dq depends on both the central ion and the ligands, roughly according to the relation

$$Dq \approx f(\text{ligand}) \times g(\text{central ion})$$

where the factor f depends only on the ligands and g depends only on the central ion. The following rules hold:

1. Influence of the central ion on Dq. For the same ligand system,

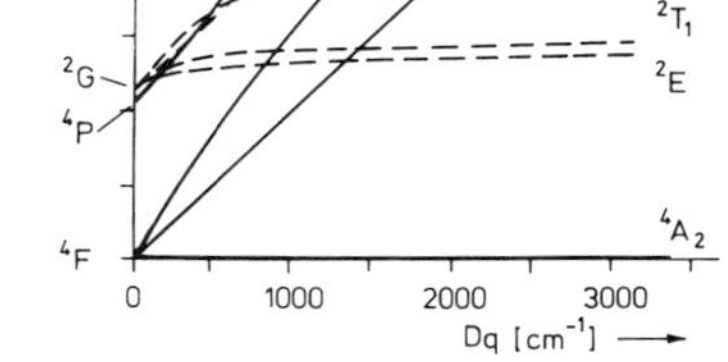

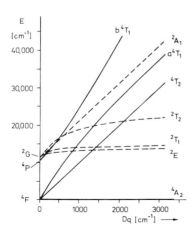

FIG. 12. Term diagram of a Cr^{3+} ion in an octahedral ligand field. (Term energies as functions of the ligand field strength Dq.)

TABLE IV. Dq Values of Six-Coordinate Transition Metal Complexes[a]

M	MCl_6	$M(H_2O)_6$	$M(CN)_6$
Ti(III)	1300	2030	—
V(III)	1100	1780	2220
Cr(III)	1370	1740	2670
Mo(III)	1920	2610	—
Fe(III)	—	1260	—
Fe(II)	—	1040	3100
Co(III)	—	1650	3240
Rh(III)	1930	2550	4450

[a] Data are expressed as reciprocal centimeters.

(a) the Dq values are very similar for transition metals of the same series and the same charge,

(b) the Dq values increase by 40 to 80% when a bivalent central ion is substituted by the corresponding trivalent ion, and

(c) the Dq values increase by 30 to 40% when going from the first to the second series of transition metal ions or from the second to the third series.

2. Influence of the ligands on Dq. For the same central ion the Dq values increase in the order of the spectrochemical series:

$$I^- < Br^- < Cl^- \sim \underline{S}CN^- \sim N_3^-$$
$$< (C_2H_5O)_2PS_2^- < F^- < (C_2H_5)_2NCS_2^-$$
$$< (NH_2)_2C\underline{O} < OH^- < (COO)_2^{2-}$$
$$\sim H_2O < \underline{N}CS^- < NH_2CH_2COO^-$$
$$< NCSHg^+ \sim NH_3 \sim C_5H_5N$$
$$< NH_2CH_2CH_2NH_2 \sim SO_3^{2-} < NH_2OH$$
$$< \underline{N}O_2^- < H^- \sim CH_3^- < \underline{C}N^-$$

An underlined atomic symbol indicates that the ligand is coordinated with that atom.

D. Treatment of Complexes by Molecular Orbital Theory

In the extended ionic model of the ligand field theory it is assumed that the electrons of the complex ion move in orbitals localized either at the central ion or at the ligands. In an important further extension of the ligand field theory, the electrons are allowed to move over the whole complex ion in molecular orbitals (molecular orbital theory of complex ions). In a common approximation the molecular orbitals are described by suitable linear combinations of atomic orbitals (LCAO approximation). For complex ions as "atomic" orbitals, the orbitals of the ligand system and the central ion orbitals d, p, and s are used.

As shown by quantum mechanics and group theory only certain linear combinations yield energetic effects:

1. The combining orbitals must have the same symmetry. (For example, in Fig. 13a the central ion orbital has the same symmetry as the orbitals of the ligand system; in Fig. 13b it has different symmetry.)
2. The energies of the combining orbitals must be of comparable magnitude for significant interaction to occur.
3. The combining orbitals must overlap.

Every pair of orbitals capable of forming linear combinations yields a stabilized (bonding) and a destabilized (antibonding) state (Fig. 14). As usual the antibonding state is labeled by an asterisk. The splitting energy is larger the smaller the energy difference between the combining orbitals and the stronger their overlap. In Fig. 15 the energy-level diagram of the molecular orbitals of an octahedral complex is represented. It is confined to σ bonds. (Only those orbitals of the individual ligands have been regarded whose shapes are invariant to rotation about the bonding axis.) The central ion orbitals t_2 (d_{xy}, d_{xz}, d_{yz}) are "nonbonding" since there are no σ orbitals of the ligands with suitable symmetry. The orbitals $e(d_{x^2-y^2}, d_{z^2})$, however, combine with ligand orbitals and yield a bonding e and an antibonding e^* state. Every ligand contributes two σ electrons to the complex ion, filling up the bonding orbitals a_1, t_1, e. Therefore, the d electrons of the central ion will occupy the

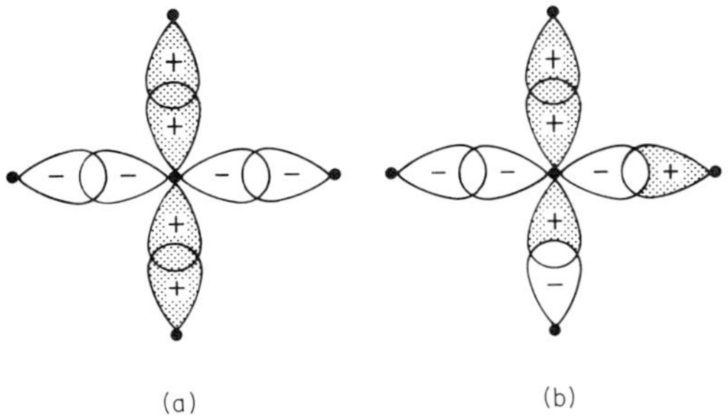

FIG. 13. Combinations of a central ion d orbital with ligand σ orbitals. The d orbital and ligand orbitals have the same (a) or different (b) symmetries.

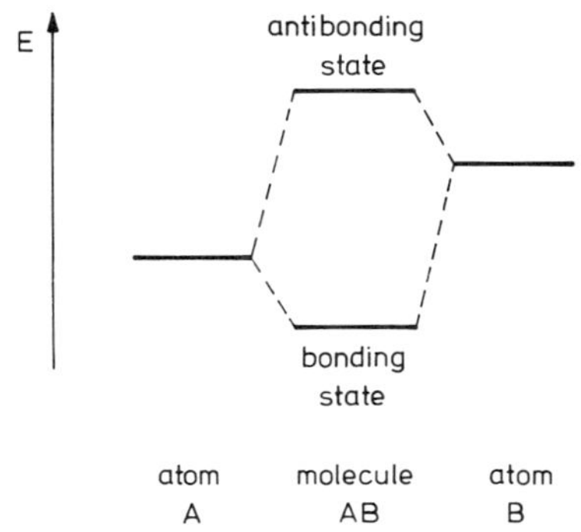

FIG. 14. Two atomic orbitals form a bonding and an antibonding state.

t_2 and e^* orbitals. The energy gap between t_2 and e^* corresponds to the ligand field parameter $\Delta \equiv 10Dq$. In a further step of the molecular orbital theory the electron–electron interaction has to be taken into account. This problem, however, can be solved only approximately.

III. Optical Properties of Complexes

The main features of the optical absorption spectra (Section I) and emission spectra of transition metal complexes can be interpreted on the basis of ligand field theory. Generally, the energies of the absorption and the emission bands correspond to energetic differences between electronic states. Therefore, an interpretation of the optical spectra will start with a comparison between the spectra and the term diagram of the complex ion, deduced from the extended ionic model or from the molecular orbital model. This method will be demonstrated by two informative examples.

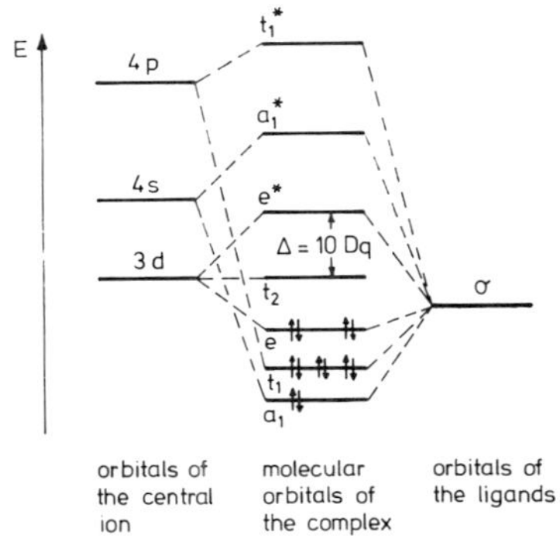

FIG. 15. Molecular orbital diagram of an octahedral complex (σ bonds only).

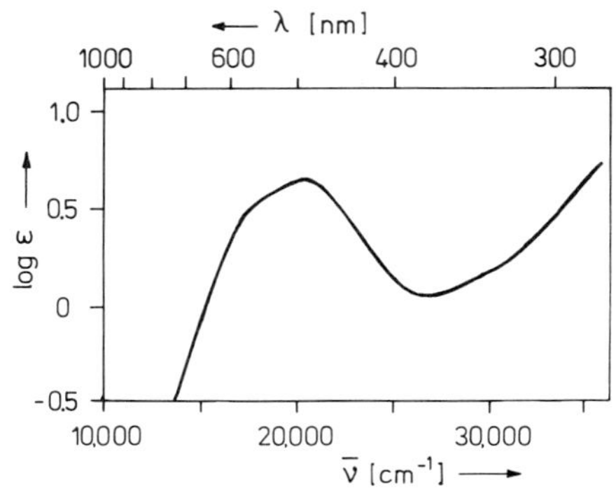

FIG. 16. Absorption spectrum of $[Ti(H_2O)_6]^{3+}$.

Figure 16 shows the absorption spectrum of the $[Ti(H_2O)_6]^{3+}$ ion consisting of one *d–d* band with its maximum at 492 nm. (The asymmetric shape of the band is due to the Jahn–Teller effect; Section V). The six-coordinate Ti^{3+} ion is a d^1 ion. From Table III and Fig. 11 it follows that an octahedral ligand field splits the ^2D state of the free d^1 ion into the low-lying $^2T_2$ ground state and a ^2E state at higher energies. By the absorption of a photon with energy $E(^2E) - E(^2T_2)$ the complex ion will be excited from its ground state $^2T_2$ into the state ^2E. The excitation energy in an octahedral d^1 ion is by definition equal to $\Delta \equiv 10Dq$. From the wavelength of the absorption maximum of 492 nm, it follows that Dq has a value of ~2030 cm^{-1}. In the molecular orbital theory the 492-nm band corresponds to the transition between the nonbonding t_2 state and the antibonding e^* state (see Fig. 15). The strong increase in absorption below ~350 nm belongs to charge transfer transitions, not covered by the extended ionic model.

The absorption spectrum of ruby is shown in Fig. 17. Two relatively strong bands I and II and three very weak absorptions J_1, J_2, and J_3 can be seen. At wavelengths below 300 nm a very strong increase in the absorption due to charge transfer transitions is observed (not shown in Fig. 17). Ruby is an Al_2O_3 crystal wherein single Al^{3+} ions are substituted by Cr^{3+} ions. The absorption spectrum is due to the Cr^{3+} ions (d^3 ions) since Al^{3+} does not have any *d* electrons. Every Cr^{3+} ion is surrounded by six oxygen ions forming an octahedron. The three lowest terms of the free Cr^{3+} ion are ^4F (ground state), ^4P, and ^2G. In the presence of the ligand field, the terms ^4F and ^2G split into three and four progeny terms, respectively. The resulting term diagram is given in Fig. 18. A comparison with the absorption spectrum yields the following assignment: the relatively intense bands I and II belong to the quartet–quartet transitions $^4A_2 \rightarrow {}^4T_2$ and $^4A_2 \rightarrow {}^4aT_1$, respectively, whereas J_1, J_2, and J_3 are due to the quartet–doublet transitions $^4A_2 \rightarrow {}^2E$, $^4A_2 \rightarrow {}^2T_1$, and $^4A_2 \rightarrow {}^2T_2$, respectively.

The significant intensity differences between the high-energy charge transfer bands ($\lambda < 300$ nm), the bands I and II, and the weak bands J_1, J_2, and J_3 originate in the different nature of the corresponding transitions. As shown by quantum theory, the absorption of light by molecules (composed of atoms that are not too heavy) is most effective if during the absorption process (1) one electron will change the quantum number of its orbital angular momentum by 1 and (2) the total spin of the electron system remains constant. Both of these criteria are fulfilled by the high-energy charge transfer transitions. In the $d \rightarrow d$ transitions, however, none of the elec-

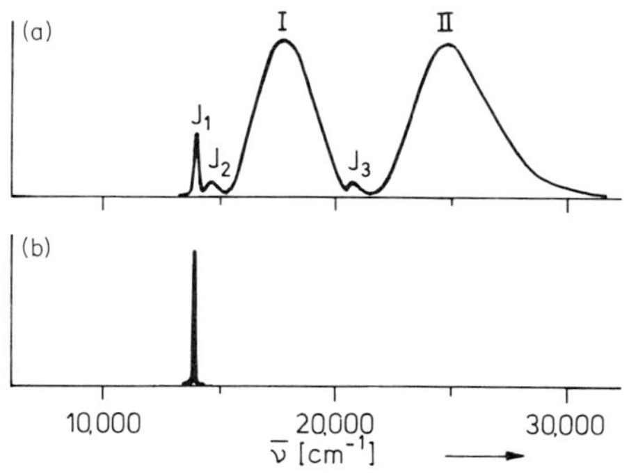

FIG. 17. Absorption (a) and emission (b) spectra of ruby.

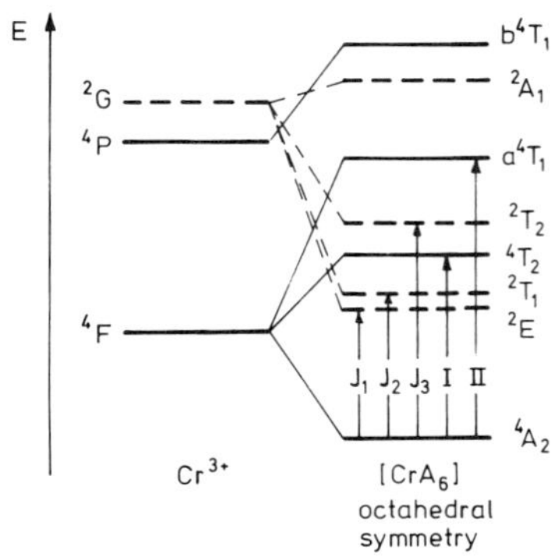

FIG. 18. Splitting of the three lowest Russell–Saunders terms of Cr^{3+} in an octahedral ligand field (cf. Fig. 12).

trons changes the value of its orbital angular momentum. Therefore, the $d \rightarrow d$ transitions will be distinctly weaker than the fully allowed charge transfer transitions. Among the $d \rightarrow d$ transitions the processes preserving the total spin show a significantly stronger absorption ("normal" bands like I and II) than the transitions that change the spin (intercombination bands like J_1, J_2, and J_3).

Several complex ions exhibit the emission of light. The emission spectrum of Cr^{3+} in ruby has the shape seen in Fig. 17. This emission has an interesting history. First, by the absorption of light the octahedral Cr^{3+} is excited from its ground state $^4A_2$ to a higher state. Because of the absorption properties a very high efficiency of excitation is expected for charge transfer transitions and a lesser efficiency for quartet–quartet transitions. Starting from the excited state the complex can deliver energy to its surroundings by nonradiative processes until it reaches the lowest excited state ^2E. The final deactivation into the ground state $^4A_2$ can occur in a single step by the emission of a photon corresponding to the energy gap between ^2E and $^4A_2$.

Ruby was the first crystalline compound to exhibit optical laser properties. The ruby laser works as follows. The quartet terms $^4T_2$ and $^4aT_1$ were excited by irradiation into the broad absorption bands I and II (optical pumping). Within a period of $<10^{-10}$ sec nonradiative transitions into the ^2E state take place, as shown above. The ^2E state is stable for a relatively long time ($\sim 5 \times 10^{-3}$ sec) before the photon emission occurs. Therefore, by optical pumping more and more Cr^{3+} centers occupy the ^2E state, and finally the number of ^2E excited centers is larger than the number of Cr^{3+} ions in the ground state (population inversion). When this "laser condition" is fulfilled, the accumulated energy can be emitted as an intense beam of photons with energy $E(^2E) - E(^4A_2)$, the brilliant red beam of the ruby laser.

IV. Magnetic Properties of Complexes

Every electron has a permanent magnetic moment $\boldsymbol{\mu}$ of amount $\mu_B = 9.27 \times 10^{-24}$ J T^{-1} (Bohr's magneton), which is parallel to its spin **s**. For an electron system with total spin quantum number S the effective magnetic moment is

$$\mu_{\text{eff}} = \sqrt{4S(S+1)}\mu_B = \sqrt{n(n+2)}\mu_B$$

where n designates the number of unpaired electrons. (Paired electrons are electrons in the same orbital having opposite spins and magnetic moments, and therefore the resulting spin and magnetic moment of such a pair are zero.) According to the Pauli principle the number of unpaired d electrons can vary between 1 and 5, since there are in total five d orbitals. In a free transition metal ion the five d orbitals are energetically degenerate. Following Hund's rule the electrons will occupy the orbitals in such a way that S is maximal. The μ_{eff} values of these high-spin (or spin-free) systems calculated by the formula given above are shown in the fourth column of Table V. Transition metal complexes with compatible μ_{eff} values are denoted high-spin (spin-free) complexes (see the fifth column of Table V).

TABLE V. Theoretical and Experimental Values of the Magnetic Moment μ_{eff} of Transition Metal Complexes[a]

Number of d electrons	Ion	High-spin configuration n[b]	μ_{eff}(theor)[c]	μ_{eff}(exp)	Low-spin configuration n[b]	μ_{eff}(theor)[c]	μ_{eff}(exp)
1	Ti^{3+}	1	1.73	1.65–1.79			
2	V^{3+}	2	2.83	2.75–2.85			
3	Cr^{3+}	3	3.87	3.70–3.90			
4	Mn^{3+}	4	4.90	4.90–5.00	2	2.83	3.18
5	Fe^{3+}	5	5.92	5.70–6.0	1	1.73	2.0–2.5
6	Fe^{2+}	4	4.90	5.10–5.70	0	0	Diamagnetic
7	Co^{2+}	3	3.87	4.30–5.20	1	1.73	1.8
8	Ni^{2+}	2	2.83	2.80–3.50	0	0	Diamagnetic
9	Cu^{2+}	1	1.73	1.70–2.20			

[a] The data are expressed in Bohr magneton units.
[b] n is the number of unpaired electrons.
[c] $\mu_{\text{eff}}(\text{theor}) = [n(n+2)]^{1/2}\mu_B$.

For several transition metal complexes, however, the experimental values of μ_{eff} are significantly smaller than expected from the high-spin concept. The experimental data for such low-spin (spin-paired) complexes are given in the last column of Table V. The reason for the appearance of low-spin complexes can be directly derived from ligand field theory. As an example octahedral complexes will be considered. In the free ion the five orbitals d_{xy}, d_{xz}, d_{yz}, $d_{x^2-y^2}$, d_{z^2} have equal energies (Fig. 19). The ligand field partly removes the degeneracy, forming the threefold orbitally degenerate t_2 state and the twofold orbitally degenerate e state separated by the energy gap Δ. For a central ion with N d electrons all the following occupations of states are possible: $t_2^n e^{N-n}$ $(0 \le n \le 6, 0 \le N - n \le 4)$.

The magnetic behavior is determined mainly by the electronic ground state. To find the ground state occupations $t_2^n e^{N-n}$ for the various complex ions two antagonistic energetic effects have to be discussed. On the one side the electron system tends to correspond to Hund's rule, since electrons with parallel spins move in different orbitals, yielding a lower electron–electron repulsion energy than electrons with opposite spins in the same orbital. For example, in the case of four d electrons, from Hund's rule the occupation $t_2^3 e^1$ will be expected. The one electron in the e state, however, has an orbital energy higher by Δ than a t_2 electron. When the value of Δ becomes larger than the stabilization, which is the basis for Hund's rule, the system will prefer the occupation t_2^4 with merely two unpaired electrons and with a lower total spin. Corresponding considerations for the other octahedral low-spin d^N systems yield the data listed in the seventh column of Table V. From the arguments given above we get the following general result. Complex ions with weak ligand fields are high-spin systems, whereas complex ions with strong ligand fields show low-spin behavior.

The deviations between the experimental data in Table V and the values calculated by the μ_{eff} formula given above are due mainly to the fact that besides the spins the orbital angular momenta can also contribute to the effective magnetic moments.

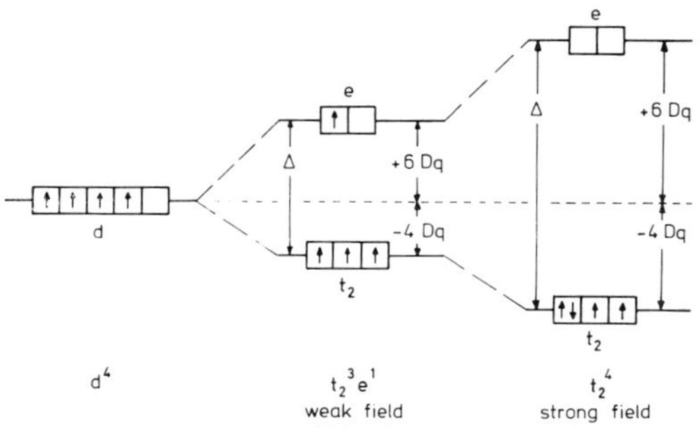

FIG. 19. Splitting of the d states by weak and by strong ligand fields. (The occupation with electrons belongs to a d^4 ion.)

V. Stabilization of Complexes

In the ionic model of Kossel and Magnus (Section II) the formation of a complex ion from the free central ion and the ligands is combined with a stabilization by the electrostatic binding energy E_{class} (Fig. 7). The resulting state corresponds to the electronic ground state of the complex. From the ligand field theory, however, it is known that the ground state term of the central ion can be split into several progeny terms, depending on its orbital angular momentum and the symmetry of the ligand field. The lowest split term coincides with the real ground state. It is stabilized by the ligand field stabilization energy (LFSE; Fig. 7).

For complex ions with an octahedral ligand system the five d states are split as shown in Fig. 19. From quantum mechanical calculations it can be seen that the t_2 state is stabilized by $-4Dq$, whereas the e state is destabilized by $+6Dq$. Therefore, in the strong-field approximation (without electron–electron interaction) for an octahedral complex ion with $t_2^n e^{N-n}$ electron system, the LFSE amounts to

$$\text{LFSE(oct)} = -[4n - 6(N - n)]Dq$$

where N is the total number of d electrons, n the number of t_2 electrons, and $N - n$ the number of e electrons. The LFSE(oct) values for high-spin and low-spin complexes for $N = 1, ..., 9$ are summarized in Table VI. They yield important information about the relative stability and several thermodynamic properties of transition metal complexes.

A. Relative Stability of Low-Spin Complexes

As shown in the preceding section octahedral complexes with d^4, d^5, d^6, and d^7 electron systems in principle can form high-spin or low-spin configurations. Why some of these transition metal ions form low-spin complexes and not the

TABLE VI. Ligand Field Stabilization Energy for Octahedral Transition Metal Complexes[a]

	High-spin configuration		Low-spin configuration	
Number of *d* electrons	Ground term	LFSE (*Dq*)	Ground term	LFSE (*Dq*)
1	$t_2^1[^2T_2]$	−4		
2	$t_2^2[^3T_1]$	−8		
3	$t_2^3[^4A_2]$	−12		
4	$t_2^3e^1[^5E]$	−6	$t_2^4[^3T_1]$	−16
5	$t_2^3e^2[^6A_1]$	0	$t_2^5[^2T_2]$	−20
6	$t_2^4e^2[^5T_2]$	−4	$t_2^6[^1A_1]$	−24
7	$t_2^5e^2[^4T_1]$	−8	$t_2^6e^1[^2E]$	−18
8	$t_2^6e^2[^3A_2]$	−12		
9	$t_2^6e^3[^2E]$	−6		

[a] Calculated in the strong-field approximation.

high-spin modification can be understood by comparison of the LFSEs of both spin configurations. From Table VI the gain of LFSE for the transition from the high-spin to the low-spin complexes amounts to $10Dq$ for d^4 and d^7 complexes and $20Dq$ for d^5 and d^6 complexes. Therefore, for strong ligand fields the low-spin complex is more stable than the high-spin complex. (In low-spin complexes the LFSE is partly compensated for by an increase in electron repulsion, since two electrons moving in the same orbital have a closer distance than otherwise.)

B. Heats of Hydration

By the dissolving of gaseous metal ions M_{gas}^{m+} in water, the corresponding hexaquo ions $[M(H_2O)_6]_{aq}^{m+}$ are formed and the heat of hydration ΔH_H is generated:

$$M_{gas}^{m} \xrightarrow{H_2O} [M(H_2O)_6]_{aq}^{m+} + \Delta H_H$$

The variation of the experimental values of $-\Delta H_H$ with the atomic number of the bivalent and trivalent metal ions of the first transition series is plotted in Fig. 20. The solid lines connecting the data points are not monotonic.

On the basis of the ionic theory it is expected that with increasing atomic number (within a series) the ionic radii decrease monotonically because the electron cloud contracts under the influence of the increasing nuclear charge. Therefore, for electrostatic reasons the heat of hydration should also increase monotonically with increasing atomic number, as indicated by the dashed lines in Fig. 20.

The discrepancy between this expected behavior and the experimental data is due to the

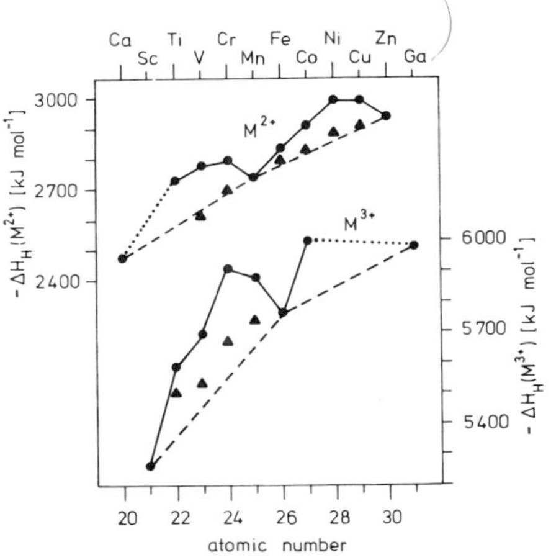

FIG. 20. Heats of hydration of transition metal ions as a function of atomic number. ●, ΔH_H(exp); ▲, $\Delta H_H - \Delta H_{lig}$.

fact that the hexaquo complexes have nonspherical symmetry. The octahedral ligand field splits the ground state terms, yielding the LFSEs given in Table VI. Therefore, the total heat of hydration ΔH_H will be composed of two portions, namely, the "classical" part ΔH_{class}, resulting from the ionic theory, and the "ligand field" part $\Delta H_{lig} \equiv$ LFSE:

$$\Delta H_H = \Delta H_{class} + \Delta H_{lig}$$

The ΔH_{class} values can be obtained by subtraction of the LFSEs from the experimental ΔH_H values. If the LFSEs are calculated with Dq values obtained from absorption spectra, the resulting ΔH_{class} values lie very close to the dashed lines in Fig. 20.

By corresponding considerations, apparent irregularities in the lattice energies of metallic halogenides, in the heats of formation and heats of reactions, and in the kinetic stability of transition metal complexes can be solved.

The structural stability of transition metal complexes is largely influenced by the Jahn–Teller effect. As Jahn and Teller have proved, the nuclear configuration of a nonlinear polyatomic molecule is unstable when its electronic ground state is orbitally degenerate. A molecule in such a situation will undergo a structural distortion such that the resulting ground state is orbitally nondegenerate. The character of the distortion can be static, yielding a permanent deformation, or dynamic by oscillating between several structures with nondegenerate ground states.

Only the following octahedral transition metal complexes have an orbitally nondegenerate ground state (see Tables V and VI):

High-spin $d^3 : {}^4A_2(t_2^3)$

$d^5 : {}^6A_1(t_2^3e^2)$

$d^8 : {}^3A_2(t_2^6e^2)$

Low-spin $d^6 : {}^1A_1(t_2^6)$

All the other octahedral complexes are Jahn–Teller unstable. In some of these complexes stability can be achieved by elongation or compression of the coordination octahedron along one of its axes. Often the distortions are expressed in the physical and chemical properties of the complexes. For example, the asymmetry of the absorption band of $[Ti(H_2O)_6]^{3+}$ (Fig. 16) is due to the Jahn–Teller effect. The distortion that splits the degenerate ground state ${}^2T_2$ into a low-lying nondegenerate level and other progeny terms at higher energy also splits the excited level ${}^2E$. Thus, two absorption bands correspond to the transitions between the ''new'' ground state and the two ${}^2E$ progeny terms. Since the maxima of these bands are very close, only one band with asymmetric shape appears.

Bibliography

Ballhausen, C. J. (1962). ''Introduction to Crystal Field Theory.'' McGraw–Hill, New York.

Cotton, F. A. (1971). ''Chemical Applications of Group Theory.'' 2nd Edition. Wiley, New York.

Gerloch, M. (1983). ''Magnetism and Ligand–Field Analysis.'' Cambridge University Press, Cambridge.

Jørgensen, C. K. (1971). ''Modern Aspects of Ligand Field Theory.'' North–Holland Publishing Company. Amsterdam.

Lever, A. B. P. (1984). ''Inorganic Electronic Spectroscopy.'' Elsevier, Amsterdam.

Schläfer, H. L., and Gliemann, G. (1969). ''Basic Principles of Ligand Field Theory.'' Wiley, New York.

Sutton, D. (1968). ''Electronic Spectra of Transition Metal Complexes.'' McGraw–Hill, London.

LIGHT SOURCES

John F. Waymouth *GTE Lighting Products*

Glossary

Arc: Name applied to a high-pressure electric discharge, originally derived from the bowed shape assumed by a horizontal unconfined discharge as a result of upward convective displacement of the center while ends remained anchored to electrodes.

Ballast: Electric circuit device for operation of a discharge lamp, combining a high open-circuit voltage for reliable initiation (ignition or starting) of the discharge, together with internal series impedance to regulate current flow to the design value and decrease the output voltage at ballast terminals to the steady-state operating voltage of the discharge at that current.

Color Rendering Index (CRI): Measure of the capability of a light source to illuminate colored objects in such a way that the colors are perceived as "normal" (see Section II).

Color temperature: Measure of the apparent color of the light emitted from a light source, being the temperature of the blackbody radiator having the closest color match. Designated as correlated color temperature if exact match is not possible (this distinction is frequently ignored in practice).

Dumet: Composite material used for lead-in wires in glass-to-metal seals for lamps using soda–lime–glass envelopes, comprising a core of low thermal expansion nickel-iron and a cladding of high-expansion copper in such proportions that the net expansion matches that of the glass.

Efficacy: Measure of performance of light sources, equal to the ratio of light output to electrical power input, normally given in lumens per watt. Since this ratio is not dimensionless, the word *efficiency* is avoided for this quantity.

Hard glass: Generic jargon term for glasses having softening and working temperatures greater than soda–lime glass but less than fused silica (quartz).

Lead-in wires: Component of a lamp through which electric current is introduced, through a glass-to-metal seal, into the interior of the hermetically sealed envelope. In industry jargon, these are termed lead wires, but that term is not used here to avoid confusion with the element lead.

Luminance: Measure of the intensity of light, equal numerically to the light flux in lumens per unit area per unit solid angle. (formerly referred to as brightness).

Polycrystalline alumina (PCA): Translucent, ceramic material used for discharge tubes of high-pressure sodium lamps (see Section V).

Press seal: Glass-to-metal seal in a lamp fabricated from fused silica (quartz), used in tungsten–halogen lamps (see Section IV) and high-intensity discharge lamps (see Section V). Fabricated by mechanically pressed heated, softened silica glass to and around thin foils of molybdenum, which serve as lead-in wires.

Resonance radiation: Radiation emitted in an atomic transition, in which the lower state of the transition pair is the lowest energy state of the atom, occupied in a large fraction of the atoms present.

Stem: Component of a lamp incorporating the glass-to-metal seals of the lead-in wires together with mating surfaces of glass ready for flame-fusion sealing to the glass envelope. The stem usually includes a tube through which air from the envelope interior can be exhausted after the stem is sealed to the envelope.

Wall-loading: Measure of the power input to a discharge lamp, in watts per unit area of wall surface. An important design parameter for most discharge lamps.

Next to the invention of the wheel, humanity's oldest and most important invention is the artificial light source, a means or device for converting some other form of energy into light. From the dawn of human history until ~200 years ago, such devices could convert only chemical energy into light, through the medium of fire. For ~100 years, commercially useful electric light sources have been available—a technological accomplishment of stupendous magnitude that has transformed our lives.

I. Introduction

Approximately 5 billion incandescent lamps, 2 billion fluorescent lamps, and 200 million high-pressure discharge lamps are in service around the world. They consume ~25% of the worldwide electric energy production. Electric energy production, in turn, accounts for ~25% of worldwide consumption of energy.

Electric lamps produce the light that makes it possible to carry on all forms of human activity far outside the sunrise-to-sunset time limitations faced by earlier societies, and thus greatly increasing our productivity. They make our streets and highways safer after dark, and they decorate and illuminate all manner of public places. Finally, they do all this at a cost to us that is one-quarter percent of our gross personal product, individually or gross national product, collectively.

This article describes the scientific and technological bases of the major electric light sources. Each section discusses the mechanisms of radiation, the energy balance and the factors that set the limits for performance and efficiency; the fabrication technology and the principal deviations from ideality; representative examples of commercially available products; and the direction of research and development toward improved future products.

II. Electromagnetic Radiation

A. Emission and Absorption of Radiation by Matter

A ray of electromagnetic radiation transiting a material substance may be characterized in terms of the number of photons of frequency ν crossing unit area per second, per unit solid angle, per hertz. As it traverses the substance, it may be diminished as a result of absorption, or it may be augmented as a result of spontaneous and stimulated emission. Stimulated emission results in photons being added to the beam, in phase and in the identical direction as the stimulating photon (i.e., within the same solid angle as the incident ray). Spontaneously emitted photons are emitted (in the absence of nuclear orientation effects not usually encountered in light sources) with equal probability in all directions. That is, the fraction of the spontaneously emitted photons within a given solid angle is equal to $d\Omega/4\pi$.

1. Radiation Transport Differential Equation

These considerations may be quantified in the radiation transport equation, Eq. (1), in which $n(u, x)$ and $n(l, x)$ are the number densities at position x of upper and lower states of the transition pair resulting in emission of frequency ν, and $A(\nu)$ is the spontaneous transition rate per second, per hertz of bandwidth, at frequency ν.

$$\mathbf{i}\frac{d\Gamma(\nu, x)}{dx} = \mathbf{i}\frac{A(\nu)}{4\pi} + k(\nu)n(u, x)\Gamma(\nu, x) - \alpha(\nu, x)\Gamma(\nu, x) \qquad (1)$$

Note that $A(\nu)$ is dimensionless. The expression $\Gamma(\nu, x)$ is the vector spectral radiance in photons per unit-area-second per hertz of bandpass per steradian, assumed for simplicity to have only an x component, and $\mathbf{i}$ is a unit vector in the x direction. The expression $\alpha(\nu)$ is the absorption coefficient of radiation of frequency (ν), and $k(\nu)$ is the stimulated emission coefficient of frequency (ν), both per unit of path length through the radiating medium.

Einstein first demonstrated that absorption, spontaneous emission, and stimulated emission coefficients are related. That is,

$$k(\nu) = \alpha(\nu, x)/(n(l, x)g_u/g_l)$$

$$\alpha(\nu, x) = \frac{A(\nu)}{8\pi\nu^2}c^2 n(l, x)g_u/g_l \qquad (2)$$

The expressions g_u, g_l are the statistical weights

of upper and lower states, respectively, and c represents the velocity of light.

Incorporating these relationships in the radiation transport equation gives the following result:

$$\mathbf{i}\,\frac{d\Gamma(\nu, x)}{dx} = \alpha(\nu, x)\left\{\frac{2\nu^2}{c^2}\left[\frac{n(u, x)g_l}{n(l, x)g_u}\right]\mathbf{i} + \left[\frac{n(u, x)g_l}{n(l, x)g_u} - 1\right]\Gamma(\nu, x)\right\} \quad (3)$$

The source of the energy input to the material that maintains a population of upper states in the face of depletion by radiation does not concern us in this section.

2. Local Thermal Equilibrium

For a system locally in thermal equilibrium, at a local temperature $T(x)$, the number densities of upper and lower states are related through a Boltzmann factor:

$$n(u, x) = n(l, x)\,\frac{g_u}{g_l}\exp(-h\nu/kT(x)) \quad (4)$$

For systems not in local thermal equilibrium (LTE) we may still define a radiation temperature from Eq. (4) for the transition in question, with the stipulation that the radiation temperature will not necessarily be the same for all possible transition pairs.

3. Blackbody Radiation

In an infinite material medium in which the temperature is independent of position, global thermal equilibrium exists, and the value of $d\Gamma(\nu, x)/dx$ becomes zero. Setting it equal to zero in Eq. (3), and solving for $\Gamma(\nu)$ yields the blackbody, or ideal radiator law, expressed in the units of photons per second per unit area per steradian per hertz of bandpass.

$$\Gamma_{\mathrm{BB}}(\nu) = \mathbf{i}\,\frac{2\nu^2}{c^2}\Big/(e^{h\nu/kT} - 1) \quad (5)$$

Therefore, the radiation transport equation may be rewritten for systems in LTE in terms of the local temperature and the local blackbody spectral radiance:

$$\mathbf{i}\,\frac{d\Gamma(\nu, x)}{dx} = \alpha(\nu, x)(1 - e^{-h\nu/kT})\{\Gamma_{\mathrm{BB}}(\nu, x) - \Gamma(\nu, x)\} \quad (6)$$

For most light sources, the value of $h\nu/kT$ is greater than or equal to 3, so that the first term $[1 - \mathrm{e}(-h\nu/kT)]$ is essentially equal to unity and is usually neglected.

Note that in Eq. (6) the temperature may vary with position and therefore the corresponding blackbody spectral radiance as well; note also that the units of spectral radiance are those chosen for the blackbody spectral radiance. Although Eq. (6) is derived in terms of photons per second, it is much more general and can be used with whatever units for blackbody radiance are convenient and familiar. Note also that the growth and decay of a ray of radiation in transiting a material medium is proportional to the absorption coefficient. Where it is less than the blackbody level, spectral radiance will increase only at those frequencies for which absorption coefficient is greater than zero. Material substances cannot emit electromagnetic radiation at any frequency at which they do not also absorb.

Therefore, determination of the radiant emission spectrum of a material substance requires a determination of its absorption spectrum.

B. Sources of Absorption

The processes that contribute to absorption and emission of radiation in the UV, visible, and IR regions of the electromagnetic spectrum are principally electronic transitions. These may include free-free and free-bound transitions of free electrons, which result in absorption and emission of radiation over wide ranges of frequency (continuum emission). This is the most characteristic feature of emission from heated metals. Many electric discharge lamps take advantage of emission and absorption by electronic transitions in isolated atoms. Absorption and emission "lines" in the radiation spectrum from such transitions are usually broadened by a variety of perturbing influences, such as (1) collisional or pressure broadening due to collisions between radiating atoms and perturbing atoms; (2) Stark broadening from the electric fields of nearby charged particles, electrons and ions, in the plasma of a discharge lamp; (3) Doppler broadening as a result of thermal motions of the radiating atoms; and (4) resonance broadening as a result of perturbation by identical atoms in the lower state of the transition pair. [*See* ATOMIC PHYSICS.]

In addition to atomic line emission, emission as a result of electronic transitions in molecules, as well as vibrational and rotational transitions, contributes absorption and emission in some media.

It is beyond the scope of this article to deal with the *a priori* calculation of the frequency-dependent absorption coefficient required for the use of Eq. (6). However, it is clear from the foregoing that the totality of absorption processes must be analyzed with full knowledge of necessary transition probabilities and broadening parameters applicable to the system in question. For those cases in which absorption coefficients can be calculated, and radiation temperature profile determined, the integration of Eq. (6), repeated for the desired range of frequencies or wavelengths and for selected angular orientation to the surface, permits calculation of emitted spectral radiance.

In many cases of interest in the science and technology of electric discharge light sources, however, necessary basic data are unknown; they must be either estimated or used as variable parameters in an empirical fitting to observational data. Research and development of light sources therefore remains an empirical science in many cases but with continual improvement in calculation models to guide the empirical program.

C. Spectral Radiance versus Position and Wavelength

Once the value of absorption coefficient as a function of frequency and position is known and temperature is known as a function of position for a material medium in local thermal equilibrium, radiance may be calculated as a function of position by integration of Eq. (6). For systems not in LTE, integration of Eq. (3) is required.

The optical density of the medium is defined as

$$\tau(\nu) = \int_0^{\bar{x}} \alpha(\nu, x)\, dx$$

In two limiting cases, optically thick, $\tau(\nu) \gg 1$, and optically thin, $\tau(\nu) \ll 1$, particularly simple results can be obtained.

1. Constant Temperature

For the optically thin case, $\Gamma(\nu, x)$ remains everywhere $\ll \Gamma_{BB}(\nu)$, and it may be neglected in comparison. Radiance increases monotonically with distance through the medium:

$$\mathbf{i}\,\frac{d\Gamma(\nu, x)}{dx} = \alpha(\nu, x)\Gamma_{BB}(\nu) = \mathbf{i}\,\frac{A(\nu)n(u, x)}{4\pi} \qquad \left(\frac{h\nu}{kT} \gtrsim 3\right) \quad (7)$$

For the nonoptically thin case of constant temperature, integration of Eq. (6) gives:

$$\Gamma(\nu, x) = \Gamma_{BB}(\nu)\{1 - e^{-\alpha(\nu)\cdot x}\} \quad (8)$$

For $\tau \gtrsim 3$, radiance approaches the blackbody level. Wherever absorption coefficients are sufficiently large that the substance is optically thick, it is not necessary to know the absorption coefficient exactly; radiance is everywhere equal to local blackbody value. Because of the relatively large absorption coefficient for free-free transitions of electrons in metals as a result of large free electron density, and because temperature inside a heated wire is essentially independent of position, this case corresponds reasonably well to the situation inside the metal filament of an incandescent lamp. The internal spectral radiance essentially equals the blackbody level from the UV to the IR.

2. Nonconstant Temperature: Self-Reversed Lines

A common situation in electric discharge light sources is optically thick emission of atomic line radiation from a discharge in LTE with a position-dependent temperature, as shown in Fig. 1. Although the absorption coefficient at the line's center may be high, leading to a large optical depth, absorption coefficient decreases with increasing frequency shift from line center because of the broadening processes. Dependent on the wavelength shift from line center, τ may be either $\gg 1$, 1, or $\ll 1$. Integration of Eq. (6) for these three cases leads to the result shown in Fig. 1. At the line center where absorption coefficient is high, spectral radiance is essentially everywhere equal to the local blackbody value, rising from a low level at $x = 0$ to a maximum coincident with maximum temperature and decreasing to a very low value at $x = D$. In the far wings of the line, where optical depth is low, there is essentially no absorption of any radiation emitted into the ray, and radiance increases monotonically to a maximum at $x = D$ but reaches only a relatively low level. In the vicinity of $\tau = 1$, however, spectral radiance continues to increase for all those values of x for which it is less than local blackbody radiance and decreases for those values of x for which the converse is true. The distance scale over which these changes can take place, however, is $1/\alpha$.

Therefore, the value of emergent radiance at $x = D$ is much greater than blackbody at $x = D$. It typically reaches 10–20% of blackbody spectral radiance at maximum temperature.

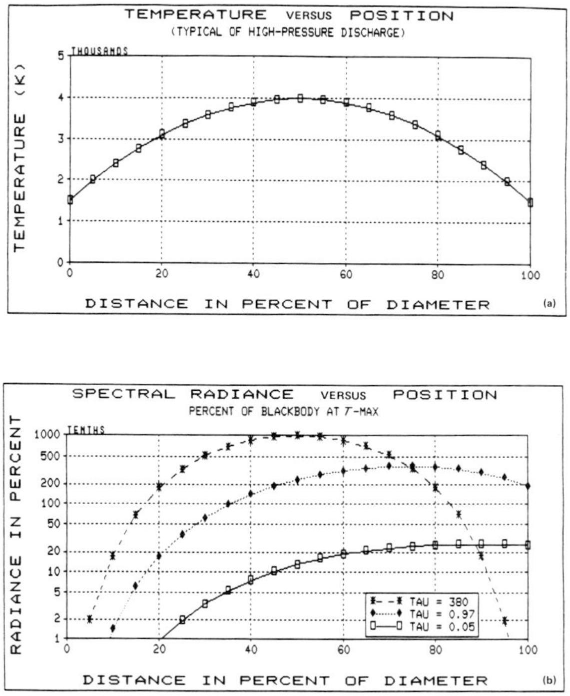

FIG. 1. (a) Profile of temperature along a diameter through an electric discharge in local thermal equilibrium (LTE) (typical). (b) Positively directed spectral radiance along a diameter through the LTE discharge of (a) for three different values of optical depth between temperature maximum and discharge tube wall. Radiance for $\tau = 380$ is indistinguishable from local blackbody radiance at the temperature corresponding to each position.

The frequency or wavelength distribution in the emitted line (see Fig. 2) shows a minimum (reversal) at the center wavelength of the atomic line, with maxima in emission on either side. Such emission lines are commonly referred to as self-reversed. The optical depth between temperature maximum and escape point is typically about unity at wavelength of maximum emission.

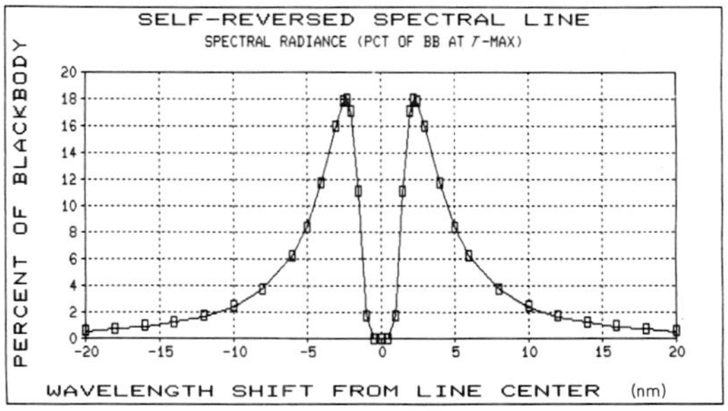

FIG. 2. Spectral distribution of emitted atomic resonance line radiation for temperature profile of Fig. 1(a), illustrating self-reversal, calculated for sodium resonance line (589.0–589.6 nm) for 0.1 atm pressure in a tube 1.0 cm in diameter. Line center (reversal minimum) corresponds to $\tau = 380$ in Fig. 1(b); maxima correspond to $\tau = 0.97$; 10-nm shift from line center (either side) corresponds to $\tau = 0.05$.

D. Reflection at Bounding Surfaces

The integration of the radiation transport equation does not of itself permit calculation of the radiation emitted by a bounded material medium. There is an interface at the boundary where the radiating medium meets the external environment and in general a mismatch of indices of refraction. As a result of the difference in the indices of reflection, there is a reflection loss so that a portion of the internally generated radiation does not escape. For discharge lamps in which the radiating plasma is contained in a transparent vessel, the reflection losses are relatively small approximately 4–5% at each of several glass surfaces. It is more severe in discharges contained in translucent vessels, which embody many scattering centers within the vessel wall that result in significant diffuse reflection of escaping radiation. For incandescent metal sources—such as tungsten-filament lamps—however, it is extremely significant because of the large index of refraction of the metal, especially in the far IR range.

The escaping flux is equal to $(1 - r)\Gamma_{BB}$, which is usually expressed as $\varepsilon\Gamma_{BB}$, where $\varepsilon = (1 - r)$ is called the emittance. The reflectance, r, of a metal surface can be approximately calculated by treating the free electrons of the metal as a free-electron gas, having a plasma frequency greater than the radiation frequency. Provided collision frequency of electrons in the metal is small in comparison to radiation frequency, a simplified Drude formula gives for $1 - r$, where ρ is electric resistivity in ohm centimeters, and λ is wavelength in centimeters:

$$\varepsilon(\lambda) = 0.365\left(\frac{\rho}{\lambda}\right)^{1/2} - 0.0464\left(\frac{\rho}{\lambda}\right) \qquad (9)$$

Figure 3 shows the observed spectral emittance of tungsten as a function of wavelength, together with the values calculated from Eq. (9). The simplified model is a fairly accurate representation of the IR emittance. It is clear that reflection at the surface drastically reduces IR radiation escape, by as much as 90% at 10 μm, for example. Therefore, even though spectral radiance internal to a heated tungsten body reaches the blackbody level over the entire range of optical frequencies, escaping radiance is at maximum less than 50% of the blackbody value in the visible, declining toward 10% at 10 μm. As is shown in Section IV, this has important consequences for the efficacy of tungsten-filament lamps.

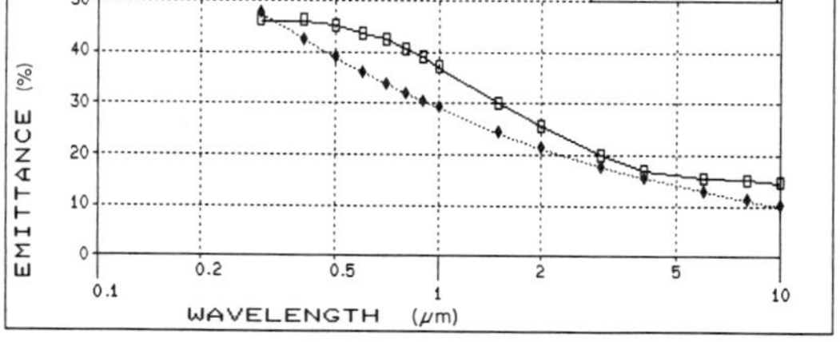

FIG. 3. Radiant emittance of tungsten as a function of wavelength, experimentally measured, and calculated from Eq. (9).

III. Light

A. Electromagnetic Radiation and the Eye

The proper measure of the "goodness" of artificial light sources is not how well they emit electromagnetic radiation, but how well they emit electromagnetic radiation that can be perceived and detected by the eye—that is, light. Therefore, of concern in light source development is not only radiant power, but also the radiant power weighted by the biological action spectra of vision. These correspond to two distinct perceptions of light, luminance (formerly called brightness) and color. There prove to be two distinct action spectra for luminance: scotopic, or dark-adapted, and photopic, or light-adapted. Under the vast majority of situations involved in applications of artificial light sources, the luminance level is high enough that the eye is light-adapted, and the photopic action spectrum is the proper one to use. In photopic vision, there are three sets of photoreceptors, called cones, sensitive to red, green, and blue radiations, respectively. In combination, these are sensitive to the wavelength band of the electromagnetic spectrum between approximately 380 nm and 780 nm.

Signal processing in the eye–brain system is such that luminance information comes from the sum of the responses of red (long wavelength) cones and green (intermediate wavelength) cones. Color information comes from a combination of the luminance signal and the differences between the responses of the red, green, and blue (short wavelength) cones.

The relative spectral sensitivity functions of these responses have been determined from an extended series of luminance and color matching experiments by a number of standard observers who have been selected to eliminate various pathologies from consideration. The average values of these functions have been agreed on by deliberations of the *Commission Internationale de L'Eclairage* (International Commission on Illumination), known as the CIE.

1. Luminance and Lumens

The luminance function is designated as $\overline{y(\lambda)}$, and the total light output of a light source in lumens is determined from the convolution integral over the wavelength interval (or range) of the radiated spectral power distribution $P(\lambda)$ weighted by the $\overline{y(\lambda)}$ function:

$$L = k \int \overline{y(\lambda)} P(\lambda)\, d\lambda \qquad (10)$$

The coefficient k has been arbitrarily set at 683 lm/W so that the lumen output value determined according to Eq. (10) should agree with comparison photometry based on older so-called standard candles. In this older definition, one standard candle emits 1 lm/sr. The values of the Y function as a function of wavelength are shown in Fig. 4. The luminous efficacy of a light source is determined by dividing its total lumen output by the input power required to maintain it in a constant light-emitting state and is measured in lumens per watt.

2. Color

The color of light can be expressed in terms of two indices, x and y, determined from three other functions, X, Y, and Z, called tristimulus values:

$$x = \frac{X}{X + Y + Z}$$
$$y = \frac{Y}{X + Y + Z} \qquad (11)$$

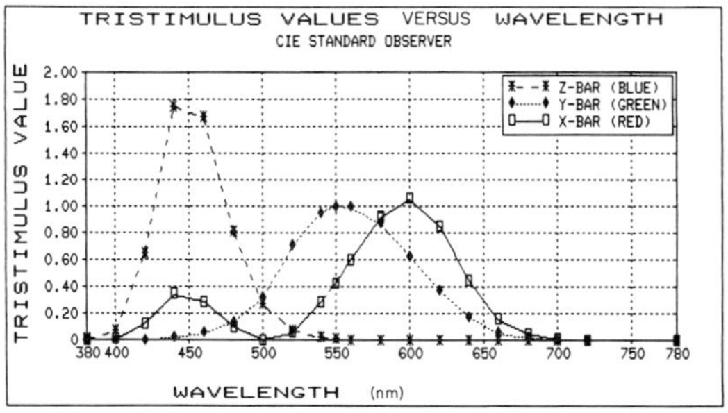

FIG. 4. Values at 20-nm intervals of the red, green, and blue tristimulus functions for computing color properties of light sources. Note that although these are ultimately dependent on the spectral responses of the three different types of retinal cones, they are not identically equal to those response functions. The Y-bar (green) function is the same as the photopic action spectrum for luminance.

The functions X, Y, Z are themselves determined from convolution integrals over the spectral power distribution, weighted according to the tristimulus functions $\overline{x(\lambda)}$, $\overline{y(\lambda)}$, and $\overline{z(\lambda)}$. The $\overline{y(\lambda)}$ function is the same one used for luminance calculations. All three functions are shown in Fig. 4. The x and y values may be measured directly by photometers with suitably calibrated filters, which are in effect analog computers for calculating the convolution integrals.

Figure 5 shows the locus of monochromatic spectrum colors on the x–y plane, forming the CIE 1931 chromaticity diagram (x–y diagram). Color points x,y for nonmonochromatic radiation sources lie in the space enclosed by the locus of spectrum colors. The x,y value for the sum of two sources of color x',y' and x'',y'' are found along a line joining the two x,y coordinates, which is a useful additive property. The curved line extending through the center of the diagram is the locus of colors of blackbody sources of the indicated temperatures. The color points for daylight also fall on or near the blackbody locus, toward the high-temperature end. For reasons probably rooted in evolution, the preferred color domain for most artificial light sources is also on or near the blackbody locus; x,y points above the locus are perceived as too

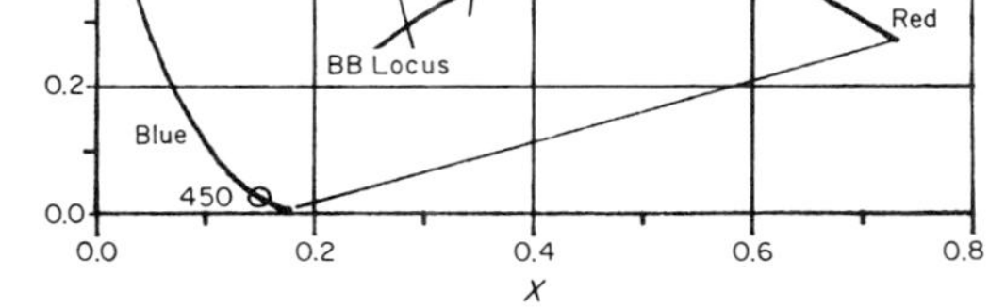

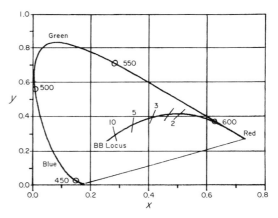

FIG. 5. CIE chromaticity (x–y) diagram: outer curve is the locus of monochromatic spectrum colors, labeled at selected wavelengths (nm); all real colors are contained within the bounded region. The inner curve is the locus of colors of blackbody radiators ranging from low temperatures at the right to high temperatures at the left; selected temperatures are labeled (in 1000 K). Light sources perceived as white have x–y values near the blackbody (BB) locus between 2500 K and 5000 K.

green, those below as gloomy and purple. Therefore a common, although far from exact, representation of the color of a light source is its correlated color temperature (or just color temperature): the temperature of the blackbody source having the closest color match. The x–y diagram, although useful for representing colors of light sources, suffers from the fact that equal perceptible color differences are not represented by equal vector distances between x,y points in different parts of the diagram. Therefore, other systems for color representation are also in use, but these do not concern us here.

3. Color Rendering

Color rendition is another property of light sources. Color rendering is a measure of the degree of distortion in the *apparent* colors of colored pigments perceived when they are illuminated by the source in question, in comparison to their apparent colors when they are illuminated by a standard source. For example, a source emitting monochromatic blue light and monochromatic red light in such proportions that the composite color lies on the blackbody locus at a color temperature of 3000 K will cause a green pigment to appear black or purple in comparison to the blackbody of the same color temperature—although the colors of the light emitted from the two sources are indistinguishable. The tristimulus values of the light reflected from a pigment can be calculated using formulas identical with those of Eq. (10), except that they also include the spectral reflectance of the pigment as a weighting factor.

The color rendering index (CRI) of a light source is computed by calculating the shifts in a uniform color space of the color coordinates in a series of standard pigments illuminated by the light source from the computed color coordinates for the same pigments illuminated by a standard source of the same color temperature. For color temperatures less than 5000 K, the reference source is a blackbody; for color temperatures greater than 5000 K, it is a standard daylight. Continuous spectrum sources, such as incandescent lamps, have high CRIs, near 100, since their spectra are nearly blackbody. Multiline spectrum sources, such as some high-pressure discharge lamps, have CRIs ranging from 50 to 80. Fluorescent lamps also have CRIs of 60 and greater. CRI values less than 40 are generally not desirable for illuminating spaces occupied by humans.

IV. Incandescent Lamps

A. Introduction

The most common form of electric light source is the incandescent lamp, which consists of a solid filament, heated by the passage of electric current, in a hermetically sealed glass envelope from which all traces of oxidizing gases have been removed. Figure 6 is a schematic diagram illustrating the principal components of such a lamp. Present-day incandescent lamps use a tungsten filament in a coiled or multiply-coiled helix. Most types use an inert gas filling in the bulb to retard evaporation of the filament, thereby permitting higher filament temperatures for a given design life.

B. Radiation Mechanism

The radiation mechanism in incandescent lamps is the continuous spectrum resulting from deflection and unquantized radiation of valence electrons (traveling freely through the conduction band of the solid) by collisions with nuclei, each other, and lattice phonons. The optical depth is great enough that the internal radiation flux reaches the blackbody level throughout the UV–visible–IR spectrum. A large index of refraction causes reflection losses in the escape of this radiation from the surface, yielding an effective emittance of ~0.45 in the visible, decreasing to approximately 0.10 to 0.15 at 10-μm wavelength in the IR. Thus, tungsten emits a larger fraction of total radiation into the visible (giving approximately 30–40% higher luminous efficacy) than a blackbody at the same temperature, with a comparable increase in this visible frac-

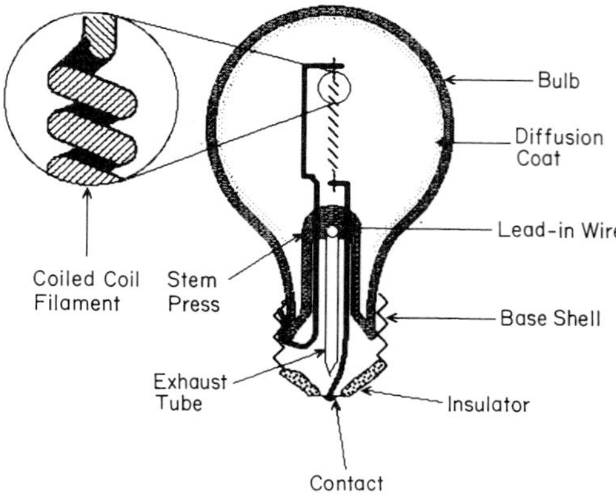

FIG. 6. Schematic diagram, in section, illustrating components of a typical incandescent lamp.

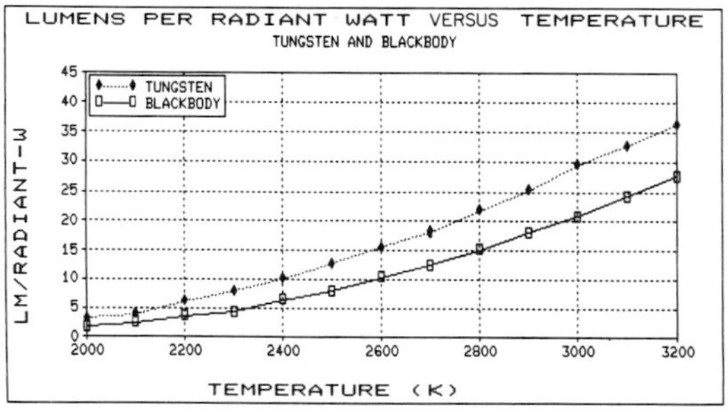

FIG. 7. Plots of luminous efficacy versus temperature for tungsten and blackbody incandescent radiators. The higher luminous efficacy for tungsten is the result of its higher radiant emittance in the visible in comparison to the IR range (see Fig. 3).

tion (and luminous efficacy) with increasing temperature (see Fig. 7). For efficient incandescent lamps, the temperature of the radiator must be as high as possible, yet consistent with constraints on service life. Visible spectral power distribution is blackbodylike, with a color temperature of 50 to 100 K higher than true; the CRI is in the high 90s.

C. Energy Balance

Ohmic heating by the energizing current raises filament temperature to dissipate power by radiation, convective cooling by the gas filling, and solid conduction to filament supports and electric lead-ins. The power consumption of the lamp at a given input voltage is determined by the filament resistance, a function of the length and cross-sectional area of the wire and resistivity of the wire material. Resistivity of tungsten increases strongly with temperature, and is 15-fold less at room temperature than at operating temperature; inrush current at initial switch-on is correspondingly higher than operating current. At normal operating temperatures (~2750 K), resistivity is ~80 $\mu\Omega$ cm. For a 100-W lamp operating from a 120-V line and requiring a resistance of 144 Ω, the ratio of cross-sectional area to length is ~5 nm. This dictates wires a few hundredths of a millimeter in diameter for total filament lengths of ~0.5 m. Even more slender filaments are required for operation at lower wattages or from 240-V power lines. For a given filament design, electric power input and filament temperature increase with increasing line voltage.

The gaseous convection loss from the filament is minimized by coiling the filament into a helix or multiple helix because of the existence at the hot surface of a stationary boundary layer of gas, with thickness comparable to the diameter of the helices. Thus, the effective surface area cooled by the gaseous convection is that of the cylindrical envelope of the helix, much less than that of the filament wire itself. The effective radiating surface is also smaller than that of the filament wire surface as a result of the coiling, but by not so great a factor. This is because radiation emitted into the interior of the helix does have a reasonable probability of escape between the turns, after one to several reflections, absorptions, and reemissions. In typical household incandescent lamps, 10–15% of the input power is lost in gaseous convection, 80–85% in radiation, and the balance in conduction to the filament supports and electric lead-ins. The reduction in evaporation rate resulting from the gas fill permits ~300°C higher operating temperature for equal life as in vacuum, which results in as much as 80% increase in luminous efficacy of the emitted radiation, more than justifying a 10–15% reduction due to gaseous convection loss.

D. Performance Limitations Resulting from Material Limitations

Maximizing luminous efficacy of incandescent lamps requires as high a radiator temperature as possible. Evaporation of the filament material and the maintenance of mechanical strength at elevated temperatures limit the permissible temperature so that tungsten is the material of choice.

1. Vaporization

Vaporization of tungsten varies as $\exp(-105000/T)$, which at 2750 K equates to a fourfold increase per 100 degrees and is the principal determinant of lamp life. Failure occurs when less than 1% of the filament mass has evaporated. A thin spot along the length of the filament has higher resistance and higher I-squared-R heating because the same total current must pass through every cross-sectional area. It consequently operates at a higher temperature and vaporizes faster than adjacent spots, becoming thinner faster. Failure generally occurs when the thinnest point along the length of the filament is reduced in diameter by ~50%. High inrush current at switch-on frequently causes failure at the weakest spot. However, the same mechanism could cause failure under steady burning conditions within a few hours. The lives of incandescent lamps are not significantly dependent on the number of switch-ons per operating hour.

Thin spots, or hot spots, may originate from nonuniformities in wire diameter or nonuniformities in coil turn spacing (caused by the coiling process itself), distortions in mounting of the filament, or shifts during operation at the elevated temperatures ("squirm" and "sag").

Both luminous efficacy and evaporation rate depend on filament temperature, reflected in an empirical "LPW/DL" law: design life varies as the inverse seventh or eighth power of design lumens-per-watt. Consequently, the sum of lamp plus electricity cost to produce a given illumination is the minimum at an optimum design life. If the design life is too short, although efficacy will be the greatest and energy cost the least, the cost of bulbs and replacement bulbs is too high. And if design life is too long, although lamp cost is minimized, energy cost increases. In household use (no labor cost for bulb replacement) the bulb life of ~1000 hr gives the minimum total cost of light. In commercial or industrial use, replacement labor cost may exceed the cost of the bulb itself; thus, longer design lives are needed.

Life and luminous efficacy of an incandescent lamp are strongly affected by operation at service voltages other than the design value. Operation at 10% greater than design voltage will shorten lamp life by a factor of 3, but it will give 35% more light. Operation at 10% less than design voltage will lengthen life 400% at the cost of 28% less light.

Incorporating an inert gas filling in the bulb obstructs the flow of vapor from the filament, converting the rate-limiting step from primary vaporization to diffusion. The dependence on filament temperature remains, however, since the density gradient is determined by the equilibrium pressure of tungsten vapor at the filament surface, which has the exact same temperature dependence as the primary evaporation rate. The loss rate of filament material is dependent on the diffusion coefficient of tungsten in the gas; life increases approximately linearly with pressure, and increases with atomic mass number of the gas. Household lamps are generally filled with argon plus a few percent of nitrogen at ~1 atm of operating pressure. The nitrogen prevents the establishment of an electric discharge in the gas between the lead-in wires. Krypton fill is used in certain premium types for higher efficiency; the lower diffusion coefficient of tungsten in krypton permits slightly higher filament temperature for equal life, and the convective losses in krypton are smaller.

2. Mechanical Strength

Wire for lamp filaments must initially be ductile enough to coil to a mandrel diameter comparable with wire diameter, without splitting or "green-stick" fracture. But the filaments must become rigid and nonductile in operation at 75% of melting temperature so that the turns of the coil do not shift, and the wire does not stretch. Control of the microstructure, not only of the as-drawn wire but also after recrystallization at elevated temperature, produces this astonishing result.

Non-sag tungsten for lamp use incorporates approximately 30–50 ppm of elemental potassium introduced in compound form in the powder preparation stage of a powder-metallurgy process. Controlled wire-drawing in multiple stages, with intermediate anneals, results in a fine-grained fibrous-looking microstructure of elongated grains parallel to the wire axis. The potassium, which is insoluble in tungsten, is dispersed as uniformly as possible throughout the wire and is concentrated as minute globules along grain boundaries. The fibrous microstructure imparts to the wire a flexibility analogous to rope so that the wire can be bent easily without fracture.

At temperatures between 1500 K and 2000 K (much less than the service temperature), the tungsten recrystallizes, and the small fibrous grains grow to sizes comparable with the wire diameter. Without potassium dopant, the preferred crystal habit would be an equiaxed hexagonal structure (see Fig. 8) with many grain boundaries approximately perpendicular to the wire axis, along which slippage or sliding occurs at elevated temperatures so that the wire "sags" or "squirms." With potassium-doped wire, however, the recrystallization is quite different. Insoluble and volatile at the recrystallization temperature, the potassium globules vaporize and create voids distributed in long rows parallel to the wire axis. The rows of voids act as barriers to grain boundary migration so that propagation of grain boundaries across the wire is greatly inhibited in comparison to propagation along the wire axis. The resulting recrystallized structure, also shown in Fig. 8, then comprises elongated interlocking grains (with greater than

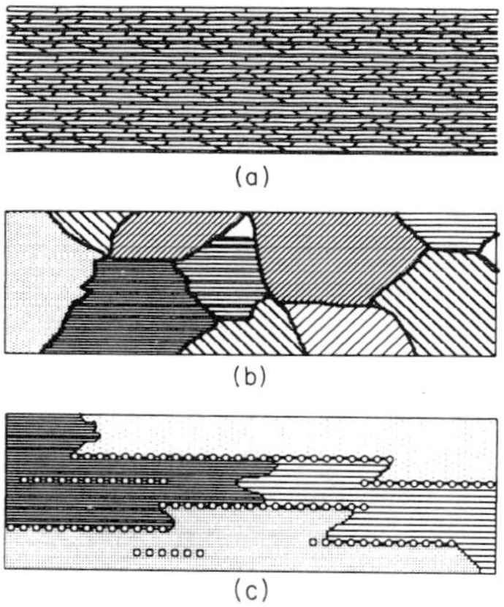

FIG. 8. Schematic diagram illustrating tungsten metal microstructure: (a) as-drawn, fibrous; (b) recrystallized, undoped wire, equiaxed; (c) recrystallized, potassium-doped wire, interlocking.

10 : 1 aspect ratio in high-quality wire) oriented along the wire axis, with few if any perpendicular grain boundaries. The long-grain boundaries exhibit much greater resistance to sliding than short perpendicular boundaries, which greatly increases the hot strength of the wire.

E. Fabrication Technology

Assembly and processing of incandescent lamps takes place on highly automated machine groups operating at speeds between one and two finished lamps per second, essentially without operator intervention. Such manufacturing methods are not only necessary to maintain low costs, but also to cope with the sheer volume of production required to fill the demand, ~1 billion lamps per year in the United States alone.

Lamp manufacture begins with fabrication of tungsten wire coils, typically wound on molybdenum or steel wire mandrels, which are acid-dissolved after stress-relieving. Primary coil-winding is done fully automatically at speeds in excess of 10,000 rpm, with precision of pitch better than 1%. Secondary coil-winding is slower but equally automatic and precise. Glass bulbs are made of soda–lime glass, blown into rotating molds at speeds of a thousand parts per minute.

Stem presses are fabricated by automatically sealing lead-in wires into a press, fusing glass to metal with gas-oxygen and gas-air fires. The lead-in wires themselves are a controlled-thermal-expansion composite comprising a low-expansion nickel-iron core and a high-expansion cladding of copper (Dumet) in such proportions as to provide an expansion match to the glass. After glassworking, the filament supports are automatically bent, and the coiled filaments are automatically fed and mounted. Meanwhile, a light-diffusing particulate coating is applied electrostatically to the inside of the bulb, and both bulb and mount are automatically transferred to the sealing machine where the glass of the bulb is fused to the glass of the stem with gas-oxygen fires. Automatically transferred to an exhaust machine, the sealed bulbs are exhausted and backfilled with gas through an exhaust tube integral with the stem, after which the exhaust tube is fused closed and cut off by gas fires. The evacuated bulb is transferred to a basing machine where the external leads are threaded to and affixed to the base, and the filaments are "flashed" to recrystallize the wire in its high-temperature microstructure. Automatic testing and packaging follow.

1. Influence of Impurities

Certain impurities substantially degrade the life and lumen maintenance performance of incandescent lamps, even when their filament temperatures are exactly as specified. An important object of the process and material control is to minimize these impurities. The elements hydrogen, oxygen, and carbon and the transition metals iron, nickel, and chromium have significant deleterious effects.

Carbon can cause formation of tungsten carbides, resulting in brittleness of the filament and susceptibility to fracture under mechanical shock. Since graphite is the preferred lubricant for the wire-drawing process, it is plain that cleaning processes to remove carbon must be under very careful control. Transition metals result in exaggerated grain growth and tend to defeat the purpose of the potassium doping in the recrystallization process. Many of the tools and jigs and fixtures involved in the assembly process are made of steel, and the lead-in wires themselves are typically made of nickel-plated steel. Contamination of filaments and coils from these sources must be monitored and controlled to a minimum.

Oxygen in gaseous form is a particularly damaging impurity since it reacts with the tungsten filament, thus forming volatile tungsten oxides. As little as 10 parts per billion of oxygen in the gas will remove tungsten from the surface of the filament as fast as it vaporizes at 2750 K. That is, the oxygen will cut the life of the lamp in half. Water vapor is a particularly troublesome form of volatile oxygen since the reaction to form tungsten oxide at the filament surface releases hydrogen. The tungsten oxide evaporates to the lower temperature bulb wall, at which temperature the reaction reverses and the evolved hydrogen reduces the tungsten oxide to tungsten, thus reforming water to return to the filament to react again.

Largely to control the water content, present day incandescent lamps contain one or more getters—active chemical compounds that react with and remove water, oxygen, hydrogen, or all three, from the gaseous atmosphere of the lamp to minimize the degree of attack on the tungsten filament. Common getters include phosphorus and its compounds and active metals such as zirconium, aluminum, and their alloys. Specific formulations are proprietary to the several manufacturers. Most manufacturers use proprietary automated on-line spectroscopic detection of oxygen and water vapor to cull out leakers and contaminated lamps that would be very short-lived in service.

F. Commercially Available Products and Performance Characteristics

Table I enumerates the performance characteristics of a limited number of commercially available products, while Fig. 9 is a photograph illustrating a sampling of the variety of incandescent lamp types that are available.

G. Areas of Research and Development

The major deficiency of incandescent lamps is an unfavorable fraction of the emitted radiation in the visible spectrum, less than 10%, resulting in poorer luminous efficacy than other sources. The search for materials with greater selectivity of emittance, or of selective emitter surface coatings compatible with high-temperature tungsten, is a low-level concern in many laboratories. A more promising avenue may be the use of selective reflective materials on the envelope that reflect IR rays back to the filament while transmitting visible rays, thereby reducing the power input required to keep the filament at a given temperature and produce a given amount of light. There are a variety of different reflective materials having suitable optical properties. But a major problem remains: the returning radiation must in fact hit and be absorbed by the filament. This requires significant improvement in mechanical precision of the envelope geometry and of coil location in the center, at manufacture, as well as similar improvements in subsequent movement of the coil—both due to mechanical shock in shipping, and due to sag or squirm in operation. Research and development

TABLE I. Representative Incandescent Lamps (120 V)

Power (W)	Bulb type[a]	Current (A)	Rated life (hr)	Light output (lm)	Efficacy (lm/W)	Color temperature[b] (K)
6	S14	0.050	1500	40	6.7	2370
10	S14	0.083	1500	86	8.6	2450
25	A19	0.208	2500	235	9.4	2550
40[c]	A19	0.333	1500	445	11.1	2770
60[c]	A19	0.500	1000	870	14.5	2800
100[c]	A19	0.833	750	1,710	17.1	2870
150[c]	A21	1.250	750	2,780	18.5	2900
200[c]	A23	1.670	750	3,830	19.2	2930
300	PS30	2.500	1000	5,960	19.9	2940
500	PS35	4.170	1000	10,600	21.2	2960
1000	PS52	8.330	1000	23,100	23.1	3030
1500	PS52	12.500	1000	33,620	22.4	3070

[a] S = spherical, A = common household lamp shape, PS = pear-shaped. Number gives maximum diameter in $\frac{1}{8}$ inches.
[b] Color rendering index for all types is essentially 100.
[c] Most common household types; ratings are for lamp with diffusing powder-coated bulbs (soft white). For all other types, ratings are for inside-frost bulbs.

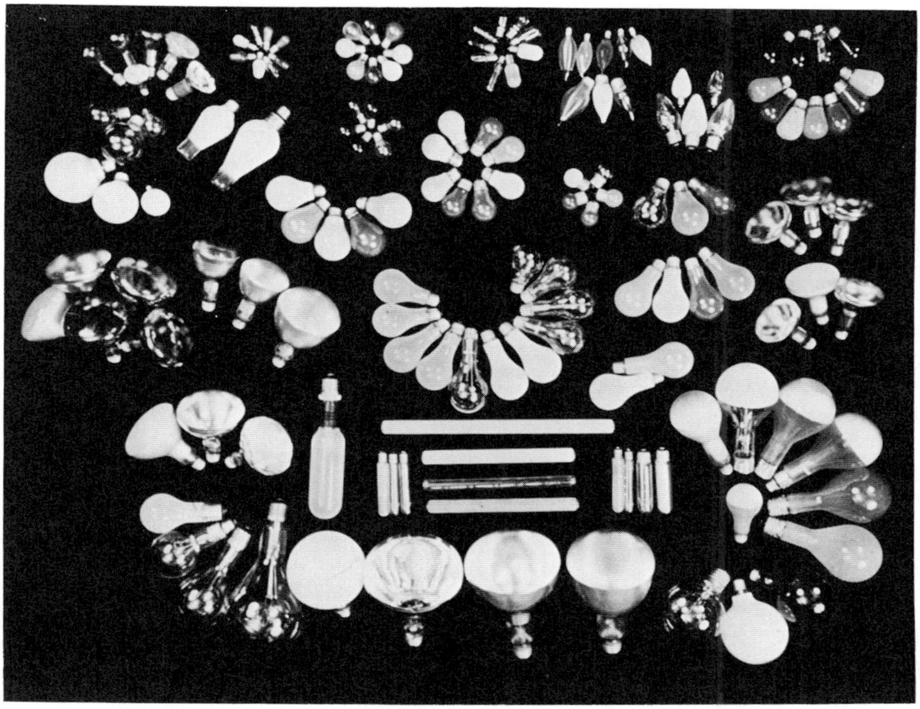

FIG. 9. Sample of the variety of types of incandescent lamps.

aimed at solution of these problems in a cost-effective way is an active area of concern in several organizations.

V. Tungsten–Halogen Lamps

A. Similarities to Incandescent Lamps

Tungsten–halogen (T–H) lamps, comprising a tungsten-filament radiator in a transparent glass envelope with a gas filling, are substantially the same as incandescent lamps in all aspects of their radiation generation and energy balance. Shared characteristics include dependence of efficacy and life on filament temperature and many of the limitations on performance resulting from material limitations.

B. Unique Features of Tungsten–Halogen Lamps

Tungsten–halogen (T–H) lamps use much higher gas filling pressures than do their incandescent counterparts, typically 5–10 atm in operation, depending on type. Consequently, the life of the filament against evaporation in T–H lamps at the same temperature would be several times longer; the gain is taken instead by operating the filament at higher temperatures to result in about 20% higher efficacy for equal life. To safely contain internal pressures greater than 1 atm requires small-diameter, heavy-walled vessels fabricated of refractory glasses operating at much higher temperatures than the bulb of an incandescent lamp. To prevent early blackening of the bulb by evaporated tungsten due to its close proximity to the filament, the T–H lamp makes use of a chemical cleaning cycle in which gaseous halogens react with evaporated tungsten, forming volatile halides that do not condense on the hot bulb walls, thereby keeping the walls clean. The tungsten halides decompose on the hot filament, redepositing the tungsten on them. Unfortunately, the temperature dependence of the redeposition is not the same as that of evaporation, and tungsten is not redeposited on the hottest spots from which it primarily evaporates. Thus the halogen cycle is not a regenerative one that of itself lengthens the life of the filament.

1. Principal Construction Features

Figure 10 shows the principal construction features of the two principal types of T–H

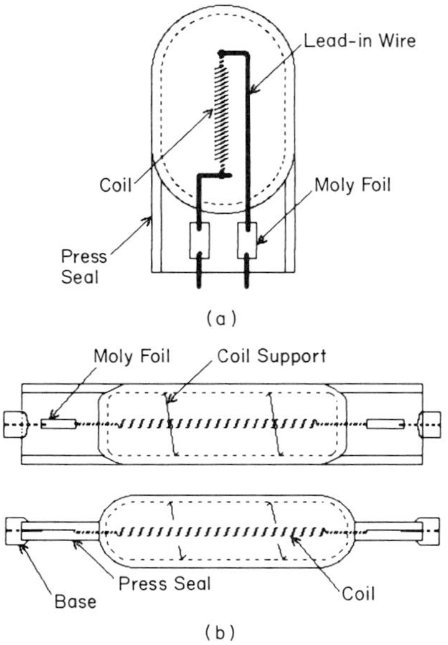

FIG. 10. Schematic diagram, illustrating components of typical T–H lamps. (a) Single-ended type, with press seal incorporating two molybdenum-foil feedthroughs. (b) Double-ended, shown in top and side views to illustrate geometry of press-seal; the coil support is usually a spiral tantalum or molybdenum wire loop affixed to the coil and loosely contacting the quartz wall, to center and support the elongated coiled filament.

lamps: single-ended and double-ended. The most common glass used for such lamps is either pure fused silica (quartz) or Vycor brand of high-silica glass (Corning Glass Works), which have softening temperatures near 1500°C and safe service temperatures of 900 to 1000°C. Glass-to-metal seals for electric lead-ins for these glasses use a very thin molybdenum foil with thickness to width ratio of 1/80 or less and having a very shallow taper at the edge to less than 25% of the thickness. This configuration permits the molybdenum to yield like plastic to accommodate the factor of 10 to 12 difference in thermal expansion between quartz and molybdenum without developing sufficient stress in the surrounding glass to cause it to fail. Such seals are susceptible to oxidation failure when operated at high temperature in air. For each type of T–H lamp, a maximum seal temperature is specified to ensure that seal failure does not occur before normal filament burnout.

Quartz and Vycor envelopes require extremely elevated temperatures for glassworking operations, which make lamp sealing slow and therefore expensive. For some types of T–H lamps, in which relatively high-production volumes are needed, aluminosilicate glasses (hard glass) are used. The sealing temperature of these glasses is 300–400°C less than quartz or Vycor, and thermal expansion is comparable to that of molybdenum. Thus rigid molybdenum wire lead-ins can be used and rapid sealing cycles used.

2. Chemical Cleaning Cycle

Tungsten–halogen lamps use reversible reactions of the form

$$W + X \leftrightarrow WX(g)$$

$$W + X + O \leftrightarrow WOX(g)$$

in which X is a halogen (usually iodine or bromine). The reactions proceed to the right at low temperatures to react with evaporated tungsten, forming volatile products that do not condense on the wall of the bulb, which therefore remains clean despite its close proximity to the filament. The maintenance of light output during the life of the lamp is therefore essentially 100%. In contact with the tungsten filament at elevated temperatures, the halides and oxyhalides decompose, redepositing tungsten on the filament, and releasing halogen. Careful control of the cycle is needed to ensure that clean-up is sufficiently rapid to prevent wall-blackening, without being so rapid as to erode the low-temperature tungsten-filament legs before normal burnout occurs. This is accomplished by (1) selection of halogen and halogen pressure and (2) control of the oxygen pressure.

C. Practical Problems

1. Fabrication Technology

The fabrication technology of T–H lamps is different from that for incandescent lamps in three respects. Tungsten–halogen lamps require (1) higher glassworking temperatures, (2) longer sealing times, and (3) preflushing of the vessel with inert gas before sealing to prevent oxidation of the filament during sealing. Filaments are recrystallized (stabilized) by firing in atmosphere furnaces before assembly to improve accuracy of filament positioning, especially in lamps for use in projection optical systems. Filling the vessel to pressures greater than atmospheric poses another unique problem in T–H lamp fabrication, solved by condensing out the fill gas into liquid form in the bulb with liquid nitrogen coolant before sealing so that flame sealing of the exhaust tube can be done in the conventional way, with less-than-atmospheric internal pressure. A final major technological difference is the necessity to dispense accurate amounts of corrosive halogens automatically on the exhaust machines.

As a result of these differences, the manufacture of many types of T–H lamps is not nearly as automated as it is for incandescent lamps. Only in the manufacture of types produced in quantities of millions per year, such as automotive headlamps, are fully integrated automatic machine groups for mount assembly, sealing, exhausting and filling, and basing used. For other types, of lower production volume, automated and semiautomated, highly flexible machines (capable of rapid type change) are used for the individual processes, and the parts are manually transferred from machine to machine.

2. Influence of Accidental Impurities on Chemistry

The cyclic halogen cleanup reactions in a T–H lamp are critically dependent on oxygen content since the oxyhalide reaction is in parallel with the halide reaction. Oxygen is present as an impurity in the tungsten itself, as well as in lead-in wires and supports. Moreover, variations in the degree of oxidation protection at sealing lead to variations in oxygen content of the lamp. Carbon, again an unavoidable impurity in the tungsten, serves to getter oxygen as carbon monoxide, in which form it is substantially inert. Hydrogen forms water from oxygen, providing water-cycle bulb blackening in parallel with evaporation. Thus, depending on the relative amounts of carbon, hydrogen, and oxygen, the role of the oxygen may be accelerated cleanup (and filament-leg erosion), neutral, or accelerated blackening.

The fact that substantial fractions of the inputs of all of these quantities result from the normal impurity contents of the lamp materials requires extremely close material control and compensatory adjustment of process to produce uniform product.

3. Mechanical Strength Problems Exaggerated

All the mechanical strength problems of incandescent lamps are present in T–H lamps to an exaggerated degree because of the higher operating temperatures of T–H filaments. Most manufacturers establish more stringent specifications for wire in T–H lamps than in incandescent lamps to avoid sag and squirm in operation. The problem of filament strength, as well as leg erosion, has in the past prevented development of low-wattage 120-V types because of the extremely fine filament wire they require. Improved materials, processes, and process control now permit manufacture of 120-V lamps having as little as 45 W.

D. Commercially Available Products and Performance Characteristics

The principal applications of T–H lamps have been in two areas: outdoor floodlighting (using high-wattage double-ended types and projection-type applications, photographic or audiovisual (using single-ended types). Single-ended quartz or Vycor T–H lamps have been widely used in Europe for automotive headlamps. Hard glass halogen capsules in sealed-beam-type outer envelopes have recently been introduced for this application in the United States, where they provide equal low-beam performance at two-thirds the electric power, and brighter high-beam performance at equal power in comparison to the incandescent product. Use in studio, theater, and television (STTV) applications, although small in absolute numbers, has revolutionized that illumination technology. Tables II and III summarize the characteristics of some double-ended and single-ended types, respectively. Recent application of aluminosilicate (hard glass) T–H capsules in sealed reflector (PAR) lamps has resulted in cost-effective products that compete with traditional incandescent applications, providing equal illumination and life, with very substantial energy savings. Table IV provides a comparison of performance of hard glass T–H PAR lamps with their incandescent predecessors. Figure 11 is a photograph illustrating a sampling of some of the various types.

E. Principal Areas of Research and Development

The development of low-wattage, 120-V, hard glass T–H capsules that can be inexpensively manufactured at high production speeds has opened new opportunities for T–H lamps in traditional incandescent applications, with energy savings of 20% or more. Many organizations are actively investigating the extension of this ad-

TABLE II. Representative Double-Ended Tungsten–Halogen Lamps

Power (W)	Type[a]	Length (in.)	Line (V)	Current (A)	Rated life (hr)	Light output (lm)	Efficacy (lm/W)	Color temperature[b] (K)
500	500T3Q/CL	$4\frac{1}{16}$	120	4.17	2000	11,100	22.2	3000
1000	1000T6Q/CL	$5\frac{5}{8}$	120	8.33	2000	22,000	22.2	3000
1000	1000T3Q/CL	$10\frac{1}{16}$	240	4.17	2000	21,500	21.5	3000
1500	1500T3Q/CL	$10\frac{1}{16}$	240	6.25	2000	35,800	23.9	3000
1500	1500T3Q/CL	$10\frac{1}{16}$	277	5.42	2000	34,400	22.9	3000

[a] T = Tubular, Number is diameter in $\frac{1}{8}$ in., Q = quartz, CL = clear.
[b] Color rendering index for all types is essentially 100.

vantage to residential illumination. Such a product would be indistinguishable in function and operation from the present-day incandescent lamp but would provide the same illumination with less electric power consumption. Application of the selective-reflector principle to T–H lamps is also being actively pursued.

VI. High-Intensity Discharge Lamps

High-intensity discharge (HID) lamps convert into radiation the power dissipation of an electric current passing through a gaseous medium at a pressure greater than or equal to 1 atm. Much higher radiating temperatures can be achieved than in any incandescent solid; appropriate selection of the gaseous medium results in favorable spectral distributions of radiated power, with a much smaller fraction of IR rays. As a result, such sources are very bright, and are 3–10 times as efficient as incandescent lamps. Figure 12 shows a schematic diagram illustrating the principal components of such a lamp.

Three principal types of HID lamps are distinguished by their radiating species: high-pressure mercury (mercury), high-pressure sodium (sodium, or HPS), and metal halide (M-H). Each comprises an inner discharge tube (arc tube) containing the high-pressure gas or vapor enclosed in a hermetically sealed outer envelope (jacket). The outer jacket is required for thermal insulation, protection of the arc tube seals from oxidation, and absorption of any short wave-

TABLE III. Representative Single-Ended Tungsten–Halogen Lamps

Power (W)	Type[a]	Length (in.)	Line (V)	Current (A)	Rated life (hr)	Light output (lm)	Efficacy (lm/W)	Color temperature[b] (K)
100	100Q/CL	$2\frac{3}{4}$	120	0.833	1000	1,800	18.0	3000
250	250Q/CL	$3\frac{1}{8}$	120	2.080	2000	5,000	20.0	3000
300	ELH[c]	$1\frac{3}{4}$	120	2.500	35	c	c	3350
600	DYV[d]	$2\frac{1}{2}$	120	5.000	75	17,500	29.1	3200
500	BTL[e]	$4\frac{1}{4}$	120	4.170	500	11,000	22.0	3050
750	BTN[e]	$4\frac{3}{8}$	120	6.250	500	17,000	22.7	3050
1,000	BTR[e]	$4\frac{3}{8}$	120	8.330	200	28,000	28.0	3200
1,500	CXZ[f]	8	120	12.500	325	38,500	25.7	3200
5,000	DPY[f]	11	120	41.700	500	143,000	28.6	3200
10,000	DTY[f]	15	120	83.300	300	291,000	29.1	3200

[a] Three-letter designations have no dimensional significance.
[b] Color rendering index for all types is essentially 100.
[c] Single-ended T–H capsule prefocused in ellipsoidal reflector for film projection applications.
[d] Principal application is in overhead projectors.
[e] Medium prefocus base for replacement of incandescent types in stage lighting.
[f] Prefocus bi-post base; primary application in studio and TV lighting.

TABLE IV. Comparison of Performance of Parabolic-Aluminized-Reflector (PAR) Lamps: Standard Incandescent versus PAR with Internal Hard-Glass Halogen (HGH) Capsule

	Center beam intensity (candela)[a]	Beam ½-angle[b] (degrees)	Field ½-angle[c] (degrees)
90-W HGH-narrow spot	22,000	4	9
150-W incandescent PAR spot	17,000	4	18
45-W HGH spot	5,000	6–7	13–15
75-W incandescent PAR spot	4,800	6–7	13–15
45-W HGH flood	1,800	14	20
75-W Incandescent PAR flood	1,800	15	24

[a] One Candela = 1 lm/sr.
[b] Angular deviation between center of beam and ½-maximum intensity.
[c] Angular deviation between center of beam and $\frac{1}{10}$-maximum intensity.

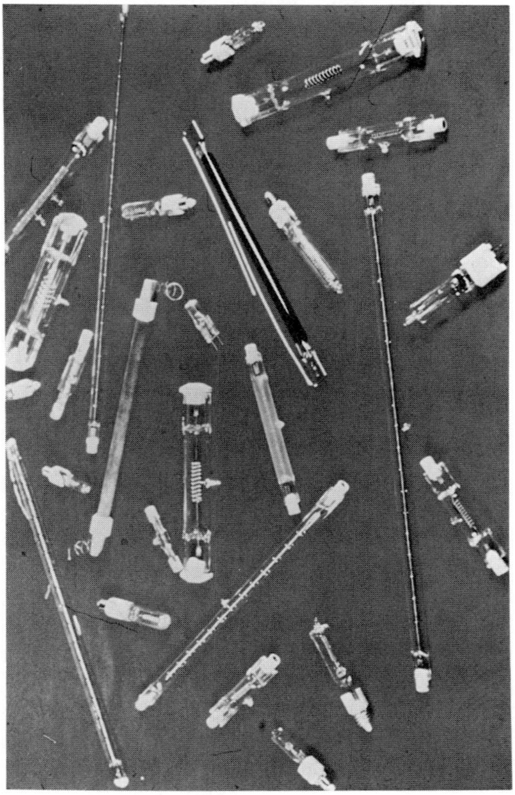

FIG. 11. Sample of double-ended and single-ended T–H lamp types.

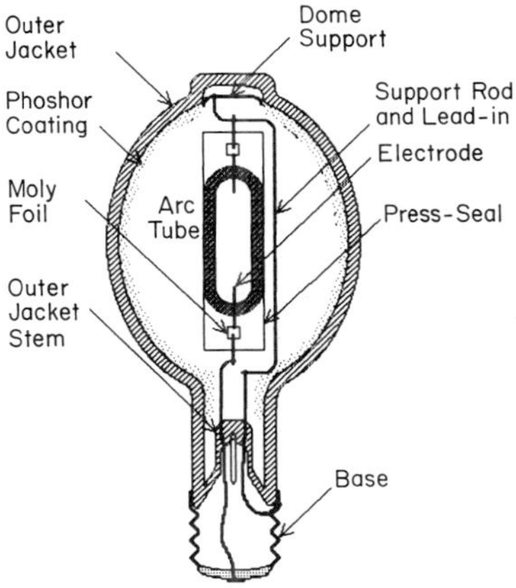

FIG. 12. Schematic diagram illustrating principal components of HID lamps, shown in section. Additional components (not shown) in many types are included to facilitate ignition.

length UV rays that may be emitted from the arc tube. Arc tubes for mercury and M-H lamps are quartz, similar to T–H lamp capsules; arc tubes for HPS lamps are fabricated from translucent polycrystalline alumina (PCA) to withstand corrosion by hot molten and gaseous sodium.

A. Radiation Mechanism

The passage of current ionizes the gaseous medium, converting it to a ''plasma'' containing high densities of free electrons plus positive ions in approximately equal concentrations but with little or no net charge density. The gas offers resistance to the passage of current because electrons collide with gas atoms. The I-squared-R power dissipation heats the gas to very high temperatures. Unlike a metallic conductor, the gas has very low thermal conductivity; there is a large temperature gradient between the center axis and the walls. The gas at the center reaches temperatures far greater than the boiling point of any material, while the walls of the arc tube remain at modest temperatures (1000–1500 K, depending on type). Rapid collisions sharing energy among electrons, ions, gas atoms, and excited gas atoms promote local thermal equilibrium (LTE), and the radiating properties are described by Eq. (6) of Section I, with absorption coefficients determined by the optical transitions of the gaseous medium. Such a discharge is called a high-pressure arc discharge, or arc.

The emitted radiation consists primarily of the line spectra of the elements present in the gas:

mercury in mercury lamps, and sodium in HPS lamps. Although mercury vapor is also present in the gas in HPS lamps, the temperature is insufficient to excite mercury to states that contribute to absorption in the visible wavelengths, and mercury lines are essentially absent from the spectrum.

Metal halide lamps contain atomic metal radiators that either do not vaporize at wall temperatures accessible to quartz or react vigorously with quartz at those temperatures. They are introduced into the arc tube in the form of metal iodides, which are quite volatile at ~1000 K and relatively nonreactive to quartz. The metal iodides participate in a halogen cycle, similar to that in T–H lamps. Iodide molecules evaporate from the tube wall and enter the high-temperature core of the arc where they dissociate, freeing metal atoms to contribute their optical transitions to the radiation of the gas mixture. Free metal and iodine atoms diffuse, or are convected, back into the low temperature regions of the discharge and chemically recombine to metal iodide, preventing condensation on, or reaction with, the quartz wall by metal atoms. The emitted radiation is dominated by the line spectrum of the added metals, with contributions from mercury (which is also present), and minor radiation from metal iodide molecules. Arc temperatures at the core are too low to excite iodine significantly, and its emission lines are barely detectable.

In all three types of HID lamps, the absorption spectra exhibit broadening of the natural line widths by a variety of processes: (1) Stark broadening due to perturbation of energy levels by electric fields from electrons and ions; (2) resonance broadening by the interaction of excited atoms with neighboring identical nonexcited atoms; and (3) van der Waals broadening caused by interaction of excited atoms with nearby foreign atoms. Calculation of the absorption coefficient as a function of wavelength requires knowledge of the broadening mechanisms, as well as of the density of absorbing atoms, and of the probabilities of their optical transitions. Calculation of the spectral radiance at the arc tube wall requires knowledge of the radial temperature profile. Nevertheless, accurate radiation transport calculations have been available for some time for HPS lamps and are becoming available for M-H lamps. In all three types, optical depths range from very thin to very thick. Because of the large temperature gradients, self-reversed lines are common. Spectral radiances at emission line maxima approach 50% or more of the blackbody level at the arc axis temperature for strong nonresonance lines and 25% or more of that level for resonance lines. Infrared transitions in most atoms, between upper energy levels near the ionization limit, are not strongly excited at the arc temperatures. Their contribution to the absorption spectrum is weak, as are corresponding emission lines. By design, electron density is maintained at a sufficiently low level that free-free transitions of electrons colliding with each other and with ions, leading predominantly to emission in the IR, are minimized. The consequent weak emission of HID lamps in the IR contributes strongly to their high efficacy. Proper choice of radiating atoms can favor emission in the visible over the UV wavelengths as well. M-H lamps permit the choice of radiating atoms that provide for emission of all colors, so that the CRI is also high.

Figure 13 shows spectral power distributions of the radiation emitted from the three types of HID lamps. These spectra are taken on instruments with relatively wide spectral bandwidth and do not reveal the self-reversed nature of the spectral lines except in the case of the sodium resonance lines at 589 nm in the HPS lamp.

B. Energy Balance

1. Arc Discharge

Electric power is dissipated in the arc tube in three modes: heating electrodes to electron-emitting temperatures, heat conduction through the radial temperature gradient in the gas to the walls, and radiation from the high temperature gaseous medium. Table V shows the approximate percentages of power dissipation in these modes for 400-W mercury, HPS, and M-H lamps. Electrode loss is minimized by designing the lamp to operate at as low a current, and as high a voltage drop, for a given power as is practical. Voltage drop between electrodes increases with increasing interelectrode spacing (arc length) and with increasing gas pressure. Heat conduction loss is approximately a constant loss per unit length of arc. The percentage lost in heat conduction is minimized by operation at as high a power input per unit length as possible, that is, operation with as short an arc length for a given power input as possible. Maximizing voltage drop while minimizing arc length dic-

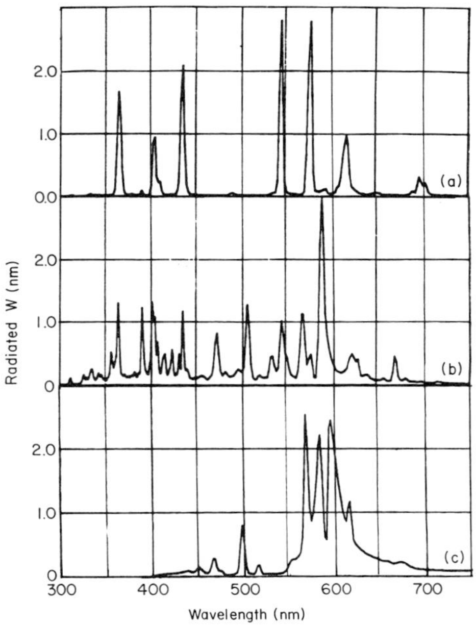

FIG. 13. Spectral distribution of radiated power (W/nm) of HID lamp types in use in the United States, all at 400-W input power. (A) Mercury lamp with phosphor-coated outer jacket; strong peaks at 365, 405, 436, 546, and 578 nm are atomic lines of mercury, while the peak at 615 nm is red emission from the phosphor, excited by UV from the arc tube; color temperature = 4000 K, CRI = 45. (B) Sodium-scandium M-H lamp; the mercury lines are visible in the spectrum, the strong line at 590 nm is due to sodium, and the balance is due to groups of lines emitted by scandium atoms (unresolved at the spectrometer bandpass used here); color temperature = 4000 K, CRI = 65. (C) HPS lamp; all radiation is from sodium, the major yellow peak with a minimum at 590 being the self-reversed resonance line of sodium (see Fig. 2); color temperature = 2100 K, CRI = 22.

tates high gas pressures, 1–10 atm, depending on type.

2. Lamp–Electrical-Circuit System

Gases are normally insulators; to establish current flow through a gas requires generation of free electrons and ions. This is accomplished in discharge lamps such as HID lamps by application of sufficiently high potential across the discharge tube terminals so that a single initial electron may gain enough energy to ionize a gas atom. This creates an ion–electron pair, the electron of which gains enough energy to create a new ion–electron pair, and so on, in an avalanche, which eventually results in sufficient free electrons in the gas to carry the required discharge current at the desired potential drop. The necessary starting, (ignition) and breakdown potential is typically several times higher than the ultimate operating voltage. Therefore, the electrical circuit must provide a high open-circuit voltage for ignition but must include current-limiting impedance to drop the voltage across the lamp terminals to the operating value, which is relatively independent of current, once the discharge is ignited. If the circuit had no current-limiting impedance, but continuously applied the ignition voltage, the electron avalanche would continue to grow unabated, and current would rapidly rise to destructive levels.

The electric circuit device that performs these functions is called a ballast. In principle, the current-limiting impedance could be resistive; however, I-squared-R dissipation in the resistance would add to power consumption of the circuit without contributing any light, thus reducing system efficacy. Since HID lamps operate on

TABLE V. Approximate Percentages of Power Dissipation in High-Intensity Discharge Lamps

Lamp type	Electrode loss	Heat conduction plus wall absorption	Radiation		
			IR	UV	Visible
Mercury[a]	12	38	10	24	16
Metal halide	12	25	17	19	31
High-pressure sodium[b]	4	37	32	0	27

[a] Low wall-loading in mercury lamps results in large conduction loss, which together with unfavorable fraction of radiation in UV results in low efficiency of visible radiation in comparison to other types.

[b] High thermal conductance of sodium vapor results in large heat conduction loss; strong IR emission lines of sodium also reduce fraction radiated in the visible rays. Visible radiation is predominantly near the maximum of the photopic response curve; therefore, luminous efficacy is high.

alternating current, the necessary impedance in their ballasts is reactive: either inductive or inductive plus capacitive, minimizing power dissipation in the ballast. Many HID lamps require ignition voltages greater than 120 V; the ballasts also include step-up transformers to increase the open-circuit voltage to the ignition value.

High-pressure sodium lamp ballasts and some M-H ballasts provide the ignition voltage in the form of very brief pulses of several kilovolts peak from a circuit that is disabled once the lamp is ignited. On alternating current, the discharge must also be reignited each half cycle; the peak instantaneous voltage required to accomplish this is typically 30% more than the instantaneous arc voltage during the majority of the half cycle. The ballast must provide the necessary reignition voltage under operating conditions with the pulse-voltage circuit inactive.

The ignition voltage required is a strongly increasing function of gas pressure. Therefore, all HID lamps use a low pressure of a rare gas as a starting gas, typically 20–100 Torr, and provide the required high operating pressure by mercury vapor. At ignition, the mercury is cold and condensed out, with a vapor pressure of a millitorr, and does not result in a high-ignition voltage. In operation, the arc tube wall is hot, all the mercury content of the capsule is in the gas phase, and the pressure is at the high level necessary to provide the design value of operating voltage. Use of mercury vapor to provide the high pressure has the added advantage that heat conductance of mercury is very low, minimizing heat conduction loss.

Less than ideal transformers and reactances result in power dissipation in the ballast, essentially proportional to volt-amperes handled, the product of open-circuit voltage times the operating current. The open-circuit voltage required is determined by ignition requirements of the lamp. Minimizing lamp current for a given power requires that operating voltage of the lamp be as high as possible, that is, as close to ignition voltage as possible. Typical commercial ballast systems for HID lamps have losses of 10 to 15% of lamp power.

C. Performance Limitations Resulting from Material Limitations

Unlike incandescent lamps, HID lamps do not embody a single mechanism that is the primary determinant of lamp life; there is not a one-to-one inverse correspondence between efficacy and life. Moreover, lives of HID lamps are prodigiously long; most mercury and HPS types have rated lives of 24,000 hr, while M-H lamps have rated lives from 7500 to 20,000 hr. Since typical operating hours in dusk-to-dawn outdoor service or two-shift indoor commercial service are 4000 hr per year, these rates represent operating lifetimes of 2 to 6 years. Nevertheless, design choices that lead to higher efficacy are constrained by material limitations that result in shorter life.

Failure mechanisms in mercury and HPS lamps include (1) exhaustion of electron-emitting activator material from the electrodes, resulting in failure to ignite or reignite each half cycle; (2) gas contamination, resulting in ignition failure; (3) arc tube seal failure, resulting in loss of hermeticity; (4) excessive arc tube blackening by evaporants from the electrode; or (5) wall material degradation, causing decrease in output to unacceptable levels and requiring replacement before failure. Metal halide and HPS lamps also may suffer from loss of radiating atomic species by unwanted chemical reactions that consume them irreversibly, therefore causing loss of light output as well as failure to reignite.

These considerations dictate materials of the arc tube, electrodes, and electrode activator compounds to minimize rates of adverse processes. All of the processes described, however, occur more rapidly as temperature is increased. While efficiency increases as input power per unit length is increased, so does arc tube temperature, and with it the rate of the adverse reactions discussed in the preceding paragraph. These constraints are generally embodied in the form of rule-of-thumb design rules regarding acceptable wall-loading (arc power input per unit area of arc tube wall surface). Experience indicates that acceptable lamp lives in mercury lamps are obtained at wall-loadings of 10 to 12 W/cm^2; M-H designs are commonly found at 13 to 17 W/cm^2; and HPS can use designs at 15 to 20 W/cm^2 by virtue of the more refractory nature of PCA. For all types, efficacy increases as wall-loading increases, and most designs are at or near these limits. In some cases in which somewhat shorter life is permitted, higher wall-loadings than the values cited may be used.

Molybdenum foil seals in both mercury and M-H lamps have adequate life at much higher temperatures than in T–H lamps because they are protected from oxidation by an inert atmosphere in the outer jacket. The electrical lead-in in HPS lamps involves a niobium (also known as columbium) metal member, chosen for expansion match to PCA and sealed with a polycrystalline oxide mixture, fusible without melting either niobium or PCA. The niobium is protected from oxidation by a vacuum in the outer jacket. In HPS lamps, resistance of sealing compounds to attack by sodium sets a limit to maximum seal temperature, thereby limiting the cold spot temperature that determines maximum pressure of sodium vapor inside the arc tube.

D. Practical Considerations

1. Fabrication Technology

Fabrication of mercury and M-H lamps involves aspects similar to a combination of T–H and incandescent lamp fabrication since two hermetically sealed vessels are required: one of fused quartz, incorporating molybdenum foil seals, and an outer jacket of glass using a stem seal similar to an incandescent lamp. The major qualitative difference is that processing of mercury arc tubes also involves dispensing a precisely determined quantity of mercury into a precisely determined internal volume of arc tube since those two factors determine operating pressure when all the mercury is vaporized. To that difference in M-H lamps is added a requirement for also dispensing extremely hygroscopic iodide salts without any contact with the atmosphere. The salts themselves are dehydrated in advance to only a few parts per million of water content, and they must be handled in atmosphere glove boxes free of moisture and oxygen to a few parts per million.

Wide differences exist among manufacturers and types in the level of automation of manufacture of mercury lamps. Some popular types are manufactured on fully integrated production lines that seal and process the arc tube automatically, mount it on the outer jacket stem press automatically, and seal and process the outer jacket automatically at speeds of dozens per minute. For others, one or more stages of the process involve jigs-and-fixtures manual operations.

Metal halide lamp manufacturing is much less automated because of lower production volumes and more difficult and demanding process requirements. With most manufacturers, arc tube fabrication is primarily a scaled-up laboratory type of process. Arc tube processing takes place on automatic exhaust machines. Final assembly and outer jacket processing usually proceeds through the mercury lamp line, sharing equipment and processes.

High-pressure sodium lamp manufacture is a different ceramic-based technology. Polycrystalline alumina tubes themselves are manufactured either by a press-and-sinter ceramic process, or an extrusion-sinter process, using as raw material a very pure alumina powder of precisely specified surface area, to which controlled quantities of sintering aid compounds have been added. The resultant translucent tubing has total diffuse transmittance of 95% or more, and single-wall inline transmittance of 10%. Arc tube sealing, exhausting, and filling may be either a two-step process or single step, depending on manufacturer. In the two-step process, both niobium end caps are cemented at once with a fusible oxide mixture to the tube ends in a vacuum or atmosphere furnace; one of the end caps is equipped with an exhaust tube. The arc tube is evacuated and mercury and sodium fillings are dispensed through the exhaust tube in a separate process, after which the niobium exhaust tube is pinched shut in a cold weld. In the one-step process, each end of the arc tube is sealed separately. The second seal is made in an atmosphere furnace containing the desired fill pressure of starting gas, with mercury-sodium amalgam already dispensed into the tube, residing at the cool first sealed-end; there is no exhaust tube, and no separate exhaust and filling process. The final assembly into an outer jacket and outer jacket processing are similar to those for mercury lamps, and they may share equipment.

2. Unfavorable Reactions and the Effects of Impurities

In all three classes of HIDS lamps, gaseous impurities that interfere with ignition or reignition must be minimized. Hydrogen is a particularly troublesome species since it is a principal component of water vapor, a common and difficult impurity to remove. In addition to surface contaminations, dissolved hydroxyl in quartz is a major problem. This is dissociated photolytically by UV rays from the discharge, and the liberated hydrogen diffuses rapidly into the arc tube interior. Manufacturing processes for quartz tubes are tailored to reduce the hydroxyl content to a parts-per-million level; optical absorption in an IR absorption band of OH is used as a quality-control tool. Because of rapid diffusion of hydrogen through hot quartz, moisture in the outer jacket must also be minimized since it may also be dissociated by UV light, and the liberated hydrogen may diffuse through the arc tube wall into the interior. Hydrogen is especially harmful in M-H lamps because of reaction with iodide salts, forming HI and liberating metal. The metal reacts with quartz and is lost to the halogen cycle; the hydrogen iodide is gaseous and interferes with electron avalanche growth in ignition by capturing free electrons.

Oxygen is also deleterious, especially in M-H and HPS lamps, because it promotes reaction of metal atoms with arc tube wall material. Hydrocarbon vapors in the outer jacket are also decomposed thermally and photolytically, liberating damaging hydrogen as well as depositing amorphous carbon on the arc tube wall surface, reducing optical transmission.

In addition to the foregoing, two adverse reactions in M-H lamps must be minimized. The inadvertent reaction of free metals with the quartz wall of the arc tube—as a result of some failure to complete the halogen cycle—causes a loss of metal, reduction in partial pressure of metal vapor ultimately entering the arc, and consequently of radiation emitted by the metal. In addition, such reactions also liberate silicon metal, which reacts with iodine to form volatile silicon tetraiodide. This compound decomposes at the electrode temperature, and deposits molten silicon on the electrode. The molten silicon fluxes recrystallization and regrowth of the electrode, drastically distorting its shape and degrading its performance. This becomes one of the life-limiting processes in M-H lamps by adversely affecting the reignition process every half cycle, ultimately to the point that the ballast capability to reignite does not suffice.

The second adverse reaction is the electrolytic loss of sodium from sodium iodide in the arc tube fill. In operation, there are always a few parts per million of sodium ions dissolved in quartz in contact with sodium iodide as a result of reaching thermochemical equilibrium in the reversible reaction between the quartz and the iodide. The quantity is not harmful to the quartz, nor does it represent a significant depletion of sodium from the initial dose dispensed. However, sodium ions are mobile in quartz, and it has been found that negative charging of the outer surface of the quartz arc tube by photoelectrons emitted from various parts of the outer jacket will attract the sodium ions to the outer surface to be neutralized and evaporate. The depletion of the ionic concentration in the inner surface then permits the forward reaction to proceed to provide more sodium ions, which are electrolyzed in turn, until eventually a very substantial fraction of the original sodium dose has been lost. Outer jacket designs providing minimum photoelectric-emitting surfaces are used to mitigate this problem.

E. Commercially Available Products and Performance Characteristics

HID lamps are primarily used in outdoor floodlighting, street and highway lighting, and indoor industrial and commercial applications in which their exceptionally long service lives and high efficacies outweigh their high initial cost and the added expense of the required ballasts. In such service, relatively high mounting heights have been traditional so that large areas could be illuminated from relatively few fixtures. This has dictated in the past that the more popular types were from 8000 to 100,000 lm in the United States and from 5000 to 50,000 lm in Europe. However, the increasing application of HPS and M-H lamps in lower ceiling height indoor commercial service, requiring smaller lumen packages—4000 to 10,000 lm—has resulted in many new lower wattage types being introduced within the last few years.

Because of the relatively small fraction of visible radiation output by mercury lamps, they provide only 50% of the efficacy of HPS and M-H lamps, or, conversely, they require twice the electrical power consumption to produce a given level of illumination. In addition, the absence of any red emission lines in the visible spectrum of mercury means that the CRI of mercury lamps is poor; the vast majority of such lamps in service today use a red-emitting phosphor coating applied to the inside surface of the outer jacket. Ultraviolet light emission from the arc is converted to red light by the phosphor, providing acceptable color rendering for most purposes. As a result of lower electrical power consumption by HPS and M-H lamps, the total cost of light obtained with these sources is less than that of mercury lamps. High-pressure sodium and M-H applications are expanding at a much more rapid rate, and are supplanting mercury lamps in many installations.

The most common type of HPS lamp is designed to operate with sodium pressure that gives maximum efficacy, with a CRI of ~ 22. At lower sodium pressures, there are insufficient sodium atoms in the vapor to provide all the sodium radiation that might be obtained. At higher sodium pressures, there is excessive resonance broadening of the sodium resonance line; this has the effect of shifting radiation away from the yellow region of the spectrum and into orange-red, where the eye is less sensitive. As a result, although the CRI may be improved to 60 to 80, and total efficiency of radiation slightly increased, luminous efficacy decreases ~25% for a CRI of 50 to 60 and about 60% for a CRI of 70 to 80. The higher sodium pressure also causes more rapid rates of adverse reactions with tube wall and sealing cement; life ratings are typically reduced by 50% or more. Although these lamps are commercially available from several manufacturers, they have not won wide acceptance in the marketplace.

Several different metal-iodide combinations are available in M-H lamps from different manufacturers. The preferred combination in the United States and in Japan uses a blend of sodium and scandium iodides. Scandium provides a multiline spectrum throughout the visible spectral range, similar to the rare earth elements, and results in a CRI of ~65, suitable for most commercial applications. Sodium increases the efficacy and permits adjustment to color temperatures from 3000 to 5000 K, which is the preferred range in the United States. In Europe, a mixture of indium, thallium, and sodium iodides has been used: indium for blue emission, thallium for green, and sodium for yellow and orange. A gamut of color temperatures is possible, depending on mixture ratios.

Also common in Europe is a dysprosium–holmium–thallium–iodide mixture, with or without sodium. The rare earth elements have multiline emission spectra giving good color rendition. Thallium adds green, improving efficacy. In the absence of sodium, the color temperature of this mixture is ~6000 K; with sodium added, it can be lowered to the 3500 to 4000 K range.

Table VI gives representative data for various examples of commercially available products in the mercury, HPS, and M-H families. Figure 14 shows some of the variety of types and sizes available.

F. Research and Development

Since efficacy of HID lamps increases with increasing wall-loading, there is active research for materials capable of operation at higher temperatures in more corrosive environments. A major focus of development is extending the

TABLE VI. Representative High-Intensity Discharge Lamps

Power (W)	Bulb[a] (type/MOL)	Operating[b] (V)	Current (A)	Rated life (hr)	Light output (lm)	Efficacy (lm/W)	Color temperature (K)	Color rendering index
Mercury lamps[c]								
175	BT28/8$\frac{5}{16}$	130	1.5	24,000	8,500	49	4,000	45
400	BT37/11$\frac{1}{2}$	135	3.2	24,000	23,000	58	4,000	45
1000	BT56/15$\frac{3}{8}$	265	4.0	16,000	55,000	55	4,000	45
Metal-halide lamps[d]								
100	ED17/5$\frac{7}{16}$	100	1.1	5,000	8,500	85	3,200	65
175	BT28/8$\frac{5}{16}$	130	1.5	7,500	14,000	80	4,400	65
400	BT37/11$\frac{1}{2}$	135	3.2	20,000	34,000	85	4,000	65
1000	BT56/15$\frac{3}{8}$	265	4.3	12,000	110,000	110	3,900	65
1500	BT56/15$\frac{3}{8}$	265	6.3	3,000	155,000	103	3,700	65
High-pressure sodium								
35	B17/5$\frac{1}{2}$	52	0.9	16,000	2,250	64	1,900	22
50	B17/5$\frac{1}{2}$	52	1.25	24,000	4,000	80	2,100	22
70	B17/5$\frac{1}{2}$	52	1.70	24,000	6,300	90	2,100	22
150	ED23$\frac{1}{2}$/7$\frac{1}{2}$	55	3.25	24,000	16,000	107	2,100	22
250	E18/9$\frac{3}{4}$	100	2.75	24,000	26,100	104	2,100	22
400	E18/9$\frac{3}{4}$	100	4.25	24,000	50,000	125	2,100	22

[a] Letters designate bulb shape; digits are diameter in $\frac{1}{8}$ in. MOL = maximum overall length.

[b] All lamps must be operated with appropriate ballasts rated for the line-supply voltage to regulate current and operating voltage of the discharge of these values.

[c] Data for phosphor-coated mercury lamps only.

[d] Ratings are for clear scandium-sodium types only.

FIG. 14. Sample of HID lamp types.

range of lamp sizes to lower wattages and lumens output, with minimal loss of efficacy, in both the HPS and the M-H families. A practical deficiency of all types of M-H lamps is variation in color, both initially and in the course of the operating lifetime, as a result of variations in ratios of radiating constituents and variations in arc tube temperature. Considerable development is being expended to reduce these variations. Since M-H lamps may use any of ~50 metals as iodides, singly or in combination, a semi-infinite set of possibilities is available, and low-level exploratory activities to examine these continues. Research into M-H lamps focuses on developing more accurate arc models, which include not only radiation transport but also deal with the thermochemistry of molecules, atoms, and radicals, together with the detailed radial and axial energy balances and transport, all in a self-consistent way. Research and development activity to improve HPS lamp color without such large penalties in efficacy or life is a concern in many laboratories.

VII. Fluorescent Lamps

The fluorescent lamp is a discharge lamp in which UV radiation emitted by a low-pressure discharge in a mixture of mercury vapor and a noble gas is converted to visible light by a fluorescent phosphor on the inside of the discharge tube wall. Fluorescent lamps operate at wall-loadings of 0.04–0.20 W/cm^2—much lower than those for HID lamps. However, since fluorescent lamps require no outer jacket, overall they yield 2000–4000 lm/L of lamp volume, ~10% as much as HID lamps. Figure 15 is a schematic diagram illustrating the major components of a fluorescent lamp. Since there are a wide variety of fluorescent phosphors emitting nearly every color of the rainbow, and these may be used in blends or multilayered coatings, a very large range of colors and CRIs is available from this family of lamps, without significant change in the discharge medium itself.

A. Radiation Mechanisms

1. Discharge Plasma

The UV radiation is created by the passage of electric current through a mixture of mercury vapor at a few millitorr pressure, and a noble gas (usually argon, krypton, or neon, or some combination of them) at a few torr pressure. The power density is adjusted to result in a coldest spot temperature, ~40°C, at which the saturated mercury vapor pressure is ~6 mtorr. At this pressure, the maximum efficiency of generation for the 254-nm resonance radiation of mercury is obtained, corresponding to the $^3P_1$-$^1S_0$ transition. The discharge is very far from LTE; electron temperature is greater than radiation temperature (which is itself different for the several

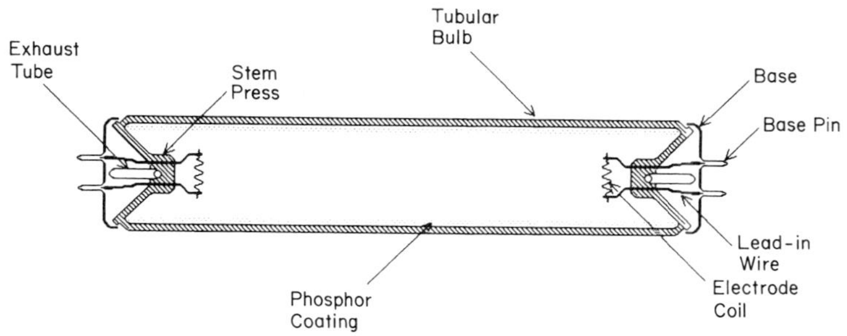

FIG. 15. Schematic diagram of the principal components of a typical fluorescent lamp, shown in section.

energy levels of the mercury atom), and both are very much greater than the gas-kinetic temperature. The energy inputs and flows that maintain these temperature differences are discussed in Section VII,B. The equation describing radiation transport is Eq. 3 of Section I. The discharge has an optical depth of 50 to 100 at the center of the resonance line, about unity for some of the stronger visible and near-UV lines, and much less than unity for other emission lines. There is essentially no excitation of the radiation of the noble gas. The large optical depth of the resonance line results from the fact that the lower level of this transition is the ground state of the mercury atom, occupied in ~99% of the atoms present. Escape of this radiation from the plasma is therefore by a number of sequential absorptions and reemissions. This process, referred to in the literature as "imprisonment of resonance radiation," has the effect of prolonging the effective radiative lifetime of the excited state, thus increasing the chance for dissipation of excitation energy by some nonradiative transition. Efficiency of generation of resonance radiation therefore depends on mercury atom number density (and hence vapor pressure) as follows: at low pressures since there are insufficient mercury atoms to be excited by electrons, which consequently dissipate energy in other, nonuseful, ways, increasing pressure results in efficiency increase; at high mercury pressures since imprisonment time is too long, and too great a fraction of energy input to creating excited mercury atoms is dissipated in nonradiative transitions, increasing pressure results in efficiency decrease. Optimum mercury pressure results from balancing these two competing trends.

In this non-LTE case, calculation of radiation flux density via Eq. 3 of Section I is extremely complex, so much so that it has not been solved exactly. To integrate Eq. (3) for radiation flux requires knowledge of $n(u, r)$, the radial density distribution of mercury atoms in the $^3P_1$ upper state of the transition pair. However, instead of being constrained to an LTE value, this number density must be determined by solving coupled rate equations involving electron-collision transitions to and from the state, as well as radiation emission and absorption transitions. The rates of electron-collision transitions are proportional to local electron density, which in turn depends on the local rate of production and ambipolar diffusion loss. Much of the production of new electrons comes from ionization of mercury atoms in the very $^3P_1$ state whose concentration is to be calculated. Thus, the total problem involves solution of coupled integrodifferential equations.

So far, model calculations in such discharges have arbitrarily decoupled the equations to obtain a reasonably tractable problem. The radial distribution of excited atoms has been calculated (and with it the imprisonment time), assuming it was determined only by emission and absorption processes in a decaying ensemble of excited atoms. The imprisonment time is then used as a constant in the solution of the radial electron density and collision rate equations. Despite the arbitrary nature of the assumptions, this route to solution has given excellent correspondence to experiment. This can only mean that the actual radial distribution of excited atoms in the discharge is not far removed from the one calculated on the basis of radiation transport alone. Adding to the complexity of radiation transport in the system is that the 185-nm resonance transition (between $^1P_1$ and $^1S_0$ states) of mercury must be considered along with the 254-nm resonance transition.

2. Phosphors

Ultraviolet radiation reaching the walls of the discharge tube is absorbed by and converted to visible light by coatings of luminescent phosphor powders applied to them. Such phosphors are composed of inorganic crystalline materials, optically transparent in the pure state but synthesized to incorporate specific luminescent centers to absorb the desired wavelengths of UV light and emit visible rays. Such luminescent centers are typically strongly coupled to ligand fields of the solid; therefore, excitation by a UV photon creates excited state complexes in high vibrational energy states. These interact with lattice phonons to relax states of the excited manifold to lower vibrational energy before radiating. Consequent to loss of energy by phonon relaxation, the energy of the photon emitted on reradiation is substantially less than that of the absorbed one.

For all but the rare earth activators, coupling to the crystal fields results in emission over a broad band of wavelengths instead of narrow lines. Skillful empirical selection of activators and host crystals has over the years led to a library of phosphors that absorb well at 254 and 185 nm UV wavelengths and emit photons at longer wavelengths. Many peak-emission wavelengths from 300 to 800 nm are available, all with quantum efficiencies that approach unity.

Note that although near-unity quantum efficiency may be obtained, energy efficiency is only ~50% since a UV photon carries 4.86 eV of energy, whereas a visible photon at the maximum of the eye sensitivity curve only carries 2.23 eV. Note that radiation output from the phosphor surface far exceeds blackbody radiation at the phosphor temperature (~40°C), in apparent violation of the fundamental conclusion of Section I. The luminescent centers, however, are radiatively coupled by UV photons to excited mercury atoms, which are in turn collisionally coupled to the electron gas in the plasma; the latter have an effective temperature of ~11,000 K. The blackbody radiance at that temperature could set the maximum thermodynamic limit to radiation output; the radiance of the phosphor surface is much less than that level.

Figure 16 illustrates spectral power distributions of (a) a fluorescent lamp intended as a substitute for an incandescent lamp, (b) the conventional "cool white" fluorescent color used in many commercial installations, and (c) a fluorescent lamp used in photocopy applications.

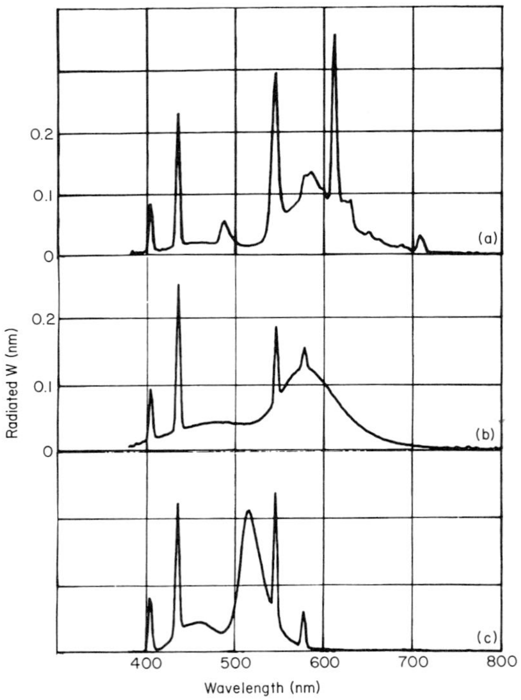

FIG. 16. Spectral distribution of radiated power (W/nm) of several fluorescent lamp types, all at 40-W input power. (a) Phosphor system including premium rare earth phosphors, intended for service as incandescent lamp substitute; color temperature = 3000 K, CRI = 75. (b) Standard cool white, the most common color for commercial applications; color temperature = 4200 K, CRI = 62. (c) Fluorescent lamp for photocopy applications, scale in arbitrary units. Since photoreceptor is not the human eye, color temperature and CRI are inappropriate designations and are not given. Visible mercury lines at 405, 436, 546, and 578 nm are evident in these spectral power distributions.

B. Energy Balance

1. Discharge Plasma

Passage of electric current through the gas imparts energy to it, producing (1) a continuing supply of new electron–ion pairs by ionization of the mercury constituent of the gas to maintain it in the plasma state, and (2) excited mercury atoms that radiate their characteristic spectrum. Because gas pressures are a small fraction of an atmosphere, the principal loss process for ions and electrons is by diffusion to the walls. Since radial electric fields in the plasma retard diffusion of electrons and enhance diffusion of ions, both species are constrained to diffuse to the wall at the same rate (ambipolar diffusion). Once at the wall, they recombine to reform neutral mercury atoms.

The energy input and dissipation process may be considered to take place in three stages:

1. Free electrons in the plasma are accelerated by the axial gradient of potential between anode and cathode.
2. As a result of frequent collisions, electrons share with each other energy gained in acceleration, establishing a steady-state electron energy distribution which is approximately maxwellian in character, with a "temperature" of ~11,000 K, ~1 eV.
3. The electrons dissipate their energy in collisions with atoms in the gas.

The high energy fraction of this distribution, greater than a few eV, may make inelastic collisions with mercury atoms, exciting them to states from which they may radiate on relaxation to the ground state. In a fraction of the cases, the mercury atom may receive enough energy to detach a valence electron, resulting in a new electron/positive-ion pair. The low energy fraction of electrons have insufficient energy to make exciting collisions (for which a threshold energy is required). The electrons can, however, make so-called collisions of the second kind, colliding with an excited mercury atom and extracting the excitation energy as kinetic energy, leaving the formerly excited atom in a state of lower excitation. Collisions of this kind by electrons substitute radiationless transitions for radiative transitions of excited atoms, reducing the amount of radiation emitted.

All electrons, low energy as well as high, make elastic collisions with gas atoms that transfer a small fraction of electron kinetic energy to the gas atom. Although the fraction of energy lost in any one collision is small, elastic collisions are very frequent; therefore, cumulative loss by this process represents a significant power dissipation.

Steady-state electron temperature is determined by the equality between rate of gain of energy by the entire ensemble of electrons from acceleration in the axial potential gradient and by the total rate of energy loss by the ensemble of electrons by all the energy loss processes that occur. The rate of ionization of mercury by high-energy electrons is proportional to the fraction of electrons having the threshold ionization energy, that is, exponentially dependent on electron temperature. There is a unique value of electron temperature at which rate of ionization exactly equals rate of loss and electron concentration in the plasma remains constant. Electron temperature increases monotonically with increasing axial potential gradient, and there is consequently a unique value of axial potential gradient which will result in the exact value of the electron temperature required to maintain the discharge in the steady state. The ballast circuit then must include internal impedance that decreases potential applied to the lamp terminals when current through the lamp increases so that the discharge can operate stably. Transient changes in electron density and current result in the alteration of discharge potential and potential gradient that produces changes of the opposite sign in electron density.

The efficiency of the discharge is determined by the ratio of power dissipated by electrons which is radiated as 254-nm resonance radiation to total power dissipated by electrons in all processes. Typically, for a 40-W fluorescent lamp, 10–15% of the input power is dissipated in electrode losses, 23% as elastic collision loss, 2% as visible and near-UV radiation, 8–9% as 185-nm resonance radiation, and 55% as 254-nm UV radiation. The astonishing efficiency of conversion of power in the plasma into 254-nm resonance radiation is the reason for the technological importance of this type of light source. Even after reduction by a factor 2 in conversion at near unity quantum efficiency to visible rays by a phosphor, it still permits high luminous efficacy (80 lm/W in commodity types, and up to 100 lm/W in premium types).

This section demonstrates the importance of the fraction of high energy electrons in the distribution (i.e., the electron temperature) in determining efficiency of the device. Electron temperature is amenable to control by the lamp designer, through adjustment of the ambipolar diffusion loss rate of electrons and ions. If diffusion rate is increased, so does the electron temperature required for steady-state operation. Diffusion rate is determined by the tube diameter and by pressure and atomic mass number of the noble gas. The heavier the gas or the higher its pressure, the lower the diffusion rate and the lower the electron temperature. The smaller the tube diameter, the faster the diffusion loss rate and the higher the electron temperature. However, noble gas pressure and type also determine elastic scattering loss by an ensemble of electrons having a given temperature. Equally, tube diameter is a determining factor in the imprisonment time for resonance radiation. Moreover, at a given current, current density increases with decreasing diameter, and with it, electron density increases. The higher the electron density, the greater is the probability of a collision of the second kind before radiation; as a result, efficiency decreases with increasing current density. Thus, ultimate performance of the device depends in a very complex way on a multiply connected set of variables.

The development of reasonably accurate discharge models incorporating rate constants for ~25 different collision processes as well as radiation transport was a major step forward in the understanding of the physics of this unique device. However, it did not result in significant improvement in efficiency of standard fluorescent lamps, which had already been optimized well by patient, empirical Edisonian techniques.

2. Lamp–Electrical-Circuit System

As in the case of HID lamps, fluorescent lamps require a higher applied potential for ignition than for steady-state operation. They too are operated on alternating current so that the necessary current limiting impedance can be reactive rather than resistive. Ignition potential is greatly reduced by heating the cathodes to electron-emitting temperatures to provide many free electrons to initiate avalanches in the breakdown process. The cathodes themselves are multiply-coiled helices of tungsten, the interstices of which are impregnated with alkaline-earth oxides for enhanced electron emission. They are heated by the passage of current through the tungsten wire of the helices.

There are two principal methods of accomplishing this during ignition. The simplest is the switch-start system, preferred in most of the world except in the United States. At starting, the two filaments are momentarily connected in series across the output terminals of the ballast so that the short circuit current of the ballast (limited by the internal impedance) flows through them, heating them to emission temperatures. After a brief interval the switch opens, applying the open-circuit potential of the ballast (together with any transient pulses of potential resulting from interruption of current in a circuit containing inductance) to the terminals of a lamp with heated cathodes, which then ignites. In the rapid-start ballast system, preferred in the United States, individual filament transformers wound on the ballast core continually supply 3.75 V to the cathodes, and the resulting current flow heats them to a sufficient temperature to emit electrons. Although this heating is not required during operation, since power received from the discharge end losses is adequate to keep the cathodes hot, the heater power has in the past been left connected during operation.

Recent concern with energy savings has resulted in introduction of lamps incorporating internal bimetal switches that disconnect one of the electrode terminals in operation, interrupting the flow of heater current. Ballast-lamp combinations in which the interruption is accomplished by the ballast have also been introduced.

As is the case in HID lamps, there are power losses in the ballast that must be added to lamp power to determine system power and efficacy. Commodity-type ballasts typically have ballast loss of 15% of lamp power. Again, recent concern with energy saving has resulted in the introduction of premium ballasts in which ballast loss is reduced by 50%. A great deal of engineering activity has recently been expended in development of electronic ballasts using semiconductor components and operating the lamps at hf, ~25 kHz; less lossy impedance can be easily provided at such frequencies, and the lamp itself is ~10–15% more efficient (primarily because of reduced electrode loss). Accordingly, up to 30% energy savings for a given illumination level over commodity lamps operated on commodity ballasts can be achieved with such a system. Unfortunately, electronic ballasts are much more expensive than copper and iron ones. In addition, premium lamp types and premium magnetic ballast types achieve equally impressive energy savings at lower cost. Consequently, market acceptance of electronic ballasts has been limited.

C. Performance Limitations Resulting from Materials Limitations

Fluorescent lamps are also extremely long-lived devices, with rated lives up to 20,000 hr at 3 burning hours per start on rapid-start circuits. There is not a fundamental relationship between efficiency and lamp life, as in incandescent lamps. Lamp life is primarily determined by the erosion of electron emission material from the cathodes. Since the process of ignition results in momentarily enhanced erosion, lamp life is adversely affected by increasing numbers of ignitions per thousand burning hours. A lamp with 20,000 hr life rating at 3 hr per start will last 40,000 hr if simply ignited once and never shut off. A lamp which is started once per minute of operation, will last 2000–5000 starts, only a few hundred hours. Lamps that are intended for service requiring many ignitions per hour are operated on ballasts supplying continuous filament heat, even when the lamp is not operating, to minimize damage to the electrodes at starting.

Electron emission materials that are more durable, but have equivalent electron emission as the alkaline earth oxides, would increase the flexibility of operation of fluorescent lamps in intermittent service. But no such materials have been found.

A major material limitation in fluorescent lamp operation is in the durability of fluorescent phosphors. These deteriorate in operation as a result of photolytic decomposition and color center formation, ion bombardment, and chemical reactions with mercury, glass, and impurity gases. The rate of deterioration of phosphors under these influences increases with the wall-loading (i.e., the flux density of UV rays and ions) and with wall temperature. The degree of this deterioration depends on the particular type of phosphor. Standard cool white fluorescent lamps, the most common type, lose ~15–20% of their output over the rated life of the lamp. Doubling the power input to achieve higher light output from a given size lamp, results in more than twice as much lumen depreciation, despite many years of empirical development to improve the phosphor durability.

Since a major obstacle to application of fluorescent lamps as substitutes for incandescent lamps is the size of the fluorescent lamp to achieve a given light output, it is plain that this material limitation has been a significant one. Recently developed rare earth–based phosphors have been found to be much more durable under high-loading conditions and to be hardly affected by operation at double and triple the customary wall-loading. Thus, most compact fluorescent lamps intended for incandescent replacement service have used these phosphors. The cost of these materials, however, is many times that of conventional phosphors, and for the present the cost appears to restrict these applications to commercial rather than residential service.

D. Practical Considerations

1. Fabrication Technology

Fabrication technology of fluorescent lamps has much in common with high-speed incandescent lamp manufacturing. It is highly automated with automatic transfer of parts in process from one station to another and little or no manual handling. There are two principal differences: first, the necessity to apply a uniform coating of powdered fluorescent materials to the inside wall of the tubular bulb, and, second, the constraints imposed by processing of electrode materials and the evacuation of very large internal lamp volumes through exhaust tubes of small diameter (limited by the capability of flame-seal rapidly and reliably).

The phosphor itself is manufactured off the site by blending raw materials of controlled particle size and firing at elevated temperatures to synthesize the proper compounds. The necessity for control of particle size in firing results from the fact that these materials are very susceptible to mechanical damage in the usual types of milling processes common to formulating paints. The application of the phosphor to the bulb is basically to make a paint with the phosphor as a pigment, flow-coating over the inside surface of the bulb to a thickness controlled by viscosity and drying. The remaining binder is removed by pyrolysis, passing the coated bulbs through furnaces at nearly the melting temperature of the glass, with axial air flow to react with the carbon and hydrogen constituents.

After coating and binder burnout, the stems with lead-in wires, electrodes, and exhaust tubes, are flame-sealed to the ends of the bulbs, and the assembly is transferred automatically to the exhaust machine. Because alkaline earth oxides used for the electron emission mix are extremely reactive to moisture, these materials are applied to the electrode coils as alkaline earth carbonates, and the carbonates are decomposed to oxides by heating as part of the evacuation process. Because of the large volume of gas to be exhausted and the small size of the exhaust tube, conventional vacuum evacuation is not fast enough. Therefore, the air and carbon dioxide are removed from the bulb by flushing inert gas in one exhaust tube and out the other; the entire process takes place in the viscous flow regimen instead of in the free-molecule flow. In this way, several liter-atmospheres of air can be removed and replaced by the noble gas filling in a fraction of a minute. Basing, ageing, testing, and packing are automatic, at production speeds as high as 50 to 100 lamps per minute.

In common with all other light sources, fluorescent lamps are sensitive to certain impurities, which must be effectively removed even at the extremely high processing speeds dictated by necessity for low-cost manufacture. Water vapor, the bête noir of all lamps, is troublesome in fluorescent lamps as well. It dissociates in the discharge, liberating hydrogen that attacks the phosphor and liberating oxygen that reacts with the electron emission coating, which "poisons" the cathode, and with mercury vapor, which forms solid deposits of dark mercury oxides on the surface of the phosphor. Residual hydrocarbons from the phosphor coating application result in carbon deposition on the phosphor as well as the liberation of hydrogen that will further damage the phosphor. If the bakeout temperature is increased too much, alkali from the glass will react with the phosphor, damaging it initially. Thus the baking process must be very critically controlled. Hydrogen and water vapor will also act to increase the ignition potential of the lamp in early life; this is usually a transient effect, however, because of cleanup during operation by the reactions noted. Such gas contamination may in extreme cases prevent the lamp from igniting the first time that it is placed in service, thus causing premature lamp failure. Testing for this effect, as well as cleanup of small amounts of impurities, is the purpose of the ageing step in the manufacturing process.

E. Commercially Available Products and Performance Characteristics

Fluorescent lamps are used primarily in indoor commercial lighting, where their high efficacy and low brightness make pleasantly diffused illumination of large areas possible at low total cost of light. Only a modest CRI, ~60, is required for this service, and most fluorescent lamps use phosphors with these characteristics. Retail merchandising places more stringent requirements on color rendition, and applications as incandescent substitutes requires not only a high CRI, but also color temperatures comparable with incandescent lamps, ~3000 K. These are obtained, together with improved resistance to degradation at high loadings, by recently developed phosphors based on rare earth compounds.

Table VII presents characteristics of fluorescent lamps intended for commercial and merchandising illumination, while Table VIII gives the characteristics of compact fluorescent lamps intended as substitutes for incandescent lamps. Figure 17 is a photograph illustrating various types of fluorescent lamps.

F. Research and Development

Research and Development in fluorescent lamp technology is focused on three areas: development of more efficient fluorescent lamps for commercial and merchandising service; development of improved phosphors; and development of compact fluorescent lamps for incandescent replacement, with the eventual hope that they can supplant incandescent lighting in many residential applications.

The first of these areas involves a range of activities from changes of diameter, fill-gas mixture and pressure, and phosphor improvements, to fundamental studies aimed at increasing the primary efficiency of generation of resonance ra-

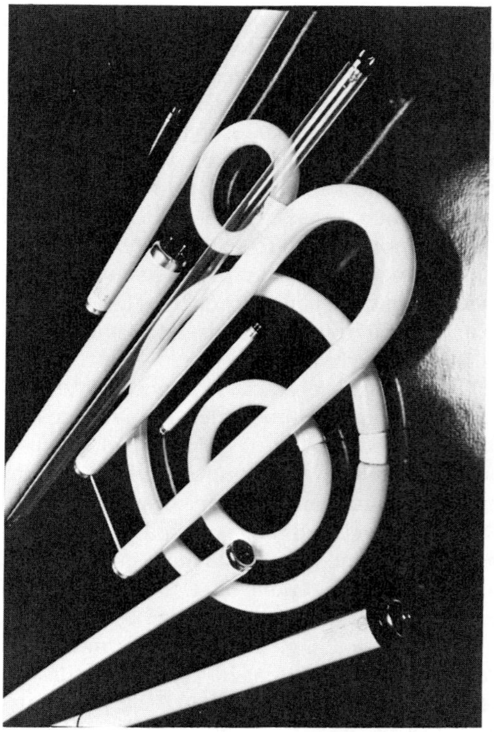

FIG. 17. Typical types of fluorescent lamps used in industrial and commercial applications.

TABLE VII. Representative Fluorescent Lamp Types for Industrial and Commercial Applications (United States Only)

Power (W)	Bulb[a]	Type	Operating current (V)	(A) (Nominal)	Rated life (hr)	Light output (lm)	Efficacy (lm/W)	Color temperature (K)	Color rendering index
Standard types									
40	48T12	CW/RS[b]	105	0.425	20,000	3150	79	4200	62
75	96T12	CW/IS	195	0.425	12,000	6300	84	4200	62
110	96T12	CW/HO	150	0.800	12,000	9200	84	4200	62
40	22.5T12U	CW/RS	105	0.425	18,000	3000	75	4200	62
Energy-saving retrofit types[c]									
34	48T12	Standard[d]/RS	85	0.425	20,000	2925	86	4150	48
34	48T12	Deluxe[d]/RS	85	0.425	20,000	2925	86	4100	67
60	96T12	/IS	155	0.425	12,000	5850	98	Available in standard & deluxe	
95	96T12	/HO	130	0.800	12,000	8800	104	Available in standard & deluxe	
34	22.5T12U	Standard[d]	85	0.425	18,000	2800	82	4150	48
Energy-saving new equipment types[e]									
32	48T8	Cool	135	0.265	20,000	2900	91	4100	75
32	48T8	Warm	135	0.265	20,000	2900	91	3100	75

[a] Nominal length in inches—tubular—diameter in $\frac{1}{8}$ in.
[b] Phosphor color/ballast type: CW = cool white, see Fig. 16 for spectral power distribution. RS = rapid start, IS = instant start, HO = high output.
[c] Retrofit types are physically interchangeable with standard types and operate at lower power on same ballasts by virture of lower design operating voltages.
[d] Generic nomenclature to represent two principal high-efficacy phosphor systems.
[e] Use premium high-efficacy phosphor system combining high efficacy and high CRI; require special ballast.

diation. It has been discovered, for example, that there is a slight isotopic effect in the imprisonment time. Increasing the concentration of the 196 isotope to ~4%, (normally present to only 0.15% in natural mercury, which has six stable isotopes), reduces imprisonment time by ~10%, which can be translated into 3 to 5% higher efficiency of generation of resonance radiation. Although this may not seem like a large reduction, it translates into a 1–2 W reduction per lamp for equal light output. Over the life of the lamp, this amounts to a reduction of 20 to 40 kW hr of energy, a substantial amount, worth approximately $2–4. If mercury enriched to the required amount can be obtained at a cost of $1–10 per gram, the value of energy savings can justify the increased cost of lamp manufacture. Investigation of the possibility of such an isotopic enrichment, either by photochemical or other techniques developed for uranium, is proceeding under the sponsorship of the U.S. Department of Energy.

Phosphor development is an activity that has been ongoing since the introduction of the fluorescent lamp more than 40 years ago. In the past, phosphor development has focused on extending the range of colors available and on evolutionary improvements in quantum efficiency and lumen maintenance of existing commercial phosphors. The primary focus at the present time is on discovering less expensive substitutes for the rare earth phosphors that nevertheless retain the high efficacy, good color, and extreme durability under high loading of those materials.

The real ferment in the field is in the development of a compact fluorescent for incandescent replacement. The chief obstacle is that radiation transport and electric characteristics of fluorescent lamps dictate that the discharge component is long and slender and requires a ballast. Incandescent lamps, however, are short and fat, and the fixtures that hold them allow little or no room for a ballast. To date, most of the approaches are the topological equivalent to spaghetti: a long slender tube is bent into a contorted continuous bundle, sometimes with a ballast tucked in among its segments. A cover is then placed over the entire bundle, which is then sold as a compact fluorescent lamp for $10 or more. A major problem with this approach is

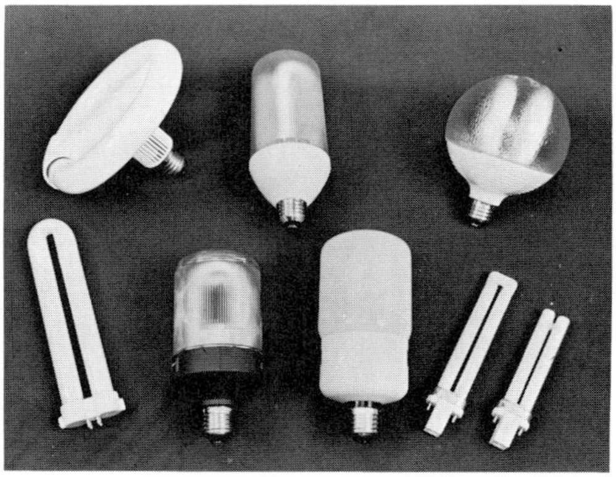

FIG. 18. Sample of fluorescent lamp types used as substitutes for incandescent lamps.

that bending glass tubing is slow, dictating production at no more than 10 to 20 pieces per minute instead of 50 to 100. Also, ballasts are costly and heavy and will outlive several lamps (so it is wasteful to attach them integrally and throw them away when the lamps fail). Furthermore, the ballasts will not fit in most incandescent lamp sockets and are too costly for all but the most dedicated devotees of life-cycle costing.

Consequently, although there are hundreds, or perhaps thousands of designs patented or disclosed around the world, only one or two have achieved even a modest measure of success in the marketplace (see Fig. 18). A prime example is the SL lamp (TM - N.V. Philips Gloeilampenfabrieken), which has achieved a secure market niche in Europe, principally in incandescent downlight applications in indoor commercial lighting. The long life and minimized labor cost to replace the SL lamp is more important than its high efficacy in the relative success of this lamp (See column 2 of Table VIII).

A great deal more success is expected in the future from new designs of single-ended low-wattage fluorescent lamps intended for new fixture applications in interior commercial lighting

TABLE VIII. Representative Compact Single-Ended Fluorescent Lamp Types for Incandescent Lamp Substitutes

	Retrofittable[a]		New equipment only	
Type	Circular with central ballast	Folded-U in light-diffusing cover	Linked parallel tubes (twin tube)	Double-D folded
Shape	Ring-shaped	Jar-shaped or globular	Two-finger-shaped	Square
Ballast	Integral	Integral	Separate	Separate
Lamp/ballast/system wattage[b]	22/5.3/27.3	13/5/18	13/5/18	16/5/21
Light output (lm)[b]	1080	900[e]	900	1050
Efficacy (system)[b]	40	50	50	50
Equivalent incandescent lamp	75 W/16 lm/W	60 W/14.5 lm/W	60 W/14.5 lm/W	75 W/16 lm/W
Color temperature/color rendering index	3000/67	2700/80	2700/80	2800/80
Life (hr)	7500–12,000	5000[e]	10,000	5000
Size (mm)	203	72 diameter × 175 long	26 wide × 188 long	134 square
Weight (g)	450[c]	520[c]	45 (lamp only)	60 (lamp only)
Principal manufacturers	All major U.S.	Philips, Toshiba, Hitachi, Matsushita, Mitsubishi[d]	All major U.S. and European	Thorn (England)

[a] Retrofittable types will fit in some incandescent lamp sockets as direct replacements. Retail prices of $7–20 make economics uncertain for residential user. Long life minimizes lamp replacement costs in commercial applications, making economics more attractive.

[b] Most common or popular type.

[c] Integral ballast contributes 80% of the weight.

[d] Philips, Toshiba, and Matsushita manufacture this type with the folded-U tubular lamp hermetically sealed with nonhermetic cover. Hitachi and Mitsubishi manufacture it with a hermetically sealed evacuated outer cover, and nonhermetically sealed internal folded-U lamp.

[e] An electronically ballasted version of this type of product is available, with 18 W power consumption, 1100 lumens, approximately equivalent to 75 W incandescent, with rated life 10,000 hr.

that would otherwise be served by long-life incandescent lamps: hotel corridor applications, with 8000 burning hours per year, for example. A prime example of this type of lamp is the twin-tube U-shaped lamp noted in column 3 of Table VIII. Long life, high efficiency, and relatively low cost for the lamp combine to make the product highly competitive in the marketplace.

Meanwhile, the search for the ultimate replacement for the residential incandescent lamp continues.

VIII. Summary

A. Cost Comparison

Table IX compares several measures of cost for the different families of lamps described in this article. Included are costs of the lamps and the electric power to operate them; ballast, fixture, installation, and maintenance costs are not included. Costs indicated are based on 1985 prices for lamps and electricity. Changes since then have been about equal to inflation, and have not altered relative rankings.

Based on lamp cost alone per thousand lumens of light output, incandescent lamps are the least expensive. Allowing for the fact that discharge lamps outlast incandescent manyfold, a somewhat more realistic measure of lamp cost is the cost per million lumen-hours, for which the fluorescent lamp is least expensive. Operation of lamps and delivery of light requires consumption of electrical power, at a cost per million lumen-hours indicated in column 4 of Table IX, assuming $0.06/kW hr electricity cost. The least expensive light source in this regard is the HPS lamp, by virtue of its very high efficacy. Life cycle cost per million lumen-hours is the sum of lamp and power cost, and is given in column 5 of Table IX. Note that cost of electric power is 70–95% of the total so that HPS lamps are again the least expensive, even though their lamp cost per million lumen hours 33% more than that of the fluorescent.

For this reason, HPS lamps have become the light source of choice for nearly all kinds of outdoor lighting, where their relatively poor CRI and undesirably low color temperature are not fatal flaws. For indoor commercial applications, fluorescent and M-H are preferred, despite their higher cost of light, because of more favorable color temperature and CRI in comparison to HPS. Despite the preference for the other sources, however, there are increasing numbers of indoor HPS applications (driven by cost considerations); for many industrial applications, color is relatively unimportant, and for indoor commercial applications, careful choice of decor emphasizing reds, oranges, yellows, and browns minimizes unfavorable color distortions. Mercury lamps appear to be marked for obsolescence; in fact, in the United States, sales of HPS lamps have exceeded sales of mercury lamps in

TABLE IX. Comparison of Lamp Costs, Operating Costs, and Total Life-Cycle Costs for Major Lamp Families[a]

Lamp family	Lamp cost $/thousand lm	Lamp cost $/million lm hr	Electrical power cost $/million lm hr	Life-cycle cost $/million lm hr (%)[b]	
Incandescent	0.69[c]	0.92	3.81	4.73	(80.5%)
Tungsten–halogen	2.34	1.17	2.70	3.87	(69.8%)
Fluorescent	1.25	0.052	0.84	0.89	(94.2%)
Mercury	1.67	0.069	1.19	1.26	(94.5%)
Metal halide	2.32	0.116	0.937	1.05	(89.0%)
High-pressure sodium	1.66	0.069	0.53	0.60	(88.5%)

[a] 1985 lamp prices and electrical costs ($.06/kWh); relative rankings not changed appreciably since then. Price does not include ballast, fixture, or installation cost.
[b] Figures in parentheses are percentage of life-cycle costs represented by electric energy.
[c] Least expensive types are set in boxes.

every year since 1983, and sales of HPS lamps are growing faster.

B. New Market Developments (1991)

Despite the advantages of more efficient light sources with respect to "total cost of light," illustrated in Table IX, the penetration of the market by energy-efficient lamp products since 1987 has been slower than anticipated. In particular, the replacement of incandescent lamps by compact fluorescent in residential service has been disappointing.

The principal obstacle to this substitution is the high first cost of compact fluorescent lamps compared with incandescent bulbs. The residential purchaser has strongly resisted paying a higher first cost, even with the anticipation of recouping the higher price in reduced electric bills later.

In the last year or two, however, a new factor has entered into the decision-making process. This is the growing shortage of electric generating capacity in some areas of the country, especially the Northeast. In New England, the electric power distribution system has been overloaded on several occasions of high peak consumption, requiring a 5% reduction in line voltage.

In this situation of small or even negative reserve capacity, utilities have recognized that substitution of light sources of reduced power consumption for equal light output offers a means of reducing peak power demand. For example, substituting an 18 W electronically ballasted compact fluorescent lamp for a 75 W incandescent reduces peak demand by 57 W, thereby adding 57 W to reserve capacity to meet other peak load requirements. (See note *e*, Table VIII.)

The enhancement of reserve capacity has offered a powerful economic incentive for this substitution. The utility buys such lamps wholesale and leases them to residential customers at \$0.20/month. The residential customer is freed from having to pay the high first cost of the energy-efficient product but enjoys the savings on the electric bill. For a lamp used 100 hr per month, the electric power savings is 5.7 kW hr, saving about \$0.57 per month. The net savings to the residential consumer is the power cost savings less the lease cost, or \$0.37 per month per lamp. This is available without the necessity of any initial investment.

The \$0.20 monthly lease payment at 10% interest would amortize the approximate \$12 wholesale cost in 84 months, 7 yr. If the lamp is used 100 hr per month, this is 8400 hr, less than the 10,000 hr rated life of the lamp, at which replacement would be needed. Thus, the utility is able to amortize its investment. The real advantage to the utility is found in the cost of the effective increase in reserve capacity: \$12 for 57 W increase, \$210 per kW. The cost of adding generating capacity is more than \$1000 per kW. Consequently, from the utility point of view, improving reserve capacity by leasing energy-efficient lamps is much more economical. Equally important, this advantage is recognized by Public Utility Commissions, which allow incorporating the investment into calculations for ratemaking.

A further advantage is the time required to achieve a capacity increase. The time scale for building and commissioning new power plants is now a decade or more, when they can be built at all. Substituting an energy-saving equivalent for an existing lamp produces immediate reduction in peak demand.

Although the economic incentives to utility and customer of this substitution have been illustrated by a particular example, the same incentives exist for other substitutions which reduce power consumption while preserving illumination. Utility rebate programs have provided major commercial and industrial users with incentives to replace standard fluorescent systems by energy-saving equivalents such as are listed in Table VII, for example.

It may seem a paradox that it is to the economic advantage of a utility to subsidize the capital cost of a light source substitution that will reduce the sales of electric power. The arithmetic of low-cost addition to reserve capacity in a capacity-short utility is the driving force.

Bibliography

Elenbaas, W. (1972). "Light Sources." Crane Russak and Co., New York.

Kaufman, J. E., and Haynes, H. (Eds.) (1981). "Ies Lighting Handbook," Illuminating Engineering Society, New York.

Waymouth, J. F. (1971). "Electric Discharge Lamps," (1971). MIT Press, Cambridge, Massachusetts.

Waymouth, J. F., and Levin, R. E. eds. (1980). "Designer's Handbook, Light Source Applications," GTE Marketing Services, West Seneca, New York.

LINEAR ALGEBRA

Stanley I. Grossman *University of Montana*

GLOSSARY

Augmented matrix: Square matrix with an additional column adjoined on the right.

Basis: Set of vectors in a vector space that is linearly independent and that spans the vector space.

Determinant: Number assigned to a square matrix.

Dimension of a vector space: Number of vectors in a basis.

Eigenvalue and eigenvector: If T is a linear transformation from a vector space V to itself, or if A is a square matrix, then λ is an eigenvalue of T or A if there is a nonzero vector $\mathbf{v} \in V$ such that $T\mathbf{v} = \lambda\mathbf{v}$ (or $A\mathbf{v} = \lambda\mathbf{v}$); $\mathbf{v}$ is called an eigenvector of T or A corresponding to λ.

Identity matrix: Square matrix with 1's on the main diagonal and 0's everywhere else.

Inverse of a square matrix: Inverse of square matrix A, denoted A^{-1}, is a matrix having the property that $AA^{-1} = A^{-1}A = I$, the identity matrix.

Isomorphism: Linear transformation that is one to one and onto.

Linearly dependent vectors: A set of vectors is linearly dependent if it is not linearly independent.

Linearly independent vectors: Vectors $\mathbf{v}_1, \mathbf{v}_2, \ldots, \mathbf{v}_n$ are linearly independent if $c_1\mathbf{v}_1 + c_2\mathbf{v}_2 + \cdots + c_n\mathbf{v}_n = \mathbf{0}$ occurs only when $c_1 = c_2 = \cdots = c_n = 0$.

Linear transformation: Function T that takes one vector space V to another vector space W and that satisfies $T(\alpha\mathbf{x} + \beta\mathbf{y}) = \alpha T\mathbf{x} + \beta T\mathbf{y}$ for all vectors $\mathbf{x}$ and $\mathbf{y}$ in V and all scalars α and β.

$m \times n$ Matrix: Rectangular array of numbers arranged in m rows and n columns.

n Vector: Ordered set of n numbers.

Row reduction: Process of solving a system of linear equations by performing simplifying operations on an augmented matrix.

Square matrix: Matrix in which $m = n$.

Subspace: Subset of a vector space that is itself a vector space.

Vector space: Set of objects, called vectors, together with two operations called addition and scalar multiplication that satisfy ten axioms (given on p. 743).

If you look up the word "linear" in a dictionary, you will find something like the following: **lin-e-ar** /lin′ēər/ *adj* **1**: of, consisting of, or using lines. In mathematics, the word linear means a good deal more than that. Nevertheless, much of the theory of elementary linear algebra is, in fact, a generalization of properties of straight lines.

A modern course in linear algebra is usually divided into two related but somewhat distinct parts: matrix theory and the theory of vector spaces and linear transformations. A matrix is a rectangular array of numbers. A vector space is a set of objects, called vectors, that have a number of specified properties. A linear transformation is a function L which takes a vector from one vector space V to a vector in another (possibly the same) vector space W and satisfies the conditions

$$L(\mathbf{x} + \mathbf{y}) = L(\mathbf{x}) + L(\mathbf{y})$$
$$L(\alpha\mathbf{x}) = \alpha L(\mathbf{x})$$

for every scalar (usually real number).

The equation of a straight line through the origin is

$$y = mx$$

where m is its slope. We shall show that the set $\mathbb{R}$ of real numbers is a vector space. Let the function L be defined by

$$L(x) = mx$$

Then,

$$L(x + y) = m(x + y) = mx + my$$
$$= L(x) + L(y)$$
$$L(\alpha x) = m \cdot \alpha x = \alpha \cdot mx = \alpha L(x)$$

so that L is a linear transformation with $V = W = R$. This shows that the set of straight lines through the origin is a set of graphs of linear transformations. In fact, the definition of a linear transformation was motivated by the desire to extend, to more general settings, properties of these lines. [*See* ALGEBRAIC EQUATIONS.]

In this article we shall discuss many of the principal ideas in the theory of matrices, vector spaces, and linear transformations. In so doing, we shall state many theorems. Because of space limitations, no proofs are given; however, mathematical proof is an intrinsic part of the study of linear algebra, and the interested reader is encouraged to consult an appropriate linear algebra text to see these essential proofs.

I. Vectors and Matrices

A. VECTORS

The study of vectors began essentially with the work of the great Irish mathematician, Sir William Rowan Hamilton (1805–1865). Hamilton was a genius who, by the age of 12 years, had mastered not only the languages of continental Europe but also Greek, Latin, Sanskrit, Hebrew, Chinese, Persian, Arabic, Malay, Hindi, Bengali, and several others as well. In his twenties, Hamilton turned to science, and his treatises on mechanics and optics provided the basis for much of modern physics.

In his thirties, this remarkable man began his research in mathematics. His desire to find a way to represent certain objects in a plane and in space led to the development of what we now call vectors. Throughout Hamilton's life, and for the remainder of the nineteenth century, there was considerable debate over the usefulness of vectors. At the end of the century, the great British physicist Lord Kelvin wrote that vectors, "although beautifully ingenious, have been an unmixed evil to those who have touched them in any way [and] ... have never been of the slightest use to any creature."

But Kelvin was wrong. Today nearly all branches of classical and modern physics are represented by means of the language of vectors. Vectors are also used with increasing frequency in the social and biological sciences.

We define an n-component row vector to be an ordered set of n numbers written as

$$(x_1, x_2, \ldots, x_n) \tag{1}$$

An n-component column vector is an ordered set of n numbers written as

$$\begin{pmatrix} x_1 \\ x_2 \\ \vdots \\ x_n \end{pmatrix} \tag{2}$$

In (1) or (2), x_1 is called the first component of the vector; x_2 is the second component; and so on. In general, x_k is called the kth component of the vector.

For simplicity, we shall often refer to an n-component row vector as a row vector or an n-vector. Similarly, we shall use the term column vector (or n vector) to denote an n-component column vector. Any vector whose entries are all zero is called a zero vector.

Notation. Vectors are usually denoted by lower case boldface letters.

We use the symbol $\mathbb{R}^n$ to denote the set of all n vectors

$$\begin{pmatrix} a_1 \\ a_2 \\ \vdots \\ a_n \end{pmatrix}$$

where each a_i is a real number. Similarly, we use the symbol $\mathbb{C}^n$ to denote the set of all n vectors

$$\begin{pmatrix} c_1 \\ c_2 \\ \vdots \\ c_n \end{pmatrix}$$

where each c_i is a complex number. We shall discuss more general sets of vectors when we define vector spaces in Section II.

1. Equality of Vectors

Two column (or row) vectors **a** and **b** are equal if and only if they have the same number of components and their corresponding components are equal. In symbols, the vectors

$$\mathbf{a} = \begin{pmatrix} a_1 \\ a_2 \\ \vdots \\ a_n \end{pmatrix}, \qquad \mathbf{b} = \begin{pmatrix} b_1 \\ b_2 \\ \vdots \\ b_n \end{pmatrix}$$

are equal if and only if $a_1 = b_1$, $a_2 = b_2$, ..., $a_n = b_n$.

2. Addition of Vectors

Let

$$\mathbf{a} = \begin{pmatrix} a_1 \\ a_2 \\ \vdots \\ a_n \end{pmatrix}, \qquad \mathbf{b} = \begin{pmatrix} b_1 \\ b_2 \\ \vdots \\ b_n \end{pmatrix}$$

be n vectors. Then, the sum of **a** and **b** is defined by

$$\mathbf{a} + \mathbf{b} = \begin{pmatrix} a_1 + b_1 \\ a_2 + b_2 \\ \vdots \\ a_n + b_n \end{pmatrix}$$

When dealing with vectors, we shall refer to numbers as scalars (which may be real or complex, depending on whether the vectors in question are real or complex).

3. Scalar Multiplication of Vectors

Let

$$\mathbf{a} = \begin{pmatrix} a_1 \\ a_2 \\ \vdots \\ a_n \end{pmatrix}$$

be a vector and α a scalar. Then, the product $\alpha\mathbf{a}$ is given by

$$\alpha\mathbf{a} = \begin{pmatrix} \alpha a_1 \\ \alpha a_2 \\ \vdots \\ \alpha a_n \end{pmatrix}$$

That is, to multiply a vector by a scalar, we simply multiply each component of the vector by the scalar.

There are several ways in which two vectors can be multiplied together. One of these is given below.

4. Scalar Product

Let

$$\mathbf{a} = \begin{pmatrix} a_1 \\ a_2 \\ \vdots \\ a_n \end{pmatrix}, \qquad \mathbf{b} = \begin{pmatrix} b_1 \\ b_1 \\ \vdots \\ b_n \end{pmatrix}$$

be two n vectors. Then, the scalar product of **a** and **b**, denoted $\mathbf{a} \cdot \mathbf{b}$, is given by

$$\mathbf{a} \cdot \mathbf{b} = a_1b_1 + a_2b_2 + \cdots + a_nb_n$$

Because of the notation used, the scalar product of two vectors is often called the dot product of the vectors. Note that the scalar product of two n vectors is a scalar (that is, a number).

EXAMPLE 1. $(6, 3, 2, -5) \cdot (4, -1, 0, 2) = (6) \cdot (4) + (3)(-1) + (2)(0) + (-5)(2) = 11$.

B. Matrices

An $m \times n$ matrix A is a rectangular array of mn numbers arranged in m rows and n columns:

$$A = \begin{pmatrix} a_{11} & a_{12} & \cdots & a_{1j} & \cdots & a_{1n} \\ a_{21} & a_{22} & \cdots & a_{2j} & \cdots & a_{2n} \\ \vdots & \vdots & & \vdots & & \vdots \\ a_{m1} & a_{m2} & \cdots & a_{mj} & \cdots & a_{mn} \end{pmatrix}$$

The ijth component of A, denoted a_{ij}, is the number appearing in the ith row and jth column of A. We shall sometimes write the matrix A as $A = (a_{ij})$. Usually, matrices are denoted by capital letters.

If A is an $m \times n$ matrix, with $m = n$, then A is called a square matrix. An $m \times n$ matrix with all components equal to zero is called the $m \times n$ zero matrix.

An $m \times n$ matrix is said to have the size $m \times n$. Two matrices $A = (a_{ij})$ and $B = (b_{ij})$ are equal if (a) they have the same size and (b) corresponding components are equal.

Each vector in $\mathbb{R}^n$ or $\mathbb{C}^n$ is a special kind of matrix. Thus, for example, the n-component row vector $(a_1, a_2, ..., a_n)$ is a $1 \times n$ matrix, whereas the n-component column vector

$$\begin{pmatrix} a_1 \\ a_2 \\ \vdots \\ a_n \end{pmatrix}$$

is an $n \times 1$ matrix.

Historical note. The term "matrix" was first used in 1850 by the British mathematician James Joseph Sylvester (1814–1897) to distinguish matrices from determinants (which we shall discuss in Section I.E). In fact, the term matrix was intended to mean "mother of determinants."

The algebra of matrices, that is, the rules by which matrices can be added and multiplied, was developed by the English mathematician Arthur Cayley (1821–1895) in 1857. Matrices arose with Cayley in connection with linear transformations of the type

$$x' = ax + by, \qquad y' = cx + dy$$

where a, b, c, d are real numbers, and which may be thought of as mapping the point (x, y) into the point (x', y'). Clearly, the transformation above is completely determined by the four coefficients a, b, c, d, and so the transformation can be symbolized by the square array

$$\begin{pmatrix} a & b \\ c & d \end{pmatrix}$$

which we have called a (square) matrix. We shall discuss linear transformations in Section III.

1. Addition of Matrices

Let $A = (a_{ij})$ and $B = (b_{ij})$ be two $m \times n$ matrices. Then, the sum of A and B is the $m \times n$ matrix $A + B$ given by

$$A + B = (a_{ij} + b_{ij})$$

$$= \begin{pmatrix} a_{11} + b_{11} & a_{12} + b_{12} & \cdots & a_{1n} + b_{1n} \\ a_{21} + b_{21} & a_{22} + b_{22} & \cdots & a_{2n} + b_{2n} \\ \vdots & \vdots & & \vdots \\ a_{m1} + b_{m1} & a_{m2} + b_{m2} & \cdots & a_{mn} + b_{mn} \end{pmatrix}$$

That is, $A + B$ is the $m \times n$ matrix obtained by adding the corresponding components of A and B.

2. Multiplication of a Matrix by a Scalar

If $A = (a_{ij})$ is an $m \times n$ matrix and if α is a scalar, then the $m \times n$ matrix αA is given by

$$\alpha A = (\alpha a_{ij}) = \begin{pmatrix} \alpha a_{11} & \alpha a_{12} & \cdots & \alpha a_{1n} \\ \alpha a_{21} & \alpha a_{22} & \cdots & \alpha a_{2n} \\ \vdots & \vdots & & \vdots \\ \alpha a_{m1} & \alpha a_{m2} & \cdots & \alpha a_{mn} \end{pmatrix}$$

In other words, $\alpha A = (\alpha a_{ij})$ is the matrix obtained by multiplying each component of A by α.

The definition of the product of two matrices is based on the definition of the scalar product of two vectors.

3. Product of Two Matrices

Let $A = (a_{ij})$ be an $m \times n$ matrix whose ith row is denoted $\mathbf{a}_i$. Let $B = (b_{ij})$ be an $n \times p$ matrix whose jth column is denoted $\mathbf{b}_j$. Then, the product of A and B is an $m \times p$ matrix $C = (c_{ij})$, where

$$c_{ij} = \mathbf{a}_i \cdot \mathbf{b}_j \tag{3}$$

That is, the ijth element of AB is the scalar product of the ith row of A ($\mathbf{a}_i$) and the jth column of B ($\mathbf{b}_j$). If we write this out, we obtain

$$c_{ij} = a_{i1}b_{1j} + a_{i2}b_{2j} + \cdots + a_{in}b_{nj}$$

Note. Two matrices can be multiplied together only if the number of columns of the first is equal to the number of rows of the second. Otherwise the vectors $\mathbf{a}_i$ and $\mathbf{b}_j$ will have different numbers of components, and the scalar product in Eq. (3) will not be defined.

EXAMPLE 2

$$\begin{pmatrix} 2 & 0 & -3 \\ 4 & 1 & 5 \end{pmatrix} \begin{pmatrix} 7 & -1 \\ 2 & 5 \\ -3 & 1 \end{pmatrix}$$

$$= \begin{pmatrix} (2)(7) + (0)(2) + (-3)(-3) & (2)(-1) + (0)(5) + (-3)(1) \\ (4)(7) + (1)(2) + (5)(-3) & (4)(-1) + (1)(5) + (5)(1) \end{pmatrix}$$

$$= \begin{pmatrix} 23 & -5 \\ 15 & 6 \end{pmatrix}$$

Note. Matrix products do not in general commute; that is, $AB \neq BA$ in general. It sometimes happens that $AB = BA$, but this is the exception not the rule. In fact, it may occur that AB is defined, whereas BA is not. Thus, we must be careful of order when multiplying two matrices together.

C. Matrices and Systems of Linear Equations

Consider the following system of two linear equations in two unknowns:

$$\begin{aligned} a_{11}x_1 + a_{12}x_2 &= b_1 \\ a_{21}x_1 + a_{22}x_2 &= b_2 \end{aligned} \tag{4}$$

Each equation in (4) is the equation of a straight line. Thus, the system has no solution if the lines are parallel and not coincident; one solution if the lines intersect at one point; and an infinite number of solutions if the lines are coincident. This is illustrated in Fig. 1. Now consider the following systems of m equations in n unknowns:

$$\begin{aligned} a_{11}x_1 + a_{12}x_2 + \cdots + a_{1n}x_n &= b_1 \\ a_{21}x_1 + a_{22}x_2 + \cdots + a_{2n}x_n &= b_2 \\ \vdots \qquad \vdots \qquad\qquad \vdots \quad & \\ a_{m1}x_1 + a_{m2}x_2 + \cdots + a_{mn}x_n &= b_m \end{aligned} \tag{5}$$

We define the matrix

$$A = \begin{pmatrix} a_{11} & a_{12} & \cdots & a_{1n} \\ a_{21} & a_{22} & \cdots & a_{2n} \\ \vdots & \vdots & & \vdots \\ a_{m1} & a_{m2} & \cdots & a_{mn} \end{pmatrix}$$

the vector

$$\mathbf{x} = \begin{pmatrix} x_1 \\ x_2 \\ \vdots \\ x_n \end{pmatrix}$$

and the vector

$$\mathbf{b} = \begin{pmatrix} b_1 \\ b_2 \\ \vdots \\ b_m \end{pmatrix}$$

Since A is an $m \times n$ matrix and $\mathbf{x}$ is an $n \times 1$ matrix, the matrix product $A\mathbf{x}$ is defined as an $m \times 1$ matrix. It can be shown that the system (6) has no solution, a unique solution, or an infinite number of solutions.

In order to solve the system (5), we write the system as an *augmented matrix:*

$$\left(\begin{array}{cccc|c} a_{11} & a_{12} & \cdots & a_{1n} & b_1 \\ a_{21} & a_{22} & \cdots & a_{2n} & b_2 \\ \vdots & \vdots & & \vdots & \vdots \\ a_{mn} & a_{m2} & \cdots & a_{mn} & b_m \end{array}\right) \tag{6}$$

In (6), the first row is read $a_{11}x_1 + a_{12}x_2 + \cdots + a_{1n}x_n = b_1$, and so on. We then *row reduce* the system by performing *elementary row operations* on the augmented matrix.

1. Elementary Row Operations

1. Multiply (or divide) one row by a nonzero number.
2. Add a multiple of one row to another row.
3. Interchange two rows.

None of these operations changes the set of solutions to the system.

The process of applying elementary row operations to simplify an augmented matrix is called *row reduction:*

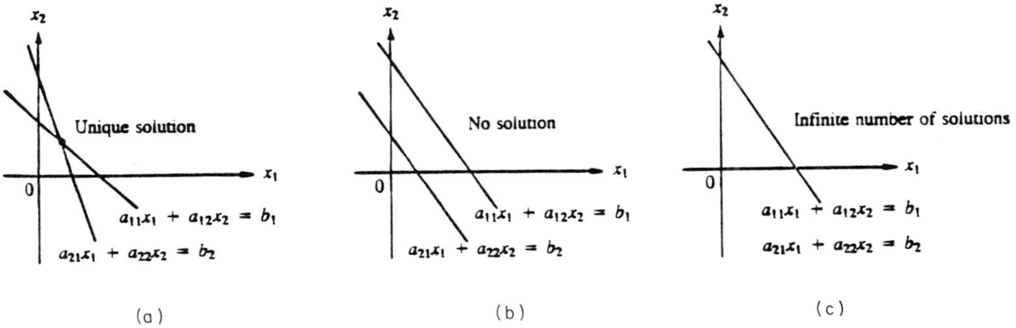

FIG. 1. (a) Lines not parallel; one point of intersection. (b) Lines parallel; no points of intersection. (c) Lines coincide; infinite number of points of intersection.

1. $M_i(c)$ represents "multiply the ith row of a matrix by the number c."
2. $A_{i,j}(c)$ represents "multiply the ith row by c, and add it to the jth row."
3. $P_{i,j}$ represents "interchange (permute) rows i and j."
4. $A \leftrightarrow B$ indicates that the augmented matrices A and B are equivalent; that is, the systems they represent have the same solution.

EXAMPLE 3. We solve the system

$$\begin{aligned} 2x_1 + 4x_2 + 6x_3 &= 18 \\ 4x_1 + 5x_2 + 6x_3 &= 24 \\ 3x_1 + x_2 - 2x_3 &= 4 \end{aligned} \tag{7}$$

by first writing the system using an augmented matrix, and then row reducing:

$$\left(\begin{array}{ccc|c} 2 & 4 & 6 & 18 \\ 4 & 5 & 6 & 24 \\ 3 & 1 & -2 & 4 \end{array}\right) \xrightarrow{M_1(\frac{1}{2})} \left(\begin{array}{ccc|c} 1 & 2 & 3 & 9 \\ 4 & 5 & 6 & 24 \\ 3 & 1 & -2 & 4 \end{array}\right)$$

$$\xrightarrow[A_{1,3}(-3)]{A_{1,2}(-4)} \left(\begin{array}{ccc|c} 1 & 2 & 3 & 9 \\ 0 & -3 & -6 & -12 \\ 0 & -5 & -11 & -23 \end{array}\right)$$

$$\xrightarrow{M_2(-\frac{1}{3})} \left(\begin{array}{ccc|c} 1 & 2 & 3 & 9 \\ 0 & 1 & 2 & 4 \\ 0 & -5 & -11 & -23 \end{array}\right)$$

$$\xrightarrow[A_{2,3}(5)]{A_{2,1}(-2)} \left(\begin{array}{ccc|c} 1 & 0 & -1 & 1 \\ 0 & 1 & 2 & 4 \\ 0 & 0 & -1 & -3 \end{array}\right)$$

$$\xrightarrow{M_3(-1)} \left(\begin{array}{ccc|c} 1 & 0 & -1 & 1 \\ 0 & 1 & 2 & 4 \\ 0 & 0 & 1 & 3 \end{array}\right)$$

$$\xrightarrow[A_{3,2}(-2)]{A_{3,1}(1)} \left(\begin{array}{ccc|c} 1 & 0 & 0 & 4 \\ 0 & 1 & 0 & -2 \\ 0 & 0 & 1 & 3 \end{array}\right)$$

The last augmented matrix reads $x_1 = 4$, $x_2 = -2$, $x_3 = 3$. This, evidently, is the unique solution to the system (7).

EXAMPLE 4. Let us solve the system

$$\begin{aligned} 2x_1 + 4x_2 + 6x_3 &= 18 \\ 4x_1 + 5x_2 + 6x_3 &= 24 \\ 2x_1 + 7x_2 + 12x_3 &= 30 \end{aligned}$$

We row reduce:

$$\left(\begin{array}{ccc|c} 2 & 4 & 6 & 18 \\ 4 & 5 & 6 & 24 \\ 2 & 7 & 12 & 30 \end{array}\right) \xrightarrow{M_1(\frac{1}{2})} \left(\begin{array}{ccc|c} 1 & 2 & 3 & 9 \\ 4 & 5 & 6 & 24 \\ 2 & 7 & 12 & 30 \end{array}\right)$$

$$\xrightarrow[A_{1,3}(-2)]{A_{1,2}(-4)} \left(\begin{array}{ccc|c} 1 & 2 & 3 & 9 \\ 0 & -3 & -6 & -12 \\ 0 & 3 & 6 & 12 \end{array}\right)$$

$$\xrightarrow{M_2(-\frac{1}{3})} \left(\begin{array}{ccc|c} 1 & 2 & 3 & 9 \\ 0 & 1 & 2 & 4 \\ 0 & 3 & 6 & 12 \end{array}\right)$$

$$\xrightarrow[A_{2,3}(-3)]{A_{2,1}(-2)} \left(\begin{array}{ccc|c} 1 & 0 & -1 & 1 \\ 0 & 1 & 2 & 4 \\ 0 & 0 & 0 & 0 \end{array}\right)$$

This is equivalent to the system of equations

$$\begin{aligned} x_1 \qquad - x_3 &= 1 \\ x_2 + 2x_3 &= 4 \end{aligned}$$

This is as far as we can go. There are now only two equations in the three unknowns x_1, x_2, x_3, and there are an infinite number of solutions. To see this, let x_3 be chosen. Then, $x_2 = 4 - 2x_3$, and $x_1 = 1 + x_3$. This will be a solution for any number x_3. We write these solutions in the form $(1 + x_3, 4 - 2x_3, x_3)$. For example, if $x_3 = 0$, we obtain the solution (1, 4, 0). For $x_3 = 10$, we obtain the solution (11, −16, 10).

EXAMPLE 5. Let us solve the system

$$\begin{aligned} 2x_1 + 4x_2 + 6x_3 &= 18 \\ 4x_1 + 5x_2 + 6x_3 &= 24 \\ 2x_1 + 7x_2 + 12x_3 &= 40 \end{aligned} \tag{8}$$

Proceeding as before, we obtain

$$\left(\begin{array}{ccc|c} 2 & 4 & 6 & 18 \\ 4 & 5 & 6 & 24 \\ 2 & 7 & 12 & 40 \end{array}\right) \xrightarrow{M_1(\frac{1}{2})} \left(\begin{array}{ccc|c} 1 & 2 & 3 & 9 \\ 4 & 5 & 6 & 24 \\ 2 & 7 & 12 & 40 \end{array}\right)$$

$$\xrightarrow[A_{1,3}(-2)]{A_{1,2}(-4)} \left(\begin{array}{ccc|c} 1 & 2 & 3 & 9 \\ 0 & -3 & -6 & -12 \\ 0 & 3 & 6 & 22 \end{array}\right)$$

$$\xrightarrow{M_2(-\frac{1}{3})} \left(\begin{array}{ccc|c} 1 & 2 & 3 & 9 \\ 0 & 1 & 2 & 4 \\ 0 & 3 & 6 & 22 \end{array}\right)$$

$$\xrightarrow[A_{2,3}(-3)]{A_{2,1}(-2)} \left(\begin{array}{ccc|c} 1 & 0 & -1 & 1 \\ 0 & 1 & 2 & 4 \\ 0 & 0 & 0 & 10 \end{array}\right)$$

$$\xrightarrow{M_3(-\frac{1}{10})} \left(\begin{array}{ccc|c} 1 & 0 & -1 & 1 \\ 0 & 1 & 2 & 4 \\ 0 & 0 & 0 & 1 \end{array}\right)$$

The last equation now reads $0x_1 + 0x_2 + 0x_3 = 1$, which is impossible, since $0 \neq 1$. Thus, system (5) has no solution.

In the last three examples, the row-reduction process we employed is called Gauss–Jordan elimination.

D. Homogeneous Systems of Equations

The general $m \times n$ system of linear equations (6) is called homogeneous if all the constants b_1, b_2, ..., b_m are zero. That is, the general homogeneous system is given by

$$\begin{aligned} a_{11}x_1 + a_{12}x_2 + \cdots + a_{1n}x_n &= 0 \\ a_{21}x_1 + a_{22}x_2 + \cdots + a_{2n}x_n &= 0 \\ \vdots \qquad \vdots \qquad\quad \vdots \quad &\ \ \vdots \\ a_{m1}x_1 + a_{m2}x_2 + \cdots + a_{mn}x_n &= 0 \end{aligned} \qquad (9)$$

Homogeneous systems arise in a variety of ways. We can use them to determine whether a set of vectors is linearly independent or dependent (Section I.G). They also arise in the computation of the eigenvalues and eigenvectors of a matrix (Section IV.A).

For the general linear system, there are three possibilities: no solution, one solution, or an infinite number of solutions. For the general homogeneous system, the situation is simpler. Since $x_1 = x_2 = \cdots = x_n = 0$ is always a solution (called the trivial solution or zero solution), there are only two possibilities: Either the zero solution is the only solution, or there are an infinite number of solutions in addition to the zero solution. (Solutions other then the zero solution are called nontrivial solutions.)

E. Determinants

Consider the following system of two equations in two unknowns:

$$\begin{aligned} a_{11}x_1 + a_{12}x_2 &= b_1 \\ a_{21}x_1 + a_{22}x_2 &= b_2 \end{aligned} \qquad (10)$$

Multiplying the first equation in (11) by $-a_{21}$ and the second by a_{11} and then adding, we obtain

$$(a_{11}a_{22} - a_{12}a_{21})x_2 = a_{11}b_2 - a_{21}b_1$$

If $a_{11}a_{22} - a_{12}a_{21} \neq 0$, then we can divide by it to obtain

$$x_2 = \frac{a_{11}b_2 - a_{21}b_1}{a_{11}a_{22} - a_{12}a_{21}}$$

Once we know x_2, we can solve either of the equations in (11) for x_1, and the system has a unique solution. We define the determinant of the matrix

$$A = \begin{pmatrix} a_{11} & a_{12} \\ a_{21} & a_{22} \end{pmatrix}$$

by

$$\det A = \begin{vmatrix} a_{11} & a_{12} \\ a_{21} & a_{22} \end{vmatrix} = a_{11}a_{22} - a_{12}a_{21} \qquad (11)$$

Evidently, the system (10) has a unique solution if and only if $\det A \neq 0$.

This result can be extended to systems of n equations in n unknown. First, we define the determinant of an $n \times n$ matrix.

There are several ways to define a determinant, and this is one of them. It is important to realize that "det" is a function that assigns a *number* to a *square* matrix.

We shall define the determinant of an $n \times n$ matrix inductively. In other words, we use our knowledge of a 2×2 determinant to define a 3×3 determinant, use this to define a 4×4 determinant, and so on. We start by defining a 3×3 determinant.

1. 3 × 3 Determinant

Let

$$A = \begin{pmatrix} a_{11} & a_{12} & a_{13} \\ a_{21} & a_{22} & a_{23} \\ a_{31} & a_{32} & a_{33} \end{pmatrix}$$

Then,

$$\begin{aligned} \det A &= |A| \\ &= a_{11}\begin{vmatrix} a_{22} & a_{23} \\ a_{32} & a_{33} \end{vmatrix} - a_{12}\begin{vmatrix} a_{21} & a_{23} \\ a_{31} & a_{33} \end{vmatrix} \\ &\quad + a_{13}\begin{vmatrix} a_{21} & a_{22} \\ a_{31} & a_{32} \end{vmatrix} \end{aligned} \qquad (12)$$

Note the minus sign before the second term on the right side of Eq. (12).

EXAMPLE 6. Let

$$A = \begin{pmatrix} 3 & 5 & 2 \\ 4 & 2 & 3 \\ -1 & 2 & 4 \end{pmatrix}$$

Then,

$$|A| = \begin{vmatrix} 3 & 5 & 2 \\ 4 & 2 & 3 \\ -1 & 2 & 4 \end{vmatrix} = 3\begin{vmatrix} 2 & 3 \\ 2 & 4 \end{vmatrix}$$

$$-5\begin{vmatrix} 4 & 3 \\ -1 & 4 \end{vmatrix} + 2\begin{vmatrix} 4 & 2 \\ -1 & 2 \end{vmatrix}$$

$$= 3 \cdot 2 - 5 \cdot 19 + 2 \cdot 10 = -69$$

There is a simpler method for calculating 3 × 3 determinants. From Eq. (12) we have,

$$\begin{vmatrix} a_{11} & a_{12} & a_{13} \\ a_{21} & a_{22} & a_{23} \\ a_{31} & a_{32} & a_{33} \end{vmatrix}$$

$$= a_{11}(a_{22}a_{33} - a_{23}a_{32}) - a_{12}(a_{21}a_{33} - a_{23}a_{31}) + a_{13}(a_{21}a_{32} - a_{22}a_{31})$$

or

$$\begin{aligned} |A| = {} & a_{11}a_{22}a_{33} + a_{12}a_{23}a_{31} \\ & + a_{13}a_{21}a_{32} - a_{13}a_{22}a_{31} \\ & - a_{12}a_{21}a_{33} - a_{11}a_{32}a_{23} \end{aligned} \tag{13}$$

We write A and adjoin to it its first two columns:

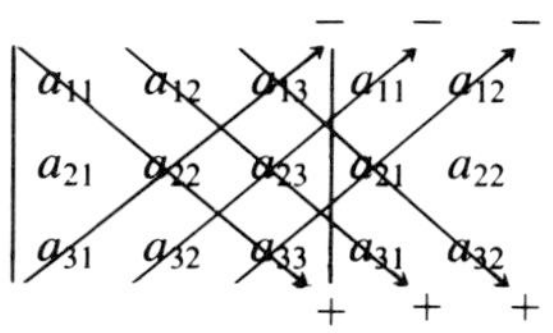

We then calculate the six products, put minus signs before the products with arrows pointing upward, and add. This gives the sum in Eq. (13).

EXAMPLE 7. We calculate

and multiplying as indicated, we obtain

$$\begin{aligned} |A| &= (3)(2)(4) + (5)(3)(-1) + (2)(4)(2) \\ &\quad -(-1)(2)(2) - 2(3)(3) - (4)(4)(5) \\ &= 24 - 15 + 16 + 4 - 18 - 80 = -69 \end{aligned}$$

Note. The method just given will not work for $n \times n$ determinants if $n \neq 3$. If you try something analogous for 4 × 4 or higher order determinants, you will get the wrong answer.

Before defining $n \times n$ determinants, we first note that in Eq. (13),

$$\begin{pmatrix} a_{22} & a_{23} \\ a_{32} & a_{33} \end{pmatrix}$$

is the matrix obtained by deleting the first row and first column of A;

$$\begin{pmatrix} a_{21} & a_{23} \\ a_{31} & a_{33} \end{pmatrix}$$

is the matrix obtained by deleting the first row and second column of A; and

$$\begin{pmatrix} a_{21} & a_{22} \\ a_{31} & a_{32} \end{pmatrix}$$

is the matrix obtained by deleting the first row and third column of A. If we denote these three matrices by M_{11}, M_{12}, and M_{13}, respectively, and if $A_{11} = \det M_{11}$, $A_{12} = -\det M_{12}$, and $A_{13} = \det M_{13}$, then Eq. (12) can be written

$$\det A = |A| = a_{11}A_{11} + a_{12}A_{12} + a_{13}A_{13} \tag{14}$$

2. Minor

Let A be an $n \times n$ matrix, and let M_{ij} be the $(n-1) \times (n-1)$ matrix obtained from A by deleting the ith row and jth column of A; M_{ij} is called the ijth minor of A.

3. Cofactor

Let A be an $n \times n$ matrix. The ijth cofactor of A, denoted A_{ij}, is given by

$$A_{ij} = (-1)^{i+j}|M_{ij}| \tag{15}$$

That is, the ijth cofactor of A is obtained by taking the determinant of the ijth minor and multiplying it by $(-1)^{i+j}$. Note that

$$(-1)^{i+j} = \begin{cases} 1 & \text{if } i+j \text{ is even} \\ -1 & \text{if } i+j \text{ is odd} \end{cases}$$

We now consider the general $n \times n$ matrix. Here,

$$A = \begin{pmatrix} a_{11} & a_{12} & \cdots & a_{1n} \\ a_{21} & a_{22} & \cdots & a_{2n} \\ \vdots & \vdots & & \vdots \\ a_{n1} & a_{n2} & \cdots & a_{nn} \end{pmatrix}$$

4. $n \times n$ Determinant

Let A be an $n \times n$ matrix. Then, the determinant of A, written det A or $|A|$, is given by

$$\det A = |A| = a_{11}A_{11} + a_{12}A_{12} + a_{13}A_{13} + \cdots + a_{1n}A_{1n} = \sum_{k=1}^{n} a_{1k}A_{1k} \quad (16)$$

The expression on the right-hand side of Eq. (16) is called an expansion of cofactors.

In Eq. (16) we defined the determinant by expanding by cofactors using components of A in the first row. We shall soon see that the same answer is obtained by expanding in any row or column of A.

F. Facts about Determinants

Expanding determinants by cofactors can be a tedious affair. Fortunately, there are a number of rules that make the computation of determinants fairly easy.

Basic Theorem. Let

$$A = \begin{pmatrix} a_{11} & a_{12} & \cdots & a_{1n} \\ a_{21} & a_{22} & \cdots & a_{2n} \\ \vdots & \vdots & & \vdots \\ a_{n1} & a_{n2} & \cdots & a_{nn} \end{pmatrix}$$

be an $n \times n$ matrix. Then,

$$\det A = a_{i1}A_{i1} + a_{i2}A_{i2} + \cdots + a_{in}A_{in} = \sum_{k=1}^{n} a_{ik}A_{ik} \quad (17)$$

for $i = 1, 2, \ldots, n$. That is, we can calculate det A by expanding by cofactors in any row of A. Furthermore,

$$\det A = a_{1j}A_{1j} + a_{2j}A_{2j} + \cdots + a_{nj}A_{nj} = \sum_{k=1}^{n} a_{kj}A_{kj} \quad (18)$$

Since the jth column of A is

$$\begin{pmatrix} a_{1j} \\ a_{2j} \\ \vdots \\ a_{nj} \end{pmatrix},$$

Eq. (18) indicates that we can calculate det A by expanding by cofactors in any column of A. We now list some properties of determinants.

PROPERTY 1. If any row or column of A is the zero vector, then det $A = 0$.

PROPERTY 2. If the ith row or the jth column of A is multiplied by the constant c, then det A is multiplied by c. That is, if we call this new matrix B, then

$$|B| = \begin{vmatrix} a_{11} & a_{12} & \cdots & a_{1n} \\ a_{21} & a_{22} & \cdots & a_{2n} \\ \vdots & \vdots & & \vdots \\ ca_{i1} & ca_{i2} & \cdots & ca_{in} \\ \vdots & \vdots & & \vdots \\ a_{n1} & a_{n2} & \cdots & a_{nn} \end{vmatrix} = c\begin{vmatrix} a_{11} & a_{12} & \cdots & a_{1n} \\ a_{21} & a_{22} & \cdots & a_{2n} \\ \vdots & \vdots & & \vdots \\ a_{i1} & a_{i2} & \cdots & a_{in} \\ \vdots & \vdots & & \vdots \\ a_{n1} & a_{n2} & \cdots & a_{nn} \end{vmatrix} = c|A|$$

PROPERTY 3. Let

$$A = \begin{pmatrix} a_{11} & a_{12} & \cdots & a_{1j} & \cdots & a_{1n} \\ a_{21} & a_{22} & \cdots & a_{2j} & \cdots & a_{2n} \\ \vdots & \vdots & & \vdots & & \vdots \\ a_{n1} & a_{n2} & \cdots & a_{nj} & \cdots & a_{nn} \end{pmatrix}$$

$$B = \begin{pmatrix} a_{11} & a_{12} & \cdots & \alpha_{1j} & \cdots & a_{1n} \\ a_{21} & a_{22} & \cdots & \alpha_{2j} & \cdots & a_{2n} \\ \vdots & \vdots & & \vdots & & \vdots \\ a_{n1} & a_{n2} & \cdots & \alpha_{nj} & \cdots & a_{nn} \end{pmatrix}$$

$$C = \begin{pmatrix} a_{11} & a_{12} & \cdots & a_{1j} + \alpha_{1j} & \cdots & a_{1n} \\ a_{21} & a_{22} & \cdots & a_{2j} + \alpha_{2j} & \cdots & a_{2n} \\ \vdots & \vdots & & \vdots & & \vdots \\ a_{n1} & a_{n2} & \cdots & a_{nj} + \alpha_{nj} & \cdots & a_{nn} \end{pmatrix}$$

Then, det C = det A + det B. In other words, suppose that A, B, and C are identical except for the jth column and that the jth column of C is the sum of the jth columns of A and B. Then, det C = det A + det B. The same statement is true for rows.

PROPERTY 4. Interchanging any two rows (or columns) of A has the effect of multiplying det A by -1.

PROPERTY 5. If one row (column) of A is a constant multiple of another row (column), then det $A = 0$.

PROPERTY 6. If a multiple of one row (column) of A is added to another row (column) of A, then the determinant is unchanged.

PROPERTY 7. Let

$$A = \begin{pmatrix} a_{11} & a_{12} & a_{13} & \cdots & a_{1n} \\ 0 & a_{22} & a_{23} & \cdots & a_{2n} \\ 0 & 0 & a_{33} & \cdots & a_{3n} \\ \vdots & \vdots & \vdots & & \vdots \\ 0 & 0 & 0 & \cdots & a_{nn} \end{pmatrix}$$

be an upper triangular matrix. That is, all the components of A below the main diagonal are zero. Then, det $A = a_{11}a_{22}a_{33} \cdots a_{nn}$. That is, the determinant of an upper triangular matrix is equal to the product of its diagonal components. A similar result holds for a lower triangular matrix.

EXAMPLE 8. We calculate

$$|A| = \begin{pmatrix} 1 & 3 & 5 & 2 \\ 0 & -1 & 3 & 4 \\ 2 & 1 & 9 & 6 \\ 3 & 2 & 4 & 8 \end{pmatrix}$$

There is already a zero in the first column, so it is simplest to reduce other elements in the first column to zero. We then continue to reduce, aiming for a triangular matrix:

1. Multiply the first row by -2 and add it to the third row and multiply the first row by -3 and add it to the fourth row,

$$|A| = \begin{pmatrix} 1 & 3 & 5 & 2 \\ 0 & -1 & 3 & 4 \\ 0 & -5 & -1 & 2 \\ 0 & -7 & -11 & 2 \end{pmatrix}$$

2. Multiply the second row by -5 and -7 and add it to the third and fourth rows, respectively,

$$|A| = \begin{pmatrix} 1 & 3 & 5 & 2 \\ 0 & -1 & 3 & 4 \\ 0 & 0 & -16 & -18 \\ 0 & 0 & -32 & -26 \end{pmatrix}$$

3. Factor out -16 from the third row (using Property 2),

$$|A| = -16 \begin{pmatrix} 1 & 3 & 5 & 2 \\ 0 & -1 & 3 & 4 \\ 0 & 0 & 1 & \frac{9}{8} \\ 0 & 0 & -32 & -26 \end{pmatrix}$$

4. Multiply the third row by 32 and add it to the fourth row,

$$|A| = -16 \begin{pmatrix} 1 & 3 & 5 & 2 \\ 0 & -1 & 3 & 4 \\ 0 & 0 & 1 & \frac{9}{8} \\ 0 & 0 & 0 & 10 \end{pmatrix}$$

Now we have an upper triangular matrix and $|A| = -16(1)(-1)(1)(10) = (-16)(-10) = 160$.

Theorem 1. Let A be an $n \times n$ matrix. Then the system $A\mathbf{x} = \mathbf{b}$ has a unique solution for every n vector $\mathbf{b}$ if and only if det $A \neq 0$. In particular, if det $A \neq 0$, then the only solution to the homogeneous system $A\mathbf{x} = \mathbf{0}$ is the zero solution.

PROPERTY 8. Let A and B be $n \times n$ matrices. Then, det AB = det A det B; that is, the determinant of the product is the product of the determinants.

G. Linear Independence and Homogeneous Systems

In the study of linear algebra, one of the central ideas is that of the linear dependence or independence of vectors. In this section we shall define what we mean by linear independence and show how it is related to the theory of homogeneous systems of equations. When we return to linear independence in Section II.C, we shall see how this concept is central to the theory of vector spaces.

Is there a special relationship between the vectors $\mathbf{v}_1 = \binom{1}{2}$ and $\mathbf{v}_2 = \binom{2}{4}$? Of course, we see that $\mathbf{v}_2 = 2\mathbf{v}_1$, or, writing this equation in another way,

$$2\mathbf{v}_1 - \mathbf{v}_2 = \mathbf{0} \tag{19}$$

What is special about the vectors

$$\mathbf{v}_1 = \begin{pmatrix} 1 \\ 2 \\ 3 \end{pmatrix}, \quad \mathbf{v}_2 = \begin{pmatrix} -4 \\ 1 \\ 5 \end{pmatrix}, \quad \mathbf{v}_3 = \begin{pmatrix} -5 \\ 8 \\ 19 \end{pmatrix}$$

This question is more difficult to answer at first. It is easy to verify, however, that $\mathbf{v}_3 = 3\mathbf{v}_1 + 2\mathbf{v}_2$, or, rewriting,

$$3\mathbf{v}_1 + 2\mathbf{v}_2 - \mathbf{v}_3 = \mathbf{0} \tag{20}$$

It appears that the two vectors in Eq. (19) and the three vectors in Eq. (20) are more closely related than an arbitrary pair of two-vectors or an arbitrary triple of three-vectors. In each case we say that the vectors are linearly dependent. In general, we have the following important definition.

1. Linearly Dependent Vectors

The set of vectors $\mathbf{v}_1, \mathbf{v}_2, \ldots, \mathbf{v}_n$ is linearly dependent if there exist scalars $c_1, c_2, \ldots, c_n$ not all zero such that

$$c_1\mathbf{v}_1 + c_2\mathbf{v}_2 + \cdots + c_n\mathbf{v}_n = \mathbf{0} \tag{21}$$

With this definition we see that the vectors in Eq. (19) $[c_1 = 2, c_2 = -1]$ and Eq. (20) $[c_1 = 3, c_2 = 2, c_3 = -1]$ are linearly dependent.

2. Linearly Independent Vectors

The set of vectors $\mathbf{v}_1, \mathbf{v}_2, \ldots, \mathbf{v}_n$ is linearly independent if it is not linearly dependent. Put in another way, $\mathbf{v}_1, \mathbf{v}_2, \ldots, \mathbf{v}_n$ is linearly independent if the equation $c_1\mathbf{v}_1 + c_2\mathbf{v}_2 + \cdots + c_n\mathbf{v}_n = \mathbf{0}$ holds only for $c_1 = c_2 = \cdots = c_n = 0$.

How do we determine whether a set of vectors is linearly dependent or independent? The case for two vectors is easy.

Theorem 2. Two vectors are linearly dependent if and only if one is a scalar multiple of the other.

In general, the m vectors

$$\mathbf{v}_1 = \begin{pmatrix} a_{11} \\ a_{21} \\ \vdots \\ a_{m1} \end{pmatrix}, \quad \mathbf{v}_2 = \begin{pmatrix} a_{12} \\ a_{22} \\ \vdots \\ a_{m2} \end{pmatrix}, \quad \ldots, \quad \mathbf{v}_n = \begin{pmatrix} a_{1n} \\ a_{2n} \\ \vdots \\ a_{mn} \end{pmatrix}$$

are linearly independent if and only if the zero solution is the only solution to the homogeneous system

$$c_1\mathbf{v}_1 + c_2\mathbf{v}_2 + \cdots + c_n\mathbf{v}_n = \mathbf{0}$$

If $n = m$, we have the following result. Let A denote the matrix whose columns are $\mathbf{v}_1, \mathbf{v}_2, \ldots, \mathbf{v}_n$.

Theorem 3. The n vectors $\mathbf{v}_1, \mathbf{v}_2, \ldots, \mathbf{v}_n$ are linearly independent if and only if $\det A \neq 0$.

EXAMPLE 9. The vectors

$$\begin{pmatrix} 2 \\ -1 \\ 4 \end{pmatrix}, \quad \begin{pmatrix} 3 \\ 5 \\ 2 \end{pmatrix}, \quad \begin{pmatrix} 3 \\ -8 \\ 10 \end{pmatrix}$$

are linearly dependent because

$$\begin{vmatrix} 2 & 3 & 3 \\ -1 & 5 & -8 \\ 4 & 2 & 10 \end{vmatrix} = 0$$

H. Inverse of a Square Matrix

3. Identity Matrix

The $n \times n$ identity matrix I_n is the $n \times n$ matrix with 1's down the main diagonal and 0's everywhere else. That is, $I_n = (b_{ij})$, where

$$b_{ij} = \begin{cases} 1 & \text{if } i = j \\ 0 & \text{if } i \neq j \end{cases}$$

Theorem 4. Let A be a square $n \times n$ matrix. Then,

$$AI_n = I_n A = A$$

That is, I_n commutes with every $n \times n$ matrix and leaves it unchanged after multiplication on the left or right.

Notation. From now on we shall write the identity matrix simply as I, since if A is $n \times n$, the products IA and AI are defined only if I is also $n \times n$.

4. Inverse of a Square Matrix

Let A and B be $n \times n$ matrices. Suppose that

$$AB = BA = I$$

Then, B is called the inverse of A and is written as A^{-1}. We then have

$$AA^{-1} = A^{-1}A = I$$

If A has an inverse, then A is said to be invertible.

REMARK 1. From this definition it immediately follows that $(A^{-1})^{-1} = A$ if A is invertible.

REMARK 2. This definition does not state that every square matrix has an inverse. In fact, there are many square matrices that have no inverse.

Theorem 5. Let A and B be invertible $n \times n$ matrices. Then AB is invertible, and

$$(AB)^{-1} = B^{-1}A^{-1}$$

Let A be an $n \times n$ matrix and consider the system $A\mathbf{x} = \mathbf{b}$. If A is invertible, we can multiply on both sides by A^{-1} to obtain

$$I\mathbf{x} = A^{-1}A\mathbf{x} = A^{-1}\mathbf{b} \qquad \mathbf{x} = A^{-1}\mathbf{b}$$

This suggests the following result.

Theorem 6. The system $A\mathbf{x} = \mathbf{b}$ has a unique solution if and only if A is invertible. If A^{-1} exists, then the unique solution is $\mathbf{x} = A^{-1}\mathbf{b}$.

When is a matrix invertible?

Theorem 7. A is invertible if and only if det $A \neq 0$.

If A is invertible, how do we compute A^{-1}? There are two standard methods.

5. Procedure for Computing the Inverse of a Square Matrix *A* by Using Row Reduction

Step 1. Write the augmented matrix $(A \mid I)$.

Step 2. Use row reduction to reduce the matrix A to I or a matrix with a row of zeros.

Step 3. Decide if A is invertible. (a) If A can be reduced to the identify matrix I, then A^{-1} will be the matrix to the right of the vertical bar. (b) If the row reduction of A leads to a row of zeros to the left of the vertical bar, then A is not invertible.

Example 10. Compute

$$\begin{pmatrix} 2 & 4 & 6 \\ 4 & 5 & 6 \\ 3 & 1 & -2 \end{pmatrix}^{-1}$$

We first put I next to A in an augmented matrix form

$$\left(\begin{array}{ccc|ccc} 2 & 4 & 6 & 1 & 0 & 0 \\ 4 & 5 & 6 & 0 & 1 & 0 \\ 3 & 1 & -2 & 0 & 0 & 1 \end{array}\right)$$

and then carry out the row reduction:

$$\xrightarrow{M_1(\frac{1}{2})} \left(\begin{array}{ccc|ccc} 1 & 2 & 3 & \frac{1}{2} & 0 & 0 \\ 4 & 5 & 6 & 0 & 1 & 0 \\ 3 & 1 & -2 & 0 & 0 & 1 \end{array}\right)$$

$$\xrightarrow[A_{1,3}(-3)]{A_{1,2}(-4)} \left(\begin{array}{ccc|ccc} 1 & 2 & 3 & \frac{1}{2} & 0 & 0 \\ 0 & -3 & -6 & -2 & 1 & 0 \\ 0 & -5 & -11 & -\frac{3}{2} & 0 & 1 \end{array}\right)$$

$$\xrightarrow{M_2(\frac{1}{3})} \left(\begin{array}{ccc|ccc} 1 & 2 & 3 & \frac{1}{2} & 0 & 0 \\ 0 & 1 & 2 & \frac{2}{3} & -\frac{1}{3} & 0 \\ 0 & -5 & -11 & -\frac{3}{2} & 0 & 1 \end{array}\right)$$

$$\xrightarrow[A_{2,3}(5)]{A_{2,1}(-2)} \left(\begin{array}{ccc|ccc} 1 & 0 & -1 & -\frac{5}{6} & \frac{2}{3} & 0 \\ 0 & 1 & 2 & \frac{2}{3} & -\frac{1}{3} & 0 \\ 0 & 0 & -1 & \frac{11}{6} & -\frac{5}{3} & 1 \end{array}\right)$$

$$\xrightarrow{M_3(-1)} \left(\begin{array}{ccc|ccc} 1 & 0 & -1 & -\frac{5}{6} & \frac{2}{3} & 0 \\ 0 & 1 & 2 & \frac{2}{3} & -\frac{1}{3} & 0 \\ 0 & 0 & 1 & -\frac{11}{6} & \frac{5}{3} & -1 \end{array}\right)$$

$$\xrightarrow[A_{3,2}(-2)]{A_{3,1}(1)} \left(\begin{array}{ccc|ccc} 1 & 0 & 0 & -\frac{8}{3} & \frac{7}{3} & -1 \\ 0 & 1 & 0 & \frac{13}{3} & -\frac{11}{3} & 2 \\ 0 & 0 & 1 & -\frac{11}{6} & \frac{5}{3} & -1 \end{array}\right)$$

Since A has now been reduced to I, we have,

$$A^{-1} = \begin{pmatrix} -\frac{8}{3} & \frac{7}{3} & -1 \\ \frac{13}{3} & -\frac{11}{3} & 2 \\ -\frac{11}{6} & \frac{5}{3} & -1 \end{pmatrix} = \frac{1}{6}\begin{pmatrix} -16 & 14 & -6 \\ 26 & -22 & 12 \\ -11 & 10 & -6 \end{pmatrix}$$

Check:

$$A^{-1}A = \frac{1}{6}\begin{pmatrix} -16 & 14 & -6 \\ 26 & -22 & 12 \\ -11 & 10 & -6 \end{pmatrix} \times \begin{pmatrix} 2 & 4 & 6 \\ 4 & 5 & 6 \\ 3 & 1 & -2 \end{pmatrix} = \frac{1}{6}\begin{pmatrix} 6 & 0 & 0 \\ 0 & 6 & 0 \\ 0 & 0 & 6 \end{pmatrix} = I$$

We can also verify that $AA^{-1} = I$.

The second method uses determinants.

Before using determinants to calculate inverses, we need to define the adjoint of a matrix $A = (a_{ij})$. Let $B = (A_{ij})$ be the matrix of cofactors of A. Then,

$$B = \begin{pmatrix} A_{11} & A_{12} & \cdots & A_{1n} \\ A_{21} & A_{22} & \cdots & A_{2n} \\ \vdots & \vdots & & \vdots \\ A_{n1} & A_{n2} & \cdots & A_{nn} \end{pmatrix} \tag{22}$$

6. The Adjoint

Let A be an $n \times n$ matrix, and let B, given by Eq. (22), denote the matrix of its cofactors. Then the adjoint of A, written adj A, is the transpose of the $n \times n$ matrix B; that is,

$$\text{adj } A = B^t = \begin{pmatrix} A_{11} & A_{21} & \cdots & A_{n1} \\ A_{12} & A_{22} & \cdots & A_{n2} \\ \vdots & \vdots & & \vdots \\ A_{1n} & A_{2n} & \cdots & A_{nn} \end{pmatrix}$$

Note. The transpose of a matrix A is the matrix obtained by interchanging the rows and columns of A.

Theorem 8. Let A be an $n \times n$ matrix. If det $A \neq 0$, then

$$A^{-1} = (\det A)^{-1} \text{ adj } A$$

EXAMPLE 11. Compute

$$A^{-1} = \begin{pmatrix} 2 & 4 & 3 \\ 0 & 1 & -1 \\ 3 & 5 & 7 \end{pmatrix}^{-1}$$

First, we note that det $A = 3 \neq 0$. Also,

$$B = \begin{pmatrix} 12 & -3 & -3 \\ -13 & 5 & 2 \\ -7 & 2 & 2 \end{pmatrix}$$

$$\text{adj } A = \begin{pmatrix} 12 & -13 & -7 \\ -3 & 5 & 2 \\ -3 & 2 & 2 \end{pmatrix}$$

so that

$$A^{-1} = \frac{1}{3}\begin{pmatrix} 12 & -13 & -7 \\ -3 & 5 & 2 \\ -3 & 2 & 2 \end{pmatrix} = \begin{pmatrix} 4 & -\frac{13}{3} & -\frac{7}{3} \\ -1 & \frac{5}{3} & \frac{2}{3} \\ -1 & \frac{2}{3} & \frac{2}{3} \end{pmatrix}$$

II. Vector Spaces

A. Basic Properties

1. Real Vector Space

A real vector space V is a set of objects, called vectors, together with two operations called addition and scalar multiplication, that satisfy the ten axioms listed below.

Notation. If $\mathbf{x}$ and $\mathbf{y}$ are in V and if α is a real number, then we write $\mathbf{x} + \mathbf{y}$ for the sum of $\mathbf{x}$ and $\mathbf{y}$ and $\alpha\mathbf{x}$ for the scalar product of α and x.

2. Axioms of a Real Vector Space

1. If $\mathbf{x} \in V$ and $\mathbf{y} \in V$, then $\mathbf{x} + \mathbf{y} \in V$ (closure under addition).
2. For all $\mathbf{x}$, $\mathbf{y}$, and $\mathbf{z}$ in V, $(\mathbf{x} + \mathbf{y}) + \mathbf{z} = \mathbf{x} + (\mathbf{y} + \mathbf{z})$ (associative law of vector addition).
3. There is a vector $\mathbf{0} \in V$ such that for all $\mathbf{x} \in V$, $\mathbf{x} + \mathbf{0} = \mathbf{0} + \mathbf{x} = \mathbf{x}$ ($\mathbf{0}$ is called the additive identity).
4. If $\mathbf{x} \in V$, there is a vector $-\mathbf{x}$ in V such that $\mathbf{x} + (-\mathbf{x}) = \mathbf{0}$ ($-\mathbf{x}$ is called the additive inverse of $\mathbf{x}$).
5. If $\mathbf{x}$ and $\mathbf{y}$ are in V, then $\mathbf{x} + \mathbf{y} = \mathbf{y} + \mathbf{x}$ (commutative law of vector addition).
6. If $\mathbf{x} \in V$ and α is a scalar, then $\alpha\mathbf{x} \in V$ (closure under scalar multiplication).
7. If $\mathbf{x}$ and $\mathbf{y}$ are in V and α is a scalar, then $\alpha(\mathbf{x} + \mathbf{y}) = \alpha\mathbf{x} + \alpha\mathbf{y}$ (first distributive law).
8. If $\mathbf{x} \in V$ and α and β are scalars, then $(\alpha + \beta)\mathbf{x} = \alpha\mathbf{x} + \beta\mathbf{x}$ (second distributive law).

9. If $\mathbf{x} \in V$ and α and β are scalars, then $\alpha(\beta\mathbf{x}) = \alpha\beta\mathbf{x}$ (associative law of scalar multiplication).

10. For every vector $\mathbf{x} \in V$, $1\mathbf{x} = \mathbf{x}$ (the scalar 1 is called a multiplicative identity).

EXAMPLES OF VECTOR SPACES.

1. The space $\mathbb{R}^n$. Let $V = \mathbb{R}^n = \{(x_1, x_2, \ldots, x_n): x_i \in \mathbb{R} \text{ for } i = 1, 2, \ldots, n\}$.
2. Let $V = \{0\}$; that is, V consists of the single number 0. This space is called a trivial vector space.
3. Let $V = \{(x, y): y = mx$, where m is a fixed real number, and x is an arbitrary real number$\}$; that is, V consists of all points in $\mathbb{R}^2$ lying on the line $y = mx$ passing through the origin with slope m.
4. $V = \{(x, y, z): ax + by + cz = 0\}$; that is, V is the set of points in $\mathbb{R}^3$ lying on the plane passing through the origin with normal vector (a, b, c).
5. Let $V = P_n$, the set of polynomials with real coefficients of degree less than or equal to n. If $p \in P_n$, then

$$p(x) = a_n x^n + a_{n-1}x^{n-1} + \cdots + a_1 x + a_0$$

where each a_i is real. The sum $p(x) + q(x)$ is defined in the obvious way: If

$$q(x) = b_n x^n + b_{n-1}x^{n-1} + \cdots + b_1 x + b_0,$$

then

$$p(x) + q(x) = (a_n + b_n)x^n + (a_{n-1} + b_{n-1})x^{n-1} + \cdots + (a_1 + b_1)x + (a_0 + b_0)$$

6. The set of $m \times n$ matrices with real components, M_{mn}, forms a vector space for any integers m and n.
7. $V = C[0, 1]$ is the set of real-valued continuous functions defined on the interval $[0, 1]$, with $(f + g)(x) = f(x) + g(x)$ and $(\alpha f)(x) = \alpha[f(x)]$.

Theorem 9. Let V be a vector space. Then,

1. $\alpha\mathbf{0} = \mathbf{0}$ for every real number α;
2. $0 \cdot \mathbf{x} = \mathbf{0}$ for every $\mathbf{x} \in V$;
3. If $\alpha\mathbf{x} = \mathbf{0}$, then $\alpha = 0$ or $\mathbf{x} = \mathbf{0}$ (or both);
4. $(-1)\mathbf{x} = -\mathbf{x}$ for every $\mathbf{x} \in V$.

B. Subspaces

1. Subspace

Let H be a nonempty subset of a vector space V and suppose that H is itself a vector space under the operations of addition and scalar multiplication defined on V. Then, H is said to be a subspace of V.

Theorem 10. A nonempty subset H of the vector space V is a subspace of V if the two closure rules hold.

2. Rules for Checking Whether a Subset is a Subspace

1. If $\mathbf{x} \in H$ and $\mathbf{y} \in H$, then $\mathbf{x} + \mathbf{y} \in H$.
2. If $\mathbf{x} \in H$, then $\alpha\mathbf{x} \in H$ for every scalar α.

Some examples of subspaces now follow.

EXAMPLE 12. $\mathbf{0}$ is a subspace of every vector space. It is called the trivial subspace.

EXAMPLE 13. Every vector space V is a subspace of itself.

EXAMPLE 14. $\Pi = \{(x, y, z): ax + by + xz = 0;\ a, b, c \text{ real}\}$ is a subspace of $\mathbb{R}^3$.

EXAMPLE 15. If P_n denotes the vector space of polynomials of degree $\leq n$, and if $0 < m < n$, then P_m is a proper subspace of P_n, as is easily verified.

EXAMPLE 16. Let M_{mn} denote the vector space of $m \times n$ matrices with real components, and let $H = \{A \in M_{mn}: a_{11} = 0\}$. Then H is a subspace of M_{mn}.

EXAMPLE 17. $P_n[0, 1] \subset C[0, 1]$ because every polynomial is continuous and P_n is a vector space for every integer n; so that each $P_n[0, 1]$ is a subspace of $C[0, 1]$.

EXAMPLE 18. Let $C'[0, 1]$ denote the set of functions with continuous first derivatives defined on $[0, 1]$. Since every differentiable function is continuous, we have $C'[0, 1] \subset C[0, 1]$. Since the sum and scalar multiple of two differentiable functions are differentiable, we see that $C'[0, 1]$ is a subspace of $C[0, 1]$.

Theorem 11. Let H_1 and H_2 be subspaces of a vector space V. Then, $H_1 \cap H_2$ is a subspace of V.

C. Linear Independence, Linear Combination, and Span

We discussed the linear independence of vectors in $\mathbb{R}^n$ in Section I.G. We now extend this definition to abstract vector spaces.

1. Linear Dependence and Independence

Let $\mathbf{v}_1, \mathbf{v}_2, \ldots, \mathbf{v}_n$ be n vectors in a vector space V. Then, the vectors are said to be linearly dependent if there exist n scalars $c_1, c_2, \ldots, c_n$ not all zero such that

$$c_1\mathbf{v}_1 + c_2\mathbf{v}_2 + \cdots + c_n\mathbf{v}_n = \mathbf{0} \tag{23}$$

If the vectors are not linearly dependent, they are said to be linearly independent.

EXAMPLE 19. The vectors 1, x, x^2, x^3 are linearly independent in P_3.

EXAMPLE 20. The vectors 1, x, x^2, x^3, ..., x^n, ..., are linearly independent in $C[0, 1]$.

2. Linear Combination

Let $\mathbf{v}_1, \mathbf{v}_2, \ldots, \mathbf{v}_n$ be vectors in a vector space V. Then, any expression of the form

$$a_1\mathbf{v}_1 + a_2\mathbf{v}_2 + \cdots + a_n\mathbf{v}_n \tag{24}$$

where $a_1, a_2, \ldots, a_n$ are scalars is called a linear combination $\mathbf{v}_1, \mathbf{v}_2, \ldots, \mathbf{v}_n$.

3. Span of a Vector Space

The vectors $\mathbf{v}_1, \mathbf{v}_2, \ldots, \mathbf{v}_n$ in a vector space V are said to span V if every vector in V can be written as a linear combination of them. That is, for every $\mathbf{v} \in V$, there are scalars $a_1, a_2, \ldots, a_n$ such that

$$\mathbf{v} = a_1\mathbf{v}_1 + a_2\mathbf{v}_2 + \cdots + a_n\mathbf{v}_n \tag{25}$$

EXAMPLE 21. The vectors

$$\mathbf{i} = \begin{pmatrix} 1 \\ 0 \\ 0 \end{pmatrix} \quad \mathbf{j} = \begin{pmatrix} 0 \\ 1 \\ 0 \end{pmatrix} \quad \mathbf{k} = \begin{pmatrix} 0 \\ 0 \\ 1 \end{pmatrix}$$

span $\mathbb{R}^3$.

EXAMPLE 22. The vectors 1, x, x^2, x^3 span P_3.

Theorem 12. Any set of n linearly independent vectors in $\mathbb{R}^n$ spans $\mathbb{R}^n$.

4. Span of a Set of Vectors

Let $\mathbf{v}_1, \mathbf{v}_2, \ldots, \mathbf{v}_n$ be n vectors in a vector space V. The span of $\{\mathbf{v}_1, \mathbf{v}_2, \ldots, \mathbf{v}_n\}$ is the set of linear combinations of $\mathbf{v}_1, \mathbf{v}_2, \ldots, \mathbf{v}_n$; that is,

$$\text{span}\{\mathbf{v}_1, \mathbf{v}_2, \ldots, \mathbf{v}_n\} = \{\mathbf{v}: \mathbf{v} = a_1\mathbf{v}_1 + a_2\mathbf{v}_2 + \cdots + a_n\mathbf{v}_n\} \tag{26}$$

where $a_1, a_2, \ldots, a_n$ are scalars.

Theorem 13. span$\{\mathbf{v}_1, \mathbf{v}_2, \ldots, \mathbf{v}_n\}$ is a subspace of $\mathbf{V}$.

Theorem 14. The span of two nonzero vectors in $\mathbb{R}^3$ that are not parallel is a plane passing through the origin.

D. Basis and Dimension

1. Basis

A set of vectors $\mathbf{v}_1, \mathbf{v}_2, \ldots, \mathbf{v}_n$ forms a basis for V if (a) $\{\mathbf{v}_1, \mathbf{v}_2, \ldots, \mathbf{v}_n\}$ is linearly independent; (b) $\{\mathbf{v}_1, \mathbf{v}_2, \ldots, \mathbf{v}_n\}$ spans V. From Theorem 12 we have Theorem 15.

Theorem 15. Every set of n linearly independent vectors in $\mathbb{R}^n$ is a basis in $\mathbb{R}^n$.

EXAMPLE 23. $\{1, x, x^2, x^3\}$ is a basis for P_3.

Theorem 16. If $\{\mathbf{v}_1, \mathbf{v}_2, \ldots, \mathbf{v}_n\}$ is a basis for V and if $\mathbf{v} \in V$, then there exists a unique set of scalars $c_1, c_2, \ldots, c_n$ such that $\mathbf{v} = c_1\mathbf{v}_1 + c_2\mathbf{v}_2 + \cdots + c_n\mathbf{v}_n$.

Theorem 17. If $\{\mathbf{u}_1, \mathbf{u}_2, \ldots, \mathbf{u}_m\}$ and $\{\mathbf{v}_1, \mathbf{v}_2, \ldots, \mathbf{v}_n\}$ are bases for the vector space V, then $m = n$; that is, any two bases in a vector space V have the same number of vectors.

2. Dimension

The dimension of a vector space V, denoted by dim V, is the number of vectors in a basis of V. If this number if finite, then V is called a finite dimensional vector space; otherwise, V is called an infinite dimensional vector space. If $V = \{\mathbf{0}\}$, then V is said to be zero dimensional. We write the dimension of V as dim V.

EXAMPLE 24. dim $\mathbb{R}^n = n$.

EXAMPLE 25. dim $P_3 = 4$.

EXAMPLE 26. dim $M_{mn} = mn$.

EXAMPLE 27. $C[0, 1]$ is infinite dimensional.

Theorem 18. Let H be a subspace of the finite dimensional vector space V. Then H is finite dimensional, and dim $H \leq$ dim V.

E. Inner Product Spaces

1. Inner Product Space

The complex vector space V is called an inner product space if for every pair of vectors $\mathbf{u}$ and $\mathbf{v}$ in V, there is a unique complex number $(\mathbf{u}, \mathbf{v})$ called the inner product of $\mathbf{u}$ and $\mathbf{v}$, such that if $\mathbf{u}$, $\mathbf{v}$, and $\mathbf{w}$ are in V and $\alpha \in \mathbb{C}$, then

1. $(\mathbf{v}, \mathbf{v}) \geq 0$;
2. $(\mathbf{v}, \mathbf{v}) = 0$ if and only if $\mathbf{v} = \mathbf{0}$;
3. $(\mathbf{u}, \mathbf{v} + \mathbf{w}) = (\mathbf{u}, \mathbf{v}) + (\mathbf{u}, \mathbf{w})$;
4. $(\mathbf{u} + \mathbf{v}, \mathbf{w}) = (\mathbf{u}, \mathbf{w}) + (\mathbf{v}, \mathbf{w})$;
5. $(\mathbf{u}, \mathbf{v}) = \overline{(\mathbf{v}, \mathbf{u})}$;
6. $(\alpha\mathbf{u}, \mathbf{v}) = \alpha(\mathbf{u}, \mathbf{v})$;
7. $(\mathbf{u}, \alpha\mathbf{v}) = \bar{\alpha}(\mathbf{u}, \mathbf{v})$.

The overbars in conditions (5) and (7) denote the complex conjugate.

Note. If $(\mathbf{u}, \mathbf{v})$ is real, then $\overline{(\mathbf{u}, \mathbf{v})} = (\mathbf{u}, \mathbf{v})$, and we can remove the overbar from (5).

EXAMPLE 28. $\mathbb{R}^n$ is an inner product space with $(\mathbf{u}, \mathbf{v}) = \mathbf{u} \cdot \mathbf{v}$.

EXAMPLE 29. $C[0, 1]$ is an inner product space with $(f, g) = \int_0^1 f(t)g(t)\,dt$.

EXAMPLE 30. $\mathbb{C}^n$ is an inner product space with $(\mathbf{x}, \mathbf{y}) = x_1\bar{y}_1 + x_2\bar{y}_2 + \cdots + x_n\bar{y}_n$.

2. Orthogonality and Norm

Let V be an inner product space and suppose that $\mathbf{u}$ and $\mathbf{v}$ are in V. Then, (a) $\mathbf{u}$ and $\mathbf{v}$ are orthogonal if $(\mathbf{u}, \mathbf{v}) = 0$; (b) the norm of $\mathbf{u}$, denoted $|\mathbf{u}|$, is given by

$$|\mathbf{u}| = \sqrt{(\mathbf{u}, \mathbf{u})} \tag{27}$$

Note. Equation (27) makes sense, since $(\mathbf{u}, \mathbf{u}) \geq 0$.

EXAMPLE 31. In $\mathbb{R}^3$,

$$\left|\begin{pmatrix} 1 \\ 2 \\ -3 \end{pmatrix}\right| = \sqrt{14}; \qquad \begin{pmatrix} 1 \\ 2 \\ -3 \end{pmatrix}$$

and

$$\begin{pmatrix} 5 \\ -4 \\ -1 \end{pmatrix}$$

are orthogonal.

EXAMPLE 32. In $C[0, 2\pi]$, the functions $\sin t$ and $\cos t$ are orthogonal, since

$$\begin{aligned}(\sin t, \cos t) &= \int_0^{2\pi} \sin t \cos t\,dt \\ &= \frac{1}{2}\int_0^{2\pi} \sin 2t\,dt \\ &= -\tfrac{1}{4}(\cos 2t)\big|_0^{2\pi} = 0\end{aligned}$$

Also, $|\sin t| = (\sin t, \sin t)^{1/2} = \pi^{1/2}$.

3. Orthonormal Set

The set of vectors $\mathbf{v}_1, \mathbf{v}_2, \ldots, \mathbf{v}_n$ is an orthonormal set in V if

$$(\mathbf{v}_i, \mathbf{v}_j) = 0 \qquad \text{for} \quad i \neq j \tag{28}$$

$$|\mathbf{v}_i| = \sqrt{(\mathbf{v}_i, \mathbf{v}_i)} = 1 \tag{29}$$

If only Eq. (28) holds, the set is said to be orthogonal.

The Gram–Schmidt orthogonalization process can always be used to turn a basis $\mathbf{v}_1, \mathbf{v}_2, \ldots, \mathbf{v}_n$ into an orthonormal basis $\mathbf{u}_1, \mathbf{u}_2, \ldots, \mathbf{u}_n$:

Step 1. $\mathbf{u}_1 = \mathbf{v}_1/|\mathbf{v}_1|$ has norm 1.

Step 2. $\mathbf{v}_2' = \mathbf{v}_2 - (\mathbf{v}_2, \mathbf{u}_1)\mathbf{u}_1$ satisfies $(\mathbf{v}_2', \mathbf{u}_1) = 0$.

Step 3. If $\mathbf{u}_2 = \mathbf{v}_2'/|\mathbf{v}_2'|$, then $\{\mathbf{u}_1, \mathbf{u}_2\}$ is an orthonormal set.

Step 4. If $\mathbf{u}_1, \mathbf{u}_2, \ldots, \mathbf{u}_k$ $(k < m)$ have been constructed, let

$$\begin{aligned}\mathbf{v}_{k+1}' = \mathbf{v}_{k+1} &- (\mathbf{v}_{k+1}, \mathbf{u}_1)\mathbf{u}_1 \\ &- (\mathbf{v}_{k+1}, \mathbf{u}_2)\mathbf{u}_2 - \cdots - (\mathbf{v}_{k+1}, \mathbf{u}_k)\mathbf{u}_k\end{aligned}$$

Then, $\mathbf{v}_{k+1}'$ is orthogonal to $\mathbf{u}_1, \mathbf{u}_2, \ldots, \mathbf{u}_k$, and if $\mathbf{u}_{k+1} = \mathbf{v}_{k+1}'/|\mathbf{v}_{k+1}'|$, then $\{\mathbf{u}_1, \mathbf{u}_2, \ldots, \mathbf{u}_k, \mathbf{u}_{k+1}\}$ is an orthonormal set.

4. Orthogonal Matrix

The $n \times n$ matrix Q is called orthogonal if Q is invertible and

$$Q^{-1} = Q^t \tag{30}$$

EXAMPLE 33.

$$Q = \begin{pmatrix} 1/\sqrt{2} & -1/\sqrt{6} & 1/\sqrt{3} \\ 1/\sqrt{2} & 1/\sqrt{6} & -1/\sqrt{3} \\ 0 & 2/\sqrt{6} & 1/\sqrt{3} \end{pmatrix}$$

is orthogonal.

Theorem 19. The $n \times n$ matrix Q is orthogonal if and only if the columns of Q form an orthonormal basis for $\mathbb{R}^n$.

F. Orthogonal Projections

In this section we assume that V is a finite dimensional inner product space.

1. Orthogonal Projection

Let H be a subspace of V with orthonormal basis $\{\mathbf{u}_1, \mathbf{u}_2, \ldots, \mathbf{u}_k\}$. If $\mathbf{v} \in V$, then the orthogonal projection of $\mathbf{v}$ onto H, denoted $\text{proj}_H\,\mathbf{v}$, is given by

$$\begin{aligned}\text{proj}_H\,\mathbf{v} = (\mathbf{v}, \mathbf{u}_1)\mathbf{u}_1 &+ (\mathbf{v}, \mathbf{u}_2)\mathbf{u}_2 \\ &+ \cdots + (\mathbf{v}, \mathbf{u}_k)\mathbf{u}_k\end{aligned} \tag{31}$$

Note that $\text{proj}_H\,\mathbf{v} \in H$. Let $B = \{\mathbf{u}_1, \mathbf{u}_2, \ldots, \mathbf{u}_n\}$ be an orthonormal basis for $\mathbb{R}^n$, and let $\mathbf{v} \in \mathbb{R}^n$. Then,

$$\begin{aligned}\mathbf{v} = (\mathbf{v} \cdot \mathbf{u}_1)\mathbf{u}_1 &+ (\mathbf{v} \cdot \mathbf{u}_2)\mathbf{u}_2 \\ &+ \cdots + (\mathbf{v} \cdot \mathbf{u}_n)\mathbf{u}_n\end{aligned} \tag{32}$$

That is, $\mathbf{v} = \text{proj}_{\mathbb{R}^n}\,\mathbf{v}$.

2. Orthogonal Complement

Let H be a subspace of V. Then, the orthogonal complement of H, denoted $H^{\perp}$, is given by

$$H^{\perp} = \{\mathbf{x} \in V: (\mathbf{x}, \mathbf{h}) = 0 \quad \text{for every} \quad \mathbf{h} \in H\} \tag{33}$$

Theorem 20. If H is a subspace of $\mathbb{R}^n$, then (a) $H^{\perp}$ is a subspace of $\mathbb{R}^n$; (b) $H \cap H^{\perp} = \{\mathbf{0}\}$; and (c) dim $H^{\perp} = n -$ dim H.

The spaces H and $H^{\perp}$ allow us to "decompose" any vector V.

Theorem 21. Let H be a subspace of V, and let $\mathbf{v} \in V$. Then there exists a unique pair of vectors $\mathbf{h}$ and $\mathbf{p}$ such that $\mathbf{h} \in H$, $\mathbf{p} \in H^{\perp}$, and

$$\mathbf{v} = \mathbf{h} + \mathbf{p} = \text{proj}_H\, \mathbf{v} + \text{proj}_{H^{\perp}}\, \mathbf{v} \tag{34}$$

III. Linear Transformations

A. Basic Properties

1. Linear Transformation

Let V and W be vector spaces. A linear transformation T from V into W is a function that assigns to each vector $\mathbf{v} \in V$ a unique vector $T\mathbf{v} \in W$ and that satisfies, for each $\mathbf{u}$ and $\mathbf{v}$ in V and each scalar α,

$$T(\mathbf{u} + \mathbf{v}) = T\mathbf{u} + T\mathbf{v} \tag{35}$$

$$T(\alpha\mathbf{v}) = T\mathbf{v} \tag{36}$$

Notation. We write T: $V \rightarrow W$ to indicate that T takes V into W.

Terminology. Linear transformations are often called linear operators or linear mappings.

EXAMPLE 34. Let A be an $m \times n$ matrix. Then, the function $T\mathbf{v} = A\mathbf{v}$ is a linear transformation from $\mathbb{R}^n$ to $\mathbb{R}^m$.

EXAMPLE 35. Let V and W be vector spaces and define T: $V \rightarrow W$ by $T\mathbf{v} = \mathbf{0}$ for every $\mathbf{v}$ in V; T is called the zero transformation.

EXAMPLE 36. Let V be a vector space and define I: $V \rightarrow V$ by $I\mathbf{v} = \mathbf{v}$ for every $\mathbf{v}$ in V; I is called the identity transformation or identity operator.

EXAMPLE 37. Let H be a subspace of a vector space V. We define the orthogonal projection transformation P: $V \rightarrow H$ by

$$P\mathbf{v} = \text{proj}_H\, \mathbf{v}$$

EXAMPLE 38. Let J: $C[0, 1] \rightarrow \mathbb{R}$ be defined by $Jf = \int_0^1 f(x)\, dx$; J is a linear transformation. It is called an integral operator.

EXAMPLE 39. If $C'[0, 1]$ denotes the set of continuously differentiable functions on $[0, 1]$, then D: $C'[0, 1] \rightarrow C[0, 1]$ defined by $Df = f'$ is a linear operator. It is called a differential operator.

B. Range and Kernel

Theorem 22. Let T: $V \rightarrow W$ be a linear transformation. Then, for all vectors $\mathbf{u}$, $\mathbf{v}$, $\mathbf{v}_1$, $\mathbf{v}_2$, ..., $\mathbf{v}_n$ in V and all scalars $\alpha_1, \alpha_2, \ldots, \alpha_n$,

$$T(\mathbf{0}) = \mathbf{0}$$

$$T(\mathbf{u} - \mathbf{v}) = T\mathbf{u} - T\mathbf{v}$$

$$T(\alpha_1\mathbf{v}_1 + \alpha_2\mathbf{v}_2 + \cdots + \alpha_n\mathbf{v}_n) = \alpha_1 T\mathbf{v}_1 + \alpha_2 T\mathbf{v}_2 + \cdots + \alpha_n T\mathbf{v}_n$$

Note. In T($\mathbf{0}$) = $\mathbf{0}$, the $\mathbf{0}$ on the left is the zero vector in V, whereas the $\mathbf{0}$ on the right is the zero vector in W.

An important fact about linear transformations is that they are completely determined by what they do to basis vectors.

Theorem 23. Let V be a finite dimensional vector space with basis $B = \{\mathbf{v}_1, \mathbf{v}_2, \ldots, \mathbf{v}_n\}$. Let $\mathbf{w}_1, \mathbf{w}_2, \ldots, \mathbf{w}_n$ be n vectors in W. Suppose that T_1 and T_2 are two linear transformations from V to W such that $T_1\mathbf{v}_i = T_2\mathbf{v}_i = \mathbf{w}_i$ for $i = 1, 2, \ldots, n$. Then for any vector $\mathbf{v} \in V$, $T_1\mathbf{v} = T_2\mathbf{v}$; that is, $T_1 = T_2$.

1. Kernel and Range of a Linear Transformation

Let V and W be vector spaces, and let T: $V \rightarrow W$ be a linear transformation. Then, (a) the kernel of T, denoted ker T, is given by

$$\ker T = \{\mathbf{v} \in V: T\mathbf{v} = \mathbf{0}\} \tag{37}$$

(b) the range of T, denoted range T, is given by

$$\text{range } T = \{\mathbf{w} \in W: \mathbf{w} = T\mathbf{v} \quad \text{for some} \quad \mathbf{v} \in V\} \tag{38}$$

Theorem 24. If T: $V \rightarrow W$ is a linear transformation, then (a) ker T is a subspace of V; (b) range T is a subspace of W.

2. Nullity and Rank of a Linear Transformation

If T is a linear transformation from V to W, then we define

$$\text{nullity of } \quad T = \nu(T) = \dim \ker T \tag{39}$$

$$\text{rank of } \quad T = \rho(T) = \dim \text{range } T \tag{40}$$

EXAMPLE 40. Let H be a subspace of a finite dimensional vector space V and define $T\mathbf{v} = \text{proj}_H \mathbf{v}$. Clearly, range $T = H$. We can write any $\mathbf{v} \in V$ as $\mathbf{v} = \mathbf{h} + \mathbf{p} = \text{proj}_H \mathbf{v} + \text{proj}_{H^\perp} \mathbf{v}$. If $T\mathbf{v} = \mathbf{0}$, then $\mathbf{h} = \mathbf{0}$, which means that $\mathbf{v} = \mathbf{p} \in H^\perp$. Thus, ker $T = H^\perp$, $\rho(T) = \dim H$, and $\nu(T) = \dim H^\perp = n - \rho(T)$.

EXAMPLE 41. Let T: $\mathbb{R}^n \to \mathbb{R}^m$ be given by $T\mathbf{v} = A\mathbf{v}$, where A is an $m \times n$ matrix. Then, ker $T = \{\mathbf{v}: A\mathbf{v} = \mathbf{0}\}$ and range $T = \{\mathbf{w}: A\mathbf{v} = \mathbf{w}$ for some $\mathbf{v} \in \mathbb{R}^n\}$. These two subspaces are called, respectively, the kernel and range of the matrix A. Dim kernel A is called the nullity of A and is denoted by ν, and dim range A is called the rank of A and is denoted by ρ.

Theorem 25. Let A be an $m \times n$ matrix. Then $\rho(A) + \nu(A) = n$.

Theorem 26. Let A be an $n \times n$ matrix. Then A is invertible if and only if $\rho(A) = n$.

Theorem 27. The system $A\mathbf{x} = \mathbf{b}$ has at least one solution if and only if A and the augmented matrix $(A, \mathbf{b})$ have the same rank.

C. Matrix Representation of A Linear Transformation

In Example 34 we saw that every $m \times n$ matrix A gives rise to a linear transformation from $\mathbb{R}^n$ to $\mathbb{R}^m$. This result has a very general converse.

Theorem 28. Let $B_1 = \{\mathbf{v}_1, \mathbf{v}_2, \ldots, \mathbf{v}_n\}$ be a basis for the vector space V, let $B_2 = \{\mathbf{w}_1, \mathbf{w}_2, \ldots, \mathbf{w}_m\}$ be a basis for the vector space W and suppose that T: $V \to W$ is a linear transformation. Then there exists a unique $m \times n$ matrix A_T such that

$$(T\mathbf{v})_{B_2} = A_T(\mathbf{v})_{B_1} \tag{41}$$

for every $\mathbf{v} \in V$. In Eq. (41), $(T\mathbf{v})_{B_2}$ denotes the representation of $T\mathbf{v}$ in W as a linear combination of the vectors in B_2. The notation $(\mathbf{v})_{B_1}$ denotes the representation of $\mathbf{v} \in V$ as a linear combination of the vectors in B_1.

1. Transformation Matrix

The matrix A_T in Theorem 28 is called the transformation matrix corresponding to T.

EXAMPLE 42. Let T: $\mathbb{R}^3 \to \mathbb{R}^4$ be defined by

$$T\begin{pmatrix} x \\ y \\ z \end{pmatrix} = \begin{pmatrix} x - y \\ y + z \\ 2x - y - z \\ -x + y + 2z \end{pmatrix}$$

Then,

$$A_T = \begin{pmatrix} 1 & -1 & 0 \\ 0 & 1 & 1 \\ 2 & -1 & -1 \\ -1 & 1 & 2 \end{pmatrix}$$

EXAMPLE 43. Let T: $P_3 \to P_2$ be defined by $Tf = f'$. Using the bases $B_1 = \{1, x, x^2, x^3\}$ in P_3 and $B_2 = \{1, x, x^2\}$ in P_2,

$$A_T = \begin{pmatrix} 0 & 1 & 0 & 0 \\ 0 & 0 & 2 & 0 \\ 0 & 0 & 0 & 3 \end{pmatrix}$$

2. Symmetric and Hermitian Matrices

The real $n \times n$ matrix A is symmetric if $A^t = A$. The complex $n \times n$ matrix A is Hermitian if $A^* = A$, where A^* denotes the conjugate transpose of A (the conjugate of each entry of the transpose of A).

3. Self-Adjoint Operator

A linear operator is called self-adjoint if its matrix representation is symmetric (in the real case) or Hermitian.

D. Isomorphisms

In this section we introduce some important terminology and then state a theorem which says that all n-dimensional vector spaces are "essentially" the same.

1. One-to-One Transformation

Let T: $V \to W$ be a linear transformation. Then, T is one to one, written 1–1, if

$$T\mathbf{v}_1 = T\mathbf{v}_2 \quad \text{implies that } \mathbf{v}_1 = \mathbf{v}_2 \tag{42}$$

That is, T is 1–1 if every vector $\mathbf{w}$ in the range of T is the image of exactly one vector in V.

Theorem 29. Let T: $V \to W$ be a linear transformation. Then, T is 1–1 if and only if ker $T = \{\mathbf{0}\}$.

2. Onto Transformation

Let T: $V \to W$ be a linear transformation. Then, T is said to be onto W or, simply, onto if for every $\mathbf{w} \in W$ there is at least one $\mathbf{v} \in V$ such that $T\mathbf{v} = \mathbf{w}$; that is, T is onto W if and only if range $T = W$.

Theorem 30. Let T: $V \to W$ be a linear transformation and suppose that $\dim V = \dim W = n$:

(a) if T is 1–1, then T is onto; (b) if T is onto, then T is 1–1.

Theorem 31. Let T: $V \to W$ be a linear transformation. Suppose that dim $V = n$ and dim $W = m$. Then, (a) if $n > m$, T is not 1–1; (b) if $m > n$, T is not onto.

3. Isomorphism

Let T: $V \to W$ be a linear transformation. Then T is an isomorphism if T is 1–1 and onto.

4. Isomorphic Vector Spaces

The vector spaces V and W are said to be isomorphic if there exists an isomorphism T from V onto W. In this case, we write $V \cong W$.

EXAMPLE 44. Let T: $\mathbb{R}^3 \to P_2$ be defined by

$$T\begin{pmatrix} a \\ b \\ c \end{pmatrix} = a + bx + cx^2$$

It is easy to verify that T is linear. Suppose that

$$T\begin{pmatrix} a \\ b \\ c \end{pmatrix} = \mathbf{0} = 0 + 0x + 0x^2$$

Then, $a = b = c = 0$; that is, ker $T = \{\mathbf{0}\}$, and T is 1–1. If $p(x) = a_0 + a_1x + a_2x^2$, then,

$$p(x) = T\begin{pmatrix} a_0 \\ a_1 \\ a_2 \end{pmatrix}$$

This means that range $T = P_2$ and T is onto. Thus, $\mathbb{R}^3 \cong P_2$.

EXAMPLE 45. Let $V = \{f \in C'[0, 1]: f(0) = 0\}$ and $W = C[0, 1]$. Let D: $V \to W$ be given by $Df = f'$. Suppose that $Df = Dg$. Then, $f' = g'$ or $(f - g)' = 0$ and $f(x) - g(x) = c$, a constant. However, $f(0) = g(0) = 0$, so that $c = 0$ and $f = g$. Thus, D is 1–1. Let $g \in C[0, 1]$, and let $f(x) = \int_0^x g(t)\,dt$. Then, from the fundamental theorem of calculus, $f \in C'[0, 1]$ and $f'(x) = g(x)$ for every $x \in [0, 1]$. Moreover, since $\int_0^0 g(t)\,dt = 0$, we have $f(0) = 0$. Thus, for every g in W, there is an f in V such that $Df = g$. Hence, D is onto and we have shown that $V \cong W$.

Theorem 32. Let V and W be two real finite-dimensional vector spaces with dim V = dim W. Then, $V \cong W$.

Theorem 33. If A is an invertible $n \times n$ matrix, then the mapping T: $\mathbb{R}^n \to \mathbb{R}^n$ defined by $T\mathbf{v} = A\mathbf{x}$ is an isomorphism.

Theorem 34. If T: $V \to W$ is an isomorphism, then there exists an isomorphism T^{-1}: $W \to V$ defined as follows: If $T\mathbf{v} = \mathbf{w}$, then $T^{-1}\mathbf{w} = \mathbf{v}$; T^{-1} is called the inverse transformation of T.

Theorem 35. Let A_T be the matrix representation of an isomorphism T: $V \to W$, where dim V = dim $W = n$. Then A_T is invertible, and A_T^{-1} is the matrix representation of T^{-1}.

E. Isometries

1. Isometry

Let V and W be real (or complex) inner product spaces and let T: $V \to W$ be a linear transformation. Then, T is an isometry if, for every $\mathbf{v}_1$, $\mathbf{v}_2 \in V$,

$$(\mathbf{v}_1, \mathbf{v}_2) = (T\mathbf{v}_1, T\mathbf{v}_2) \tag{43}$$

That is, an isometry is a linear transformation that preserves the inner product.

Theorem 36. If T: $V \to W$ is an isometry, then (a)

$$|\mathbf{v}_1|_V = |T\mathbf{v}_1|_W \tag{44}$$

and (b) T is an isomorphism. Because of Eq. (44), isometries are said to be norm preserving.

2. Isometrically Isomorphic Vector Spaces

Two vector spaces V and W are said to be isometrically isomorphic if there exists a linear transformation T: $V \to W$ that is both an isometry and an isomorphism.

Theorem 37. Any two n-dimensional real or complex inner product spaces are isometrically isomorphic.

Theorem 38. If T: $V \to W$ is an isometry, then T^{-1}: $W \to V$ is also an isometry.

3. Unitary Matrix

A complex $n \times n$ matrix U is called unitary if $U^* = U^{-1}$. If U is real and unitary, then $U^* = U^t$ and U is called orthogonal.

Theorem 39. A linear transformation T: $V \to W$ is an isometry if and only if its matrix representation matrix is unitary.

Theorem 40. If $T: V \to W$ is an isometry and if $\mathbf{v}_1, \mathbf{v}_2, \ldots, \mathbf{v}_n$ is an orthonormal basis for V, then $T\mathbf{v}_1, T\mathbf{v}_2, \ldots, T\mathbf{v}_n$ is an orthonormal basis for W.

Corollary. The columns of a unitary matrix form an orthonormal set of vectors.

IV. Eigenvalues and Eigenvectors

A. Definitions and Examples

Let $T: V \to V$ be a linear transformation. In a great variety of applications, it is useful to find a vector $\mathbf{v}$ in V such that $T\mathbf{v}$ and $\mathbf{v}$ are parallel; that is, we seek a vector $\mathbf{v}$ and a scalar λ such that

$$T\mathbf{v} = \lambda\mathbf{v} \tag{45}$$

If $\mathbf{v} \neq \mathbf{0}$ and λ satisfy Eq. (45), then λ is called an eigenvalue of T, and $\mathbf{v}$ is called an eigenvector of T corresponding to the eigenvalue λ. The purpose of this section is to investigate properties of eigenvalues and eigenvectors. If V is finite dimensional, then T can be represented by a matrix A_T. For that reason we shall discuss eigenvalues and eigenvectors of $n \times n$ matrices.

1. Eigenvalue and Eigenvector

Let A be an $n \times n$ matrix with real components. The number λ (real or complex) is called an eigenvalue of A if there is a nonzero vector $\mathbf{v}$ in $\mathbb{C}^n$ such that

$$A\mathbf{v} = \lambda\mathbf{v} \tag{46}$$

The vector $\mathbf{v} \neq \mathbf{0}$ is called an eigenvector of A corresponding to the eigenvalue λ.

Note. The word "eigen" is the German word for "own" or "proper." Eigenvalues are also called proper values, or characteristic values, and eigenvectors are called proper vectors, or characteristic vectors.

Remark. A matrix with real components can have complex eigenvalues and eigenvectors. That is why in the definition we have asserted that $\mathbf{v} \in \mathbb{C}^n$.

Theorem 41. Let A be an $n \times n$ matrix. Then λ is an eigenvalue of A if and only if

$$p(\lambda) = \det(A - \lambda I) = 0 \tag{47}$$

2. Characteristic Equation and Polynomial

Equation (47) is called the characteristic equation of A; $p(\lambda)$ is called the characteristic polynomial of A. Note that $p(\lambda)$ is a polynomial of degree n.

By the fundamental theorem of algebra, any polynomial of degree n with real or complex coefficients has exactly n roots (counting multiplicities). By this we mean, for example, that the polynomial $(\lambda - 1)^5$ has five roots, all equal to the number 1. Since any eigenvalue of A is a root of the characteristic equation of A, we conclude that, counting multiplicities, every $n \times n$ matrix has exactly n eigenvalues.

Theorem 42. Let λ be an eigenvalue of the $n \times n$ matrix A, and let $E_\lambda = \{\mathbf{v}: A\mathbf{v} = \lambda\mathbf{v}\}$. Then E_λ is a subspace of $\mathbb{C}^n$.

3. Eigenspace

Let λ be an eigenvalue of A. The subspace E_λ is called the eigenspace of A corresponding to the eigenvalue λ.

Theorem 43. Let A be an $n \times n$ matrix, and let $\lambda_1, \lambda_2, \ldots, \lambda_m$ be distinct eigenvalues of A with corresponding eigenvectors $\mathbf{v}_1, \mathbf{v}_2, \ldots, \mathbf{v}_m$. Then, $\mathbf{v}_1, \mathbf{v}_2, \ldots, \mathbf{v}_m$ are linearly independent; that is, eigenvectors corresponding to distinct eigenvalues are linearly independent.

The characteristic equation can be factored:

$$p(\lambda) = (\lambda - \lambda_1)^{r_1}(\lambda - \lambda_2)^{r_2} \cdots (\lambda - \lambda_m)^{r_m} = 0 \tag{48}$$

4. Algebraic Multiplicity

The numbers $r_1, r_2, \ldots, r_m$ are called the algebraic multiplicities of the eigenvalues $\lambda_1, \lambda_2, \ldots, \lambda_m$, respectively.

5. Geometric Multiplicity

Let λ be an eigenvalue of the matrix A. Then the geometric multiplicity of λ is the dimension of the eigenspace corresponding to λ (which is the nullity of the matrix $A - \lambda I$); that is, the geometric multiplicity of $\lambda = \dim E_\lambda = \nu(A - \lambda I)$.

Theorem 44. Let λ be an eigenvalue of A. Then the geometric multiplicity of λ is less than or equal to the algebraic multiplicity of λ.

Note. The geometric multiplicity of an eigenvalue is never zero. This follows from the definition, which states that if λ is an eigenvalue, then there exists a *nonzero* eigenvector corresponding to λ.

6. Procedure for Computing Eigenvalues and Eigenvectors

1. Find $p(\lambda) = \det(A - \lambda I)$.
2. Find the roots $\lambda_1, \lambda_2, \ldots, \lambda_m$ of $p(\lambda) = 0$.
3. Corresponding to each eigenvalue λ_i, solve the homogeneous system $(A - \lambda_i I)\mathbf{v} = \mathbf{0}$ to find the eigenvectors.

EXAMPLE 46. Let $A = \begin{pmatrix} 4 & 2 \\ 3 & 3 \end{pmatrix}$. Eigenvalues are $\lambda_1 = 1$ and $\lambda_2 = 6$, with corresponding eigenspaces $E_1 = \text{span}\{\begin{pmatrix} 2 \\ -3 \end{pmatrix}\}$ and $E_6 = \text{span}\{\begin{pmatrix} 1 \\ 1 \end{pmatrix}\}$.

EXAMPLE 47. Let $A = \begin{pmatrix} 3 & -5 \\ 1 & -1 \end{pmatrix}$. Eigenvalues are $\lambda_1 = 1 + i$ and $\lambda_2 = 1 - i$, with corresponding eigenspaces $E_{1+i} = \text{span}\{\begin{pmatrix} 2+i \\ 1 \end{pmatrix}\}$ and $E_{1-i} = \text{span}\{\begin{pmatrix} 2-i \\ 1 \end{pmatrix}\}$.

Theorem 45. The complex eigenvalues and eigenvectors of a real matrix occur in complex conjugate pairs.

EXAMPLE 48. Let $A = \begin{pmatrix} 4 & 1 \\ 0 & 4 \end{pmatrix}$. Then $\lambda = 4$ is an eigenvalue of algebraic multiplicity 2. The geometric multiplicity is 1 because $E_4 = \text{span}\{\begin{pmatrix} 1 \\ 0 \end{pmatrix}\}$.

EXAMPLE 49. Let

$$A = \begin{pmatrix} 3 & 2 & 4 \\ 2 & 0 & 2 \\ 4 & 2 & 3 \end{pmatrix}$$

The eigenvalues are $\lambda_1 = 8$ and $\lambda_2 = -1$ (of algebraic multiplicity 2). Then,

$$E_8 = \text{span}\left\{\begin{pmatrix} 2 \\ 1 \\ 2 \end{pmatrix}\right\}$$

and

$$E_{-1} = \text{span}\left\{\begin{pmatrix} 1 \\ -2 \\ 0 \end{pmatrix}, \begin{pmatrix} 0 \\ -2 \\ 1 \end{pmatrix}\right\}$$

so the geometric multiplicity of -1 is 2.

Let A be an $n \times n$ matrix. Then A has n linearly independent eigenvectors if and only if the geometric multiplicity of every eigenvalue is equal to its algebraic multiplicity. In particular, A has n linearly independent eigenvectors if all the eigenvalues are distinct (since then the algebraic multiplicity of every eigenvalue is 1).

B. Summary

We summarize here many of the results in this article.

Theorem 46. Let A be an $n \times n$ matrix. Then the following ten statements are equivalent; that is, if one is true, all are true:

1. A is invertible;
2. the only solution to the homogeneous system $A\mathbf{x} = \mathbf{0}$ is the trivial solution ($\mathbf{x} = \mathbf{0}$);
3. the system $A\mathbf{x} = \mathbf{b}$ has a unique solution for every n vector $\mathbf{b}$;
4. A can be row reduced to the $n \times n$ identity matrix I_n;
5. the rows (and columns) of A are linearly independent.
6. $\det A \neq 0$;
7. $\nu(A) = 0$;
8. $\rho(A) = n$;
9. the linear transformation T from $\mathbb{R}^n$ to $\mathbb{R}^n$ defined by $T\mathbf{x} = A\mathbf{x}$ is an isomorphism.
10. zero is not an eigenvalue of A.

C. Similar Matrices and Diagonalization

1. Similar Matrices

Two $n \times n$ matrices A and B are said to be similar if there exists an invertible $n \times n$ matrix C such that

$$B = C^{-1}AC \tag{49}$$

The function defined by Eq. (49) that takes the matrix A into the matrix B is called a similarity transformation.

Note. $C^{-1}(A_1 + A_2)C = C^{-1}A_1C + C^{-1}A_2C$ and $C^{-1}(\alpha A)C = \alpha C^{-1}AC$, so that the function defined by Eq. (49) is in fact a linear transformation. This explains the use of the word "transformation" in the definition.

Theorem 47. If A and B are similar $n \times n$ matrices, then A and B have the same characteristic equation and therefore have the same eigenvalues.

2. Diagonalizable Matrix

An $n \times n$ matrix A is diagonalizable if there is a diagonal matrix D such that A is similar to D.

Theorem 48. An $n \times n$ matrix A is diagonalizable if and only if it has n linearly independent eigenvectors. In that case, the diagonal matrix

D, similar to A is given by

$$D = \begin{pmatrix} \lambda_1 & 0 & 0 & \cdots & 0 \\ 0 & \lambda_2 & 0 & \cdots & 0 \\ 0 & 0 & \lambda_3 & \cdots & 0 \\ \vdots & \vdots & \vdots & & \vdots \\ 0 & 0 & 0 & \cdots & \lambda_n \end{pmatrix}$$

where $\lambda_1, \lambda_2, \ldots, \lambda_n$ are the eigenvalues of A. If C is a matrix whose columns are linearly independent eigenvectors of A, then $D = C^{-1}AC$.

Theorem 49. Let A be an $n \times n$ Hermitian matrix. Then the eigenvalues of A are real.

Theorem 50. Let A be a Hermitian $n \times n$ matrix. If λ_1 and λ_2 are distinct eigenvalues with corresponding real eigenvectors $\mathbf{v}_1$ and $\mathbf{v}_2$, then $\mathbf{v}_1$ and $\mathbf{v}_2$ are orthogonal.

Theorem 51. Let A be a Hermitian $n \times n$ matrix. Then, A has n real orthonormal eigenvectors.

Remark. It follows from Theorem 51 that the geometric multiplicity of each eigenvalue of A is equal to its algebraic multiplicity.

3. Unitarily Diagonalizable Matrix

An $n \times n$ matrix A is said to be unitarily diagonalizable if there exists a unitary matrix U such that

$$U^*AU = D \tag{50}$$

where $D = \text{diag}(\lambda_1, \lambda_2, \ldots, \lambda_n)$ and $\lambda_1, \lambda_2, \ldots, \lambda_n$ are the eigenvalues of A.

Note. Remember that U is orthogonal if $U^* = U^{-1}$; hence, Eq. (50) could be written as $U^{-1}AU = D$.

Theorem 52. Let A be a real $n \times n$ matrix. Then A is unitarily diagonalizable if and only if A is symmetric.

D. Quadratic Forms and Conic Sections

A quadratic form in two variables is an expression of the form

$$F(x, y) = ax^2 + bxy + cy^2 \tag{51}$$

where $|a| + |b| + |c| \neq 0$.

Theorem 53. Let

$$A = \begin{pmatrix} a & b/2 \\ b/2 & c \end{pmatrix}$$

Then, if $\mathbf{v} = \binom{x}{y}$, the quadratic form (51) can be written

$$F(x, y) = A\mathbf{v} \cdot \mathbf{v} \tag{52}$$

That is, each quadratic form can be written in the form of Eq. (52), where A is a symmetric matrix. Conversely, if A is a symmetric matrix, then Eq. (52) defines a quadratic form $F(x, y) = A\mathbf{v} \cdot \mathbf{v}$. Since A is real and symmetric, there exists an orthogonal matrix Q such that $Q^tAQ = D$, where D is the diagonal matrix of eigenvalues of A. Let $\binom{x'}{y'} = \mathbf{v}' = Q^t\mathbf{v}$. Then, in the new variables x' and y', Eq. (52) can be rewritten

$$F(x', y') = D\mathbf{v}' \cdot \mathbf{v}' = a'x'^2 + c'y'^2 \tag{53}$$

where a' and c' are the eigenvalues of A.

Let us take another look at the matrix Q. Since Q is real and orthogonal, $1 = \det QQ^{-1} = \det QQ^t = \det Q \det Q^t = \det Q \det Q = (\det Q)^2$. Thus, $\det Q = \pm 1$. If $\det Q = -1$, we can interchange the rows of Q to make the determinant of this new Q equal to 1. Then, it can be shown that

$$Q = \begin{pmatrix} \cos\theta & -\sin\theta \\ \sin\theta & \cos\theta \end{pmatrix}$$

for some number θ with $0 \leq \theta < 2\pi$. That is, Q represents the linear transformation that rotates a vector through an angle θ.

Theorem 54. *Principal axes theorem in* $\mathbb{R}^2$. Let

$$ax^2 + bxy + cy^2 = d \tag{54}$$

be a quadratic equation in the variables x and y. Then there exists a unique number θ in $[0, 2\pi)$ such that Eq. (54) can be written in the form

$$a'y'^2 + c'y'^2 = d \tag{55}$$

where x', y' are the axes obtained by rotating the x and y axes through an angle of θ in the counterclockwise direction. Moreover, the numbers a' and c' are the eigenvalues of the matrix

$$A = \begin{pmatrix} a & b/2 \\ b/2 & c \end{pmatrix}$$

The x' and y' axes are called the principal axes of the graph of the quadratic equation [Eq. (54)].

We can use Theorem 54 to identify three important conic sections. Recall that the standard equations of a circle, ellipse, and hyperbola are

circle $\quad x^2 + y^2 = r^2$

ellipse $\quad \dfrac{x^2}{a^2} + \dfrac{y^2}{b^2} = 1$

hyperbola $\frac{x^2}{a^2} - \frac{y^2}{b^2} = 1$ or $\frac{y^2}{a^2} - \frac{x^2}{b^2} = 1$

EXAMPLE 50. We identify the conic section whose equation is

$$x^2 - 4xy + 3y^2 = 6 \tag{56}$$

Here, $A = \begin{pmatrix} 1 & -2 \\ -2 & 3 \end{pmatrix}$ with eigenvalues $2 - \sqrt{5}$ and $2 + \sqrt{5}$. Then Eq. (56) can be rewritten

$$\frac{y'^2}{6/(2+\sqrt{5})} - \frac{x'^2}{6/(\sqrt{5}-2)} = 1$$

This is a standard hyperbola rotated through an angle

$$\theta = \cos^{-1} \frac{2}{\sqrt{10 - 2\sqrt{5}}} \approx 31.7^0$$

Theorem 55. If

$$A = \begin{pmatrix} a & b/2 \\ b/2 & c \end{pmatrix},$$

then the quadratic equation $ax^2 + bxy + cy^2 = d$ with $d \neq 0$ is the equation of

1. a hyperbola if $\det A < 0$;
2. an ellipse, circle, or degenerate conic section if $\det A > 0$.
3. a pair of straight lines or a degenerate conic section if $\det A = 0$;
4. if $d = 0$, then the quadratic equation is the equation of two straight lines if $\det A \neq 0$ and the equation of a single line if $\det A = 0$.

A quadratic form can be defined in any number of variables.

Quadratic Form

Let

$$\mathbf{v} = \begin{pmatrix} x_1 \\ x_2 \\ \vdots \\ x_n \end{pmatrix}$$

and let A be a symmetrix $n \times n$ matrix. Then, a quadratic form in $x_1, x_2, \ldots, x_n$ is an expression of the form

$$F(x_1, x_2, \ldots, x_n) = \mathbf{Av} \cdot \mathbf{v} \tag{57}$$

E. Jordan Canonical Form

As we have seen, $n \times n$ matrices with n linearly independent eigenvectors can be brought into an especially nice form by a similarity transformation. Fortunately, as "most" polynomials have distinct roots, "most" matrices will have distinct eigenvalues; however, matrices that are not diagonalizable (that is, do not have n linearly independent eigenvectors) do arise in applications. In this case, it is still possible to show that the matrix is similar to another, simpler matrix, but the new matrix is not diagonal, and the transforming matrix C is harder to obtain.

To discuss this case fully, we define the matrix N_k to be the $k \times k$ matrix

$$N_k = \begin{pmatrix} 0 & 1 & 0 & \cdots & 0 \\ 0 & 0 & 1 & \cdots & 0 \\ \vdots & \vdots & \vdots & & \vdots \\ 0 & 0 & 0 & \cdots & 1 \\ 0 & 0 & 0 & \cdots & 0 \end{pmatrix} \tag{58}$$

Note that N_k is the matrix with 1's above the main diagonal and 0's everywhere else. We next define a $k \times k$ Jordan block matrix $B(\lambda)$ by

$$B(\lambda) = \lambda I + N_k = \begin{pmatrix} \lambda & 1 & 0 & \cdots & 0 & 0 \\ 0 & \lambda & 1 & \cdots & 0 & 0 \\ \vdots & \vdots & \vdots & & \vdots & \vdots \\ 0 & 0 & & \cdots & \lambda & 1 \\ 0 & 0 & & \cdots & 0 & \lambda \end{pmatrix} \tag{59}$$

Note. We can (and often will) have a 1×1 Jordan block matrix. Such a matrix takes the form $B(\lambda) = (\lambda)$.

Jordan Matrix

A Jordan matrix J has the form

$$J = \begin{pmatrix} B_1(\lambda_1) & 0 & & 0 \\ 0 & B_2(\lambda_2) & \cdots & 0 \\ \vdots & \vdots & & \vdots \\ 0 & 0 & \cdots & B_r(\lambda_r) \end{pmatrix}$$

where each $B_j(\lambda_j)$ is a Jordan block matrix. Thus, a Jordan matrix is a matrix with Jordan block matrices down the diagonal and zeros everywhere else.

Theorem 56. Let A be an $n \times n$ matrix. Then, there exists an invertible $n \times n$ matrix C

such that

$$C^{-1}AC = J \tag{60}$$

where J is a Jordan matrix whose diagonal elements are the eigenvalues of A. Moreover, J is unique except for the order in which the Jordan blocks appear; J is called the Jordan canonical form of the matrix A.

Theorem 57. Let λ_i be an eigenvalue of A with algebraic multiplicity r_i and geometric multiplicity s_i. If $\lambda_1, \lambda_2, \ldots, \lambda_k$ are the eigenvalues of A, then the number of 1's above the diagonal of the Jordan canonical form of A equals

$$(r_1 - s_1) + (r_2 - s_2) + \cdots + (r_k - s_k)$$

$$= \sum_{i=1}^{k} r_i - \sum_{i=1}^{k} s_i = n - \sum_{i=1}^{k} s_i$$

There are procedures for computing the Jordan canonical form when A is not diagonalizable, but these are too involved to be discussed in this survey article.

F. The Cayley–Hamilton Theorem

If $p(x) = a_0 + a_1x + a_2x^2 + \cdots + a_nx^n$ and if A is a square matrix, then $p(A)$ is defined by

$$p(A) = a_0I + a_1A + a_2A^2 + \cdots + a_nA^n$$

Theorem 58. *The Cayley–Hamilton theorem.* Every square matrix satisfies its own characteristic equation; that is, if $p(\lambda) = 0$ is the characteristic equation of A, then $p(A) = 0$.

V. Two Applications of Linear Algebra

A. Linear Systems of Differential Equations

Consider the following system of n linear differential equations in n unknown functions:

$$\begin{aligned} x_1'(t) &= a_{11}x_1(t) + a_{12}x_2(t) + \cdots + a_{1n}x_n(t) \\ x_2'(t) &= a_{21}x_1(t) + a_{22}x_2(t) + \cdots + a_{2n}x_n(t) \\ &\vdots \qquad\qquad\qquad\qquad \vdots \\ x_n'(t) &= a_{n1}x_1(t) + a_{n2}x_2(t) + \cdots + a_{nn}x_n(t) \end{aligned} \tag{61}$$

where the a_{ij}'s are real numbers. The system (65) is called an $n \times n$ first-order system of linear differential equations. The term "first order" means that only first derivatives occur in the system.

Now, let

$$\mathbf{x}(t) = \begin{pmatrix} x_1(t) \\ x_2(t) \\ \vdots \\ x_n(t) \end{pmatrix}$$

Here, $\mathbf{x}(t)$ is called a vector function.

$$\mathbf{x}'(t) = \begin{pmatrix} x_1'(t) \\ x_2'(t) \\ \vdots \\ x_n'(t) \end{pmatrix}$$

Then, if we define the $n \times n$ matrix

$$A = \begin{pmatrix} a_{11} & a_{12} & \cdots & a_{1n} \\ a_{21} & a_{22} & \cdots & a_{2n} \\ \vdots & \vdots & & \vdots \\ a_{n1} & a_{n2} & \cdots & a_{nn} \end{pmatrix},$$

the system (65) can be written in the form

$$\mathbf{x}'(t) = A\mathbf{x}(t) \tag{62}$$

1. The Matrix e^A

Let A be an $n \times n$ matrix with real (or complex) entries. Then, e^A is an $n \times n$ matrix defined by

$$e^A = I + A + \frac{A^2}{2!} + \frac{A^3}{3!} + \frac{A^4}{4!} + \cdots \tag{63}$$

Theorem 59. The series in (63) converges for every square matrix A.

Theorem 60. Each column of e^{At} is a solution vector to the system (62), and the columns of e^{At} are linearly independent.

The matrix e^{At} is called the principal matrix solution to (62).

Theorem 61. If A is diagonalizable, then $e^{At} = Ce^{Dt}C^{-1}$, where D is the diagonal matrix of eigenvalues of A and C is a matrix of linearly independent eigevectors of A.

Theorem 62. If $D = \text{diag}\{\lambda_1, \lambda_2, \ldots, \lambda_n\}$, then $e^{Dt} = \text{diag}\{e^{\lambda_1 t}, e^{\lambda_2 t}, \ldots, e^{\lambda_n t}\}$, where $\text{diag}\{\lambda_1, \lambda_2, \ldots, \lambda_n\}$ denotes the diagonal matrix with numbers $\lambda_1, \lambda_2, \ldots, \lambda_n$ along the main diagonal.

Theorem 63. If A is not diagonalizable, then there exists an invertible matrix C such that $e^{At} = Ce^{Jt}C^{-1}$, where J is the Jordan canonical form of A.

B. Multivariate Statistics[1]

In the theory of multivariate analysis, we consider the joint distribution of n random variables $y_1, y_2, \ldots, y_n$, which we generally write as the elements of a column vector $\mathbf{y}$, where

$$\mathbf{y} = \begin{pmatrix} y_1 \\ y_2 \\ \vdots \\ y_n \end{pmatrix}$$

We call this a random $n \times 1$ vector. We are generally interested in the (arithmetic) mean, called the expected value, of each component, in the variance of each component, and the covariance of each pair of elements of $\mathbf{y}$.

The mean of $\mathbf{y}$, which we denote by $\boldsymbol{\mu}$, is an $n \times 1$ vector whose ith component is the mean of y_i; that is,

$$\boldsymbol{\mu} = \begin{pmatrix} \mu_1 \\ \vdots \\ \mu_n \end{pmatrix} = \begin{pmatrix} E(y_1) \\ \vdots \\ E(y_n) \end{pmatrix} = E(\mathbf{y})$$

where $E(y_i)$ represents the expected value of the random variable y_i and $E(\mathbf{y})$ is defined in terms of these elements.

To systematize the variances and covariances of the elements of $\mathbf{y}$, we define an $n \times n$ matrix V, called the covariance of $\mathbf{y}$. The ijth element v_{ij} of V, when $i \neq j$, is the covariance of y_i and y_j; the ith diagonal element v_{ii} of V is the variance of y_i. Thus, the matrix V is a symmetric matrix and is nonnegative. Often, nothing more is known about V; conversely, it is sometimes known that V has a certain form or pattern. The theory of multivariate analysis often centers around an analysis of a covariance matrix V. When this is the case, it may be necessary to find the determinant of V, the eigenvalues of V, the inverse of V if it exists, and perhaps to determine these and other quantities for certain submatrices of V. Among other things, it is often necessary to find marginal and conditional distributions of a subset of $\mathbf{y}$; sometimes it is required to find the moments of $\mathbf{y}$ or the moment generating (or characteristic) function of $\mathbf{y}$. Also, it may be necessary to transform from the vector $\mathbf{y}$ to a new vector $\mathbf{x}$, and this transformation may require the evaluation of a certain determinant called the Jacobian; it may be necessary to find maximum likelihood or least squares estimators of parameters in the distribution of $\mathbf{y}$. Many of these problems can be solved by manipulating vectors and matrices.

[1] Adapted from the introduction in Graybill, *Introduction to Matrices with Applications to Statistics*.

1. Linear Model

The theory of the linear model (sometimes referred to as the general linear hypothesis) can be considered as a part of multivariate analysis; however, it is often considered as a separate subject.

The model can be written as $\mathbf{y} = X\boldsymbol{\beta} + \mathbf{e}$, where $\mathbf{y}$ is an $n \times 1$ random vector of observations; X is an $n \times p$ known matrix of constants; $\boldsymbol{\beta}$ is a $p \times 1$ vector of unknown parameters; and $\mathbf{e}$ is a vector of unknown errors. The e_i terms are generally assumed to have a mean of zero and to have variance σ^2 (unknown), and each pair e_i, e_j, $i \neq j$, is assumed to be uncorrelated.

We can write this model as $\mathbf{y} = \boldsymbol{\mu} + \mathbf{e}$, where $\boldsymbol{\mu} = X\boldsymbol{\beta} = E(\mathbf{y})$ and one of the objectives is to estimate $\boldsymbol{\beta}$ and σ^2. The method of estimation is usually least squares or maximum likelihood. If we denote the estimators by $\hat{\boldsymbol{\beta}}$ and $\hat{\sigma}^2$, respectively, then $\hat{\boldsymbol{\mu}} = X\hat{\boldsymbol{\beta}}$ is a formula for predicting the mean of $\mathbf{y}$ for various values of the matrix X. The system of equations $\mathbf{y} = X\boldsymbol{\beta}$ will in general not have a solution $\boldsymbol{\beta}$ for an observed vector $\mathbf{y}$ and matrix X. If no solution exists, it may be desirable to find some kind of approximate (say, least squares) solution.

Often, we want to test certain hypotheses about the parameters β_i. This is generally done by the technique called analysis of variance. The procedure is to partition $\mathbf{y}'\mathbf{y}$ into a set of quadratic forms such that the following equation obtains:

$$\mathbf{y}'\mathbf{y} = \mathbf{y}'A_1\mathbf{y} + \mathbf{y}'A_2\mathbf{y} + \cdots + \mathbf{y}'A_k\mathbf{y}.$$

The procedures available to test certain hypotheses require that each quadratic form $\mathbf{y}'A_i\mathbf{y}$ be distributed as a noncentral chi-square variable and that the set of quadratic forms be pairwise independent.

Bibliography

Crowe, M. J. (1967). "A History of Vector Analysis," Univ. of Notre Dame Press, South Bend, Indiana.

Fox, L. (1965). "An Introduction to Numerical Linear Algebra," Oxford Univ. Press, New York.

Gantmacher, F. R. (1959). "Matrix Theory," Vols. 1 and 2, Chelsea, Bronx, New York.

Graybill, F. A. (1969). "Introduction to Matrices with Applications in Statistics," Wadsworth, Belmont, California.

Grossman, S. I. (1991). "Elementary Linear Algebra," 4th ed., Saunders, Philadelphia.

Halmos, P. R. (1958). "Finite-Dimensional Vector Spaces," 2nd ed., Van Nostrand-Reinhold, Princeton.

Noble, B., and Daniel, J. W. (1977). "Applied Linear Algebra," 2nd ed., Prentice-Hall, Englewood Cliffs, New Jersey.

Strang, G. (1980). "Linear Algebra and Its Applications," 2nd ed., Academic Press, Orlando.

LINEAR PROGRAMMING

M. J. Fryer *European Business School*

GLOSSARY

Artificial variable: Nonnegative variable introduced to enable an initial basic feasible solution to be found.

Basic feasible solution: Feasible solution in which all but m variables are zero. Such a point corresponds to a vertex of the feasible region.

Basis: Set of nonzero variables in a nondegenerate basic feasible solution.

Coefficient matrix: $m \times n$ Matrix of the coefficients of the n variables (including slack variables) in the m equality constraints.

Degenerate basic feasible solution: Feasible solution in which all but $m - d$ variables are zero, with $d > 0$.

Feasible region: Set of points satisfying all the constraints (including any nonnegativity conditions).

Feasible solution: Any point in the feasible region (not necessarily optimal).

Optimal basic feasible solution: Basic feasible solution that corresponds to the (constrained) optimum value of the objective function.

Slack variable: Nonnegative variable used to convert an inequality constraint to an equation.

Linear programming is concerned with optimizing a linear function whose variables are required not only to be nonnegative but also to satisfy a given system of linear inequality or equality constraints. It arises most often in problems of optimizing the use of scarce resources.

As we shall see, such a problem can be written without loss of generality as

$$\text{Maximize} \quad z = \sum_j c_j x_j$$

$$\text{subject to} \quad \sum_j a_{ij} x_j = b_i, \quad i = 1, \ldots, m$$

$$b_i \geq 0, \quad i = 1, \ldots, m$$

$$x_j \geq 0, \quad j = 1, \ldots, n > m$$

where the x's are nonnegative variables whose values are to be determined, and the a's, b's, and c's are known constants. The m constraints are assumed to be linearly independent (i.e. none may be written as a linear combination of any of the others). The problem can also be written in matrix form as

$$\text{Maximize} \quad z = \mathbf{c}'\mathbf{x}$$

$$\text{subject to} \quad \mathbf{Ax} = \mathbf{b}, \qquad \mathbf{b} \geq \mathbf{0}, \quad \mathbf{x} \geq \mathbf{0}$$

where $\mathbf{A}$ is an $m \times n$ matrix (of rank m) whose i,j element is a_{ij}, and $\mathbf{x}$, $\mathbf{b}$, and $\mathbf{c}$ are column vectors of the x's, b's, and c's, respectively. The prime denotes a transpose.

I. Historical Background

Although many early papers had been written (some as far back as 1826), and theorems proved concerning the existence of solutions for systems of linear inequalities, it was not until the early years of the World War II that serious interest was taken in the subject. This interest stemmed from the fact that several seemingly unconnected problems could be written as linear programs. For example, in 1939 Kantorovich discussed a whole range of models aimed at increasing the efficiency of industrial production processes whose mathematical forms were often linear programs. In 1941, Hitchcock proposed a model to describe the problem of minimizing the total cost of transporting a commodity from a set of distribution points to a set of destinations. This turned out to be a very special type of linear program for which he was able to propose a solution technique.

In 1944, von Neumann and Morgenstern published a book on game theory in which the problem of optimizing one's returns when in strict competition with a rival could be written as a linear program; however, it was not until 1947 that Dantzig [as part of the U.S. Air Force research project Scientific Computation of Optimum Programs (SCOOP)] proposed his now famous simplex algorithm for solving the general linear program. The research team had been working on an interindustry type of economic model based on the input/output analysis of Leontief, and this had lead to a general linear program, as opposed to the more specific forms described earlier. This general solution technique sparked the interest of many researchers and soon led not only to implementations of the algorithm and its variants on the early large-scale computers but also to algorithms for the solution of associated problems, such as integer programs (in which one or more of the variables are also required to be integers) and, later, to quadratic programs (in which the constraints are still linear but the objective function is quadratic). With the present availability of computers of all sizes, much work has been going into finding numerically stable and compact versions of the existing algorithms and developing new algorithms that will handle even larger problems. [*See* COMPUTER ALGORITHMS; OPERATIONS RESEARCH.]

II. Major Areas of Application

The application of linear programming techniques has permeated most areas of operations research and economics, both military and civil—the list seems endless; however, there are a group of "standard" problems that form the basic models for many of them, although each application requires its own refinements. The *diet problem* is concerned with producing a balanced meal at minimum cost. Suppose a nutritionist requires a particular meal to contain at least c_1 units of carbohydrates, c_2 units of protein, c_3 units of fiber, etc.; then these have to be obtained from the foods $F_1, F_2, \ldots,$ presently available. Suppose that food F_i, costing \$$p_i$ per kilo, contains a_{ij} units of c_j; then if x_i represents the amount of this food purchased, the problem can be modeled as

$$\begin{aligned} &\text{Minimize} \quad \sum_i p_i x_i \\ &\text{subject to} \quad \sum_i x_i a_{ij} \geq c_j, \qquad j = 1, 2, \ldots, \\ &\qquad\qquad\qquad x_i \geq 0, \qquad i = 1, 2, \ldots \end{aligned}$$

a linear program with inequality constraints. This model, in common with all linear models, assumes constant returns to scale, so that no benefit is to be obtained from buying in bulk. It also assumes that any amount of each food may be purchased. These assumptions become less restrictive the greater the number of meals that are to be produced.

The *blending problem* is concerned with mixing various ingredients to produce a mix of a given standard. Consider the problem of an oil company that sells three grades of fuel oil that are of a guaranteed quality with regard to impurities such as sulfur and to thermal capacity. It must blend together the available fuel oils from its refineries and from other importers to make up products with the required specifications so as to minimize its cost (or maximize the profit). Suppose that for each oil j the company wishes to produce g_i gallons of product i ($i = 1, 2, 3$) and that there are k_j gallons available at a cost of \$$c_j$ per gallon. Suppose also that (a) the sulfur content of fuel j is s_j%, but for product i it should be no greater than S_i%; and (b) the thermal capacity of fuel j is t_j per gallon, but for product i it should be at least T_i per gallon. Then, if x_{ij} gallons of fuel j are to be used to produce grade i, the problem can be written

$$\text{Minimize} \quad \sum_i \sum_j c_j x_{ij}$$

$$\begin{aligned} &\text{subject to} \quad \sum_i x_{ij} \leq k_j, \qquad j = 1, \ldots \\ &\left.\begin{aligned} &\sum_j x_{ij} \geq g_i \\ &\sum_j x_{ij} s_j \leq S_i \sum_j x_{ij} \\ &\sum_j x_{ij} t_j \geq T_i \end{aligned}\right\} \quad i = 1, 2, 3 \\ &\qquad x_{ij} \geq 0, \qquad \text{for all} \quad i \text{ and } j \end{aligned}$$

When the third set of constraints is rearranged, this becomes a linear program with inequality constraints.

TABLE I. Trim-Loss Combinations

	Width (m)			
Combination	1	1.7	3.5	Waste
1	5	0	0	0
2	3	1	0	0.3
3	1	2	0	0.6
4	1	0	1	0.5

The *trim-loss problem* is illustrated by the following example. A manufacturer produces polyethylene in sheets 5 m wide × 100 m long. He is prepared to sell the sheeting in 100-m lengths but cut to any width to satisfy his customers' demands. He obviously wishes to do this in such a way as to minimize any waste. Suppose, on a particular day he has orders for eighty 1-m, forty 1.7-m, and thirty 3.5-m widths; how should the order be made up? Consider all sensible combinations of the three widths that will fit into 5 m, as shown in Table I. Suppose that x_i sheets are cut with combination i, then the constraints are

$$5x_1 + 3x_2 + 1x_3 + 1x_4 \geq 80$$
$$0x_1 + 1x_2 + 2x_3 + 0x_4 \geq 40$$
$$0x_1 + 0x_2 + 0x_3 + 1x_4 \geq 30$$
$$x_1, \ldots, x_4 \geq 0$$

If overproduction is to be included in the loss, then the amount corresponding to the first order is given by $x_5 = 5x_1 + 3x_2 + x_3 + x_4 - 80$. If x_6 and x_7 denote the corresponding overproduction on the other two orders, the problem is

$$\text{Minimize} \quad 0x_1 + 0.3x_2 + 0.6x_3 + 0.5x_4 + x_5 + 1.7x_6 + 3.5x_7$$

subject to

$$5x_1 + 3x_2 + x_3 + x_4 - x_5 = 80$$
$$x_2 + 2x_3 - x_6 = 40$$
$$x_4 - x_7 = 30$$

where $x_1, \ldots, x_7$ are nonnegative integers. This is a linear program with equality constraints, but it is the fact that the variables are also required to be integers that makes the solution more difficult.

The *knapsack problem* (also an integer problem) gets its name from the following situation. A climber wishes to take as much useful equipment and food as possible on a lengthy climb but is limited by the total weight W he can comfortably carry. If the "value" to him (or utility) of item i is u_i and its weight is w_i, then his problem can be modeled as

$$\text{Maximize} \quad \sum_i x_i u_i$$
$$\text{subject to} \quad \sum_i x_i w_i \leq W$$

where x_i is a nonnegative integer for all i.

There are many other "standard" problems in linear programming, and some of these are dealt with later in the context of their special solution algorithms. [*See* LINEAR SYSTEMS OF ALGEBRAIC EQUATIONS (COMPUTER SCIENCE).]

III. The Simplex Algorithm

A. A Graphical Example

Consider the following two-dimensional linear program with inequality constraints:

$$\text{Maximize} \quad z = 3x_1 + 2x_2$$
$$\text{subject to} \quad 4x_1 + 4x_2 \leq 21 \qquad (1)$$
$$-2x_1 + x_2 \leq 2 \qquad (2)$$
$$2x_1 + x_2 \leq 8 \qquad (3)$$
$$2x_1 - x_2 \leq 6 \qquad (4)$$
$$x_1 \geq 0 \qquad (5)$$
$$x_2 \geq 0 \qquad (6)$$

The set of points satisfying the constraints (the feasible region) is shown shaded in Fig. 1. The lines producing the shading are all of the form $3x_1 + 2x_2 = z$, for various values of z, the direction in which z increases being shown by the arrow. From this it can be seen that the largest value of z within the feasible region is at the vertex C with coordinates $(\frac{11}{4}, \frac{5}{2})$.

For a two-dimensional problem with a bounded feasible region this type of reasoning

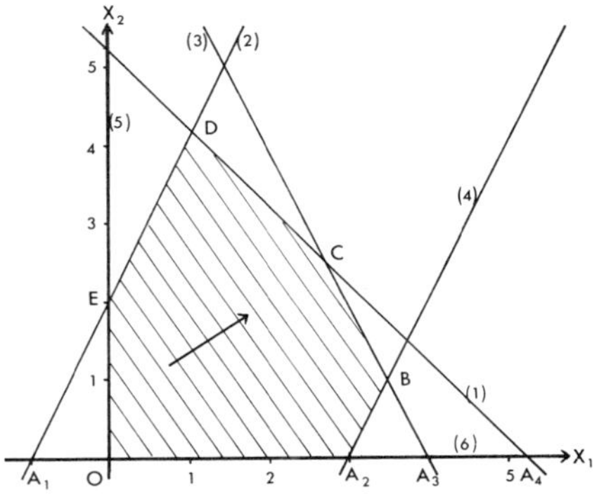

FIG. 1. The feasible region with the contours of the objective function superimposed.

will always lead to the conclusion that the optimum lies at a vertex (and possibly at any point along a whole boundary line). This result is, however, not restricted to two-dimensional problems but is quite general. Consequently, one technique for obtaining the solution to a linear program is to evaluate the objective function at each of the feasible vertices and to choose that one (or perhaps those) with the largest value of z. However, after a little thought this can be seen not to be such a sensible strategy, since if there are just 10 inequality constraints in 10 nonnegative variables—a very modest problem—then there are some ${}^{20}C_{10} = 184{,}756$ vertices (not all feasible), and the number rises dramatically as either the number of variables or constraints is increased. Fortunately, Dantzig produced a solution strategy, known as the simplex algorithm, which enables much larger problems to be solved in a reasonable amount of computer time. The idea behind the algorithm is, having found one feasible vertex, to move along a boundary edge of the feasible region to a neighboring vertex that has a higher value for the objective function. In this way only a fraction of the total number of feasible vertices are actually visited.

B. The Tabular Solution

The solution strategy assumes that the problem has a finite nonempty feasible region (so that at least one feasible point exists) and that the right-hand side (RHS) of each constraint is positive. The first stage is to rewrite the constraints, where necessary, so that the RHS terms are positive and then convert each inequality into an equality by incorporating a nonnegative "slack" variable. The two-dimensional example is then increased to one of six dimensions, becoming

Maximize $z = 3x_1 + 2x_2$

subject to

$$\begin{aligned} 4x_1 + 4x_2 + x_3 \quad\quad\quad\quad &= 21 \\ -2x_1 + x_2 \quad + x_4 \quad\quad &= 2 \\ 2x_1 + x_2 \quad\quad + x_5 \quad &= 8 \\ 2x_1 - x_2 \quad\quad\quad + x_6 &= 6 \end{aligned}$$

$$x_1, x_2, \ldots, x_6 \geq 0$$

The importance of this step is that a boundary of the feasible region can now be defined simply by a single variable being set zero. For example, in Fig. 1 boundary (1) is defined by $x_3 = 0$. Similarly, the vertex C (the intersection of two boundaries) is defined by x_3 and x_5, both being zero. Generally, if there were m equations in n variables (including the slacks), a vertex would be defined by $n - m$ variables being set zero. The other variables are necessarily positive except in so-called degenerate cases.

The simplex algorithm requires that all feasible vertices be nondegenerate. In two-dimensions this means that only two boundary lines should pass through any feasible vertex (i.e., that only two variables should be zero at each such vertex). Generally, only $n - m$ variables should be zero at a feasible vertex. (Techniques to circumvent this restriction are discussed later.) Here, the vertex defined by $x_1 = 0$ and $x_2 = 0$ is feasible, since it corresponds to $x_3 = 21$, $x_4 = 2$, $x_5 = 8$, and $x_6 = 6$, with $z = 0$. These nonzero variables are said to form the "basis," and the constraints are said to be in "standard form" with respect to the basis when each variable in the basis occurs in one and only one constraint, each has a unit coefficient, and, furthermore, the RHS terms are all positive. It is these properties that make the computation of the values for the basis variables so straightforward. For ease of computation, the problem is displayed in a tabular form in the first part of Table II. The elements of columns 3–9 in rows 3–6 correspond to the coefficients of x_1–x_6 and the RHS element for each of the constraints. The coefficients of the objective function are placed in the top row above the corresponding variable, and its initial value 0 above the RHS column. The z row is repeated in row 7 to give this section (or tableau) the same structure as later tableaux. Each current basis variable is listed in column 2 alongside the constraint in which it appears, its value being given by the RHS entry. The algorithm now requires that a neighboring vertex be found in a direction of z increasing, hence, this new vertex must have two variables zero, just one of them being chosen from x_1 and x_2. Now the coefficients in the objective function of both x_1 and x_2 are positive, so z increases as either is increased. Suppose it is decided to make x_1 positive (the x_1 column is now known as the pivot column). As a general rule, when there is a choice it is best to choose the variable with the largest positive coefficient in the objective function to correspond to the pivot column, since on average this leads to the smallest number of iterations. One of the variables must now leave the basis, but which? Consider each in turn: If x_3 leaves the basis, then $x_3 = 0$, and the constraints give $x_1 = \frac{21}{4}$ $x_4 = \frac{25}{2}$,

TABLE II. Tabular Solution

Basis:		3	2	0	0	0	0	0	
μ	x	x_1	x_2	x_3	x_4	x_5	x_6	RHS	Ratio
0	x_3	4	4	1	0	0	0	21	21/4
0	x_4	−2	1	0	1	0	0	2	$2/-2 < 0$
0	x_5	2	1	0	0	1	0	8	8/2 = 4
0	x_6	[2]	−1	0	0	0	1	6	6/2 = (3)
	z^a	(3)	2	0	0	0	0	0	
0	x_3	0	6	1	0	0	−2	9	3/2
0	x_4	0	0	0	1	0	1	8	Infinite
0	x_5	0	[2]	0	0	1	−1	2	(1)
3	x_1	1	$-\frac{1}{2}$	0	0	0	$\frac{1}{2}$	3	<0
	z	0	$(\frac{7}{2})$	0	0	0	$-\frac{3}{2}$	−9	
0	x_3	0	0	1	0	−3	[1]	3	(3)
0	x_4	0	0	0	1	0	1	8	8
2	x_2	0	1	0	0	$\frac{1}{2}$	$-\frac{1}{2}$	1	<0
3	x_1	1	0	0	0	$\frac{1}{4}$	$\frac{1}{4}$	$\frac{7}{2}$	14
	z	0	0	0	0	$-\frac{7}{4}$	$(\frac{1}{4})$	$-\frac{25}{2}$	
0	x_6	0	0	1	0	−3	1	3	
0	x_4	0	0	−1	1	3	0	5	
2	x_2	0	1	$\frac{1}{2}$	0	−1	0	$\frac{5}{2}$	
3	x_1	1	0	$-\frac{1}{4}$	0	1	0	$\frac{11}{4}$	
	z	0	0	$-\frac{1}{4}$	0	−1	0	$-\frac{53}{4}$	

[a] The z row can be interpreted as either the updated objective function or the Lagrangian. In the latter case, the column headed μ gives the values of the local multipliers.

$x_5 = -\frac{5}{2}$, and $x_6 = \frac{9}{2}$. Similarly, if $x_4 = 0$, then $x_1 = -1$, $x_3 = 25$, $x_5 = 10$, $x_6 = 8$. If $x_5 = 0$, then $x_1 = 4$, $x_3 = 5$, $x_4 = 10$, $x_6 = -2$, and if $x_6 = 0$, then $x_1 = 3$, $x_3 = 9$, $x_4 = 8$, $x_5 = 2$. These points correspond to the vertices A_4, A_1, A_3, and A_2, respectively in Fig. 1. Of course only A_2 is feasible, and this can be seen from the values for x_1 alone, since the only feasible vertex along $x_1 > 0$ must be the nearest to $x_1 = 0$. Hence the smallest positive value for x_1 is chosen (obtained by forming the ratio of the RHS term to the coefficient of x_1 in each of the constraints). The row that contains this least positive ratio is known as the pivot row, and the element at the intersection of the pivot row and pivot column as the pivot element. The first iteration of the simplex procedure is now complete and the working is shown in a tabular form as the first section (or *tableau*) of Table II.

The elements that define the pivot row and columns are in parentheses, and the pivot element is in square brackets. For the moment we disregard the first column. Before the second iteration is started it is algebraically convenient to put the constraints in standard form with respect to the new basis (x_3, x_4, x_5, x_1). To achieve this, the coefficient of the pivot element is reduced to unity by dividing the fourth constraint by 2. The coefficient of x_1 in all the other constraints is then made zero by subtracting suitable multiples of the reduced pivot row. This process is known as "pivoting." In this example, the following row transformations are performed:

$$r_4' = \tfrac{1}{2}r_4, \qquad r_2' = r_2 + 2r_4'$$
$$r_1' = r_1 - 4r_4' \qquad r_5' = r_5 - 2r_4'$$

where r_i denotes the existing row i and r_i' the new row i, So that, for example, the new first row is obtained by subtracting 4 times the new fourth row from the existing first row. This leads to the equivalent set of constraints:

$$\begin{aligned} 6x_2 + x_3 \qquad\qquad &- 2x_6 = 9 \\ x_4 \qquad &+ x_6 = 8 \\ 2x_2 \qquad\qquad &+ x_5 - x_6 = 2 \\ x_1 - \tfrac{1}{2}x_2 \qquad\qquad &+ \tfrac{1}{2}x_6 = 3 \end{aligned}$$

which is in standard form with respect to the new basis so that the current solution $x_3 = 9$, $x_4 = 8$, $x_5 = 2$, $x_1 = 3$ (with $x_2 = x_6 = 0$) can be read directly from the RHS column. Now, in order to be able to decide which variable should enter the basis at the next stage, the z function must be written in terms of the nonbasis variables only. This is accomplished by using the pivot row to eliminate the pivot variable from the z function, giving

$$z - 9 = \tfrac{7}{2}x_2 - \tfrac{3}{2}x_6$$

where that the current value of z is 9. These computations are shown in the second tableau of Table II. The process is continued as before, this time bringing x_2 into the basis. This iteration leads to the vertex B and the next to vertex C, the optimum. These computations are summarized in the remaining tableaux of Table II.

C. Practical Problems in Using the Algorithm

1. Minimization

A minimization problem can be solved by maximizing the negative of the objective function, since min $z = -\max(-z)$.

2. The Initial Basic Feasible Solution

The simplex algorithm requires that an initial basic feasible solution be known, and if all the constraints are initially inequalities similar in form to those of the example, then the slack variables will provide such an initial basis. However, this will not always be the case, as can be seen from the following example:

$$\text{Maximize} \quad z = 2x_1 + 3x_2 + 4x_3$$

$$\text{subject to} \quad \begin{aligned} 3x_1 - x_2 + x_3 &\leq 4 \\ x_1 + x_2 + x_3 &\geq 5 \\ 2x_1 + x_2 - 3x_3 &= 6 \\ x_1, x_2, x_3 &\geq 0 \end{aligned}$$

If slack variables x_4 and x_5 are introduced, the constraints become

$$\begin{aligned} 3x_1 - x_2 + x_3 + x_4 &= 4 \\ x_1 + x_2 + x_3 - x_5 &= 5 \\ 2x_1 + x_2 - 3x_3 &= 6 \\ x_1, x_2, \ldots, x_5 &\geq 0 \end{aligned}$$

This time there is no obvious initial basic feasible solution, even though x_4 has a positive sign. Of course it is possible in such a small problem to find an initial feasible basis by setting two variables zero at a time and solving for the remainder until a feasible solution is obtained, but this is not a sensible strategy for larger problems. Instead, the dimensions of the problem are increased by adding nonnegative "artificial" variables, one for each constraint that is not in standard form with respect to some existing variables. Now, since these artificial variables have nothing to do with the problem at hand, they must be made zero in the final solution. To accomplish this, the problem is solved in two stages. In the first, a new objective function is used that is constructed so that the artificial variables will be forced to become zero at its optimum. For this example the two artificial variables x_6 and x_7 are added, and the first stage then consists of solving the following problem:

$$\text{Maximize} \quad z = -x_6 - x_7$$

subject to

$$\begin{aligned} 3x_1 - x_2 + x_3 + x_4 &= 4 \\ x_1 + x_2 + x_3 - x_5 + x_6 &= 5 \\ 2x_1 + x_2 - 3x_3 + x_7 &= 6 \\ x_1, x_2, \ldots, x_7 &\geq 0 \end{aligned}$$

The iterations are performed as usual until x_6 and x_7 both leave the basis. The optimum value for z is zero, and when this is attained, the values for the other variables will then correspond to a feasible solution to the original problem. In stage 2, the artificial variables are discarded and the original objective function used to complete the solution. (Remember to eliminate the basis variables from the objective function before choosing the pivot column!)

An alternative approach is to incorporate the artificial variables directly into the original objective function. If their coefficients are chosen to be both large and negative, then, provided they are large enough, the artificial variables will be forced to be zero at the optimum of this extended problem. The remainder of the solution will, of course, be the solution for the original problem.

3. Degenerate Solutions

If at a feasible vertex one or more basis variables happen also to be zero (e.g., in two dimensions when three or more boundary lines pass through a vertex), then the solution is said to be degenerate, and the simplex algorithm breaks down. The technique used to circumvent this difficulty is to replace any "offending zeroes" in the RHS column by ϵ, a small undefined positive constant. This has the effect of moving the corresponding boundaries slightly to produce extra vertices, each with the correct number of boundaries passing through them. The computations continue in terms of ϵ until the degeneracy has disappeared, at which time each ϵ is set zero.

In certain circumstances, multiple degeneracies can result in "cycling"; that is, a sequence of iterations repeating itself for ever. This can be overcome by the simple expedient of choosing from among alternative pivot columns at random. Fortunately, cycling seems to occur very infrequently in practice.

4. Multiple Solutions

If in the final tableau a nonbasis variable has a zero coefficient in the objective function, then that variable can be introduced into the basis without changing the value of z. Consequently, the objective function will attain its maximum value at more than one vertex, and, in fact, at any point on the line segment joining them. This can be very useful in practical problems because a subsidiary objective function can then be used to choose from among these alternative solutions.

5. Infinite Solutions

Although the simplex algorithm requires the feasible region to be bounded, it is robust enough to handle unbounded regions. If a pivot column corresponds to a boundary that has no finite vertex in the direction of its variable increasing, then the ratio column will have no finite positive terms. This situation usually reflects a poorly defined problem.

6. Unconstrained Variables

In many problems, not all of the variables will be constrained to be nonnegative. Such problems can be accommodated by replacing each unconstrained variable by the difference of two nonnegative variables. For example, if x is not required to be nonnegative, it would be replaced by $x_1 - x_2$, say, where $x_1 \geq 0$ and $x_2 \geq 0$.

IV. The Revised Simplex Algorithm

A. The Lagrange Formulation

An alternative derivation of the simplex algorithm is obtained through the use of Lagrange multipliers and recourse to the Kuhn–Tucker theorem. This leads naturally to the revised simplex algorithm.

After all slack variables have been incorporated, the corresponding Lagrangian with multipliers $\lambda_1, \ldots, \lambda_m$ is

$$L = \sum_j c_j x_j - \sum_i \lambda_i \left(\sum_j a_{ij} x_j - b_i \right)$$

with $x_j \geq 0\ j = 1, \ldots, n$. The Kuhn–Tucker necessary and sufficient conditions for an optimum solution to this problem (assuming that the feasible region is finite and contains at least one internal point) are

$$\left.\begin{aligned} \partial L/\partial x_j &= c_j - \sum_i \lambda_i a_{ij} \leq 0 \quad &(7)\\ x_j &\geq 0 \quad &(8)\\ x_j\, \partial L/\partial x_j &= 0 \quad &(9)\end{aligned}\right\} j = 1, \ldots, n$$

$$\partial L/\partial \lambda_i = -\sum_j a_{ij} x_j + b_i = 0 \qquad i = 1, \ldots, m \qquad (10)$$

Conditions (8) and (10) just require the optimal solution to be feasible, whereas condition (9) (the complementary slackness condition) states that if $x_j > 0$, then $\partial L/\partial x_j$, the coefficient of x_j in L, should be zero. In other words, the multipliers are chosen to make the coefficients in L of the basis variables zero. In this case we see from Eq. (7) that the multipliers have to satisfy a linear constraint. Now since there are m multipliers, there cannot in general be more then m such constraints. Hence only $n - m$ of the x_j's will be zero, a condition that corresponds to a vertex solution. The simplex algorithm insists that at every iteration, conditions (8)–(10) be satisfied and that the basis variables should be chosen to improve condition (7) at the next stage. It is instructive to consider the iterative procedure in matrix terms. The pivoting operation can be considered as premultiplying the constraint matrices by the inverse of a nonsingular matrix $\mathbf{B}$ such that at each iteration, the constraints after pivoting, $\mathbf{A}_1\mathbf{x} = \mathbf{b}_1$, are related to the original constraints as follows:

$$\begin{aligned} L &= \mathbf{c}'\mathbf{x} - \boldsymbol{\lambda}'(\mathbf{Ax} - \mathbf{b}) \\ &= \mathbf{c}'\mathbf{x} - \boldsymbol{\lambda}'(\mathbf{BB}^{-1})(\mathbf{Ax} - \mathbf{b}) \\ &= \mathbf{c}'\mathbf{x} - (\boldsymbol{\lambda}'\mathbf{B})(\mathbf{B}^{-1}\mathbf{Ax} - \mathbf{B}^{-1}\mathbf{b}) \\ &= \mathbf{c}'\mathbf{x} - \boldsymbol{\mu}'(\mathbf{A}_1\mathbf{x} - \mathbf{b}_1) \end{aligned}$$

where $\boldsymbol{\mu}' = \boldsymbol{\lambda}'\mathbf{B}$, $\mathbf{A}_1 = \mathbf{B}^{-1}\mathbf{A}$, and $\mathbf{b}_1 = \mathbf{B}^{-1}\mathbf{b}'$.

If "local" multipliers $\boldsymbol{\mu}$ are used, then it can be seen from the structure of $\mathbf{A}_1$ that $\boldsymbol{\mu}_i$, the ith element of $\boldsymbol{\mu}$, equals $c_{[i]}$, the coefficient in z of the ith basis variable $x_{[i]}$. Consequently, the coefficient of x_p in L can be obtained as $c_p - \sum_i c_{[i]}x_{[i]}$. For example, in the last tableau in Table II, the coefficient of x_3 in the Lagrangian is obtained as

$$0 - \{0(1) + 0(-1) + 2(\tfrac{1}{2}) + 3(-\tfrac{1}{4})\} = -\tfrac{1}{4}$$

Numerically, L is identical to the updated z row, but its direct computation makes it easier to use when, for example, alternative objective functions are being considered. The computation of the coefficients in L (still referred to as z in the tableaux) requires an additional column consisting of the $c[i]$, shown as the first column of Table II. If the original basis is represented by $\mathbf{x}_{[0]}$ and its corresponding coefficients in the objective function by $\mathbf{c}_{[0]}$, then $\mathbf{c}_{[0]} - \boldsymbol{\lambda}$ is the coefficient of $\mathbf{x}_{[0]}$ in L at each iteration; hence $\boldsymbol{\lambda}$ can easily be recovered from the tableaux.

The revised simplex algorithm uses the same ideas as the simplex algorithm; it is just the method of obtaining $\mathbf{A}_1$, $\mathbf{b}_1$ and $\boldsymbol{\lambda}$ that varies. Instead of working in terms of local multipliers, it uses the original multipliers $\boldsymbol{\lambda}$, relating each iteration directly back to the original tableau by calculating a new **B** and its inverse. For this reason, it can be made computationally more compact and stable, depending on the numerical algorithm actually used to invert or update **B**.

B. Postoptimal Analysis

Having found an optimal solution to a particular linear program, it is often useful to check how sensitive the result is to changes in one or more of the coefficients. Rather than to change these coefficients and then solve the modified problem *ab initio*, it is usually more convenient and informative to modify the solution of the original problem.

A change, no matter how drastic, in the objective function is easily dealt with because the existing solution will always correspond to a basic feasible solution to the modified problem. A recomputation of the Lagrangian (z row), as discussed in Section IV,A will determine whether the original solution is still optimal, and the iterations can continue if required. The effect of changing coefficients or constants in the constraints can most easily be obtained by writing the change as a linear combination of the basis columns of the initial tableau. The corresponding change in the final tableau will be the same linear combination of those columns in that final tableau. Having absorbed these changes into the final tableau, some pivoting might be necessary to reduce the constraints to standard form again for the evaluation of the Lagrange coefficients. If the solution is still feasible, the iterations can continue as required; if it is not, recourse to another algorithm (such as the dual simplex algorithm) may be necessary. Note that a change in the RHS of constraint i adds λ_i times that change to the value of the objective function (provided that the basis remains optimal) as can be seen from the form of the Lagrangian.

V. Duality

A. The Dual Problem

Associated with each linear program is a "dual" problem, also a linear program, whose formulation and results are closely interwoven with those of the original problem (the "primal"). In fact, the variables of the one are the Lagrange multipliers of the other, and the values of the two objective functions (when finite) are equal. In some circumstances the dual is simpler to solve than the original problem, so its solution is obtained and, using the relationships between the two problems, the solution of the primal deduced. In others (such as the transportation problem), the primal problem is solved in conjunction with the dual. The relationship between the two problems is most easily expressed if the primal problem is rewritten in its equivalent inequality form (replacing an equality by two inequalities, if necessary): If the primal is

$$\begin{aligned} \text{Maximize} \quad & \mathbf{c}'\mathbf{x} \\ \text{subject to} \quad & \mathbf{A}\mathbf{x} \le \mathbf{b} \\ & \mathbf{x} \ge \mathbf{0} \end{aligned}$$

then the dual is

$$\begin{aligned} \text{Minimize} \quad & \mathbf{b}'\boldsymbol{\lambda} \\ \text{subject to} \quad & \mathbf{A}'\boldsymbol{\lambda} \ge \mathbf{c} \\ & \boldsymbol{\lambda} \ge \mathbf{0} \end{aligned}$$

where **b** need not be positive. Note that the maximization problem has constraints with "$\le$" and that the minimization problem has constraints with "$\ge$." The Lagrangian of the primal is

$$\begin{aligned} L_1 &= \mathbf{c}'\mathbf{x} - \boldsymbol{\lambda}'(\mathbf{A}\mathbf{x} - \mathbf{b}) \\ &= -(-\mathbf{b}'\boldsymbol{\lambda} - \mathbf{x}'(\mathbf{c} - \mathbf{A}'\boldsymbol{\lambda})) \\ &= -L_2 \end{aligned}$$

where L_2 is the Lagrangian of the dual, with **x** taking on the role of the multipliers. The Kuhn–Tucker conditions for both problems are identical, and so the optimal solutions of both are the same (if either is finite). Rewriting the dual in the form of the primal and obtaining its dual shows that the dual of a dual is the primal.

For example, to find the dual of the program

$$\begin{aligned} \text{Minimize} \quad & w = 3x_1 + 2x_2 + x_3 \\ \text{subject to} \quad & x_1 + x_2 - x_3 \le 5 \\ & 2x_1 + x_2 + x_3 \ge 6 \\ & x_1 + x_2 + x_3 = 4 \\ & x_1, x_2, x_3 \ge 0 \end{aligned}$$

the objective function is first converted to a maximization and the equality constraint then replaced by the two inequalities

$$x_1 + x_2 + x_3 \le 4$$

$$x_1 + x_2 + x_3 \ge 4$$

The constraints are now rewritten so that the inequalities become "≤," giving

$$\begin{aligned} \text{Maximize} \quad & z = -3x_1 - 2x_2 - x_3 \\ \text{subject to} \quad & x_1 + x_2 - x_3 \le 5 \\ & -2x_1 - x_2 - x_3 \le -6 \\ & x_1 + x_2 + x_3 \le 4 \\ & -x_1 - x_2 - x_3 \le -4 \\ & x_1, x_2, x_3 \ge 0 \end{aligned}$$

The solution to this primal is $\mathbf{x} = (2, 0, 2)$, with the multipliers $\boldsymbol{\lambda} = (0, 2, 1, 0)$, obtained as minus the coefficients of the slack variables in the optimum Lagrangian. The optimum value of z is -8.

The dual of this problem is

$$\begin{aligned} \text{Minimize} \quad & u = 5\lambda_1 - 6\lambda_2 + 4\lambda_3 - 4\lambda_4 \\ \text{subject to} \quad & \lambda_1 - 2\lambda_2 + \lambda_3 - \lambda_4 \ge -3 \\ & \lambda_1 - \lambda_2 + \lambda_3 - \lambda_4 \ge -2 \\ & -\lambda_1 - \lambda_2 + \lambda_3 - \lambda_4 \ge -1 \\ & \lambda_1, \lambda_2, \lambda_3, \lambda_4 \ge 0 \end{aligned}$$

The solution of this dual is found (after making the RHS elements positive and adding slack variables) to be $\boldsymbol{\lambda} = (0, 2, 1, 0)$, with the multipliers $\mathbf{x} = (2, 0, 2)$ and -8 as the optimum value of u. The relationships between the final tableaux of the two problems are summarized in Table III. Note that, due to the relationship between the last two constraints of the primal, the coefficient of λ_4 is always minus that of λ_3. Consequently, a new variable λ_5 can be defined as $\lambda_5 = \lambda_3 - \lambda_4$, a variable that can take both positive and negative values. The dual can then be written in the alternative form:

$$\begin{aligned} \text{Minimize} \quad & u = 5\lambda_1 - 6\lambda_2 + 4\lambda_5 \\ \text{subject to} \quad & \lambda_1 - 2\lambda_2 + \lambda_5 \ge -3 \\ & \lambda_1 - \lambda_2 + \lambda_5 \ge -2 \\ & -\lambda_1 - \lambda_2 + \lambda_5 \ge -1 \\ & \lambda_1, \lambda_2 \ge 0, \quad \lambda_5 \text{ unconstrained} \end{aligned}$$

This is an example of the more general result that the dual of an equality constraint is an unconstrained variable.

TABLE III. Relationship between Primal and Dual Solutions[a]

Primal →	Main variables			Slack variables				
↓	x_1	x_2	x_3	x_4	x_5	x_6	x_7	
Solution	2	0	2	5	0	0	0	− L_2 (z)
L_1 (z)	0	−1	0	0	−2	−1	0	− Solution
	λ_5	λ_6	λ_7	λ_1	λ_2	λ_3	λ_4	
	Slack variables			Main variables				↑ ← *Dual*

[a] For the *primal* problem, read the headings at the top and left of the table; for the *dual* problem, read the headings at the bottom and right of the table.

B. The Dual Algorithm

The close relationship between primal and dual problems can sometimes be used to good effect to move via nonfeasible basic solutions to an optimal solution. If the coefficients of the Lagrangian for such a nonfeasible basis should all happen to be nonpositive, then it can be shown that the corresponding solution of the dual is basic feasible, although not optimal. This is as a consequence of the relationships set out in Table III, which are true not only for optimal solutions but also for individual tableaux. By performing the usual operations to determine the pivot row and column for the dual within the primal tableau, then pivoting as normal, an improved solution to the dual is found that corresponds to a less nonfeasible solution to the primal. These iterations proceed until the optimal solution for the dual is obtained, which must also be optimal for the primal. As an example consider the following pair of problems:

Primal

$$\begin{aligned} \text{Minimize} \quad & x_1 + 2x_2 + 3x_3 \\ \text{subject to} \quad & x_1 + x_2 + x_3 \ge 3 \\ & 2x_1 - x_3 \ge 1 \\ & x_1 + 2x_2 - x_3 \ge 1 \\ & x_1, x_2, x_3 \ge 0 \end{aligned}$$

Dual

$$\begin{aligned} \text{Maximize} \quad & 3\lambda_1 + \lambda_2 + \lambda_3 \\ \text{subject to} \quad & \lambda_1 + 2\lambda_2 + \lambda_3 \le 1 \\ & \lambda_1 + 2\lambda_3 \le 2 \\ & \lambda_1 - \lambda_2 - \lambda_3 \le 3 \\ & \lambda_1, \lambda_2, \lambda_3 \ge 0 \end{aligned}$$

Adding slack variables the problems can be written as follows:

Primal

$$
\begin{aligned}
\text{Maximize} \quad & -x_1 - 2x_2 - 3x_3 \\
\text{subject to} \quad & -x_1 - x_2 - x_3 + x_4 = -3 \\
& 2x_1 + x_3 + x_5 = -1 \\
& x_1 - 2x_2 + x_3 + x_6 = -1 \\
& x_1, \ldots, x_6 \geq 0
\end{aligned}
$$

Dual

$$
\begin{aligned}
\text{Maximize} \quad & 3\lambda_1 + \lambda_2 + \lambda_3 \\
\text{subject to} \quad & \lambda_1 + 2\lambda_2 + \lambda_3 + \lambda_4 = 1 \\
& \lambda_1 + 2\lambda_3 + \lambda_5 = 2 \\
& \lambda_1 - \lambda_2 - \lambda_3 + \lambda_6 = 3 \\
& \lambda_1, \ldots, \lambda_6 \geq 0
\end{aligned}
$$

Note that (0, 0, 0, −3, −1, −1) is a nonfeasible basic solution of the primal and that (0, 0, 0, 1, 2, 3) is a basic feasible solution of the dual. Consider the first tableau in the solution of the dual as shown in Table IV. Now the same computations can be carried out on the primal problem, the pivot row being obtained first by choosing the most negative RHS element and then the pivot column being defined by the smallest positive ratio of the nonbasis coefficients in z to the coefficients in the pivot row. These calculations are repeated on each tableau of the primal after the usual pivoting operations have been performed. The full solution is shown in Table V. Note that, if a nonbasis variable had a zero coefficient in the z row during the computations, then this should be treated as if it were a degeneracy and the zero replaced by $-\epsilon$ ($\epsilon > 0$). The dual algorithm is most often used to best effect in a postoptimal situation, when it is required to add an extra constraint to a problem that has already been solved. An example of its use for this purpose is given in Section VI.

TABLE IV. Dual Problem: Initial Table

Basis: μ	λ	3 λ_1	1 λ_2	1 λ_3	0 λ_4	0 λ_5	0 λ_6	0 RHS	Ratio
0	λ_4	[1]	2	1	1	0	0	1	(1)
0	λ_5	1	0	2	0	1	0	2	2
0	λ_6	1	−1	−1	0	0	1	3	3
	z	(3)	1	1	0	0	0	0	

TABLE V. Primal Problem: Dual Simplex Algorithm

Basis: μ	x	−1 x_1	−2 x_2	−3 x_3	0 x_4	0 x_5	0 x_6	0 RHS
0	x_4	[−1]	−1	−1	1	0	0	(−3)
0	x_5	−2	0	1	0	1	0	−1
0	x_6	1	−2	1	0	0	1	−1
	z	−1	−2	−3	0	0	0	0
Ratio		(1)	2	3	—	—	—	
−1	x_1	1	1	1	−1	0	0	3
0	x_5	0	2	3	−2	1	0	5
0	x_6	0	[−3]	0	1	0	1	(−4)
	z	0	−1	−2	−1	0	0	3
Ratio		—	($\frac{1}{3}$)	$-\infty$	−1	—	—	
−1	x_1	1	0	1	$-\frac{2}{3}$	0	$\frac{1}{3}$	$\frac{5}{3}$
0	x_5	0	0	3	$-\frac{4}{3}$	1	$\frac{2}{3}$	$\frac{7}{3}$
−2	x_2	0	1	0	$-\frac{1}{3}$	0	$-\frac{1}{3}$	$\frac{4}{3}$
	z	0	0	−2	$-\frac{4}{3}$	0	$-\frac{1}{3}$	$\frac{13}{3}$

C. An Economic Interpretation of Duality

In many linear programs derived from economic problems it is possible to provide an economic interpretation of the corresponding dual. As a simple example, let us consider the following problem of maximizing the profit to be made from manufacturing a range of products from a given set of raw materials:

$$\text{Maximize profit} = \sum_{j=1}^{n} c_j x_j$$

subject to

$$\sum_{j=1}^{n} a_{ij} x_j \leq b_i, \qquad i = 1, \ldots, m$$

$$x_j \geq 0, \qquad j = 1, \ldots, n$$

in which x_j represents the number of units of product j to be produced and c_j the corresponding unit profit in dollars, say. The constraints represent restrictions on the amounts of the various inputs (raw materials) that are available. So, for example, no more than b_i units of input i are available, a_{ij} of these being required for each unit of product j. The dual problem is

$$\text{Minimize} \quad Q = \sum_{i=1}^{m} b_i \lambda_i$$

subject to

$$\sum_{i=1}^{m} a_{ij} \lambda_i \geq c_j, \qquad j = 1, \ldots, n$$

$$\lambda_i \geq 0, \qquad i = 1, \ldots, m$$

By considering the dimensions of the terms in constraint j, it can be seen that λ_i must have the dimensions of dollars per unit of input i, since the units of c_j are dollars per unit of product j and of a_{ij} the amount of input i per unit of product j. Economists have christened the optimal value of λ_i the "shadow price" of input i. With this nomenclature, the dual problem can be seen to be

$$\text{Minimize } Q = \sum_{i=1}^{m} \begin{array}{c}\text{Shadow price associated}\\ \text{with input } i\end{array}$$

$$= \text{Total shadow price of all inputs}$$

subject to

$$\sum_{i=1}^{m} \begin{pmatrix}\text{Shadow price of the amount of input}\\ i \text{ used per unit of product } j\end{pmatrix}$$

$$\geq \begin{pmatrix}\text{Unit profit of}\\ \text{product } j\end{pmatrix}, \qquad j = 1, \ldots, n,$$

$$\text{Shadow price of input } i \geq 0, \qquad i = 1, \ldots, m$$

From the complementary slackness conditions it can be seen that if dual constraint j is a strict inequality, then the corresponding multiplier x_j is zero so that there is no production of product j. In economic terms, it does not pay the manufacturer to produce product j if the total shadow price of the components for that product is greater than the corresponding profit.

We recall that λ_i represents the amount by which the primal objective function is increased for a unit increase in b_i (provided that the optimal basis remains unchanged). Now, if constraint i of the primal is not binding, then the supply for input i is strictly greater than its demand. Hence, an additional unit of b_i will not affect the overall profit. This fact is reflected in that the shadow price of input i (λ_i) is zero, and so input i does not contribute to the total shadow price in the dual objective function.

VI. Integer Programming

In many problems it is quite natural to require some variables not only to be nonnegative but also to be integers, such as a variable representing the number of people in the workforce, or, in a more extreme case, when using a zero–one variable to indicate the absence or presence of an attribute. In general, it does not suffice to find a noninteger optimal solution and then convert each variable to an integer by taking its integer part or rounding to the nearest integer, since these techniques can give very misleading suboptimal results, especially when dealing with relatively small integers. Instead, several techniques have been suggested for moving from an optimal solution of the corresponding noninteger problem to the optimal integer solution. Most of these fall into one of two categories: branch and bound, and cutting-plane methods. In the former, the constraints of the original problem are modified sequentially to produce a "tree" of problems, each branch being continued only until it is known to be suboptimal or to result in an integer solution. In the second, extra constraints are added to the original problem, cutting corners from the feasible region that cannot contain the integer solution, until the optimal integer solution is found. Although zero–one problems can be solved by these techniques, more efficient algorithms have been developed for their solution. In particular, many scheduling and combinatoric problems can better be solved by dynamic programming or network analysis.

A. Branch and Bound Methods

Let us assume that the integer linear program P_I is one of maximization, with one or more variables required to be an integer. Dakin's method obtains successively better lower bounds for the objective function of P_I in an iterative fashion: The first such bound is taken to be $-\infty$. The corresponding noninteger problem P_0 is first solved by using the simplex algorithm. Suppose that x_i is required to be integer yet is not so in this solution. If $x_i = b_i$ (not an integer) and $[b_i]$ represents the largest integer not greater than b_i, then x_i must satisfy just one of the extra constraints:

$$x_i \leq [b_i], \qquad x_i \geq [b_i] + 1$$

Each of these constraints is added in turn to P_0, so that the original problem has branched into two enlarged problems P_{11} and P_{12}, only one of which can lead to the optimal solution of P_I. These are both solved (by using the techniques of postoptimal analysis) and their solutions inspected. If either produces an integer solution whose objective function is higher than the current lower bound, then this becomes the new lower bound. If at any stage in this process, there is no problem P_{ij} with a noninteger solution whose objective function is higher than the current lower bound, then that lower bound is the solution to the original problem. Otherwise, that problem P_{ij} with a noninteger solution that has the highest value for the objective function is split into two, as discussed above, and the whole process repeated (omitting any redundant constraints).

B. Cutting-Plane Methods

These methods usually distinguish between "pure" integer programs, in which all variables (including the slack variables) are required to be integers, and "mixed"-integer programs, in which some variables are not required to be integers.

1. Gomory's Pure Integer Algorithm

Since all variables, including the slack variables, are required to be integers, any fractions have to be cleared before slack variables are included and the problem solved by the simplex algorithm. Suppose that at least one basis variable x_i has a noninteger value in the optimal tableau and that the defining constraint has the form

$$x_i + f_{i1}y_1 + f_{i2}y_2 + \cdots + f_{ir}y_r = g_i$$

where g_i is a positive noninteger, and $y_1, \ldots, y_r$ represents the current nonbasis variables. Each coefficient f is now written as the sum of $[f]$, the largest integer not greater than f, and f', the remainder such that $0 < f' < 1$. If g_i is also written in this form, the defining equation can be rewritten as

$$x_i = \{[g_i] - [f_{i1}]y_1 - [f_{i2}]y_2 - \cdots - [f_{ir}]y_r\} + \{g_i' - f_{i1}'y_1 - f_{i2}'y_2 - \cdots - f_{ir}'y_r\}$$

The first expression in braces represents an integer, since each term is an integer by construction. Now, since x_i is to be an integer, the second term must also be an integer; but since $g_i' < 1$ and the other terms can only subtract from it, the term in braces must represent an integer of less than 1 (i.e., an integer of less than or equal 0) giving

$$g_i' - f_{i1}'y_1 - f_{i2}'y_2 - \cdots - f_{ir}'y_r \leq 0$$

The equation of the cutting plane is therefore;

$$-f_{i1}'y_1 - f_{i2}'y_2 - \cdots - f_{ir}'y_r + s = -g_i'$$

where the slack variable s must also be a nonnegative integer. This constraint is added to the linear program, and the solution process can be continued with the dual algorithm. For example, if in the problem considered in Section III, all the variables are required to be integers, then the solution found is not feasible, since neither x_1 nor x_2 is an integer. The defining constraint for x_1 is

$$x_1 - \tfrac{1}{4}x_3 + x_5 = \tfrac{11}{4}$$

which can be written

$$x_1 = \{2 + x_3 - x_5\} + \{\tfrac{3}{4} - \tfrac{3}{4}x_3 - 0x_5\}$$

so that the Gomory cut for x_1 is

$$-\tfrac{3}{4}x_3 - 0x_5 + x_7 = -\tfrac{3}{4}$$

where x_7 is a nonnegative integer slack variable. This extra constraint can now be added to the original problem and the iterations continued with the dual algorithm until an optimal solution is found. If this is still not integer, the process is repeated. The computations for this example are given in Table VI.

2. Gomory's Mixed-Integer Algorithm

Let us again suppose that x_i is required to be integer but is not so in the final tableau and that with the previous notation, the defining equation for x_i is of the form

$$x_1 + f_{i1}y_1 + f_{i2}y_2 + \cdots + f_{ir}y_r = g_i = [g_i] + g_i'$$

In this situation it is no longer possible to assume that all the other variables are integers, so the following argument is used. Since x_i must be integer, then either $x_i \leq [g_i]$ or $x_i \geq [g_i] + 1$. This

TABLE VI. Pure Integer Problem: Cutting-Plane Method

Basis:		3	2	0	0	0	0	0	0
μ	x	x_1	x_2	x_3	x_4	x_5	x_6	x_7	RHS
0	x_6	0	0	1	0	−3	1	0	3
0	x_4	0	0	−1	1	3	0	0	5
2	x_2	0	1	$\frac{1}{2}$	0	−1	0	0	$\frac{5}{2}$
3	x_1	1	0	$-\frac{1}{4}$	0	1	0	0	$\frac{11}{4}$
0	x_7	0	0	$[-\frac{3}{4}]$	0	0	0	1	$(-\frac{3}{4})$
	z	0	0	$-\frac{1}{4}$	0	−1	0	0	$-\frac{53}{4}$
Ratio		—	—	$(\frac{1}{3})$	—	$-\infty$	—	—	
0	x_6	0	0	0	0	−3	1	$\frac{4}{3}$	2
0	x_4	0	0	0	1	3	0	$-\frac{4}{3}$	6
2	x_2	0	1	0	0	−1	0	$\frac{2}{3}$	2
3	x_1	1	0	0	0	1	0	$-\frac{1}{3}$	3
0	x_3	0	0	1	0	0	0	$-\frac{4}{3}$	1
	z	0	0	0	0	−1	0	$-\frac{1}{3}$	−13

is equivalent to

$$\begin{aligned} g_i' &\le f_{i1}y_1 + \cdots + f_{ir}y_r \\ &= \sum_k f_{ik}y_k \le \sum_{k+} f_{ik}y_k \end{aligned}$$

or

$$g_i' - 1 \ge \sum_k f_{ik}y_k \ge \sum_{k-} f_{ik}y_k$$

where $\Sigma_{k+} f_{ik}y_k$ is the sum over those terms for which $f_{ik} > 0$, and $\Sigma_{k-} f_{ik}y_k$ is the sum over the other terms. The second of these terms can be rewritten as

$$\frac{\sum_{k-} f_{ik}y_k}{g_i' - 1} \ge 1$$

or, equivalently,

$$\frac{g_i' \sum_{k-} f_{ik}y_k}{g_i' - 1} \ge g_i'$$

and the iterations continued with the help of the dual algorithm. Further cuts may have to be added at later stages until x_1 becomes an integer.

VII. Special Algorithms

A. Dantzig's Transportation Algorithm

Let us consider the problem of transporting a particular commodity as cheaply as possible from a chain of m warehouses to n customers (sometimes referred to as the Hitchcock problem). Suppose that warehouse W_i has w_i units available for despatch, customer C_j requires c_j units, the cost of transporting a single unit from W_i to C_j is a_{ij}, and the actual number transported is x_{ij}. Then, if the total supply equals the total demand and the costs of transportation are proportional to the number of items transported the problem can be written as follows:

Minimize $\displaystyle\sum_i \sum_j a_{ij}x_{ij}$

subject to

$$\begin{array}{llllll}
x_{11} + x_{12} + \cdots + x_{1n} & & & & & = w_1 \\
 & x_{21} + x_{22} + \cdots + x_{2n} & & & & = w_2 \\
 & & \cdots & & & \\
 & & & & x_{m1} + x_{m2} + \cdots + x_{mn} & = w_m \\
x_{11} & + x_{21} & \cdots & + x_{m1} & & = c_1 \\
\quad x_{12} & \quad + x_{22} & \cdots & \quad + x_{m2} & & = c_2 \\
 & & \cdots & & & \\
\qquad x_{1n} & \qquad + x_{2n} & \cdots & & + x_{mn} & = c_n
\end{array}$$

Combining these alternatives gives the Gomory mixed cut:

$$g_i' \le \sum_{k+} f_{ik}y_k + \left[g_i' \sum_{k-} f_{ik}y_k \Big/ \left(g_i' - 1\right)\right]$$

The fractions may now be cleared, a nonnegative slack variable (not required to be integer) included, and this new constraint added to the problem. For example, if in the problem discussed in Section III, x_1 (only) is required to be an integer, then its defining equation,

$$x_1 + -\tfrac{1}{4}x_3 + x_5 = \tfrac{11}{4} = 2 + \tfrac{3}{4}$$

gives $\Sigma_{k-} f_{ik}y_k \equiv -\frac{1}{4}x_3$ and $\Sigma_{k+} f_{ik}y_k \equiv x_5$. The corresponding Gomory mixed cut is $\frac{3}{4} \le x_5 + 3x_3$, which becomes $-4x_5 - 3x_3 + x_7 = -3$, with the inclusion of the nonnegative slack variable x_7. This is now added to the original problem

where $x_{ij} \ge 0$ for all i, j. Since the $m + n$ constraints are linearly dependent (the sum of the first m equals that of the remainder, so that one equation could be removed without changing the model), only $m + n - 1$ variables are required to form a basis.

This problem could, of course, be solved by the simplex algorithm but owing to the form and sparseness of the coefficient matrix, a much simpler algorithm can be developed using the concept of duality. The dual of this linear program is

Minimize $\displaystyle\sum_i \lambda_i w_i + \sum_j v_j c_j$

subject to $\lambda_i + v_j \le a_{ij}$, for all i, j

where λ_i and v_j are unrestricted in sign.

It is this symmetric relationship between λ_i, v_j, and a_{ij} terms that leads to a simplification of the solution to the primal problem. Suppose that

TABLE VII. Unit Transportation Costs

		Customer			No. of units available
		C_1	C_2	C_3	
	Warehouse				
	W_1	3	5	4	20
	W_2	2	1	6	20
	W_3	4	1	3	10
No. of units required:		10	15	20	

at a particular vertex x_{ij} is in the basis of the primal, then the Kuhn–Tucker conditions require that its coefficient should be zero in the Lagrangian. This, in turn, implies that the corresponding slack variable of the dual should also be zero. Hence, for such a route, $\lambda_i + v_j = a_{ij}$. Since there are $n + m - 1$ basis variables, there are this number of (dual) equations for the $n + m$ dual variables. A solution can be obtained by arbitrarily setting one of these dual variables zero and solving for the remainder. The coefficients in the Lagrangian of the dual slack variables are $a_{ij} - \lambda_i - v_j$, which are the values of the corresponding nonbasis primal variables in its Lagrangian. The most negative of these (since it is a minimization) is used to pinpoint a new basis variable for the primal problem. All this information can be conveniently stored in a tabular form for the primal problem. The technique is demonstrated with the following problem in which there are just three warehouses and three customers. Suppose that the unit transportation costs and the numbers of items available for supply and required for delivery are as given in Table VII. Since the supply is greater than the demand, a "dummy" customer C_4 is added to take the surplus, having zero associated transportation costs. This information is now transferred to Table VIII in preparation for the next stage. The unit transportation cost is shown in the bottom right-hand corner of its corresponding cell. The first row and column are reserved for the values of the dual variables. In this problem a nondegenerate basic feasible solution requires $n + m - 1 = 6$ routes to be used. Several methods are available for finding such a set of routes, the more complex the method, the fewer the number of iterations required on average to find the optimal solution. Perhaps the most sensible balance between effort and effectiveness is the "least cost" method, which is employed here. In this method as many units as possible are transported along the cheapest available route. This necessarily requires the other routes in either its row or column to remain unused. This process is repeated with the remaining routes until the table is completed. Here there are three routes with zero unit cost. Suppose it is (arbitrarily) decided to send as many units as possible from W_3 to C_4 [route (3,4)], then $x_{34} = 5$ and, consequently, $x_{24} = x_{14} = 0$. These values are shown in the middle of their respectively cells in Table VIII. The cheapest remaining routes are (2,2) and (3,2), with a unit cost of 1. Suppose (again arbitrarily) that route (2,2) is filled to capacity, giving $x_{22} = 15$; then, $x_{12} = x_{32} = 0$. Route (2,1) now becomes the cheapest, so $x_{21} = 5$ and $x_{23} = 0$. Next, route (1,1) is filled, giving $x_{11} = 5$ and $x_{31} = 0$. There is now no choice left for the remaining elements of Table VIII.

TABLE VIII. Transportation Problem: Initial Table

λ	ν	3 C_1	2 C_2	4 C_3	1 C_4	Available
0	W_1	5_3	${}_30_5$	15_4	${}_{-1}0_0$	20
−1	W_2	5_2	15_1	${}_30_6$	${}_00_0$	20
−1	W_3	${}_20_4$	${}_00_1$	5_3	5_0	10
Required:		10	15	20	5	50

The dual problem associates with row i a variable λ_i and with column j a variable ν_j (termed shadow costs) which, provided route (i,j) is in the basis, must satisfy $\lambda_i + \nu_j = a_{ij}$. Consequently, for this basis the shadow costs satisfy the following six equations in seven variables:

$$\lambda_1 + \nu_1 = 3, \qquad \lambda_2 + \nu_2 = 1,$$

$$\lambda_1 + \nu_3 = 4, \qquad \lambda_3 + \nu_3 = 3,$$

$$\lambda_2 + \nu_1 = 2, \qquad \lambda_3 + \nu_4 = 0$$

If λ_1 is arbitrarily chosen to be zero, then $\nu_1 = 3$, $\nu_3 = 4$ etc. This solution sequence is carried out directly on Table VIII itself (using the nonzero routes only). The Lagrange coefficients of these basis routes are zero, but for the unused routes they are given by $a_{ij} - \lambda_i - \nu_j$. So that for route (2,3), for example, the coefficient is $6 - (-1) - 4 = 3$, this value being entered in the Table VIII (to the left of the corresponding value for x_{23}). Since this is a minimization problem, the negative of a Lagrange coefficient shows the potential reduction in the objective function for each unit increase in that variable if it were to be brought into the basis. Here there is just one

TABLE IX. Transportation Problem: Change of Basis

λ	ν	3 C_1	2 C_2	4 C_3	1 C_4	Available
0	W_1	5_3	0_5	$15 - \theta_4$	$0 + \theta_0$	20
−1	W_2	5_2	15_1	0_6	0_0	20
−1	W_3	0_4	0_1	$5 + \theta_3$	$5 - \theta_0$	10
Required:		10	15	20	5	50

such negative value: that for route (1,4). Hence, x_{14} should be brought into the next basis, and one (and only one) variable must become zero. Suppose that θ units are transported along route (1,4), then since C_4 needs five units, θ must be subtracted from x_{34}. Since W_3 has ten units, θ must be added to x_{33} (not to a zero route or else two variables would be entering the basis). This process of balancing row and column totals using basis routes only is continued until all are satisfied, as shown in Table IX. The maximum value for θ is now chosen consistent with $x_{ij} \geq 0$. In Table IX the value for x_{34} restricts θ to be no greater than 5. Choosing $\theta = 5$ then corresponds to x_{34} leaving the basis, and gives the new feasible solution shown in Table X (with θ set 0).

New values for the shadow costs are now calculated and the coefficients for the Lagrangian obtained. This time there are no negative coefficients, so this is an optimum solution. Note, however, that the coefficient of x_{32} is zero, suggesting that there is an alternative basis leading to the same value of the objective function. As can be seen from Table X, transporting θ units along route (3,2) and bringing x_{32} into the basis requires x_{11} to leave, the new value for x_{32} being given by $\theta = 5$. The Lagrange coefficients confirm that this is the only alternative solution.

The nature of the transportation problem, with all the coefficients being either 0 or 1, results in all basic feasible solutions being integers (provided that the row and column totals are also integers). This is one of the few linear programs that automatically produces an integer solution.

TABLE X. Transportation Problem: Optimal Solution and Alternative

λ	ν	3 C_1	2 C_2	4 C_3	0 C_4	Available
0	W_1	$5 - \theta_3$	$_3 \quad 0_5$	$10 + \theta_4$	5_0	20
−1	W_2	$5 + \theta_2$	$15 - \theta_1$	$_3 \quad 0_6$	$_10_0$	20
−1	W_3	$_2 \quad 0_4$	$_00 + \theta_1$	$10 - \theta_3$	$_10_0$	10
Required:		10	15	20	5	50

As with the simplex method, this algorithm requires the basic feasible solutions to be nondegenerate. If degeneracy occurs during the computation it will be as a result of the value chosen for θ setting two (or more) variables zero. This degeneracy can easily be overcome by replacing all but one of these new zeroes by an ϵ, a small positive constant, and proceeding with the calculations until the ϵ is no longer needed to break any degeneracy, at which time it is set zero. If the degeneracy occurs when finding the initial basic feasible solution, then a row and a column are completed by the same element. The easiest way to proceed is to recompute the initial basic solution after adding ϵ (>0) to each row total and $m\epsilon$ to just one column total. Again, ϵ is set zero as soon as it has fulfilled its purpose.

B. The Assignment Problem: The Hungarian Algorithm

The assignment problem concerns the matching of one group of items to another group of the same size on a one-to-one basis so as to optimize some criterion of matching. This might be the matching of tasks to machines to maximize efficiency or the matching of men to jobs to minimize total cost. Take, for example, the latter problem in which there are n men and n jobs, and the costs c_{ij} associated with man i doing job j are known; then this problem can be written as

$$\text{Minimize} \quad \sum_i \sum_j c_{ij} x_{ij}$$

$$\text{subject to} \quad \sum_j x_{ij} = 1, \qquad i = 1, \ldots, n$$

$$\sum_i x_{ij} = 1, \qquad j = 1, \ldots, n$$

where $x_{ij} = 0$ or 1 for all i, j. This zero–one integer program is a special case of the transportation problem with the row and column totals all equal to 1, so Dantzig's algorithm could be used for its solution. It should be noted that any optimal solution will involve only n nonzero variables (corresponding to the particular assignment), whereas $2n - 1$ variables are in any basis. The solution is therefore highly degenerate, although this can be handled by the techniques mentioned above. However, a simpler algorithm exists, known as the Hungarian method after the Hungarian mathematician Egerváry

TABLE XI. Assignment of Men to Jobs: Cost Matrix

		Job				
		1	2	3	4	5
	1	5	6	7	2	2
	2	6	9	11	6	5
Man	3	5	4	6	3	1
	4	4	6	7	7	6
	5	4	6	7	1	2

who proved a theorem in combinatorics on which the algorithm relies. The algorithm also depends on a result that holds true even for the transportation problem: that the optimal basis remains unchanged if a constant is added or subtracted from all the unit costs in any row or column. The *value* of the objective function does of course change. So, if $c_{ij} \geq 0$ for all i, j and by such additions and subtractions the cost matrix can be reduced so that n zeroes occur to correspond to a feasible assignment, then this must have a minimum cost. The technique is most easily explained by means of an example. Suppose that the costs c_{ij} of five men doing five jobs are as in Table XI.

Stage 1

1. For each row in turn subtract the row minimum from each element in its row.
2. For each column in turn subtract the column minimum from each element in its column.

(The results of these operations are shown in Table XII.)

TABLE XII. The Assignment Problem: Stages 1 and 2

		Job				
		1	2	3	4	5
	1	3	2	2	0	0
	2	1	2	3	1	0
Man	3	4	1	2	2	0
	4	0	0	0	3	2
	5	3	3	3	0	1

Stage 2. Cover all the zeroes with as few horizontal and vertical lines as possible. In this case, three such lines are necessary. This is equivalent to just three minimal cost matchings being found, so this does not correspond to a feasible solution.

Stage 3

1. Add the minimum of the uncovered costs (here, 1) to each element in each covered row and then to each element in each covered column.
2. Subtract this value from all the elements.

(The result of these steps is shown in Table XIII.) This time five lines are necessary, indicating that a feasible matching is available. The only such matching is shown in square brackets, though the solution will not always be unique. If only four or fewer lines had been required, stages 2 and 3 would be repeated until a feasible solution is found. If some of the original costs c_{ij} had been negative, then the simple expedient of adding a large enough number to all the costs would make them nonnegative and allow the algorithm to work.

If, instead of minimizing cost, the problem had been to maximize profits or some other utility, then the elements should be subtracted from the largest element, and the alternative minimization problem solved.

VIII. Matrix Game Theory

Von Neumann's theory of competition predates Dantzig's work, yet it contains many of the basic results of duality theory. It is the so-called two-person zero-sum game that provides

TABLE XIII. The Optimal Assignment

		Job				
		1	2	3	4	5
	1	2	1	1	0	[0]
	2	[0]	1	2	1	0
Man	3	3	[0]	1	2	0
	4	0	0	[0]	4	3
	5	2	2	2	[0]	1

a natural interpretation of the concept of duality. These games between two opponents are such that the rules are assumed to be strictly defined (as opposed, for example, to the rules in the "game" of business), and the outcomes (in money or utilities) are known in advance for each possible outcome. Furthermore, one player's gains are assumed to be the other's losses, no wealth being created or destroyed. [*See* GAME THEORY.]

Let us consider the following game between players A and B, which involves them simultaneously calling one of numbers 1 or 2. The amount received by A from B for each combination of calls is shown in Table XIV (note that B's payoffs are minus those shown in the table). Suppose that both players are cautious; then they might argue as follows:

A: "If I call 1 then the worst that can happen is that I win \$1, but if I call 2 then I can be forced to lose \$1. So my optimum strategy is to call 1."

This best-of-the-worst outcome for A is known as the maximin value of the game and is denoted by α.

B: "If I call 1 I can at worst lose \$1, yet if I call 2 I can be made to lose \$3. So my optimal strategy is to call 1."

This best outcome for b is known as the minimax value of the game (measured in terms of the payoff to A) and is denoted by β. Its name comes from the fact that it is the minimum of the column maxima. In this problem $\alpha = \beta = 1$, and the element (1,1), corresponding to both players calling 1, is the equilibrium (saddle point) of the game. It is an equilibrium point, since it pays neither opponent to move unilaterally from his optimum strategy, and it is a saddle point because it is both a row minimum and a column maximum. The common value of α and β is known as the value of the game V, since that is the amount expected by both players. Now, not all games possess such a saddle point. It can be shown that "games of full information" (in which moves are made sequentially, all previous moves being known to both players) always possess a saddle point, whereas others may not. Table XV gives an alternative payoff matrix for the game just considered. This game is not of full information, since the calls are made simultaneously. Here, the maximin value of the game is -2, with A calling 2, and the minimax value is 2 with B calling 1, so $\alpha \neq \beta$, and no equilibrium exists. However, if the players take a long-term view, considering their payoffs over many games, then it can be shown that a saddle-point equilibrium exists if they choose not to play just a single strategy (a pure strategy) but to mix their strategies in a random manner according to fixed probabilities.

TABLE XIV. Matrix of Payoffs to A

		B calls 1	B calls 2
A calls	1	1	2
	2	−1	3

TABLE XV. Alternative Payoff Matrix (Payoffs to A)

		B calls 1	B calls 2
A calls	1	2	−3
	2	−2	4

Let us consider a general two-person zero-sum game in which A has pure strategies $A_1, A_2, \ldots, A_r$, and B has $B_1, B_2, \ldots, B_s$, for which the payoff to A for the mix of actions A_i, B_j is a_{ij}. Suppose that A's optimum mixed strategy (leading to payoff V_A) requires that he play his pure strategies $A_1, \ldots, A_r$ with probabilities $p_1, \ldots, p_r$, where $\sum_i p_i = 1$. Then, no matter how B plays from among his s strategies, the value of the game to A must be at least V_A, provided that he plays his optimal mixed strategy. Suppose that B chooses to play his pure strategy B_j; then the payoff to A satisfies

$$p_1 a_{ij} + p_2 a_{2j} + \cdots + p_r a_{rj} \geq V_A$$

where $\sum_i p_i = 1$, and this result must be true for all values of j.

If x_i defined as $x_i = p_i/V_A$, then these inequalities become

$$x_1 a_{1j} + x_2 a_{2j} + \cdots + x_r a_{rj} \geq 1$$

and $\sum_i p_i = 1$ becomes $\sum_i x_i = 1/V_A$. So, to maximize V_A, A should minimize $1/V_A$, and so, from A's point of view, the problem is to find x_1,

$x_2, \ldots, x_r$ to

$$\begin{aligned}\text{Minimize}\quad & x_1 + x_2 + \cdots + x_r \\ \text{subject to}\quad & a_{11}x_1 + a_{21}x_2 + \cdots + a_{r1}x_r \geq 1 \\ & \vdots \\ & a_{1s}x_1 + a_{2s}x_2 + \cdots + a_{rs}x_r \geq 1 \\ & x_1, x_2, \ldots, x_r \geq 0.\end{aligned}$$

Now, from B's point of view, if his optimum mixed strategy (leading to payoff V_B to A) requires that he use his pure strategies $B_1, \ldots, B_s$ with probabilities $q_1, \ldots, q_s$, where $\Sigma_j q_j = 1$, then if A plays A_i and B plays his optimal mixed strategy,

$$q_1(-a_{i1}) + q_2(-a_{i2}) + \cdots + q_s(-a_{is}) \geq -V_B$$

This can be rewritten as

$$a_{i1}q_1 + a_{i2}q_2 + \cdots a_{is}q_s \leq V_B$$

and must be true for all i.

This time, y_j is defined by $y_j = q_j/V_B$, and $\Sigma_j q_j = 1$ becomes $\Sigma_j y_j = 1/V_B$. Now, B wishes to maximize $-V_B$ or to minimize V_B or, equivalently, to maximize $1/V_B$. Hence, from B's point of view, the problem is to

$$\begin{aligned}\text{Maximize}\quad & y_1 + y_2 + \cdots + y_s \\ \text{subject to}\quad & a_{11}y_1 + a_{12}y_2 + \cdots + a_{1s}y_s \leq 1 \\ & \vdots \\ & a_{r1}y_1 + a_{r2}y_2 + \cdots + a_{rs}y_s \leq 1 \\ & y_1, y_2, \ldots, y_s \geq 0.\end{aligned}$$

These two problems, the game from the point of view of the two opponents, are duals, and hence not only do they give the optimal values for the two sets of probabilities, but also show that at the optimum $V_A = -V_B$, this common value being the value of the game.

IX. Quadratic Programming

Quadratic programming is concerned with optimizing a quadratic function of the variables subject to linear and nonnegativity constraints. At first sight it would appear that none of the techniques so far considered could be of much use in the solution of such a problem. Fortunately, the use of the Kuhn–Tucker conditions leads to what is almost a linear program. A modification of the simplex method can then be used to find a point that satisfies these conditions and thereby obtain a solution to the original quadratic program.

Let us consider the following example:

$$\begin{aligned}\text{Maximize}\quad & -10x_1^2 + 4x_1x_2 - 10x_2^2 + 7x_1 + 13x_2 \\ \text{subject to}\quad & 2x_1 + 2x_2 \leq 1 \\ & x_1, x_2 \geq 0\end{aligned}$$

The Lagrangian for this problem is

$$L = -10x_1^2 + 4x_1x_2 - 10x_2^2 + 7x_1 + 13x_2 - \lambda(2x_1 + 2x_2 - 1)$$

and the Kuhn–Tucker necessary conditions are

$$\begin{aligned}\partial L/\partial x_1 &= -20x_1 + 4x_2 + 7 - 2\lambda \leq 0 \\ x_1 \geq 0;&\quad x_1\,\partial L/\partial x_1 = 0 \\ \partial L/\partial x_2 &= 4x_1 - 20x_2 + 13 - 2\lambda \leq 0 \\ x_2 \geq 0;&\quad x_2\,\partial L/\partial x_2 = 0 \\ \partial L/\partial \lambda &= -2x_1 - 2x_2 + 1 \geq 0 \\ \lambda \geq 0;&\quad \lambda\,\partial L/\partial \lambda = 0\end{aligned}$$

The objective function can be shown to be concave, and this ensures that a solution to these conditions will lead to the unique maximum of the objective function.

Adding nonnegative slack variables x_3, x_4, x_5, these conditions become

$$\begin{aligned}20x_1 - 4x_2 + 2\lambda - x_3 &= 7 \\ x_1 \geq 0;\quad x_1x_3 &= 0 \\ -4x_1 + 20x_2 + 2\lambda - x_4 &= 13 \\ x_2 \geq 0;\quad x_2x_4 &= 0 \\ 2x_1 + 2x_2 + x_5 &= 1 \\ \lambda \geq 0;\quad \lambda x_5 &= 0 \\ x_3, x_4, x_5 &\geq 0\end{aligned}$$

where the product conditions (complementary slackness conditions) have been written in terms of the slack variables. For example, $\partial L/\partial x_1 = -x_3$, so that $x_1\,\partial L/\partial x_1 = 0$ becomes $x_1x_3 = 0$. The problem is how to find a feasible solution to this set of constraints. Now there are six variables, and from the three complementary slackness conditions it follows that at least three of these variables must be zero at any feasible solution. Since there are three main constraints and at most three variables may be nonzero, any feasible solution must also be basic. Moreover, such a solution must also satisfy the complementary slackness conditions, and so the pairs of variables x_1, x_3; x_2, x_4 and λ, x_5 may not both be nonnegative, or, equivalently, they may not both belong to the same (nondegenerate) basis. Consequently, the simplex algorithm can be used to move between bases until these extra conditions also hold. As usual, in order to find an initial basic feasible solution to these constraints, artificial variables are often needed. Here, two such variables x_6 and x_7 are needed to complete an initial basis. The temporary objective function

$$\max z = -x_6 - x_7$$

is used until x_6 and x_7 are removed from the basis. At this stage, provided that the complementary slackness conditions have been properly incorporated, a feasible solution will have been found. This will correspond to the optimum of the original quadratic program.

The steps in this modified simplex algorithm are shown in Table XVI. The extra column at the left of each tableau gives in brackets the name of any variable that cannot enter the basis without the corresponding basis variable leaving. For example, even though the coefficient of λ in the z row is positive in the first tableau, λ cannot be brought into the basis unless the ratio column requires x_5 to leave. This is not the case in this tableau, and so this positive value must be disregarded when choosing the pivot column. The final tableau shows that the optimum is attained at $x_1 = \frac{1}{8}$, $x_2 = \frac{3}{8}$.

If the objective function had not been concave then this method would have given a stationary point, not necessarily the maximum; however, by switching between possible bases that satisfy the complementary slackness conditions, all the stationary points could have been found and the optimum determined by evaluation of the objective function at each of these points (together with any at infinity).

X. Recent Developments

A. The Ellipsoid Algorithm

During the 1970s, several Soviet authors, including Iudin, Nemirovskii, and Shor, published results describing a method for detecting whether or not a feasible solution exists for a set of constraints of the form $\mathbf{Ax} \le \mathbf{b}$. Their method involves constructing a set of ellipsoids E_0, E_1, ..., E_j, ..., each of which contains at least one feasible point (if one exists). At the jth step, the center x_j of E_j is checked for feasibility. If it is feasible, then the algorithm ends. If not, one of the constraints must be violated, and so a new, smaller, ellipsoid E_{j+1} is generated, circumscribing the half of E_j that contains points that satisfy this constraint, and the iterations continue.

Khachiyan modified this method and was able to show that the algorithm can be used to find a feasible point, if one exists, in a precomputable number of iterations. If more than this number are required, then it is concluded that there is no feasible solution to the problem.

TABLE XVI. A Modified Simplex Solution of a Quadratic Program

	Basis		0	0	0	0	0	0	−1	−1	0	
	μ	x	x_1	x_2	λ	x_3	x_4	x_5	x_6	x_7	RHS	Ratio
	−1	x_6	20	−4	2	−1	0	0	1	0	7	<0
	−1	x_7	−4	20	2	0	−1	0	0	1	13	$\frac{13}{20}$
(λ)	0	x_5	2	[2]	0	0	0	1	0	0	1	($\frac{1}{2}$)
		z	16	(16)	4	−1	−1	0	0	0	20	
	−1	x_6	24	0	2	−1	0	2	1	0	9	$\frac{9}{2}$
	−1	x_7	−24	0	[2]	0	−1	−10	0	1	3	($\frac{3}{2}$)
(x_4)	0	x_2	1	1	0	0	0	$\frac{1}{2}$	0	0	$\frac{1}{2}$	∞
		z	0	0	4	−1	−1	−8	0	0	12	
	−1	x_6	[48]	0	0	−1	1	12	1		6	($\frac{1}{8}$)
(x_5)	0	λ	−12	0	1	0	$-\frac{1}{2}$	−5	0		$\frac{3}{2}$	<0
(x_4)	0	x_2	1	1	0	0	0	$\frac{1}{2}$	0		$\frac{1}{2}$	$\frac{1}{2}$
		z	(48)	0	0	−1	1	12	0		6	
(x_3)	0	x_1	1	0	0	$-\frac{1}{48}$	$\frac{1}{48}$	$\frac{1}{4}$			$\frac{1}{8}$	
(x_5)	0	λ	0	0	1	$-\frac{1}{4}$	$-\frac{1}{4}$	−2			3	
(x_4)	0	x_2	0	1	0	$\frac{1}{48}$	$-\frac{1}{48}$	$\frac{1}{4}$			$\frac{3}{8}$	
		z	0	0	0	0	0	0			0	

In his now famous 1979 paper, Khachiyan published this result together with a technique for using it to prove (for the first time) that a linear program could be solved in "polynomial-time." That is, the upper bound for the number of computations required for the solution of a problem of size N is TN^t, where T and t are constants independent of N. This contrasts with the simplex algorithm for which the corresponding upper bound is known to be exponential (i.e., Rr^N for constants R and r independent of N).

The press became very excited with this result, predicting that the new algorithm would revolutionize the solution of linear programs and hence have a great impact on the commercial world. Even at this stage, it was possible to see that their predictions might have been a little overoptimistic. First, the number of computations quoted are *upper* bounds, corresponding to the *worst* that can happen. In most practical problems the simplex algorithm has been found to converge to the optimum much more quickly than its upper bound might suggest. Second, in Khachiyan's algorithm $t = 6$, and the constant T can be large due to the high computational accuracy required. Hence, a problem might have to be extremely large before the upper bounds are even equal. Khachiyan suggests several ways of using this ellipsoid algorithm to solve a linear program. One involves using the general relationship that the objective function corresponding to any feasible solution of the primal (maximization) problem is never greater than the objective function of the dual (minimization) problem at any feasible point. In the notation of Section V,A, $\mathbf{c}'\mathbf{x} \leq \mathbf{b}'\boldsymbol{\lambda}$. Hence, provided that there is a unique finite optimum to either of these problems, the set of constraints

$$\mathbf{Ax} \leq \mathbf{b}, \qquad -\mathbf{A}'\boldsymbol{\lambda} \leq -\mathbf{c}, \qquad -\mathbf{x} \leq 0,$$
$$-\boldsymbol{\lambda} \leq 0, \qquad \mathbf{b}'\boldsymbol{\lambda} - \mathbf{c}'\mathbf{x} \geq 0$$

has only one solution, $\mathbf{x}^*, \boldsymbol{\lambda}^*$, the optimal solution vectors to the primal and dual problems, respectively.

Another suggestion involves finding an interior feasible point $\mathbf{x}_0$ and adding the constraint $\mathbf{c}'\mathbf{x} \geq \mathbf{c}'\mathbf{x}_0$ to the feasible region. The algorithm is then used to find an internal point $\mathbf{x}_1$ to this reduced feasible region. This will of necessity correspond to a higher value for the objective function. This process is repeated until the sequence of points has converged sufficiently for the optimum vertex to be ascertained.

Various techniques for updating E_j to E_{j+1} have been suggested by Khachiyan and subsequent authors, but it is now generally agreed that the algorithm, though theoretically important, will never be of much practical use.

B. Karmarkar's Algorithm

A more recent polynomial-time algorithm by Karmarkar has been shown to be not only more efficient than the ellipsoid algorithm (here, $t = 3.5$ rather than 6) but also more stable in the sense that round-off errors are not compounded. Karmarkar assumes the problem to be in a particular form, namely

$$\begin{aligned} &\text{minimize} \quad z = \mathbf{c}'\mathbf{x} \\ &\text{subject to } \mathbf{Ax} = 0 \\ &\qquad (1,1, \ldots 1)\mathbf{x} = 1 \\ &\qquad \mathbf{x} \geq \underline{0} \end{aligned}$$

These last two sets of constraints form a simplex. He also makes a very restrictive assumption that the optimum value of z is zero! The basic idea of the algorithm is as follows. Starting with an internal feasible point $\mathbf{a}_0$, a projective transformation is made. This has the property that the simplex is transformed onto itself and $\mathbf{a}_0$ is transformed to the center, $\mathbf{a}_c$, of the simplex.

Next, the largest spheroid, center $\mathbf{a}_c$, that will fit within the transformed feasible region is constructed. To find the point $\mathbf{a}_1$ that optimizes the transformed objective function (or rather, a related "potential function") within the spheroid is now straightforward. A further projective transformation is used to bring $\mathbf{a}_1$ to the center of the simplex, and the process repeated until the points converge to a vertex (in the original space). Many techniques have been suggested to overcome the restricted form of the problem, and there are examples of implementations of the algorithm being used to solve certain problems in times comparable with (or even faster) than the simplex algorithm. Generally, however, the simplex method is still thought to be the more efficient method, especially when degeneracies are present.

It has been shown that Karmarkar's algorithm is in fact a special case of the "logarithmic barrier function" method that has long been used to solve nonlinear programming problems. It might be, therefore, that other cases of this more general method could lead to even faster solutions to rival or outpace the simplex algorithm.

BIBLIOGRAPHY

Bland, R. G., Goldfarb, D., and Todd, M. J. (1981). The ellipsoid method: A survey, *Oper. Res.* **29,** 1039–1091.

Boffey, T. B. (1982). "Graph Theory in Operations Research," Macmillan, London.

Dantzig, G. B. (1963). "Linear Programming and Extensions," Princeton Univ. Press, Princeton, New Jersey.

Ferris, M. C., and Philpott, A. B. "On the Performance of Karmarkar's Algorithm." *J. Opl. Res. Soc.* **39**(3), 257–270.

Fletcher, R. (1981). "Practical Methods of Optimization," Vol. II, Wiley, New York.

Fryer, M. J., and Greenman, J. V. (1987). "Optimisation Theory: Applications in O. R. and Economics," Edward Arnold, London.

Hillier, F. S., and Lieberman, G. J. (1986). "Introduction to Operations Research," 4th ed., Holden-Day, San Francisco, California.

Intriligator, M. D. (1971). "Mathematical Optimization and Economic Theory," Prentice-Hall, Englewood Cliffs, New Jersey.

Karmarkar, N. (1984). A new polynomial-time algorithm for linear programming, *Combinatorics* **4**, 373–395.

Luce, D. R., and Raiffa, H. (1957). "Games and Decisions," Wiley, New York.

Wagner, H. M. (1975). "Principles of Operations Research," 2nd ed., Prentice-Hall (International) Englewood Cliffs, New Jersey.

Walsh, G. R. (1985). "An Introduction to Linear Programming," 2nd ed., Wiley, New York.

LINEAR SYSTEMS OF ALGEBRAIC EQUATIONS (COMPUTER SCIENCE)

Victor Pan *Columbia University, New York; State University of New York at Albany; City University of New York*

GLOSSARY

Condition (condition number): Product of the norms of a matrix and of its inverse; condition of the coefficient matrix characterizes the sensitivity of the solution of the linear system to input errors.

Error matrix (error vector): Difference between the exact and approximate values of a matrix (of a vector).

Gaussian elimination: Algorithm that solves a linear system of equations via successive elimination of its unknowns, or, equivalently, via decomposition of the input coefficient matrix into a product of two triangular matrices.

$m \times n$ matrix: Two-dimensional array of mn entries represented in m rows and n columns. A sparse matrix is a matrix filled mostly with zeros. A sparse matrix is structured if the locations of all its nonzero entries follow some regular patterns.

Norms of vectors (matrices): Nonnegative values that characterize the magnitudes of those vectors (matrices).

Pivot: Entry in the northwest corner of the coefficient matrix, which defines the current elimination step of the solution to that system; pivoting is a policy of interchanging the rows and/or the columns of the matrix such that its certain entry of sufficiently large magnitude is moved to the northwest corner.

A linear system of algebraic equations (also called a linear system of equations and simultaneous linear equations) is the set of equations of the form,

$$\begin{aligned} a_{11}x_1 + a_{12}x_2 + \cdots + a_{1n}x_n &= b_1 \\ &\vdots \\ a_{m1}x_1 + a_{m2}x_2 + \cdots + a_{mn}x_n &= b_m \end{aligned}$$

where $a_{11}, a_{12}, \ldots, a_{mn}, b_1, b_2, \ldots, b_m$ are given constants, and $x_1, x_2, \ldots, x_n$ are unknown values. The main problem is to compute a solution to such a system, that is, a set of values, $c_1, c_2, \ldots, c_n$, such that the substitution of $x_1 = c_1, x_2 = c_2, \ldots, x_n = c_n$ simultaneously satisfies all the equations of that system, or to determine that the system is inconsistent, that is, it has no solution.

I. Introduction and Preliminaries

A. Subject Definition

Our subject is the systems

$$\begin{aligned} a_{11}x_1 + a_{12}x_2 + \cdots + a_{1n}x_n &= b_1 \\ &\vdots \\ a_{m1}x_1 + a_{m2}x_2 + \cdots + a_{mn}x_n &= b_m \end{aligned} \tag{1}$$

and algorithms for their solution, with particular attention to linear systems important in computational practice and to their solution on modern computers. We include inconsistent systems and systems having nonunique solution (compare Examples 2 and 3). [Nonunique solution of Eq. (1) always means infinitely many solutions.]

EXAMPLE 1. $m = n = 3$:

$$10x_1 + 14x_2 + 0 * x_3 = 7$$
$$-3x_1 - 4x_2 + 6x_3 = 4$$
$$5x_1 + 2x_2 + 5x_3 = 6$$

where $x_1 = 0$, $x_2 = 0.5$, $x_3 = 1$ is the unique solution.

EXAMPLE 2. $m = 3, n = 2$ (overdetermined systems, $m > n$):

$$2x_1 - x_2 = 3.2$$
$$-2x_1 - 2x_2 = -10.6$$
$$0 * x_1 - 6x_2 = -18$$

The system is inconsistent.

EXAMPLE 3. $m = 2, n = 3$ (underdetermined systems, $m < n$):

$$x_1 + x_2 + x_3 = 5, \qquad -x_1 + x_2 + x_3 = 3$$

The system has infinitely many solutions, $x_1 = 1$, $x_2 = 4 - x_3$ for any x_3.

Usually, we assume that all the inputs a_{ij} and b_i are real numbers; the extensions to complex and other inputs (Boolean rings, path algebras) being possible and frequently straightforward.

B. Variety of Applications, Ties with the Computer Technology. Vast Bibliography. Packages of Subroutines

Here are some large subjects, important in computational practice: numerical solution of differential and partial differential equations, mathematical programming and operations research, combinatorial computations, fitting data by curves, interpolation by polynomials and polynomial computations. These and many other practically important subjects have a common feature: Computationally, the problems are reduced to solving linear systems [Eq. (1)], probably the most frequent operation in the practice of numerical computing. Special packages of computer subroutines, such as LINPACK and LAPACK, are available for solving linear systems. The bibliography on the subject is vast; luckily, the book by G. H. Golub and C. F. van Loan systematically and successfully exposes a variety of most important basic and advanced topics. Some other texts, containing further references, are listed at the end of this article. In particular, several major topics are covered in the volume edited by E. Spedicato (especially see pages 1–92), whereas the reviews by K. A. Galligan, R. J. Plemmons, and A. H. Sameh, by M. T. Heath, E. Ng, and B. W. Peyton, and by J. M. Ortega and R. G. Voight survey the applications of vector and parallel computers to solving systems [Eq. (1)]. [*See* NUMERICAL COMPUTING.]

The development and study of modern algorithms for systems [Eq. (1)] has been greatly influenced by practical and theoretical applications of linear systems and by the development of modern computer technology. More recent vector and parallel computers have turned out to be very effective for solving linear systems, which has motivated both further development of those computers and the study and design of algorithms for linear systems. [*See* COMPUTER ALGORITHMS.]

C. Sparsity, Structure, and Computer Representation of Linear Systems

A linear system [Eq. (1)] can be defined by its extended matrix,

$$W = \begin{bmatrix} a_{11} & a_{12} & \cdots & a_{1n} & b_1 \\ \vdots & \vdots & & \vdots & \vdots \\ a_{m1} & a_{m2} & \cdots & a_{mn} & b_m \end{bmatrix} \qquad (2)$$

which occupies $m \times (n + 1)$ working array in a computer. The first n columns of W form the $m \times n$ coefficient matrix A of the system. The last column is the right-hand-side vector $\mathbf{b}$.

EXAMPLE 4. The extended matrices of systems of Examples 1 and 2 are

$$\begin{bmatrix} 10 & 14 & 0 & 7 \\ -3 & -4 & 6 & 4 \\ 5 & 2 & 5 & 6 \end{bmatrix}, \qquad \begin{bmatrix} 2 & -1 & 3.2 \\ -2 & -2 & -10.6 \\ 0 & -6 & -18 \end{bmatrix}$$

Since the primary storage space of a computer is limited, the array [Eq. (2)] should not be too large; 100×101 or 200×201 can be excessively large for some computers. Practically, systems with up to, say, 100,000 equations, are handled routinely, however; because large linear systems arising in computational practice are usually sparse (only a small part of their coefficients are nonzeros) and well structured (the nonzeros in the array follow some regular patterns). Then special data structures enable users to store only nonzero coefficients (sometimes only a part of them). The algorithms for solving such special systems are also much more efficient than in the case of general dense systems.

Consider, for instance, tridiagonal systems, where $a_{ij} = 0$, unless $-1 \leq i - j \leq 1$. Instead of storing all the $n^2 + n$ input entries of A and $\mathbf{b}$, which would be required in case of a dense system, special data structures can be used to store only the $4n - 2$ nonzero entries. The running time of the program solving such a system (which can be roughly measured by the number of arithmetic operations used) is also reduced from about $\frac{2}{3}n^3$ for dense systems to $8n - 13$ for tridiagonal systems. (substitute $n = 10{,}000$ to see the difference). The structure of some linear systems may not be immediately recognized. For instance, in Section II,A, solving the Laplace equation $\partial^2 u/\partial x^2 + \partial^2 u/\partial y^2 = 0$ is reduced to a system that is not tridiagonal but is block tridiagonal, that is, its coefficient matrix can be represented as a tridiagonal matrix whose entries are in turn matrices, specifically in the model example of a small size:

$$A = \begin{bmatrix} -4 & 1 & 1 & 0 \\ 1 & -4 & 0 & 1 \\ 1 & 0 & -4 & 1 \\ 0 & 1 & 1 & -4 \end{bmatrix} = \begin{bmatrix} B_2 & I_2 \\ I_2 & B_2 \end{bmatrix} \tag{3}$$

$$B_2 = \begin{bmatrix} -4 & 1 \\ 1 & -4 \end{bmatrix}, \qquad I_2 = \begin{bmatrix} 1 & 0 \\ 0 & 1 \end{bmatrix}$$

Block tridiagonal structures can be also effectively exploited, particularly in cases where the blocks are well structured. [*See* LINEAR ALGEBRA.]

D. Specifics of Overdetermined and Underdetermined Linear Systems

Overdetermined linear systems [Eq. (1)] with m greatly exceeding n (say, $m = 1000$; $n = 2$) arise when we try to fit given data by simple curves, in statistics, and in many other applications; such systems are usually inconsistent. A quasi-solution $x_1^*, \ldots, x_n^*$ is sought, which minimizes the magnitudes of the residuals, $r_i = b_i - (a_{i1}x_1^* + \cdots + a_{in}x_n^*)$, $i = 1, \ldots, n$. Methods of computing such a quasi-solution vary with the choice of the minimization criterion, but usually the solution is ultimately reduced to solving some regular linear systems [Eq. (1)] (where $m = n$) (see Sections II,E; IV,A; and IV,C).

A consistent underdetermined system [Eq. (1)] always has infinitely many solutions (compare Example 3) and is frequently encountered as part of the problem of mathematical programming, where such systems are complemented with linear inequalities and with some optimization criteria.

E. General and Special Linear Systems. Direct and Iterative Methods. Sensitivity to Errors

Generally, the efforts to identify fully the structure of a system [Eq. (1)] are generously awarded at the solution stage. Special cases and special algorithms are so numerous, however, that we shall first study the algorithms that work for general linear systems [Eq. (1)]. We shall follow the customary pattern of subdividing the methods for solving systems [Eq. (1)] into direct and iterative. The direct methods are more universal; they apply to general and special linear systems, but for many special and/or sparse linear systems, the special iterative methods are superior (see Section VIII). If the computations are performed with infinite precision, the direct methods solve Eq. (1) in finite time, whereas iterative methods only compute better and better approximations to a solution with each new iteration (but may never compute the solution exactly). That difference disappears in practical computations, where all arithmetic operations are performed with finite precision, that is, with round-off errors. In principle, the round-off errors may propagate and greatly, or even completely, contaminate the outputs. This depends on the properties of the coefficient matrix, on the choice of the algorithms, and on the precision of computation. A certain amount of study of the sensitivity of the outputs to round-off error is normally included in texts on linear systems and in current packages of computer subroutines for such systems; stable algorithms are always chosen, which keep output errors lower. In general, direct methods are no more or no less stable than the iterative methods. [*See* ALGEBRAIC EQUATIONS.]

II. Some Examples of Applications

Next we present a few simple examples that demonstrate how frequently practical computations and important theoretical problems are reduced to solving linear systems of algebraic equations (more examples are presented in Sections VI,B and VII,D) (Those readers not interested in the present section may proceed to Section III, consulting Section II as they are referred to it.)

A. Numerical Solution of the Laplace Equation

We consider the Laplace equation $\partial^2 u/\partial x^2 + \partial^2 u/\partial y^2 = 0$ on the square region $0 \leq x, y \leq 1$, provided that the function $u(x, y)$ is given on the boundary of that region; $u(x, y)$ models the temperature distribution through a square plate with fixed temperature on its sides. To compute $u(x, y)$ numerically, we superimpose a mesh of horizontal and vertical lines over the region as shown by

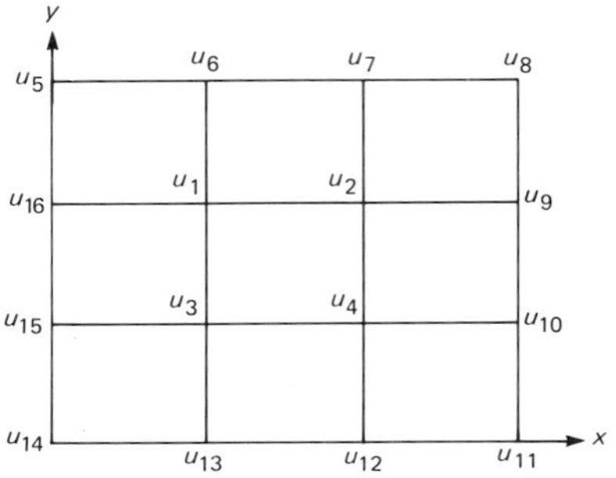

so that u_1 denotes the point $(\frac{1}{3}, \frac{2}{3})$; u_2 denotes the point $(\frac{2}{3}, \frac{2}{3})$; u_7 denotes $(\frac{2}{3}, 1)$, and so on; $u_5, u_6, \ldots, u_{16}$ are given; and u_1, u_2, u_3, u_4 are unknowns. Then we replace the derivatives by divided differences,

$$\partial^2 u/\partial x^2 \text{ by } u(x-h, y) - 2u(x, y) + u(x+h, y)$$

$$\partial^2 u/\partial y^2 \text{ by } u(x, y-h) - 2u(x, y) + u(x, y+h)$$

where $h = \frac{1}{3}$. This turns the Laplace equation into a linear system that can be equivalently derived if we just assume that the temperature at an internal point of the grid equals the average of the temperatures at the four neighboring points of the grid;

$$\begin{aligned}
-4u_1 + u_2 + u_3 \qquad\qquad &= -u_6 - u_{16} \\
u_1 - 4u_2 \qquad\qquad + u_4 &= -u_7 - u_9 \\
u_1 \qquad - 4u_3 + u_4 &= -u_{13} - u_{15} \\
u_2 + u_3 - 4u_4 &= -u_{10} - u_{12}
\end{aligned}$$

The coefficient matrix A of the system is the block tridiagonal of Eq. (3). With smaller spacing we may obtain a finer grid and compute the temperatures at more points on the plate. Then the size of the linear system will increase, say to N^2 equations in N^2 unknowns for larger N; but its $N^2 \times N^2$ coefficient matrix will still be block tridiagonal of the following special form (where blank spaces mean zero entries),

$$\begin{bmatrix}
B_N & I_N & & & \\
I_N & B_N & I_N & & \\
 & I_N & B_N & \ddots & \\
 & & \ddots & \ddots & I_N \\
 & & & I_N & B_N
\end{bmatrix}$$

$$B_N = \begin{bmatrix}
-4 & 1 & & \\
1 & -4 & \ddots & \\
 & \ddots & \ddots & 1 \\
 & & 1 & -4
\end{bmatrix}$$

Here, B_N is an $N \times N$ tridiagonal matrix, and I_N denotes the $N \times N$ identity matrix (see Section II,D). This example demonstrates how the finite difference method reduces the solution of partial differential equations to the solution of linear systems [Eq. (1)] by replacing derivatives by divided differences. The matrices of the resulting linear systems are sparse and well structured.

B. Solving a Differential Equation

Let us consider the following differential equation on the interval $\{t: 0 \leq t \leq 1\}$, $d^2x/dt^2 + x = g(t)$, $x(0) = 0$, $x(1) = 1$ [where $g(t)$ is a given function, say $g(t) = \log(t+1)$ or $g(t) = e^t$]. Let $t_0 = 0$; $t_1, t_2, t_3, t_4, t_5 = 1$ be the one-dimensional grid of six equally spaced points on the interval $\{t: 0 \leq t \leq 1\}$, so $t_1 = \frac{1}{5}$, $t_2 = \frac{2}{5}$, $t_3 = \frac{3}{5}$, $t_4 = \frac{4}{5}$, $h = \frac{1}{5}$. Denote $x_0 = x(t_0) = x(0) = 0$, $x_1 = x(t_1)$, $\ldots$, $x_5 = x(t_5) = x(1) = 1$, replace the derivative d^2x/dt^2 by the divided differences so that $(d^2x/dt^2)|_{t=t_2} = (x_1 - 2x_2 + x_3)/h^2$ and similarly at $t = t_1$, $t = t_3$, and $t = t_4$; and arrive at the tridiagonal system defined by the following extended matrix:

$$\begin{bmatrix}
h^2-2 & 1 & 0 & 0 & h^2 g(t_1) - x_0 \\
1 & h^2-2 & 1 & 0 & h^2 g(t_2) \\
0 & 1 & h^2-2 & 1 & h^2 g(t_3) \\
0 & 0 & 1 & h^2-2 & h^2 g(t_4) - x_5
\end{bmatrix}$$

Using a finer grid with more points t, we may compute the solution $x(t)$ at more points. The derived linear system would have greater size but the same tridiagonal structure.

C. Hitchcock Transportation Problem. Linear Programming Problem

We consider a communication system having three sources, 1, 2, and 3, with supplies s_1, s_2, and s_3 and two sinks, 1 and 2, with demands d_1 and d_2, respectively, such that $d_1 + d_2 = s_1 + s_2 + s_3$. Let every source be connected with every sink by a communication line. Suppose that the quantities x_{ij} must be delivered from source i to sink j for every pair i, j such that

$$\sum_{j=1}^{2} x_{ij} = s_i, \qquad i = 1, 2, 3$$

$$\sum_{j=1}^{3} x_{ij} = d_j, \qquad j = 1, 2$$

One of these equations can be deleted, for the sums of the first three and of the last two equations coincide with one another. Thus, we arrive at an underdetermined system of four equations with six unknowns having two free variables; say x_{22} and x_{32}, which can be chosen arbitrarily, then x_{11}, x_{12}, x_{21}, x_{31} will be uniquely defined. For instance, let $s_1 = s_2 = s_3 = 2$, $d_1 = d_2 = 3$. Choose $x_{22} = x_{32} = 1$, then $x_{11} = x_{12} = x_{21} = x_{31} = 1$; choose $x_{22} = 2$, $x_{32} = 0$, then $x_{11} = x_{12} = 1$, $x_{21} = 0$, $x_{31} = 2$, and so on. In such situations some additional requirements are usually imposed. Typically, it is required that all the variables x_{ij} be nonnegative and that a fixed linear function in those variables take its minimum value; for example,

$$\begin{aligned}
&\textit{minimize} \quad x_{11} + x_{12} + x_{21} + 2x_{22} + 2x_{31} + x_{32} \\
&\text{subject to} \quad x_{11} + x_{12} = 2 \\
&\qquad x_{21} + x_{22} = 2 \\
&\qquad x_{31} + x_{32} = 2 \\
&\qquad x_{11} + x_{21} + x_{31} = 3 \\
&\qquad x_{12} + x_{22} + x_{32} = 3 \\
&\qquad x_{ij} \geq 0 \quad \text{for} \quad i = 1, 2, 3, \quad j = 1, 2
\end{aligned}$$

In this case, $x_{11} = x_{12} = 1$, $x_{21} = x_{32} = 2$, $x_{22} = x_{31} = 0$ is the unique solution. This example is a specific instance of the Hitchcock transportation problem, generally defined as follows:

$$\text{minimize} \quad \sum_{i=1}^{p} \sum_{j=1}^{q} c_{ij} x_{ij}$$

$$\text{subject to} \quad \sum_{j=1}^{q} x_{ij} = s_i, \qquad i = 1, \ldots, p$$

$$\sum_{i=1}^{p} x_{ij} = d_j, \quad j = 1, \ldots, q$$

$$x_{ij} \geq 0 \qquad \text{for} \quad \text{all } i \quad \text{and } j$$

Here s_i, d_j and c_{ij} are given for all i, j. (In our specific example above, $p = 3$, $q = 2$, $s_1 = s_2 = s_3 = 2$, $d_1 = d_2 = 3$, $c_{11} = c_{12} = c_{21} = c_{32} = 1$, $c_{22} = c_{31} = 2$.) The linear equations form an underdetermined but sparse and well-structured system.

The Hitchcock transportation problem is in turn an important particular case of the linear programming problem (l.p.p.). The l.p.p. is known in several equivalent forms, one of which follows:

$$\text{minimize} \quad \sum_{j=1}^{m} c_j x_j$$

$$\text{subject to} \quad \sum_{j=1}^{m} a_{ij} x_{ij} = b_i, \quad i = 1, \ldots, n$$

$$x_j \geq 0, \quad j = 1, \ldots, m$$

In this representation, the general l.p.p. includes an underdetermined system of linear equations complemented with the minimization and nonnegativity requirements. Solving the l.p.p. can be reduced to finite number of iterations, each reduced to solving one or two auxiliary linear systems of equations; such systems either have n equations with n unknowns (in the simplex algorithms for l.p.p.) or are overdetermined, in which case their least-squares solutions are sought (in ellipsoid algorithms, in Karmarkar's algorithm). The least squares solutions to overdetermined linear systems are studied in Sections II,E; IV,A; and IV.C. [*See* LINEAR PROGRAMMING.]

D. Some Matrix Operations. Special Matrices

The study of linear systems [Eq. (1)] is closely related to the study of matrices and vectors. In this section we shall reduce $n \times n$ matrix inversion (which is theoretically important and has some practical applications, for instance, in statistics) to solving n systems [Eq. (1)], where $m = n$. We shall also list some special matrices and recall some basic concepts of matrix theory.

Generally, a $p \times q$ array is called a $p \times q$ matrix; in particular $p \times 1$ and $1 \times p$ matrices are called vectors of dimension p. Deletion of any r rows and s columns for $r < p$ and $s < q$

turns a $p \times q$ matrix into its $(p - r) \times (q - s)$ submatrix. The coefficient matrix A of Eq. (1) has size $m \times n$; the extended matrix W has size $m \times (n + 1)$; the last column of W is vector $\mathbf{b}$ of dimension m. The unknowns $x_1, x_2, \ldots, x_n$ form a (column) vector $\mathbf{x}$ of dimension n. Of course, that notation may change; for instance, in the next section we shall replace $\mathbf{x}$ by $\mathbf{c}$ and $\mathbf{b}$ by $\mathbf{f}$.

The transpose of a matrix V is denoted by V^{T}, so $\mathbf{x}^{\mathrm{T}} = [x_1, \ldots, x_n]$, $\mathbf{x} = [x_1, \ldots, x_n]^{\mathrm{T}}$. For a complex matrix $V = [v_{gh}]$, its Hermitian transpose is defined $V^{\mathrm{H}} = [v^*_{hg}]$, v^*_{hg} being the complex conjugate of v_{hg}. $V^{\mathrm{T}} = V^{\mathrm{H}}$ for a real V. A matrix V is called symmetric if $V = V^{\mathrm{T}}$ and Hermitian if $V = V^{\mathrm{H}}$. For two column vectors $\mathbf{u}$ and $\mathbf{v}$ of the same dimension p, their inner product (also called their scalar product or their dot product), is defined as follows,

$$\mathbf{u}^{\mathrm{T}}\mathbf{v} = u_1v_1 + u_2v_2 + \cdots + u_pv_p$$

This is extended to define the $m \times p$ product of an $m \times n$ matrix A by an $n \times p$ matrix B, $AB = [a_{i1}b_{1k} + a_{i2}b_{2k} + \cdots + a_{in}b_{nk}, i = 1, \ldots, m; k = 1, \ldots, p]$; that is, every row $[a_{i1}, \ldots, a_{in}]$ of A is multiplied by every column $[b_{1k}, \ldots, b_{nk}]^{\mathrm{T}}$ of B to form the $m \times p$ matrix AB. For instance, if $A = [1, 2]$, $B = [1, 2]^{\mathrm{T}}$, then $AB = [5]$ is a 1×1 matrix, $BA = [\begin{smallmatrix}1 & 2\\ 2 & 4\end{smallmatrix}]$ is a 2×2 matrix, $AB \neq BA$. The m equations of Eq. (1) can be equivalently represented by a single matrix–vector equation, $A\mathbf{x} = \mathbf{b}$. For instance, the system of Eq. (1) takes the following form,

$$\begin{bmatrix} 10 & 14 & 0 \\ -3 & -4 & 6 \\ 5 & 2 & 5 \end{bmatrix} \begin{bmatrix} x_1 \\ x_2 \\ x_3 \end{bmatrix} = \begin{bmatrix} 7 \\ 4 \\ 6 \end{bmatrix}.$$

(For control, substitute here the solution vector $[x_1, x_2, x_3]^{\mathrm{T}} = [0, 0.5, 1]^{\mathrm{T}}$ and verify the resulting equalities.)

Hereafter I_n denotes the unique $n \times n$ matrix (called the identity matrix) such that $AI_n = A$, $I_nB = B$ for all the matrices A and B of sizes $m \times n$ and $n \times p$, respectively. All the entries of I_n are zeros except for the diagonal entries, equal to 1. (Check that $I_2A = A$ for $I_2 = [\begin{smallmatrix}1 & 0\\ 0 & 1\end{smallmatrix}]$ and for arbitrary A.) In the sequel, I (with no subscript) denotes the identity matrix I_n for appropriate n; similarly, 0 denotes a null matrix (filled with zeros) of appropriate size.

An $n \times n$ matrix A may (but may not) have its inverse, that is, an $n \times n$ matrix $X = A^{-1}$ such that $XA = I$. For instance, $A^{-1} = [\begin{smallmatrix}1 & -2\\ 0 & 1\end{smallmatrix}]$ if $A = [\begin{smallmatrix}1 & 2\\ 0 & 1\end{smallmatrix}]$; but the matrix $[\begin{smallmatrix}2 & 2\\ 1 & 1\end{smallmatrix}]$ has no inverse. Matrices having no inverse are called singular. All the nonsquare matrices are singular. Linear system $A\mathbf{x} = \mathbf{b}$ has unique solution $\mathbf{x} = A^{-1}\mathbf{b}$ if and only if its coefficient matrix A is nonsingular. If $XA = I$, then always $AX = I$; so computing the kth column of $X = A^{-1}$ amouns to solving the system of Eq. (1) where $\mathbf{b}$ is the kth coordinate vector whose kth entry is 1 and whose other entries are zeros, $k = 1, 2, \ldots, n$. Computing the inverse of an $n \times n$ matrix A is equivalent to solving n such linear systems with the common coefficient matrix A.

The maximum r, such that A has a $r \times r$ nonsingular submatrix, is called the rank of A and is denoted as rank(A). An $m \times n$ matrix A has full rank if $\mathrm{rank}(A) = \min\{m, n\}$.

Theorem 1. If the system of Eq. (1) is consistent, then its general solution is uniquely defined by the values of $n - r$ free parameters, where $r = \mathrm{rank}(A)$.

The sum $A + B = [a_{ij} + b_{ij}]$ and the difference $A - B = [a_{ij} - b_{ij}]$ are defined for two matrices A and B of the same size; the product $cA = Ac = [ca_{ij}]$ is defined for a matrix A and a scalar c. The customary laws of arithmetic (except for $AB = BA$) are extended to the case where the operations are performed with matrices, $A + B = B + A$, $(A + B) + C = A + (B + C)$, $-A = (-1)A$, $(AB)C = A(BC)$, $(A + B)C = AC + BC$, $C(A + B) = CA + CB$, $c(A + B) = cA + cB$.

Further, $(AB)^{\mathrm{T}} = B^{\mathrm{T}}A^{\mathrm{T}}$, $(AB)^{-1} = B^{-1}A^{-1}$, $(A^{-1})^{\mathrm{T}} = (A^{\mathrm{T}})^{-1}$. Linear forms and linear equations can be defined over matrices, say $AX + BY = C$, where A, B, C, X, Y are matrices of appropriate sizes, A, B, C are given and X, Y are unknown. Such a matrix equation can be also rewritten as a system of linear equations, the entries of X and Y playing the role of unknowns. If $B = 0$, $C = I$, we arrive at the matrix equation $AX = I$, which defines $X = A^{-1}$.

Finally, definitions of and the customary notation for some special matrices used in special linear systems [Eq. (1)] are given in Table I.

E. Approximating Data by Curves. Overdetermined Linear Systems. Normal Equations. Reduction to Linear Programming Problems

In many applications we need to define a simple curve (function) that approximates to (that is, passes near) a given set of points on a plane $\{(x_i, f_i), i = 1, \ldots, N\}$. [The objectives can be to compress $2 \times N$ array representing those points where N is large or to retrieve the information and to suppress the noise or to replace a func-

TABLE I. Customary Notation for Special Matrices

1. Diagonal, $A = \text{diag}[a_{11}, \ldots, a_{nn}]$:	$a_{ij} = 0$, unless $i = j$
2. Lower triangular, $A = L$:	$a_{ij} = 0$, unless $i \geq j$
2a. Unit lower triangular:	$a_{ii} = 1$ for all i
3. (Unit) upper triangular, $A = U, A = R$:	the transpose of 2 (of item 2a)
4. Band with bandwidth (g, h):	$a_{ij} = 0$, unless $g \leq i - j \leq h$
4a. Tridiagonal:	$a_{ij} = 0$, unless $-1 \leq i - j \leq 1$
5. (Strictly) row-diagonally dominant:	$2\|a_{ii}\| > \sum_{j=1}^{n} \|a_{ij}\|$ for all i
6. (Strictly) column-diagonally dominant:	$2\|a_{jj}\| > \sum_{i=1}^{n} \|a_{ij}\|$ for all j
7. Hermitian (real symmetric):	$A = A^H$ (in real case, $A = A^T$)
8. Positive definite:	$\bar{x}^H A \bar{x} > 0$ for all vectors $\bar{x} \neq \bar{0}$
9. Unitary (real orthogonal), $A = Q$:	$A^H A = I$ (real case, $A^T A = I$)
10. Toeplitz:	$a_{ij} = a_{i+1,j+1}$, for all $i, j < n$
11. Hankel:	$a_{ij} = a_{i+1,j-1}$, for all $i < n, j > 1$
12. Vandermonde:	$a_{ij} = a_j^{i-1}$ for all i, j; a_j distinct

tion $f(x)$ by an approximating polynomial, which can be computed at any point using only few arithmetic operations.]

i:	1	2	3	4	5	6	7	8
x_i:	0.1	0.2	0.3	0.5	0.7	1.0	1.4	2.0
f_i:	0.197	0.381	0.540	0.785	0.951	1.11	1.23	1.33

A model example with eight points, where in fact $f_i = \tan^{-1} x_i$ (in practice, hundreds or thousands of input points are not an unusual case) is shown in the accompanying tabulation. To find a straight line $c_0 + c_1 x$ passing through all the eight points (x_i, f_i), we would have to satisfy the following system of eight equations with two unknowns c_0 and c_1, $c_0 + c_1 x_i = f_i$, $i = 1, \ldots, 8$. This is a typical example of an overdetermined linear system $A\mathbf{c} = \mathbf{f}$, that has no solution. Every (overdetermined) linear system $A\mathbf{c} = \mathbf{f}$, however, has a least-squares solution vector $\mathbf{c} = \mathbf{c}^*$ minimizing the Euclidean norm of the residual vector $\mathbf{r} = \mathbf{f} - A\mathbf{c}$, $\mathbf{r} = [r_1, r_2, \ldots, r_N]^T$, $\|\mathbf{r}\|_2 = (\sum_{i=1}^{N} r_i^2)^{1/2}$. In our case, $N = 8$, and $\mathbf{r} = [r_1, r_2, \ldots, r_8]^T$, $\mathbf{c} = [c_1, c_2]^T$, $\mathbf{f} = [0.197, 0.381, 0.540, 0.785, 0.951, 1.11, 1.23, 1.33]^T$, and

$$A = \begin{bmatrix} 1 & 1 & 1 & 1 & 1 & 1 & 1 & 1 \\ 0.1 & 0.2 & 0.3 & 0.5 & 0.7 & 1.0 & 1.4 & 2.0 \end{bmatrix}^T$$

In some cases a vector $\mathbf{c}$ is sought that minimizes another norm of $\mathbf{r}$ (rather than Euclidean); but the minimization of the Euclidean norm of $\mathbf{r}$ [or of a weighted Euclidean norm $(\sum_{i=1}^{N} w_i r_i^2)^{1/2}$ for a fixed set of positive weights $w_1, \ldots, w_N$] is most customary because simple solution methods are available. Computing a least squares solution $\mathbf{c}$ to an overdetermined linear system $A\mathbf{c} = \mathbf{f}$ is called regression in statistics. When the computation is with finite precision, computing such a solution $\mathbf{c}$ is equivalent to solving the system of normal equations, $A^T A\mathbf{c} = A^T\mathbf{f}$. In the previous example the normal equations take the following form:

$$\begin{bmatrix} 8 & 6.2 \\ 6.2 & 7.84 \end{bmatrix} \begin{bmatrix} c_0 \\ c_1 \end{bmatrix} = \begin{bmatrix} 6.524 \\ 6.8081 \end{bmatrix}$$

The latter system defines the desired least-squares solution vector $\mathbf{c}^T = [c_0, c_1] = [0.368119, 0.577265]$ (here the entries of $\mathbf{c}$ are given with six decimals).

When the computation is done with finite precision, using normal equations is not always recommended because for some matrices A, higher precision of computation is required in order to solve the system of normal equations correctly. For example, let us consider the problem of least-squares fitting by a straight line, $c_0 + c_1 x$, to the set of data, shown in the accompanying tabulation.

i:	1	2	3	4
x_i:	970	990	1000	1040
f_i:	4	2	0	−3

Then, $\mathbf{f} = [4, 2, 0, -3]^T$,

$$A^T = \begin{bmatrix} 1 & 1 & 1 & 1 \\ 970 & 990 & 1000 & 1040 \end{bmatrix}$$

which gives the following system $A^TA\mathbf{c} = A^T\mathbf{f}$ of normal equations

$$\begin{bmatrix} 4 & 4000 \\ 4000 & 4002600 \end{bmatrix} \begin{bmatrix} c_0 \\ c_1 \end{bmatrix} = \begin{bmatrix} 3 \\ 2740 \end{bmatrix}$$

The solution $c_1 = -0.1$, $c_0 = 100.75$ defines the straight line $-0.1x + 100.75$. Next, we assume that the computation is with chopping to four decimals, that is, every number is a floating-point decimal number, and its fraction (mantissa) is chopped to its four most significant digits. We then arrive at $c_1 = -0.13$, $c_0 = 130.7$. The substantial error arises because of the large entries of A^TA. To counter this difficulty, we linearly transform the basis $1, x$ of the representation of the straight line into the more suitable basis $1, x - 1000$ and seek the straight line $c_0^* + c_1^*(x - 1000)$. (That basis is in fact orthogonal: The two vectors $[1, 1, 1, 1]$ and $[x_1 - 1000, x_2 - 1000, x_3 - 1000, x_4 - 1000] = [-30, -10, 0, 40]$, representing the values of the basis functions 1 and $x - 1000$ at x_1, x_2, x_3, x_4, are orthogonal to each other; that is, their inner product equals $-30 - 10 + 0 + 40 = 0$). Using that basis we may rewrite the previous tabulation as shown in the accompanying one here. We then arrive at

i:	1	2	3	4
$x_i - 1000$:	−30	−10	0	40
f_i:	4	2	0	−3

the normal equations, $A^TA\mathbf{c}^* = A^T\mathbf{f}$, where

$$A^T = \begin{bmatrix} 1 & 1 & 1 & 1 \\ -30 & -10 & 0 & 40 \end{bmatrix}$$

so that $4c_0^* = 3$, $2600c_1^* = -260$, $c_0^* = 0.75$, and $c_1^* = c_1 = -0.1$. This defines the desired straight line, $c_0^* + c_1^*(x - 1000) = 0.75 - 0.1(x - 1000) = -0.1x + 100.75$. The latter approach, with the orthogonalization of the basis via its linear transformation, leads to the methods of QR-factorization of a matrix A (see Section IV,A).

Our model examples of the approximation to the given data by a straight line can be immediately extended to the approximation by algebraic polynomials of higher degree, by trigonometric polynomials, and so on. For instance, fitting by a quadratic curve $c_0 + c_1x + c_2x^2$ leads to an overdetermined system $c_0 + c_1x_i + c_2x_i^2 = f_i$, $i = 1, \ldots, N$, of the form $A\mathbf{c} = \mathbf{f}$, whose least-square solution can be found by the usual methods. Here, $\mathbf{c} = [c_0, c_1, c_2]^T$, and A is a $3 \times N$ matrix $A = [x_i^j, i = 1, \ldots, N, j = 0, 1, 2]$.

Minimizing the least deviation norm of the residual vector $\|\mathbf{r}\|_1 = \sum_{i=1}^N |r_i|$ is a little harder than regression. The problem is equivalent to the linear programming problem (l.p.p.) of the following form:

$$\text{minimize} \quad \|\mathbf{q}\|_1 = \sum_{i=1}^{N} q_i$$

$$\text{subject to} \quad \mathbf{q} \geq \mathbf{f} - A\mathbf{c}, \qquad \mathbf{q} \geq -\mathbf{f} + A\mathbf{c}$$

The latter inequalities imply that every coordinate q_i of the vector $\mathbf{q}$ is not less than $|r_i| = |f_i - \mathbf{A}_i^T\mathbf{c}|$ where $\mathbf{A}_i^T$ denotes the ith row of A.

Similarly, the minimization of the maximum norm of $\mathbf{r}$, $\|\mathbf{r}\|_\infty = \max_{1 \leq i \leq N} |r_i|$, is equivalent to the l.p.p. of the following form:

$$\text{minimize} \quad q$$

$$\text{subject to} \quad q \geq f_i - \mathbf{A}_i^T\mathbf{c},$$

$$q \geq -f_i + \mathbf{A}_i^T\mathbf{c}, \quad i = 1, 2, \ldots, N$$

The latter inequalities imply that $q \geq |f_i - A_i^T\mathbf{c}|$ for all i.

III. Gaussian Elimination and Triangular Factorization

Gaussian elimination and its modifications are the most customary direct algorithms for the general linear system of Eq. (1), $A\mathbf{x} = \mathbf{b}$. The subroutine versions usually include pivoting and rely on triangular factorizations of the coefficient matrix A; computing is performed with finite precision. We initially assume infinite precision and no pivoting in order to facilitate the presentation. Systems with nonsquare matrices A are studied further in Section IV; Section VI contains some special algorithms for special systems [Eq. (1)] that are most important in applications; and Section V contains further estimates for time and space required to solve a general linear system.

A. Solving Triangular Systems by Back Substitution

Let $A = [a_{ij}]$ be an $n \times n$ upper triangular matrix; that is, $a_{ij} = 0$ if $i > j$ (similarly, A is a lower triangular if $a_{ij} = 0$, where $i < j$). There can be two cases.

Case 1. All the diagonal entries a_{ii} are nonzero. In that case, the system is nonsingular and has a unique solution.

EXAMPLE 5.

$$\begin{aligned} x_1 + 2x_2 - x_3 &= 3 \\ -2x_2 - 2x_3 &= -10 \\ -6x_3 &= -18 \end{aligned}$$

Compute $x_3 = -18/(-6) = 3$. Substitute this value into the second equation and obtain $-2x_2 - 6 = -10$, so $-2x_2 = -4$, $x_2 = 2$. Substitute $x_2 = 2$, $x_3 = 3$ into the first equation and obtain $x_1 + 4 - 3 = 3$, $x_1 = 2$. In general, if A is an $n \times n$ triangular matrix, this back substitution algorithm can be written as follows.

For $i = n, n - 1, \ldots, 1$

If $a_{ii} = 0$, end (the system is singular)

Else $x_i := \left(b_i - \sum_{j=i+1}^{n} a_{ij}x_j\right) \Big/ a_{ii}$

The computation consists mostly of operations of the form, $c: = c + gh$. The amount of computational work required to perform such an operation on a computer using a floating-point finite-precision arithmetic is called a flop. The number of flops used is a customary measure for the amount of work required in algorithms for systems [Eq. (1)]. Frequently, the terms of lower order are ignored; for instance, we may say that the above back substitution algorithm requires $n^2/2$ flops. In that algorithm, operations are grouped into inner product computations; computing inner products can be simplified on some serial computers.

Case 2. Some diagonal entries are zeros. In that case the system is singular, that is, is inconsistent or has infinitely many solutions (compare Theorem 1).

EXAMPLE 6.

$$\begin{aligned} 0 * x_1 + 2x_2 - x_3 &= 3 \\ -2x_2 - 2x_3 &= -10 \\ -6x_3 &= -18 \end{aligned}$$

Back substitution shows an inconsistency: $x_3 = 3$, $x_2 = 2$, $4 - 2 = 3$.

EXAMPLE 7.

$$\begin{aligned} x_1 + 2x_2 - x_3 &= 3 \\ 0 * x_2 - 2x_3 &= -6 \\ -6x_3 &= -18 \end{aligned}$$

Back substitution yields $x_3 = 3$; x_2 is a free variable; $x_1 = 6 - 2x_2$.

B. Forward Elimination Stage of Gaussian Elimination

Every system [Eq. (1)] can be reduced to triangular form using the following transformations, which never change its solutions:

1. Multiply equation i (row i of the extended matrix W) by a nonzero constant.
2. Interchange equations i and k (rows i and k of W).
3. Add a multiple of equation i to equation k (of row i to row k of W).

EXAMPLE 8.

$$\begin{aligned} 10x_1 + 14x_2 &= 7 \\ -3x_1 - 4x_2 + 6x_3 &= 4 \\ 5x_1 + 2x_2 + 5x_3 &= 6 \end{aligned}$$

Step 1. Multiply the first equation by the multipliers $m_{21} = -\frac{3}{10}$ and $m_{31} = \frac{5}{10}$; subtract the results from the second and the third equations, respectively; and arrive at the system

$$\begin{aligned} 10x_1 + 14x_2 &= 7 \\ 0.2x_2 + 6x_3 &= 6.1 \\ -5x_2 + 5x_3 &= 2.5 \end{aligned}$$

Step 2. Multiply the second equation by the multiplier $m_{32} = -5/0.2 = -25$ and subtract the results from the third equation. The system becomes triangular:

$$\begin{aligned} 10x_1 + 14x_2 &= 7 \\ 0.2x_2 + 6x_3 &= 6.1 \\ 155x_3 &= 155 \end{aligned}$$

For the general system [Eq. (1)], where $m = n$, the algorithm can be written as follows.

ALGORITHM 1. FORWARD ELIMINATION. Input the $n^2 + n$ entries of the extended matrix $W = [w_{ij}, i = 1, \ldots, n; j = 1, \ldots, n+1]$ of the system of Eq. (1), which occupies $n \times (n + 1)$ working array:

For $k = 1, \ldots, n - 1$,

For $i = k + 1, \ldots, n$,

$w_{ik}: = w_{ik}/w_{kk}$

For $j = k + 1, \ldots, n + 1$,

$w_{ij}: = w_{ij} - w_{ik}w_{kj}$

In $n - 1$ steps, the diagonal entries w_{ii} and the superdiagonal entries w_{ij}, $i < j$, of the working array W are overwritten by the entries of the extended matrix U of an upper triangular system equivalent to the original system [Eq. (1)], provided that in the kth step the denominator w_{kk} (called the pivot) is nonzero for $k = 1, \ldots, n - 1$. For general system Eq. (1), the algorithm requires about $n^3/3$ flops, that is, more than $n^2/2$ flops used in back substitution. The multipliers m_{ik} usually overwrite the subdiagonal entries w_{ik} of the array (the previous contents are no longer needed and are deleted). Thus, the space of $n^2 + n$ units of an $n \times (n + 1)$ array suffices to solve the general system Eq. (1), including the space for input and output. Additional n^2 (or $n^2 + n$) units of space are provided to save the inputs A (and $\bar{b}$) in some subroutines. The entire computational process of forward elimination can be represented by the sequence of $n \times (n + 1)$ matrices $W^{(0)}, \ldots, W^{(n-1)}$, where $W^{(k-1)}$ and $W^{(k)}$ denote the contents of the working arrays before and after elimination step k, respectively, $k = 1, \ldots, n - 1$; $W^{(0)} = W$, whereas $W^{(n-1)}$ consists of the multipliers (placed under the diagonal) and of the entries of U.

EXAMPLE 9. The sequence $W^{(0)}$, $W^{(1)}$, $W^{(2)}$ represents forward elimination for a system of three equations of Example 1:

$$\begin{bmatrix} 10 & 14 & 0 & 7 \\ -3 & -4 & 6 & 4 \\ 5 & 2 & 5 & 6 \end{bmatrix} \rightarrow \begin{bmatrix} 10 & 14 & 0 & 7 \\ -0.3 & 0.2 & 6 & 6.1 \\ 0.5 & -5 & 5 & 2.5 \end{bmatrix}$$

$$\rightarrow \begin{bmatrix} 10 & 14 & 0 & 7 \\ -0.3 & 0.2 & 6 & 6.1 \\ 0.5 & -25 & 155 & 155 \end{bmatrix}$$

The presented algorithm works if and only if the pivot entry (k, k) is zero in none step k, $k = 1, \ldots, n - 1$, or, equivalently, if and only if for none k the $(n - k) \times (n - k)$ principal submatrix of the coefficient matrix A is singular. (A $p \times p$ submatrix of A is said to be the principal if it is formed by the first p rows and by the first p columns of A.) That assumption always holds (so the validity of the above algorithm is assured) in the two important cases where A is row or column diagonally dominant and where A is Hermitian (or real symmetric) positive definite (compare the list of special matrices in Section II,D). (For example, the system derived in Sections II,A is simultaneously row and column diagonally dominant and real symmetric; multiplication of all the inputs by -1 makes that system also positive definite. The product $V^{H}V$ for a nonsingular matrix V is a Hermitian positive definite matrix, which is real symmetric if V is real.)

Next, we assume that in some step k the pivot entry (k, k) is 0. Then we have two cases.

Case 1. The entries $(k, k), (k + 1, k), \ldots, (s - 1, k)$ are zeros; the entry (s, k) is nonzero, where $k < s \leq n$. In that case interchange rows s and k, bringing a nonzero entry into the pivot position; then continue the elimination.

EXAMPLE 10.

$$\begin{bmatrix} 10 & 14 & 0 & 7 \\ -3 & -4.2 & 6 & 4 \\ 5 & 2 & 5 & 6 \end{bmatrix} \rightarrow \begin{bmatrix} 10 & 14 & 0 & 7 \\ -0.3 & 0 & 6 & 6.1 \\ 0.5 & -5 & 5 & 2.5 \end{bmatrix}$$

$$\rightarrow \begin{bmatrix} 10 & 14 & 0 & 7 \\ 0.5 & -5 & 5 & 2.5 \\ -0.3 & 0 & 6 & 6.1 \end{bmatrix}$$

Case 2. The pivot entry (k, k) and all the subdiagonal entries (s, k) for $s > k$ equal 0. In that case continue elimination, skipping the kth elimination step and leaving the (k, k) entry equal to 0. For underdetermined systems, apply complete pivoting (see Section III,C). Some subroutines end the computation in Case 2, indicating that the system is singular.

EXAMPLE 11.

$$\begin{bmatrix} 10 & 14 & 0 & 7 & 6 \\ -3 & -4.2 & 5 & 4 & 5 \\ 5 & 7 & 5 & 5 & 7 \\ 10 & 14 & 5 & 9 & 4 \end{bmatrix}$$

$$\rightarrow \begin{bmatrix} 10 & 14 & 0 & 7 & 6 \\ -0.3 & 0 & 5 & 6.1 & 6.8 \\ 0.5 & 0 & 5 & 1.5 & 4 \\ 1 & 0 & 5 & 2 & -2 \end{bmatrix}$$

$$\rightarrow \begin{bmatrix} 10 & 14 & 0 & 7 & 6 \\ -0.3 & 0 & 5 & 6.1 & 6.8 \\ 0.5 & 0 & 5 & 1.5 & 4 \\ 1 & 0 & 1 & 0.5 & -6 \end{bmatrix}$$

No row interchange is required in order to eliminate all the subdiagonal nonzero entries in the second column in Step 2.

The forward-elimination algorithm can be immediately extended to overdetermined and underdetermined systems.

EXAMPLE 12. Forward elimination for an underdetermined system:

$$\begin{bmatrix} 10 & -7 & 1 & 0 \\ -3 & 2 & 0 & 1 \end{bmatrix} \rightarrow \begin{bmatrix} 10 & -7 & 1 & 0 \\ -0.3 & -0.1 & 0.3 & 1 \end{bmatrix}$$

Summarizing, forward elimination with pivoting reduces arbitrary linear system Eq. (1) to triangular form and, respectively, to either Case 1 or Case 2 of the previous section (see the end of Section III,C for complete classification).

Forward elimination and back substitution together are called Gaussian elimination algorithm. There exist several modifications of that algorithm. In one of them, Jordan's, the back substitution is interwoven throughout the elimination; that is, every pivot equation times appropriate multipliers is subtracted from all the subsequent and preceding equations; this turns the system into diagonal form in n elimination steps. [Each step, but the first, involves more flops, so the resulting solution of the general system of Eq. (1) becomes more costly.] In the case of systems of two equations, Jordan's version is identical to the canonical Gaussian elimination.

C. Gaussian Elimination Performed with Finite Precision. Pivoting Policies. Complete Pivoting for Singular Systems

Gaussian elimination, as presented in the previous sections, may easily fail in practical computations with finite precision, because such computations may greatly magnify the round-off errors if the pivot entries are close to 0.

EXAMPLE 13. Let the following sequence of working arrays represent Gaussian elimination performed on a computer with chopping to five decimals (see Section II,E about such chopping):

$$\begin{bmatrix} 10 & 14 & 0 & 7 \\ -3 & -4.198 & 6 & 3.901 \\ 5 & 2 & 6 & 7 \end{bmatrix}$$

$$\rightarrow \begin{bmatrix} 10 & 14 & 0 & 7 \\ -0.3 & 0.002 & 6 & 6.001 \\ 0.5 & -5 & 6 & 3.5 \end{bmatrix}$$

$$\rightarrow \begin{bmatrix} 10 & 14 & 0 & 7 \\ -0.3 & 0.002 & 6 & 6.001 \\ 0.5 & -2500 & 15006 & 15005 \end{bmatrix}$$

Solving the resulting upper triangular system, we obtain the following approximation to the solution:

$$x_3 = 0.99993, \qquad 0.002x_2 + 6 * (0.99993) = 6.001$$

$$x_2 = 0.75, \qquad 10x_1 + 14 * (0.75) = 7$$

$$x_1 = -0.35$$

This greatly differs from the correct solution, $x_1 = 0$, $x_2 = 0.5$, $x_3 = 1$, because the division (at the second elimination step) by the small diagonal entry 0.002 has magnified the round-off errors.

The algorithm can be made more *stable* (less sensitive to the errors) if the rows of working array are appropriately interchanged during the elimination. First, the following policy of row interchange is called (unscaled) partial pivoting. Before performing the kth elimination step, choose (the least) i such that $|w_{ik}|$ is maximum over all $i \geq k$ and interchange rows i and k. Row i is called pivotal, the entry w_{ik} is called the pivot entry of step k. Keep track of all the row interchanges. In some subroutines row interchanges are not explicit but are implicitly indicated by pointers. (Each step k may be preceded by scaling the equations by factors of 2^s on binary computers to make $\max_j |w_{ij}|$ in all rows $i \geq k$ lying between 1 and 2. Such scaling is expensive, however, so it is rarely repeated for $k > 1$.)

ALGORITHM 2. FORWARD ELIMINATION WITH UNSCALED PARTIAL PIVOTING.

For $h = 1, \ldots, n$

  $p_h = h$ (initialization)

For $k = 1, \ldots, n - 1$

  Find the smallest $i \geq k$ such that $|w_{ik}| \geq |w_{lk}|$ for all $l \geq k$

  If $w_{ik} = 0$, end (A is singular)

  Else swap the contents of p_k and p_i
  Swap rows k and i of W

  For $i = k + 1, \ldots, n$

    $w_{ik} := w_{ik}/w_{kk}$

    For $j = k + 1, \ldots, n + 1$

      $w_{ij} := w_{ij} - w_{ik}w_{kj}$

If $w_{nn} = 0$, end (A is singular).

In our previous example, partial pivoting after the first elimination step would change the working array W as follows:

$$\begin{bmatrix} 10 & 14 & 0 & 7 & 1 \\ -0.3 & 0.002 & 6 & 6.001 & 2 \\ 0.,5 & -5 & 6 & 3.5 & 3 \end{bmatrix}$$

$$\rightarrow \begin{bmatrix} 10 & 14 & 0 & 7 & 1 \\ 0.5 & -5 & 6 & 3.5 & 3 \\ -0.3 & 0.002 & 6 & 6.001 & 2 \end{bmatrix}$$

Here, the last column is the vector **p**, which monitors the row interchanges. Further computation with chopping to five decimals would give the correct solution, $x_3 = 1$, $x_2 = 0.5$, $x_1 = 0$.

Next, we discuss Complete (total) pivoting. Both rows and columns of W can be interchanged in elimination step k to bring the absolutely maximum coefficient in the left side of the last $n - k + 1$ equations of the current system to the pivot position (k, k); that is, after that interchange $|w_{kk}| \geq \max_{ij=k,\ldots,n} |w_{ij}|$. Two auxiliary vectors $[1, 2, \ldots, n]$ are formed to monitor the row and column interchanges.

EXAMPLE 14. Here are the pivot entries in the first elimination step for the system

$$200x_1 - 1000x_2 = 2200, \qquad x_1 - x_2 = 0$$

1. For unscaled partial pivoting, $a_{11} = 200$.
2. For complete pivoting, $a_{12} = -1000$.

Solution of some systems [Eq. (1)] (called ill-conditioned) is sensitive to input errors and to round-off errors, no matter which algorithm is applied (see Sections III,I and III,J). For other systems (well-conditioned, such as in the first example of this section), the output errors in the presence of round-off depend on the algorithm, in particular, on pivoting. Theoretical estimates (Section III,J) show that complete pivoting prevents the solution from any substantial magnification of input and round-off errors in the case of well-conditioned systems. Practical computations show that even unscaled partial pivoting has similar properties for almost all well-conditioned systems [although it fails for some specially concocted instances of Eq. (1)]. Unscaled partial pivoting requires only $n(n - 1)/2$ comparisons versus about $n^3/3$ in complete pivoting; therefore in practice, safe and inexpensive unscaled partial pivoting is strongly preferred, except for underdetermined systems, for which Gaussian elimination with complete pivoting or the methods of Section IV,B are recommended.

The triangular systems, to which the original systems [Eq. (1)] are reduced by forward elimination with complete pivoting, can be completely classified. We assume infinite precision of computation. Then there can be exactly two cases. (The reader may use examples from Section III,A.)

Case 1. All the diagonal (pivot) entries are nonzero; the triangular system has exactly r equations, $r = \text{rank}(A) \leq n$. In that case, $x_{r+1}, \ldots, x_n$ are free variables; for an arbitrary set of their values, back substitution defines unique set of values of $x_1, \ldots, x_r$ satisfying the original system of Eq. (1), (compare Theorem 1). If $r = n$, the system of Eq. (1) is nonsingular and has a unique solution.

Case 2. The triangular system includes one or more equations of the form, $0 = b_i^*$, where b_i^* is a constant. If at least one of those constants is nonzero, the original system is inconsistent. Otherwise, those equations become the identities, $0 = 0$ and can be deleted. The remaining triangular system belongs to Case 1.

D. Solving Several Systems with Common Coefficient Matrix. Matrix Inversion

Matrix inversion and many other problems are reduced to solving several linear systems [Eq. (1)] with the same coefficient matrix A and distinct vectors **b**.

EXAMPLE 15. The two systems represented by their working arrays

$$W = \begin{bmatrix} 10 & -7 & 1 \\ -3 & 2 & 0 \end{bmatrix}, \qquad W^* = \begin{bmatrix} 10 & -7 & 0 \\ -3 & 2 & 1 \end{bmatrix}$$

define the inverse A^{-1} of their common coefficient matrix A. Represent these two systems by a 2×4 working array and apply forward elimination to that array (compare also Example 12 of Section III,B):

$$\begin{bmatrix} 10 & -7 & 1 & 0 \\ -3 & 2 & 0 & 1 \end{bmatrix} \rightarrow \begin{bmatrix} 10 & -7 & 1 & 0 \\ -0.3 & -0.1 & 0.3 & 1 \end{bmatrix}$$

Both systems have been simultaneously reduced to upper triangular form, so back substitution immediately gives the solutions $x_2 = -3$, $x_1 = -2$ to the first system and $x_2 = -10$, $x_1 = -7$ to the second. This defines the inverse matrix $A^{-1} = \left[\begin{smallmatrix} -2 & -7 \\ -3 & -10 \end{smallmatrix}\right]$. (Verify that $AA^{-1} = A^{-1}A = I$ for $A = \left[\begin{smallmatrix} 10 & -7 \\ -3 & 2 \end{smallmatrix}\right]$.)

In the elimination stage for k systems with a common $m \times n$ matrix A (as well as for an underdetermined system with $n = m + k - 1$), $m^3/3 + km^2/2$ flops and $(k + m)m$ units of storage space are used; for matrix inversion $k = m$, it is easier to solve the system $A\mathbf{x} = \mathbf{b}$ than to invert A. The back substitution stage involves $km^2/2$ flops for the k systems and $(k + m/2)m$ for the underdetermined system.

E. Block Matrix Algorithms

Arithmetic operations with matrices can be performed the same as those with numbers, except that singular matrices cannot be inverted, and the communitive law no longer holds for multiplications (see Section II,D). If the coefficient matrix is represented in block matrix form, as in Eq. (3) then we may perform block Gaussian elimination operating with matrix blocks the same as with numbers and taking special care when divisions and/or pivoting are needed. The block version can be highly effective. For instance, we represent the linear system of Section II,A as follows [compare Eq. (3)]:

$$\begin{bmatrix} B_2 & I_2 \\ I_2 & B_2 \end{bmatrix} \begin{bmatrix} \mathbf{y} \\ \mathbf{z} \end{bmatrix} = \begin{bmatrix} \mathbf{c} \\ \mathbf{d} \end{bmatrix}, \qquad \mathbf{c} = \begin{bmatrix} -u_6 - u_{16} \\ -u_7 - u_9 \end{bmatrix}$$

$$\mathbf{d} = \begin{bmatrix} -u_{13} - u_{15} \\ -u_{10} - u_{12} \end{bmatrix}, \qquad B_2 = \begin{bmatrix} -4 & 1 \\ 1 & -4 \end{bmatrix}$$

where I_2 is the 2×2 identity matrix, and $\mathbf{y}$, $\mathbf{z}$ are two-dimensional vectors of unknowns. Then block forward elimination transforms the extended matrix as follows:

$$\begin{bmatrix} B_2 & I_2 & \mathbf{c} \\ I_2 & B_2 & \mathbf{d} \end{bmatrix} \rightarrow \begin{bmatrix} B_2 & I_2 & \mathbf{c} \\ B_2^{-1} & C_2 & \mathbf{f} \end{bmatrix}$$

Here, $C_2 = B_2 - B_2^{-1}$ and $\mathbf{f} = \mathbf{d} - B_2^{-1}\mathbf{c}$. Block back substitution defines the solution vectors

$$\mathbf{z} = C_2^{-1}\mathbf{f}, \qquad \mathbf{y} = B_2^{-1}(\mathbf{c} - \mathbf{z}) = B_2^{-1}(\mathbf{c} - C_2^{-1}\mathbf{f})$$

The recent development of computer technology greatly increased the already high popularity and importance of block matrix algorithms (and consequently, of matrix multiplication and inversion) for solving linear systems, because block matrix computations turned out to be particularly well suited and effective for implementation on modern computers and supercomputers.

F. *PLU* Factorization. Computing the Determinant of a Matrix

If Gaussian elimination requires no pivoting, then by the end of the elimination stage, the working array contains a lower triangular matrix L (whose subdiagonal entries are filled with the computed multipliers and whose diagonal entries are 1's) and the extended matrix $\hat{U} = A^{(n-1)}$ of the upper triangular system, equivalent to Eq. (1). The coefficient matrix U of that system is an upper triangular submatrix of $\hat{U}$. In Example 8,

$$L = \begin{bmatrix} 1 & 0 & 0 \\ -0.3 & 1 & 0 \\ 0.5 & -25 & 1 \end{bmatrix},$$

$$\hat{U} = \begin{bmatrix} 10 & 14 & 0 & 7 \\ 0 & 0.2 & 6 & 6.1 \\ 0 & 0 & 155 & 155 \end{bmatrix},$$

$$U = \begin{bmatrix} 10 & 14 & 0 \\ 0 & 0.2 & 6 \\ 0 & 0 & 155 \end{bmatrix}$$

For that special instance of Eq. (1), $W = L\hat{U}$, $A = LU$; similarly for the general system of Eq. (1), unless pivoting is used. Moreover, Gaussian elimination with partial pivoting can be reduced to a certain interchange of the rows of W (and of A), defined by the output vector $\mathbf{p}$ (see Algorithm 2 in Section III,C), and to Gaussian elimination with no pivoting. Any row interchange of W is equivalent to premultiplication of W by an appropriate permutation matrix P^{-1} (say, if $P^{-1} = \left[\begin{smallmatrix} 0 & 1 \\ 1 & 0 \end{smallmatrix}\right]$, then rows 1 and 2 are interchanged), so Gaussian elimination with pivoting computes matrices P, L, and $\hat{U}$ such that $P^{-1}W = L\hat{U}$, $P^{-1}A = LU$, $W = PL\hat{U}$, $A = PLU$; that is, the LU factors of $P^{-1}A$ and the $L\hat{U}$ factors of $P^{-1}W$ are computed. PLU factorization is not unique, it depends on pivoting policy; the elimination with no pivoting gives $P = I$, $W = L\hat{U}$, $A = LU$.

When PLU factors of A are known, solving the system $A\mathbf{x} = \mathbf{b}$ is reduced to the interchange of the entries of $\mathbf{b}$ and to solving two triangular systems

$$L\mathbf{y} = P^{-1}\mathbf{b}, \qquad U\mathbf{x} = \mathbf{y} \tag{4}$$

for the total cost of n^2 flops. The back substitution of Section III,A saves $n^2/2$ of those flops, but computing the PLU factors of A saves $n^2/2$ of the "elimination flops," because the last column of the matrix $\hat{U}$ need not be computed. In fact, two ways of solving the system $A\mathbf{x} = \mathbf{b}$, that is, via PLU factorization and via Gaussian elimination of Sections III,A and III,B lead to exactly the same computations (within the order of performing the operations). In subroutine packages, the solution based on PLU factorization is usually preferred. Among its many applications, PLU factorization of A leads to very effective computation of the determinant of an $n \times n$ matrix A, $\det A = \det P \det U = (\det P) u_{11} u_{22}, \ldots, u_{nn}$, where $u_{11}, \ldots, u_{nn}$ denotes the diagonal entries of U and where $\det P = (-1)^s$, s being the total number of all the row interchanges made during the elimination.

Gaussian elimination applied to overdetermined or underdetermined systems also computes PLU factorizations of their matrices (see Sections IV,A–IV,C about some other important factorizations in cases $m \neq n$).

G. Some Modifications of *LU* Factorization. Choleski's Factorization. Block Factorizations of a Matrix

If all the principal submatrices of an $n \times n$ matrix A are nonsingular, LU factors of A can be computed; furthermore, LDM^T factors of A can be computed where $DM^T = U$, D is a diagonal matrix, $D = \mathrm{diag}(u_{11}, \ldots, u_{nn})$, so both L and M^T are unit triangular matrices (having only 1's on their diagonals). If the LDM^T factors of A are known, solving the system $A\mathbf{x} = \mathbf{b}$ can be reduced to solving the systems $L\mathbf{y} = \mathbf{b}$, $D\mathbf{z} = \mathbf{y}$, $M^T\mathbf{x} = \mathbf{z}$, which costs only $n^2 + n$ flops, practically as many as in case where the LU factors are known. The following modification of Gaussian elimination computes the LDM^T factors of A.

ALGORITHM 3. LDM^T FACTORIZATION

For $k = 1, \ldots, n$

For $g = 1, \ldots, k-1$

$u_g := a_{gg} a_{gk}$

$v_g := a_{kg} a_{gg}$

$$a_{kk} := a_{kk} - \sum_{j=1}^{k-1} a_{kj} u_j$$

If $a_{kk} = 0$, end (A has no LDM^T-factors)
Else

For $i = k+1, \ldots, n$,

$$a_{ik} := \left(a_{ik} - \sum_{j=1}^{k-1} a_{ij} u_j\right) \Big/ a_{kk},$$

$$a_{ki} := \left(a_{ki} - \sum_{j=1}^{k-1} v_j a_{jk}\right) \Big/ a_{kk}$$

Algorithm 3 requires $n^3/3$ flops and $n^2 + 2n$ units of storage space. It keeps low the number of updatings of the values a_{ij} stored in the working array so that each a_{ij} is updated only in a single inner loop of the form $a_{kk} := a_{kk} - \sum_j a_{kj} u_j$ or $a_{ik} := (a_{ik} - \sum_j a_{ij} u_j)/a_{kk}$, or $a_{ki} := (a_{ki} - \sum_j v_j a_{ji})/a_{kk}$, where computing inner products is the main operation (easy on many serial computers).

Algorithm 3, for LDM^T factorization, is a simple extension of Crout's algorithm, which computes LD and M^T, and of Doolittle's algorithm, which computes L and $U = DM^T$. If A is symmetric and has only nonsingular principal submatrices, then $L = M$, so Algorithm 3 computes the LDL^T factorization of A. If A is symmetric and positive definite, then all the diagonal entries of D are positive, so the matrix $\sqrt{D} = \mathrm{diag}[\sqrt{d_{11}}, \ldots, \sqrt{d_{nn}}]$ can be computed; then Choleski's factorization, $A = GG^T$, $G = L\sqrt{D}$ can be computed. Algorithm 4 computes Choleski's factorization using $n^3/6$ flops and only $n(n+1)/2$ units of storage space.

ALGORITHM 4. CHOLESKI'S FACTORIZATION

For $k = 1, \ldots, n$

$$a_{kk} := \left(a_{kk} - \sum_{j=1}^{k-1} a_{kj}^2\right)^{1/2}$$

If $a_{kk} = 0$, end (A is not positive definite)
Else

For $i = k+1, \ldots, n$

$$a_{ik} := \left(a_{ik} - \sum_{j=1}^{k-1} a_{ij} a_{kj}\right) \Big/ a_{kk}$$

For complex Hermitian matrices, the factorizations LDL^T and GG^T are replaced by LDL^H and LL^H, respectively. The factorizations of A presented can be generally extended to the case where A is a block matrix, provided that the given and the computed block matrices can be inverted as required. For instance, let A be a 2×2 block-matrix,

$$A = \begin{bmatrix} A_{11} & A_{12} \\ A_{21} & A_{22} \end{bmatrix} \tag{5}$$

Then,

$$A = \begin{bmatrix} I & 0 \\ A_{21}A_{11}^{-1} & I \end{bmatrix} \begin{bmatrix} A_{11} & 0 \\ 0 & B \end{bmatrix} \begin{bmatrix} I & A_{11}^{-1}A_{12} \\ 0 & I \end{bmatrix} \tag{6}$$

$$A^{-1} = \begin{bmatrix} I & -A_{11}^{-1}A_{12} \\ 0 & I \end{bmatrix} \begin{bmatrix} A_{11}^{-1} & 0 \\ 0 & B^{-1} \end{bmatrix} \begin{bmatrix} I & 0 \\ -A_{21}A_{11}^{-1} & I \end{bmatrix} \tag{7}$$

provided that $B = A_{22} - A_{21}A_{11}^{-1}A_{12}$ and A_{11} and B are nonsingular. This is the block version of the LDM^T factorization for A and of the respective triangular factorization of A^{-1}.

H. Error and Residual Vectors. Vector and Matrix Norms. Condition Number

The error of an approximation $\mathbf{x}^*$ to the solution $\mathbf{x}$ to Eq. (1) is measured by the error vector, $\mathbf{e} = \mathbf{x} - \mathbf{x}^*$. The error magnitude is measured by a norm $\|\mathbf{e}\|$ of $\mathbf{e}$ and by the relative error norm, $\|\mathbf{e}\|/\|\mathbf{x}\|$; $\mathbf{e}$ is not known until $\mathbf{x}$ is computed; as a substitution, the residual vector $\mathbf{r}$, its norm $\|\mathbf{r}\|$, and the relative residual norm $\|\mathbf{r}\|/\|\mathbf{b}\|$ are used. Here, $\mathbf{r} = \mathbf{r}(\mathbf{x}^*) = \mathbf{b} - A\mathbf{x}^*$, so $\mathbf{r} = A\mathbf{e}$, $\mathbf{e} = A^{-1}\mathbf{r}$ if A is nonsingular; a vector norm is nonuniquely defined by the following properties:

1. $\|\mathbf{v}\| \geq 0$ for all vectors $\mathbf{v}$, $\|\mathbf{v}\| = 0$ if and only if $\mathbf{v}$ is a null vector, filled with zeros.
2. $\|q\mathbf{v}\| = |q| * \|\mathbf{v}\|$ for all vectors $\mathbf{v}$ and all complex numbers q.
3. $\|\mathbf{u} + \mathbf{v}\| \leq \|\mathbf{u}\| + \|\mathbf{v}\|$ for all pairs of vectors $\mathbf{u}$ and $\mathbf{v}$ of the same dimension.

Maximum (Chebyshev's, uniform) norm, $\|\mathbf{v}\|_\infty = \max_i |v_i|$ and Hölder's norms, $\|\mathbf{v}\|_p = (\sum_i |v_i|^p)^{1/p}$, for $p = 1$ (least deviation norm) and $p = 2$ (Euclidean norm) are most customary vector norms. (Here, $\mathbf{v} = [v_i]$ is a vector.)

Every vector norm can be extended to its subordinate matrix norm,

$$\|A\| = \max_{\mathbf{v} \neq \mathbf{0}} \|A\mathbf{v}\|/\|\mathbf{v}\| \tag{8}$$

Chebyshev's and Hölder's norms define the matrix norms $\|A\|_\infty$, $\|A\|_p$. Also, the Frobenius norm (F norm) is a customary matrix norm, $\|A\|_F = (\sum_{i=1}^m \sum_{j=1}^n |a_{ij}|^2)^{1/2}$, where A is an $m \times n$ matrix $[a_{ij}]$. All the matrix norms have properties 1–3 (see above) of the vector norms (where $\mathbf{v}$ and $\mathbf{u}$ are replaced by matrices); the subordinate matrix norms satisfy also the inequalities

$$\|AB\| \leq \|A\| * \|B\|, \ \|A\mathbf{v}\| \leq \|A\| * \|\mathbf{v}\| \tag{9}$$

for all matrices A, B and vectors $\mathbf{v}$ such that AB and $A\mathbf{v}$ are defined. Here are some further properties of matrix norms.

Theorem 2. For any $m \times n$ matrix $A = [a_{ij}]$,

$$\|A\|_\infty = \max_i \sum_j |a_{ij}|,$$

$$\|A\|_1 = \max_j \sum_i |a_{ij}|,$$

$$\|A\|_2^2 \leq \|A\|_1 * \|A\|_\infty$$

$$\|A\|_\infty/\sqrt{n} \leq \|A\|_2 \leq \sqrt{m}\ \|A\|_\infty$$

$$\|A\|_1/\sqrt{m} \leq \|A\|_2 \leq \sqrt{n}\ \|A\|_1$$

$$\max_{i,j} |a_{ij}| \leq \|A\|_2 \leq \sqrt{mn} \max_{i,j} |a_{ij}|,$$

$$\|A\|_2 \leq \|A\|_F \leq \sqrt{n}\ \|A\|_2$$

The condition number of A [$\text{cond}(A) = \|A\| * \|A^{-1}\|$ if A is nonsingular, $\text{cond}(A) = \infty$ otherwise] is used in the error-sensitivity analysis for Eq. (1). Cond(A) depends on the choice of a matrix norm, but $\text{cond}(A) \geq \|I\| \geq 1$ in any of the cited norms.

EXAMPLE 16

$$A = \begin{bmatrix} 10 & -7 \\ -3 & 2 \end{bmatrix}, \qquad A^{-1} = \begin{bmatrix} -2 & -7 \\ -3 & -10 \end{bmatrix}$$

$$\|A\|_1 = 17; \quad \|A^{-1}\|_1 = 13,$$

$$\text{cond}_1(A) = \|A\|_1 \|A^{-1}\|_1 = 221$$

Hereafter, we shall use only the three subordinate matrix norms, $\|A\|_1$ (1-norm), $\|A\|_2$ (2-norm), $\|A\|_\infty$ (maximum norm). For the subordinate matrix norms, the equations $A\mathbf{x} = \mathbf{b}$, $\mathbf{x} = A^{-1}\mathbf{b}$, $\mathbf{r} = A\mathbf{e}$, $\mathbf{e} = A^{-1}\mathbf{r}$ imply that

$$(1/\text{cond}(A))(\|\mathbf{r}\|/\|\mathbf{b}\|) \leq \|\mathbf{e}\|/\|\mathbf{x}\| \leq \text{cond}(A)\|\mathbf{r}\|/\|\mathbf{b}\| \tag{10}$$

$$\text{cond}(A) \geq (\|\mathbf{e}\|/\|\mathbf{x}\|)/(\|\mathbf{r}\|/\|\mathbf{b}\|) \tag{11}$$

I. Sensitivity of Linear Systems to Input Errors

The solution to a linear system can be sensitive to input errors even if the computations are performed with infinite precision.

EXAMPLE 17.

$$\begin{bmatrix} 780 & 563 \\ 913 & 659 \end{bmatrix} \begin{bmatrix} x_1 \\ x_2 \end{bmatrix} = \begin{bmatrix} 217 \\ 254 \end{bmatrix}$$

The correct solution is $x_1 = 1$, $x_2 = -1$. For the approximation $x_1^* = 0.341$, $x_2^* = -0.087$, we have the error and the residual vectors

$$\mathbf{e} = [0.659, -0.913]^T \qquad \mathbf{r} = [-0.001, 0]^T$$

so for that specific matrix, the addition of 0.001 to b_2, which is a very small perturbation of the vector $\mathbf{b} = [217; 254]^T$, changes the solution from $\mathbf{x} = [1, -1]^T$ to $\mathbf{x}^* = [0.341, -0.087]^T$. Furthermore, $\|\mathbf{e}\|_\infty = 0.913$, $\|\mathbf{x}\|_\infty = 1$, $\|\mathbf{r}\|_\infty = 10^{-3}$, $\|\mathbf{b}\|_\infty = 254$, so Eq. (11) implies that

$$\text{cond}_\infty(A) \geq 0.913 * 254 * 10^3 > 0.2 * 10^6$$

Thus, in that example the linear system is ill-conditioned (its coefficient matrix A has a large condition number) and is sensitive to the input errors even if the computation is performed with infinite precision. Systems like Eq. (1) are not very sensitive to the input errors if the condition number of A is not large (then the system is called well conditioned). The latter fact follows from the next perturbation theorem, which bounds the output errors depending on the perturbation of inputs (on the input error) and on cond(A).

Perturbation Theorem. Let A, E be $n \times n$ matrices, **x**, **e**, **b**, and $\boldsymbol{\Delta}$ be n-dimensional vectors, such that $A\mathbf{x} = \mathbf{b}$, $(A + E)(\mathbf{x} - \mathbf{e}) = \mathbf{b} + \boldsymbol{\Delta}$, $\text{cond}(A)\|E\| \leq \|A\|$. Then,

$$\frac{\|\mathbf{e}\|}{\|\mathbf{x}\|} \leq \frac{\text{cond}(A)}{1 - \text{cond}(A)\|E\|/\|A\|}\left(\frac{\|E\|}{\|A\|} + \frac{\|\boldsymbol{\Delta}\|}{\|\mathbf{b}\|}\right)$$

If $\boldsymbol{\Delta} = \mathbf{0}$, then $\|\mathbf{e}\|/\|\mathbf{x} - \mathbf{e}\| \leq \text{cond}(A)\|E\|/\|A\|$.

Remark. The $\text{cond}(A^{\mathrm{T}}A)$ may be as large as $(\text{cond}(A))^2$, so the transition from the system of Eq. (1) to $A^{\mathrm{T}}A\mathbf{x} = A^{\mathrm{T}}\mathbf{b}$ is not generally recommended, even though the latter system is symmetric.

J. Sensitivity of Algorithms for Linear Systems to Round-Off Errors

The output errors may also be influenced by the round-off errors. The smaller such an influence, the higher *numerical stability* of the algorithm, which is a subject of major concern to users. J. H. Wilkinson applied his nontrivial techniques of backward error analysis to estimate that influence in cases where Gaussian elimination was applied. It turned out that the resulting output error bounds were the same as if the output errors stemmed entirely from some input errors. (This result is easily extended to computing LDM^{T} factorization and Choleski's factorization.) To state the formal estimates, we define (a) the matrix $|V|$ of the absolute values of the entries of a matrix $V = [v_{ij}]$, so $|V| = [|v_{ij}|]$; and (b) the unit round-off u for a given computer, u only depends on a floating-point finite precision (of d digits with a base β) u being the minimum positive value such that the computer represents $1 + u$ and 1 with finite precision as two distinct values; $u < \beta^{1-d}$. The desired estimates can be derived by analyzing the expressions $a_{ik} = \sum_{j=0}^{s} l_{ij}u_{jk}$, $s = \min\{i, k\}$, where $L = [l_{ij}]$, $U = [u_{jk}]$, $u_{ji} = l_{ij} = 0$ if $j > i$, $l_{ii} = 1$ for all i, $A = [a_{ij}]$, $A = LU$.

Theorem 3. Let L^*, U^*, and $\mathbf{x}^*$ denote approximations to the LU-factors of A and to the solution **x** to $A\mathbf{x} = \mathbf{b}$ computed on a computer with unit round-off u. Then

$$|L^*U^* - A| \leq 3\,\text{un}\{|A| + |L^*| * |U^*|\}$$

$(A - E)\mathbf{x}^* = \mathbf{b}$ where $|E| \leq \text{un}(3|A| + 5|L^*| * |U^*|\}$; here and hereafter the values of an order of $0(u^2)$ are ignored.

If PLU factorization of A has been computed, it suffices to replace A by PA^{-1} in Theorem 3. With pivoting, the entries of $|L^*|$ are bounded by 1, so $\|L^*\|_\infty \leq n$, and furthermore,

$$\|E\|_\infty \leq \text{nu}\{3\|A\|_\infty + 5n\|U^*\|_\infty\} \tag{12}$$

In the case where complete pivoting is applied, $\|U^*\|_\infty$ can be estimated by using Wilkinson's bound,

$$\max_{i,j} |u_{ij}| \leq (2 \cdot 3^{1/2} \ldots n^{1/(n-1)}n)^{1/2} \max_{i,j} |a_{ij}| \tag{13}$$

Many years of computational practice have convinced us that the latter bound is almost always pessimistic, even where unscaled partial pivoting is applied. The latter observation and the perturbation theorem of Section III,I imply that Gaussian elimination with complete pivoting never (and with partial pivoting rarely) greatly magnifies the input or round-off errors, unless the system of Eq. (1) is ill-conditioned, so that Gaussian elimination with pivoting is quite stable numerically. This analysis can be extended to some block matrix algorithms, in particular, to the block factorization (5)–(7) for Hermitian (real symmetric) and positive definite matrices A.

K. Iterative Improvement of Computed Soluton and Condition Estimation

Let good approximations L^*U^* to the LU factors of $A = LU$ be computed. Then set $\mathbf{x}(0) = \mathbf{e}(0) = \mathbf{0}$, $\mathbf{r}(0) = \mathbf{b}$, and successively compute $\mathbf{r}(i + 1) = \mathbf{r}(i) - A\mathbf{e}(i)$, in n^2 flops; $\mathbf{e}(i + 1)$ from $L^*U^*\mathbf{e}(i + 1) = \mathbf{r}(i + 1)$, in n^2 flops [see Eq. (4)]; $\mathbf{x}(i + 1) = \mathbf{x}(i) + \mathbf{e}(i + 1)$, in n flops, for $i = 0, 1, 2, \ldots$. If the computations are done with infinite precision and if A is well conditioned, say, if $3\,\text{cond}(A)\|A - L^*U^*\| < \|A\|$, then it can be shown that $\mathbf{x}(i + 1)$ rapidly converges to the solution **x** to $A\mathbf{x} = \mathbf{b}$. Moreover, it can be shown that it is sufficient to use the d-bit precision with $d > \log_2 \text{cond}(A)$ while computing $\mathbf{e}(i)$ and to use the (double) $2d$-bit precision while computing $\mathbf{r}(i + 1)$ in the above algorithm in order to assure that every iteration decreases the error $\|\mathbf{x} -$

$\mathbf{x}(i)\|$ by a constant factor, c, $0 < c < 1$. Thus, more and more correct digits of $\mathbf{x}$ are computed with each new iteration.

That algorithm of iterative improvement (by J. H. Wilkinson) can be extended to the case where an approximation C to A is available such that $\|C^{-1}A - I\|$ is sufficiently small and the system $C\mathbf{e} = \mathbf{r}$ can be quickly solved for $\mathbf{e}$. In particular $C = L^*U^*$ was implicitly defined above by its factors L^* and U^*. Since the progress in iterative improvement to $\mathbf{x}$ depends on cond(A), this suggests using the same algorithm of iterative improvement as an effective heuristic condition estimator. Indeed, to estimate the progress of iterative improvement, we only need an order of n^2 flops, whereas computing cond(A) generally requires us to invert A and costs more than n^3 flops.

IV. Orthogonal Factorization and Singular Linear Systems

Solving linear systems via orthogonal factorization of the coefficient matrix is a stable method, particularly effective for singular and ill-conditioned linear systems.

A. Application to Overdetermined Systems

We again consider computing a least-squares solution to an overdetermined linear system, $A\mathbf{c} = \mathbf{f}$ (see Section II,E). We assume that A is an $m \times n$ matrix. The problem is equivalent to computing solution to the normal equations, $A^{T}A\mathbf{c} = A^{T}\mathbf{f}$, which amounts to the requirements that $\partial(\|\mathbf{r}(\mathbf{c})\|_2^2)/\partial c_j = 0$ for all j, where $\mathbf{r}(\mathbf{c}) = \mathbf{f} - A\mathbf{c}$ is the residual vector, $\mathbf{c} = [c_0, \ldots, c_n]^T$, and $\|\mathbf{v}\|_2^2 = \sum_j v_j^2$. The symmetric matrix A^TA can be computed in $mn^2/2$ flops. The matrix A^TA is positive definite if it is nonsingular; then the normal equations can be solved via Choleski's factorization in $n^3/6$ flops, so computing a least squares solution to $A\mathbf{c} = \mathbf{f}$ costs about $0.5\, n^2(m + n/3)$ flops. The best methods of orthogonal factorization require about $n^2(m - n/3)$ flops, but they are substantially more stable and can also be extended to the case of singular A^TA. Iterative improvement of computed approximations to a least-squares solution to $A\mathbf{c} = \mathbf{f}$ is possible based on the following equivalent representation of the normal equations:

$$\begin{bmatrix} I & A \\ A^T & 0 \end{bmatrix} \begin{bmatrix} \mathbf{r} \\ \mathbf{c} \end{bmatrix} = \begin{bmatrix} \mathbf{f} \\ \mathbf{0} \end{bmatrix}$$

Remark 2. The problem of minimizing $\|\mathbf{f} - A\mathbf{c}\|_2$ can be immediately extended to the problem (called the weighted least-squares problem) of minimizing $\|D(\mathbf{f} - A\mathbf{c})\|_2$ for a diagonal matrix $D = \text{diag}[d_1, \ldots, d_m]$ with positive entries on the diagonal. The methods of solution remain the same, they are just applied to the system $(DA)\mathbf{c} = D\mathbf{f}$. In Section II,E, we transformed the specific overdetermined system $A\mathbf{c} = \mathbf{f}$, with

$$A^T = \begin{bmatrix} 1 & 1 & 1 & 1 \\ 970 & 990 & 1000 & 1040 \end{bmatrix}$$

$\mathbf{f}^T = [4, 2, 0, -3]$, into the system $AU\mathbf{c}^* = \mathbf{f}$, such that $\mathbf{c} = U\mathbf{c}^*$,

$$c_0 = c_0^* - 1000c_1^*, \qquad c_1 = c_1^*$$

$$U = \begin{bmatrix} 1 & -1000 \\ 0 & 1 \end{bmatrix};$$

$$(AU)^T = \begin{bmatrix} 1 & 1 & 1 & 1 \\ -30 & -10 & 0 & 40 \end{bmatrix},$$

$$(AU)^TAU = \begin{bmatrix} 4 & 0 \\ 0 & 2600 \end{bmatrix}$$

This changed the normal equations from the system $4c_0 + 4000c_1 = 3$, $4000c_0 + 4002600c_1 = 2740$ to the much more simple and more stable system, $4c_0^* = 3$, $2600c_1^* = -260$. Such a trick can be extended to the general overdetermined system $A\mathbf{c} = \mathbf{f}$ if a matrix U can be computed such that $(AU)^TAU$ is a nonsingular diagonal matrix. It is customary to apply that approach seeking $R = U^{-1}$ (rather than U) such that $A = QR$, Q^TQ is diagonal (or, furthermore, $Q^TQ = I$) and R is an $n \times n$ upper triangular matrix. When such QR factors of A have been computed, the normal equations, $A^TA\mathbf{c} = A^T\mathbf{f}$, can be immediately simplified as follows. We substitute $A = QR$, $A^T = R^TQ^T$, $Q^TQ = I$ in the system $A^TA\mathbf{c} = A^T\mathbf{f}$ and arrive at the system $R^TR\mathbf{c} = R^TQ^T\mathbf{f}$.

Case 1. A^TA is nonsingular. Then, all the diagonal entries of R^T are nonzeros, and the system can be premultiplied by $(R^T)^{-1}$, reduced to the upper triangular system $R\mathbf{c} = Q^T\mathbf{f}$, and then solved by back substitution.

Case 2. A^TA is singular (see Section IV,C).

Algorithm 5 computes QR factorization of A using mn^2 flops and $n(m + n/2)$ space (A is overwritten by Q and $\mathbf{a}_{\cdot h}$ denotes column h of A).

ALGORITHM 5 (MODIFIED GRAM–SCHMIDT).

For $h = 1, \ldots, n$

$r_{hh} := \|\mathbf{a}_{\cdot h}\|_2$

For $i = 1, \ldots, m$,

$a_{ih} := a_{ih}/r_{hh}$

For $j = h + 1, \ldots, n$

$$r_{hj} := \sum_{i=1}^{m} a_{ih} a_{ij}$$

For $i = 1, \ldots, m$

$a_{ij} := a_{ij} - a_{ih} r_{hj}$

However, a faster algorithm, also completely stable (called the Householder transformation or Householder reflection), computes R and $Q^{\mathrm{T}}\mathbf{f}$ using $n^2(m - n/3)$ flops and mn space. The algorithm can be used for the more general purpose of computing an $m \times m$ orthogonal matrix $Q = Q_{m,m}$ and an $m \times n$ upper triangular matrix $R = R_{m,n}$ such that $A = QR$, $Q^{\mathrm{T}}Q = QQ^{\mathrm{T}} = I$. Previously we considered QR factorization, where Q had size $m \times n$ and R had size $n \times n$. Such QR factors of A can be obtained by deleting the last $m - n$ columns of $Q_{m,m}$ and the last $m - n$ rows of R (those last rows of R form a null matrix, for R is upper triangular). Householder transformation of A into R is performed by successive premultiplications of A by the Householder orthogonal matrices $H_k = I - 2\mathbf{v}_k\mathbf{v}_k^{\mathrm{T}}/\mathbf{v}_k^{\mathrm{T}}\mathbf{v}_k$, $k = 1, 2, \ldots, r$, where $r \le n$, and usually $r = n$. The vector $\mathbf{v}_k$ is chosen such that the premultiplication by H_k makes zeros of all the subdiagonal entries of column k of the matrix $A_k = H_{k-1}H_{k-1} \cdots H_1A$ and does not affect its columns $1, 2, \ldots, k - 1$. Such a choice of $\mathbf{v}(k)$ for $k = 1, 2$ is shown below for the matrix A of our previous example. Here is the general rule. Zero the first $k - 1$ entries of column k of A_k and let $\mathbf{a}(k)$ denote the resulting vector. Then $\mathbf{v}_k = \mathbf{a}(k) \pm \|\mathbf{a}(k)\|_2\mathbf{i}(k)$ where $\mathbf{i}(k)$ is the unit coordinate whose kth entry is 1 and whose other entries are zeros; the sign + or − is chosen the same as for the entry k of $\mathbf{a}(k)$ (if that entry is 0, choose, say, +).

Remark 3. A modification with column pivoting is sometimes performed prior to premultiplication by H_k for each k in order to avoid possible complications where the vector $\mathbf{a}(k)$ has small norm. In that case, column k of A is interchanged with column s such that $s \ge k$ and $\|\mathbf{a}(s)\|_2$ is maximum. Finally, QR factors are computed for the matrix AP, where P is the permutation matrix that monitors the column interchange. Column pivoting can be performed using $O(mn)$ comparisons.

When only the vector $Q^{\mathrm{T}}\mathbf{f}$ and the matrix $R_{m,n}$ must be computed, the vector $\mathbf{f}$ is overwritten by successively computed vectors $H_1\mathbf{f}$, $H_2H_1\mathbf{f}$, ..., and the matrices $H_1, H_2, \ldots$, are not stored. If the matrix Q is to be saved, it can be either explicitly computed by multiplying the matrices H_i together $[Q = (H_rH_{r-1} \cdots H_1)^{\mathrm{T}}]$ or implicitly defined by saving the vectors $\mathbf{v}_1, \mathbf{v}_2, \ldots, \mathbf{v}_r$.

EXAMPLE 18. HOUSEHOLDER TRANSFORMATION WITH NO COLUMN PIVOTING. For the matrix A of Example 17, $\mathbf{v}_1^{\mathrm{T}} = [3, 1, 1, 1]$, so

$$A_1^{\mathrm{T}} = \begin{bmatrix} -2 & 0 & 0 & 0 \\ -2000 & 0 & 10 & 50 \end{bmatrix},$$

$$\mathbf{v}_2^{\mathrm{T}} = [0,\ \sqrt{2600},\ 10,\ 50],$$

$$A_2^{\mathrm{T}} = \begin{bmatrix} -2 & 0 & 0 & 0 \\ -2000 & -\sqrt{2600} & 0 & 0 \end{bmatrix}$$

Givens transformation (Givens rotation) is sometimes applied to compute QR factors of A, although it requires $2n^2(m - n/3)$ flops and seems generally inferior to the Householder transformation. The Givens' method uses successive premultiplications of A by rotation matrices that differ from the identity matrix I only in their 2×2 submatrices of the following form, $\left[\begin{smallmatrix} c & d \\ -d & c \end{smallmatrix}\right]$, where $c^2 + d^2 = 1$. Each such premultiplication zeros a new entry of A.

B. Computing the Minimum 2-Norm Solution to an Underdetermined System

Gaussian elimination with complete pivoting solves an underdetermined system $A\mathbf{x} = \mathbf{b}$ with an $m \times n$ matrix A, $m \le n$, in $0.5\ m^2(n - m/3)$ flops, but does not define the unique solution having minimum 2-norm. The solution having minimum 2-norm can be computed by using $m^2(n - m/3)$ flops as follows. Apply the Householder transformation with column pivoting (see Remark 3) to the *transposed* matrix A^{T} and compute its factorization $A^{\mathrm{T}}P = QR$, where

$$R = \begin{bmatrix} R_{11} & R_{12} \\ 0 & 0 \end{bmatrix}$$

and R_{11} is an $r \times r$ nonsingular triangular matrix, $r = \operatorname{rank}(A)$, $Q = [Q_1, Q_2]$, and Q_1 is a square matrix. Then the minimum 2-norm solution $\mathbf{x}$ to the system $A\mathbf{x} = \mathbf{b}$ can be computed,

$$\mathbf{x} = Q_1\mathbf{y}, \quad \begin{bmatrix} R_{11}^{\mathrm{T}} \\ R_{12}^{\mathrm{T}} \end{bmatrix} \mathbf{y} = P^{-1}\mathbf{b}$$

unless the latter system (and then also the system $A\mathbf{x} = \mathbf{b}$) is inconsistent.

C. Applications to Overdetermined Systems of Deficient Rank

Householder transformation with column pivoting can be applied to a matrix A in order to compute the least-squares solution to $A\mathbf{c} = \mathbf{f}$ even where A does not have full rank, that is, where $r = \text{rank}(A) < n \leq m$. That algorithm first computes the factorization $AP = QR$ where

$$R = \begin{bmatrix} R_{11} & R_{12} \\ 0 & 0 \end{bmatrix}$$

and R_{11} is an $r \times r$ nonsingular upper triangular matrix. Then the general solution to $A^{\mathrm{T}}A\mathbf{c} = A^{\mathrm{T}}\mathbf{f}$ (that is, the general least-squares solution to $A\mathbf{c} = \mathbf{f}$) is computed as follows:

$$\mathbf{c} = P^{-1} \begin{bmatrix} R_{11}^{-1}(\mathbf{g} - R_{12}\mathbf{b}) \\ \mathbf{b} \end{bmatrix}$$

where the vector $\mathbf{g}$ consists of the first r entries of $Q^{\mathrm{T}}\mathbf{f}$, and the vector $\mathbf{b}$ consists of the last $n - r$ entries of $P\mathbf{c}$. The latter $n - r$ entries can be used as free parameters in order to define a specific solution (the simplest choice is $\mathbf{b} = 0$). Formally, infinite precision of computation is required in that algorithm; actually, the algorithm works very well in practice, although it fails on some specially concocted instances, somewhat similarly to Gaussian elimination with unscaled partial pivoting.

A little more expensive [$n^2(m + 17n/3)$ flops and $2mn^2$ space versus $n^2(m - n/3)$ and mn^2 in the Householder transformation] but completely stable algorithm relies on computing the *singular value decomposition* (SVD) of A. Unlike Householder's transformation, that algorithm always computes the least-squares solution of the minimum 2-norm. The SVD of an $m \times n$ matrix A is the factorization $A = U\Sigma V^{\mathrm{T}}$, where U and V are two square orthogonal matrices (of sizes $m \times m$ and $n \times n$, respectively), $U^{\mathrm{T}}U = I_m$, $V^{\mathrm{T}}V = I_n$, and where the $m \times n$ matrix Σ may have nonzero entries only on the diagonal; the (i, i) diagonal entry of Σ is denoted σ_i and is called the ith *singular value* of A; $\sigma_1 \geq \sigma_2 \geq \cdots \geq \sigma_p \geq 0$, $p = \min\{m, n\}$, so $p = n$ if $m \geq n$. Matrix Σ consists of its largest principal $p \times p$ diagonal submatrix, diag $[\sigma_1, \ldots, \sigma_p]$, banded with zeros.

EXAMPLE 19. The matrix $A = [0.4, 0.3]$ has the SVD,

$$[0.4, 0.3] = [1][0.5, 0] \begin{bmatrix} 0.8 & 0.6 \\ -0.6 & 0.8 \end{bmatrix}$$

The normal equations $A^{\mathrm{T}}A\mathbf{c} = A^{\mathrm{T}}\mathbf{f}$ are equivalent to the system $\Sigma^{\mathrm{T}}\,\Sigma V^{\mathrm{T}}\mathbf{c} = \Sigma^{\mathrm{T}}U^{\mathrm{T}}\mathbf{f}$; $\Sigma^{\mathrm{T}}\,\Sigma = \text{diag}[\sigma_1^2, \ldots, \sigma_n^2]$ is an $n \times n$ matrix, for $m \geq n$. When the SVD of A is available, the minimum 2-norm solution is obtained by setting $\mathbf{c} = V(\Sigma^{\mathrm{T}}\,\Sigma)^*U^{\mathrm{T}}\mathbf{f}$; the $n \times n$ matrix $(\Sigma^{\mathrm{T}}\,\Sigma)^* = \text{diag}[\sigma_1^{-2}, \ldots, \sigma_r^{-2}, 0, \ldots, 0]$ of rank $r = \text{rank}(\Sigma)$ is called the *pseudo-inverse* of A.

As one of the by-products of computing the SVD of A, the number σ_1/σ_r can be computed. That number equals $\text{cond}_2(A) = \|A\|_2 * \|A^{-1}\|_2$ for nonsingular matrices A and extends both the definition of the condition number of a matrix and its applications to error analysis to the case of singular matrices.

D. Orthogonalization Methods for a System with a Square Matrix

Methods of orthogonal factorization are also useful for systems $A\mathbf{x} = \mathbf{b}$ with a square $n \times n$ matrix A in the cases where A is ill-conditioned or singular. Householder orthogonalization solves such systems in $2n^3/3$ flops; SVD requires $6n^3$ flops.

V. Asymptotic and Practical Acceleration of Solving General Linear Systems

The upper estimates of $\geq n^3/3$ flops in algorithms for the linear systems of Eq. (1) for $m = n$ have led to a popular conjecture of the 1950s and 1960s that a nonsingular linear system of n equations cannot be solved using less than cn^3 arithmetic operations for some positive constant c. This was proven to be wrong in 1968. The result followed from Strassen's $n \times n$ matrix multiplication (hereafter referred to as *MM*) using $o(n^{2.81})$ arithmetic operations and recently successively implemented on the CRAY supercomputer. The block decomposition (5)–(7) of Section III,G reduces $2n \times 2n$ matrix inversion to two $n \times n$ matrix inversions and to six $n \times n$ *MM*s and recursively to several *MM*s of decreasing sizes; it follows that $o(n^{2.81})$ arithmetic operations suffice to invert an $n \times n$ matrix A and, consequently, to solve the system $A\mathbf{x} = \mathbf{b}$. Due to the new techniques of algorithmic design, the exponent 2.81 of *MM* of 1968 decreased to 2.522 in 1978–1979, below 2.52 in 1980, and below 2.4 in 1986. Consequently, in

1986 the asymptotic acceleration of *MM* already implied the complexity bound $o(n^{2.4})$ (rather than n^3) for solving linear systems.

Numerical stability of all such fast $n \times n$ matrix multipliers has been both theoretically proven in the most general case (by D. Bini and G. Lotti in 1980) and experimentally confirmed, but only the algorithms supporting the upper bounds cn^d for d from 2.775 (Pan, 1984, part III) to 2.81 (Strassen) have the overhead constants $c = c(d)$ small enough to compete with the classical algorithm.

Here is a distinct approach, promising some practical improvement. Suppose that we seek the product $A\mathbf{b}$ of a 1000×1000 matrix A by a vector $\mathbf{b}$, both filled with zeros and ones and use a computer with 100 bit precision. Each entry of $A\mathbf{b}$ is at most 1000 and occupies at most 10 bits, so that 10 entries of $A\mathbf{b}$ can be easily computed and stored by using one arithmetic operation and a single word of memory, thus almost by 10 times improving the classical approach. The algorithm can be extended to matrices and vectors whose entries are bounded by integers (see Pan, 1984; Bini and Pan, 1992).

VI. Direct Solution of Some Special Linear Systems

Many special linear systems $A\mathbf{x} = \mathbf{b}$ can be solved by special efficient algorithms [recall, for example, Choleski's method for symmetric positive-definite systems (Section III,G)]. Next, some typical special systems are considered (compare the end of Section II,D).

A. Banded, Block-Banded, Banded-Symmetric, and Symmetric Systems

A matrix $A = [a_{ij}]$ has bandwidth (p, q) if $a_{ij} = 0$ whenever $i + p < j < i - q$. Such a matrix can be stored by using less than $(p + q + 1)n$ memory words. The general $n \times n$ lower triangular matrix has bandwidth $(0, n - 1)$; a tridiagonal matrix has bandwidth $(1, 1)$. Banded system frequently arise in applications. Their effective solution may rely on decompositions of A into the product of banded triangular matrices. In particular, if the bandwidth of A is (p, q) and if A has LU factors, then L and U have bandwidths $(0, q)$ and $(p, 0)$, respectively; $pqn + r(n - (p^2 + q^2)/2) + r^3/3$ flops, where $r = \min\{p, q\}$, suffice to compute the factors L and U. Then it remains to use $(p + q + 1)n - (p^2 + q^2)/2$ flops to solve the system $A\mathbf{x} = \mathbf{b}$. Partial pivoting partially destroys the band structure of A; however, the resulting PLU factorization of A defines matrices U still having bandwidth $(p + q, 0)$ and L having at most $p + 1$ nonzero entries per column. Consequently, a substantial flop saving is still possible.

Many banded systems are symmetric positive definite and/or diagonally dominant. In those cases, pivoting is unnecessary, and the band structure can be fully exploited; one-half of the flops used can be further saved if A has Choleski's factorization.

$PLDL^{\mathrm{T}}P^{\mathrm{T}}$ factorization of an $n \times n$ symmetric matrix A (where P is a permutation matrix) can be computed, say, by Aasen's algorithm, using about $n^3/6$ (rather than $n^3/3$) flops and $O(n^2)$ comparisons for pivoting, even if A is not positive definite and has no Choleski's factorization.

In many applications, linear systems have block-band structure. In particular, the numerical solution of partial differential equations is frequently reduced to solving block tridiagonal systems (see Section II,A). For such systems, block triangular factorizations of A and block Gaussian elimination are effective. Such systems can be also solved in the same way as usual banded systems with scalar coefficients. This would save flops against dense systems of the same size, but the algorithms exploiting the block structure are usually far more effective.

Apart from triangular factorization and Gaussian elimination, there exist other effective direct methods for block-banded systems. For instance, the odd–even reduction (the cyclic reduction) is effective for solving symmetric block tridiagonal systems $A\mathbf{x} = \mathbf{b}$ with $(2^s - 1) \times (2^s - 1)$, matrices of the form

$$A = \begin{bmatrix} D & F & & & \\ E & D & F & & \\ & \ddots & \ddots & \ddots & \\ & & & & F \\ & & & E & D \end{bmatrix} = PBP^{\mathrm{T}} = P \begin{bmatrix} D & & & F & & \\ & \ddots & & E & \ddots & F \\ & & D & & & E \\ E & F & & D & & \\ & \ddots & F & & \ddots & \\ & & E & & & D \end{bmatrix} P^{\mathrm{T}}$$

Here, the blanks show the block entries filled with zeros; P and P^{T} are permutation matrices such that the matrix B obtained from the original matrix A by moving all the 2^{s-1} odd numbered rows and columns of A into the first 2^{s-1} positions. The first 2^{s-1} steps of Gaussian elimination eliminate all the subdiagonal nonzero blocks in the first 2^{s-1} columns of the resulting matrix. The $(2^{s-1} - 1) \times (2^{s-1} - 1)$ matrix in the right lower corner is again a block tridiagonal block Toeplitz matrix, so the reduction is recursively repeated until the system is reduced to a single block equation. (For an exercise, apply this algorithm to the system of Section II,A for the 4×6 grid, $n = 15$, $s = 4$.)

B. Toeplitz, Hankel, and Vandermonde Systems and their Correlation to Polynomial Operations

Many scientific computations (for signal processing, for partial differential equations, in statistics, for approximation of functions by polynomials, and so on) are reduced to solving Toeplitz or Hankel systems $A\mathbf{x} = \mathbf{b}$, having Toeplitz or Hankel matrix A. A Hankel matrix becomes a Toeplitz matrix by appropriate row interchange (reflecting the rows about the median row), so we shall consider only Toeplitz systems. An $m \times n$ Toeplitz matrix is defined by its first row and its first column, which requires only $m + n - 1$ units of storage space.

EXAMPLE 20. Toeplitz matrices:

$$\begin{bmatrix} 1 & 0 & -1 & 0 & 0 & 0 \\ 0 & 1 & 0 & -1 & 0 & 0 \\ 0 & 0 & 1 & 0 & -1 & 0 \end{bmatrix}, \quad \begin{bmatrix} 1 & 4 & 5 & 6 \\ 2 & 1 & 4 & 5 \\ 3 & 2 & 1 & 4 \end{bmatrix},$$

$$\begin{bmatrix} 1 & 2 & 3 \\ 2 & 1 & 2 \\ 3 & 2 & 1 \end{bmatrix}$$

EXAMPLE 21. Polynomial Division and Solving a Triangular Toeplitz System. Given two polynomials,

$$w(t) = u_4t^4 + u_3t^3 + u_2t^2 + u_1t + u_0$$
$$v(t) = v_2t^2 + v_1t + v_0$$

we compute the quotient $q(t) = q_2t^2 + q_1t + q_0$ and the remainder $r(t) = r_1t + r_0$ of the division of $u(t)$ by $v(t)$ such that $u(t) = v(t)q(t) + r(t)$ or, equivalently, such that

$$\begin{bmatrix} v_2 & 0 & 0 \\ v_1 & v_2 & 0 \\ v_0 & v_1 & v_2 \\ 0 & v_0 & v_1 \\ 0 & 0 & v_0 \end{bmatrix} \begin{bmatrix} q_2 \\ q_1 \\ q_0 \end{bmatrix} + \begin{bmatrix} 0 \\ 0 \\ 0 \\ r_1 \\ r_0 \end{bmatrix} = \begin{bmatrix} u_4 \\ u_3 \\ u_2 \\ u_1 \\ u_0 \end{bmatrix}$$

Computing the coefficients q_2, q_1, q_0 of $q(t)$ is equivalent to solving the triangular Toeplitz system,

$$\begin{bmatrix} v_2 & 0 & 0 \\ v_1 & v_2 & 0 \\ v_0 & v_1 & v_2 \end{bmatrix} \begin{bmatrix} q_2 \\ q_1 \\ q_0 \end{bmatrix} = \begin{bmatrix} u_4 \\ u_3 \\ u_2 \end{bmatrix}$$

When $q(t)$ is known, $r(t)$ is immediately computed, $r(t) = u(t) - v(t)q(t)$. For example, if $u(t) = t^4 + t^3 + t^2 + t + 1$, $v(t) = t^2 - 1$, then, $q(t) = t^2 + t + 2$, $r(t) = 2t + 3$, so the vector $\mathbf{q} = [1, 1, 2]^T$ is the solution of the triangular Toeplitz system,

$$\begin{bmatrix} 1 & 0 & 0 \\ 0 & 1 & 0 \\ -1 & 0 & 1 \end{bmatrix} \begin{bmatrix} 1 \\ 1 \\ 2 \end{bmatrix} = \begin{bmatrix} 1 \\ 1 \\ 1 \end{bmatrix}$$

In general, computing the quotient of division of a polynomial of degree $n + k$ by a polynomial of degree $k + 1$ is equivalent to solving a triangular Toeplitz system of size n. Solving both problems via fast Fourier transform involves $O(n \log n)$ arithmetic operations with a small overhead.

Solving a general Toeplitz system is also closely related to polynomial computations, namely, to computing Pade' approximants to a power series and to computing the greatest common divisor of two polynomials. Trench's algorithm of 1964 and other similar algorithms solve a Toeplitz system with an $n \times n$ matrix in $O(n^2)$ arithmetic operations (with a small overhead); algorithms of 1980 use only $O(n \log^2 n)$ with substantial overhead, and less than $8\, n \log^2 n$ are used in the more recent algorithms.

Vandermonde systems have the coefficient matrix A of the form $A = [a_{j+1}^i, i, j = 0, 1, \ldots, n]$. Solving system $A^T\bar{p} = \bar{\mathbf{f}}$ with such a matrix A^T is equivalent to computing a polynomial $p(t) = p_0 + p_1t + \cdots + p_nt^n$ that interpolates to a function $f(t)$ at some points $t_0, t_1, \ldots, t_n$, where $\mathbf{p} = [p_i]$, $\mathbf{f} = [f(t_i)]$, $i = 0, 1, \ldots, n$. That correlation can be exploited in order to solve the systems $A^T\mathbf{p} = \mathbf{f}$ using n^2 flops, where A is an $n \times n$ Vandermonde matrix.

Numerical stability is frequently a problem in computations with polynomials and thus in the Toeplitz, Hankel, and Vandermonde computations.

Toeplitz, Hankel, and Vandermonde matrices are special cases of more general classes of structured matrices associated with operators of shift (displacement) and scaling; such an association enables us to extend the algorithms for Toeplitz linear systems to the systems of the cited general classes (see author's book with D. Bini).

C. Fast Fourier Transform Methods for Poisson Equations

Special linear systems arise from the Poisson equation,

$$\partial^2 u/\partial x^2 + \partial^2 u/\partial y^2 = f(x, y)$$

on a rectangle, $0 \leq x \leq a$, $0 \leq y \leq b$. [The Laplace equation of Section II,A is a special case where $f(x, y) = 0$.] If finite differences with N points per variable replace the partial derivatives, the resulting linear system has N^2 equations. Such systems can be solved in $O(N^2 \log N)$ flops with small overhead by special methods using fast Fourier transform (FFT) versus an order of N^4 flops, which would be required by Gaussian elimination for that special system. Storage space also decreases from $2N^3$ to N^2 units. Similar saving of time and space from $O(N^7)$ flops, $2N^5$ space units to $O(N^3 \log N)$ flops and N^3 space units is due to the application of FFT to the solution of Poisson equations on a three-dimensional box.

VII. Direct Algorithms for Sparse and Well-Structured Linear Systems

A. Sparse Linear Systems and the Associated Graphs

The coefficient matrices of banded and block-banded linear systems of Section VI,A are sparse, that is, filled mostly with zeros, and have some regular patterns for all the nonzero entries. Linear systems with those two features arise most frequently in applications (compare the regular patterns of banded and block-banded systems, where nonzeros are grouped about the diagonal). Such sparse and structured systems can be solved efficiently using special fast direct or iterative algorithms and special data structures allowing the storage of only nonzero coefficients. To see the structure of the coefficient matrix A and to choose appropriate data structures for its representation, replace the nonzero entries of A by ones. The resulting $n \times n$ matrix, $B = [b_{ij}]$, filled with zeros and ones, can be interpreted as the adjacency matrix of a (directed) graph $G = (V, E)$ consisting of the vertex set $V = \{1, 2, \ldots, n\}$ and of the edge set E such that there exists arc(i, j) from vertex i to vertex j if and only if $b_{ij} = 1$ or, equivalently, if and only if $a_{ij} \neq 0$. Note that the graph G is undirected if the matrix A is symmetric. The special data structures used in graph algorithms (linked lists, stacks, queues) are extended to the computations for linear systems.

B. Fill-In; Pivoting (Elimination Order) as a Means of Decreasing Fill-In

In the process of Gaussian elimination (with, say partial pivoting), applied to a sparse system, some zero entries of the working array may be filled with nonzeros. The set of such entries is called fill-in. Large fill-in leads to increasing both time and space used for solving linear systems. Some special pivoting policies (called orderings) of Gaussian elimination have been developed in order to keep fill-in low. Pivoting used for stabilization (see Section III) is respectively modified to avoid conflicts. Typically, a certain degree of freedom is introduced by applying threshold (rather than partial or complete) stabilization pivoting such that a pivot in the first elimination step can be any entry (i, l) such that $|a_{i1}| \geq t \max_h |a_{h1}|$, where t is a chosen tolerance value $0 < t < 1$ (and similarly in the further steps). The resulting freedom in pivoting is used to keep the fill-in low. In the important cases of symmetric positive-definite and/or symmetric diagonally dominant systems $A\mathbf{x} = \mathbf{b}$, no stabilization pivoting is needed, so the problem is simplified. To decrease the fill-in, rows and columns of A are interchanged such that the symmetry of A is preserved; the resulting triangular factorization takes the form $A = PLL^{T}P^{T}$, where L is a lower triangular matrix and P is a permutation matrix, which defines the elimination order.

C. Some Policies of Pivoting for Sparse Systems

The most universal elimination ordering is given by the Markowitz's rule, reduced to the minimum degree rule in the symmetric case. Let p_i and q_j denote the numbers of nonzeros in row i and column j of the coefficient matrix A, respectively. Then the Markowitz rule requires us to choose the nonzero entry (i, j) that minimizes the value $(p_i - 1)(q_j - 1)$ and to move that entry into the pivot position (1, 1) in the first elimination step. (The ties can be broken arbitrarily.) The same rule is applied to the subsystem of $n - k + 1$ remaining (last) equations in elimination step k for $k = 2, 3, \ldots, n - 1$. In the symmetric case, $p_i = q_i$ for all i, so the Markowitz rule is reduced to minimization of p_i [rather than of $(p_i - 1)(q_i - 1)$]. For instance, let A be symmetric.

$$A = \begin{bmatrix} x & x & x & x & \cdots & x \\ x & x & & & & \\ x & & x & & & \\ x & & & x & & \\ \vdots & & & & \ddots & \\ x & & & & & x \end{bmatrix}$$

where all the nonzero entries of A are located on the diagonal, in the first row, and in the first column and are denoted by x. Then the fill-in of Gaussian elimination with no pivoting would make the matrix dense, which would require an increase in the storage space from $3n - 2$ to n^2 units. With the Markowitz rule for this matrix, no fill-in will take place.

There also exist general ordering policies that

(1) decrease the bandwidth (Cuthill–McKee) or the profile (reversed Cuthill–McKee, King) of a symmetric matrix A [the profile of a symmetric matrix A equals $\sum_{i=1}^{n} (i - \min_{a_{ij} \neq 0} j)$];

(2) reduce the matrix A to the block diagonal form or to the block triangular form with the maximum number of blocks (policies 1 and 2 amount to computing all the connected components or all the strongly connected components, respectively, of the associated graph G;

(3) represent symmetric A as a block matrix such that elimination of the block level causes no fill-in (tree partitioning algorithms for the associated graph G). Effective dissection algorithms customarily solve linear systems whose associated graphs G have small separators, that is, can be partitioned into two or more disconnected subgraphs of about equal size by removing relatively few vertices. For instance, in many applications G takes the form of an $\sqrt{n} \times \sqrt{n}$ grid on the plane. Removing $2\sqrt{n} - 1$ vertices of the horizontal and vertical medians separates G into four disconnected grids, each with $(n + 1 - 2\sqrt{n})/4$ vertices. This process can be recursively repeated until the set of all the separators includes all the vertices. The nested dissections of this kind define the elimination orders (where the separator vertices are eliminated in the order-reversing the process of dissection), which leads to a great saving of time and space. For instance, for the $\sqrt{n} \times \sqrt{n}$ plane grid, the nested dissection method requires $O(n^{1.5})$ flops with small overhead, rather than $n^3/3$. Furthermore the triangular factors L and U of PA (or Choleski's factor L and L^T of PAP^T in the symmetric case) are filled with only $O(n)$ nonzeros, so $O(n)$ flops suffice in the substitution stage, which makes the method even more attractive where the right side $\mathbf{b}$ varies and the coefficient matrix A is fixed.

D. Solving Path Algebra Problems via Their Reduction to Linear Systems. Exploiting Sparsity

Although effective algorithms for solving sparse linear systems exploit some properties of the associated graphs, many combinatorial problems can be effectively solved by reducing them to linear systems of equations whose coefficient matrix is defined by the graph, say, is filled with the weights (the lengths) of the edges of the graph. In particular, that reduction is applied to path algebra problems, such as computing shortest or longest paths between some fixed pairs or between all pairs of vertices, computing paths having bounded length, counting the numbers of circuits or of distinct paths between two given vertices, and testing graphs for connectivity. Numerous applications include the problems of vehicle routing, investment and stock control, network optimization, artificial intelligence and pattern recognition, encoding and decoding of information, and so on. The resulting linear systems are usually sparse; special techniques (such as the Markowitz rule and nested dissection) can be extended to this case.

VIII. Iterative Algorithms for Sparse and Special Dense Linear Systems

Iterative algorithms are recommended for some linear systems $A\mathbf{x} = \mathbf{b}$ as an alternative to direct algorithms. An iteration usually amounts to one or two multiplications of the matrix A by a vector and to a few linear operations with vectors. If A is sparse, small storage space suffices. This is a major advantage of iterative methods where the direct methods have large fill-in. Furthermore, with appropriate data structures, arithmetic operations are actually performed only where both operands are nonzeros; then, $D(A)$ or $2D(A)$ flops per iteration and $D(A) + 2n$ units of storage space suffice, where $D(A)$ denotes the number of nonzeros in A. Finally, iterative methods allow implicit symmetrization, when the iteration applies to the symmetrized system $A^TA\mathbf{x} = A^T\mathbf{b}$ without explicit evaluation of A^TA, which would have replaced A by less sparse matrix A^TA.

Consider the two classical iterative methods: Jacobi and Gauss–Seidel. Hereafter, $\mathbf{x}^{(s)} = [x_1^{(s)}, \ldots, x_n^{(s)}]^T$ denotes the approximation to the solution vector x computed in iteration s, $s = 1, 2, \ldots$.

ALGORITHM 6 (JACOBI)

$$x_i^{(s+1)} = \frac{b_i - \sum_{j=1}^{i-1} a_{ij}x_j^{(s)} - \sum_{j=i+1}^{n} a_{ij}x_j^{(s)}}{a_{ii}}$$

$$i = 1, \ldots, n$$

ALGORITHM 7 (GAUSS–SEIDEL)

$$x_i^{(s+1)} = \frac{b_i - \sum_{j=1}^{i-1} a_{ij}x_j^{(s+1)} - \sum_{j=i+1}^{n} a_{ij}x_j^{(s)}}{a_{ii}}$$

$$i = 1, \ldots, n$$

Example 22. $4x_1 - x_2 = 7$, $-x_1 + 4x_2 = 2$, $x_1 = 2$, $x_2 = 1$ is the solution. Let $x_1^{(0)} = x_2^{(0)} = 0$. Then, the Jacobi iterations give $x_1^{(1)} = 1.75$, $x_2^{(1)} = 0.5$, $x_1^{(2)} = 1.875$, $x_2^{(2)} = 0.9375$, and so on. The Gauss–Seidel iterations give $x_1^{(1)} = 1.75$, $x_2^{(1)} = 0.9375$, $x_1^{(2)} = 1.984375$, $x_2^{(2)} = 0.99609375$, and so on.

The Jacobi and Gauss–Seidel iterations can be expressed in matrix form. Let us represent A as follows: $A = L + D + U$, where $D = \text{diag}[a_{11}, \ldots, a_{nn}]$, and L and U are lower and upper triangular matrices whose diagonals are filled with zeros.

Example 23

$$A = \begin{bmatrix} 4 & -1 \\ -1 & 4 \end{bmatrix}, \qquad D = \text{diag}[4, 4]$$

$$L = \begin{bmatrix} 0 & 0 \\ -1 & 0 \end{bmatrix}, \qquad U = \begin{bmatrix} 0 & -1 \\ 0 & 0 \end{bmatrix}$$

Then, we may rewrite Algorithm 6 (Jacobi) as $D\mathbf{x}^{(s+1)} = \mathbf{b} - (L + U)\mathbf{x}^{(s)}$, and Algorithm 7 (Gauss–Seidel) as $(D + L)\mathbf{x}^{(s+1)} = \mathbf{b} - U\mathbf{x}^{(s)}$. Here is a more general iteration scheme.

ALGORITHM 8. Let $A = P - N$, where A and P are nonsingular (and P is readily invertible). Let $P\mathbf{x}^{(s+1)} = \mathbf{b} + N\mathbf{x}^{(s)}$, $s = 0, 1, \ldots$.

Examples. In Jacobi iteration, $P = D$, $N = -(L + U)$; in Gauss–Seidel iteration, $P = D + L$, $N = -U$.

THEOREM 3. Algorithm 8 converges to the solution $\mathbf{x} = A^{-1}\mathbf{b}$ to the system $A\mathbf{x} = \mathbf{b}$ if there exists a matrix norm such that $\rho = \|P^{-1}N\| < 1$. Furthermore in that norm $\|\mathbf{x} - \mathbf{x}^{(s)}\| \le \rho^s\|\mathbf{x} - \mathbf{x}^{(0)}\|$.

COROLLARY 1. Jacobi iteration converges if A is a diagonally dominant matrix; Gauss-Seidel iteration converges if A is symmetric positive definite.

It is known that the greatest lower bound $\rho(W)$ on all the norms $\|W\|$ of a matrix W equals the absolute value of the absolutely largest eigenvalue λ of W; the eigenvalues of W are the values λ such that $\det(W - \lambda I) = 0$; $\rho(W)$ is called the spectral radius of W. Theorem 3 implies that $\rho(P^{-1}N)$ defines the convergence rate of Algorithm 8. Estimating $\rho(P^{-1}N)$ is generally harder than solving linear systems $A\mathbf{x} = \mathbf{b}$, but for many specific choices of P and N, such estimates are readily available.

Appropriate variation of the splitting $A = P - N$ may imply smaller spectral radius $\rho(P^{-1}N)$ and thus faster convergence. In particular, we may try to accelerate the Jacobi or Gauss–Seidel iteration, choosing a positive β and modifying the splitting $A = P^* - N^*$ of those iterations as follows: $A = (1 + \beta)P^* - (N + \beta P^*)$. In fact the customary variation of Gauss-Seidel, called the successive overrelaxation (SOR) method, is a bit different: $A = P - N$, $P = (D + \omega L)$, $N = ((1 - \omega)D - \omega U)$, $\omega > 1$; ω is called the relaxation parameter [$\omega = 1$ means Gauss-Seidel splitting, $A = (D + L) - (-U)$]. For some linear systems, we know how to choose appropriate ω in order to obtain dramatic acceleration of the convergence of Gauss–Seidel; in other cases, ω is defined by additional analysis or by heuristics. There exists a modification of SOR called the symmetric SOR (SSOR) method, which amounts to combining SOR with implicit symmetrization of the system $A\mathbf{x} = \mathbf{b}$.

Another modification (frequently combined with SSOR) is the Chebyshev semi-iterative acceleration, which replaces the approximation $\bar{x}^{(k+1)}$ by

$$\mathbf{y}^{(k+1)} = \omega_{k+1}[\mathbf{y}^{(k)} - \mathbf{y}^{(k-1)} + \gamma P^{-1}(\mathbf{b} - A\mathbf{y}^{(k)})] + \mathbf{y}^{(k-1)}$$

where $\mathbf{y}^{(0)} = \mathbf{x}^{(0)}$, $\mathbf{y}^{(1)} = \mathbf{x}^{(1)}$, and γ and ω_{k+1} are some scalars, responsible for the acceleration and somewhat similar to the relaxation parameter ω of SOR. Some of these and other iterative methods are sometimes applied in block form.

The algorithms solve the linear systems that arise from a PDE discretized over a sequence of d-dimensional grids $G_0, \ldots, G_k$, rather than over a single grid, as in Section II,A. The grid G_{i+1}

refines G_i and has by about 2^d times more points. The solution on a coarser grid G_i is simpler, but it supplies a good initial approximation to the solution on G_{i+1}, and then $O(1)$ iteration steps refine this approximation. It was recently observed that adding $O(1)$ bits of storage space per a solution point in each transition to a finer grid also suffices, which means the overall storage space of $O(n)$ binary bits ($n = N_k$ is the number of points in the finest grid G_k), and for constant coefficient linear PDEs, this also means that only a constant number, $O(1)$, of binary bits are needed in each of $O(n)$ arithmetic operations of this process. The search for the most effective preconditioning is the area of active research. Here is one of the versions, where $(\mathbf{u}, \mathbf{v})$ denotes $\mathbf{u}^{\mathrm{T}}\mathbf{v}$, and the matrix B is precomputed. If $B = I$, this becomes the original conjugate gradient algorithm.

PRECONDITIONED CONJUGATE GRADIENT ALGORITHM

$\mathbf{r}^{(0)} = \mathbf{b} - A\mathbf{x}^{(0)}$, $\mathbf{q}^{(0)}: = B^{-1}\mathbf{r}^{(0)}$, $\mathbf{r}^{(0)}: = \mathbf{q}^{(0)}$

For $k = 0, 1, \ldots$

$$c_k: = (\mathbf{r}^{(k)}, \mathbf{r}^{(k)})/(\mathbf{p}^{(k)}, A\mathbf{p}^{(k)}))$$

$$\mathbf{x}^{(k+1)}: = \mathbf{x}^{(k)} + c_k\mathbf{p}^{(k)}$$

If not converged, do

$$\mathbf{r}^{(k+1)}: = \mathbf{r}^{(k)} - c_kA\mathbf{p}^{(k)}, \quad \mathbf{q}^{(k+1)}: = B^{-1}\mathbf{r}^{(k+1)}$$

$$d_k = (\mathbf{r}^{(k+1)}, \mathbf{q}^{(k+1)})/(\mathbf{r}^{(k)}, \mathbf{q}^{(k)}),$$

$$\mathbf{p}^{(k+1)} = \mathbf{q}^{(k+1)} + d_k\mathbf{p}^{(k)}$$

Conjugate gradient methods are closely related to the Lanczos method, also used as an iterative algorithm for symmetric linear systems. A large and growing class of highly effective methods for linear systems arising from partial differential equations (PDEs) is known as multigrid and multilevel methods. For some linear systems (defined on grids) the alternating direction implicit (ADI) method is also effective. The multigrid methods solve a large class of problems on a grid of n points with sufficiently high precision within $O(n)$ flops.

Several most popular iterative algorithms for linear systems $A\mathbf{x} = \mathbf{b}$ rely on the residual minimization in the Krylov subspace, so that the successive approximations $\mathbf{x}_0, \mathbf{x}_1, \ldots, \mathbf{x}_k$ to the solution minimize the residual norms $\|\mathbf{r}_i\|$ where $\mathbf{r}_i = C(\mathbf{b} - A\mathbf{x}_i)$, $i = 0, 1, \ldots, k$, and $C = I$ or $C = A^H$ (conjugate gradient and orthogonalization techniques). Sometimes the minimization is replaced by a related but weaker requirement, such as orthogonality of $\mathbf{r}_i$ to $B^j\mathbf{r}_0$ for all $j < i$, where $B = A^*$ (BIOMIN or CGS). The power of this approach is due to the three term relations expressing $\mathbf{x}_i$ through $\mathbf{x}_j$ for $j < i$, so that every iteration step is essentially reduced to one or two matrix-by-vector multiplications. Many algorithms of this class compute the exact solution $\mathbf{x} = A^{-1}\mathbf{b}$ in n steps (in the absence of round-off errors), but much fewer steps are needed in order to compute a good approximation to many linear systems (even under round-off). The convergence rate is defined by the eigenvalues of A or of A^HA (singular values of A), and there are various techniques of preconditioning, which replace A by matrices CAD for appropriate readily invertible matrices C and D and which accelerate the convergence of such methods for many linear systems.

IX. Influence of the Development of Vector and Parallel Computers on Solving Linear Systems

The development of vector and parallel computers has greatly influenced methods for solving linear systems, for such computers greatly speed up many matrix and vector computations. For instance, the addition of two n-dimensional vectors or of two $n \times n$ matrices or multiplication of such a vector or of such a matrix by a constant requires n or n^2 arithmetic operations, but all of them can be performed in one parallel step if n or n^2 processors are available. Such additional power dramatically increased the previous ability to solve large linear systems in a reasonable amount of time. This development also required revision of the previous classification of known algorithms in order to choose algorithms most suitable for new computers. For instance, Jordan's version of Gaussian elimination (Section III,B) is slow on serial computers, but seems more convenient on many parallel machines because $n - 1$ nonzeros in a column are eliminated in each elimination step. This is better suited to parallel computation with, say $n - 1$ processors than the usual Gaussian elimination, where $n - k$ nonzeros are eliminated in step k and k varies from 1 to $n - 1$. Variation of k complicates synchronization of the computation on all processors and communication among them. Similar problems characterize the additive steps of computing inner products, so the designer of parallel algorithms does not always adopt usual tendency of the designer of sequential algorithms to exploit maximally the inner product computation. In another example, computing the inverse A^{-1} of A (and, consequently, computing the solution $\mathbf{x} = A^{-1}\mathbf{b}$ to $A\mathbf{x} = \mathbf{b}$) can be performed via Newton's iterations, $B_{h+1} = 2B_h - B_hAB_h$, $h = 0, 1, \ldots$. If A is a well-conditioned $n \times n$ matrix, then the choice $B_0 = tA^T$, $t = 1/(\|A\|_1\|A\|_\infty)$ ensures that $\|A^{-1} - B_h\|$ is already sufficiently small, when $h = O(\log n)$. Matrix multiplications can be performed rapidly on some parallel computers, so Newton's algorithm can be useful for solving linear systems on some parallel machines, although as a sequential algorithm it is certainly inferior to Gaussian elimination.

It is frequently effective to use block representation of parallel algorithms. For instance, a parallel version of the nested dissection algorithm of Section VIII,C for a symmetric positive-definite matrix A may rely on the following recursive factorization of the matrix $A_0 = PAP^T$, where P is the permutation matrix that defines the elimination order (compare Sections III,G–III.I):

$$A_h = \begin{bmatrix} X_h & Y_h^T \\ Y_h & Z_h \end{bmatrix}$$

where $Z_h = A_{h+1} + Y_hX_h^{-1}Y_h^T$ for $h = 0, 1, \ldots, d - 1$, and X_h is a block diagonal matrix consisting of square blocks of rapidly decreasing sizes, say, $(2^{-h}n)^{0.5} \times (2^{-h}n)^{0.5}$, so

$$A_h^{-1} = \begin{bmatrix} I & -X_h^{-1}Y_h^T \\ 0 & I \end{bmatrix} \begin{bmatrix} X_h^{-1} & 0 \\ 0 & A_{h+1}^{-1} \end{bmatrix} \begin{bmatrix} I & 0 \\ -Y_hX_h^{-1} & I \end{bmatrix}$$

Such a reclassification of the available algorithms for linear systems due to the recent and current development of computer technology is an area of active research. Making the final choice for practical implementation of parallel algorithms requires some caution. The following quotient q is a good measurement for the speedup due to using a certain parallel algorithm on p processors:

$$q = \frac{\text{Execution time using the fastest known sequential algorithm on one processor}}{\text{Execution time using a parallel algorithm on } p \text{ processors.}}$$

The execution time includes various synchronization and communication overheads, which means that in fact only part of the whole computational work can be performed in parallel. The overheads are usually machine dependent and are harder to estimate, so theoretical analysis frequently ignores them and tends to give overly optimistic estimates for the power of various parallel algorithms.

BIBLIOGRAPHY

Anderson, E., Bai, Z., Bischof, C., Demmel, J., Dongarra, J., DuCroz, J., Greenbaum, A., Hammarling, S., McKenney, A., and Sorensen, D. (1990). LAPACK Working Note 20, LAPACK: A Portable Linear Algebra Library for High Performance Computers, CS 90-105, Computer Science Department, University of Tennessee, Knoxville, Tenn. (LAPACK user's guide will be published by *SIAM*).

Bini, D., and Pan, V. (1992). "Algebraic and Numerical Computations with Matrices and Polynomials, Research Notes in Theoretical Computer Science." (2 volumes.) Birkhauser, Boston.

Chvatal, V. (1983). "Linear Programming," Freeman, San Francisco, California.

Dongarra, J., Bunch, J. R., Moler, C. B., and Stewart, G. W. (1978). "LINPACK Users Guide," SIAM Publ., Philadelphia, Pennsylvania.

Eisenstat, S. C., Elman, H., Schultz, M. H., and Sherman, A. H. (1979). *In* "Advances in Computer Methods for Partial Differential Equations" (R. Vichnevetsky and R. S. Stepleman, eds.), Vol. III, IMACS, Rutgers Univ. Press, New Brunswick, New Jersey.

Gallivan, K. A., Plemmons, R. J., and Sameh, A. H. (1990). Parallel algorithms for dense linear algebra computations. *SIAM Review* **32**(1), 54–135.

George, J. A., and Liu, J. W. (1981). "Computer Solution of Large Sparse Positive Definite Systems," Prentice-Hall, Englewood Cliffs, New Jersey.

Golub, G. H., and van Loan, C. F. (1983 and 1989). "Matrix Computations," Johns Hopkins Press, Baltimore, Maryland.

Gondran, M., and Minoux, M. (1984). "Graphs and Algorithms," Wiley (Interscience), New York.

Hageman, L. A., and Young, D. M. (1981). "Applied Iterative Methods," Academic Press, New York.

Heath, M. T., Ng, E., and Peyton, B. W. (1991). Parallel algorithms for sparse linear systems. *SIAM Review* **33**(3), 420–460.

Lawson, C. L., and Hanson, R. J. (1974). "Solving Least Squares Problems," Prentice-Hall, Englewood Cliffs, New Jersey.

Ortega, J. M., and Voight, R. G. (1985). Solution of partial differential equations on vector and parallel computers, *SIAM Rev.* **27**(2), 149–240.

Pan, V. (1984). "How to Multiply Matrices Faster," Lecture Notes in Computer Science 179, Springer-Verlag, Berlin.

Pissanetsky, S. (1984). "Sparse Matrix Technology," Academic Press, New York.

Spedicato, E. (editor) (1991). "Computer Algorithms for Solving Linear Algebraic Equations (the State of Art)," NATO ASI Series, Series F: Computer and Systems Sciences, vol. 77, Springer-Verlag, Berlin, 1991.

LIPIDS AND POLYMERS, MONOLAYERS

Herman E. Ries, Jr. *The University of Chicago*

GLOSSARY

Collapse pressure: Maximum stable pressure above which, on further compression, the pressure falls rapidly or remains constant.

Compressibility: Change in area per unit change in pressure for a given area.

Extrapolated area: Molecular area obtained by extending to zero pressure the steep upper linear part of a pressure–area isotherm.

Lipid: Compound with a fatty-acid-type structure, insoluble or difficultly soluble in water but soluble in nonpolar organic solvents.

Monolayer: Film one molecule thick; also known as a monomolecular film.

Polymer: Relatively large molecule composed of many small molecules or monomers.

It is difficult to do any work in the laboratory or in the outside world without dealing almost entirely with surfaces or interfaces. Considerable interest therefore focuses on the thin adsorbed films that form at interfaces. The ultimate thin adsorbed film is the monomolecular film or monolayer. Monolayers play important roles in biology, catalysis, friction, rust prevention, and in the formation of emulsions and foams. In addition much attention is now focused on the modification of solid surfaces by transferred monolayers.

The basic structure of cell membranes is a lipid bilayer. The inner and outer monolayers of the bilayer control many physiological processes. In fact the lipid bilayer structure in cell membranes was first elucidated by monolayer techniques. Polymers in the form of proteins are also important components of cell membranes. Monolayers of lipids and polymers are considered to be bimembrane mimetic systems.

I. Experimental Techniques

Monolayers can be controlled and manipulated best at the water–air interface. One of the most reliable and versatile techniques for the study of monolayers under controlled conditions is the Langmuir–Adam–Harkins film balance (Fig. 1). Also in use is a Wilhelmy technique in which the change in surface tension of the film-covered surface is measured with a suspended vertical plate.

The film balance consists essentially of a long shallow trough containing distilled water on which the film is spread, a horizontal float and torsion-wire system for surface-pressure measurements, and brass barriers for sweeping the surface and compressing the film. The trough and barriers, which are coated with Teflon, are carefully cleaned before each experiment. Currently a Teflon float and FEP (fluorinated ethylene–propylene) Teflon foils are used in preference to the mica float and platinum foils of earlier systems. Thus the use of contaminating wax coatings is entirely avoided.

A large cabinet encloses the apparatus to minimize contamination and water evaporation. Pressure and area adjustments are made from outside the cabinet. Temperature and humidity control are important. Temperatures are usually in the range of 20 to 25°C and rarely vary more than 0.1°C during an individual experiment. Before a film is spread, the water surface is swept many times to remove surface contamination. A Pyrex weighing pipet, or a micrometer syringe,

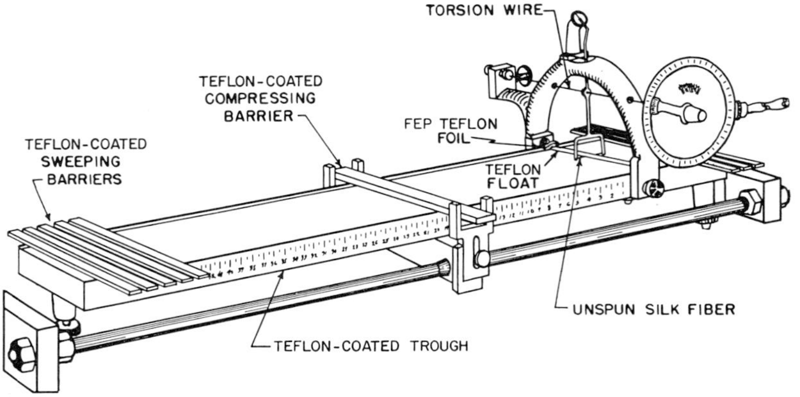

FIG. 1. Film-balance apparatus.

is used to spread a few drops of a dilute solution of the film-forming material in a volatile solvent, such as benzene, hexane, or chloroform. Pressure–area isotherms are then obtained by reducing the area in small decrements and measuring the corresponding surface pressures. The surface pressure is the difference between the surface tension of the clean water surface behind the float and the reduced surface tension of the film-covered surface in front of the float.

A Langmuir–Blodgett method is used to transfer film samples from the water surface to electron-microscope grids sandwiched between a small glass plate and a coating film such as collodion. The collodion surface may be coated with vapor-deposited silicon monoxide to improve wettability. In the transfer procedure the plate is slowly raised and the film is simultaneously compressed at such a rate that the surface pressure remains constant. Automated systems are now available in which pressure–area isotherms are recorded directly and films are transferred to solid surfaces at constant pressure.

II. Pressure–Area Isotherms

A pressure–area isotherm is a plot of surface area, usually in square angstroms ($Å^2$) per molecule, against surface pressure in dynes per centimeter (dyn/cm) at a constant temperature. Pressure–area isotherms are, in many respects, the two-dimensional analogs of pressure–volume isotherms for three-dimensional systems. Many properties of the monolayer and its components molecules are provided by pressure–area isotherms.

A. Molecular Area

Extrapolation of the steep upper linear portion of a pressure–area isotherm to zero pressure is the conventional method for obtaining a molecular area. For vertically oriented molecules this is the cross-sectional area of the molecule. Molecular areas are also of interest at other pressures; for example, at the collapse pressure where the tightest packing occurs.

B. Film Thickness (Molecular Orientation)

Calculation of the thickness of the compressed film is straightforward near the collapse pressure. Because small particles of the bulk material appear at collapse, the density of the monolayer near this pressure approaches that of the bulk material. The mass of the compound spread is simply divided by this density to obtain the volume of the film. The volume divided by the area yields the film thickness. If, for example, this thickness value is in agreement with the length of the molecule, vertical orientation is indicated. On the other hand, if the thickness approaches the diameter of a hydrocarbon chain, as for some polymers, horizontal orientation is demonstrated.

C. Compressibility

Compressibility is related to the overall packing of the molecules in the monolayer. It is the change in area per unit change in surface pressure for a given area:

$$(a_0 - a_1)/a_0 f_1$$

where a_0 is the extrapolated area at zero pressure and a_1 is a smaller area at pressure f_1. Film rigidity is of course inversely related to compressibility and is thus related to both intramolecular and intermolecular packing as well as to the attractive and repulsive forces of the polar groups involved.

D. Collapse Pressure

For relatively rigid stable films of low compressibility, the collapse pressure is the maximum stable pressure above which the pressure falls off rapidly as the film breaks. For less rigid, more compressible films, the rate of compression will affect the collapse pressure. Isotherms for highly compressible films may bend over gradually and approach the horizontal. Such an equilibrium pressure is arbitrarily referred to as a liquid-type collapse pressure.

III. Lipids

A great many film-forming compounds are of the lipid type, insoluble or difficultly soluble in water and soluble in several organic solvents. These compounds are of critical importance in stabilizing biological membranes and of commercial importance as detergents and emulsifying agents. They also play important roles in the reduction of friction, wear, and corrosion.

A. Steric Acid and Related Compounds

Among the many film-forming compounds, stearic acid has one of the simplest molecular structures. It is the classical compound in monolayer studies. As shown schematically in Fig. 2, stearic acid has a relatively long hydrocarbon

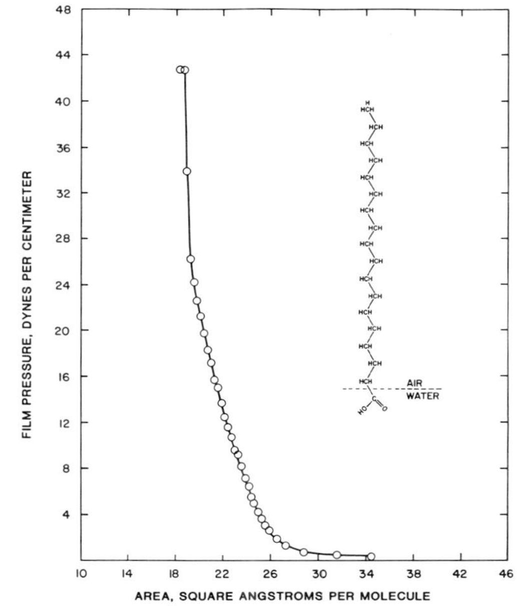

FIG. 2. Pressure–area isotherm for stearic acid and schematic of the stearic acid molecule.

chain (18 carbon atoms) and a fairly strong polar group (COOH) at one extremity. The pressure–area isotherm in Fig. 2 gives an extrapolated area of 20.6 Å^2/molecule. A calculated film thickness is approximately 25 Å. These values are in good agreement with the molecular spacing and length for stearic acid obtained from X-ray diffraction data. Vertical orientation is clearly indicated. The collapse pressure is 42 dyn/cm and the compressibility is 0.0015 cm/dyn (Table I).

TABLE I. Monolayer Properties of Lipids

Lipid	Area[a] (Å^2/molecule)	Collapse pressure (dyn/cm)	Compressibility[b] (cm/dyn)
Stearic acid	20.6	42	0.0015
Cholesterol	39.0	43	0.0012
Lecithin (20°C)			
Low pressure	69.0	(4)[c]	0.0543
High pressure	38.5	38	0.0054
n-Hexatriacontanoic acid	20.4	58	0.0034
Cerebronic (2-hydroxytetracosanoic) acid	26.0	68	0.0047

[a] Extrapolated area at zero pressure.
[b] Compressibility is $(a_0 - a_1)/a_0 f_1$, where a_0 is the extrapolated area at zero pressure and a_1 is a smaller area at pressure f_1.
[c] Pressure at inflection point.

Experiments with a closely related compound, *n*-hexatriacontanoic acid (36 carbon atoms), twice as long as stearic acid, yield an almost identical cross-sectional area, 20.4 Å^2/molecule, and double the film thickness, 50 Å. Thus further proof of vertical orientation is provided. The collapse pressure, 58 dyn/cm, for the 36-carbon compound is much higher than that for stearic acid because of the greater cohesion of the longer hydrocarbon chains. Cerebronic (2-hydroxytetracosanoic) acid, with a stronger polar group on a 24-carbon atom chain, gives a stable maximum pressure of 68 dyn/cm, but an increased molecular area and compressibility because of the bulkiness of its polar extremity. Monolayers of alcohols with a long straight hydrocarbon chain and a terminal hydroxy group give similar results and thus provide additional evidence for vertical orientation.

B. Cholesterol

Cholesterol is an important component of biomembranes and plays a significant role in cardiovascular and other diseases. A schematic drawing of the cholesterol molecule and the isotherm for its monolayer are shown in Fig. 3.

The monolayer properties of cholesterol are among the most remarkable in surface chemistry. Cholesterol forms an extremely strong and stable film in spite of its relatively weak polar group and bulky hydrocarbon structure. However, the polar hydroxy group is located at one extremity, the ideal location to produce vertical orientation of the molecule. Moreover, the hydrocarbon portion, which appears bulky because of its multiple-ring structure, packs tightly both intramolecularly and intermolecularly. The compact nature of the cholesterol structure is apparent in the molecular model shown with that for stearic acid in Fig. 4.

FIG. 4. Molecular models showing vertical orientation of (a) stearic acid and (b) cholesterol. [From Ries, H. E., Jr. (1984). *Colloids Surf.* **10,** 283–300.]

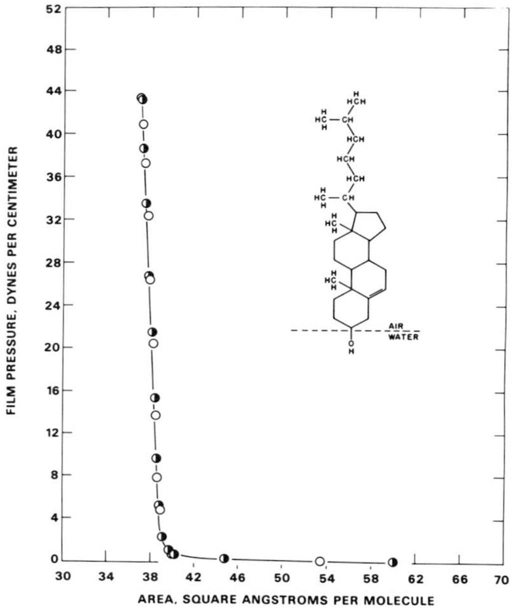

FIG. 3. Pressure–area isotherms for cholesterol and schematic of the cholesterol molecule. [From Ries, H. E., Jr. (1984). *Colloids Surf.* **10,** 283–300.]

The extrapolated area for the cholesterol molecule is only 39 Å^2, which is approximately equal to that for two straight hydrocarbon chains. Collapse occurs at 43 dyn/cm, which is only slightly higher than that for stearic acid, although the latter compound has a stronger polar group and a relatively long straight hydrocarbon chain. The thickness of the cholesterol monolayer, calculated at a molecular area of 39 Å^2, is 15 Å, the vertical length of the oriented molecule. Most striking is the extremely low compressibility of the cholesterol monolayer, 0.0012 cm/dyn.

These monolayer properties of cholesterol undoubtedly bear directly on the role of cholesterol in cell membranes and in many diseases.

C. Lecithin

Lecithin is also one of the principal lipids in cell membranes. Pressure–area isotherms at several temperatures and a schematic drawing of a synthetic lecithin, β, γ-dipalmitoyl-DL-α-glycerylphosphorylcholine, are shown in Fig. 5.

Although both the hydrocarbon and polar portions of the lecithin molecule are bulky, the isotherms demonstrate a strong and well-behaved monolayer. Considerable temperature sensitivity is indicated. At 20°C, the isotherm shows an initial pressure rise near 69 $Å^2$/molecular and a pronounced inflection at 50 $Å^2$ and 4 dyn/cm. The isotherm then rises steeply to a collapse pressure close to 38 dyn/cm. The extrapolated area is 38.5 $Å^2$/molecule and the compressibility is relatively high, 0.0054 cm/dyn. The area value is clearly consistent with that expected for two vertically oriented hydrocarbon chains. However, the compressibility may indicate a reorganization in molecular packing as pressure is increased, possibly due to the bulky polar groups.

Of special interest is the rather pronounced temperature effect. The extrapolated area at the higher pressures increases linearly with temperature. The pressure at the inflection point, 50 $Å^2$, also increases linearly with temperature. An intramolecular and/or intermolecular reorganization evidently takes place at 50 $Å^2$. Reorganizations of this type may be critical in the structure and function of biological membranes.

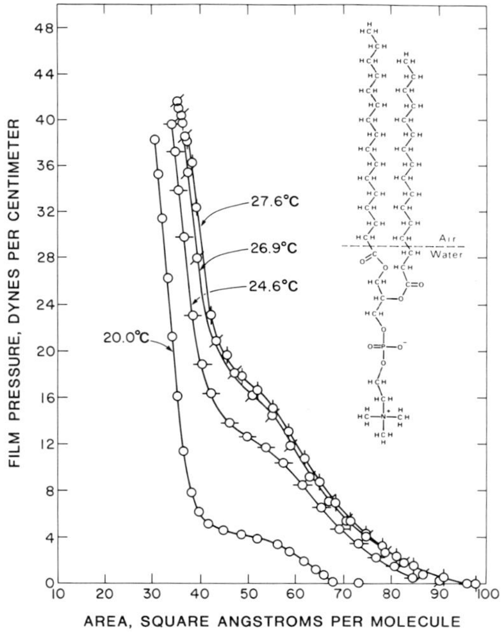

FIG. 5. Pressure–area isotherms for a synthetic lecithin at several temperatures. [Reprinted with permission from Ries, H. E., Jr., Matsumoto, M., Uyeda, N., and Suito, E. (1975). *In* "Monolayers," (E. D. Goddard, ed.), p. 286. Amer. Chem. Soc., Washington, D.C. Copyright 1975 American Chemical Society.]

IV. Polymers

Polymers are important as the fibers, films, and plastics of the modern world as well as the proteins and nucleic acids of living organisms. Polyvinyl acetate and polymethyl methacrylate are model polymers of commercial importance. The gramicidins are antibiotics, biomembrane-channel formers, and, in some respects, protein models.

A. Polyvinyl Acetate

Polyvinyl acetate (PVAc) has a relatively simple structure and may be considered a surface-chemistry model for many polymers including proteins. The structure and orientation of PVAc are shown schematically in the form of three monomer units in Fig. 6.

Extrapolation of the central linear portion of the isotherm for PVAc gives 1.9 m^2/mg or 27 $Å^2$/monomer unit (see Fig. 6 and Table II). The film thickness that corresponds to this area is 5 Å Horizontal orientation of the polymer is thus demonstrated. Compressibility of the monolayer is high, 0.0252 cm/dyn, as might be expected for long molecules that lie flat on the water surface. Collapse occurs gradually at about 25 dyn/cm, a relatively high pressure for a film of such molecules.

The compression–expansion isotherms of Fig. 6 are of special interest. Essentially no hysteresis is observed. Moreover complete compression and expansion can be performed rapidly and all points fall on the equilibrium isotherm. After collapse and the subsequent release of pressure, the polymer molecules evidently move extremely rapidly across the water surface to occupy the available area. Such experiments also establish the fact that essentially no molecules are lost by dissolution, evaporation, or leakage.

B. Polymethyl Methacrylate

Polymethyl methacrylates (PMMA) are widely used for making transparent glasslike

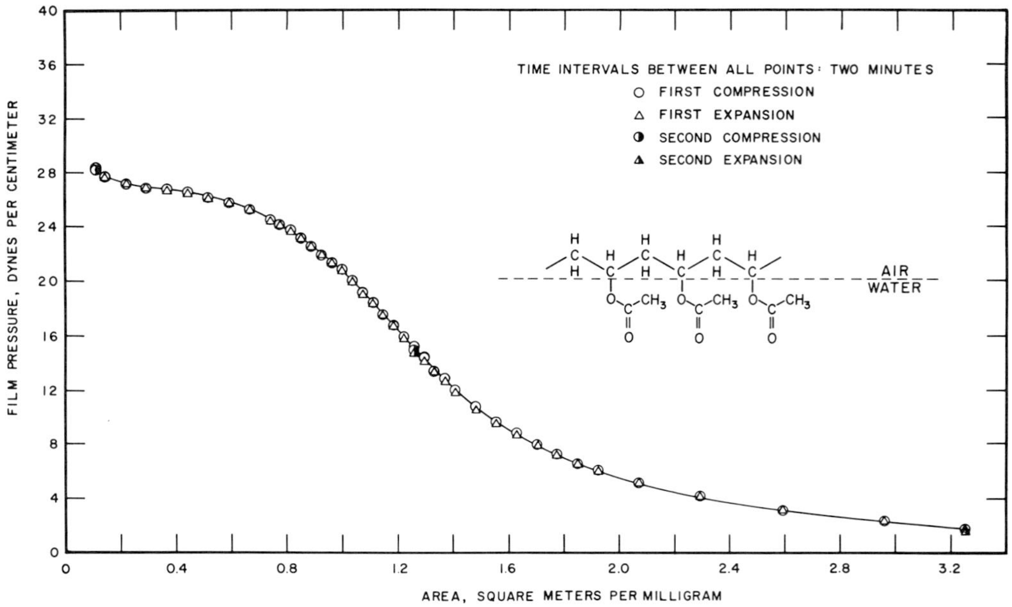

FIG. 6. Compression–expansion isotherms for polyvinyl acetate.

solids known as Lucite and Plexiglass. Monolayer techniques have been used to distinguish among several stereoregular isomers of PMMA. These are isomers that differ in the orientation of the side groups on the backbone chain. In the atactic isomer the distribution of side groups is random, in the isotactic the side groups are all oriented in the same direction, and in the syndiotactic the side groups alternate in orientation. Isotherms for the three stereoisomers, as well as a schematic drawing of the isotactic form, are shown in Fig. 7.

The three isotherms effectively coincide in the central region, 10 to 18 dyn/cm. Significant differences appear at lower and higher pressures. The extrapolated area for the common central linear region is 1.0 m^2/mg, or 17 Å^2/monomer unit. Film thickness calculations give about 9 Å. PMMA is evidently more tightly packed than PVAc. The isotactic isotherm may be divided into three distinct segments with inflection points at 8 and 18 dyn/cm and final collapse at 24 dyn/cm. At low pressures, the long tail of the isotherm is similar to that for PVAc, perhaps

TABLE II. Monolayer Properties of Polymers

Polymer	Area[a,b] (m^2/mg)	Collapse pressure (dyn/cm)	Compressibility[c] (cm/dyn)
Polyvinyl acetate	1.9 (27)	25	0.0252
Polymethyl methacrylate			
(atactic)	1.0 (17)	18	0.0192
Valine-gramicidin A			
Low pressure	1.2 [386]	17[d]	0.0263
High pressure	0.51 [160]	63	0.0062
Valinomycin	2.0 [370]	23	0.0147

[a] Extrapolated area at zero pressure.
[b] Parentheses indicate square angstroms per monomer unit; square brackets indicate square angstroms per molecule.
[c] Compressibility is $(a_0 - a_1)/a_0 f_1$, where a_0 is the extrapolated area at zero pressure and a_1 is a smaller area at pressure f_1.
[d] Pressure at inflection point.

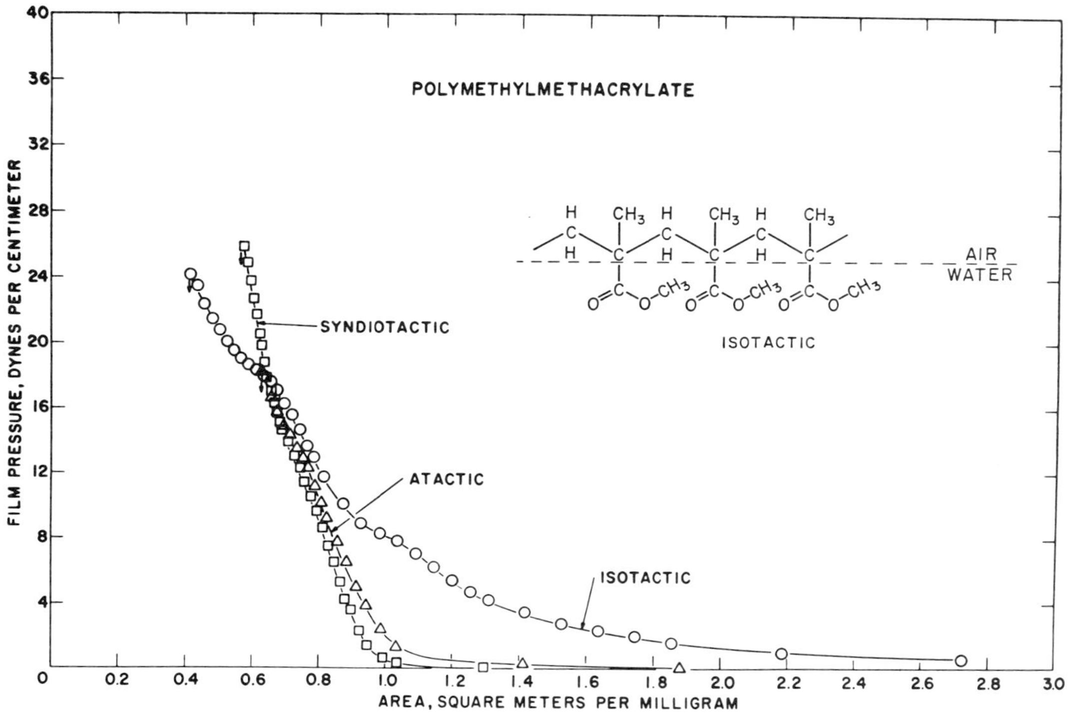

FIG. 7. Pressure–area isotherms for atactic, isotactic, and syndiotactic polymethylmethacrylate. [Reprinted with permission from Beredjick, N., Ahlbeck, R. A., Kwei, T. K., and Ries, H. E., Jr. (1960). *J. Polym. Sci.* **46,** 268–270. Copyright © 1960 John Wiley & Sons, Inc.]

indicating a fully extended structure. The syndiotactic isotherm consists of two linear segments with an inflection point at 18 dyn/cm followed by a steep rise to collapse at 26 dyn/cm. At low pressures the syndiotactic molecules are clearly more tightly packed or more condensed than the isotactic molecules. The atactic isotherm effectively coincides with much of that for the syndiotactic, but collapse occurs at 18 dyn/cm, considerably below the collapse pressures for the other two isomers.

The marked differences as well as the similarities in monolayer properties for these three stereoisomers suggest that much light may be shed on the problems of stereoregularity by such studies. The differentiation and characterization of stereoregular polymers is important in both basic and applied research.

C. Gramicidins and Valinomycin

Gramicidins are transmembrane channel formers that bridge the distance from the exterior to the interior of the cell. Valine-gramicidin A (VGA), a linear pentadecapeptide, is an antibiotic and a model for the hydrophobic portions of integral membrane proteins. The isotherm and structure of VGA are presented in Fig. 8. Also shown for purposes of comparison are the isotherm and structure for valinomycin, a cyclic dodecadepsipeptide. Valinomycin is an ionophore and also an antibiotic.

Extrapolation of the low-pressure portion of the VGA isotherm gives an area of 386 Å^2/molecule, or an area per amino acid group of approximately 25 Å^2. Thus the VGA molecule lies essentially flat at low surface pressures. Horizontal orientation is also demonstrated by the average film thickness of 8 Å calculated at the extrapolated zero pressure. Consistent with this horizontal orientation is a high compressibility, 0.0263 cm/dyn. However, following the inflection point at about 17 dyn/cm and 200 Å^2, the isotherm rises steeply to give a surprisingly low compressibility, 0.0062 cm/dyn, and high collapse pressure, 63 dyn/cm. Perhaps, a helical or folded configuration of the polymer under pressure accounts for this unexpected behavior.

The isotherm for valinomycin is quite different from that for VGA, although the extrapo-

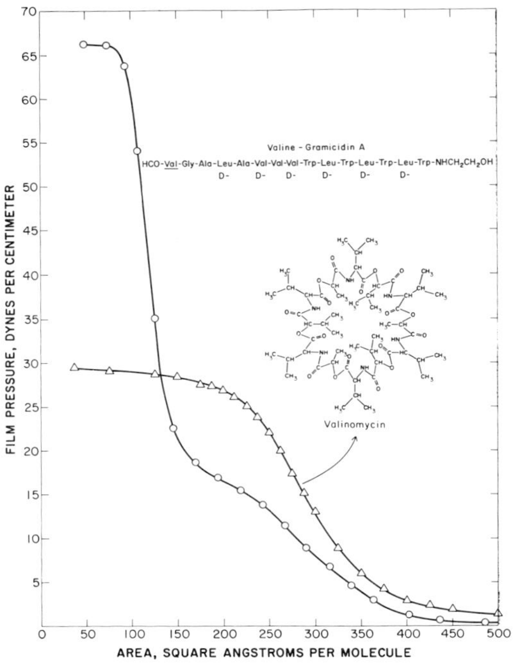

FIG. 8. Pressure–area isotherms for valine-gramicidin A and valinomycin. [From Ries, H. E., Jr., and Swift, H. (1987). *J. Colloid Interface Sci.* **117,** 584.]

lated area for valinomycin, 370 Å^2/molecule. The VGA molecule has three more monomer or component groups than valinomycin. However, the latter is a cyclic structure that encloses some empty space and undoubtedly packs intermolecularly with greater difficulty than the linear VGA. Evidently the valinomycin molecules remain essentially flat throughout the compression and the monolayer undergoes a liquid-type collapse at 23 dyn/cm.

In recent work pressure-area isotherms for valinomycin have shown significant differences when the film is spread from four different volatile solvents: benzene, chloroform, *n*-hexane, and cyclohexane. This pronounced effect of the spreading solvent is in sharp contrast to that found with long-chain lipid-type compounds which show no significant solvent effect.

Isotherms obtained with the four different solvents are presented in Fig. 9; data and calculations therefrom are presented in Table III. The highly polar internal ring structure of valinomycin in contrast to the relatively small terminal polar group of a typical lipid may account for the difference. Care must therefore be exercised in the selection of a spreading solvent for highly polar compounds.

V. Mechanism for Monolayer Collapse

Considerable light has been shed on the mechanism for monolayer collapse by electron-microscope studies of transferred films. Figure 10 shows schematically four stages in a proposed

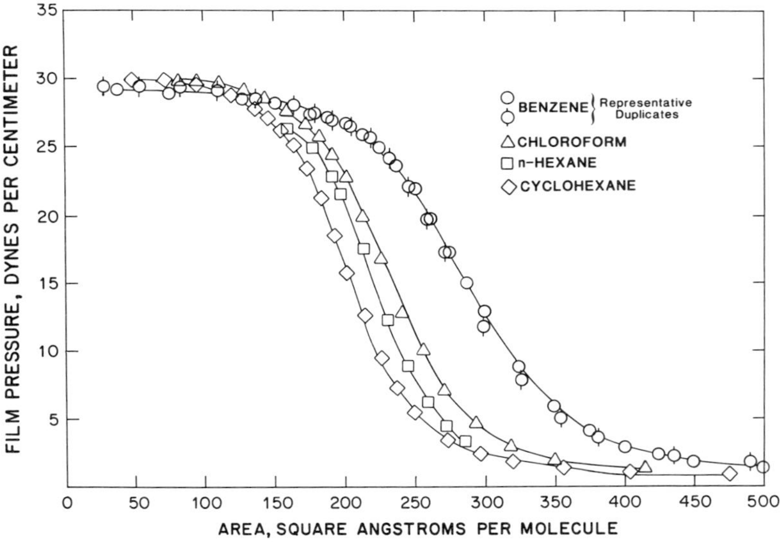

FIG. 9. Pressure–area isotherms for valinomycin spread from four different solvents.

TABLE III. Effect of the Spreading Solvent on Monolayers of Valinomycin

Solvent	Area[a] (A^2/molecule)	Collapse pressure (dyn/cm)	Compressibility[b] (cm/dyn)
Benzene	370	23	0.0150
Chloroform	300	23	0.0145
n-Hexane	280	24	0.0135
Cyclohexane	260	23	0.0141

[a] Extrapolated area at zero pressure.
[b] Compressibility is $(a_0 - a_1)/a_0 f_1$, here a_0 is the extrapolated area at zero pressure and a_1 is a smaller area at pressure f_1.

collapse mechanism for a typical lipid-type monolayer. Small circles represent the polar groups, and straight lines the long hydrocarbon chains of the molecules.

In the first, or weakening, stage of collapse, some lipid molecules are forced up from the water surface to form small blisters in the film. Because of the mutual attraction of the polar groups and the cohesion of the long hydrocarbon chains, the molecules then rise in closely packed folds or ridges two molecules thick. The double-layer ridges may then bend and break. Collapsed fragments of the final stage are thus two molecules thick and rest on the monolayer that remains.

The proposed mechanism is strongly supported by electron-microscope studies of transferred films that have been shadowcast with a platinum-palladium alloy. In Fig. 11A tall narrow ridges normal to the direction of compression are clearly shown for a collapsing film of a lipid, cerebronic (2-hydroxytetracosanoic) acid. Figure 11B shows a long flat ribbon from a collapsed film of cholesterol resting on the monolayer.

VI. Related Studies

Because of the importance of monolayers in basic and applied research, a wide variety of techniques has been applied to their study. Surface-potential, radiotracer, and fluorescence techniques have been used for a number of years. Electron diffraction, grazing incidence X-ray diffraction, and the measurement of thin-film viscosity are used in current studies. Optical methods such as ellipsometry and multiple-internal-reflection infrared spectroscopy continue to be of interest. The quantitative transfer of monolayers to solid surfaces has opened a wide area of related studies that include various forms

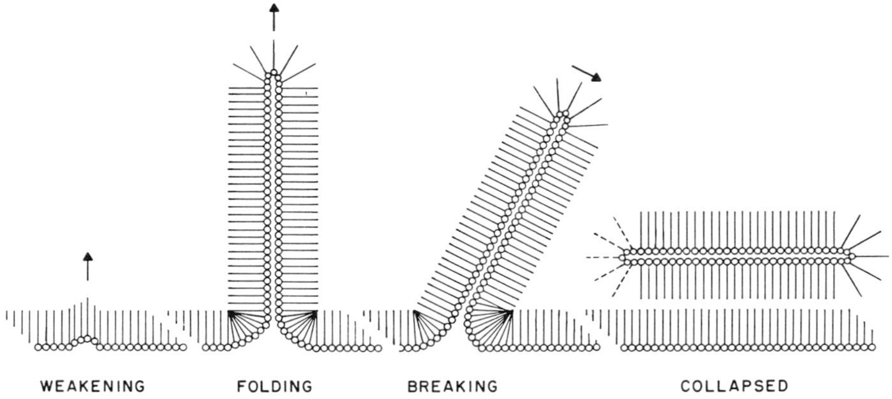

FIG. 10. Mechanism for monolayer collapse. [Reprinted with permission from Ries, H. E., Jr., and Swift, H. (1987). *Langmuir* **3,** 853. Copyright 1987 American Chemical Society.]

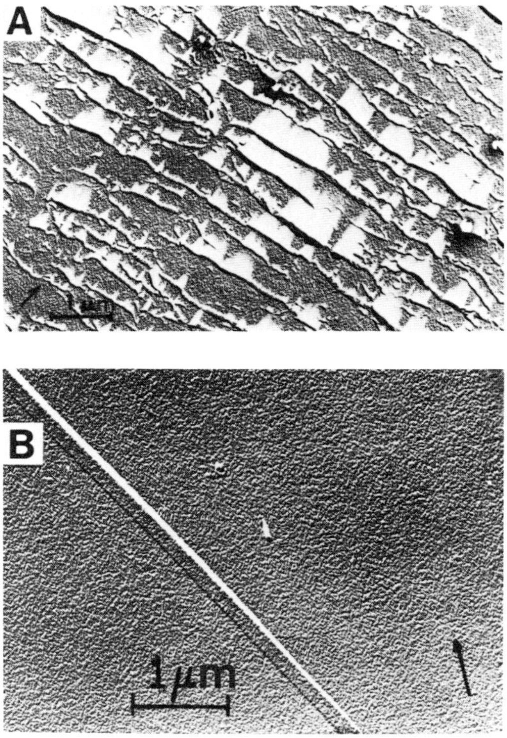

FIG. 11. Electron micrographs of collapsing and collapsed films: (A) tall folds or ridges of a collapsing monolayer of cerebronic acid; (B) narrow platelet or ribbon of a collapsed monolayer of cholesterol. Arrows indicate the direction of shadowcasting and shadows appear as light areas. [Reprinted with permission from Ries, H. E., Jr., and Swift, H. (1987). *Langmuir* **3,** 853. Copyright 1987 American Chemical Society.]

of electron microscopy and scanning tunneling microscopy.

Fundamental studies on carefully controlled systems are also in progress in an effort to understand equilibrium, relaxation, and phase changes in monolayer systems. Monolayers of mixtures and related diffusion experiments are now opening new areas that bear directly on the complex systems encountered in both the laboratory and the outside world.

Bibliography

Adam, N. K. (1941). "The Physics and Chemistry of Surfaces," 3rd Ed. Oxford Univ. Press, London.

Adamson, A. W. (1982). "Physical Chemistry of Surfaces," 4th Ed. Wiley, New York.

Chemistry and Physics of Lipids, Special Issue on Phospholipid Phase Transitions, **57**(2 and 3), March 1991.

Gaines, G. L., Jr. (1966). "Insoluble Monolayers at Liquid–Gas Interfaces." Wiley (Interscience), New York.

Goddard, E. D. (1975). "Monolayers," Advances in Chemistry Series 144. Amer. Chem. Soc., Washington, D. C.

Harkins, W. D. (1952). "The Physical Chemistry of Surface Films." Van Nostrand-Reinhold, Princeton, New Jersey.

Ries, H. E., Jr. (1961). Monomolecular films, *Sci. Am.* **204,** 152–164.

Ries, H. E., Jr. (1984). *Colloids Surf.* **10,** 283–300.

Ries, H. E. Jr. (1990). *Langmuir* **6,** 883–885.

Ries, H. E., Jr., and Swift, H. (1987). *Langmuir* **3,** 853–855.